ATOMIC WEIGHTS BASED ON CARBON-12
(IUPAC, 1961)

			IIIA	IVA	VA	VIA	VIIA	INERT GASES
								HELIUM 2 He 4.0026
			BORON 5 B 10.811	CARBON 6 C 12.01115	NITROGEN 7 N 14.0067	OXYGEN 8 O 15.9994	FLUORINE 9 F 18.9984	NEON 10 Ne 20.183
	IB	IIB	ALUMINUM 13 Al 26.9815	SILICON 14 Si 28.086	PHOSPHORUS 15 P 30.9738	SULFUR 16 S 32.064	CHLORINE 17 Cl 35.453	ARGON 18 Ar 39.948
CKEL 28 Ni 8.71	COPPER 29 Cu 63.54	ZINC 30 Zn 65.37	GALLIUM 31 Ga 69.72	GERMANIUM 32 Ge 72.59	ARSENIC 33 As 74.9216	SELENIUM 34 Se 78.96	BROMINE 35 Br 79.909	KRYPTON 36 Kr 83.80
ADIUM 46 Pd 06.4	SILVER 47 Ag 107.870	CADMIUM 48 Cd 112.40	INDIUM 49 In 114.82	TIN 50 Sn 118.69	ANTIMONY 51 Sb 121.75	TELLURIUM 52 Te 127.60	IODINE 53 I 126.9044	XENON 54 Xe 131.30
TINUM 78 Pt 5.09	GOLD 79 Au 196.967	MERCURY 80 Hg 200.59	THALLIUM 81 Tl 204.37	LEAD 82 Pb 207.19	BISMUTH 83 Bi 208.980	POLONIUM 84 Po 210	ASTATINE 85 At 211	RADON 86 Rn 222

LINIUM 64 Gd 7.25	TERBIUM 65 Tb 158.924	DYSPROSIUM 66 Dy 162.50	HOLMIUM 67 Ho 164.930	ERBIUM 68 Er 167.26	THULIUM 69 Tm 168.934	YTTERBIUM 70 Yb 173.04	LUTETIUM 71 Lu 174.97
RIUM 96 Cm 42	BERKELIUM 97 Bk 243	CALIFORNIUM 98 Cf 245	EINSTEINIUM 99 Es 253	FERMIUM 100 Fm 254	MENDELEVIUM 101 Md 256	NOBELIUM 102 No 254	LAWRENCIUM 103 Lr 259

the ENCYCLOPEDIA of the CHEMICAL ELEMENTS

Edited by

CLIFFORD A. HAMPEL
Consulting Chemical Engineer
Skokie, Illinois

REINHOLD BOOK CORPORATION
A subsidiary of Chapman-Reinhold, Inc.
New York   Amsterdam   London

CONTRIBUTORS

JOHN B. ADEMEC, Development and Research Department, International Nickel Company, Inc., 67 Wall Street, New York, N.Y. 10005. *Nickel.*

A. C. ANDREWS, Professor of Chemistry, Department of Chemistry, Kansas State University, Manhattan, Kans. 66502. *Hydrogen.*

EVAN H. APPELMAN, Chemistry Division, Argonne National Laboratory, 9700 South Cass Avenue, Argonne, Ill. 60439. *Astatine.*

F. E. BACON, Research and Development Department, Mining and Metals Division, Union Carbide Corp., P.O. Box 579, Niagara Falls, N.Y. 14302. *Chromium.*

RUSSELL BALDOCK, Chemistry Division, Oak Ridge National Laboratory, P.O. Box X, Oak Ridge, Tenn. 37830. *Isotopes. I. Pre-World War I Status; Isotopes. II. Post-World War I Developments.*

JELKS BARKSDALE, Department of Chemistry, University of Alabama, Auburn, Ala. 36830. *Titanium.*

B. J. BEAUDRY, Associate Metallurgist, Ames Laboratory, Institute for Atomic Research, Iowa State University, Ames, Ia. 50010. *Erbium, Holmium, Lutetium.*

ROBERT M. BESANÇON, Physical Sciences Administrator, U.S. Air Force Materials Laboratory, Wright-Patterson Air Force Base, Ohio 45433. *Atoms.*

L. W. BRANDT, Research Director, Helium Research Center, U.S. Department of the Interior, Bureau of Mines, P.O. Box 10085, Amarillo, Tex. 79106. *Helium.*

JANET Z. BRIGGS, Director of Technical Information, Climax Molybdenum Company, a division of AMAX (American Metal Climax Inc.), 1270 Avenue of the Americas, New York, N.Y. 10020. *Molybdenum.*

LEE S. BUSCH, The Brush Beryllium Company, Elmore, Ohio 43416. *Beryllium.*

S. C. CARAPELLA, JR., Research Superintendent, Central Research Laboratories, American Smelting and Refining Company, South Plainfield, N.J. 07080. *Antimony, Arsenic.*

HOWARD C. CLARK, Professor, Department of Chemistry, University of Western Ontario, London, Ontario, Canada. *Fluorine.*

EDWARD H. CONROY, Manager of Quality Control Department, Frasch Sulphur Division, Texas Gulf Sulphur Company, Newgulf, Tex. 77462. *Sulfur.*

GERHARD A. COOK, Union Carbide Corp., Linde Division Research Laboratory, P.O. Box 44, Tonawanda, N.Y. 14150. *Oxygen.*

W. CHARLES COOPER, Head, Research Division, Noranda Research Centre, 240 Hymus Boulevard, Pointe Claire, Quebec, Canada. *Tellurium.*

BURRIS B. CUNNINGHAM, Professor of Chemistry, University of California, Lawrence Radiation Laboratory, Berkeley, Calif. 94720. *Berkelium, Californium, Curium.*

JAMES W. CURRIER, Growth Sciences Center, International Minerals and Chemical Corp., Libertyville, Ill. 60048. *Phosphorus.*

ADRIAN H. DAANE, Head, Department of Chemistry, Kansas State University, Manhattan, Kans. 66502. *Scandium, Yttrium.*

BERNARD E. DAVIS, Research Metallurgist, Wah Chang Albany Corp., P.O. Box 460, Albany, Ore. 97321. *Tungsten.*

ANDRE J. DE BETHUNE, Professor of Chemistry, Boston College, Chestnut Hill, Mass. 02167. *Electrode Potentials of the Elements.*

ORONZIO DE NORA, Founder and Head, Oronzio de Nora-Impianti Elettrochimici, Via Bistolfi 35, Milan, Italy. *Chlorine.*

WILLIAM D. EHMANN, Professor of Chemistry, University of Kentucky, Lexington, Ky. 40506. *Prevalence of the Elements.*

iii

CONTRIBUTORS

LeRoy Eyring, Chairman, Department of Chemistry, Arizona State University, Tempe, Ariz. 85281. *Praseodymium, Terbium.*

Paul Fields, Chemistry Division, Argonne National Laboratory, 9700 South Cass Avenue, Argonne, Ill. 60439. *Lawrencium, Nobelium.*

L. M. Foster, IBM Corporation, Thomas J. Watson Research Center, P.O. Box 218, Yorktown Heights, N.Y. 10598. *Gallium.*

Arnold M. Friedman, Chemistry Division, Argonne National Laboratory, 9700 South Cass Avenue, Argonne, Ill. 60439. *Radium.*

Patrizio Gallone, Research Director, Oronzio de Nora-Impianti Elettrochimici, Via Bistolfi 35, Milan, Italy. *Chlorine.*

Harry C. Gatos, Department of Metallurgy and Materials Science and Center for Materials Science and Engineering, Massachusetts Institute of Technology, Cambrige, Mass. 02139. *Germanium.*

Gary Gerard, Kaiser Aluminum & Chemical Corp., Metals Division Research, Permanente, Calif. 95014. *Aluminum.*

N. J. Goetzinger, Rare Earth Division, American Potash & Chemical Corp., 258 Ann Street, West Chicago, Ill. 60185. *Gadolinium.*

Nathaniel Grier, Senior Investigator, Merck Sharp & Dohme Research Laboratories, Rahway, N.J. 07065. *Mercury.*

R. R. Grinstead, Research Laboratories, The Dow Chemical Company, 2800 Mitchell Drive, Walnut Creek, Calif. 94598. *Copper (Biochemical Behavior).*

William H. Gross, Metal Products Department, The Dow Chemical Company, Midland, Mich. 48640. *Magnesium.*

Karl A. Gschneidner, Jr., Associate Professor and Metallurgist, Department of Metallurgy and Institute for Atomic Research, Iowa State University, Ames, Ia. 50010. *Cerium, Ytterbium.*

French Hagemann, Associate Director, Chemistry Division, Argonne National Laboratory, 9700 South Cass Avenue, Argonne, Ill. 60439. *Actinium.*

Clifford A. Hampel, Consulting Chemical Engineer, 8501 Harding Avenue, Skokie, Ill. 60076. *Barium, Hafnium, Iron, Lithium, Manganese, Rhenium, Strontium.*

Leonard Harris, Plant Metallurgist, Cerro de Pasco Corp., La Oroya, Peru. *Lead.*

R. A. Hemstreet, Central Research Laboratory, Air Reduction Company, Inc., Murray Hill, N.J. 07971. *Argon, Neon.*

Charles K. Hersh, Manager, Propellant Research, IIT Research Institute, 10 W. 35th Street, Chicago, Ill. 60616. *Nitrogen.*

Alvin J. Herzig, President, Climax Molybdenum Company of Michigan, a division of AMAX (American Metal Climax Inc.), 1600 Huron Parkway, Ann Arbor, Mich. 48195. *Molybdenum.*

James C. Hindman, Chemistry Division, Argonne National Laboratory, 9700 South Cass Avenue, Argonne, Ill. 60439. *Neptunium.*

Herbert E. Howe, Central Research Laboratories American Smelting and Refining Company, South Plainfield, N.J. 07080. *Bismuth, Thallium.*

Earl K. Hyde, University of California, Lawrence Radiation Laboratory, Berkeley, Calif. 94720. *Francium.*

Herbert H. Hyman, Chemistry Division, Argonne National Laboratory, 9700 South Cass Avenue, Argonne, Ill. 60439. *Noble Gases.*

Saul Isserow, Manager, Materials Research, Nuclear Metals Division, Whittaker Corp., West Concord, Mass. 01781. *Allotropy.*

C. A. Johnson, Professor of Chemistry, College of Medicine, University of Illinois, 1853 W. Polk Street, Chicago, Ill. 60612. *Iron (Biochemical and Biological Aspects).*

Leslie H. Juel, Technical Director, Graphite Products Division, Great Lakes Carbon Corp., P.O. Box 667, Niagara Falls, N.Y. 14302. *Carbon.*

R. A. King, Research Engineer, General Metallurgical Research, Research and Corporate Development, Cominco Ltd., Trail, British Columbia, Canada. *Indium.*

W. R. King, Kaiser Aluminum & Chemical Corp. Metals Division Research, Permanente, Calif. 95014. *Aluminum.*

George R. Kotrba, 6452 Fireside Drive, Chicago Ridge, Ill. 60415. *Silver.*

A. Labbauf, Jones & Laughlin Steel Corp., Graham Research Laboratory, 900 Agnew Road, Pittsburgh Pa. 15230. *Carbon-12 Scale of Atomic Masses.*

Percy E. Landolt, Consulting Engineer, 595 Madison Avenue, New York, N.Y. 10022. *Lithium.*

F. C. Lanning, Department of Chemistry, Kansas State University, Manhattan, Kans. 66502. *Silicon.*

Carol M. Lauer, Union Carbide Corp., Linde Division Research Laboratory, P.O. Box 44, Tonawanda, N.Y. 14150. *Oxygen.*

ROBERT S. LEHTO, Superintendent of Zinc Refining, Cerro de Pasco Corp., La Oroya, Peru. *Zinc.*

S. C. LIANG, Head, General Metallurgical Research, Research and Corporate Development, Cominco Ltd., Trail, British Columbia, Canada. *Indium.*

M. H. LIETZKE, Group Leader, Chemistry Division, Oak Ridge National Laboratory, P.O. Box X, Oak Ridge, Tenn. 37830. *Atomic Number, Polonium.*

KENNETH L. LINDSAY, Process Research Supervisor, Industrial Chemical Research, Ethyl Corporation, P.O. Box 341, Baton Rouge, La. 70821. *Sodium.*

ROBERT M. MACINTOSH, Manager, Tin Research Institute, Inc., 483 West Sixth Avenue, Columbus, Ohio 43201. *Tin.*

A. G. MADDOCK, University Chemical Laboratory, Lensfield Road, Cambridge, England. *Protactinium.*

CHARLES L. MANTELL, Consulting Chemical Engineer, 457 Washington Street, New York, N.Y. 10013. *Calcium.*

J. H. McCLAIN, Wah Chang Albany Corp., P.O. Box 460, Albany, Ore. 97321. *Zirconium.*

W. A. E. McBRYDE, Dean, Faculty of Science, University of Waterloo, Waterloo, Ontario, Canada. *Iridium, Osmium, Palladium, Platinum, Platinum Metals, Rhodium, Ruthenium.*

JACK F. MILLS, Chemicals Department Research Laboratory, The Dow Chemical Company, 335 Building, Midland, Mich. 48641. *Iodine.*

JOHN MILSTED, Chemistry Division, Argonne National Laboratory, 9700 South Cass Avenue, Argonne, Ill. 60439. *Einsteinium, Fermium, Mendelevium.*

WILLIAM N. MINER, CMF-5, Los Alamos Scientific Laboratory, University of California, P.O. Box 1663, Los Alamos, N. Mex. 87544. *Plutonium.*

THERALD MOELLER, Professor of Inorganic Chemistry, Department of Chemistry and Chemical Engineering, Noyes Chemical Laboratory, University of Illinois, Urbana, Ill. 61801. *Lanthanide Elements.*

JOHN L. MORIARTY, JR., Director of Research, Lunex Company, Pleasant Valley, Ia. 52767; present address: 1917 Perry Street, Davenport, Ia. 52803. *Lanthanum, Neodymium.*

HAROLD P. MORRIS, Head, Nutrition and Carcinogenesis Section, Laboratory of Biochemistry, National Cancer Institute, Bethesda, Md. 20014. *Iodine (Physiological Aspects).*

C. EDWARD MOSHEIM, Group Leader, Kawecki Chemical Company, Boyertown, Pa. 19512. *Cesium, Rubidium.*

ROBERT A. PENNEMAN, CMF-4, Los Alamos Scientific Laboratory, University of California, P.O. Box 1663, Los Alamos, N. Mex. 87544. *Americium.*

E. A. PERETTI, Head, Department of Metallurgical Engineering and Materials Science, College of Engineering, University of Notre Dame, Notre Dame, Ind. 46556. *Copper.*

JACK E. POWELL, Department of Chemistry and Institute for Atomic Research, Iowa State University, Ames, Ia. 50010. *Dysprosium, Thulium.*

P. F. REIGLER, Group Leader, Analytical Laboratories, The Dow Chemical Company, Midland, Mich. 48640. *Bromine.*

J. A. REYNOLDS, United Kingdom Atomic Energy Authority, Culham Laboratory, Culham, Abingdon, Berks., England. *Nuclear Fusion.*

S. J. RIMSHAW, Senior Scientist, Isotopes Development Center, Oak Ridge National Laboratory, P.O. Box X, Oak Ridge, Tenn. 37830. *Technetium.*

HAROLD W. ROBINSON, Head of the Assay Department, Engelhard Industries, Inc., 113 Astor Street, Newark, N.J. 07114. *Gold.*

G. E. RYSCHKEWITSCH, Professor, Department of Chemistry, University of Florida, Gainseville, Fla. 32601. *Bonding, Ionic Compounds.*

R. T. SANDERSON, Department of Chemistry, Arizona State University, Tempe, Ariz. 85281. *Bonding, Chemical; Electronegativity; Electronic Configuration; Periodic Law and Periodic Table.*

JAMES C. SCHAEFER, Project Director, Crystal-Solid State Division, Harshaw Chemical Company, 2240 Prospect Avenue, Cleveland, Ohio 44106. *Boron.*

FRANK F. SCHMIDT, Research Metallurgist, Nonferrous Metallurgy Division, Battelle Memorial Institute, Columbus, Ohio 43201; present address: Manager, Quality Control, Worthington Steel Co., 1152 Industrial Boulevard, Louisville, Ky. 40219. *Niobium.*

E. A. SCHOELD, Research Superintendent, Potash Company of America, P.O. Box 31, Carlsbad, N. Mex. 88220. *Potassium.*

FRED W. SCHONFELD, CMF-5, Los Alamos Scientific Laboratory, University of California,

P.O. Box 1663, Los Alamos, N. Mex. 87544. *Plutonium.*

FELIX SCHREINER, Chemistry Division, Argonne National Laboratory, 9700 South Cass Avenue, Argonne, Ill. 60439. *Krypton.*

GLENN T. SEABORG, Chairman, U.S. Atomic Energy Commission, Washington, D.C. 20545. *Transuranium Elements, Uranium.*

HENRY SELIG, Chemistry Division, Argonne National Laboratory, 9700 South Cass Avenue, Argonne, Ill. 60439; present address: Professor of Chemistry, Department of Inorganic and Analytical Chemistry, Hebrew University, Jerusalem, Israel. *Xenon.*

WALTER L. SILVERNAIL, Rare Earth Division, American Potash & Chemical Corp., 258 Ann Street, West Chicago, Ill. 60185. *Samarium.*

A. A. SMITH, JR., Assistant to the Director of Research, Research Department, American Smelting and Refining Company, South Plainfield, N.J. 07080. *Cadmium.*

FRANK H. SPEDDING, Director, Ames Laboratory, Institute for Atomic Research, Iowa State University, Ames, Ia. 50010. *Erbium, Holmium, Lutetium.*

D. B. SPRINGER, Development and Research Department, International Nickel Company, Inc., 67 Wall street, New York, N.Y. 10005. *Nickel.*

LAWRENCE STEIN, Chemistry Division, Argonne National Laboratory, 9700 South Cass Avenue, Argonne, Ill. 60439. *Radon.*

ELLIS P. STEINBERG, Chemistry Division, Argonne National Laboratory, 9700 South Cass Avenue, Argonne, Ill. 60439. *Nuclear Fission.*

JOHN R. STONE, Superintendent, Development Department, American Smelting and Refining Company, P.O. Box 151, Perth Amboy, N.J. 08861. *Selenium.*

R. W. STOUGHTON, Group Leader, Chemistry Division, Oak Ridge National Laboratory, P.O. Box X, Oak Ridge, Tenn. 37830. *Atomic Number, Polonium.*

G. L. THOMPSON, Rare Earth Division, American Potash & Chemical Corp., 258 Ann Street, West Chicago, Ill. 60185. *Europium.*

JAMES W. TRURAN, Institute for Space Studies, Goddard Space Flight Center, NASA, 475 Riverside Drive, New York, N.Y. 10027. *Origin of the Elements.*

RALPH H. WEHRMANN, Consultant, 10062 Betty Jane Lane, Dallas, Tex. 75229. *Tantalum.*

FRITZ WEIGEL, Head, Radiochemistry Laboratory, Institute of Inorganic Chemistry, University of Munich, Meiserstrasse 1, 8·Munchen 2, West Germany. *Promethium.*

GLENN B. WENGERT, Section Leader, Analytical Laboratories, The Dow Chemical Company, Midland, Mich. 48640. *Bromine.*

THOMAS P. WHALEY, Manager, Inorganic and Physical Chemistry, Growth Sciences Center, International Minerals and Chemical Corp., Libertyville, Ill. 60048. *Phosphorus.*

C. E. T. WHITE, Manager, Electronic Materials Division, Cominco American Inc., Spokane, Wash. 99215. *Indium.*

CARL R. WHITTEMORE, Deloro Stellite, Division of Deloro Smelting and Refining Co., Ltd., Belleville, Ontario, Canada. *Cobalt.*

HARLEY A. WILHELM, Departments of Chemistry and Metallurgy and Institute for Atomic Research, Iowa State University, Ames, Ia. 50010. *Thorium.*

AUGUST F. WITT, Department of Metallurgy and Materials Science and Center for Materials Science and Engineering, Massachusetts Institute of Technology, Cambridge, Mass. 02139. *Germanium.*

PREFACE

"The Encyclopedia of the Chemical Elements" has been prepared to meet the need for a single volume devoted to the chemical elements. Its object is to present in a concise and authoritative manner information on the nature, properties and behavior of each of the 103 elements.

The emphasis in the articles about the individual elements is on the elemental form, so this is not a book on general inorganic chemistry. Indeed, its compilation is based on the realization that inorganic chemistry books do not provide sufficient information about the elements themselves. This book includes material on the discovery and history of each element, its prevalence, sources, derivation, physical properties (an aspect given scanty treatment in inorganic chemistry books) and chemical properties, the importance of the element and its compounds, applications of the element, and its biological and biochemical nature, including toxicological factors. A short reference list accompanies each article for supplemental reading.

In addition to an article on each of the 103 elements, the book contains about 20 articles of a general nature on related subjects. Among their titles are: "Periodic Law and Periodic Table," "Noble Gases," "Lanthanide Elements," "Transuranium Elements," "Isotopes," "Electronic Configuration," "Origin of the Elements," and "Prevalence of the Elements." A complete tabulation of the electrode potentials of the elements is included.

Recent advances in knowledge about the elements have been covered. This is especially valuable to readers seeking information about the transuranium and other actinide elements, the rare earth elements, the noble gases (with their newly discovered chemical activity), and the many hitherto uncommon or rare metals, all of which have gained increasing attention in recent years.

The entries in the book have been prepared by 104 knowledgeable individuals, and their contributions make the book more authoritative and valuable than one which a single author or two or more coauthors could produce. The entries are arranged in encyclopedic fashion in alphabetical sequence, and each is a self-contained entity.

The sequence of sections in each of the articles about the individual elements is similar insofar as possible. However, as might be expected, the emphasis varies somewhat from entry to entry depending on the background of the respective contributor. One of the major jobs of the Editor was to maintain the desired balance of coverage about each element, but strict uniformity of treatment was not possible, so variety will be found among the entries. In fact, this variety is bound to be encountered in all encyclopedic books prepared with the aid of a multitude of authors.

The length of the articles ranges from 1400 to 7000 words according to a scale worked out by the Editor so that the final book would contain the desired number of pages. While opinions may vary about how much space should have been assigned to each entry, it is obvious that those on elements like oxygen, sulfur and chlorine should be longer than those on antimony, bromine and gold, which in turn should be allotted more space than entries on actinium, cesium and erbium, to cite a few examples. The well-known fact that it is easier to write a long letter or report than a short one applies as well to the writing of articles. Thus, another of the major problems facing the Editor was to trim overlong manuscripts down to requested length. Had this not been done, "The Encyclopedia of the Chemical Elements" would have been approximately 50% longer, a situation adverse to the purpose and cost of the book.

The success of the book has been, of course, vitally dependent on the cheerful cooperation of the 104 contributors, and to each of these busy individuals I again express my sincere appreciation for sharing their knowledge and experience via their contributions.

I wish to acknowledge especially the assistance and advice given by Paul Fields of Argonne National Laboratory about authors for articles on the individual actinide elements; by Herman H. Hyman of Argonne National Laboratory about writers for articles on the noble (or rare) gases; and by Karl A. Gschneidner, Jr., of the Ames Laboratory for contributors of articles on the rare earth elements. Special appreciation is due W. A. E.

McBryde of the University of Waterloo, Canada, for preparing individual articles about each of the six platinum metals along with the general one on "Platinum Metals"; and Glenn T. Seaborg of the U.S. Atomic Energy Commission for reviewing the articles on the individual transuranium elements in addition to writing the entries on "Uranium" and "Transuranium Elements."

The support and advice of Gessner G. Hawley of Reinhold, whose idea it was that this book should be prepared, and the all-important processing of the manuscripts and proofs by Alberta Gordon and her associates at Reinhold, have been of great import and value to the Editor.

Without the encouragement offered by my wife, Merrylyn, and her willingness to listen to a variety of complaints by the Editor about improperly prepared articles, long-delayed receipt of manuscripts, and other factors affecting the smooth preparation of the book, the project would have been much more difficult to handle and complete.

CLIFFORD A. HAMPEL

Skokie, Illinois
March, 1968

A

ACTINIUM

Discovery

Actinium, atomic number 89, mass 225, was discovered by Debierne in 1899 and independently by Giesel in 1902, in the rare earth fraction of pitchblende residues. The name actinium (*aktis*, ray) was proposed by Debierne.

The genetic relationships of the members of the actinium decay series were determined during the next twenty years by radiochemical studies (Fig. 1). The parent of the series, U^{235}, and the mass numbers of all its members were established by Dempster in 1935, by mass spectrometric analysis.

Occurrence

Actinium-227 occurs in small amounts in all uranium ores. Two other isotopes of actinium are also found in trace amounts in nature, mesothorium II (Ac^{228}) and Ac^{225}. Mesothorium II, a 6.13-hr beta emittor, is a decay product of thorium-232.

Although actinium-225 is not normally considered a naturally occurring isotope because the parent Np^{237} is geologically short-lived, trace amounts are found in ore concentrates, resulting from reaction of neutrons with uranium and thorium to form the parent Np^{237} and U^{233} via the reactions

$$U^{238}(n,2n)\ U^{237} \rightarrow Np^{237} \text{ and}$$
$$Th^{232}(n,\gamma)\ Th^{233} \rightarrow U^{233}.$$

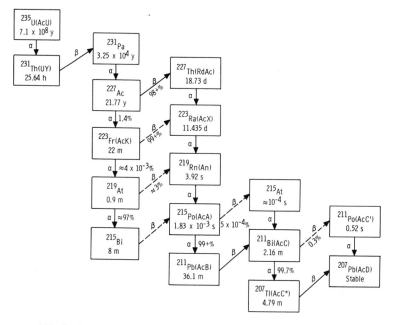

FIG. 1. Decay scheme of the uranium-actinium radioactive series.

TABLE 1. ISOTOPES OF ACTINIUM

Isotope	Types of Radiation	Half-life	Energy of Principal Radiations, MeV
Ac^{221}	α	$\ll$ 1 sec	7.6
Ac^{222}	α	4.2 sec	6.998(93%), 6.952(6%)
Ac^{223}	α (99%) EC (1%)	2.2 min	α 6.657 (37.5%) 6.643 (42.1%) 6.561 (13.3%)
Ac^{224}	α (10%) EC (90%)	2.9 hr	α 6.205 (32%), 6.139 (26%), 6.044 (32%) γ 0.217 (62%), 0.133 (28%)
Ac^{225}	α	10.0 day	5.829 (52%) 5.793 (28%), 5.732 + 5.724 (12%)
Ac^{226}	β^- (80%) EC (20%)	29 hr	β^- 1.2 max; γ 0.253 (11%), 0.230 (47%), 0.185 (9%), 0.158 (32%)
Ac^{227}	α (1.4%) β^- (98.6%)	21.8 yr	α 4.989 (48.7%), 4.936 (36.1%) 4.866 (6.9%) 4.849 (5.5%) β 0.046 max.
Ac^{228}	β^-, γ	6.13 hr	β^- 2.11 max; γ 1.587 (8% complex), 0.96 (20% complex), 0.908 (25%), 0.34 (15% complex)
Ac^{229}	β^-	66 min	0.9 (predicted)
Ac^{230}	β^-	< 1 min	2.2 max.
Ac^{231}	β^-, γ	15 min	β 2.1 max; γ 0.71, 0.39, 0.28, 0.185

Eight additional isotopes of actinium have been produced artificially by nuclear reactions A list of the isotopes of actinium is given in Table 1.

Nuclear Properties

Actinium-227. Actinium-227 decays with a 21.8-year half-life primarily by weak beta-particle emission.

Alpha-branching decay of actinium-227 was first observed in 1914 and in 1939, the product of such decay, the new element, francium (AcK) was isolated. Reported values of the alpha-branching range from 1.25-1.45%. The energy of the alpha particle is 4.95 MeV. The upper limit of the thermal neutron fission cross section is 2×10^{-24} cm^2.

Actinium-228. The beta spectrum of Ac^{228} (MsTh-2) is complex but no alpha branching occurs and the maximum energy of the beta particles is 2.1 MeV. MsTh-2 decays with a 6.13-hour half-life to form 1.9-year radiothorium (Th^{228}).

Actinium-225. This isotope is particularly useful for radioactive tracer studies because of its favorable 10.0-day half-life. It may be assayed by alpha counting after allowing eight hours for transient equilibrium of the four alpha-emitting daughters. Actinium-225 is obtained as a decay product of U^{233} which is produced by neutron irradiation of Th^{232}.

Preparation and Isolation of Actinium

Actinium-227 is the only isotope of actinium sufficiently long-lived to permit separation of macro amounts of the element. It has never been isolated in greater than trace amounts from natural sources because of its low abundance and its chemical similarity to lanthanum and the lighter rare earths which are present in much greater concentrations in the ores.

Milligram amounts of actinium have been produced by the transmutation of radium in a neutron reactor via the reactions

$$Ra^{226} (n,\gamma) Ra^{227}; Ra^{227} \xrightarrow[41.2 \text{ min}]{\beta^-} Ac^{227}.$$

Since radium can readily be purified from rare earths the difficult lanthanum-actinium separation is avoided. Solvent extraction or ion exchange procedures are preferred for the separation of actinium from radium and daughter products because they are more easily adapted to the remotely controlled shielded operations necessary for radiation protection.

Actinium Metal

Actinium metal has been prepared by reduction of actinium trifluoride with lithium vapor at 1100–1275°C.

Physical Properties

Actinium metal is silvery white, melting at 1050 (± 50)°C. The vapor pressure at 1600°C is about 0.007 mm. The estimated boiling point is 3200 (± 300)°C.

The optical absorption spectrum of actinium in $1M$ HCl has been examined in the visible and ultraviolet ranges. As expected from the lack of color in actinium solutions no absorption occurs in the region 400 to 1000 mμ. There is a slight absorption in the 300–400 mμ region and a pronounced peak at 250 mμ.

Lub in 1937 measured seven lines in the visible and ultraviolet region of the emission spectrum of actinium in samples of lanthanum oxide containing 1% of actinium which were prepared by M. Curie. These measurements were confirmed and the list of lines greatly extended by Meggers, Fred and Tomkins in 1951 using a one milligram sample of pure actinium oxide in a hollow cathode discharge supplemented by smaller spark excited samples. A fairly complete term analysis has been obtained for Ac (II) which resembles Y (II) more closely than La (II) or Sc (II). The f electron is less firmly bound in Ac (II) than in La (II). The Ac (I) term analysis is as yet fragmentary; the ground state is $6d\,7s^2\ ^2D_{3/2}$ with a doublet splitting of 2231.4 cm^{-1}. From the hyperfine structure the indicated nuclear spin of Ac^{227} is 3/2.

Chemical Properties

The chemical behavior of actinium is very similar to that of the tripositive rare earths, particularly to that of its lower homolog, lanthanum. The only known oxidation state in aqueous solution is $+3$. Its high basicity and large atomic radius (1.11 Å) place actinium intermediate between lanthanum, the most basic tripositive rare earth and the dipositive alkaline earths. The formal electrode potential of actinium for the reaction $Ac \rightarrow Ac^{+3}$(SHE) is 2.6 volts. The metal is highly reactive and cannot be prepared by electrolysis from aqueous solution.

Coprecipitation. The coprecipitation of trace amounts of actinium from solution with comparatively large amounts of insoluble precipitates is summarized in Table 2. Lanthanum is the preferred carrier for actin-

TABLE 2. COPRECIPITATION OF TRACER ACTINIUM WITH VARIOUS PRECIPITATES

Carrier	Conditions	% Carried
Hydroxides of Al, Fe, Y, Zr, and rare earths	complete precipitation of carrier with NH_4OH or NaOH	~100
$Th_2O_7.4H_2O$	precipitation with H_2O_2 from dilute HNO_3 solution	0
$BaCl_2.2H_2O$	precipitation from concentrated HCl	0
LaF_3	precipitation with HF, HNO_3 conc. $< 5N$, low NH_4^+ concentration	~100
$Zr\,(IO_3)_2$	precipitation with KIO_3, 0.2N HNO_3, low NH_4^+ conc.	70–97
$BiPO_4$	precipitation with H_3PO_4 from hot 0.1N HNO_3 low NH_4^+ conc.	95
	Same, except 1N NHO_3	4
$LaPO_4$	neutralization of hot H_3PO_4 solution with NH_4OH	~100
$La_2(C_2O_4)_3$	Hot ammoniacal or slightly acid solution	~100
$La_2(CO_3)_3$	alkaline solution	~100
$ZrO(H_2PO_4)_2$	precipitation with H_3PO_4 from 1 M HNO_3	< 1
$BaSO_4$	precipitation with H_2SO_4 from dilute HNO_3 solution	11–96
$PbSO_4$	precipitation from 6 M H_2SO_4	~90
acid-insoluble sulfides (PbS, Bi_2S_3)	precipitation from acid solution	0

ium where subsequent lanthanum-actinium separation is not required.

Separation of Actinium from other Elements

Precipitation. Actinium is separated along with rare earth elements by the usual rare earth group separation procedures based upon the insolubility of the oxalates, fluorides, and hydroxides. Thorium may be precipitated as the thiosulfate or iodate from slightly acid solution leaving actinium in solution but the separation is somewhat erratic. Precipitation of thorium peroxyhydroxide from hot, slightly acidic solution with excess hydrogen peroxide is a good method of separation. Radium remains in solution when actinium hydroxide is precipitated from a carbonate-free solution of ammonia. Radium chromate precipitates from boiling solution buffered with sodium acetate leaving actinium in solution. Heavy elements which form acid-insoluble sulfides may be separated from actinium by precipitation from slightly acid solutions. Impurities such as iron and aluminum may be conveniently removed by precipitation of actinium as the insoluble oxalate.

Solvent Extraction. TTA (Thenoyltrifluoroacetone) in nonpolar solvent is a useful extractant for separation of actinium from radioactive daughter elements. However, the extraction is highly pH dependent and the solvent apparently undergoes radiolytic decomposition at high radiation levels. Tributyl phosphate and the di(2-ethyl hexyl) and di(octyl-phenyl) esters of orthophosphoric acid (HDEHP and HDOϕP), although somewhat lacking in specificity, are particularly useful solvents since they may be used in systems sufficiently acidic to avoid hydrolysis of actinium and require no salting-out agents.

Chromatographic Separation. Actinium can be readily and completely separated from other elements, including the rare earths, with "Dowex"-50 cation exchange resin.

Actinium and lanthanum separation has been accomplished on an anion exchange ("Dowex"-1) column using 4.4 M $LiNO_3$ eluant but with less efficiency than a cation exchange system. In this case, the distribution coefficient of Ac lies between that of Nd and Sm instead of the expected position beyond La. There is no evidence for anionic complexes of actinium.

Actinium Compounds

A number of pure actinium compounds have been prepared and characterized by x-ray

TABLE 3. CRYSTALLINE STRUCTURE OF COMPOUNDS OF ACTINIUM AND LANTHANUM

Compound	Symmetry	Type of Structure	Lattice Constants, Å				Calculated Density g/cc
AcF_3	Hexagonal	LaF_3	4.27	± 0.01	7.53	± 0.02	7.88
LaF_3	Hexagonal	LaF_3	4.140	± 0.001	7.336	± 0.001	5.93
$AcCl_3$	Hexagonal	UCl_3	7.62	± 0.02	4.55	± 0.02	4.81
$LaCl_3$	Hexagonal	UCl_3	7.468	± 0.003	4.366	± 0.003	3.84
$AcBr_3$	Hexagonal	UCl_3	8.06	± 0.04	4.68	± 0.02	5.85
$LaBr_3$	Hexagonal	UCl_3	7.951	± 0.003	4.501	± 0.003	5.07
AcOF	Cubic	CaF_2	5.931	± 0.002			8.28
LaOF	Cubic	CaF_2	5.76	± 0.02			6.00
AcOCl	Tetragonal	PbFCl	4.24	± 0.02	7.07	± 0.03	7.23
LaOCl	Tetragonal	PbFCl	4.113	± 0.003	6.871	± 0.009	5.41
AcOBr	Tetragonal	PbFCl	4.27	± 0.02	7.40	± 0.03	7.89
LaOBr	Tetragonal	PbFCl	4.147	± 0.003	7.376	± 0.012	6.11
Ac_2O_3	Hexagonal	La_2O_3	4.07	± 0.01	6.29	± 0.02	9.19
La_2O_3	Hexagonal	La_2O_3	3.93	± 0.01	6.12	± 0.02	6.57
Ac_2S_3	Cubic	Ce_2S_3	8.97	± 0.01			6.75
La_2S_3	Cubic	Ce_2S_3	8.706	± 0.001			5.01
$AcPO_4.1/2H_2O$	Hexagonal	$LaPO_4.1/2H_2O$	7.21	± 0.02	6.64	± 0.03	5.48
$LaPO_4.1/2H_2O$	Hesagonal	$LaPO_4.1/2H_2O$	7.081	± 0.005	6.468	± 0.008	4.28

diffraction patterns. The preparations were conducted on a ten microgram scale to minimize radiation health hazards and fogging of the x-ray film by gamma radiation which grows in rapidly after purification. In all cases where the actinium compound was identified it was isostructural with the corresponding lanthanum compounds and exhibited only the trivalent state (Table 3).

Detection and Determination

If present in sufficient quantity (> 0.01 microgram), actinium may be detected and determined by its characteristic emission spectrum. However, since it is most frequently encountered in trace concentration, the most useful analytical method is radio-assay. Ac^{227} emits such weak radiations that determination is usually based upon measurement of the more energetic daughter activities.

Physiological Behavior of Actinium

Although actinium is primarily a beta-emittor, in view of its five alpha-emitting daughters, it should be classed as a hazardous radioactive poison of high specific alpha activity along with radium and the trans-uranium elements plutonium, americium, and curium. The metabolic behavior of actinium in the rat is almost indistinguishable from that of the lanthanide rare earths. The most important characteristic is the tendency for actinium to accumulate and to be tenaciously retained by the skeleton in the superficial layers of the bone structure. The rate of elimination of actinium from the body is much less than the rate of radioactive decay.

References

1. Bagnall, K. W., "Chemistry of the Rare Radioelements," 150–165, New York, Academic Press, 1957.
2. Hagemann, F., "The Chemistry of Actinium," in G. T. Seaborg and J. J. Katz, "The Actinide Elements," Natl. Nuclear Energy Series IV, Vol. 14A, 14–44, New York, McGraw-Hill, 1954.
3. Herr, W., "Actinium and Isotope," in W. Fresenius and G. Jander, Eds., "Handbuch der Analytischen Chemie," Berlin, Springer Verlag, 1956.
4. Hyde, E. K., Perlman I., and Seaborg, G. T., "The Nuclear Properties of the Heavy Elements," Vol. 2, New Jersey, Prentice-Hall, 1964.
5. Katz, J. J., and Seaborg, G. T., "The Chemistry of the Actinide Elements," 5–15, London, Methuen, 1957.
6. Kirby, H. W., "The Analytical Chemistry of Actinium," in H. A. Elion and D. C. Stewart, "Progress in Nuclear Energy," Series 9, Analytical Chemistry Vol. 8, Part 1, Oxford, 1967.
7. Pietsch, E., "Actinium and Isotope," in "Gmelins Handbuch der anorganische Chemie," System number 40, Berlin, Verlag Chemie, 1942.
8. Salutsky, M. L., "Actinium" in C. L. and D. W. Wilson, "Comprehensive Analytical Chemistry," Vol. IC, 492–496, Amsterdam, Elsevier, 1962.
9. Sedlet, J., "Actinium, Astatine, Francium, Polonium, and Protactinium," in I. M. Koltoff and P. J. Elving, "Treatise on Analytical Chemistry," Vol. 6, Part II, Section A, 439–485, New York, Interscience, 1964.
10. Stevenson, P. C., and Nervik, W. E., "The Radiochemistry of the Rare Earths, Scandium, Yttrium, and Actinium," United States Atomic Energy Commission, NAS-NS-3020, 1961.

FRENCH HAGEMANN

ALLOTROPY

Allotropy is the existence of a substance in two or more different forms. Polymorphism is a more suitable term, especially for different crystalline phases, but the term allotropy has been generally adopted for the elements. It is applied even when the forms are not crystalline, such as the different forms of liquid sulfur or helium or the 0_2–0_3 (ozone) forms of molecular oxygen. The different forms, designated as allotropes or polymorphs, are thermodynamically different and therefore manifest significant differences in various properties, both physical and chemical. Thus, allotropes can differ in atomic configuration and dimensions (hence in density), melting and boiling points, color, and thermal conductivity. In addition, allotropes show marked differences in reactivity with various reagents and in solubility in different solvents. The conditions for the preparation of an element can determine which allotrope is obtained.

The transformation between the allotropes is unidirectional if one of the forms always has a higher free energy, being metastable and requiring an energy input for its initial formation. In most cases, the transformation is reversible and is governed by the same physicochemical considerations that govern other phase equilibria such as melting and vaporization. Thus, a single-component two-phase system is univariant, i.e., according to the phase rule either the temperature or the the pressure, but not both, may be independently specified for the coexistence of two phases. The relation between the equilibrium temperature and pressure is determined, according to the Clapeyron equation, by the enthalpy and volume changes associated with the phase transformation, $dp/dt = \dfrac{\triangle H}{T \triangle V}$. The coexistence of three phases of a uniquely defined composition is an invariant situation, i.e., the temperature and pressure are defined by the composition and are unique properties of the substance.

From a practical point of view, it is very important that the temperature for transformation between two phases of an element (usually specified at atmospheric pressure) can be altered by the presence of other elements. If these solute elements dissolve to different extents in the allotropes of the base element, the dependence of the free energies of the individual allotropes on temperature is so modified as to shift the equilibrium temperature, i.e., the temperature at which the free energies are equal. The allotrope in which solubility is greater is stabilized since the temperature at which it prevails has been lowered or raised, depending on whether it is the high- or low-temperature phase (The situation is analogous to depression of the melting point by a solute that is more soluble in the liquid than in the solid.) The dependence of the transformation temperature on solute concentration is of course an essential aspect of the phase diagram for the base element and the solute.

Another important consideration in the relation between the allotropes is the delay in reaching equilibrium, especially in the presence of solutes. A metastable phase may persist, a situation that is not necessarily undesirable and is in fact often exploited to retain a desirable allotrope. This situation may be encouraged by incorporation of solute elements that, even if they do not effect retention of the desirable allotrope under equilibrium conditions, are so effective in retarding attainment of equilibrium that, for all practical purposes, they have effected retention of a metastable phase.

Examples of allotropy are so abundant that allotropy is the rule rather than the exception, especially when one considers the effect of pressure as well as temperature on phase stability. Even at atmospheric pressure some elements exhibit many crystalline forms: uranium, 3; manganese, 4; plutonium, 6! More extended information can be found in the entries on these elements and also others, such as helium, hydrogen, carbon, phosphorus, and sulfur, in which allotropy plays an important part. The following two paragraphs respectively cite examples of metallic and nonmetalic elements in which allotropy has to be taken into account.

The most common example of the manipulation of allotropy is found in the heat treatment of steel to obtain phases with the desired metallurgical properties. Carbon is the most prominent of the alloying elements introduced for the effect on the relative stability of the phases. In other metallic systems, consideration has to be given to the differences between properties of the allotropes. Thus, it may be essential to avoid transformations that can lead to dimensional changes or deterioration of mechanical properties (grey tin). In alloy systems, attention must be paid to the partitioning of solute elements between phases; such partitioning can cause serious inhomogeneities (the hexagonal alpha phase of titanium or zirconium versus the body-centered cubic beta). Transformations may be used to wipe out preferred orientation imparted by working (beta-phase treatment of uranium worked in the alpha phase). Metals difficult to work in their common structure may become workable in a structure stable under different conditions.

Nonmetallic elements provide some of the classical examples of allotropy. White phosphorus is obtained by condensation from the vapors in the usual reduction. The more stable red allotrope can be obtained by heating at 240–250°C in the presence of a catalyst such as iodine. It differs from white phosphorus in its substantially lower reactivity and in its insolubility in a variety of solvents. A black allotrope can be obtained under pressure. Another white allotrope is stable below $-77°K$. Sulfur has a variety of allotropic forms in both the solid and liquid phases—as discussed in its entry. The well-known allotropy of graphite and diamond has provided the basis for the goal of preparing the more valuable form, an accomplishment requiring the extreme conditions of temperature and pressure where it is the stable allotrope.

References

1. Cottrell, A. H., "Theoretical Structural Metallurgy," New York, St. Martin's Press, Inc. 1955.
2. Hume-Rothery, William, and Raynor, G. V., "The Structure of Metals and Alloys," 3rd Ed., London, The Institute of Metals, 1954.
3. Klement, William, Jr., and Jayaraman, Aiyasami, chapter on "Phase Relations and Structure of Solids at High Pressures," in "Progress In Solid State Chemistry," H. Reiss, Editor, Vol. 3, New York, Pergamon Press, 1967.

SAUL ISSEROW

ALUMINUM

History

Aluminum is the most abundant (8.13%) metallic element in the earth's crust and, after oxygen and silicon, the third most abundant of all elements. Because of its strong affinity to oxygen, it is not found in the elemental state but only in combined forms such as oxides or silicates.

The metal derives its name from *alumen,* the Latin name for alum. In 1761 L. B. G. de Morveau proposed the name *alumine* for the base in alum, and in 1787 Lavoisier definitely identified it as the oxide of a still undiscovered metal. In 1807 Sir Humphrey Davy proposed the name *alumium* for this metal and later agreed to change it to *aluminum.* Shortly thereafter, the name *aluminium* was adopted to conform with the "ium" ending of most elements, and this spelling is now in general use throughout the world. Aluminium was also the accepted spelling in the United States until 1925 when the American Chemical Society officially reverted to *aluminum.*

Hans Christian Oersted is now generally credited with having been the first to prepare metallic aluminum. He accomplished this in 1825 by heating anhydrous aluminum chloride with potassium amalgam and distilling off the mercury. Frederick Wöhler improved the process between 1827 and 1845 by substituting potassium for the amalgam and by developing a better method for dehydrating aluminum chloride. In 1854 Henri Sainte-Claire Deville substituted sodium for the relatively expensive potassium and, by using sodium aluminum chloride instead of aluminum chloride, produced in a pilot plant near Paris the first commercial quantities of aluminum. Several plants using essentially this process were subsequently built in France and in Great Britain, but none survived for long the advent in 1886 of the electrolytic process, which has dominated the industry ever since.

The development of the electrolytic process dates back to Sir Humphrey Davy who in 1807 attempted unsuccessfully to electrolyze a mixture of alumina and potash. Later, in 1854 Robert Wilhelm von Bunsen and Sainte-Claire Deville independently prepared aluminum by electrolysis of fused sodium aluminum chloride, but this process was not exploited for lack of an economic source of electricity. Gramme's invention of the dynamo (in 1866) changed this and paved the way for the invention of the modern process. In 1886 Charles Martin Hall of Oberlin, Ohio, and Paul L. T. Héroult of France, both 22 years old at the time, discovered and patented almost simultaneously the process in which alumina is dissolved in molten cryolite and decomposed electrolytically. This reduction process, generally known as the Hall-Héroult process, has successfully withstood many attempts to supplant it; it remains the only method by which aluminum is being produced today in commercial quantities.

Raw Materials and Manufacture

Bauxite. Most of the aluminum produced today is made from bauxite. The only other ore serving as a raw material for aluminum is nepheline (a sodium potassium aluminum silicate) which is being used increasingly in the Soviet Union for lack of adequate indigenous bauxites.

Bauxite derives its name from the village of Les Baux in southern France where it was discovered in 1821. The term is generic. It refers to an ore or to a mixture of minerals rich in hydrated aluminum oxides, formed by the weathering of aluminous rocks such as nepheline, feldspars, serpentine, clays, etc. During weathering the silicates are decomposed and the decomposition products (silica, lime, soda, potash, etc.) are leached out, leaving behind a residue enriched in alumina, iron oxide, and titanium oxide but still containing some silica. In tropical and subtropical regions the weathering process is more intense, and this is where most of the large bauxite deposits are found, at or near the surface.

Most bauxites contain 40–60% alumina, either as the trihydrate gibbsite (also called hydrargillite) or as the monohydrates boehmite and diaspore. The tropical bauxites contain primarily gibbsite. Boehmite prevails in bauxites found in a broad belt along the northern Mediterranean. These deposits, extending from Spain through southern France, Italy, Yugoslavia, Austria, and Hungary through Greece, provide the base for the European aluminum industry. Predominantly diasporic bauxites, found largely in countries in the temperate zone, are less desirable for alumina extraction because of their poorer solubility in caustic. At 150°C, for example, diaspore is virtually insoluble in 100 gpl Na_2O, while the solubilities of gibbsite and boehmite are 124 and 66 gpl Al_2O_3, respectively.

The most objectionable contaminant in bauxites is silica, particularly the so-called "reactive silica," which ties up soda and alumina in the extraction process to form insoluble sodium aluminum silicates. For economic reasons the conventional, so-called Bayer alumina processes generally limit the reactive silica content in the bauxite to 5–6%. (Special circumstances have resulted in at least one Arkansas plant using bauxite with up to 18% SiO_2. This is not a straight Bayer plant, however.)

The annual world output of bauxite (dry equivalent) reached 36.5 million long tons in 1965, more than twice the amount (17.7 million tons) mined in 1955. The aluminum industry accounted for about 90% of the bauxite used. (The remainder went into abrasives, refractories, chemicals, aluminous cements, and other products.) Estimated world reserves at the end of 1965 stood at more than 5.7 billion tons.

Based on the rule of thumb that 4 tons of bauxite are required to produce 1 ton of aluminum, the reserves should meet the requirements of the industry for some 220 years at 1965 production levels. Moreover, new ore deposits are being discovered considerably faster than the rate at which bauxite is currently being used, and this situation should prevail for some time to come.

Bayer Process. Bauxite cannot be used directly in the electrolytic reduction to aluminum; it must be refined first. The refining process predominantly in use today is the so-called Bayer process, named after the Austrian, Karl Joseph Bayer who patented it in 1888. Basically, ground bauxite is digested under pressure with a caustic solution that dissolves the alumina and silica while leaving most of the impurities behind as an insoluble residue. The resulting sodium aluminate liquor is held for a while to allow "desilication" (precipitation of silica as sodium aluminum silicate) to take place and is then clarified by settling with starch and then filtering. The residue, called "red mud," is washed countercurrently and eventually discarded, while the clarified liquor is diluted, cooled, and seeded with alumina trihydrate from a previous cycle. Seeding promotes hydrolysis of the aluminate liquor (a step generally referred to as "decomposition" in Europe and "precipitation" in North America), and the resulting trihydrate crystals are filtered off or classified. In the United States the fine product fraction is returned to serve as seed in future precipitations and the coarse fraction is washed and calcined at >1100°C to nonhygroscopic anhydrous alumina. This product is then shipped to reduction plants.

Bayer plants are very large by conventional standards. For example, a plant producing 1000 tons of alumina per day must accommodate a stream of about 3000 gallons per minute. The following raw materials are used in the production of one ton of alumina by the Bayer process:

Bauxite (from Jamaica), tons
(dry basis) — 2.3
Soda ash, pounds — 180
Lime, pounds — 140
Starch, pounds — 11
Fuel, Btu — 10,000

Caustic soda reacts with most siliceous materials in the bauxite to produce an insoluble sodium aluminum silicate which precipitates with the mud. Because this ties up roughly 1 ton of soda and 1 ton of alumina for each ton of silica, the Bayer process is economically unsuitable for the treatment of bauxites containing more than 5–6% reactive silica unless provisions are made to recover the alumina and soda values from the red mud. In the so-called "combination process," developed by Alcoa for the treatment of Arkansas ores containing 10–18% SiO_2, the red mud is mixed with limestone and soda ash and calcined at 1300°C ("lime-soda sinter"); on cooling, the sinter is leached with water to give sodium aluminate liquor, and calcium silicate, which is discarded along with the other impurities.

Many other alkaline sinter processes have been proposed, and some were actually used in various countries primarily during World War II, when traditional supply routes were disrupted and producers had to rely on domestic ores. Few of these processes survive. A notable exception is the soda-lime sinter process used increasingly in the Soviet Union for the treatment of nepheline. This mineral, a sodium potassium aluminum silicate, is available in almost unlimited quantity in Siberia where large hydroelectric power projects are being developed to accommodate a considerable expansion of aluminum capacity.

The by-products of the nepheline process are about 9 tons of Portland cement and 1 ton of soda and potash per ton of alumina produced.

World War II was also responsible for the fairly widespread use of acid processes for the extraction of alumina from siliceous ores such as clays. Various acids and acid salts (hydrochloric, sulfuric, nitric, sulfurous; ammonium sulfate, sodium bisulfate) were used, alone or in combination; but important obstacles (poor product purity, inadequate acid recovery) could not be overcome, and all these processes were abandoned at the end of the war.

Detailed descriptions of the Bayer process and of alternate alumina processes are given in References 1–3.

The Reduction Process

Primary aluminum is now produced exclusively by the Hall-Héroult electrolytic process. The

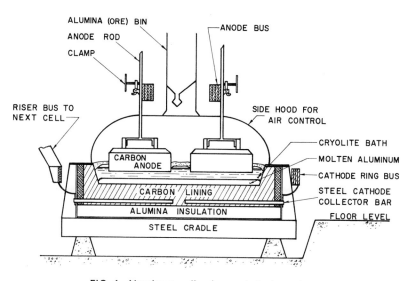

FIG. 1. Aluminum cell using prebaked anodes.

basic process has not changed since its discovery more than 80 years ago, but the productivity of the cells has been improved dramatically over the years.

Two types of cells (also called "pots") are in common use today: one, the "prebaked" cell, uses multiple prebaked anodes; the other, called Soderberg cell, uses a continuous self-baking anode.

A typical prebake cell, shown schematically in Fig. 1, consists of a rectangular steel shell, lined with insulating brick and an inner carbon lining. The cell holds the molten cryolite-alumina electrolyte, commonly called "bath". The carbon bottom is covered by a pad of molten aluminum serving as the cathode. The anodes are prebaked carbon blocks, suspended into the electrolyte by steel rods which connect them to the anode bus. The cathodic current is collected from the carbon bottom by imbedded steel bars that protrude through the shell to connect with the cathode bus.

The bath is covered by a crust of frozen electrolyte which supports a blanket of alumina. At periodic intervals, portions of the crust are broken and fed into the cell along with some alumina from the top. During electrolysis, aluminum is deposited on the metal pad and the oxygen, liberated at the anode, reacts with the carbon to CO_2, some of which is reduced to CO by secondary reactions. At 24–48 hour intervals, aluminum is tapped from the cell by a cast iron siphon, taken to holding furnaces (where it is fluxed, degassed, and also alloyed) and eventually cast. As the anodes are consumed, they are regularly lowered into the bath to maintain a constant anode-to-cathode distance. After about 1–3 weeks, depending on operating conditions, only a stub remains of the anode block and this is replaced by a new anode.

The need for changing the anodes (each cell has 20–54 anodes and there may be as many as 1000 cells in a plant) and particularly the cost of maintaining fabricating and rodding facilities led to the development (in 1923) and extensive use of the Soderberg cell. In this cell, shown schematically in Fig. 2, the anode is self-baking and continuous. A carbon paste of about two-thirds coke and one-third pitch is fed at intervals into a steel casing open at the top and bottom and supended above the furnace. Rows of studs (also called pins or stubs) are inserted into the paste at several levels, both to supply current and to support the mass. The paste moves down in the casing at the rate at which the anode is consumed; and by the time it reaches a certain point above the bath, it is fully baked, the necessary heat having been supplied by the molten bath and by the electrical resistance of the carbon. Eventually the lowest row of studs must be pulled, cleaned, and reinserted at a higher level into the paste; but this, apart from the height adjustment of the anode after

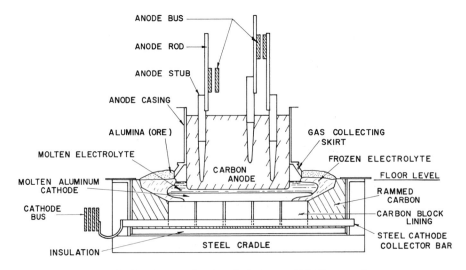

FIG. 2. Aluminum cell using Soderberg self-baking anodes.

tapping, is the only labor directly related to anode handling.

There are some disadvantages to Soderbergs, however, (mainly a complex fume collection system), and most new plants again tend to use prebaked cells.

Other modern trends include the use of silicon rectifiers replacing the old mercury arc, and extensive automation of such cell operations as crust breaking, feeding, anode adjustment, etc. Some plants have also started modifying the electrolyte with compounds that increase its conductivity and thus the productivity of the cell. Lithium fluoride is such a compound.

The location of reduction plants continues to be determined by the availablity of a dependable supply of cheap power. The significance of a cheap power source is brought into focus by the statistic that 4.2% of all the electricity produced in the United States in 1965 was consumed by the aluminum industry.

The operating parameters for prebaked and Soderberg cells are similar. For a 100,000-amp cell, the cell voltage ranges 4–5 v; the temperature, 950–975°C; bath depth, 5–8 inches; Al pad depth, 2–15 inches; anode current density, 4–9 amp/in^2; and the anode-cathode distance, 1.5–2.0 inches. Some typical performance data for such cells are: Al production, 1500–1560 lb/day; current efficiency, 85–88%, d-c power consumption, 6–8 kwh/lb Al; anode carbon consumption, 0.45–0.53 lb/lb Al; cell life, 800–1500 days.

Various aspects of the reduction process are described in References 1, 4–6. Reference 7 gives a detailed historical account of the reduction process from its infancy to the present time.

Alternate Reduction Processes

Many attempts have been made over the years to supplant the conventional process, mainly because electrolytic reduction facilities require a high capital investment (about $800 per annual short ton of reduction capacity). None has been successful thus far although the probability of future success is much enhanced by the great strides being made in materials technology.

The most promising alternate processes are nonelectrolytic and they may use either alumina or aluminum alloys as the starting material. In the former, called "carbothermic" processes, a proper charge of alumina and carbon is heated to 2000–2500°C in an electric furnace. This produces, as a function of the stoichiometry and temperature, a mixture of carbides, oxycarbides, and aluminum from which the metal is generally separated by fluxing. Many variations of the carbothermic process have been proposed involving disproportionation of aluminum nitride, carbide, or subsulfide; use of plasma jets; and many others.

Among the processes using aluminum alloys as the starting material, the "subhalide" process is one of the more prominent. Aluminum from an Al-Fe-Si alloy, obtained readily by carbothermic reduction of bauxite, reacts selectively at 1200°C with $AlCl_3$ vapor to produce a subchloride, $AlCl$, vapor which decomposes on cooling to 800°C into its original components. The metal is tapped off and $AlCl_3$ is recirculated.

Other processes rely on the selective extraction of aluminum from aluminum alloys by mercury, zinc, magnesium, or other metals followed by a crude separation and distillation. Some of these processes were used during World War II for the recovery of Al from scrap.

Still other processes propose electrolyzing aluminum halides, aluminum sulfide, cryolite, aluminates, aluminum alkyls, and many other compounds. With the possible exception of the aluminum chloride electrolysis, none of these latter processes is considered a serious threat to the established Bayer-Hall technology.

Electrolytic Refining and Superpurity Aluminum

Aluminum produced in commercial cells is usually 99.5–99.8% pure, with iron and silicon the principal impurities. Metal of a consistently higher purity is obtained by subsequent refining. Of the several existing processes, the electrolytic or "three-layer processes" generally give a metal >99.99% pure; zone refining and chemical refining via subhalides or aluminum alkyls can produce metal >99.9999%.

Most of the superpurity aluminum is produced electrolytically in various modifications of the Hoopes cell, developed at Alcoa

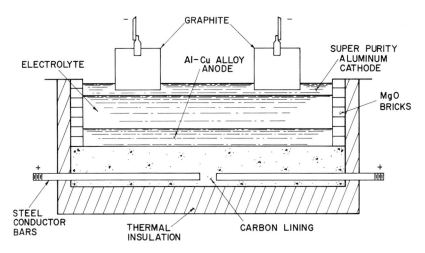

FIG. 3. Three-layer aluminum refining cell.

in 1924. In principle, all three-layer processes rely on transferring aluminum from a lower anodic layer containing the molten impure aluminum in the form of an Al-Cu (25–33%) alloy, through an intermediate layer of fused salts, to the top cathodic layer of purified aluminum (Fig. 3). Refined aluminum is removed periodically from the top as more impure aluminum is added to the copper alloy. The power requirements are about the same here as in the electrolytic reduction of alumina.

The composition of the electrolyte is the main distinguishing feature between the various three-layer processes. Where the old Hoopes process used 60% cryolite and 40% BaF_2 at 950–1000°C, the Pechiney process uses 60% $BaCl_2$ and 40% chiolite (AlF_3. 1.5NaF) at 750°C. The Swiss Aluminium process uses an exclusively fluoridic bath; 48% AlF_3, 18% NaF, 18% BaF_2, and 16% CaF_2 at 740°C.

Superpurity aluminum (99.99%) sells for about twice the price of primary metal.

Economic Aspects

Since 1900 the world production of primary aluminum has increased at an average rate of 10% per year. Indications are that this rate will be maintained at least through 1980, although consumption in the United States (where the per capita consumption is consider-

ably higher than in the rest of the world) is expected to grow at a somewhat slower rate. The world production of primary metal, 1900–1965, is given in Table 1, along with United States production for the more recent years. The consumption in the United States is currently more than 43 lb per capita, by far the largest in the world.

TABLE 1. WORLD PRODUCTION OF PRIMARY ALUMINUM, 1900-1965 AND AVERAGE U.S. MARKET PRICE

Year	Production, short tons	Average price in U.S., cents/lb	U.S. Production, short tons
1900	7700	32.7	
1910	45,000	22.0	
1920	133,100	33.3	
1930	289,300	23.8	
1940	851,400	18.8	206,280
1950	1,628,000	17.6	717,112
1960	4,906,000	26.0	2,014,497
1965	7,122,000	24.5	2,754,000
1966		24.5	2,968,000

Physical Properties of Aluminum

Atomic Structure and Crystalline Form. Aluminum, atomic number 13, is the second element in the third group of the periodic system of elements. The atomic mass is 26.9815 on the basis $C^{12} = 12.000$.

The neutral aluminum atom has a radius of 1.43 Å, and the electronic configuration in the ground state is $1s^2 2s^2 2p^6 3s^2 3p^1$, term symbol $^2P_{\frac{1}{2}}$.

The strength with which an electron is bound to an atom can be measured by the ionization energy for that electron. To remove the first valence electron from the $3p$ orbital of aluminum requires 137.3 and for the second and third from the $3s$ orbital 430.6 and 652.1 kcal/g-atom. Thus, the $3p$ electron in aluminum is considerably more weakly bound than either of the two $3s$ electrons. Ordinarily aluminum is trivalent (Al^{+3}), but the monovalent form (Al^+) is known in the high-temperature compounds AlCl and AlF, among others.

Aluminum has only one stable isotope of mass number 27. Several artificial radioisotopes are known. They are listed in Table 2. The thermal neutron capture cross section for Al^{27} is 0.23×10^{-24} cm^2 (0.23 barns).

The long-lived form of Al^{26} is probably the most useful for radiotracer work.

TABLE 2. ISOTOPES OF ALUMINUM

Half-life	Type of decay	Energy of radiation, MeV	Some typical modes of formation
Al²³ 0.13 sec			
Al²⁴ 2.1 sec	β^+	~8.8, 4.5 Mg²⁴	(p, n)
	γ	1.37–7.1	
Al²⁵ 7.2 sec	β^+	3.24 Mg²⁵	(p, n)
	γ	0.58–1.6	
Al²⁶ᵐ 6.6 sec	β^+	3.21 Mg²⁵	(d, n)
		Mg²⁶	(d, 2n)
Al²⁶ 7.4 × 10⁵y	ec	Mg²⁵	(d, n)
	β^+	1.16 Mg²⁶	(p, n)
	γ	1.83, 1.12 Al²⁷	(n, 2n)
Al²⁷ 100% abundance (stable)		—	
Al²⁸ 2.30 min	β^-	2.87 Al²⁷	(n, γ)
	γ	1.78 Al²⁷	(d, p)
		P³¹	
Al²⁹ 6.6 min	β^-	2.5, 1.4 Al	(α, 2p)
	γ	1.28, 2.43 Mg	(α, p)
Al³⁰ 3.3 sec	β^-	5.05 Si	(n, γ)
	γ	2.26, 3.52	

It is interesting to note that the first demonstration of the possibility of producing artificially radioactive elements was made in 1934 by I. Curie and F. Joliot by bombarding aluminum with alpha particles to produce the 2.3-minute P³⁰ activity:

$$Al^{27} + He^4 \rightarrow n^1 + P^{30}$$

$$P^{30} \xrightarrow[2.3\ m]{\beta^+} Si^{30}.$$

The crystalline form of aluminum has a face-centered cubic lattice with a unit-cell dimension of 4.04958 ± 0.000025 Å (25°C). The space group is Fm3m – O_h^5. The distance between an atom and one of its 12 nearest neighbors is 2.86 Å.

Electron density calculations indicate that the aluminum atom in the crystal lattice is in the state of a doubly charged positive ion.

Density. The density for a metal with 99.996% Al, 0.0020% Si, 0.001% Cu, 0.0003% each of Na, Ca, and Mg, and 0.0001% Fe at 20°C is 2.6989 g/cc.

For a metal with 99.996% Al the density above the melting point is given by the expression,

$$d = 2.368 - 0.000265\ (t - 658),$$

from which the density of the metal at the temperature of production (950°C) is calculated to be 2.291 g/cc.

Melting and Boiling Points. The melting point of aluminum depends on its purity. For a 99.5% Al metal the melting point is 658°C, and for 99.996% Al metal it is 660.24°C.

The normal boiling point (760 mm Hg) of aluminum of 99.998% purity is 2467°C (2740°K).

Thermal Expansion. For an aluminum with a purity of 99.996% the linear thermal expansion coefficient in the temperature range −200°C to 500°C is shown in the following table.

Temperature range, °C	Average coefficient, 10⁻⁶ cm/cm/°C
−200 to 20	18.0
−150 to 20	19.9
−100 to 20	21.0
−50 to 20	21.8
20 to 100	23.6
20 to 200	24.5
20 to 300	25.5
20 to 400	26.4
20 to 500	27.4

Thermal Conductivity. The thermal conductivity of aluminum depends strongly on its purity. At 200°C it has the values 0.5, 0.53, and 0.82 cal/cm/sec/°C for metals of purity 99.5%, 99.7%, and 99.9% Al. The thermal conductivity is only a weak function of temperature.

Viscosity and Surface Tension. The viscosity of 99.996% Al metal at 700, 800, and 900°C is 1.12, 1.00, and 0.90 centipoise. The viscosity of less pure metal is greater.

The surface tension of molten aluminum against a vacuum is a linear function of the temperature, t°C, and is given by the expression,

$$\sigma = 865 - 0.14\,(t - 660)\ \text{dyne/cm.}$$

At 950°C the value is then 824 dyne/cm.

Electrical Conductivity. The electrical conductivity of aluminum depends on its purity and increases with decrease in impurities. A 99.999% Al metal at 20°C has 65.45% of the conductivity of copper, the value being 38.02×10^4 mho/cm. The temperature coefficient of electrical resistivity (20°C) is 0.00429 per °C for 99.996% Al.

The various metal impurities in aluminum may be divided into 3 groups depending on their effect:

1. Titanium, vanadium, chromium, and manganese depress the conductivity very strongly.

2. Magnesium, copper, and silver decrease the conductivity less strongly.

3. Beryllium, silicon, iron, nickel, zinc, and gold have the smallest effect.

Below 1.4°K aluminum becomes superconductive.

Mechanical Properties. The modulus of elasticity of 99.996% pure aluminum is 9×10^6 lb/in².

Other mechanical properties are as follows:

Property	Annealed	Cold-rolled (75% of original thickness)
Tensile strength, psi	6800	16,300
Yield strength, psi	1700	15,400
Elongation, %†	60	5
Brinell hardness‡	17	27

† Sheet specimens.
‡ 500-kg load, 10-mm ball.

Some mechanical properties of commercial-grade aluminum (99.6 + %) are given in Table 3.

Miscellaneous Properties. The reflectivity of aluminum for electromagnetic radiation is exceeded only by that of freshly deposited silver. Aluminum evaporated onto glass reflects 85–90% of the incident light over the wavelength range of 3,000 to 12,000 Å. Aluminum is silver-white when pure, but it usually has a blue tinge.

Aluminum is weakly paramagnetic with a susceptibility of 0.60×10^{-6} c.g.s. units.

TABLE 3. TYPICAL MECHANICAL PROPERTIES OF 106 ALLOY†

(99.6 + % Aluminum)

Temper	Tensile str., psi	Yield str., psi	Elongation, % ‡	Brinell hardness§	Shear str., psi	Fatigue limit, psi‖
0	10,000	4,000	43	19	7,000	3,000
H12	12,000	11,000	16	23	8,000	4,000
H14	14,000	13,000	12	26	9,000	5,000
H16	16,000	15,000	8	30	10,000	6,500
H18	19,000	18,000	6	35	11,000	6,500

† These typical properties are average for various forms, sizes, and methods of manufacture, and may not exactly describe any one particular product. Modulus of elasticity (average of tension and compression moduli), 10,000,000 psi for tempers shown. Compression modulus is about 2% greater than tension modulus.
‡ Sheet specimens, ¹⁄₁₆″ thick.
‖ 500-kg load, 10-mm ball.
§ Based on 500,000,000 cycles using R. R. Moore-type rotating-beam machine.

Chemical Properties

The chemical activity of aluminum is very high as is seen in the very high energies of formation of its compounds with oxygen, the halogens, carbon and sulfur. The standard (unit activities at 25°C compared to the hydrogen-hydrogen ion couple as zero) oxidation-reduction potential is 1.67 volts for the couple $Al \rightarrow Al^{+3} + 3e^{-}$.

When exposed to air, aluminum forms a thin (0.2 μm), nonporous but very strongly bonded coating of aluminum oxide. This coating protects the metal from further oxidation and imparts a high resistance to corrosion. As the temperature is increased, the thickness of the coating becomes greater.

Finely divided aluminum is extremely rapidly oxidized at high temperature, a property which finds application in high explosives and solid rocket propellant mixtures.

Aluminum is only superficially attacked by pure water at ordinary temperatures. At 180°C pure aluminum is rapidly oxidized by water. Dilute or cold concentrated sulfuric acid has very little effect, and the pure metal is essentially unattacked by concentrated nitric acid. Concentrated and dilute hydrochloric acid solutions dissolve aluminum with hydrogen evolution. Hot concentrated sulfuric acid reacts to form sulfur dioxide. Perchloric acid slowly dissolves aluminum, the reaction being accelerated if the metal is in contact with platinum which lowers the hydrogen overvoltage potential.

Strong alkalis attack aluminum violently by dissolving the protective oxide coating and reacting to form hydrogen.

Aluminum at high temperature (ca. 1000°C) reduces many oxides including alumina. The Goldschmidt reaction, generalized in the equation for a metal M,

$$2Al + 3MO \rightarrow Al_2O_3 + 3M,$$

is used to prepare alloys and for welding. Aluminum will attack silica, silicates, and glass at temperatutes of about 600°C. Aluminum reacts with its own oxide at 1490°C in a vacuum to produce AlO.

Aluminum reacts with many elements and compounds. Some of these reactions and conditions for reaction are summarized in Table 4.

The mono- and divalent compounds of aluminum, such as AlCl and AlS, are stable only at high temperature and decompose into aluminum and trivalent compounds at lower temperatures.

TABLE 4. SOME REACTIONS OF ALUMINUM

Reactant	Product	Conditions for reaction
Cl_2	$AlCl_3$	~100°C
$AlCl_3$	AlCl	~1000°C
S	Al_2S_3	>1000°C
Al_2S_3	AlS or Al_2S	1300°C in vacuum
N_2	AlN	>1100°C
C	Al_4C_3	~2000°C or 1000°C in presence of cryolite
CO	$Al_4C_3 + Al_2O_3$	~1000°C
B	AlB_2 and AlB_{12}	~2000°C

Thermochemical Properties. The chemical thermodynamic properties of aluminum are listed in Tables 5 and 6.

In Table 5, the superscript ° refers to the element in its standard state. C_p° is the heat capacity at constant pressure. S_T° is absolute entropy at temperature T, °K. The expression

TABLE 5. HEAT, TEMPERATURE AND ENTROPY OF FUSION AND VAPORIZATION FOR ALUMINUM

Type of process	State Initial	Final	Pressure mm Hg	Temp. °K	°C	ΔH, kcal/mole	ΔS, cal/deg/mole
Fusion	Solid	Liquid		933	660	2.55	2.8
Vaporization	Liquid	Gas	760	2740	2467	70.7	26

$- (F_T^\circ - H_{298}^\circ)/T$ denotes the free energy function in the standard state at temperature T, $^\circ$K, and is defined as $S_T^\circ - (H_T^\circ - H_{298}^\circ)/T$. The term $H_T^\circ - H_{298}^\circ$ indicates the heat content (enthalpy) in the standard state at temperature T, $^\circ$K, less the heat content in the standard state at 298.15°K.

TABLE 6. ALUMINUM THERMOCHEMICAL PROPERTIES

Reference state is solid 0°K to 932°K, liquid 932°K to 2736°K and Ideal Atomic Gas 2736°K to 6000°K.

| T, $^\circ$K | Cal/mole/deg | | | kcal/mole |
	C_P°	S_T°	$-(F_T^\circ - H_{298}^\circ)/T$	$H_T^\circ - H_{298}^\circ$
0	0.000	0.000	Infinite	-1.094
298	5.820	6.769	6.769	0.000
1000	7.000	17.506	10.192	7.313
2000	7.000	22.358	15.201	14.313
2800	4.970	50.501	18.191	90.467
5000	5.130	53.402	33.104	101.489

From: JANAF Thermochemical Tables, The Dow Chemical Co., Midland, Michigan, 1960.

Corrosion

Aluminum resists corrosion better than indicated by its position in the emf series or by its free energy. An ennobling oxide is responsible for this improvement. This natural oxide film is approximately 50 Å thick. It is continuous over the surface and inert to a wide variety of environments. It is tough, but if mechanically damaged, it reforms instantaneously in air or water to give the same protection as the original film.

Principal uses of aluminum depend on its resistance to atmospheric environments and to the fact that its corrosion products are nontoxic and colorless. In some applications, aluminum has withstood the rigors of weathering for over 80 years.

Due to its amphoteric nature, aluminum is usually attacked in strongly acid or alkaline solutions; however, the metal is resistant to 80 + % nitric acid, 100% sulfuric acid, and ammonia. Aluminum and its alloys are also resistant to most organic acids, alcohols, ketones, aldehydes, esters, halogenated hydrocarbons, petrochemicals, hydrogen peroxide, molten sulfur, and many other chemicals.

The performance of aluminum and its alloys in the presence of a number of specific chemicals is described in Reference 8. Galvanic attack occurs when aluminum is used indiscriminately in contact with more noble metals.

Alloying brings about changes in the corrosion resistance of aluminum. Copper is the most detrimental addition. Manganese and silicon have little effect. Magnesium improves corrosion resistance except when large quantities are present in susceptible structures. Zinc provides no improvement; however, its addition produces a more electronegative alloy which makes a good cathodic cladding for alloys that are less resistant to corrosion.

When attack occurs, an accumulation of corrosion products shields the metal surface and usually stifles further attack. More protective films may be applied by electrochemical and chemical means. Typical finishing techniques are anodizing, chemical conversion, coating, painting, porcelain enameling, and others. Finishing of aluminum and its alloys is treated in detail in References 9 and 10.

Alloys

Pure aluminum has good working and forming properties and high ductility but low mechanical strength. The strength properties may be improved by alloying, by strain hardening (cold working), and by solution heat treatment and aging. Aluminum alloys are generally divided into two basic types—casting and wrought—and a commonly used designation system has been established for each type.

For casting alloys, the system consists of 2 or 3 digits categorized as shown in Table 7.

TABLE 7. DESIGNATION OF CASTING ALLOYS

Designation	Major alloying element
0– 99	Silicon
100–199	Copper
200–299	Magnesium
300–399	Silicon-copper, silicon-magnesium, or silicon-copper-magnesium
400–499	Manganese
500–599	Nickel
600–699	Zinc
700–799	Tin

A 4-digit system (Table 8) is used for wrought alloys—those that would be found in sheet, plate, rod, extrusions, forgings, etc.

TABLE 8. ALUMINUM ASSOCIATION DESIGNATIONS FOR WROUGHT ALLOYS

Designation	Major alloying element
1000–1999	99% aluminum and greater
2000–2999	Copper
3000–3999	Manganese
4000–4999	Silicon
5000–5999	Magnesium
6000–6999	Magnesium-silicon
7000–7999	Zinc
8000–8999	Other elements
9000–9999	Unused series

In the 1000 series the last two digits signify the purity of the alloy in hundredths of a per cent; e.g., 1050 stands for 99.50% aluminum. The second digit, if other than zero, signifies that one or more elements are closely controlled.

In the 2000 through 8000 series the last two digits are assigned arbitrarily. The second digit, if other than zero, signifies a modification of a standard alloy; e.g., 7175 designates a modification of basic 7075 alloy. Experimental alloys are marked by a prefix "X".

The Aluminum Association also uses a systematic letter notation to indicate the form and heat treatment of the alloy:

F: as fabricated.

O: annealed, recrystallized.

H: stain-hardened (wrought products only). The H is always followed by 2 or more digits.

T: Thermally treated to produce stable tempers other than F, O, or H. The T is always followed by one or more digits.

The means by which the alloys are strengthened classifies them roughly into two categories, non-heat-treatable and heat-treatable alloys.

Non-heat-treatable alloys rely on the hardening effect of elements such as maganese, silicon, iron, and magnesium for their initial strength. They are further strengthened by various degrees of cold working, denoted by the "H" series of tempers.

Heat-treatable alloys, containing elements such as copper, magnesium, zinc, and silicon, are strengthened by heat treatment and artificial aging, but they also may be cold-worked after an initial heat treatment.

The alloy and temper designations for aluminum and standards for mill products are revised annually by the Aluminum Association (Ref. 11).

Applications

In the United States the consumption of aluminum is roughly divided among the following applications: building and construction, 25%; transportation equipment including automobiles, 25%; electrical, 16%; consumer durables, 10%; containers and packaging, 8%; machinery and equipment, including chemical equipment, 8%; and miscellaneous other uses, 8%.

Hygienic Aspects

Aluminum is inert in the the body. When introduced under the skin of animals, it causes nothing more than a mechanical irritation. A comprehensive review by the Kettering Laboratory showed that aluminum, alumina, and alumina trihydrate are not injurious to the pulmonary system, but fibrosis has been reported in animals exposed to prolonged inhalation of heavy concentrations of aluminum dust. When inhaled together with silica, even a small amount of aluminum dust has been found to prevent silicosis in humans. Prophylaxis and therapy of this disease by inhalation of aluminum is still used in some countries but this practice is now on the wane.

In contrast to copper and a number of other metals, aluminum does not accelerate the loss of vitamins in cooking. The aluminum intake due to cooking in aluminum utensils is insignificant. Because some writers had warned of ill effects due to cooking in aluminum, the Council of Foods and Nutrition of the American Medical Association concluded after a study in 1951 that "the use of aluminum cooking utensils is in no way injurious to health."

The fact that aluminum compounds have been used for years in the therapy of peptic ulcers and gastric hyperacidity without any apparent ill effects shows conclusively that the oral toxicity of aluminum is practically negligible. Ingested aluminum traverses the alimentary tract without absorption and is evacuated in the feces.

References

1. Pearson, T. G., "The Chemical Background of the Aluminum Industry," Roy. Inst. Chem. (London), Lectures, Monographs, Repts., No. 3 (1955).
2. Gerard, Gary, and Stroup, P. T., Editors, "Extractive Metallurgy of Aluminum," Vol. 1, New York, Interscience Publishers, 1963.
3. Ginsberg, Hans, and Wrigge, F. W., "Tonerde und Aluminium," Vol. 1, Berlin, Walter de Gruyter, 1964.
4. Gerard, Gary, Editor, "Extractive Metallurgy of Aluminum," Vol. 2, New York, Interscience Publishers, 1963.
5. Edwards, J. D., Frary, F. C., and Jeffries, Z., "Aluminum and Its Production," Vol. 1, New York, McGraw-Hill Book Co., 1930.
6. Beljajew, A. I., Rapoport, M. B., and Firsanova, L. A., "Metallurgie des Aluminiums," Vol. 1, Berlin, VEB Verlag Technik, 1956 (Translation from Russian).
7. Ferrand, Louis, "Histoire de la Science et des Techniques de l'Aluminium et ses Développements Industriels," 2 vols., Largentière (Ardèche), France, Imprimerie Humbert et Fils, 1960.
8. American Society for Metals, "Metals Handbook," Vol. 1, "Properties and Selection of Metals," 1961; Vol. 2, "Heat Treating, Cleaning, and Finishing," 1964, Metals Park, Ohio, American Society for Metals.
9. Wernick, S., and Pinner, R., "The Surface Treatment and Finishing of Aluminum and Its Alloys," Teddington, England, Robert Draper Ltd., 1959.
10. Kissin, G. H., Editor, "Finishing of Aluminum," New York, Reinhold Publishing Corp., 1963.
11. "Standards for Aluminum Mill Products," 9th ed., New York, The Aluminum Association, 1966.

GARY GERARD AND
W. R. KING

AMERICIUM

Americium is the third man-made element heavier than uranium, the two preceding ones being neptunium and plutonium. The atomic number of americium, symbol Am, is 95. Isotopes 240 and lighter undergo K electron capture while isotopes 244 and heavier are short-lived beta emitters. Two longest-lived isotopes are Am^{241}, half-life 433 years and Am^{243}, half-life 7700 years, with alpha energies of 5.48 and 5.27 MeV, respectively. Gamma radiation accompanies the alpha emission.

The known isotopes of americium, with their radioactivity decay characteristics and some method of production, are given on page 747 in the article on **Transuranium Elements.**

Since americium is relatively short-lived and has no long-lived precursor, it is not found as one of the naturally occurring elements. It is made in nuclear reactors by multiple neutron capture in plutonium, which results in formation of the plutonium isotopes Pu^{241} and Pu^{243}. These undergo beta decay to form the corresponding americium isotopes as follows: Pu^{241} (β^-, 13.2 yr.) Am^{241}, and Pu^{243} (β^-, 5 hr.) Am^{243}. The lower mass americium isotope can be separated easily from plutonium even at the parts-per-million level at which it occurs in the usual grade of plutonium, resulting in the availability of Am^{241} in kilogram amounts. Until recently, the longer-lived Am^{243} was available in very limited quantities, but production of Cm^{244} for isotopic power uses will make kilogram quantities of Am^{243} as well.

The production of gram amounts of Am^{243} involves multiple neutron capture in Pu^{239} and requires a high neutron flux (exceeding 10^{15} neutrons/cm^2 sec) and efficient heat removal from the Pu target, which is completely consumed. Through loss of plutonium by fission of Pu^{239} and Pu^{241}, the yield of Am^{243} is but a few per cent of the original plutonium starting material. The path to Am^{243} starting with Am^{241} is not favorable since the intermediate isotope Am^{242} decays primarily by 16-hr beta emission.

Chemical or metallurgical work with amercium must be done with great care to avoid personal contamination. As little as one-fiftieth of a microgram of Am^{241} is the allowable body burden (bone). The health hazard arises both from alpha activity (the 241 isotope is about three times as active as radium) and gamma radiation. There is associated with alpha decay a 59 KeV gamma which makes hand exposure a serious problem when gram amounts of Am^{241} are handled.

Use of one-quarter inch x-ray glass (equivalent to one-half its thickness of lead) is quite useful; it permits visibility and reduces the penetrating radiation effectively. Work with americium is usually done in totally enclosed systems, or within enclosures which are maintained at a slightly negative pressure.

A discussion of the properties of americium can logically begin with its electronic configuration, which places it in perspective with its neighbors in the Periodic Table of elements. Its electronic configuration is $[Rn]5f^66d^17s^2$, and it is thus one f electron short of being the center of the actinide series. It is a member of the second inner transition (or actinide) series. Its analog is europium in the first inner transition series, i.e., the lanthanide or rare earth series.

Members of inner transition series differ only by the number of f electrons and, therefore, have a strong chemical similarity. This chemical similarity (when in the same valence state) predominates over the repetition of chemical similarity at intervals of 8, 18, 32 electrons, which is a fundamental rule of chemical periodicity. That, plus the ease in obtaining several actinide valence states, makes exact comparison of actinide and lanthanide chemistry difficult. Nonetheless, americium in its usual trivalent state is the first of the transuranium elements to resemble the lanthanides in much of its chemistry. For example, trivalent americium shows solubility behavior similar to trivalent rare earths. Also, in several ion exchange and solvent extraction processes Am(III) is concentrated with the light lanthanides. One striking *difference* between americium and its lanthanide analog europium, is the ready formation of compounds of divalent europium and the lack of true compounds of divalent americium. Other major differences involve the existence of compounds of pentavalent and hexavalent americium, valence states which have no lanthanide counterpart. Aqueous solutions of Am^{+3}, AmO_2^+, and AmO_2^{++} can be prepared, each essentially free of the other oxidation states. The simple Am^{+4} (aq) ion is unstable and is not found in aqueous solution, but is known as a fluoride complex.

Metallic americium has been prepared by reduction of the trifluoride by barium metal or of the dioxide by lanthanum metal. These are high-temperature reactions (1200°C) and are carried out in vacuum. The metal is very reactive and dissolves cleanly in aqueous acid. Americium metal is silvery, and in its usual form is double-hexagonal close-packed, $a = 3.47$, $c = 11.24$ with a calculated metallic radius of 1.73 Å. The melting point is close to 1000°C and the density is 13.67 g/cc at 20°C, much lower than the densities of the three preceding elements, U, Np, and Pu, which have densities of nearly 20. The surface of the metal reacts with limited amounts of oxygen or hydrogen to form AmO and AmH_2.

Divalent americium has been observed by means of its paramagnetic resonance spectrum at low temperature when americium was present to 0.1 wt % in a CaF_2 matrix. Initially Am^{+3} is observed, but electrons are set free in the lattice by effects of the americium alpha radiation and cause reduction to Am^{+2}. Heat reverses the reduction. Americium metal is much more volatile than its neighbors on either side, plutonium and curium. This volatility also suggests a tendency toward divalency, and predicts a high solubility of americium metal in a melt of its trihalide salts, since similar behavior has been observed with certain rare earths. In a study of the solubility of plutonium metal in an alkali halide melt containing $PuCl_3$, the accompanying americium solubility indicated americium divalency. However, the stability of divalent americium is obviously much less than that of Eu(II), Yb(II), and even of Sm(II). Hydrogen treatment of $AmCl_3$, $AmBr_3$, or AmI_3 does not produce the americium dihalide compounds in contrast to the behavior of europium, samarium, or ytterbium, and no Am^{+2} has been observed in aqueous solution after treatment by the most powerful reducing agents.

Trivalent americium forms precipitates of low solubility with fluoride, hydroxide, phosphate, oxalate, iodate, potassium sulfate, etc. The crystal structure of all americium trihalides have been reported. In aqueous acid solution, pink Am^{+3} (aq) ion has an absorption spectrum which is characterized by an intense, narrow absorption band at 5027 Å in solution and is little changed in solid compounds. The high specific alpha activity of Am^{241} is sufficient to cause chemical reduction of all higher oxidation states in aqueous solution to the trivalent state in a matter of hours. Complexity constants have been reported between Am^{+3} and the inorganic ions SCN^-, $CO_3^=$, NO_3^-, $SO_4^=$, F^-, and Cl^-, as well as Am^{+3} and the organic chelating ligands, ethylenediamine tetraacetic acid and alpha-hydroxy-isobutyric acid. Much of the chemistry of Am(III) is concerned with separation methods and is discussed in a later section.

Tetravalent americium is known in the form of $Am(OH)_4$, AmF_4, $(NH_4)_4AmF_8$, $LiAmF_5$, $7NaF.6AmF_4$, K_2AmF_6, $7KF.6AmF_4$, and $7RbF.6AmF_4$. A composition approximating that of the dioxide, AmO_2, is very stable but the composition is somewhat variable; microphases can exist as with PrO_2. As a solution species, Am(IV) disproportionates, yielding Am(III) and Am(V); Am(IV) also oxidizes Am(V) to Am(VI). The potential of the Am^{+4}, Am^{+3} couple is between 2.6 and 2.9 volts, far in excess of that needed to oxidize water. However, oxygen is not evolved when AmO_2 or $Am(OH)_4$ is dissolved in $HClO_4$; Am(IV) reacts instead as just described to produce Am(III), Am(V), and Am(VI). In the analogous case of Pr^{+4}, no higher state exists in aqueous solution; consequently, oxidation of water occurs, oxygen is evolved, and formation of Pr^{+3} results.

The Am(III)-Am(IV) potential is sufficiently lowered in basic solution that oxidation of $Am(OH)_3$ to $Am(OH)_4$ by hypochlorite ion occurs readily. The $Am(OH)_4$ (or hydrous oxide) dissolves readily, without disproportionation, in concentrated NH_4F solution. The absorption spectrum of this solution resembles that of AmF_4; there are many absorption bands in the region 3500 Å to 10,000 Å, with a narrow characteristic band at 4560 Å in fluoride solution. The red complex, $(NH_4)_4AmF_8$, can be crystallized from the solution. K_2AmF_6 is formed when a solution of Am^{241}(V) and KF is allowed to stand overnight to allow the alpha-induced reduction of Am(V) to Am(IV) to take place.

Pentavalent americium is readily formed upon oxidation of Am(III) in hot K_2CO_3 solution using hypochlorite ion, yielding a dense crystalline precipitate which can have the composition $KAmO_2CO_3$ or $KAmO_2$ $CO_3.2K_2CO_3$. The compounds $RbAmO_2$ CO_3, $RbAmO_2F_2$, and $KAmO_2F_2$ are known, but there is no simple compound, AmF_5, or complex fluoride compound of pentavalent americium. In the oxide system, Li_3AmO_4 has been reported. The potassium americyl(V) carbonates contain the AmO_2^+ group and dissolve in dilute acid to yield a solution of the AmO_2^+ ion; infrared studies establish that the Am(V) ion is indeed AmO_2^+. Pentavalent americium is stable in dilute acid, subject to reduction by the effects of the Am^{241} alpha radiation. The main absorption of AmO_2^+ occurs at 7150 Å with a secondary peak at 5140 Å. In strong acid, *e.g.*, $6M$ $HClO_4$, second order disproportionation is observed, $2Am(V) \rightarrow Am(IV)$ and Am(VI). The subsequent reactions of Am(IV) make the net reaction $3AmO_2^+ + 4H^+ \rightarrow 2AmO_2^{++} + Am^{+3} + 2H_2O$. The rate law has two terms and can be written $-d(AmO_2^+)/dt = k_2 (H^+)^2(AmO_2^+)^2 + k_3(H^+)^3(AmO_2^+)^2$; it always is second order in Am(V) but the apparent hydrogen ion dependence changes in different acids and at different temperatures.

Hexavalent americium occurs in sodium americyl acetate, $NaAmO_2Ac_3$, and AmO_2F_2. No simple fluoride, AmF_6, is known although attempts have been made to prepare it. No compounds containing hexavalent americium without oxygen are known. In the oxide system, Ba_3AmO_6 and Li_6AmO_6 have been reported. The aqueous ion, AmO_2^{++}, can be prepared by the direct oxidation of Am^{+3} in acid solution; however, ozone oxidation of Am(III) does take place in neutral solution, to yield Am(VI) which is slightly amphoteric, being soluble in acid and also soluble to some extent in strong base. The 9945 Å absorption characteristic in acid is absent in basic solutions.

The infrared absorption spectrum of aqueous AmO_2^{++} shows that it is similar to uranyl, UO_2^{++}. The couple AmO_2^+, AmO_2^{++} is reversible. In sodium carbonate solution (rather than potassium carbonate which yields the Am(V) salt), a soluble mahogany-colored Am(VI) carbonate results on ozone treatment of Am(III) in Na_2CO_3 at room temperature. This soluble carbonate complex of Am(VI) undergoes reduction at 95°C, precipitating Am(V)-sodium carbonate. Acid solutions of $Am^{241}O_2^{++}$ are reduced to AmO_2^+ at a rate of 4% per hour. In the case of the longer-lived Am^{243}, this rate is lowered to about 0.25% per hour. Hexavalent americium is a strong oxidizing agent similar to permanganate or ceric ions, and is reduced to AmO_2^+ by chloride ion and hydrogen peroxide.

Separation of americium from other elements by precipitation of the Am(III) state is usually not useful in separating americium cleanly from the lanthanides. However, two precipitation methods have been described: The first involves preferential precipitation of americium away from lanthanum by controlled oxalate precipitation (using hydrolysis of dimethyl oxalate); a precipitate containing 50% of the lanthanum contains 95% of the americium. The second uses fluosilicic acid to precipitate promethium (element 61) preferentially, leaving americium in solution. Usually other techniques are more useful. These are oxidation, ion exchange, and solvent extraction. The oxidation of Am(III) to Am(V) in K_2CO_3 to achieve americium-curium separation is effected by the hypochlorite oxidation of Am(III) in K_2CO_3 solution, precipitating K-Am(V)-carbonate, leaving Cm(III) amd most of the rare earths in solution. Oxidation of Am^{+3} to AmO_2^{++} in dilute acid using peroxydisulfate is a useful procedure since AmO_2^{++} is fluoride-soluble while curium or the rare earths in the (III) state are insoluble in fluoride solution; thus separation can be accomplished. Indeed, this procedure proved a valuable step in the treatment of americium targets irradiated for the purpose of producing heavier elements. The bulk of the target material (Am) could be separated quickly from the products of the bombardment, so that selective ion exchange separation could be used on the remaining heavy elements.

Trivalent americium forms a complex in saturated chloride solution. In strong HCl (or ethanolic HCl) americium is not strongly bound to Dowex-50 cation resin and can thus be separated from lanthanum. In ammonium thiocyanate, americium is retained on strong base anion exchanger and separation is readily achieved from the light rare earths which are not strongly absorbed. This thiocyanate method was used at Los Alamos and is now the basis of a large scale americium separation process at Dow Chemical Co.

Cation exchange using α-hydroxy isobutyric acid is still a valuable method for individual actinide separations.

Solvent extraction using LiCl solution and a tertiary (8-9 carbon) amine to separate the lanthanides from the actinides is the basis of a group separation scheme being used at the Oak Ridge Heavy Element Facility. The actinides can then be divided into fractions, using 2-ethylhexylphenyl phosphoric acid. Americium-curium are extracted together, but separation can be achieved as mentioned above.

Uses

The isotope Am^{241} has been used as a portable source for gamma radiography, taking advantage of the 59 KeV gamma that accompanies the majority of the alpha emission. In the past, Am^{241} has been irradiated with neutrons to produce Am^{242}, Cm^{242} and heavier actinides. However, use of Am^{243} (obtained from Pu^{242}) is a superior source. The heavier isotope Am^{243} is being used for chemical studies and as a source of Cm^{244} which is being made in kilogram quantities as an isotopic power source.

References

1. Cunningham, B. B., "Chemistry of the Actinide Elements," *Ann. Rev. Nucl. Sci.*, **14** 323–46 (1964).
2. Penneman, R. A., and Keenan, T. K., "The Radiochemistry of Americium and Curium," National Research Council Nuclear Energy Series, 3006, 1960.
3. Katz, J. J., and Seaborg, G. T., "The Chemistry of the Actinide Elements," New York, John Wiley and Sons, Inc., 1957.
4. Keenan, T. K., "Americium and Curium," *J. Chem. Ed.*, **36,** 27 (1959).
5. Rabideau, S. W., Asprey, L. B., Keenan, T. K., and Newton, T. W., "Recent Advances in the Basic Chemistry of Plutonium, Americium and Curium," *Proc. Second Int'l. Conf. Peaceful Uses of Atomic Energy*, **28,** 361 (1958).
6. Penneman, R. A., and Asprey, L. B., "A Review of Americium and Curium Chemistry," *Proc. Int'l. Conf. Peaceful Uses of Atomic Energy*, **7,** 355 (1956).
7. Seaborg, G. T., "Man-made Transuranium Elements," New York, Prentice-Hall, Inc., 1963.

Robert A. Penneman

ANTIMONY

Antimony in the form of its natural sulfide was known to the ancients and was used by them as a cosmetic and a medicine. The Old Testament refers to its use by Jezebel as a cosmetic for the eyes. The early Egyptian women also adorned their eyes with antimony sulfide as evidenced by its presence amongst the articles discovered in the ancient tombs. Pliny in his writings during the First Century A.D. describes seven remedies that can be obtained from the use of stibium (antimony sulfide).[1]

Metallic antimony was mentioned in the early works of Dioscorides written in the First Century A.D. Fragments of an unearthed Chaldean vase were found to be composed of metallic antimony by M. Berthelot and have been estimated to have been in existence probably as early as 4000 B.C.

The art of producing metallic antimony was well known by the 17th Century. Basil Valentine described its preparation in his work "Triumphal Chariot of Antimony" probably written in 1350 A.D. but published in 1604.

Libavius in 1615 described the use of iron to reduce stibnite directly to metallic antimony. Lemery in his book "Cours de Chemie" published in 1675 also describes methods for its preparation. There is no doubt that the metal was well known to the artisans of the Middle Ages.

The name antimony was obtained from the Latin term antimonium which first appeared in a Latin translation of the work by Ceber.

Occurrence

The terrestrial abundance of antimony is about 1 gram/ton compared to about 5 grams/ton for arsenic.

Over one hundred minerals of antimony have been recognized. Scattered quantities of native metallic antimony are found in nature, however they are rare. The most important mineral source of antimony is *stibnite,* antimony trisulfide. Stibnite deposits are normally small and shallow, and do not contain more than several thousand tons of ore. Ore bodies of this nature are found scattered throughout the world and are located in Algeria, Bolivia, China, Mexico, Peru and Yugoslavia. Other important commercial minerals of antimony

which resulted from the natural oxidation of stibnite are stibicontite, cervantite, valentinite and senarmontite. Kermasite, an oxysulfide ore, $2Sb_2S_3.Sb_2O_3$, is also of some economic importance. Complex ores of antimony such as argentiferous tetrahedrite, principally $3Cu_2S.Sb_2S_3$, livingstonite, $HgSb_4S_7$, and jamisonite, $Pb_2Sb_2S_5$, are also a source of antimony. Antimony is also present in copper and lead in minor quantities so small that its mineral species is not known, but of sufficient value to be recovered as a by-product element. Another important source of antimony is from the treatment of lead-base scrap material. About one-half of all antimony produced is derived from this secondary scrap source.

Recovery

Antimony metal can be recovered directly from high-grade or enriched stibnite ore by reduction with iron such as scrap iron turnings. Metallic antimony is also produced by converting low-grade stibnite ore to the oxide and reducing it with carbon, and by the direct reduction of the natural oxide ores. The metal may be recovered from tetrahedrite concentrates by leaching it directly with sodium sulfide, or first converting it to a matte and then leaching. The resulting thio-antimonate solution is electrolyzed in a diaphragm cell using an insoluble lead anode and steel cathode.[2]

The as-reduced antimony metal from these processes is normally further refined by matting and oxidation procedures to decrease the level of the common impurities, copper, iron, arsenic and sulfur. The refined metal, termed regulus, is cast and slowly cooled under a slag cover to induce a large dendritic fern-like structure on its surface, which is referred to as a starred surface. The purity of the antimony can be in the range of about 99.0 to 99.9%. Further purification can be obtained by electrorefining.[3]

Commercial antimony is usually sold in cake form weighing about 55 lb and measuring $10'' \times 10'' \times 2\frac{1}{2}''$. The current price of the metal is about 45 cents per pound.

Economic Aspects

The major source of primary antimony until 1934 was from ores mined in China. Due to wars and unfavorable political developments, new sources of antimony were developed throughout the world. Today the major sources of antimony ore for domestic consumption are from Mexico, Bolivia, South Africa and Thailand. A small quantity of antimony is recovered from domestic ore. However, to satisfy an annual industrial consumption of about 50,000 tons of antimony, about 50–55% is recovered primarily from the treatment of lead scrap from the battery industry.

Physical Properties

Elemental antimony is a brittle, silvery-white crystalline solid with a high metallic luster. It exhibits relatively poor electrical and heat conductivity. In addition to the metallic form, it can exist in two allotropic forms,[1] a yellow modification and an amorphous black modification. Both of these modifications are unstable and revert to the crystalline form. The yellow modification is formed by low-temperature oxidation of SbH_3 (stibine) with air or chlorine. The black amorphous form can be produced by rapid quenching of antimony vapor. An explosive modification of antimony also exists which is sometimes referred to as a third allotrope. It is produced by the electrolysis of antimony from a chloride, iodide or bromide electrolyte under special conditions. The deposit is considered to be in a strained amorphous condition which, when bent or scratched, will explode mildly, converting it to the crystalline form. Slow heating of the electrodeposit will convert it to the crystalline form, while sudden heating to about 125°C will cause a mild explosion. Some experimental electrodeposits of antimony from a chloride electrolyte have been observed to ignite and burn, though incompletely, to form the oxide, while drying at room temperature.

Some inconsistency regarding the volume change of antimony upon solidification has existed in the literature for some time. Recent data[4] on high-purity antimony show that it does not expand but undergoes a volume contraction of $0.79 \pm 0.14\%$ upon solidification.

Antimony has an atomic number of 51 and belongs to Group VA of the Periodic Table. It exhibits two stable isotopes, one of mass 121 (57.25% natural abundance) and the other

of mass 123 (43.75% natural abundance). Physical constants are listed in Table 1.

TABLE 1. PHYSICAL CONSTANTS

Atomic number	51
Atomic weight	121.75
Atomic volume, cc/g atom	18.4
Melting point	630.5°C
Boiling point	1635°C
Density, g/cc	
solid, 26°C	6.697
liquid, 640°C	6.49
Latent heat of fusion, cal/g	38.3
Latent heat of vaporization, cal/g	161
Specific heat, cal/g/°C	
solid, 0°C	0.0494
liquid 650 to 950°C	0.0656
Thermal conductivity cal/sec/sq cm/cm/°C	
solid, 20°C	0.045
liquid, 630 to 730°C	0.052 to 0.050
Surface tension, dyne/cm, 635°C	383
Linear coefficient of expansion micro-inches/°C at 20°C	8–11
Electrical resistivity, microhm-cm, 0°C	39.1
Magnetic susceptibility, cgs, emu/g	-0.87×10^{-6}
Nuclear absorption cross-section, thermal neutrons 2200 m/s, barns	
natural 121.76	5.7 ± 1.0
isotope 121 (57.25%)	5.9 ± 0.5
123 (42.75%)	4.1 ± 0.3
Crystal system, hexagonal (rhombohedral)	
Lattice constant	a = 4.307 Å, c = 11.273 Å
Hardness, Mohs scale	3.0–3.5

Chemical Properties

The principal valence states of antimony are $+5$, $+3$, 0 and -3. In the elemental state, antimony is quite stable and is not readily attacked by air or moisture. It will react with oxygen under controlled conditions to form the oxides $Sb_2O_3(Sb_4O_6)$, Sb_2O_4 and Sb_2O_5. Antimony will combine vigorously with the halides to form trihalides, but only forms pentahalides with fluorine and chlorine. Sulfur combines in all proportions with antimony and will form the compounds Sb_2S_3 and Sb_2S_5.

TABLE 2. CONSUMPTION OF PRIMARY ANTIMONY (SHORT TONS)

Metal Product		1962	1963	1964
Antimonial lead		6,090	6,462	5,952
Bearing metal and bearings		682	992	804
Cable covering		114	101	49
Castings		64	49	50
Collapsible tubes and foil		112	72	53
Sheet and pipe		127	81	99
Solder		172	188	149
Type metal		429	652	513
Other†		271	199	182
	Total	8,061	8,796	7,851
	Nonmetallic	7,391	7,736	7,988
	Grand total	15,452	16,532	15,839

† Includes antimony consumption in ammunition.
Data from "Minerals Yearbook."

Hydrogen does not combine directly with antimony. Stibine, antimony hydride, SbH_3, an extremely toxic gas, can be produced by the hydrolysis or action of hydrochloric acid on a compound such as Zn_3Sb_2. Stibine can also be liberated by the reduction of antimony compounds in hydrochloric acid solutions with zinc or other reducing metals.

Antimony is oxidized by nitric acid to form a gelatinous precipitate of hydrated antimony pentoxide.[5] Hydrochloric acid in the absence of air will not readily attack antimony. With sulfuric acid, antimony reacts to form an indefinite compound, probably an oxysulfate, which has low solubility in the acid. Hydrofluoric acid will react to form soluble fluorides or fluoride complexes with many insoluble antimony compounds.

It will react with many metals to form antimonides.

Uses

Antimony is used metallurgically as an additive element since the physical properties of the element are not suitable for engineering applications. Its most important use is as an alloying constituent for lead and lead-base alloys to impart hardness and stiffness, and to improve the corrosion resistance. It is also used as an alloying ingredient for tin alloys to produce britannia metal, pewter, and tin-base babbits for bearing metal applications.

A list of applications and consumption of primary antimony is given in Table 2.

It will be noted from Table 2 that the greatest consumption of primary antimony is in the production of antimonial lead. This material is used in the manufacture of battery grids and parts (2–7% Sb, 0.1–0.5% Sn, 0.02–0.5% As, bal. Pb), and in chemical hardware such as tank linings, pipes and pumps (2–6% Sb, bal. Pb). About 50% of the antimonial lead is used in battery grids.

Antimony in the form of chemical compounds, such as the trioxide, trichloride and sulfide, finds a variety of industrial applications. The trioxide is used as an opacifier in enamelizing of ceramics and metalware. It is used as a white pigment for paints. Increasing amounts of the trioxide in formulation with chlorine compounds or polymers are being used for flameproofing fabrics and plastics. It is also used in glass as a decolorizer and refining agent.

The trioxide is used in the preparation of medicine, in dye mordants and for staining dull finishes on iron and copper hardware.

Antimony sulfide is used in vulcanizing rubber, as a vermilion pigment and other pigment shades such as yellow, formed by slow oxidation of the sulfide, and blue by mixing the yellow with other pigments. It is also used to a lesser extent in fireworks, ammunition primers, tracer bullets and metals.

The greatest consumption of antimony compounds is in the form of the trioxide.

The distribution of consumption of primary antimony during the past few years has been about equal for metallic and non-metallic products.

Semiconductor Applications

Antimony of a purity exceeding 99.999% is used in semiconductor technology.[7] This material may be produced by the reduction of high-purity compounds such as the trioxide and chloride with hydrogen. Further refinement may be obtained by zone purification.

Important III-V compounds such as AlSb, InSb and GaSb are made from high-purity antimony. These compounds may be used as infrared detectors, diodes and Hall effect devices. The compound in this group of the greatest technological importance is InSb. Antimony with a purity of 99.99 + % is an important alloying ingredient in Bi_2Te_3-type alloys which can be used as thermoelectric coolers or power generators.

Hygienic Precautions

The toxicity of antimony depends upon its chemical state. Metallic antimony is relatively inert, while stibine is highly toxic. The toxicity of other compounds of antimony may be classified between these extremes.

In handling antimony and its compounds, proper ventilation should be used as determined by the nature of the processing being undertaken, in order to maintain atmospheric contamination below 0.5 mg/M^3 (calculated as antimony). Cases of dermatitis have been reported in the manufacture of antimony trioxide. Good personal sanitation must be practiced to avoid ingestion. In processes generating stibine it is recommended that the atmospheric concentrations be kept below 0.1 ppm. The recommended maximum atmospheric concentration for stibine in 8-hour exposure is 0.1 ppm parts of air.[8]

References

1. Mellor, J. W., "Comprehensive Treatise on Inorganic and Theoretical Chemistry," Vol. 9, pp. 339–586, New York, Longsman, Green & Co., 1930.
2. Wang, C. Y., "Antimony," 3rd Edition, London, Charles Griffin Co., 1952.
3. Schlain, D., Prater, J. D., and Ravitz, S., J. Electrochem. Soc., 95, 145–160 (1949).
4. Cahill, J. A., and Kirshenbaum, A. D. Trans. ASM, 56, 874–878 (1963).
5. Sneed, M. C., and Brasted, R. C., "Comprehensive Inorganic Chemistry," Vol. 5, pp. 111–152, Princeton, N.J., D. Van Nostrand Co. Inc., 1956.
6. "Minerals Yearbook," Washington, D.C., U.S. Bureau of Mines, Vol. 1, p. 211, 1964.
7. Willardson, R. H., and Goering, H. L., "Compound Semiconductors, Preparation of III–V Compounds," New York, Reinhold Publishing Corporation, 1962.
8. "Hygienic Guide Series," Detroit, Michigan, American Industrial Hygiene Association, 1959 (1960).
9. Hayward, C. R., "An Outline of Metallurgical Practices," 3rd Edition, London, D. Van Nostrand Co. Inc., 1952.
10. "Gmelins Handbuch Der Anorganischen Chemie," Parts B and B2, No. 18, Clausthal-Zellerfeld, Lubeck, Germany, Gmelin-Verlag G.M.B.H., 1949.

S. C. CARAPELLA, JR.

ARGON

Argon (Greek, *argos*, inactive), symbol Ar, is a member of the family helium (He), neon (Ne), krypton (Kr), xenon (Xe), and radon (Rn). This is the helium group, at times called rare gases, noble gases, inert gases, or Group 0 of the Periodic Table. (See article on **Noble Gases**.)

The discovery of argon was announced jointly by Rayleigh and Ramsay in 1894. It was obtained from atmospheric nitrogen as a residue after the nitrogen was reacted with hot magnesium. The discovery of argon was anticipated by Cavendish over a century before. Cavendish obtained an inert residue when an electric spark was passed through air and oxygen.

The principal isotope of argon, Ar^{40}, which comprises 99.6% of the stable isotopes of argon, most likely was formed by radioactive decay of K^{40} in the earth's crust. The argon so formed was gradually released to the atmosphere. Probably most of the argon isotopes except Ar^{40} were part of the original mass of matter which condensed to form the earth. Weathering of the earth's crust released these elements into the atmosphere. Dry atmospheric air contains about 0.94% by volume of argon.

Derivation

The atmosphere is the commercial source for argon and large quantities are obtained from air separation plants used to produce oxygen and nitrogen. During the distillation of liquid air to separate oxygen and nitrogen, argon is separated so as not to appear as an impurity in the oxygen or nitrogen. The crude argon, withdrawn either as a gas or liquid, is refined by distillation. The product, which may contain as much as 98% argon, is purified by passage over heated copper, selective adsorption, or by addition of hydrogen followed by

TABLE 1. PHYSICAL PROPERTIES OF ARGON

Abundance in universe, number of atoms per 10,000 atoms of silicon (all isotopes)	1.5×10^{-3}
Abundance in earths' crust, number of atoms per 10,000 atoms of silicon (all isotopes)	9.46×10^{-2}
Abundance in earth's crust, parts per million by weight	3.4
Abundance in dry air, parts per million by volume	9340
Stable isotopic abundance	Ar^{36} 0.337%
	Ar^{38} 0.063%
	Ar^{40} 99.600%
Atomic number	18
Atomic weight, $C^{12} = 12$	39.948
Critical point	
Temperature	150.86°K
Pressure	48.34 atm
Density	0.536 g/ml
Normal boiling point	87.28°K
Triple point	
Temperature	83.81°K
Pressure	0.6800 atm
Density	
Gas, 1 atm, 273.15°K	1.78380 g/l
Gas, normal boiling point	5.763 g/l
Liquid, normal boiling point	1.3936 g/ml
Liquid, triple point	1.418 g/ml
Solid, triple point	1.623 g/ml
Volume of gas (1 atm, 273.15°K) equivalent to unit volume of liquid at normal boiling point	781
Heat of vaporization at normal boiling point	1550 cal/g-mole
Heat of fusion at triple point	283 cal/g-mole
Heat capacity at constant pressure, gas, 1 atm, 25°C	4.969 cal/g-mole/°K
liquid, normal boiling point	10.9 cal/g-mole/°K
Sonic velocity, gas, 1 atm, 0°C	307.8 m/sec
Thermal conductivity	
gas, 1 atm, 0°C	40.5 cal/cm/sec/°K
liquid, normal boiling point	290 cal/cm/sec/°K
Viscosity	
gas, 1 atm, 25°C	226.4 μ poise
liquid, normal boiling point	2.75 m poise
Dielectric constant	
gas, 1 atm, 20°C	1.00051659
1st ionization potential	15.759 ev
Minimum excitation potential	11.548 ev

catalytic combustion and reliquefication of the argon to remove excess hydrogen. The final product is 99.994% pure. (See article on **Oxygen** for more details.)

Some argon is recovered from ammonia synthesis plants where it enters as an impurity in either the nitrogen or hydrogen supplies. It is also obtained from plants which produce hydrogen by partial oxidation of natural gas.

Argon is supplied commercially in small quantities in glass bulbs, pressurized metal cylinders, tube trailers, or in large quantity in the form of liquid which is vaporized to gas at the use point. In 1967 the annual production of argon in the United States was two billion standard cubic feet of gas. By 1971 the consumption of argon is expected to reach 4 billion standard cubic feet.

Physical Properties

Table 1 gives the physical properties of argon and its abundance in the universe as well as the earth. Table 2 lists the unstable isotopes of argon. At ambient temperatures argon is a colorless, odorless, and tasteless gas.

TABLE 2. UNSTABLE ARGON ISOTOPES

Isotope	Disintegration Mode	Half-Life
Ar^{35}	$\beta+$ (4.96 MeV 93%)[a] $\beta+$ (others 7%)[b]	1.83 sec
Ar^{37}	electron capture	35 days
Ar^{39}	$\beta-$ (0.565 MeV)	265 years
Ar^{41}	$\beta-$ (1.20 MeV 99%)[c] $\beta-$ (2.5 MeV 1%)	110 months
Ar^{42}	$\beta-$	~3.5 years

[a] γ—transition at 1.73 MeV
[b] γ—transition at 1.19 MeV
[c] γ—transition at 1.29 MeV

Chemical Properties

At the present time argon is not known to form true chemical compounds, as do krypton, xenon and radon, the heavier elements of Group 0. It does form a hydrate having a dissociation pressure of 105 atm at 0°C. Ion molecules involving argon are known spectroscopically. The following have been observed:

$$(ArKr)^+, (ArXe)^+, (Ar^{36} Ar^{40})^+,$$
$$(NeAr)^+, (ArH)^+, \text{ and } (ArD)^+.$$

These ion molecules are formed in electric discharge tubes and occur by reactions of the type:

$$Ar^+ + H_2 \rightarrow ArH^+ + H$$
$$Ar^+ + HCl \rightarrow ArH^+ + Cl$$
$$Ne^* + Ar \rightarrow (NeAr)^+ + e$$

where * indicates an excited state and e is an electron.

Argon forms a clathrate with β-hydroquinone. This clathrate is quite stable and may be stored for several weeks in air at 1 atm pressure with less than 10% loss of the argon. It is interesting to note that the β modification of hydroquinone is not stable itself. Its stability requires the presence of a component (argon) of sufficient size to stabilize the clathrate cage structure. The formula of the argon-hydroquinone clathrate would be $[C_6H_4(OH)_2]_3Ar$ if all the cavities in the cage structure were filled. Even though the argon clathrate is quite stable, a true chemical bond does not exist. The argon is held by Van der Waals forces.

Applications

Argon is the least expensive and most widely used of the helium group gases (helium runs a close second in use).

The metallurgical industry is the largest consumer of argon. Argon (and helium) are used as inert gas shields for arc welding of metals which are susceptible to oxidation or reaction with nitrogen. The argon is played about the area where the arc is applied. Inert gas shields of argon or helium have made practical the arc welding of aluminum, stainless steel, and more exotic metals.

The choice of argon or helium in arc welding depends on the desired arc temperature, metal penetration by the arc, and cleaning action of the arc. In nonconsumable arc welding a tungsten electrode is used with argon shielding if a relatively cool arc and shallow penetration are desired. If the electrode is positive relative to the work, an argon shield gives a cleaning action. Alternating current is used in argon shielded welding to prevent overheating of the electrode. Nonconsumable electrode welding gives the highest quality weld in all metals except mild steel. Nonconsumable electrode welding is extensively used in the aerospace industry for the fabrication of frames, jet engine components, and space launch vehicles.

Argon or argon-helium mixtures serve as shields in consumable electrode arc welding where the electrode is a filler wire which is melted and deposited on the work piece. The electrode is positive. With argon or argon-helium shields the filler metal is sprayed as discrete drops on the work piece. The argon-helium mixture gives deeper penetration than argon alone. Consumable electrode welding is applied to mild steel, stainless steel, and titanium and aluminum.

Argon-hydrogen mixtures are utilized in plasma jet torches where the gases are heated to temperatures of 10,000°K or higher. These torches are used for cutting operations and for coating metals with refractory materials.

For materials sensitive to atmospheric gases like oxygen and nitrogen, high-temperature preparation, refining, and fabrication are done in argon or helium atmospheres. Such materials are zirconium, niobium, tantalum, titanium, uranium, thorium, plutonium, and reactor-grade graphite. Most high-purity crystals for semiconducting applications are grown and doped in argon or helium atmospheres. Special mixtures of argon or helium containing the doping agents are used.

As in the case of arc welding, brazing of many metals requires that the metal be protected from oxygen and/or nitrogen. Hydrogen has been the preferred atmosphere for furnace brazing, but is being replaced by argon or helium where a reducing atmosphere is not required. The use of argon or helium eliminates the hazards associated with hydrogen. If a reducing atmosphere is required, argon-hydrogen mixtures may be used. Argon has largely replaced hydrogen as the atmosphere for brazing transistor junctions.

Large quantities of argon are used in the steel industry to eliminate the atmosphere during melting, pouring, casting, and annealing of special alloy steels. During the vacuum degassing of certain steels to remove carbon monoxide argon is used as a purge. Also, direct injection of argon into molten metals at ambient pressures has been used to remove dissolved gases. In many respects, the use of argon (or helium) as an inert atmosphere is an alternate to vacuum processing.

In some chemical reactions argon is used to transport a reactant to a reaction zone as well as serving as diluent to control the rate of reaction. The argon also removes the reaction products. Argon (and helium) have the advantage of being chemically inert. Typical processes are the manufacture of zirconium and titanium by the Kroll process and the production of metal hydrides.

Argon finds application as a fill gas for various light sources. Some of the "neon" signs contain argon either as pure argon or mixed with neon and/or helium. Pure argon in a colorless tube gives a blue color.

Originally incandescent lights were filled with nitrogen to protect the filament. However, most lamps now contain an argon-nitrogen fill (about 12% N_2). The argon-nitrogen fill is more effective than pure nitrogen in reducing the rate of filament evaporation. Heat losses through argon are less than in nitrogen. Consequently, it is possible to operate a filament at higher temperatures with argon (more intense light) at a fixed power consumption. Some nitrogen is needed to prevent arcing between the electrical leads. Fluorescent lights frequently contain argon with mercury vapor. Sometimes krypton and neon are also used.

Argon, with other gases such as Kr, Xe, Ne, and Hg, is used to fill specialized light sources such as mercury vapor lamps, germicidal lamps, ozone lamps, stroboscopic lights, pilot lamps, and sodium vapor lamps.

Argon, sometimes mixed with He, Ne, hydrocarbons, halogens, or carbon dioxide has been used to fill ionization chambers, proportional counters, Geiger-Muller counters, neutron fission chambers, scintillation counters, and cosmic ray counters.

Analysis of argon is used to date some geological specimens. The argon results from the decay of potassium-40.

In the laboratory argon serves as a convenient atmosphere in "dry boxes" to protect materials from moisture or reaction with atmospheric gases. Argon is occasionally employed as a carrier in gas chromatography.

References

1. Cook, G. A., Ed., "Argon, Helium and the Rare Gases," Vol. 1 and 2, New York, Interscience Publishers, 1961.

2. Hemstreet, R. A., and Kirk, B. S., "Helium Group Gases," in "Encyclopedia of Chemical Technology," Eds. Kirk and Othmer, 2nd Ed., New York, John Wiley and Sons, 1965.

R. A. HEMSTREET

ARSENIC

Arsenic has been encountered in nature by man since antiquity. Aristotle makes reference to sandarach (arsenic trisulfide) in the Fourth Century B.C. In the First Century A.D., Pliny stated that sandarach is found in gold and silver mines and arsenicum (arsenic trioxide) is composed of the same matter as sandarach. By the Eleventh Century three species of arsenic were known, the white, yellow and red—since recognized as arsenic trioxide, arsenic trisulfide (orpiment) and arsenic disulfide (realgar), respectively. Orpiment is referred to by Chaucer in the *Canterbury Tales*.

Albertus Magmus is reputed in the Thirteenth Century to be the discoverer of metallic arsenic, however, his documentation is considered vague. It was not until 1649 that J. Schroder clearly reported the preparation of metallic arsenic by reducing arsenic trioxide with charcoal. Thirty-four years later, N. Lemery also observed that metallic arsenic was produced by heating arsenic trioxide with soap and potash. By the Eighteenth Century the properties of metallic arsenic were sufficiently known to classify it as a semimetal.

Occurrence

The terrestrial abundance of arsenic is about 5 grams/ton and is found widely dispersed in nature.

Some native samples of arsenic have been found which vary in purity from about 90 to 98%. The commonly associated impurities encountered in these samples are antimony, bismuth, iron, nickel and sulfur.

Normally, arsenic is found in nature combined as sulfides, arsenides, sulfoarsenides and arsenites, and occasionally as oxide and oxychloride. The most commonly encountered minerals of arsenic are arsenopyrite or mispickel, $FeAsS$; loellingite, $FeAs_2$; enargite, $CuS.As_2S_5$; orpiment, As_2S_3; and realgar, As_2S_2. In addition to these minerals over 150 others have been identified, many of which are listed in Mellor.[1]

The bulk of the arsenic of commerce, however, is recovered as a by-product from the smelting of copper, lead, cobalt and gold ores.

Recovery

Arsenic may be obtained in the metallic form by the direct smelting of arsenopyrite at 650–700°C in the absence of air. Commercially the metal[2] is prepared by the reduction of arsenic trioxide with charcoal. The yield from this reaction has been studied experimentally.[3]

The uses of commercial metallic arsenic are quite limited. For this reason, with the exception of high-purity arsenic, it has not been produced in the United States since 1950.

Most of the arsenic of commerce is recovered as arsenic trioxide from the smelting of copper and lead concentrates. The arsenic present in these concentrates is readily oxidized and volatilized during smelting and collected in a dust flue system. This crude flue dust, which may contain around 30% arsenic trioxide, is treated further by roasting to upgrade the trioxide. Pyrite or galena concentrates are added to the flue dust to prevent undesirable arsenites from forming during roasting and to yield a clinkered residue which is suitable for additional processing. The arsenic trioxide vapor which results is condensed by passing through a series of brick chambers or rooms called kitchens. The temperature of the gases and vapors is controlled so that they enter the first kitchen at about 220°C and are cooled to 100°C or less by the time they reach the last kitchen. The arsenic trioxide recovered from the kitchens is of varying purity. This product is referred to as crude arsenic and analyzes from 90–95% pure. A higher purity oxide referred to as white arsenic is obtained by the resublimation of the crude arsenic.

The specification for the white arsenic requires that the As_2O_3 content be 99% minimum.

It has been reported that crude arsenic trioxide may also be purified by pressure leaching and recrystallization.

Economic Aspects

The world consumption of metallic arsenic is small. Most of the arsenic which is consumed in the United States is imported from Sweden. Some metal has also been obtained from Poland, Germany and Great Britain. A summary of some recent importations is given in the following table:

Import of Metallic Arsenic[4]

Year	Short Tons
1960	72
1961	66
1962	115
1963	169
1964	154

In contrast, the consumption of white arsenic (arsenic trioxide) during 1964 was approximately 30,000 tons.

Metallic arsenic is sold in lump form with a minimum purity of 99%. The 1966 price quoted for arsenic in drums of 160 pounds each is 55 cents a pound.

Physical Properties

Metallic arsenic is a steel-gray brittle crystalline material which exhibits both low heat and electrical conductivity. In addition to the metallic form referred to as α arsenic, it can exist as a black, amorphous solid referred to as vitreous arsenic or β arsenic, and also as a yellow allotrope. Other allotropes of arsenic have been reported: they are gray to black, pale reddish brown to dark brown.[1] Evidence supporting some of these other forms is meager. Metallic arsenic when heated under normal atmospheric pressure sublimes rather than melts. Molten arsenic may be obtained by heating it under pressure. The vapor pressure of molten arsenic at the melting point is reported in the literature as both 28 and 36 atmospheres. The variation in the melting point as a function of high pressures has been studied and appears to increase almost linearly with pressure up to 10 kilobars.[5] Large crystals of arsenic have been prepared by heating the metal under pressure in a sealed heavy-wall transparent quartz tube.[6] The electrical and magnetic properties of single crystals of arsenic have recently been studied.[7, 8]

According to the periodic grouping, arsenic has an atomic number of 33, is classified as a metalloid and belongs to Group VA. It exhibits only one stable isotope of mass 75 (100% natural abundance). Table 1 lists various physical constants.

TABLE 1. PHYSICAL CONSTANTS

Atomic number	33
Atomic weight	74.9216
Atomic volume, cc/g atom	13.09
Melting point (28 atmospheres)	817°C
Boiling point, 760 mm (sublimes)	613°C
Latent heat of fusion, cal/g	88.5
Latent heat of sublimation, cal/g	102
Density:	
α-metallic g/cc	5.72
β-amorphous g/cc	4.7
Electrical resistivity, ohm-cm, 20°C:	
α-metallic single crystal parallel to trigonal axis	35.6×10^{-6}
perpendicular to trigonal axis	25.5×10^{-6}
α-metallic polycrystalline	33.3×10^{-6}
β-amorphous	107
Magnetic susceptibility, cgs, emu/g:	
α-metallic single crystals, 19°C, parallel to trigonal axis	$+0.578 \times 10^{-6}$
perpendicular to trigonal axis	-0.279×10^{-6}
α-metallic polycrystalline, 240°C	$+0.015 \times 10^{-6}$
β-amorphous, 25°C	-0.301×10^{-6}
Specific heat, cal/g/°C	
α-metallic	0.082
β-amorphous	0.082
Transformation temperature, $\beta \rightarrow \alpha$	288°C
Linear coefficient of thermal expansion, inches/°C, 20°C	4.7×10^{-6}
Nuclear absorption cross-section thermal neutrons, 2200 m/s, barns	4.3
Crystal system, hexagonal (rhombohedral)	
Lattice constants, 26°C	a = 3.760 Å c = 10.548 Å
Hardness, Mohs scale	3.5

Chemical Properties

The principal valence states of arsenic are $+5, +3, 0, -3$. In the elemental state arsenic is stable in dry air. On exposure to humid or moistened air, the surface first tarnishes to a golden bronze color, which on further exposure is converted to a black oxide.

Upon heating, the vapor sublimes and burns in air to form arsenic sesquioxide, As_4O_6. This oxide is normally referred to as arsenic trioxide. A persistent garlic-like odor is noted during the oxidation of the vapor.

Arsenic will combine exothermally when heated with halogens to form trihalides. It does not form pentahalides with the exception of AsF_5. It reacts with sulfur to form the compounds As_2S_3, As_2S_2 and As_2S_5 and mixtures of various proportions. Some of these compounds, depending upon the conditions of cooling, can be obtained in the vitreous form. It will combine with many metals to form arsenides.

Hydrogen gas does not react directly with arsenic to form hydrides. Arsine, AsH_3, a highly toxic gas, can be formed chemically by the reaction of aluminum arsenide, $AlAs$, with water or HC1 acid. It can also be formed by electrochemical reduction, at the cathode, of arsenic compounds in acid solutions, or by the reduction of arsenic compounds in acid with chemically active metals such as zinc and magnesium.

Metallic arsenic is relatively inert to attack by water, caustic and nonoxidizing acids. It will react with concentrated nitric acid, and chlorinated water to form orthoarsenic acid, H_3AsO_4. It will be attacked by hydrochloric acid only in the presence of an oxidant.

Qualitatively arsenic may be detected as a yellow sulfide, As_2S_3, by precipitation from a strong solution of hydrochloric acid. Interference from other members of this group which normally would precipitate, can be prevented in a 25% or greater concentration of hydrochloric acid.

Trace amounts of arsenic may be detected by the formation of arsine from solution and thermally decomposing it according to the Marsh test, in which a black arsenic mirror forms on the inside of a small tube. The arsine may also be detected by reacting it with test paper impregnated with mercuric chloride as devised by Gutzeit.

Uses

Because of its semimetallic properties, arsenic is used in metallurgical applications as an additive metal.

Additions of $\frac{1}{2}$ to 2% of arsenic to lead assists in the manufacture of lead shot to improve its sphericity. The addition of up to 3% arsenic to lead-base bearing alloys improves both their mechanical and elevated temperature properties. A small amount of arsenic is added to lead-base battery grid metal and cable sheathing to improve the hardness of these materials.

In minor additions arsenic will improve the corrosion resistance and raise the recrystallization temperature of copper. In amounts of 0.15–0.50% arsenic will improve the elevated temperature applications of copper parts used for locomotive staybolts, firebox straps and plates. A small addition of arsenic (0.02–0.05%) to brass minimizes or prevents dezincification. It has been claimed that small additions of arsenic to brass minimizes season cracking.

The largest quantity of arsenic is used in the form of chemical compounds. It is estimated that in 1965 approximately 32,000 short tons of arsenic trioxide were consumed for this purpose.

Some of these chemical compounds and typical uses are noted as follows. Calcium arsenate is used in the control of boll weevil which damages cotton crops, and the control of crabgrass. Lead arsenate is used to control fruit pests, the most common being the codling moth. Sodium arsenite is used as a weed killer and in the control of undergrowth. Frequent applications of sodium arsenite for this purpose are made on rubber plantations in Malaya and also along railroad right-of-ways. Sodium arsenite is also used as a fungicide to control leaf rot that attacks potato plants. Trees are also debarked by applying sodium arsenite to them while the sap is running. Applications of sodium arsenite are used for aquatic weed control to clear ponds and streams. Sheep and cattle dip solutions contain sodium arsenite for control of ticks and disease carriers and their eggs. Sodium arsenate is an ingredient of Wolman salts used as a wood preservative.

White arsenic trioxide, in addition to being a basic chemical for the preparation of other arsenic salts, is used as a decolorizing agent in glass manufacture. Arsenic acid and cacodylic acid (dimethylarsinic acid) are widely used as a desiccant which facilitates the harvesting of cotton. They are also used as a total sterilant for soils. Disodium methylarsonate and ammonium methanearsonate are used in crabgrass control and also as selective herbicides. Arsanilic acid (para-amino-phenylarsonic acid) is used as a feed additive for swine and poultry. Arsenic sulfide is an ingredient in fireworks. It is also used as the compound As_2S_3 in the making of infrared lenses.

Semiconductor Applications

High-purity arsenic exceeding 99.999% is used in semiconductor technology.[9] This material may be produced from the reduction of purified arsenic compounds such as arsenic trioxide and arsenic trichloride with hydrogen or the thermal dissociation of arsine.

High-purity arsenic is used to make gallium arsenide which finds application in such semiconductor devices as diodes, transistors and lasers. Indium arsenide is used for infrared detectors and in Hall effect applications. Small quantities are also used as a dopant in germanium and silicon devices.

High-purity arsenic trichloride and arsine are used in the production of epitaxial gallium arsenide.

A series of low-melting point glasses containing high-purity arsenic have been developed for semiconductor and infrared application.[10, 11]

Hygienic Considerations

The toxicity of arsenic depends on its chemical state. Metallic arsenic and arsenious sulfides are inert or nearly so, while arsine, AsH_3, a gas, is extremely toxic. The toxicity of other arsenical compounds would be classified between these two extremes. Arsenical compounds are in general hazardous, principally because of their irritant effects on the skin. Men handling arsenic trioxide industrially wear special clothing and masks which frequently are changed; otherwise, dermatitis may result particularly in the folds of the skin or moist areas.[12]

Metallic arsenic and arsenious sulfides may be handled but it is suggested that skin contact should be avoided. Protective creams are

helpful in preventing dermatitis, but minimum exposure and strict personal hygiene are most desirable.

In processes emitting dusts and fumes, exhaust ventilation should be installed; if impractical, respirators should be used.

Poisoning by means of inhalation of dusts or fumes are unusual. Most poisoning is due to ingestion.

The recommended maximum atmospheric concentration of arsenic in dusts, fumes or mists during an eight-hour daily exposure is 0.5 mg per cubic meter.[13]

Those conditions which promote the generation of arsine should be avoided. The maximum recommended exposure limit of arsine is 0.05 ppm of vapor in air per eight-hour period.[13]

References

1. Mellor, J. W., "Comprehensive Treatise on Inorganic and Theoretical Chemistry," Vol. 9, New York, Longman, Green & Co., 1930.
2. Jones, C. H., *Chem. Met. Eng.*, **23**, 957–60 (1920).
3. Vickery, R. C., and Edwards, R. W., *Metallurgia*, **36**, 3–6 (1947).
4. Minerals Yearbook 1964, Vol. 1, Metals and Minerals, U.S. Department of Interior.
5. Chaney, P. E., and Babb, S. E., Jr., *J. Chem. Phys.*, **43**, 1071 (1965).
6. Weisberg, L. R., and Celmes, P. R., *J. Electrochem. Soc.*, **110**, 56–59 (1960).
7. Taylor, J. B., Bennett, S. L., and Heyding, R. D., *J. Phys. Chem. Solids*, **26**, 69 (1965).
8. Bennett, S. L., and Heyding, R. D., *J. Phys. Chem. Solids*, **27**, 471 (1965).
9. Willardson, R. H., and Goering, H. L., "Compound Semiconductors, Preparation of III-V Compounds," New York, Reinhold Publishing Corporation, 1962.
10. Flaschen, S., Pearson, D., and Northover, W., *J. Am. Cer. Soc.*, **43**, 274–8 (1960).
11. Jerger, J., U.S. Patents 2,883,292–5, (to Servo Corporation of America), (April 21, 1959).
12. "Hygienic Guide for Arsenic," Company Memorandum prepared by K. W. Nelson, Dept. of Hygiene, Amer. Smelting & Ref. Co., Salt Lake City, Utah.
13. "Hygienic Guide Series," Detroit, Michigan, American Industrial Hygiene Assoc., 1964, 1965.
14. "Gmelin Handbuch der Anorganischen Chemie," "System—Nummer 17, Arsen," Weinheim, Verlag Chemie, GMBH, 1952.

15. Quiring, H., "Die Metalleschen Rohstoffe-Arsen," Vol. 8, Stuttgart, Germany, Ferdenand Enke, 1946.
16. Sneed, M. C., and Brasted, R. C., "Comprehensive Inorganic Chemistry," Vol. 5, Princeton, N.J., D. Van Nostrand Co., 1956.
17. Smith, W. C., "Arsenic," in Liddell, "Handbook of Nonferrous Metallurgy," Vol. II, pp. 94–103, New York, McGraw-Hill Book Co., Inc., 1945.
18. Vallee, B. L., Ulmer, D. D., and Wacker, E. C., "Arsenic Toxicology and Biochemistry," *AMA Archives of Industrial Health*, **21**, 132–151 (1960).

S. C. CARAPELLA, JR.

ASTATINE†

Astatine, element 85, is the heaviest member of the halogen family. During the 1920's and 1930's several workers claimed to have found element 85 in natural sources. We know today, however, that all astatine isotopes are highly radioactive, and the amount of astatine present in nature is so small that these early reports must be erroneous. Minute amounts of the short-lived isotopes At^{215}, At^{218} and At^{219} exist in nature in equilibrium with the naturally occurring long-lived uranium and thorium isotopes, and traces of short-lived At^{217} are in equilibrium with the U^{233} and Np^{237} that result from interaction of thorium and uranium with naturally produced neutrons. However, the total amount of astatine present in the earth's crust is less than one ounce.

Element 85 was first characterized in 1940 by Corson, MacKenzie, and Segré, who synthesized the isotope At^{211} by bombarding bismuth with alpha particles. They observed chemical behavior somewhat similar to that of other halogens and named the new element "astatine," from the Greek "astatos," meaning "unstable." Since that time a number of astatine isotopes have been identified, and their principal nuclear properties are summarized in Table 1.

As can be seen from the table, the least unstable astatine isotopes, At^{210}, has only an 8.3-hr half-life. This corresponds to a specific activity of two curies per microgram.

†Written under the auspices of the U.S. Atomic Energy Commission.

TABLE 1. ASTATINE ISOTOPES†

Isotope	Half-life	Mode of Decay	Method of Production
At^{200}	0.8 min	α	$Au + C^{12}$
At^{201}	1.5 min	α	$Au + C^{12}$
At^{202}	3 min	α (12%) EC (88%)	$Au + C^{12}$
At^{203}	7.4 min	α (14%) EC (86%)	$Au + C^{12}$
At^{204}	9.3 min	α (4.5%) EC (95.5%)	$Au + C^{12}$
At^{205}	26 min	α (18%) EC (82%)	$Au + C^{12}$ Bi $(\alpha, 8n)$
At^{206}	29 min	α (0.9%) EC (99.1%)	$Au + C^{12}$ Bi $(\alpha, 7n)$
At^{207}	1.8 hr	α (10%) EC (90%)	$Au + N^{14}$ Bi $(\alpha, 6n)$
At^{208}	1.7 hr	α (0.5%) EC (99.5%)	Bi $(\alpha, 5n)$
At^{209}	5.5 hr	α (5%) EC (95%)	Bi $(\alpha, 4n)$
At^{210}	8.3 hr	α (0.17%) EC (99.8%)	Bi $(\alpha, 3n)$
At^{211}	7.2 hr	α (41%) EC (59%)	Bi $(\alpha, 2n)$
At^{212}	0.2 sec	α	Bi (α, n)
At^{213}	< 1 sec	α	descendant Pa^{225} [Th^{232} (p, 8n) Pa^{225}]
At^{214}	2 μsec	α	descendant Pa^{226} [Th^{232} (p, 7n) Pa^{226}]
At^{215}	10^{-4} sec	α	descendant U^{235}
At^{216}	3×10^{-4} sec	α	descendant Pa^{228} [Th^{232} (p, 5n) Pa^{228}]
At^{217}	0.018 sec	α	descendant Np^{237}
At^{218}	2 sec	α	descendant U^{238}
At^{219}	0.9 min	α (97%) β (3%)	descendant U^{235}

† Based on the data given in Hyde, E. K., Perlman, I., and Seaborg, G. T., "The Nuclear Properties of the Heavy Elements," Vol. II, pp. 1081–1082, Englewood Cliffs, New Jersey, Prentice-Hall, Inc., 1964.

Hence studies of ponderable amounts of astatine have not been possible, and nothing is known of the bulk physical properties of the element. The largest preparations of astatine to date have been about 0.05 microgram. Astatine is most efficiently obtained by bombarding bismuth with energetic alpha particles to obtain the relatively long-lived isotopes $At^{209-211}$, which can be distilled from the target by heating in air.

The atomic absorption spectrum of astatine has been measured. Two lines at 2244.01 Å and 2162.25 Å have been assigned to the transitions $^2P_{3/2}{}^0 - {}^4P_{3/2}$ and $^2P_{3/2}{}^0 - {}^4P_{5/2}$ between configurations $6p^5$ and $6p^47s$.

Extrapolation from the other halogens suggests that astatine should have about the same vapor pressure as mercury. Although no measurement of the bulk vapor pressure of astatine has been possible, the element appears to be fairly volatile. It can be distilled in vacuum at room temperature in a glass apparatus and can be condensed in a trap cooled by dry ice.

Like iodine, astatine has a strong tendency to be adsorbed on various surfaces. In the case of metallic adsorbents, chemical interaction with the surfaces is indicated. Tellurium, silver and platinum are particularly good adsorbents for astatine, and a platinum plate on which astatine is deposited must be heated to several hundred degrees centigrade before the astatine can be removed. Although astatine is not strongly adsorbed by clean glass, traces of impurities on the surface may cause the astatine to be very tightly held.

Also like the lighter halogens, astatine is more soluble in organic solvents than in water, and may be extracted from aqueous solution by a variety of solvents, among them hydrocarbons, halocarbons, and ethers.

Although astatine behaves much like iodine, there is to date no evidence for the existence of the molecule At_2. Recent mass spectral studies of astatine and its compounds have failed to reveal any signs of such a molecule. It is possible, therefore, that the elemental astatine species may be atomic At resulting from dissociation of At_2 at the very low concentrations involved in all the research carried out so far. It is also possible that the species thought of as elemental astatine may in many cases consist of organic astatine compounds formed by reaction of the astatine with impurities in the experimental systems.

Most investigations of astatine chemistry have been carried out by tracer techniques, in which the element is detected only by its radioactivity. However, very recently the compounds HAt, CH_3At, AtI, AtBr, and AtCl

have been identified by direct measurement of their masses in a mass spectrometer.

Tracer studies have shown the existence of at least four oxidation states of astatine in aqueous solution:

The "zero" or "elemental" state is characterized by extractability into nonpolar organic solvents. The species At and At_2 have usually been assumed to be present. However, organic astatine compounds may behave similarly, while in the presence of iodine the extractable species is AtI.

The -1 state is characterized by coprecipitation with insoluble iodides. It is formed by reducing higher states with strong reducing agents, such as SO_2. The species present is presumed to be At^-, the astatide ion.

The $+5$ state is characterized by coprecipitation with insoluble iodates. It is formed by oxidizing lower states with such strong oxidants as Ce^{+4} or H_5IO_6. Presumably the astatine is present as the astatine ion $AtO_3{}^-$.

An intermediate positive oxidation state of astatine is formed by oxidation of lower states with mild oxidants, such as bromine. It is characterized by its failure to extract into nonpolar organic solvents or to coprecipitate with either insoluble iodides or iodates. Species present may be intermediate oxides or oxyacids of astatine, or even polar organic astatine compounds. A recent investigation suggests that cationic astatine species may also be present in some cases. Under certain conditions polyhalide complex ions are formed. Ions of this type that have been identified are $AtI_2{}^-$, $AtIBr^-$, $AtICl^-$, $AtBr_2{}^+$, and $AtCl_2{}^-$.

No evidence has been found for the existence of perastatate—astatine in the $+7$ oxidation state.

The aqueous chemistry of astatine may be summarized by the following approximate electrode potential diagram for acid solution:

$$At^- ---- 0.3v --- At(0) --- 1.0v ---$$
$$At(+X) --- 1.5v --- AtO_3{}^-$$

Tracer techniques have been used to characterize a number of organic astatine compounds, among them: C_6H_5At, HOC_6H_4At, $p\text{-}AtC_6H_4COOH$, $p\text{-}AtC_6H_4SO_3H$, $C_6H_5AtCl_2$, $(C_6H_5)_2AtCl$, $C_6H_5AtO_2$, $At(C_5H_5N)_2ClO_4$, and $At(C_5H_5N)_2NO_3$. Astatine has also been successfully incorporated into protein molecules.

When injected as At⁻ into experimental animals, astatine concentrates in the thyroid, though not quite so selectively as does iodine. The alpha-emitting astatine isotopes offer an advantage over radioiodine in the treatment of hyperthyroidism and thyroid cancer, since the alpha particles deposit more energy in a limited area than do the beta particles of the radioiodine. Thus astatine can attack thyroid tissue without damaging the nearby parathyroid. However, astatine has shown a tendency to induce tumours in experimental animals, and this obviously presents a severe obstacle to its clinical use. To date, no clinical tests have been made of the effectiveness of astatine in treating thyroid ailments in man.

References

1. Appelman, E. H., Sloth, E. N., and Studier, M. H., *Inorg. Chem.*, **5**, 766 (1966).
2. Aten, A. H. W., Jr., *Advances Inorg. Radiochem.*, **6**, 207 (1964).
3. Corson, D. R., Mackenzie, K. R., and Segré, E., *Phys. Rev.*, **57**, 1087 (1940).
4. Hamilton, J. G., Durbin, P. W., Asling, C. W. and Johnston, M. E., *Proc. Intern. Conf. Peaceful Uses Atomic Energy, Geneva, 1955,* **10**, 175 (1955–6).
5. McLaughlin, Ralph, *J. Optical Soc. Am.*, **54**, 965 (1964).

EVAN H. APPELMAN

ATOMIC NUMBER

The atomic number of an element is the ordinal number which is equal to the number of unit positive charges carried by the nucleus of its atom. Since an atom in the ground state is electrically neutral, the atomic number is also equal to the number of electrons around the nucleus of the atom. All atoms of the same element have the same atomic number and hence the same number of protons in the nucleus; they may, however, have different numbers of neutrons in the nucleus and hence differ in mass (isotopes). The modern classification of the chemical elements is based upon the atomic numbers of the elements, starting with one for hydrogen. Hence the Periodic Law is a statement of the fact that the chemical properties of the elements are periodic functions of their atomic numbers.

The recognition of the basic nature of the atomic number in classifying the chemical elements did not come until the early Twentieth Century although the concept of atoms as elementary, indivisible and indestructible particles, of which all matter is composed, dates back to Democritus in the early Fourth Century B.C. Democritus stated that all atoms were alike and that differences in quality of matter were due to the impressions caused on our senses by different configurations and combinations of atoms. The ideas of Democritus were expressed in the poem *De Rerum Natura* by Lucretius in the First Century B.C. Other Greek philosophers attempted to describe the properties of matter by postulating four different types of atoms: earth, air, fire, and water. According to this view the various types of matter were composed of different combinations of the atoms of these basic elements. For example, metals were considered to be composed of earth atoms and fire atoms, since they could be produced by placing ores (earth) in a flame. The higher the content of fire atoms in a given metal, the shinier the metal was. These views persisted through the Middle Ages and Renaissance until near the end of the Eighteenth Century when it was realized by Lavoisier, among others, that ordinary matter could be decomposed into a rather different set of basic constituents, now termed the chemical elements. This recognition led to the practical basis for understanding the nature of chemical compounds.

The first quantitative evidence in favor of the atomic theory of matter was presented in 1808 by the British chemist John Dalton in his "New System of Chemical Philosophy." Dalton had observed that in forming compounds chemical elements always combined in certain proportions or in integer multiples thereof. He clearly recognized that these laws of constant and multiple proportions could be interpreted in term of the Greek idea of individual atoms by ascribing to the atoms of different chemical elements definite atomic weights. The atomic weights so derived describe only the relative weights of different atoms, since neither Dalton nor his contemporaries knew how much atoms actually weigh. Since hydrogen, when it is present in any known simple chemical compound, is always present in the smallest proportion by weight, the atom of hydrogen must be the lightest of all atoms. In 1816 the English physician William Prout thought it possible that all atomic weights were integral. Hence he considered that all other elements might be formed from hydrogen by some process of condensation or grouping. Prout's hypothesis fell into disfavor, however, when definite fractional atomic weights, such as those of chlorine and copper, were obtained.

The first attempt at a unified classification of the chemical elements was made by J. W. Döbereiner between 1817 and 1829, when he showed that certain triads of elements possessed close relationships between their members. For example, calcium, barium, and strontium exhibited many properties in common as did lithium, sodium, and potassium. Between 1828 and 1854 others expanded Döbereiner's suggestions by showing that similar relationships were not limited to triads of elements. For example, oxygen, sulfur, selenium, and tellurium were classified as one family, with nitrogen, phosphorus, arsenic, antimony and bismuth as another.

Other attempts at classification were made by trying to prove that the atomic weights of the elements could be expressed by an arithmetic function. Then in 1862 A. E. B. de Chancourtois plotted the atomic weights of the elements on a helical curve with corresponding points differing by 16, the approximate atomic weight of oxygen. Since this curve brought closely related elements on to corresponding points, he suggested that "the properties of the elements are the properties of numbers." Following the work of J. A. R. Newlands, who in 1863 proposed the law of octaves, Dmitri I. Mendeléev in 1869 enunciated the Periodic Law by which "the elements arranged according to the magnitude of atomic weights show a periodic change of properties."

Although Mendeléev stated the Periodic Law in terms of atomic weights, the periodic table which he published in 1871 had the elements arranged in eight vertical groups having valency from 1 to 8. In other words, Mendeléev clearly recognized that the outstanding periodic property of the elements is valency. The classification according to val-

ency, however, presented certain anomalies, since the Periodic Law was stated in terms of atomic weights. For example, only one element, hydrogen, precedes the inert gas helium of Group VIII, even though there are seven other groups. Moreover, the atomic weights of argon, cobalt, and tellurium are higher, respectively, than the atomic weights of potassium, nickel, and iodine, which they precede in the table. As became evident later, the anomaly relating to the position of hydrogen is inherent in the periodic classification. As we shall see, the anomalies relating to the atomic weight inversions are, however, no longer anomalies on an atomic number basis.

Following the discovery of the electron by J. J. Thomson in 1897 several atomic models were developed. Thomson himself developed a model which pictured the internal structure of an atom as a positive charge filling uniformly its entire body with negative electrons embedded in that charge. In 1911 Ernest Rutherford showed, on the basis of experiments involving the scattering of alpha particles, that Thomson's model was entirely wrong. Rutherford developed an atomic model which had all the positive charge and most of the atomic mass concentrated in a very small nucleus or center of the atom, with the electrons moving around the nucleus under the action of an inverse square coulomb attraction. Such a model seemed to contradict the nature of things, however, since the electrons moving in this way were expected to emit electromagnetic radiation, lose energy, and rapidly spiral into the nucleus. To explain this apparent paradox the Danish physicist Niels Bohr, who was then working with Rutherford, formulated in 1913 a revolutionary new theory in which the laws of classical mechanics did not apply to atomic mechanisms. Bohr developed a model for the hydrogen atom that enabled him to calculate the frequencies of the lines in the hydrogen spectrum. In Bohr's theory of the origin of spectra the charge on the nucleus, or the atomic number, played a fundamental role. According to Bohr's theory, the frequency ν of a spectral line is given by

$$\nu = Z^2 \frac{2\pi^2 m e^4}{h^3} \left(\frac{1}{n_2{}^2} - \frac{1}{n_1{}^2} \right) \qquad (1)$$

where Z is the atomic number; m and e are respectively the electronic mass and charge; h is Planck's constant; and n_2 and n_1 are integers, where $n_1 > n_2$.

In the same year that Bohr published his theory H. G. J. Moseley, a student in Rutherford's laboratory, came under the influence of Bohr's teaching. After the development of a simple method of x-ray spectrum analysis by the Braggs, Moseley made a detailed study of the x-ray spectra of a series of elements from aluminum to gold and found that the spectra contained three lines in the same relative position in all the elements. He also observed that in the progression from lighter to heavier elements the wavelengths of the lines as well as the relative distances between the lines decreased. The mathematical relationship between the frequency ν of the K_α spectral line and the atomic number Z was found to be

$$\nu = 0.248 \times 10^{16} \, (Z-1)^2. \qquad (2)$$

If, in Eq. (1), we set $n_2 = 1$ and $n_1 = 2$ and insert the numerical values of m, e, and h, we obtain

$$\nu = 0.246 \times 10^{16} \, Z^2. \qquad (3)$$

Except for the slight correction to Z, Eqs. (2) and (3) are almost identical, lending support to Moseley's hypothesis that quantum transitions of the type postulated by Bohr give rise to the lines in the x-ray spectra of the elements. Moseley summarized his results by stating that a certain quantity "increases by a constant amount as we pass from one element to the next using the chemical order of the elements in the periodic table." He stated further that "this quantity can only be the charge on the central positive nucleus." Assuming that iron had a positive nuclear charge of 26 (and hence 26 electrons) as the twenty-sixth element in the chemical order, Moseley showed that cobalt had 27 and nickel 28 electrons, despite the fact that nickel had a smaller atomic weight than cobalt. The method was applied to the other periodic anomalies and hence it was proved that the true order of the elements in the classification is that of atomic number, not atomic weight. Thus the atomic weight inversions in Mendeléev's table were caused by the relative abundance of the particular stable isotopes of these elements.

The atomic number also enters prominently into the theory of nuclear reactions, since it represents the number of positive changes on the nucleus. An example is the coulombic potential barrier inhibiting absorption or emission of positively charged particles as in (p,n), (α,n), (α,pn) reactions or in α-particle emission. As a special case we may consider its effect on nuclear fission, either spontaneous or particle induced. The critical energy requisite for fission to occur is the energy which must be supplied to a nucleus of an atom in order to deform it to a state where the electrostatic repulsion overcomes the binding force still holding the nucleus together. Since the repulsive force depends on the product of the positive charges on the fission fragments, it may be taken to a fair approximation as proportional to Z^2, where Z is the positive charge or atomic number of the original nucleus. The binding force holding the nucleus together is dependent on the mass number A of the nucleus. Hence, in a general way, the ease of fission of a given nucleus will be proportional to Z^2/A, since an increase in electrostatic repulsion favors fission while an increase in binding energy opposes fission. The larger the value of Z^2/A for a given nucleus, the smaller is the amount of energy which must be supplied to make it suffer fission. Using the liquid drop analogy for a nucleus, Bohr and Wheeler concluded that if Z^2/A exceeded about 45 no additional energy would be needed to cause nuclear fission to take place. Since Z^2/A might be expected to have a value of 45 for an element having an atomic number of about 120, this would seem to represent an upper limit for nuclear stability against spontaneous fission. Systematic studies on the induced fissionability of heavy nuclides vs Z^2/A for each of the neutron number-proton number types (i.e., where Z-$(A-Z)$ is even-even, even-odd, odd-even, or odd-odd) do indeed show a general increase in tendency toward fission the higher the value of Z^2/A.

References

1. Evans, R. D., "The Atomic Nucleus," New York, McGraw-Hill Book Co., Inc., 1955.
2. Glasstone, Samuel, "Sourcebook on Atomic Energy," New York, D. Van Nostrand Co., Inc., 1950.

3. Haas, A., "Atomic Theory," London, Constable and Co. Ltd., 1936.
4. Loeb, Leonard B., "Atomic Structure," New York, John Wiley & Sons, Inc., 1947.
5. Richtmyer, F. K., Kennard, E. H., and Lauritsen, T., "Introduction to Modern Physics," Fifth Edition, New York, McGraw-Hill Book Co., Inc., 1955.

M. H. LIETZKE AND R. W. STOUGHTON

ATOMS

The word "atom" is used universally in chemistry and physics to denote the smallest particle of an element which can exist either alone or in combination with other atoms of the same or of other elements and still have the properties of the given element. Breaking up an atom would yield particles that would not have the same properties as the original element. The radius of an atom is about 2 or 3×10^{-8} cm. Atoms are the building blocks from which molecules are constructed and they are the particles which occupy regularly spaced positions in the lattices of crystals. The mass of the lightest atom, the hydrogen atom, is 1.67×10^{-27} kilogram. This means that its mass is about 1840 times the mass of an electron.

Historical Development

The name "atom" was derived from the Greek word "atomos" which means uncut or indivisible; the Greek philosopher Democritus, was the first to propose the existence of such elementary particles. The idea was revived late in the Nineteenth Century in an effort to explain experimental results. Dalton's Law of Partial Pressures showed that in any mixture of gases or of vapors or of both, each constituent exerted its pressure as though the other constituents were not present. Other studies, such as the development of the kinetic theory of gases, and measurements on the combining weights of elements, brought out a more complete atom theory. In many experiments atoms behaved as though they were tiny solid spheres, in accordance with the ideas of Democritus. However, later developments indicated that the atom was anything but solid and indivisible and further that it had some waves associated with it. These results showed that the atom was far more complex than a simple solid particle.

Many important discoveries in the last half of the Nineteenth Century had a direct bearing on beliefs about the structure of matter. Studies of electrical discharges through gases and in particular of cathode rays led to the discovery of electrons, and J. J. Thomson and others showed that electrons are constituents of atoms. Later, in Lord Rutherford's laboratory elaborate experiments were carried out by Geiger and Marsden on the scattering of radioactive emanations by metal foils. The results convinced Rutherford that the positive charges in matter were concentrated in very tiny regions whose size was about 10^{-12} cm or a millionth of a millionth of a centimeter. This positively charged core or nucleus was surrounded by an equal amount of negative charge.

The Orbital Model

Albert Einstein invoked the idea of light quanta. This theory proposed that the emission of light energy occurred in certain discrete amounts called quanta or in even multiples of these amounts, but not in other amounts. The Danish scientist, Niels Bohr, tied this concept to processes in individual atoms by developing his orbital model of the atom. He postulated that the negative charge in the atom was carried by electrons which rotated in stable orbits around the positive core or nucleus of the atom. His hypothesis for the hydrogen atom was that there was one stable orbit for the single electron which rotated about the nucleus of this atom. The angular momentum of the electron in this orbit was assumed to have a value equal to $h/2\pi$ where h was the universal constant known as Planck's constant. Bohr also assumed the existence of other orbits in each of which the angular momentum was an integral multiple of $h/2\pi$. If the electron should get out into one of these orbits the atom was in an excited state which was not a stable configuration. All other orbits were considered to be impossible arrangements.

This meant that the atom could exist (at least temporarily) in states in which it had certain definite amounts of energy, but states corresponding to electrons in other orbits or other amounts of energy were ruled out.

Hydrogen atoms which were not combined into molecules were found in electrical discharges, and in the discharges the excited states corresponding to electrons in other than stable orbits also appeared. When an electron dropped from one orbit to another in which it was closer to the nucleus, Bohr's theory stated that energy was emitted and the atom lost this same amount of energy. Since only certain orbits were considered possible, only certain definite amounts of energy were emitted and these amounts corresponded to Einstein's "packets of energy." Also, energy could be absorbed by the atom in amounts equal to the amounts needed to move the electron out to specific orbits.

Atoms of elements other than hydrogen have more than one electron and these are found in specific orbits when the atoms are in their normal states. Each element is characterized by the number of electrons which makes up its normal complement. This number is also equal to the amount of positive charge which is contained in the nucleus when that amount is expressed in multiples of the charge on one proton. These numbers, which are called atomic numbers, range up to 103 which corresponds to the element lawrencium. For each kind of atom there are certain stable orbits and others which correspond to excited states of the atom. If an atom has either more or less than its normal complement of electrons in orbits around it, the atom is said to be ionized.

Extensions of Bohr's model were proposed which used elliptical orbits or shells of negative electricity to account for the results of some precise experiments. None of these have been entirely successful and Bohr's theory is not considered to be a complete picture of the atom. None the less, the model has retained its usefulness because it provided a picture of the atom which could be visualized and the model is frequently used to describe the conclusions reached by theoretical calculations based on much more complicated models of the atom.

Atomic Weights

The masses of atoms are often expressed as "atomic weights." The atomic weight of an atom is the average mass of the atoms making up a sample of the element when these masses are expressed on a proportional scale on which the average mass of the atoms of a sample of ordinary oxygen is taken as exactly 16. On such a scale, hydrogen has an atomic weight of 1.008. When using this scale, the whole number or integer nearest to the mass of a particular atom is called the mass number of that atom. This scale is sometimes called the "chemical" system. Another scale called the "physical" system is also used, especially where single atoms are to be compared. Some types of oxygen atoms are heavier than others though all have the properties of oxygen. The physical scale selects the mass of the most common form (isotope), calls it 16, and uses that as a standard. Under this system the atomic weights come out about 1.0002 times those based on the chemical scale. A conference of the International Commission on Atomic Weight recommended a value of 12 for the most abundant type or isotope of carbon as a standard.

Classification of Elements

Since all the atoms of any one element have the same amount of positive charge on each of their nuclei and this amount is different from the amount on the nuclei of any other element, the elements can be arranged in order of increasing positive charge. When this is done, it is found that these amounts are all even multiples of the charge of the first element on the list—hydrogen. Each element is assigned an atomic number which denotes its position on this list. This number also indicates the number of electrons in the orbits about the nucleus. The arrangement of the electrons, particularly the number of electrons in the outermost orbit which is occupied, determines the way in which the atom will combine with other atoms to form molecules. In an attempt to classify elements, Mendeléev found that they could be placed in groups such that those in any one group had similar chemical and physical properties and that various properties showed a continuing trend throughout the group. Names of the elements can be arranged in rows with atomic number increasing from left to right, starting a new row whenever an element is reached which is similar to hydrogen in its chemical properties. This results in a periodic chart of the elements similar to the one proposed by Mendeléev. Elements which are in any one column are those which are similar in their chemical properties. These characteristics are determined mainly by the number of electrons in the outermost orbit which is occupied.

Electron Distribution

The electrons in any atom fall into groups or classes in accordance with the amount of energy needed to remove them from the atom and these groups are called the K shell, the L shell, the M shell, etc. Experiments with x-ray photons are used to determine the energies necessary to remove electrons. For each kind of atom the electrons which are hardest to remove are the K electrons, those in the next group are L electrons, etc. The maximum number of electrons in each shell is 2 for the K shell, 8 for the L shell, 18 for the M shell, and 32 for the N shell.

If a start is made with the lightest atom, the hydrogen atom, and each element is considered in turn throughout the Periodic Table, we find that more and more orbits are occupied. The second element, helium, has two electrons for each atom and these fill the K shell. The next atoms have some electrons in the L shell. It is not always found that any given shell is filled before the next shell receives any electrons. Sometimes a shell is partially filled to a convenient semi-complete stopping place with 8 or 18 electrons in the outermost occupied orbit. Then in the following elements some electrons are placed in the next orbit before any more are placed in the semi-complete orbit. Later, this orbit is filled in. When the outermost orbit which is occupied is full, the atom is nearly inert. There are also nearly inert atoms when the M shell reaches its semi-complete point with 8 elec- trons and when the N shell has 18 electrons.

The atoms of elements just beyond the nearly inert ones have one and only one electron in the outermost shell which is occupied. This last electron revolves in a field which is similar to that of the one electron of the hydrogen atom. This results in these elements having spectra which are similar to that of hydrogen, and these atoms all have similar chemical properties. Throughout the Periodic Table there are correlations between

the chemical properties and the number of atoms in the outer orbit.

One might expect that the atoms which have several occupied shells would be considerably larger than those which have fewer occupied shells. However, the larger attractive forces, which the more strongly charged nuclei of these heavier atoms exert on the electrons, result in the stable orbits being drawn inward so that there is only a comparatively slight variation in size among all the known atoms.

The Nucleus

The nucleus or core of the atom contains all the positive charge associated with that particle. For a long time it was believed that nuclei consisted of protons and electrons. This gave way to the belief that nuclei consisted of protons and neutrons. Elements differ from each other in the number of protons in their nuclei. The lightest element, hydrogen, has only one proton in each nucleus. The next element in the Periodic Table, helium, has two, and so on throughout the table. In addition to the protons present, all atoms, except some of those of the very lightest elements, contain one or more neutral particles or neutrons. A neutron has almost exactly the same mass as the proton but differs in that it is uncharged.

It is possible for two atoms to contain the same number of protons in their nuclei and thus be atoms of the same element, but to have different numbers of neutrons and thus have different atomic masses. Such atoms are called *isotopes*. Some elements are known to exist in as many as seven or eight isotopic forms. The mass number of an atom of a particular isotope can be obtained by adding the number of neutrons in its nucleus to the number of protons in that same nucleus. Different isotopes of an element may differ widely in the stability of their nuclei.

The way in which the components of a nucleus (the nucleons) are arranged is at the present time the object of much study. One hypothesis is that these particles are in much the same form as they are when existing separately but are closely packed together in the atom. Another theory states that they exist more in the form of shells one inside the other. The nucleus is held together by forces which are extremely great when the separations are very small, but which fall off very rapidly as the distances between particles increase. The Japanese scientist, Yukawa, developed a mathematical meson theory which deals with these forces.

The nuclei of all the very heavy elements are unstable in varying degrees and decay spontaneously with the emission of radiations. This process, called *radioactivity*, was first discovered by Becquerel; it transforms an atom of one element into an atom of another element, the disintegrations following statistical laws. Some isotopes decay so slowly that it takes thousands of years for one-half of the atoms of a given sample to decay and another equal period of time for one-half of the remainder to disintegrate. Others decay so rapidly that one-half of the atoms in a given sample will decay in a tiny fraction of a second. Some isotopes of the lighter elements are also radioactive. The half-life for radioactive decay is the length of time it takes for one-half of the atoms in a given sample to decay. At least one radioactive isotope of every element has been found to occur naturally or has been prepared artificially.

Theoretical Interpretation of the Atom

Powerful mathematical methods give quantitative treatments of atomic and subatomic processes. These theories are called quantum mechanics, matrix mechanics, or wave mechanics and are primarily the results of investigations by Heisenberg, Dirac, and Schrödinger. The background for these theories comes from Louis de Broglie's realization that the circumference of the circular orbit of Bohr's atom model for hydrogen in the normal state is equal to the wavelength of the waves which can be associated with the moving electrons. This leads to the idea that in the atom there is a standing wave associated with the electron as it moves in its orbit. Erwin Schrödinger proposed that this wavelength be substituted in a classical wave equation and from this beginning he derived a wave equation for the hydrogen atom. This pictures the negative charge of the electrons as a standing wave about the nucleus. The square of the amplitude of the wave represents the probability that the electron can be found at that point.

For other atoms wave mechanics indicates a method for finding the energy values and the electron distributions for stationary states of the atoms. The mathematical difficulties, where many particles are involved, are stupendous, but successes are being achieved. This development is generally known as the modern orbital theory of atomic structure.

Atomic Energy

Much is being written at the present time about atomic energy, using the expression to refer specifically to the energy obtained from certain changes in nuclear structure. The foundation of this idea of obtaining energy in usable form from atoms can be traced to Albert Einstein who showed that matter seemed to be a form of energy and that it could be changed to other forms of energy. The amount of energy obtained is given by the equation $E = mc^2$. The energy E is given in ergs if m is the mass in grams and c is the velocity of light in centimeters per second. One gram would correspond to 9×10^{20} ergs. At the present time only a small fraction of the mass of any given sample can be converted, but this fraction still yields a vast quantity of energy.

Considering two atoms of deuterium, the heavy hydrogen isotope, each nucleus contains one proton and one neutron. At high temperatures and high pressures these will combine into one nucleus. This new nucleus has two protons and two neutrons. Thus, it is the nucleus of an atom of helium. However, if we add up the masses of the starting atoms very carefully and compare the sum with that of the helium nucleus, we find that a small amount of mass is missing. It has been converted into other forms of energy. The loss of mass is often referred to as "mass defect."

Considering any other combinations of very light nuclei which result in heavier nuclei, we find that some mass is lost in the process of *fusion*. This mass appears as some other type of energy. On the other hand, if we consider the heaviest atoms in the Periodic Table, we find that they can be broken into two nearly equal parts plus some very light particles. The sum of all the masses of the resulting particles is less than that of the original materials. This process is called *fission*, and again we have the conversion of mass into other forms of energy.

Chain reactions occur when some of the particles produced in the fission process are ones which are capable of breaking other atoms, and the geometry of the arrangement is such that there is a great enough chance of their breaking other atoms before they are absorbed by competing processes, or are lost outside of the mass of fissionable material, or are slowed down to the point where they can no longer trigger the fission process.

Atoms should be thought of as entities which are very small but none the less so complex that they stagger the imagination and offer rich fields for further research and speculation.

References

1. Boorse, Henry A., and Motz, Lloyd, Editors, "The World of the Atom," 2 Vols., New York, Basic Books, Inc., 1966.
2. Fano, U., and Fano, L., "Basic Physics of Atoms and Molecules," New York, John Wiley & Sons, Inc., 1959.
3. Cook, C. Sharp, "Modern Atomic and Nuclear Physics," New York, D. Van Nostrand Co., Inc., 1961.
4. Gamow, George, "The Atom and Its Nucleus," New York, Prentice-Hall, Inc., 1961.

ROBERT M. BESANÇON

B

BARIUM

Barium, symbol Ba, atomic number 56 and atomic weight 137.34, is located in Group IIA of the Periodic Table. It is the heaviest of the three alkaline earth elements: calcium, strontium and barium, and is the least volatile of the three.

In 1774 Scheele distinguished barium oxide from lime and recognized that a new element was present. The element was first prepared by Davy in 1808 as an amalgam by the electrolysis of a soluble barium salt on a mercury cathode. It was named barium from the Greek *barys* (heavy) which had also been applied to the oxide, baryta, and the sulfate, barite or barytes.

Occurrence

Barium constitutes 0.4–0.5% of the earth's crust. The most common barium minerals are barite or barytes, $BaSO_4$, and witherite, $BaCO_3$. The former is the chief source of barium compounds in the United States and is mined in Missouri, Georgia, Tennessee, California and Nevada. Of the estimated world production of 3 million tons annually of barite, the United States production is about 800,000 tons, chiefly from Missouri and Georgia.

Barium minerals are heavy, with a specific gravity of 4.4–4.5 compared with 2.71 for calcite, $CaCO_3$. For this reason barite is also known as heavy spar. The high density of barite permits its ready separation from clay and other material associated with many barite deposits.

The greatest tonnage of natural or crude barite is used as such, principally as a constituent of oil well drilling mud, without further processing except for washing, gravity separations to remove lighter material present in the as-mined ore, and grinding.

Derivation

Metallic or elemental barium cannot be made by the reduction with carbon of barium oxide at elevated temperature because the acetylide, BaC_2, is formed rather than the metal. Electrolysis of aqueous solutions of barium salts, such as $BaCl_2$, yields barium hydroxide at a solid cathode. When a mercury cathode is used for the electrolysis of a $BaCl_2$ solution, a barium amalgam is formed from which the mercury may be distilled in vacuum to produce barium. Guntz in 1905 used this method to obtain 98.5% metal. Electrolysis of fused barium salts has not been too successful, but a solid "carrot" of barium can be made in a bath of fused KCl and $BaCl_2$.

The most effective method of making barium is the reduction of barium oxide with aluminum or silicon in a high vacuum at elevated temperature. The reactions involved are: $4BaO + Si \rightarrow 2BaO \cdot SiO_2 + 2Ba$ (gas) and $4BaO + 2Al \rightarrow BaO \cdot Al_2O_3 + 3Ba$ (gas). The barium oxide and aluminum or silicon are briquetted and placed in a horizontal nickel-chromium steel retort. The retort is heated to 1100–1200°C for about 8 hours while a vacuum of about 0.1 mm Hg is maintained. A water-cooled condenser is fitted onto one end of the retort and the barium vapors are condensed to a liquid in that condenser. After the retort and condenser have been cooled solid barium is removed from the condenser.

Useful alloys of barium and aluminum or magnesium are readily made by the reaction of aluminum and magnesium, respectively, with barium oxide. Fusion electrolysis with a heavy metal cathode, such as zinc, lead,

43

TABLE 1. PHYSICAL PROPERTIES

Atomic number	56
Atomic weight	137.34
Atomic volume, cc/g-atom	39
Melting point, °C	729
Boiling point, °C	1637
Density, g/cc, 20°C	3.6
Crystal structure	body-centered cubic
Lattice constant	$a = 5.015$ Å
Latent heat of fusion, kcal/g-atom	1.83
Latent heat of vaporization, kcal/g-atom	41.74
Specific heat, cal/g/°C, 20°C	0.068
Electrical resistivity, microhm-cm	50
Electron work function, eV	2.5
Surface tension, dyne/cm	195
Vapor pressure, 10 mm	1049°C
100 mm	1301°C
400 mm	1518°C
760 mm	1637°C
Thermal neutron absorption cross section, barns	1.2

antimony, tin and bismuth, also produces barium alloys with the respective cathode metals.

Barium is produced by Dominion Magnesium at Haley, Ontario. The market price is some $7–10/lb.

Physical Properties

Barium is a silver-white metal slightly harder than lead that is malleable, extrudable and machinable so that it can be made into rods, wire and plate. It is the densest of the alkaline earth metals. Barium and barium compounds give green colors in flames.

Values of various physical properties are given in Table 1.

Chemical Properties

Barium forms divalent compounds since its valence electrons are $6s^2$. It is an extremely reactive element and the free energy of formation of barium compounds is very high. Barium reacts directly with water, oxygen, nitrogen, hydrogen, ammonia, the halogens, phosphorus, sulfur and most acids. The chief use for it as a "getter" or degassing agent in vacuum tubes indicates its reactivity with gases. In finely divided form barium is pyrophoric and dangerous to handle in air, making it necessary to keep the powder under an atmosphere of dry argon or helium. In massive form it can be handled safely in air during the assembly of tube components.

When barium is heated in hydrogen at about 200°C a vigorous reaction occurs to form barium hydride, BaH_2, a solid compound readily decomposed by water and acids. Barium nitride, BaN_6, decomposes violently when heated.

Barium reduces the oxides, halides and sulfides of less reactive metals to produce the corresponding metal. However, it is not more effective than calcium in such reactions and is not used for this purpose because of its much higher cost per equivalent weight of reducing agent.

As mentioned previously, barium forms alloys with many metals, among them, aluminum, magnesium, lead, nickel, calcium and cadmium.

Compounds and Their Uses

Barium forms compounds analogous to those of calcium and their properties, including color or lack thereof, closely resemble those of the corresponding calcium compounds. One prominent exception is barium hydroxide which is quite soluble in water, forming an almost 50% solution at 100°C.

Commercially, most barium compounds are derived from chemical grade barite, $BaSO_4$; witherite, $BaCO_3$, is of minor importance as a starting material. In the production of many barium compounds, the $BaSO_4$ is first reduced to the sulfide by carbon in a furnace, and the soluble BaS then is reacted to form other compounds.

Barium carbonate is probably the most important barium compound insofar as chemical applications are concerned. Precipitated $BaCO_3$ is made by the reaction of sodium carbonate or CO_2 with barium sulfide. One of its most important uses is the treatment of salt brines to remove sulfates from the solutions fed to chlorine-alkali cells; the reaction involved is $CaSO_4$ (or Na_2SO_4) $+ BaCO_3 \rightarrow BaSO_4 + CaCO_3$ (or Na_2CO_3). Barium carbonate is also used as a raw material for other barium chemicals, as a flux in ceramics, as an ingredient in optical glass and fine glassware, and as a carbon carrier in case-hardening baths.

Barium chloride and *barium nitrate* are made by the action of hydrochloric and nitric acid, respectively, on barium carbonate or barium sulfide. Barium chloride is also produced commercially by heating a mixture of barium sulfate, carbon and calcium chloride: $BaSO_4 + 4C + CaCl_2 \rightarrow BaCl_2 + CaS + 4CO$. From its other barium compounds can be made, e.g., it is used to form precipitated barium sulfate (blanc fixe) in place as in the preparation of white leather where the leather is soaked in a solution of sodium sulfate and then in a $BaCl_2$ solution to cause the precipitation of $BaSO_4$ by the reaction: $Na_2SO_4 + BaCl_2 \rightarrow BaSO_4 + 2NaCl$. Barium nitrate, $Ba(NO_3)_2$, is used to produce a green color in flares, pyrotechnic devices and tracer bullets.

Barium oxide, BaO, is made by the ignition of barium nitrate and by the decomposition of barium carbonate at high temperature in the presence of carbon. The carbon results in the formation of CO: $BaCO_3 + C \rightarrow BaO + 2CO$, which has a higher vapor pressure than does CO_2 which would form if $BaCO_3$ alone is heated. The major use of BaO is in the manufacture of lubricating oil detergents.

Barium peroxide, BaO_2, a stable material at room temperature when dry, is readily formed by heating BaO in air at about 1000°F. At a higher temperature, or at the same temperature but at a lower pressure, the BaO_2 reverts to BaO and oxygen. These alternate reactions are the basis of the Brin process for oxygen production which was used prior to the development of the air liquefaction techniques which displaced it in the early 1900's. However, the Brin process is again being examined for oxygen production. Barium peroxide when added to dilute sulfuric or phosphoric acid yields hydrogen peroxide solution which can be separated from the precipitated barium sulfate or barium phosphate: $BaO_2 + H_2SO_4 \rightarrow BaSO_4 + H_2O_2$. At one time this was the chief commercial source of hydrogen peroxide until it was displaced by the electrolytic method of producing H_2O_2.

Barium sulfate, prepared chemically as a fine white powder by the metathetical reactions of various barium compounds with sulfates, is one of the most insoluble salts known and is widely used as a filler in paper, leather, rubber goods, etc. It is also used as a paint pigment and in cosmetics. A small but vital use is in x-ray photography of the gastrointestinal tract where it provides a fine opaque contrasting medium when ingested prior to the x-ray examination.

The brilliant white paint pigment, lithopone, is a mixture of zinc sulfide and barium sulfate prepared by the joint precipitation of these compounds by the reaction: $BaS + ZnSO_4 \rightarrow BaSO_4 + ZnS$. In addition to having excellent covering power, lithopone paints are not discolored by hydrogen sulfide.

Uses of Barium Metal

There are very few uses for barium metal. The most common is a "getter" in radio tubes to remove the last traces of H_2, N_2, O_2, CO, CO_2 and H_2O. Alloys of barium with aluminum and with magnesium are also applicable for this purpose.

Thin films of barium are used as a lubricant on the rotors of anodes operating at 3500 rpm in vacuum x-ray tubes. The low vapor pressure of barium allows the anodes to operate at quite high temperatures where oils and greases would vaporize. The barium coating increases the coasting time of the rotor from 12 seconds to 8 minutes.

A high-nickel alloy of barium for spark plugs improves their operating performance.

Barium metal has been used to prepare

45

americium (q.v.) by the reduction of AmF_3 at about 1200°C and under a vacuum.

The production and use of barium metal is small in quantity, only a few tons per year.

Toxicology

All of the soluble compounds of barium are poisonous when taken by mouth. This includes barium carbonate, which although insoluble (0.002 g/100 ml water at 20°C), is dissolved by the hydrochloric acid in the stomach if ingested. The fatal dose of barium chloride is 0.8 to 1.0 g; larger amounts of less soluble compounds, such as the sulfide, may be tolerated. However, very few cases of industrial systemic poisoning have been reported.

The barium ion is a muscle stimulant. It is very toxic to the heart and may cause ventricular fibrillation. Symptoms of barium poisoning are excessive salivation, convulsive tremors, rapid pulse, high blood pressure, paralysis of the arm and leg, renal, intestinal and stomach hemorrhage, and eventually cyanosis and death.

The antidote for ingested poisonous barium compounds is to drink a solution of sodium sulfate or Glauber's salts which converts the barium ion to the insoluble harmless barium sulfate.

As mentioned previously, nontoxic barium sulfate from which all soluble barium compounds have been removed is widely used as an opaque medium for radiography of the gastrointestinal tract.

References

1. Pidgeon, L. M., "Encyclopedia of Chemical Technology," Kirk, R. A., and Othmer, D. F., Editors, 2nd Edition, Vol. 3, pp. 80–82, New York, John Wiley and Sons, 1964.
2. Priesman, L., *ibid.*, pp. 82–98.
3. "Minerals Yearbook," Vol. 1, Washington, D.C., U.S. Bureau of Mines, issued annually.
4. *Light Metals*, **34**, 77 (1944).
5. Kroll, W. J., U.S. Bur. Mines Inform. Circ. 7327, 1945.
6. Guntz, M., *Compt. rend.*, **141**, 1240 (1905).
7. Matignon, C., *Compt. rend.*, **156**, 1378 (1913).
8. Pidgeon, L. M., and Alexander, W. A., *Trans. Am. Inst. Mining Met. Engrs.*, **159**, 315 (1944).
9. Mantell, C. L., "Rare Metals Handbook," Hampel, C. A., Editor, 2nd Edition, pp. 25-28, 1961.

CLIFFORD A. HAMPEL

BERKELIUM

Discovery

In December 1949, S. G. Thompson, A. Ghiorso and G. T. Seaborg carried out an ion-exchange separation of the products formed by the irradiation of milligram quantities of Am^{241} with 35 MeV helium ions at the 60-inch cyclotron at the University of California, Berkeley. A 4.5-hour electron-capture activity eluting just ahead of curium was assigned to an isotope of a new element, atomic number 97, mass number 243, produced from Am^{241} by the reaction:

$$_{95}Am^{241} + {_2}He^4(35 \text{ MeV}) \longrightarrow {_{97}\square}^{243} + 2{_0}n^1$$

The new element was named *berkelium* (symbol Bk) for the city of Berkeley, California, where it was discovered.

Historical

The stable oxidation state of berkelium in aqueous solution is $3+$, but in 1950 Thompson, B. B. Cunningham and Seaborg found that trace amounts of berkelium in acidic aqueous solution could be oxidized to the $4+$ state by tetrapositive cerium or more powerful oxidizing agents. Coprecipitation experiments in solutions of adjusted oxidation potential showed that the potential of the Bk(IV)-Bk(III) couple in 5 M nitric acid solution was about 1.6 v.

A visible amount of berkelium was isolated for the first time by Thompson and Cunningham at the University of California Radiation Laboratory in Berkeley in 1958. Three-tenths of a microgram of the isotope of mass 249 was collected on a half-millimeter diameter sphere of cation exchange resin for measurements of the magnetic susceptibility of Bk^{3+}. The molar susceptibility was found to be approximately the same as that of Tb^{3+}, as expected for the ninth member of a $5f$ transition series.

An effort to observe lines in the absorption spectrum of Bk^{3+} on the resin was unsuccessful, but it was possible to place an upper limit of about 20 for the molar absorptivity of any such lines in the visible region of the berkelium spectrum.

The first determination of the structure of a

TABLE 1. ISOTOPES OF BERKELIUM

Mass no.	243	244	245	246	247	248	249	250
Radiation	ε	ε, α	ε, α	ε	α	β^-	β^-	β^-
Half-life	4.5 h	4.4 h	4.95 d	1.8 d	$\sim 10^4$ y	23 h	314 d	3.2 h

a, alpha particle emission; ε, orbital electron capture; β^-, negative electron emission; h, hours; d, days; y, years.

berkelium compound was carried out by Cunningham and J. C. Wallmann in 1962, using x-ray diffraction methods. Four diffraction lines obtained from 0.004 μg of berkelium were indexed on the basis of a cubic CaF_2-type structure with a = 5.33 $\pm$ 0.01 Å.

Spectral features due to Bk^{3+} were observed in the self-luminescence spectrum of 5 μg of Bk in 3 mg of $LaCl_3$ by R. G. Gutmacher, E. K. Hulet, E. F. Worden and J. G. Conway at the University of California Radiation Laboratory in 1963; in 1965 20 lines were obtained between 3400 and 4000 Å in the spark spectrum of 0.2 μg of Bk on a graphite electrode by Gutmacher, Hulet and R. Lougheed at the Livermore branch of the Lawrence Radiation Laboratory.

Efforts to determine the absorption spectrum of Bk^{3+} and Bk^{4+} in aqueous solution have recently been successful, but this work is still in progress.

Additional studies of berkelium were stimulated in 1966, partly as a result of increasing availability of the element, and partly because of advances in experimental technique. In 1966 an estimated 3000 to 5000 lines of Bk were obtained from 32 μg of Bk in an electrodeless discharge tube by Worden, Hulet, Lougheed and Conway. Measurements of the hyperfine patterns from this work yielded a spin for the Bk^{249} nucleus of 7/2.

R. D. Baybarz, of the Oak Ridge National Laboratory, identified cubic berkelium sesquioxide, while J. R. Peterson and Cunningham at Berkeley determined the crystal structures and lattice parameters of Bk_2O_3, BkO_2, BkF_3, $BkCl_3$ and BkOCl.

Although berkelium has not yet been prepared in its elemental or metallic form, it is possible to predict that the metal can be made by reduction of BkF_3 or BkF_4 with calcium.

Prevalence

Berkelium does not occur naturally. The element is made by nuclear synthesis. Known isotopes are listed in Table 1. A more detailed tabulation is given on page 751 of the article on **Transuranium Elements.**

As is evident from the table, the half-life of the most stable isotope of berkelium is only a minute fraction of the age of the earth; primordial berkelium, if it existed, would long since have disappeared from the natural environment.

Sources

Berkelium is prepared by nuclear synthesis; the lighter isotopes are made by charged particle bombardment (as in the reaction used in its discovery) and the heavier ones by neutron irradiation of large quantities of plutonium, americium or curium.

The synthesis of Bk^{249} by the prolonged neutron irradiation of Am^{243} is illustrated in Fig. 1.

In practice, because of the susceptibility of the heavy element isotopes to neutron

$$_{95}Am^{243} \longrightarrow {}_{95}Am^{244}$$
$$_{96}Cm^{244} \longrightarrow {}_{96}Cm^{245} \longrightarrow {}_{96}Cm^{246} \longrightarrow {}_{96}Cm^{247} \longrightarrow {}_{96}Cm^{248} \longrightarrow {}_{96}Cm^{249} \longrightarrow {}_{97}Bk^{249}$$

FIG. 1. Formation of Bk^{249} from $Am^{243} \longrightarrow$ = n, γ reactions; $\uparrow$, β^- decay.

induced fission, only a small fraction of the Am^{243} is converted to Bk^{249}.

An alternative method of synthesis is to expose elements of lower atomic number to the intense, but very brief (microseconds) neutron fluxes produced by nuclear explosions. Thus Bk^{249} could be formed by $_{92}U^{238} + 11_0n^1 = U^{249}$, followed by five successive β^- decays.

The decay of Bk^{249} by β^- emission produces Cf^{249} which grows in at a rate of about 0.2% per day. Frequent repurification is necessary to maintain high chemical purity in preparations of Bk^{249}.

Physical and Chemical Properties

Although berkelium has not been prepared in its elemental form, it may be anticipated that it will be a silvery metal having a density of about 14, easily soluble in dilute mineral acids and readily oxidized by air or oxygen at 500°C to produce berkelium dioxide.

Principal Compounds

Slightly soluble compounds include $Bk(OH)_3$, $Bk(OH)_4$ and BkF_3.

The following compounds have been identified by x-ray diffraction methods:

1. *BkO$_2$*. The tan-colored dioxide has been prepared by heating the sulfate in air at 1200°C and by the oxidation of Bk_2O_3 in oxygen at 600C°. It exhibits a cubic structure of the CaF_2 type with a $= 5.334 \pm 0.001$ Å.

2. *Bk$_2$O$_3$*. Berkelium dioxide is reduced to the reddish-tan sesquioxide by heating in hydrogen at around 600°C. The compound is cubic, Mn_2O_3-structure type, with a $= 10.89 \pm 0.01$ Å.

3. *BkF$_3$*. Treatment of BkO_2 with an equimolar mixture of hydrogen and HF (g) at 500°C yields the trifluoride.

The compound appears to be dimorphic but neither structure has been fully interpreted.

4. *BkCl$_3$*. Lime-green berkelium trichloride is formed by heating berkelium dioxide or sesquioxide with CCl_4 vapor or anhydrous HCl (g) at 500°C.

The compound is hygroscopic and must be handled in a dry atmosphere. It crystallizes in the hexagonal system, UCl_3-structure type, with a $= 7.38 \pm 0.01$ Å, c $= 4.13 \pm 0.01$ Å.

5. *BkOCl*. On treatment of $BkCl_3$ with an appropriate mixture of HCl (g) and H_2O (g) the pale-green oxychloride is formed by the reaction:

$$BkCl_3(s) + H_2O(g) \xrightarrow{400°C} BkOCl(s) + 2HCl(g).$$

The oxychloride is not hygroscopic. It crystallizes in the tetragonal system, PbFC-l structure type with a $= 3.97 \pm 0.01$ Å, c $= 6.71 \pm 0.03$ Å.

Importance of Berkelium

Berkelium has no technological uses at present and its limited availability has precluded an extensive investigation of its properties. However, its cerium-like oxidation behavior provides important evidence for the continuing rare earth-like character of the actinide elements beyond the point of the half-filled $5f$ subshell.

Biological Action of Berkelium

It has been shown in experiments with rats and mice that actinide elements taken into the body tend to accumulate in the skeletal system.

Here the radiations associated with these isotopes cause damage to the red-cell forming mechanism of the body.

The toxicity per unit mass of the individual isotopes varies, depending upon the type of radioactivity and half-life.

The maximum permissible body burden of Bk^{249} in the human skeleton is about 0.0004 μg.

References

1. Seaborg, G. T., "The Transuranium Elements," New Haven, Yale University Press, 328 pp., 1958.
2. Katz, J. J., and Seaborg, G. T., "The Chemistry of the Actinide Elements," London, Methuen, 508 pp., 1957.
3. Seaborg, G. T., "Man-Made Transuranium Elements," Englewood Cliffs, N.J., Prentice-Hall, Inc., 120 pp., 1963.
4. "Noveau Traite de Chemie Minerale," published under the direction of Paul Pascal Volume XV, Paris, Masson et Cie, 1962. J. R. Peterson, unpublished data.
5. Thompson, S. G., and Muga, M. L., "*Intern. Conf. Peaceful Uses Atomic Energy*," 2nd., Geneva, **28**, 331, 1958.

6. Cunningham, B. B., *J. Chem. Ed.*, **36**, 32 (1959).
7. Gutmacher, R. G., Hulet, E. K., Worden, E. F., and Conway, J. G., *J. Opt. Soc. Am.*, **53**, 506 (1963).
8. Seaborg, Glenn T., *Chem. Eng. News*, **44**, 76 (1966).
9. Peterson, J. R., and Cunningham, B. B., to be published in *J. Inorg. Nucl. Chem.*
10. Recent issues of *J. Inorg. Nucl. Chem.*, *Inorg. Chem.*, *J. Opt. Soc. Am.*, and *J. Chem. Phys.*

B. B. CUNNINGHAM

BERYLLIUM

Vauquelin discovered the element beryllium in 1797 as a constituent of the mineral beryl. In the French language the element is referred to as glucinium (Gl). This name is derived from the sweetish taste of many of its compounds.

The first metallic beryllium was produced by Wohler and Bussy in 1828. They obtained beryllium in the form of an impure powder by reducing beryllium chloride with metallic potassium.

Of particular interest is the work of the French scientist Lebeau published in 1899, which includes descriptions of the electrolysis of sodium beryllium fluoride resulting in the production of small, hexagonal beryllium crystals, and the preparation of beryllium-copper alloys by direct reduction of beryllium oxide with carbon in the presence of copper. Also of interest is the work by the German scientist Oesterheld who, in 1916, published the equilibrium diagrams of beryllium with copper, aluminum, silver, and iron.

Commercial development of beryllium in the United States was begun in 1916 by Hugh S. Cooper, who produced the first significant beryllium metal ingot, and by the Brush Laboratories Company, which started their development work under the direction of Dr. C. B. Sawyer in the early 1920's. In Germany, the Siemens-Halske Konzern began their commercial development work in 1923.

Occurrence

There are some thirty recognized minerals containing beryllium; only three are of significance, namely, beryl, $3BeO.Al_2O_3.6SiO_2$; phenacite, $2BeO.SiO_2$; and chrysoberyl, $BeO.Al_2O_3$. Of these three, only beryl is now of industrial importance. In pure form this mineral is a beryllium aluminum silicate containing approximately 14% beryllium oxide, BeO; 19% aluminum oxide, Al_2O_3; and 67% silicon dioxide, SiO_2. The pure composition is approached in the precious forms of beryl, emerald and aquamarine.

Industrial grades of beryl ore contain approximately 10 to 12% beryllium oxide. Rarely is ore of more than 12% beryllium oxide available, and the trend is toward a supply ranging from 11% downward to the marginal ores containing less than 9%. Other constituents of the ore are aluminum oxide, 17 to 19%; silicon dioxide, 64 to 70%; alkali metal oxides, 1 to 2%; iron, 1 to 2%; and minor amounts of other oxides. Feldspar, quartz, and mica are the principal mineral contaminants of commercial grades of beryl ore.

Occurrences of beryllium in the earth's crust are widely distributed and are estimated to amount to approximately 0.001%. However, beryl ore containing 10 to 12% beryllium oxide has not as yet, with one or two exceptions, been found anywhere concentrated in large enough quantities to be mined economically for its own sake. The supply is, therefore, generally obtained as a by-product of mining feldspar, lithium, or mica in pegmatite dikes and only those crystals are recovered which are large enough to be hand-sorted and cobbed. An economically successful concentration process for low-grade ores has not yet been developed, although work is progressing in that direction.

Sources

The principal producers of beryl ore are the Union of South Africa, Southern Rhodesia, Brazil, Argentina, and India. Small amounts are produced in British East Africa, French Morocco, Mozambique, Portugal, and Canada. In the United States the principal sources are located in Colorado, Maine, New Hampshire, and South Dakota. Several undeveloped deposits are located in Canada. Most of the beryl ore consumed by the beryllium industry in the United States is imported. Up to this time, the supply of hand-sorted and cobbed ore has been sufficient to meet industrial demand of 3–4000 tons/year.

Through the use of the berylometer (see below), however, large deposits of the mineral phenacite, which was formerly considered to be a rare beryllium mineral, have been found in the Beaver Flats District of Colorado, at Mt. Wheeler, Nevada, and in the very extensive Agua Chile fluorspar deposits in northern Mexico. An extremely large deposit of beryllium-bearing volcanic ash has been discovered through the use of the berylometer just west of the Thomas Range, Juab County, Utah. Beryllium resources in this district, known as the Topaz District, are so large and extend over such a vast area that many years will be required for full estimation of the reserves. Reserve exploration has been carried out continously for over three years and, already, over 15 million pounds of beryllium content have been positively established. The precise mineralogical form in which beryllium exists in the Topaz District has not yet been positively identified because the particle size of the beryllium-bearing mineral is so small that its separation has not yet been effected. Its form, however, is markedly different from any of the other known American beryllium-bearing deposits in that the beryllium content in the Topaz District can be readily extracted at high yield by simple leaching with mineral acids.

Berylometer. The berylometer is capable of detecting very small quantities of beryllium in mixtures of almost any kind. The principle is based on bombarding the sample whose analysis is desired with radiation from antimony-24. When the sample is struck by the gamma radiation from this source, the beryllium gives up one neutron per atom. A detection source of boron trifluoride or helium-3 then gives off radiation which is electronically counted. The number of counts in the sample is then compared with a standard to give a quantitative measure of the amount of beryllium in the sample. The instrument can be made portable and is widely used in geological exploration for beryllium-containing minerals.

Extraction of Metal from Beryl Ore

The production of metal from beryl ore is complicated by the fact that the desirable but minor constituent beryllium oxide is tightly bound chemically within the major constituents alumina and silica. Differences in the extraction method are primarily based on (1) the freeing of the beryllium content and (2) the subsequent treatment of the solution after the ore is solubilized to remove the alumina and silica.

In one case, the beryllium oxide content of the ore is freed by melting the ore and quenching it to retain the beryllium oxide in solid solution, then reheating to precipitate this oxide, grinding, and dissolving in sulfuric acid at high temperature and pressure. Subsequent chemical treatment and the judicious choice of pH and temperature remove the silica and alumina from the sulfate solution. The final treatment gives a beryllium hydroxide slurry which is about 97% beryllium oxide.

Another method frees the beryllium by roasting with complex fluorides and repeatedly leaching to get maximum yield and purity of beryllium hydroxide. Both processes are used commercially in the United States.

A recent innovation employs liquid-liquid extraction to replace the complex chemical treatment after the ore is dissolved in sulfuric acid. Yields and costs are improved. This process can handle the dilute solutions resulting from the treatment of low-grade domestic ore directly with sulfuric acid.

The relatively impure hydroxide resulting from both the sulfuric and complex fluoride process is further purified and converted to a double salt of ammonium beryllium fluoride. This double salt is sufficiently stable to withstand crystallization from solution and subsequent thermal decomposition to make glass-like pure beryllium fluoride. This fluoride is then heated with magnesium metal to form pure beryllium metal. It is impractical to remove all of the magnesium and magnesium fluoride from the pebble-like product of the reduction operation. Final purification is accomplished by vacuum melting of the raw beryllium metal. Standard powder metallurgy processes convert the raw metal to solid shapes, the final step being consolidation by hot pressing.

Physical Properties

Metallic beryllium is grayish in color. Large crystals of bright metallic luster are usually discernible. It is a very light metal (sp gr $= 1.85$) and known as the only such metal

TABLE 1. PHYSICAL PROPERTIES OF BERYLLIUM

		CGS Units	British Units
Atomic number	4		
Atomic weight	9.0122		
Melting point		1283°C	2345°F
Boiling point		2970°C	
Specific gravity at 4°C		1.85 g/cc	
Density			.067 lb/in.³
Crystal system	Hexagonal (close-packed)		
Lattice constant Å	a = 2.286 c = 3.584		
Latent heat of fusion		250–275 cal/g	470 BTU/lb
Latent heat of vaporization		5,917 cal/g	
Coefficient of linear expansion		μin./in./°C	μin./in./°F
25–200°C		11.5	
200–800°C		17.4	
		2% BeO	09% BeO
80°F		5.9	6.5
600°F		7.7	8.1
1200°F		8.69	8.89
Electrical conductivity, % of International Annealed Copper Standard (IACS)	40–45		
Specific heat		cal/g/°C	BTU/lb/°F
0°C		0.41	
100°C		0.50	
800°C		0.74	
80°F			0.44
800°F			0.64
1600°F			0.76
Thermal conductivity		(cal/sec/cm²/°C/cm)	(BTU/ft/ft²sec°F)
0°C		0.440	
100°C		0.404	
800°C		0.192	
80°F			0.029
800°F			0.022
1600°F			0.012
Reflectivity, white light	55%		
Sound transmission velocity		12,600 m/sec	41,300 ft/sec
Resistivity, microhm-in²/in			
80°F			1.6
800°F			6.1
1400°F			11.1
Thermal neutron absorption cross-section		0.0090 barns/atom	

combining high mechanical strength with a high melting point, 1284°C (2343°F).

Beryllium has a high permeability to x-rays, owing to its low atomic weight. Its permeability is approximately 17 times greater than that of aluminum. This makes it ideally suited for windows in x-ray tubes. The small mass of the beryllium nucleus, the small tendency of the nucleus to absorb neutrons, and particularly its low affinity for slow neutrons make beryllium more efficient than graphite in moderating the velocity of neutrons in

TABLE 2. TENSILE STRENGTH VS. TEMPERATURE, BERYLLIUM HOT-PRESSED BLOCK AND SHEET

	Room Temperature	200°F	400°F	600°F	800°F	1000°F
Hot-Pressed Block	46,000	43,000	38,000	36,000	32,000	28,000
Cross-Rolled Sheet	78,000	76,000	66,000	57,000	45,000	34,000

nuclear energy devices. In the article on **Radium**, page 588, the radium-beryllium source of neutrons is described. The physical properties of beryllium are summarized in Table 1.

Chemical Properties

Beryllium is the first element in Group II of the periodic system of elements. Its atomic number is 4, its atomic weight 9.0122, and it has a valance of 2 corresponding to $2s$ electrons in the L-shell. Only one stable isotope is known to exist.

Many chemical properties of beryllium resemble aluminum, and to a lesser extent, magnesium; notable exceptions include thermal stability of water-soluble alkali metal beryllates and solubility of alkali metal fluorides-beryllium fluoride complexes. Kinetics of formation and equilibrium constants of beryllium with alkyl acid phosphates also vary considerably from aluminum and other similar elements. These differences are utilized in commercial separation processes.

All the common mineral acids attack beryllium metal readily with the exception of nitric acid, which, if cold and concentrated, is without effect. Alkalies react with beryllium with the evolution of hydrogen to first form beryllium hydroxide. Excess alkali will convert the hydroxide to a water-soluble beryllate (such as Na_2BeO_2).

At ordinary temperatures in normal atmosphere, beryllium metal shows good resistance to oxidation. At temperatures above 700°C, nitrogen attacks beryllium forming beryllium nitride, Be_3N_2; and carbon combines with beryllium to produce beryllium carbide, Be_2C.

Compounds of Beryllium

Basic beryllium acetate [($Be_4O\{C_2H_3O_2\}_6$), m.w. = 406.35, sp gr = 1.36] is soluble in glacial acetic acid and can readily be crystal-

lized therefrom in very pure form. It is also soluble in chloroform and other organic solvents and melts at about 330°C without decomposition. It is used as a source of pure beryllium salts.

Beryllium carbide (Be_2C, m.w. = 30.036, sp gr = 1.91) is produced when beryllium metal powder, intimately mixed with carbon, is heated in the absence of air to temperatures of 900°C or greater. The finely hexagonal, crystalline beryllium carbide is hard and refractory. It is attacked vigorously by strong, hot alkali solutions forming methane gas and alkali-beryllate. It has found limited use in atomic energy applications.

Ammonium beryllium carbonate [$\{Be(NH_4 CO_3)_2.[(NH_4)_2CO_3]_2\}.(H_2O)_x$] exists in ammoniacal carbonate solutions only. Prepared by dissolving β-$Be(OH)_2$ and basic beryllium compounds in warm (50°C) aqueous mixtures of NH_4HCO_3 and $(NH_4)_2CO_3$. In concentrated ammoniacal carbonate solutions, the beryllium content can reach 2 molar. It readily decomposes on heating to 88°C, yielding NH_3, CO_2, and crystalline basic beryllium carbonate. Decomposition occurs at all conditions where NH_3 and CO_2 are lost from solution phase. At pH <7.5, beryllium precipitates as β-$Be(OH)_2$. Purified solutions are water white.

Basic beryllium carbonate [variable compositions depicted by $(BeO)_x.BeCO_3$] Value of x is dependent on concentration of NH_3 and CO_2 of solution at time of precipitation (by hydrolysis of ammonium beryllium carbonate). A white crystalline (sp gr = 2.63) compound analyzing as $BeCO_3$ can be readily recovered if terminal hydrolyzing media is greater than 0.5 molar in NH_4HCO_3 and product is dried using absolute alcohol displacement washes at room temperature. Basic carbonate is easily hydrolyzed in H_2O to β-$Be(OH)_2$ at temperatures up to 110°F and converts directly to α-Be(OH)₂ at temperatures above 160°C at corresponding steam pressure. Basic carbonate is readily dissolved in all mineral acids, evolving CO_2, but is insoluble in H_2O and organic solvents. It begins to lose CO_2, converting to BeO on heating above 300°C at atmospheric pressure, with instantaneous loss and conversion occurring above 550°C, resulting in an extremely bulky BeO.

Beryllium chloride (BeCl₂, m.p. = 440°C, b.p. = 520°C, sp gr = 1.599) is a highly deliquescent, crystalline compound. It dissolves in water readily and the solution is accompanied by hydrolysis evolving hydrogen chloride. It is soluble in ether and alcohol. Its vapor pressure is high at its melting point.

Beryllium fluoride [BeF₂, m.w. = 47.01, m.p. = (500 to 800°C), sp gr = 1.986] is the intermediate compound in the production of beryllium metal and is reduced by magnesium metal. Finely ground BeF₂ is readily soluble in water and in alcohol. It is produced by the thermal decomposition (at 900–950°C) of ammonium beryllium fluoride.

Beryllium hydroxide Be(OH)₂, is known to exist in two forms. The "alpha" hydroxide is a chemical individual of definite composition. It is a granular, crypto-crystalline powder prepared by precipitation from strongly alkaline solution of beryllate and drying at 100°C to BeO.1H₂O. The "beta" hydroxide is gelatinous and of indefinite composition. In either form beryllium hydroxide begins to decompose to beryllium oxide at 190°C, its transformation being complete at red heat.

Beryllium nitrate [Be(NO₃)₂.3H₂O, m.w. = 187.08, m.p. = 60°C] is produced commercially by dissolving beryllium oxide or hydroxide in concentrated nitric acid and crystallizing out the nitrate salt. The crystals are deliquescent and have a strong odor of nitrogen pentoxide. It is fairly unstable and decomposes completely into beryllium oxide and nitrous gases at low red heat, suiting it for introducing beryllia into incandescent mantles.

Beryllium nitride, Be₃N₂, is produced by heating beryllium metal powder in a dry, oxygen-free nitrogen atmosphere at temperatures of 700–1400°C. The hard, refractory nitride reacts with mineral acids to form the corresponding salts of beryllium and ammonia. Strong alkali solutions attack it readily liberating ammonia. It has applications in the nuclear energy program and is currently used in producing the radioactive carbon isotope (C¹⁴) for tracer uses.

Beryllium oxide (BeO, m.w. = 25.013, m.p. = 2570°C, sp gr = 3.025, sp.heat = 0.299 cal/g at 100°C and Mohs hardness = 9) is a white, high-temperature refractory. It is characterized by its excellent thermal conductivity, high electrical resistance even at elevated temperatures, and good resistance to thermal shock and to chemical attack. These important properties coupled with good strength suit it admirably for refractory crucible material. In addition, it has high dielectric strength. It has found use as a neutron reflector in power reactors. Other uses include numerous precision resistor cores, internal parts for traveling wave tubes, microwave energy windows, radomes, components of solid state devices, thermocouple protection tubes and insulators, bubbler tubes for glass tanks, etc.

Beryllium sulfate (BeSO₄.4H₂O, m.w. = 177.14, sp gr = 1.713) is readily water-soluble, of definite composition, stable and well adapted to crystallization (a saturated water solution contains 30.5% BeSO₄ by weight at 30°C and 65.2% BeSO₄ at 111°C). When heated in air it progressively loses water of crystallization, resulting in the anhydrous salt at 400°C. This is stable up to 530°C; at 550–600°C, sulfur trioxide is slowly lost and at 1000°C the conversion to beryllium oxide is complete.

Applications of Beryllium

The most significant reason for the development of beryllium metal as an industrial material has been its nuclear characteristics. As early as 25 years ago, significant amounts of money were being spent by government agencies to try to learn how to turn raw beryllium material into sizes and shapes which could be applied to nuclear requirements. In some instances, structural requirements are also needed in the beryllium. Very recent experimental nuclear applications are utilizing beryllium that has been hot-pressed to shape with strength characteristics in the order of 60,000 psi yield strength and measurable ductility.

Manufacturing techniques have become sophisticated enough that the material is more than adequate from a mechanical point of view so that utilization of the rigidity of beryllium (as measured by the modulus of elasticity) is in no way restricted by low mechanical properties. No known material exceeds beryllium's modulus-to-weight ratio and also possesses significant ductility.

Applications which fully exploit the nuclear and high modulus properties currently account for the major portion of the beryllium produced. Examples of such applications using hot-pressed machined block are heat shields, guidance systems parts, including gimbals, gyroscopes, stable platforms and accelerometers, housings, and mirrors (in this case the beryllium is used as a rigid carrier for a highly polished surface). In the case of some guidance and control parts, cold pressing (isopressing) and sintering are used to replace hot pressing. In this manner, parts can be made closer to finished size with appreciable material cost savings.

TABLE 3. ELASTIC MODULUS VS. TEMPERATURE, BERYLLIUM HOT-PRESSED BLOCK AND SHEET

Temperature, °F	Elastic Modulus × 10⁶
Room	44.5
200	44
400	43
600	42
800	41.5
1000	38

More sophisticated current applications for beryllium require that strength levels (other than modulus) be 50,000 psi yield or higher and beryllium has been rather widely applied in structures which are loaded in compression. Examples of these applications are shingles for cladding the capsule for use in the Gemini program, the inner stage joining element for stages of the Minuteman missile, and skin panels for the Agena booster. In these applications, of course, problems involving joining, chemical milling, hot forming, zinc brazing, hole drilling, and riveting have been encountered and have been successfully

solved. The working of the beryllium for these applications took place after hot pressing of a massive block and was accomplished by such techniques as ring rolling, conventional sheet rolling with cladding and, very recently, by forging.

The main driving force behind beryllium fabrication activity during the past three years has been aerospace applications. Structural applications, largely involving compressive loading and high mechanical properties, have been flight tested and in some cases are in production. The future of beryllium in structural applications appears bright.

Additions of beryllium to commercial copper-base alloys enable these materials to be precipitation-hardened to strengths approaching those of heat-treated steels. Yet, beryllium copper retains the corrosion resistance, electrical and thermal conductivities, and spark-resistant properties of copper-base alloys.

Wrought, high-strength alloys of copper with 1.6 to 2.0% Be are used in mechanical and current-carrying springs and diaphragms because of their high elastic and endurance strength (in the heat-treated state) and their good formability (in the process state).

The oxide of beryllium, when fabricated into finished shapes, has a unique combination of properties unavailable in any other design material.

The neutron properties of beryllia are combined with high-temperature resistance (melting point above 2500°C) which permit use in high-temperature reactor systems where the metal would deform or melt.

Beryllium oxide is unique among ceramic materials in that it combines extremely high electrical resistivity and dielectric strength with extremely high thermal conductivity.

Biology-Toxicology

Under some circumstances beryllium dust, mist, fume or vapor, when inhaled, may be hazardous to health. In addition, the soluble beryllium salts may produce a dermatitis on contact with the skin. There is, however, no ingestion problem.

The hazards are generally classified as (a) the acute respiratory disease, (b) the chronic disease (berylliosis), and (c) dermatitis.

Acute Disease. The acute disease, which is

principally a concern of the basic extractor, manifests itself principally as a chemical pneumonitis, though other effects such as beryllium nasopharyngitis and beryllium tracheobronchitis, also occur. It is generally accepted that the acute disease is caused by exposure to airborne dusts, mists, or fumes of the soluble salts of beryllium, especially beryllium fluoride and sometimes the sulfate. The acute disease, which is similar to the conditions caused by exposure to chlorine, phosgene, or oxides of nitrogen, has a relatively short latency period (a few days). Deaths have occurred before the disease was fully recognized but today with proper medical attention, it resolves itself in complete clinical and x-ray recovery.

Chronic Disease (Berylliosis). The chronic disease is the more important industrial hazard encountered when working with beryllium, since it has a latency period marked by a remarkable variance from a few months after exposure to as long as twenty years. Though the respiratory system is chiefly affected, it is considered by some as a systemic illness. It should be noted that no disabling cases of chronic berylliosis have been documented from exposure after 1949, at which times the disease was recognized and controls were instigated.

Beryllium oxide and perhaps other compounds, except beryl, may be hazardous on chronic exposure, though the hazard probably depends on the specific compounds involved and the degree of exposure. Nonoccupational cases caused by atmospheric pollution and contaminated workers' clothing have been reported. The greatest concentration of chronic cases occurred in the manufacture of fluorescent lamps where the compound beryllium zinc manganese silicate, probably containing excess free or unbound beryllium oxide, was used. Beryllium oxide is no longer used in this application.

Specific Medical Procedures. For people working with beryllium, preplacement and periodic medical examinations should be routine. Full-size x-rays should be made on all personnel prior to job assignment. Periodic chest x-rays should be made at yearly intervals (semiyearly at refineries) on potentially exposed personnel, and removal from exposure should be prompt at the first abnormal finding.

Dermatitis. Dermatitis is produced by skin contact with soluble salts of beryllium, especially the fluoride. Besides rash, irritation of the nose, throat, and eyes is encountered. Granuloma, which responds only to surgical excision, may result from embedded particles, usually of soluble compounds in the skin. Dermatitis is controlled by a program of good personal hygiene, frequent washing of the exposed parts of the body, as well as by a clothing program where clothing is laundered on the plant site. This practice, incidentally, also keeps the beryllium from going home with the worker, hence, preventing nonoccupational exposures.

Hygienic Controls. The methods of control, originally recommended by the Medical Advisory Committee of the Atomic Energy Commission in 1949, are as follows:

1. "The inplant atmospheric concentration of beryllium should not exceed 2 micrograms per cubic meter as an average throughout an eight-hour day."

2. "Even though the daily weighted average might be within the limits of recommendation, no personnel should be exposed to a concentration greater than 25 micrograms per cubic meter for any period of time, however short." (It is generally agreed by industrial hygiene authorities that the language "however short" is impossible to interpret realistically and should, therefore, be eliminated and replaced by a time-concentration product equal to 30 min. at a concentration of 25 micrograms per cubic meter. This change was accepted in 1964 by the American Industrial Hygiene Association in their Hygienic Guide for Beryllium and Its Compounds).

3. "In the neighborhood of a plant handling beryllium compounds the average monthly concentration should not exceed 0.01 micrograms per cubic meter."

These original recommendations above were set down as target levels only, and practical working variations from these limits were recognized and formalized by the Atomic Energy Commission in 1956, the major interpretations being the concept of a daily weighted average over a three-month period, the use of respiratory protection in concentrations over the 25 microgram per cubic meter level, and the toleration of inplant levels up to 5 micrograms per cubic meter provided engineering work is in progress to correct the exposure situation. It should be emphasized that though the levels recommended in 1949 were approached, they were never fully met in the beryllium refineries, but that no disabling chronic disease has been documented from exposures generated since 1949. There has been no difficulty experienced in meeting the Atomic Energy Commission standards in machine shops or fabricating facilities.

Engineering Control. Local exhaust ventilation is the major engineering control used in controlling concentration of airborne beryllium. With some processes, such as furnace operations, complete enclosure may be required. Machine shop operations require low-volume, high-velocity ventilated pickups. Local exhaust and process ventilation is run through air cleaners before being discharged to the atmosphere. Modern air cleaners allow ready control of recommended outplant levels of 0.01 micrograms beryllium per cubic meter, averaged over a period of one month.

References

1. "Beryllium in Aerospace Structures," The Brush Beryllium Company, Cleveland, 1963.
2. Clark, G. L., and Hawley, G. G., "The Encyclopedia of Chemistry," 2nd Ed., p. 128, New York, Reinhold Publishing Corp., 1966.
3. Darwin, G. E., and Buddery, J. H., "Beryllium," Vol. 7, New York, Academic Press, Inc., 1960.
4. Hampel, C. A., "Rare Metals Handbook," article on "Beryllium," New York, Reinhold Publishing Company, 1961.
5. Hausner, H. H., "Beryllium, Its Metallurgy and Properties," Berkeley and Los Angeles, University of California Press, 1965.
6. Kirk-Othmer, "Encyclopedia of Chemical Technology," 2d Ed., Vol. 3, "Beryllium and Beryllium Alloys," by C. W. Schwenzfeier, Jr. New York, Interscience Publishers, Inc.,, 1964.
7. White, D. W., Jr., and Burke, J. E., "The Metal Beryllium," Cleveland, The American Society for Metals, 1955.

LEE S. BUSCH

BISMUTH

Bismuth, symbol Bi, atomic number 83, atomic weight 208.98, is a metallic element located in Group VA of the Periodic Table.

Bismuth was probably not recognized as a specific metal by the early orientals, Greeks or Romans, but by the Middle Ages, Europeans were becoming aware of its specific nature, and in the Fifteenth Century Basil Valentine referred to it as wismut. The early mineralogist, Georgus Agricola, at the end of the Sixteenth Century, Latinized wismuth to bisemutum. Not until the middle of the Eighteenth Century, through the research of J. Pott, C. Geoffroy, and T. Bergman, was bismuth definitely recognized as a specific metal.

Occurrence

The abundance of bismuth in the earth's crust has been estimated to be 0.00002 weight %, about the same order of plentifulness as silver, less than tin, but more than gold.

Bismuth occurs both as native bismuth and in ores. The native bismuth is not abundant but is found in veins associated with silver, lead, zinc, and tin ores in localities such as Saxony, Bolivia, Canada, and England.

The most important ores are bismite, or bismuth ocher (Bi_2O_3); bismuthinite, or bismuth glance (Bi_2S_3); and bismutite and bismutosphaerite (carbonates).

Production

Bismuth derived from domestic and foreign ores is obtained as a by-product in the smelting and refining of lead, copper, tin, silver and gold ores. During the last decade annual world production has increased from about 5 million pounds to 9.4 million in 1965. This increase has been particularly noticeable since 1962 due to the discovery of a catalytic process which uses a bismuth compound.

The leading bismuth-producing countries in approximate order of amount produced are the following:

United States. The major producers are American Smelting and Refining Company, United States Smelting, Refining and Mining Company, and International Smelting and Refining Company.

Peru. The Cerro de Pasco Corporation is the largest producer in Peru.

Japan. Five companies operate smelters and refiners in Japan recovering bismuth from lead and copper ores.

Mexico. Bismuth is also obtained as a by-product of lead smelting and refining at the Monterrey plants of Asarco Mexicana, S.A. and Metalurgica Mexicana Peñoles.

South Korea. In South Korea bismuth is being recovered in large quantities from tungsten ores southeast of Seoul.

Bolivia. Bismuth is predominantly an output from the Tasna copper-bismuth ore body of the Corporacion Minera de Bolivia.

Canada. The Consolidated Mining and Smelting Company of Canada, Ltd., Trail, British Columbia, the Molybdenite Corporation of Canada Ltd., and the Anglo-American Molybdenite Mining Corporation are the major Canadian producers of bismuth.

Consumption and Prices

The domestic uses of bismuth for the last several decades have been in three major areas, namely, pharmaceuticals and industrial chemicals, fusible alloys, and a category referred to as other alloy uses, meaning in large, the addition of bismuth to other metals such as steel, aluminum and malleable iron.

Although varying over the years, each of these three areas of application has taken roughly about one-third of the total and along with several minor uses has consumed about 3.1 million pounds during 1966 in the United States. This represents a sharp increase in the pharmaceutical and industrial chemicals uses over the 1964 consumption of 750,000 pounds doubling to 1,500,000 pounds. This increase resulted from a mushrooming in demand for bismuth in the manufacture of a catalytic compound necessary for the manufacture of acrylic fibers. This demand should eventually ease off since the catalytic bismuth compound can be reconstituted and reused in the process.

The 1967 quoted price of $4 per pound compared to $2.35 quoted at the beginning of 1965 reflected the above mentioned demand which exceeded available supply. Prior to this heavy but apparently temporary demand, the price had been reasonably stable at $2.25 since 1950.

Recovery

The primary sources of bismuth in the world and particularly in the Western Hemisphere are by-products of the smelting and refining of lead and copper ores. Bismuth is often found in these ores and will remain with the metals after smelting.

Bismuth is partially volatilized by the high temperature of the copper converter, and is caught as a dust in the baghouse or Cottrell systems, along with other elements such as lead, arsenic, antimony, etc., which are then transferred to the lead-smelting and refining operation. The major portion of the bismuth remains with the metallic copper, however, and, during the electrolytic refining, bismuth accumulates in the anode slimes with the other impurities, i.e., lead, selenium, tellurium, arsenic, antimony, and the precious metals. The procedure for handling the slimes is such that the bismuth is collected in the lead.

Bismuth is found in most lead ores and will accompany the lead through the smelting and refining operations. Refineries that treat bullion by the furnace-kettle process will practice debismuthizing only when the bismuth content is above 0.05%. The Missouri ores containing negligible amounts of bismuth are not treated. The two most important methods for removing bismuth from lead are the Betts and the Betterton-Kroll processes.

Betterton-Kroll Process. The basic reactions of this process are the formation of high-melting compounds, such as Ca_3Bi_2 and Mg_3Bi_2, which liquate from the bath and are removed as dross. Enriched calcium and magnesium lead from a previous charge is added to softened and desilverized lead, containing bismuth ($>0.05\%$). The resulting dross is skimmed, and then the required amounts of calcium (as a lead alloy) and magnesium metal are stirred into the molten metal. The charge is cooled, and the liquating bismuth dross is skimmed. This removes bismuth to 0.02%. If it is to be removed more completely, excess calcium and magnesium plus a small amount of antimony are added.

The enriched bismuth dross is melted in small 25-ton kettles, and the dross is separated from the entrapped lead by liquation. This dross is treated with lead chloride or chlorine to remove the calcium and magnesium, and, after desilverizing the alloy by the Parkes process, further chlorination removes the lead. Final treatments with caustic soda produce a high-purity, $>99.995\%$ bismuth.

Jollivet Penarroya Process. This process is used to a limited extent in France and is based on a similar metallurgical process to the Betterton-Kroll process in which potassium is substituted for the calcium to form a $Bi_7Mg_6K_9$ compound which liquates to the top of the bath and is removed from the molten lead as dross. A bismuth-lead alloy of approximately 20% bismuth is obtained from this dross which is finally processed to separate the lead and bismuth.

Betts Electrolytic Process. In the Betts process, anodes of lead bullion are electrolytically refined in a solution of lead fluosilicate and free fluosilicic acid. Thin sheets of pure lead form the cathodes. The impurities including bismuth, are collected in the anode slimes which are filtered, dried, and smelted. The metal from this smelting is cupeled, and bismuth goes into the lead-antimony slag and the litharge. These slags are reduced to metal containing 20% or higher bismuth and are transferred to the bismuth plant for refining.

At the present time only a small portion of the bismuth recovered comes from mines worked specifically for their bismuth ore content. But bismuth can be recovered from the concentrates of high-grade sulfide and carbonate ores by smelting in small reverberatory furnaces, with carbon for reduction, iron to decompose any bismuth sulfide present, and an alkaline flux to produce a fusible slag.

If bismuth occurs as an oxide or carbonate in ores such as those found in Bolivia and Peru, or in other metallurgical products, the most satisfactory recovery is made by leaching with hydrochloric acid. The separation depends on the precipitation of bismuth oxychloride from the chloride solution by diluting. By repeated dissolution, precipitation, and use of scrap iron to remove copper, the oxychloride is purified. The dry filtrate is smelted with lime and charcoal to crude metallic bismuth.

Bismuth Refining. The final steps in the bismuth refining process are fairly standard regardless of the process used to recover bismuth up to this point. The impure bismuth is melted and treated with repeated additions of caustic and niter to remove such impurities as arsenic, antimony, tin, tellurium, selenium. The purified bismuth is then given a final treatment with caustic producing a high-purity $>99.995\%$ bismuth.

Physical Properties

Bismuth will fracture as a brittle, crystalline metal having a high metallic luster with a pinkish tinge. Rhombohedral crystals of bismuth are shown in Fig. 1. As a member of Group VA of the Periodic Table, it is in the same subgroup as phosphorus, arsenic, and antimony. Physical property data are given in Table 1.

Bismuth is one of two metals (gallium the other) which increases in volume on solidification, this expansion being 3.32%.

The thermal conductivity of bismuth is

FIG. 1. Rhombohedral crystals of bismuth.

TABLE 1. PHYSICAL PROPERTIES OF BISMUTH

Atomic number	83
Atomic weight (one stable isotope)	208.980
Atomic volume, cc/g-atom	21.3
Density	
lb/cu in. at 20°C (68°F)	0.354
g/cc ,, 20°C (68°F)	9.8
,, ,, 271°C (520°F) (solid)	9.74
,, ,, 271°C liquid	10.07
,, ,, 300°C (572°F)	10.03
,, ,, 400°C (752°F)	9.91
,, ,, 600°C (1112°F)	9.66
,, ,, 800°C (1472°F)	9.40
,, ,, 960°C (1760°F)	9.20
Melting point	271.3°C (520.4°F)
Latent heat of fusion, cal/g	12.5
Boiling point	1560°C (2840°F)
Latent heat of vaporization, cal/g at 1627°C (2960°F)	204.3
Specific heat, cal/g/°C	
20°C (68°F)	0.0294
271°C (520°F) (liquid)	0.0340
400°C (752°F)	0.0354
600°C (1112°F)	0.0376
800°C (1472°F)	0.0397
1000°C (1832°F)	0.0419
Vapor pressure, mm Hg	
920°C (1683°F)	1
1100°C (2038°F)	10
1200°C (2192°F)	100
1400°C (2552°F)	400
Thermal conductivity, cal/cm²/cm/°C/sec	
20°C (68°F)	0.020
250°C (482°F)	0.018
300°C (572°F)	0.041
400°C (752°F)	0.037
700°C (1292°F)	0.037
Coefficient of linear thermal expansion, μ in./°C	13.3
Volume expansion on solidification, %	3.32
Surface tension, dynes/cm	
300°C (572°F)	376
500°C (932°F)	363
780°C (1436°F)	344
Electrical resistivity, microhm-cm	
−100°C (−148°F)	75.6
0°C (32°F)	106.8
100°C (212°F)	160.2
300°C (572°F) (liquid)	128.9
400°C (752°F)	134.2
600°C (1112°F)	145.2
750°C (1382°F)	153.5
Crystallography	Rhombohedral
	$a_0 = 4.7457$ Å
	Axial angle 57° 14.2'
Thermal neutron absorption cross section, barns/atom	0.034 ± 0.002
Thermal neutron activation cross section, barns/atom	0.019 ± 0.002
Mechanical properties	
Modulus of elasticity in tension, psi	4.6×10^6

TABLE 1—*continued*

Shear modulus, psi	1.8×10^6
Poisson's ratio	0.33
Brinell hardness (100 kg, 10 mm ball, 30 sec.)	7
Impact strength unnotched Charpy, ft-lb	
18°C (65°F)	0.1
66°C (150°F)	0.15
93°C (200°F)	0.3
149°C (300°F)	0.5
204°C (400°F)	0.4
Creep, psi (load for deflection rate of 0.001 in./in./hr)	
66°C (150°F)	600
121°C (250°F)	450
177°C (350°F)	350
204°C (400°F)	300

Resistance of metals to attack by bismuth

Molybdenum	Good resistance to at least					1110°C (2030°F)
Tantalum	,,	,,	,, ,,	,,		900°C (1652°F)
Chromium	,.	,,	,, ,,	,,		732°C (1350°F)
Beryllium	,,	,,	,, ,,	,,		500°C (930°F)
Columbium	,,	,,	,, ,,	,,		482°C (900°F)
Aluminum	,,	,,	,, ,,	,,		300°C (570°F)
Nickel and nickel alloys–Poor resistance above						271°C (520°F)
Copper	Eutectic at	270°C (519°F)	Solubility (%)	0.2		
Manganese	,,	,, 268°C (514°F)	,,	,,	0.6	
Magnesium	,,	,, 260°C (500°F)	,,	,,	0.54	
Zinc	,,	,, 254°C (490°F)	,,	,,	2.7	
Platinum	,,	,, 266°C (511°F)	,,	,,	1.0	
Tin	,,	,, 139°C (282°F)	,,	,,	42.0	

lower than any metal with the exception of mercury.

The most diamagnetic of all metals, bismuth has a mass susceptibility of -1.35×10^6.

Bismuth displays the greatest increase in resistance when influenced by a magnetic field (Hall effect) of any of the metals. The thermal conductivity decreases in a magnetic field.

It is one of the metals in which the electrical resistance is greater in the solid than in the liquid state. The ratio of solid to liquid resistivity is 0.5 for most metals, but is approximately 2 for bismuth.

High thermoelectric effects are produced when bismuth is coupled with certain other materials. Bismuth can be extruded as wire and sheet, making the practical applications of this thermoelectric effect possible.

Because of its low absorption cross section for thermal neutrons, bismuth has attracted attention as a fuel carrier and coolant for nuclear reactors and as windows for neutron transparency in medical reactors.

Bismuth forms a number of binary, ternary, quaternary and quinary alloys which have low melting points, and the more common ones are often referred to as "fusible alloys." Table 2 gives the eutectic composition and temperature of these alloys.

Some noneutectic fusible alloys are used in safety devices, e.g., safety plugs for compressed gas cylinders and tanks, automatic sprinkler systems, and fire-door releases. Although these alloys solidify over a range of temperatures, yield temperatures have been determined for them and are given in Table 3.

In addition to their extremely low melting points, alloys of bismuth often exhibit unusual expansion and contraction characteristics. When a metal is cast, two volume changes take place: (1) volume change from liquid to solid, and (2) volume change owing to thermal contraction of both liquid and solid.

Alloys of bismuth-lead and particularly bismuth-lead-tin exhibit another volume change which occurs when the alloys are

TABLE 2. EUTECTIC COMPOSITIONS AND TEMPERATURES OF BISMUTH ALLOYS

System	Composition	Eutetic Temperature
Ag-Bi	97.5 Bi	262°C (503.6°F)
Au-Bi	82.0 Bi	240°C (464°F)
Cd-Bi	60.0 Bi	144°C (291°F)
In-Bi	33.7 Bi	72°C (161.6°F)
(two eutectics)	67.0 Bi	109°C (228°F)
Li-Bi	99.5 Bi	243°C (469°F)
Mg-Bi	59.0 Bi	551°C (1024°F)
Na-Bi	97.0 Bi	218°C (424°F)
Pb-Bi	56.5 Bi	125°C (257°F)
Sb-Bi	Miscible in liquid and solid state	
Sn-Bi	57.0 Bi	139°C (282°F)
Tl-Bi	76.5 Bi	198°C (388°F)
(two eutectics)	47.5 Bi	188°C (370°F)
Zn-Bi	97.3 Bi	254°C (489°F)
Pb-Sn-Bi	52Bi-16Sn-32Pb	96°C (205°F)
Pb-Cd-Bi	52Bi-8Cd-40Pb	92°C (198°F)
Sn-Cd-Bi	54Bi-20Cd-26Sn	102°C (216°F)
Sn-Zn-Bi	56Bi-4Zn-40Sn	130°C (266°F)
In-Sn-Bi	58Bi-16In-25Sn	79°C (174°F)
Tl-Pb-Bi	55.2Bi-33.3Pb-11.5Tl	91°C (196°F)
(two eutectics)	42.2Bi-9.8Pb-48Tl	186°C (367°F)
Tl-Sn-Bi	50Bi-35.7Sn-14.3Tl	124°C (255°F)
(two eutectics)	44Bi-31Sn-25Tl	167°C (333°F)
Pb-Sn-Cd-Bi	50Bi-10Cd-13.3Sn-26.7Pb	70°C (158°F)
In-Pb-Sn-Bi	49.4Bi-11.6Sn-18Pb-21In	57°C (135°F)
Tl-Sn-Cd-Bi	49.1Bi-18.2Cd-23.5Sn-9.2Tl	94.6°C (202°F)
In-Cd-Pb-Sn-Bi	44.7Bi-5.3Cd-8.3Sn-22.6Pb-19.1In	47°C (117°F)

TABLE 3. FREEZING TEMPERATURE RANGES AND YIELD TEMPERATURES OF NONEUTECTIC ALLOYS

Composition					Freezing Range,		Yield Temp†,	
Bi	Pb	Sn	Cd	Others	°C	°F	°C	°F
14.0	43.0	43.0	—	—	163–143	325–289	154	309
—	24.2	50.0	25.8	—	149–142	300–288	143	290
5.0	32.0	45.0	18.0	—	139–132	282–270	135	275
48.0	28.5	14.5	—	9.0Sb	263–103	505–217	116	241
59.4	14.8	25.8	—	—	114–95	237–203	100	212
52.0	31.7	15.3	1	—	92–83	198–181	90	194
42.5	37.7	11.3	8.5	—	90–70	194–158	72	161
48.0	25.6	12.8	9.6	4.0In	65–61	149–142	64	147

† Temperature at which fusible alloy will yield, as prescribed by Compressed Gas Manufacturers Association.

solidified. This is an increase in volume owing to a change in the solid structure of the alloy, a transformation accompanied by heat evolution which is readily detected. The expansion can be as high as a 1% linear increase. For the maximum expansion the composition is about 56% bismuth, 20% tin, and 24% lead, and it will decrease as the contents of the constituents are changed or as other elements, such as cadmium, antimony, or indium, are added. For example, the linear expansion of the ternary eutectic compositions is 0.8%. The reaction in the solid state is such that the rate is related to the magnitude of the expansion, i.e., the greater the expansion, the faster it occurs. At the higher magnitudes of expansion, most of it takes place in 20 to 30 minutes. Such an expansion also occurs in the bismuth-lead system with a linear increase of 0.3%, but it requires several hundred hours to reach its maximum. Contraction due to cooling would be canceled by this expansion, and various practical uses have been made of this phenomenon to grip tools, punches, and parts to be machined.

Since bismuth is one of the two metals which expands on solidification, it is not unusual that the various alloys of bismuth-lead and bismuth-tin have different liquid-to-solid volume changes. This volume change is zero at about 50% bismuth in the bismuth-tin alloy and about 70% bismuth in the bismuth-lead alloy.

The dimensional changes which usually take place in castings can be controlled by selecting a composition where volume changes (liquid-to-solid and solid transformation) are such that an accurate dimensional casting results.

Chemical Properties

Bismuth like the other members of its family, arsenic and antimony, forms two sets of compounds in which it is trivalent and pentavalent. The trivalent compounds are the more common.

Bismuth Oxides. Bismuth does not readily oxidize at ordinary temperature in dry or moist air. The silver-white luster is retained for long periods of time. Rapid oxidation at the boiling point produces the trioxide.

Bismuth trioxide, Bi_2O_3, is the best defined of the oxides, the existence of others being questioned. Other oxides which may be found are the tetroxide, Bi_2O_4, and the pentoxide, Bi_2O_5. The oxide mineral, bismite, is a bismuth trioxide.

The trioxide may be formed by ignition of bismuth hydroxide or by heating the basic nitrate in air. The latter method is used for the commercial production of bismuth trioxide. Bismuth is dissolved in hot nitric acid, and an excess of sodium hydroxide is added. Continued heating of the mixture precipitates a heavy yellow powder of bismuth trioxide.

It is sold for use in enameling for cast iron, and in porcelain painting. Although the trioxide is a basic anhydride, it will act as a weak acid in warm, very concentrated potassium hydroxide.

Bismuth tetroxide may be prepared by oxidizing bismuth trioxide, using agents such as potassium ferricyanide with concentrated potassium hydroxide or ammonium persulfate with dilute sodium hydroxide.

Bismuth pentoxide is an acid anhydride, although salts of this acid have not been prepared in the pure state. This oxide can be prepared by oxidation of bismuth trioxide, using either chlorine or an electrolytic oxidation in hot concentrated alkali, forming a scarlet red precipitate.

Bismuth hydroxide is prepared in a manner similar to that for the trioxide, with the exception that it is precipitated cold from the nitrate solution with sodium hydroxide.

Halides. The compounds of bismuth with the halogens are of the form BiX_3. They are usually formed by dissolving bismuth in nitric acid and adding a soluble halogen salt. Since the salts of trivalent bismuth hydrolyze in water to insoluble basic salts, dilution of the above solution will precipitate the oxysalt:

$$BiCl_3 + 2H_2O \rightleftharpoons Bi(OH)C_2l + 2HCl$$

This reversible reaction shows that the relative amounts of hydrochloric acid and water that are present will determine which way the reaction will go. If water is added, a white precipitate of basic chloride forms, and if hydrochloric acid is added, the precipitate dissolves. When this precipitate is dried, it gives up a molecule of water, forming BiOCl. Most other halogen salts of bismuth act as does the chloride. Bismuth chloride is used for pigment and cosmetics. Bismuth bromide is employed in veterinary medicine.

Bismuth Nitrates. The best solvent for bismuth is nitric acid. From the concentrated solution bismuth nitrate pentahydrate, $Bi(NO_3)_3 \cdot 5H_2O$, is formed. But, like other salts of bismuth, with the addition of water an oxysalt, $Bi_2O_3N_2O_5 \cdot 2H_2O$, will precipitate.

The bismuth nitrate, $Bi(NO_3)_3 \cdot 5H_2O$, is prepared by evaporation of the concentrated solution and then cooling to form the crystals.

Bismuth subnitrate is prepared by the

hydrolysis of bismuth nitrate at a given nitric acid content between temperatures of 30 and 70°C (86 and 158°F). In commercial production the hydrolysis is carried out using sodium bicarbonate to maintain the proper acidity. The quantity of water used is controlled, and the subnitrate is formed by stirring at 40-50°C (104-122°F).

Bismuth subcarbonate is prepared from bismuth subnitrate. By adding sodium bicarbonate to a suspension of the subnitrate in water, the bicarbonate is precipitated. The product obtained depends on the nature of the subnitrate suspension, the amount of water, and the temperature.

Both of these compounds, i.e., bismuth subcarbonate and bismuth subnitrate, are used in pharmacology for the treatment of diarrhea, enteritis, and gastric ulcers, and for making the alimentary canal opaque in x-ray diagnosis.

Sulfur Compounds. Bismuth trisulfide occurs in nature as bismuthinite (bismuth glance). It may be prepared by the reaction of hydrogen sulfide on a solution of bismuth salts. The trisulfide is insoluble in cold dilute mineral acids and soluble in hot dilute nitric acid or boiling concentrated hydrochloric.

Bismuth sulfate is not precipitated from an acid solution of the salt, but, if the solution is evaporated to give off fumes, a bismuth acid sulfate, $Bi_2(SO_4)_3 \cdot H_2SO_4 \cdot 6H_2O$, is formed. By heating at 350°C (662°F), the normal sulfate, $Bi_2(SO_4)_3$, can be formed.

Organic Compounds. A number of organic bismuth preparations have been used for the treatment of syphilis. Tartrates of bismuth potassium, bismuth-sodium, and bismuth-sodium-potassium as well as iodobismuthite sodium are water soluble preparations. The oil-soluble compounds are bismuth camphor-carboxylate and bismuth ethyl camphorate.

Bismuth subgallate is a water-insoluble organic compound of bismuth which is also used in the treatment of irritations of the alimentary canal.

Fabrication

The melting of bismuth may be handled in the same manner as lead. Its low melting point and the extremely low solubility of iron in bismuth permit the use of steel or cast-iron vessels. Within the range of 300-400°C (572-752°F), the rate of oxidation is low, and fluxes are not generally used.

Bismuth being a brittle metal at ordinary temperatures, is usually cast to the desired form. The liquid-to-solid expansion produces either a swelling or exudations on the open end as the casting freezes.

Bismuth at ordinary temperatures is too brittle to roll, draw, or extrude; however, above 225°C (437°F), it becomes more plastic, permitting extrusion in various shapes. Rods of 1 in. diameter to fine wires (0.010 in. diameter) have been successfully extruded. The fine wires have a reasonable ductility if bent slowly around diameters equal to their own or larger.

For protective and ornamental coatings the electrodeposition of bismuth from strongly acid solution of perchlorate has been suggested as the most satisfactory. The chloride bath is considered superior for the preparation of high-purity bismuth.

Applications

Pharmaceutical. The pharmaceutical uses are principally in indigestion remedies, cosmetics and antisyphilitic drugs. Soon after the discovery of bismuth as a distinct metal in about the Fifteenth Century, various compounds of it were recommended for a wide variety of diseases. By the latter part of the Eighteenth Century bismuth compounds were used with remarkable success in the treatment of gastric spasms and dyspepsia. After World War 1, bismuth's chemotherapeutic value in the treatment of syphilis was recognized. At the present time two main divisions of bismuth therapy are (a) the internal and external application of slightly soluble or insoluble salts in the treatment of gastric disorders and of wounds, (b) the chemotherapeutic use of bismuth by the injection of finely divided metals or insoluble salts in suspension.

Cosmetics. The present desirable "frosty" look in women's fashions has increased the use of bismuth oxychloride in cosmetics. In 1966 cosmetic manufacturers were using several hundred thousand pounds to impart pearlescence to such products as lipstick, nail polish, eye shadow, etc. The durability of this market is, of course, hard to predict.

Chemical. Bismuth chemicals have been

used in a number of production processes such as the manufacture of plastics, the synthesis of methanol, but the use of bismuth phosphomolybdate as a catalyst in the Sohio acrylonitrile process is by far the largest chemical application. The process yields acrylonitrile by air oxidation of a mixture of propylene and ammonia in the presence of bismuth phosphomolybdate. The process will be used to produce about 75% of the worldwide acrylonitrile production in 1967. The acrylonitrile is a basic chemical used in the production of acrylic fibers, acrylic paints, ABS plastic and Lucite.

Low Melting Alloys. In the past 25 years a group of bismuth-containing alloys commercially referred to as "fusible alloys" has gained wide use in a number of ingenious fabricating methods. Typical uses of these alloys in fabricating are: in foundry practice as master patterns or match plates, protective coatings for wood patterns, core boxes, etc.; as a filling when bending pipes and thin sections; in anchoring of bearings, bushings, pole pieces in magnetic chucks, punches, dies, and irregular parts to be machined; in spotting fixtures; as a liquid heat transfer medium; in soldering and sealing; in safety fuses; and in short life dies, where by cooling the alloys in liquid nitrogen ($-195.6°$C [$-320°$F]), a technique has been developed

to produce experimental sheet-metal stampings in 24 to 48 hours.

As an Additive to other Metals. Due to its brittle nature and low solid solubility in a number of other metals, bismuth has been added in the order of 0.5% to aluminum, steels, stainless steels, and other alloys to improve the machinability.

Bismuth is also added to malleable cast iron to suppress mottling, that is to say, the formation of graphite on freezing. The tendency to mottling increases with casting thickness, but the addition of 0.025% bismuth with 0.003% boron permits an increase in the section size from 1.75 to as much as 5 inches without mottling, with nominal carbon contents of 2.6% and silicon 1.4%.

Counterelectrodes. The eutectic alloys of bismuth-tin and bismuth-cadmium are sprayed as coatings against selenium to form the barrier layer (counterelectrode) in selenium rectifiers.

Thermoelectric Use. Intermetallic compounds of bismuth with tellurium or selenium have been found to be effective thermoelectric materials for making use of the Peltier effect for refrigeration. Good Peltier thermocouple materials should exhibit high thermoelectric power, low thermal conductivity, and low electrical resistivity. The semiconductor compounds, Bi_2Te_3 and Bi_2Se_3,

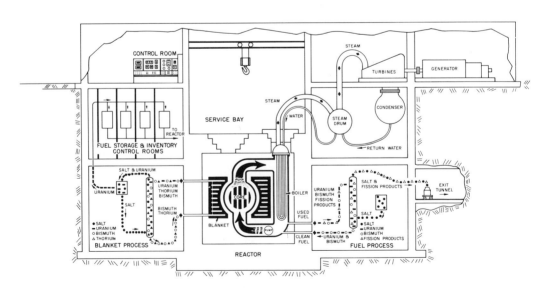

FIG. 2. Diagram of liquid metal fuel nuclear power reactor using bismuth as the carrier for the uranium fuel and the liquid metal coolant for the reactor.

have excellent combinations of these properties. A temperature difference of 29°C
(85°F) between an inner chamber and outside
conducting fins has been produced experimentally with 20 watts. It is estimated that
the present values for coefficients of performance must be increased by a factor of 2 to
be comparable to compressor-type refrigerators in home appliances.

Permanent Magnet. A permanent magnet
(named "Bismanol") of high coercive force
and maximum energy products has been
produced from MnBi by the United States
Naval Ordnance Laboratory. An energy
product of 4.3×10^6 gaussoersteds, a coercive
force of 3,400 oersteds, and a residual flux
density of 4,200 gausses have been reported
for this magnet.

Others. The liquid metal fuel reactor
(LMFR) once considered by AEC as a
possible generator of nuclear energy, used
liquid bismuth as the carrier for the fuel
(U^{235} or U^{233}) and as the coolant. The
reactor has a moderator of unclad graphite.
The design parameters are such that criticality
is reached, and self-sustained fission takes
place.

Toxicity

Toxicity is not a problem in the handling of
bismuth. It is one of the least toxic of the
heavy metals, and cases of bismuth poisoning
in industrial use have not been recorded.

References

1. Hansen, M., "Constitution of Binary Alloys,"
   2nd Ed., New York, McGraw-Hill Book Co.,
   Inc., 1958.
2. Holmes, J. F., "Survey of Methods for Removal of Bismuth," *Metal Industry* (*London*),
   99, No. 6, 110–112 (August 11, 1961); **99**,
   No. 7, 124–126 (August 18, 1961); **99**, No. 8,
   146–147 (August 25, 1961).
3. Howe, H. E., "Bismuth," chapter in "Rare
   Metals Handbook," Hampel, C. A., Editor,
   2nd Ed., New York, Reinhold Publishing
   Corp., 1961.
4. Liddell, D. M., "Handbook of Nonferrous
   Metallurgy, Recovery of Metals," pp. 143,
   193, New York, McGraw-Hill Book Co.,
   Inc., 1945.
5. Lyon, R. N., Editor, "Liquid Metals Handbook," NAVEXOS P-733 (Rev.), Washington, D.C., Atomic Energy Commission, 1952.
6. Mellor, J. W., "A Comprehensive Treatise
   on Inorganic and Theoretical Chemistry,"
   Vol. 9, p. 587, New York, Longmans, Green
   & Co., 1929.
7. "Metals Handbook," 8th Ed., pp. 863, 1199,
   Cleveland, American Society for Metals,
   1961.

HERBERT E. HOWE.

BONDING, CHEMICAL

All chemical bonding arises from electrostatic
attractions between oppositely charged components of atoms. Although every atom as a
whole is electrically neutral, it consists of a
positively charged nucleus imbedded in a
cloud of negatively charged electrons. The
electrostatic interactions between atoms must
therefore include (1) repulsions between electron clouds, (2) repulsions between nuclei,
and (3) attractions between each nucleus and
electrons of the other atom. An electron cloud,
being both nebulous and mobile, must adjust
to the influence of an external electrical field,
such as that of another atom. Such adjustment, although inherently dynamic in nature,
must inevitably lead to net attractive forces,
for the reason that coulombic forces vary
inversely with the square of the distance:
repulsive forces tend to increase the distance
thus becoming weaker, whereas attractive
forces tend to decrease the distance and grow
stronger. The net force between any two atoms
therefore tends to hold them together. Such
forces, which may be thought of as attractions
between very rapidly oscillating induced
dipoles, are called van der Waals forces. They
are so weak among small atoms, and especially if these atoms are of low polarizability
(not easily deformed), that the kinetic energy
of ordinary temperatures is too great for them
to be effective, unless some other, much
stronger attractive force is also in action.
However, van der Waals forces increase with
increasing complexity of the atoms or molecules. They become very significant even at
ordinary temperatures where the number of
electrons is relatively high and the electron
clouds are spread out over several or many
nuclei, especially when the molecular geometry permits close intermolecular approach.
Attractive forces many times stronger, per

atom-pair, than van der Waals forces are observable when atoms of all elements (except helium) having fewer than 8 outer shell electrons come in contact. Such forces produce what are known as chemical bonds, which may broadly be classified as of two principal types, *covalent* and *metallic.* The number, kind, and properties of bonds an atom can form are determined by the electronic configurations of each atom involved, and especially by the arrangement of electrons in the two outermost principal quantum levels (see **Electronic Configuration.**)

When an atom has 8 electrons in its outermost shell, or 2 in the case of helium, the nuclear charge effective at the "surface" of the atom is inadequate to attract an outside electron strongly. This is evidently because of the shielding by the intervening electron cloud. The significance of having fewer than 8 outermost electrons (or fewer than 2, in hydrogen) is that each vacancy represents a region energetically capable of accommodating an outside electron in such a way that it comes within the strong influence of the nucleus. When two atoms each having in its outer shell one half-filled orbital come together, the electron of each can expand its region of occupancy to include the vacancy of the other. In this way, both electrons come under the influence of both nuclei. The two atoms are described as sharing a pair of electrons between them. This mutual electrostatic attraction of two nuclei for the same electron pair holds the atoms together in a more stable system than that of the two separate atoms. It is called a *covalent bond.* The enthalpy difference (the energy released by formation of the bond) between the two systems is called the *covalent bond energy.* The equilibrium internuclear distance is called the *bond length.* If the two atoms at wide separation are considered to possess zero potential energy, then allowing them to approach will result in a decrease in potential energy (negative value) until a minimum is reached at a certain distance, closer than which the potential energy rises rapidly as the atoms resist further approach. This energy minimum corresponds to the bond energy and the internuclear distance at which the minimum occurs is the bond length.

Of central importance in theoretical chemis-

try is the exact mathematical description and prediction of bond energy and bond length. *In principle,* this can be accomplished through application of the Schrödinger wave equation and the methods of wave mechanics. The Schrödinger equation is:

$$\frac{\partial^2 \psi}{\partial x^2} + \frac{\partial^2 \psi}{\partial y^2} + \frac{\partial^2 \psi}{\partial z^2} + \frac{8\pi^2 m}{h^2}(E - V)\psi = 0$$

where x, y, and z are coordinates of the particle, m is its mass, h is Planck's constant, E is the total energy and V the potential energy. ψ is called the "wave function," and has physical significance in that its square is proportional to the probability of finding the electron in the position designated by the coordinates. Unfortunately, the mathematical complexities increase so rapidly as the number of particles increases that only in the simplest cases, such as the hydrogen molecule, have rigorous solutions been obtained. For applications to systems having even a few more interacting particles, grossly simplifying assumptions are essential, and the results are inevitably less reliable.

Two principal types of approach to the wave mechanical description of the covalent bond are used. One, the *valence bond* method, considers electron sharing to involve an overlap of orbitals, one from each atom, so that the atoms retain their individuality but occupy an intermediate region in common. For example, if the wave function for hydrogen atom A which holds electron (1) is $\psi_A(1)$ and the wave function for hydrogen atom B which holds electron (2) is $\psi_B(2)$, then the total wave function for the two atoms is $\Psi = \psi_A(1)\psi_B(2)$. But since electrons are indistinguishable, the total function could equally well be $\psi_A(2)\psi_B(1)$. The true function then may be some combination of the two:

$$\Psi = C_1\psi_A)1)\psi_B(2) + C_2\psi_A(2)\psi_B(1)$$

The parameters C_1 and C_2 are "mixing coefficients" giving the relative contributions of each function. The weight of each coefficient is proportional to its square. In the symmetrical example of the two identical hydrogen atoms, $C_1{}^2 = C_2{}^2$ and $C_1 = \pm C_2$. Thus two wave functions are possible:

$$\Psi_+ = \psi_A(1)\,\psi_B(2) + \psi_A(2)\,\psi_B(1)$$
$$\Psi_- = \psi_A(1)\,\psi_B(2) - \psi_A(2)\,\psi_B(1)$$

Application of the Schrödinger wave equation to calculation of the energy shows that Ψ_- corresponds to the state of parallel electron spins, leading only to increased repulsion as the internuclear distance is decreased. Ψ_+ gives an energy minimum at 0.80 Å corresponding to sharing an electron pair with opposed spins, and a bond energy of 72 kcal per mole. The observed bond length and energy in H_2 is 0.741 Å and 103.2 kcal (at $0°K$), showing that Ψ_+ accounts for about two-thirds of the energy.

Another possibility not yet considered is that both electrons may happen near the same nucleus at the same time, creating in effect the ions H^+ and H^-, for which ionic wave functions $\psi_A(1)\,\psi_A(2)$ and $\psi_B(1)\,\psi_B(2)$ should be included. The total wave function thus becomes:

$$\Psi = \psi_A(1)\,\psi_B(2) + \psi_A(2)\,\psi_B(1)$$
$$+ \lambda[\psi_A(1)\,\psi_A(2) + \psi_B(1)\,\psi_B(2)]$$
$$\text{or } \Psi = \Psi \text{ covalent} + \lambda' \,\Psi \text{ ionic}$$

The parameter λ' gives the relative contribution of the ionic wave function, which for H_2 is somewhat less than 6 kcal per mole. Consideration of additional factors improves still more the agreement between calculated and experimental values. James and Coolidge performed laborious calculations using a wave function containing 13 terms, and found the bond energy to be 102.8 kcal per mole and the bond length 0.74 Å as observed. Later extension to a 50-term wave function, with the help of modern computers gave 103.2 and 0.741, exactly as observed experimentally. In this sense the H_2 molecule may be regarded as completely "understood."

The second principal method of describing the covalent bond is in terms of molecular orbitals. According to this concept, polynuclear "molecular" orbitals may replace atomic orbitals, resembling them in possessing specific energy and spatial characteristics and in having a capacity of two electrons each. For example, in the hydrogen molecule, the two $1s$ orbitals are replaced by two molecular orbitals, different in energy. The one lower in energy concentrates the electrons between the two nuclei; it is called a *bonding* orbital and designated as σ. The one higher in energy would keep electrons away from the region between the nuclei; it is called an *anti-bonding*

orbital and designated as σ^*. Molecular orbitals are σ (sigma) if they give cylindrical symmetry about the bond axis. If they lead to nodal planes through the bond axis they are designated as π (pi).

A molecular orbital wave function is usually written as a linear combination of atomic orbital wave functions, on the basis that in the region of each nucleus, the molecular orbital must closely resemble the atomic orbital which it replaces.

$$\Psi_{M.O.} = \psi_A + \lambda\psi_B$$

λ denotes the degree to which one atomic orbital is favored over the other, and of course in homonuclear bonding as in H_2, must equal 1. Just as in the valence bond method, the potential energy change with distance can be calculated, leading to a minimum at the bond length.

Each of these two approaches to the mathematical description of bonding has certain advantages over the other, but neither is suitable for dealing simply with the complex interactions involved in most chemical bonding. For a practical understanding a more approximate and intuitive approach is an essential supplement to wave mechanical theory.

From the observed requisites for a covalent bond, namely a half-filled outer shell orbital on each atom, the number of covalent bonds an atom can form is easily seen to be equal to the number of such half-filled orbitals. In general the number of bonds is limited by the number of outermost electrons when the number of vacancies is greater, and by the number of vacancies when the number of electrons is greater. For example, across the Periodic Table, lithium with but one outermost electron and seven vacancies can form but one covalent bond; beryllium with two electrons and six vacancies can form two bonds; boron with three electrons and five vacancies can form three covalent bonds; carbon with four of each can form four covalent bonds; nitrogen with five electrons but only three vacancies can form only three covalent bonds, oxygen with six electrons but only two vacancies can form only two covalent bonds, and fluorine with seven electrons has but one vacancy and can form only one covalent bond. The formulas of compounds are thus often

67

predictable (and nearly always understandable) from the structure of the component atoms. For instance, the hydrogen atom having only one half-filled orbital can form but one covalent bond, but a carbon atom can form four, so it combines with four hydrogen atoms producing methane, CH_4.

The number of possible covalent bonds can sometimes be increased, two at a time, if one of an outer shell electron pair can be promoted to an otherwise vacant outer d orbital. This process, called "expanding the octet," creates two new half-filled orbitals at once. It allows, for example, the number of covalent bonds formed by iodine, which normally has an outer shell of one half-filled orbital and three filled orbitals or electron pairs, to be increased from one to three, then to five, then to seven. Such promotion only occurs when withdrawal of some of the electron cloud by other atoms allows the nuclear charge to become more effectively sensed in the outer d orbitals, increasing their stability. For instance, sulfur has the normal capacity to form two covalent bonds but the promoting influence of fluorine permits expansion of this capacity to form SF_4 and SF_6.

Usually an atom of a major group element uses all possible electrons in bonding, but toward the bottom of certain groups is observable a tendency for two electrons to remain aloof. This is known as the "inert pair" effect, as though the s orbital of the outermost principal quantum level tends to retain its electron pair as in the ground state instead of permitting one electron to move into a p orbital for maximum covalence. It leads to compounds in which thallium, for example, forms only one bond instead of its possible three, lead two instead of four, and bismuth three instead of five. In the transitional elements, which characteristically use underlying d orbitals as well as outermost shell orbitals in their bonding, the tendency to use fewer than the maximum possible half-filled orbitals is common, and variable valence is the rule.

The bonding orbitals of a combining atom have a strong tendency to equalize even though different in the isolated atom. This phenomenon is called "hybridization." It leads, for example, to two equal sp hybrid bonding orbitals in zinc instead of one s orbital and one p, to three equal sp^2 hybrid bonding orbitals in boron instead of one s and two p, and to four equal sp^3 hybrid bonding orbitals in carbon instead of one s and three p.

The geometry of atomic orbitals permits more than one electron pair, up to three pairs, to become involved in a given bond under certain conditions. A four-electron bond is called a double covalent bond and a six-electron bond is called a triple covalent bond. Such bonds are said to have *bond order* of 1, 2, and 3. Owing to the difficulty of concentrating so many mutually repelling electrons between the same two nuclei, a double bond is not ordinarily twice as strong as a single bond nor is a triple bond three times as strong (unless for some special reason the single bond happens to be abnormally weak). Elements of period 2, especially carbon, nitrogen, and oxygen, use p orbitals in multiple bonding, but in period 3 the elements appear much more able to use outer d orbitals instead, to increase the bond order beyond 1. In molecular orbital terminology, a multiple bond consists of a combination of a σ orbital with π orbitals, the latter being distinguished a $p\pi$ or $d\pi$ depending on the type of atomic orbitals from which they are derived.

Sophisticated explanations of the geometry of molecules involve calculations by wave mechanics of the directional nature of the pure and/or hybrid orbitals that may be involved in the bonding. A much simpler and at least equally useful explanation can be based on the recognition that electron pairs, or electrons in bonds, tend to locate as far apart as possible to minimize the electrostatic repulsions. For example, if all the electrons in the outer shell of an atom are used in only two bonds, these two invariably are directed opposite to one another, giving a bond angle of 180°. If all the electrons in the outer shell of an atom are used in three bonds, or if all but one pair are used in two bonds, the farthest apart these can be is at the corners of an equilateral triangle, giving a bond angle of 120°. If all the electrons in the outer shell of an atom are used in four bonds, or in three bonds with one lone pair of electrons not used, or in two bonds with two lone pairs left over, the bond angle is close to that of a regular tetrahedron, 109° 28'. Five exactly equivalent positions on the surface of a sphere do not exist, but the best separation of five groups of electrons, whether used in bonding or not, is at the corners of a trigonal bipyramid. Six equivalent positions for electrons, whether involved in bonds or not, are at the corners of a regular octahedron, which makes the angle between adjacent bonds 90°. In general, a lone pair is expected to exert somewhat stronger repulsion than a shared pair, and bonds exert greater repulsion the higher the bond order. These factors may modify the bond angles given above. Practically all molecular geometry can be explained, at least approximately, on the basis of this simple picture of electrostatic repulsion among groups of electrons surrounding the atomic nucleus.

Bonds of nonintegral order are common. They demonstrate two important points. One is that although extremely useful, the concept of the two-electron bond, or integral multiples of it, has limited applicability. The second is a very important principle of bonding: When an atom might equally well provide multiple bonding electrons to any one or some of several joined atoms but not all at once, it tends to provide these electrons partially but equally to all rather than just to one or some, excluding the others. Similarly, when integral covalent bonding would leave one or more outer level orbitals unoccupied, the tendency is for available bonding electrons to occupy all vacancies partially rather than one or two exclusively and the others not at all. These tendencies often result in nonintegral bond order. This phenomenon of partial utilization of electrons among several bonds in contrast to localization of electrons between a particular pair of atoms is called *resonance*. A familiar example of a compound involving resonance is benzene, C_6H_6, in whose six-membered ring each carbon atom could form a double bond to one or the other of its two neighbors but not to both. Instead it shares equally, giving a ring containing six equivalent bonds of order 1.5.

The resonance principle assumes especially great importance in bonding between atoms in each of which the number of outer vacancies exceeds the number of electrons. The tendency toward covalence would suggest that such atoms would unite to the limit of their covalent capacity and no further. But

this would leave low-energy orbitals unoccupied. Accordingly, the electrons spread out through all available orbitals, becoming delocalized instead of paired between specific atom pairs. This results in much closer packing of atoms, in fact most commonly the closest possible packing of spheres of equal radius, in which each atom on the interior is in contact with 12 neighbors. This is called *metallic* bonding. It may be regarded crudely as the electrostatic attraction between the metal cations and the continuum of valence electrons in which they are imbedded. Such bonding is usually quite strong, and imparts unique characteristics to the metallic crystal, including high lustre, electrical and thermal conductivity, and malleability and ductility. In contrast, covalently bonded substances with their relatively localized bonding electrons tend to be electrical and thermal insulators and brittle.

An important property of atoms not yet considered here is electronegativity (which see.) Covalent bonds between atoms initially different in electronegativity become unsymmetrical because the more electronegative atom acquires more than half share of the bonding electrons. Such bonds are polar, and more so the greater the initial electronegativity difference. Polarity imparts partial charge to the atoms, changing their condition and thus exerting a vital influence on the physical and chemical properties of the compound. It also contributes to bond energy, as recognized in both valence bond and molecular orbital descriptions.

Polarity in bonds to hydrogen permits the hydrogen, under certain conditions, to act as a bridge between or within molecules. Such bridges, the most common of which involve protonic hydrogen and are customarily called *hydrogen bonds*, constitute a special kind of chemical bond, weaker than ordinary covalent bonds, but having significance of highest importance, especially in biological phenomena.

The acquisition of positive charge by an atom increases its attraction for electrons, making it more prone, if it possesses low-energy vacant orbitals, to form additional covalent bonds by accepting an electron pairs from donor atoms having such pairs available. The availability of an electron pair likewise

69

increases as an atom acquires negative charge. These are important factors in causing formation of *coordinate covalent* or *coordination* bonds, which resemble ordinary covalent bonds except that one atom furnishes both bonding electrons, and the other, a vacant orbital.

When initial electronegativities are widely different, the bond polarity approaches an upper limit of complete unevenness of sharing, or in other words, total monopoly of the bonding electrons by one atom. Whether this extreme is ever actually reached is controversial, but unquestionably its close approach can be treated usefully as if the electron transfer were complete, producing negative and positive ions. The bonding is then described as the result of electrostatic attraction among oppositely charged ions. The crystal represents a balance between the net attractive forces as determined by evaluating the coulombic potential energy over the entire crystal, and the repulsion forces that result when the electronic clouds of the neighboring ions come into contact. This model is quite successful in permitting calculation of the crystal energy in good agreement with experimental measurements, for the alkali halides and some other salts, but is obviously inadequate for many compounds which nevertheless are usually classified as ionic. Whether or not the bonding is correctly described as ionic, high bond polarity unquestionably leads to very regular arrays of negatively and positively charged atoms or groups of atoms, such that no individual simple molecules exist as such in the crystal. For example, in most of the alkali halides and alkaline earth oxides and sulfides, 6:6 coordination prevails, which means that each positive atom is surrounded symmetrically by 6 negative atoms equally spaced, and each negative atom is similarly surrounded by 6 positive atoms.

There is no conclusive evidence of an abrupt transition from ionic to covalent bonding. It seems probable that to some extent anions share their electrons with the cations that surround them even in the most "ionic" of crystals. A "coordinated polymeric" model of binary compounds has recently been proposed which has distinct advantages over the ionic model. By taking into account the fact that all simple cations are potential electron

acceptors and all anions are potential electron donors, the model provides for a significant contribution of coordinate covalence to the total bonding energy. Unlike the ionic model, it is applicable over a complete range of bond polarity in nonmolecular solids, permitting accurate estimations of bond energy as the weighted sum of a covalent contribution and an ionic contribution. The weighting coefficients are determined directly from the partial charges on the atoms, which except in the alkali halides indicate that the atoms are much less ionic than usually considered. With minor modification the method of bond energy calculation is applicable also to molecular compounds. Yet, although progress is being made, much remains to be learned about bonding, especially in the solid state.

References

1. Companion, A. L., "Chemical Bonding," New York, McGraw-Hill, 1964.
2. Gray, H. B., "Electrons and Chemical Bonding," New York, Benjamin, 1964.
3. Linnett, J. W., "The Electronic Structure of Molecules," New York, John Wiley and Sons, 1964.
4. Pauling, L., "Nature of the Chemical Bond," 3rd Ed., Ithaca, N.Y., Cornell Univ. Press, 1960.
5. Phillips, C. S. G. and Williams, R. J. P., "Inorganic Chemistry," Vol. 1, New York, Oxford Univ. Press, 1965.
6. Sanderson, R. T., "Inorganic Chemistry," New York, Reinhold Publishing Corp., 1967.
7. Sebera, D. K., "Electronic Structure and Chemical Bonding," New York, Blaisdell, 1964.

R. T. SANDERSON

BONDING, IONIC COMPOUNDS

There exist a large number of chemical compounds whose composition, stability, structure, and properties can be satisfactorily accounted for by the assumption that they are composed of charged, massive particles, or ions. Ions may either be atoms with net positive or negative charges (simple ions) or charged molecules (complex ions) where the net charge can reside on a specific atom in the molecule or be distributed over several of the constituent atoms. The existence of both ion types with single or multiple charges has been amply demonstrated in a large number of examples, metals tending to form positive and nonmetals negative simple ions. Since ionic compounds are electrically neutral the number of positive charges must in a compound equal the number of negative charges; combining ratios of ions of opposite charge are thus fixed.

Bonding in ionic compounds arises from the electrostatic attraction of oppositely charged ions and can be described quantitatively by Coulomb's law. The strength of ionic bonding in solids is customarily defined in terms of the *lattice energy*, the energy released when a mole of the compound is formed from an ideal gas composed of the constituent ions in the proper proportions, or alternately, the energy absorbed in the reverse process. The lattice energy can be calculated from electrostatic theory or can be obtained from thermochemical data. Calculations for ideal ionic solids take into account that at equilibrium there exists a balance between the net electrostatic attractions which are stabilizing the structure and the repulsions between the electronic envelopes of the various ions. The total electrostatic potential energy is obtained by summing up Coulomb's law terms for all possible ion pairs. The resulting infinite series can often be simply expressed as the product of the ionic charges, q_+ and q_-, the reciprocal of the smallest of the equilibrium interionic distances, d_0, and a numerical constant, A, the *Madelung constant*. The lattice energy, U, can thus be calculated from the equation $U = q_+ \cdot q_- \cdot A \cdot N (1 - 1/n)/ d_0$, where N is Avogadro's number and n is the *Born exponent*, arising from the interelectronic repulsive potential energy function. Values of the Born exponents depend on the electron configuration of the ions and range from 5 to 11 for ions isoelectronic with He or Xe, respectively. The repulsive energy at equilibrium, represented by the $1/n$ factor in the equation, amounts to about 10 to 15% of the electrostatic energy in most ionic compounds. The Madelung constants is a function of the crystal structure and the stoichiometry and generally increases with the coordination number of the ions. In accord with the equation the strength of ionic bonding increases markedly with the ionic charge as is illustrated by the series NaF, CaO, Al_2O_3, where the lattice energies are 216, 826, 3663 kcal/mole, respectively. Since the lattice energy is a function of the reciprocal of the interionic distance an increase in ionic size weakens the bonding. In practice the effect is less pronounced than the charge effect producing, *e.g.*, a variation from 192 to only 151 kcal/mole between potassium fluoride and potassium iodide.

Direct measurement of lattice energies is complicated by the low volatility of ionic compounds and by reactions other than ionization competing in the vaporization process. Only a few determinations have therefore been made. More commonly, accurate values are obtained from thermochemical energy cycles. For instance, the lattice energy can be expressed as the difference between the energies of formation (from the elements) of the ionic solid and the separate gaseous ions, or as the difference between the heat of solvation of the gaseous ions and the heat of solution of the compound. Most frequently the lattice energy is calculated by applying the *Born-Haber cycle*, which involves several steps for which energy data can be obtained experimentally, especially for compounds of simple ions. These energies are: the heats of formation of one mole of gaseous metal atoms (S) and one mole of gaseous nonmetal atoms (D) from the elements, the ionization energies for successive removal of electrons from the metal to achieve the required positive charge ($I = I_1 + I_2 + \cdots$), the electron affinities for the consecutive attachment of electrons to the nonmetal till the proper negative charge is reached ($E = E_1 + E_2 + \cdots$), and the molar heat of formation of the solid compound from the elements (Q). The energy necessary to disrupt the ionic bonding is then obtained from Hess's law, giving for a compound M_xA_y the relation $U = xS + yD + xI - yE - Q$. When complex ions are present the energy of the bonds within the complex must also be taken into account.

Theoretical and experimental values agree well in a large number of instances, particularly when the theoretical calculations are refined to include the PV-energy of the ionic gas and small corrections for zero-point energy, Van der Waals forces, and polarization

71

in the lattice. However, when there are appreciable non-ionic contributions to the bonding experimental lattice energies are larger than the values calculated from the ionic model. This is the case, *e.g.*, in ammonium fluoride where strong *hydrogen bonds* to the fluoride ions enhance the stability of the crystal. Partial *covalent bonding* or its equivalent, extreme mutual polarization of the ions in each other's electrostatic field, will also cause an increase in lattice stability. This occurs in the silver halides which have a crystal structure similar to sodium chloride but have very low solubilities in water because of enhanced lattice stability derived from partial covalent bonding. Examples of mixed bond character are numerous and it is fair to say that purely ionic bonding, just like purely covalent bonding, represents an idealized description on one extreme of the range of intermediate bond character.

Factors which modify the importance of ionic bonding are the physical state of the compound, the oxidation number and the electronegativity of the constituent atoms. Electrostatic forces decrease with distance much less rapidly than do covalent bond forces and, unlike the latter, are not saturated over the distance of about one ionic diameter. In solids, where matter is in its most compact form, attractions between ions separated by several other ions contribute significantly to the stability of a compound. In the liquid state stabilizing ionic attractions are somewhat fewer in number since with a lower density of matter an ionic particle has, on the average, fewer neighbors within a given distance. In the gas phase, finally, stabilization by ionic bonding beyond the immediately neighboring ion is not possible because only a few ions are clustered together with large average distances between aggregates. Ionic bonding is therefore most pronounced in the solid state and occasionally even a change to pronounced covalent bonding may occur during melting or vaporization. A case in point is PBr_5 which is an ionic solid composed of PBr_4^+ and Br^- ions but in the liquid and gaseous state consists of PBr_5 molecules.

When metals form compounds which differ in the *oxidation number* of the positive ion the lowest oxidation number is associated with the most pronounced ionic bond character. Thus, $TiCl_2$, $TiCl_3$, $SnCl_2$, and UF_4 are ionic solids whereas $TiCl_4$, $SnCl_4$ and UF_6 are easily vaporized covalent liquids. This change can be explained by the polarizing effect of the positive charge which can distort the electron clouds of the surrounding ion. If the charge (or the oxidation number on simple positive ions) is high enough the resulting large distortion becomes equivalent to incipient covalent bonding. An increase in the positive charge of an ion is always accompanied by a decrease in its size so that the polarizing effect is enhanced by a greater concentration of the charge. The polarizing power of ions can be expressed as the ratio of charge to ionic radius.

The relative importance of ionic bonding can also be estimated from the *electronegativity* difference in the bond partners. Electronegativity increases towards the right and decreases towards the bottom of the *Periodic Table*. Thus, compounds between metals to the left and the bottom of the Periodic Table and nonmetals in the upper right show the greatest degree of ionic character in their bonds: in analogous compounds changes in the degree of covalent contribution to bonding are often discernible with a change in position in the Periodic Table of one of the ions. For instance, hydrides of the alkali and alkaline earth metals are distinctly ionic, having high melting points, high electrical conductivity in the molten state, produce hydrogen gas at the anode on electrolysis in fused salt solution, but are not significantly soluble in media of low polarity. In the boron family, the boron hydrides are predominantly covalent compounds with distinct molecular structures, but the lower family members form more ionic structures. Similar trends are observed for fluorides. In the halides, ionic bond character is at a maximum in the fluorides and decreases steadily in the family: the electrical conductivity in the molten state is much lower in $BeCl_2$ than it is in BeF_2. AlF_3 is a high melting ionic solid and maintains in the fused state the coordination of six fluoride ions around each aluminum ion which is appropriate to the solid state. On the other hand, $AlCl_3$, has a rather low melting point and changes to four-coordination on melting, a characteristic of covalent bond character. $AlBr_3$ exists in the solid and the liquid state as Al_6Br_6 molecules with the bonds now best described as covalent with considerable ionic character.

Ionic bonding also exists in materials other than conventional salts. Noteworthy examples are the *ion-exchange resins* which are organic polymers incorporating in their structures functional groups capable of accommodating positive or negative charges. Cation $(+$ ion$)$ exchangers contain sulfonate $(-SO_3^-)$ or carboxylate $(-CO_2^-)$ groups which hold mobile positive ions to the resin; anion $(-$ ion$)$ exchangers are based on positively charged groupings such as quaternary ammonium ions (R_4N^+) or on protonated amines. The resins are thus in essence highly polymerized organic salts which can react to replace one mobile ion by another, the ease of reaction depending, in part, on the relative strength of the ionic bonds to the fixed resin charges.

Other instances of ionic bonding are perhaps the interactions between ions and *dipolar* molecules such as water or ammonia. Such interactions are smaller in magnitude than ion-ion interactions but they are nevertheless most significant in explaining, for instance, the solubility of ionic compounds in polar solvents and the existence of solvated ionic species.

G. E. RYSCHKEWITSCH

BORON

Boron, symbol B, atomic number 5, atomic weight 10.811, is a black solid of unusual chemical and physical properties. The element is located in Group IIIA of the Periodic Table and is classed as a metalloid. Boron is a material of low density that is hard and brittle in massive form. It is important as an absorber of neutrons, its fibers can greatly increase the strength of metals and alloys, and it can raise the conductivity of copper to 103.5% of standard values when added to that metal in small amounts. Boron exists naturally as 19.57% B^{10} isotope and 80.43% as B^{11} isotope.

History

Boron compounds may have been known for about 6000 years, starting with the Bab-

ylonians. The Egyptians, Chinese, Tibetans and Arabians are reported to have used such materials. The Arabs used the expression "baurach" for a number of minerals including the now familiar borax.

Elemental boron was not known until the early Nineteenth Century when Sir Humphry Davy, Gay-Lussac, and Thenard prepared boron by reduction of boron trioxide with potassium and by electrolysis of moistened boric acid. The purity of their products was about 50%.

Fifty years later impure boron products resembling both diamond and graphite were produced. The diamond-hard material was found to be largely aluminium boride, AlB_{12}, while the graphite variety was a complex boron-aluminum-carbide. Much later a higher purity boron was made by the reduction of boron trioxide with magnesium, a form that is still commercially available. Purities of about 90% can be achieved by this procedure. The product is light brown in color and is considered to be amorphous.

Boron did not become of interest until the Twentieth Century when it was found that it formed many unusual and complex compounds. Elemental boron has generated interest since World War II and has enjoyed United States Government support for research and development in the last few years. It has been within the last twenty years that the true physical and chemical properties have been determined. High-purity boron produced by electrolysis and vapor deposition methods have made such determinations possible.

Prevalence

Boron is present to the extent of 0.001% of the earth's crust and to the extent of a few parts per million in sea water. Its mineral ores are concentrated to such an extent that boron compounds, such as borax, can be mined cheaply enough for large quantity usage.

Sources

Boron is sufficiently reactive to preclude its occurrence in the free state. The sources of combined boron are sassolite, H_3BO_3, found in Italy; colemanite, $Ca_2B_6O_{11}.5H_2O$; ulexite, $CaNaB_5O_9.8H_2O$; and kernite (rasorite), $Na_2B_4O_7.4H_2O$, in the United States. Ulexite is also found in Bolivia, Chile and Peru. Boracite, $Mg_7B_{10}Cl_2O_{30}$, is found in Germany. Russia obtains calcium and magnesium borates from the Inder deposits. The world's major source of boron is kernite from the Mojave Desert in California.

Preparation

Several methods are known for preparing the element. The products obtained vary widely in cost and purity. The methods vary from simple to very complex operations. The methods of preparation are (1) reduction of the oxide by metals; (2) hot-wire vapor deposition and thermal decomposition; and (3) fused salt electrolysis.

In the first procedure the reducing metal, preferably magnesium, aluminum or potassium, is reacted directly with a boron compound such as KBF_4 or B_2O_3. The product obtained usually varies from about 85 to 93% boron with the remainder composed of various amounts of the reducing metal, iron and suboxides of boron such as B_3O and B_7O, and borides of the reducing metal.

The most common reaction is the reduction of boric oxide, B_2O_3, with magnesium to produce a brownish technical grade powder of about 90%. Careful leaching in aqueous solutions of hydrochloric acid can provide a 93–95% pure product.

A similar reaction with aluminum produces a boron product containing various aluminum borides, particularly AlB_{12}.

Boron produced by these methods is amorphous.

In the second method various gaseous compounds of boron are mixed with hydrogen and passed over hot wires or rods. These wires or rods may be metals such as titanium, tantalum, tungsten, molybdenum or their alloys. Some investigators have used graphite and silicon carbide; each has worked out a procedure that fits his particular needs.

The procedures involved are most costly and most difficult. The yields are low and the filament upon which the boron deposits is a source of contamination. This accounts for the wide variety of materials used as filaments. These results however are gratifying, since the purest boron has been obtained.

The basic method is not new, having been described by Kosef as early as 1922 and

Warth in 1923. Not much success toward achieving a commercial production unit was noted until the United States Atomic Energy Commission built a plant in the 1950's to produce the isotope boron-10 by the hot-wire technique. The product obtained was about 95–97% boron. At that time it was dropped in favor of the Cooper electrolytic process.

Recent investigators have achieved purities of essentially 100% boron.

In practice a mixture of boron trichloride and hydrogen is caused to pass over a heated filament. Temperatures for the reactions range from 800 to 2000°C. The gases react at the hot wire or rod filament depositing a layer of boron. Initially a layer of boron and boride results. As the reaction is continued, high-purity boron deposits and the outer surface becomes larger in diameter. The final result is a rod of boron with a center composed of the original wire plus a boride. Various methods have evolved to remove the central wire. In the section on *Applications* it will be shown that removal of the wire is not necessarily desirable.

Further refining can be accomplished by subsequent zone refining techniques. Single crystal material has been made by the Czochralski crystal growth method. This method requires the introduction of a seed into a molten bath which is subsequently removed to provide a continuous rod or crystal.

The initial attempts to produce boron by vapor phase techniques were made by Weintraub. Hydrogen and boron trichloride BCl_3, were passed through a high-tension arc. Powdered boron of 99.8% purity was obtained. This method led to the vapor-phase hot-wire reaction techniques.

Hot-tube reaction methods involving the reaction of hydrogen with the halides of boron can be used to produce a high-purity product. The mechanism is the same as the hot-filament procedure. The walls of the vessels or tubes provide a greater source of contamination than a filament. Power requirements are also much greater.

In the third method boron compounds such as B_2O_3, KBF_4 and BF_3 are dissolved in molten salts such as KCl and KF. These baths are electrolyzed to produce a very fine powdered boron. The purity obtained ranges from

95 to 99.8%. The impurities are generally iron, carbon and oxygen.

Preparation of boron by electrolysis dates back to the time of Davy, but it wasn't until 1951 that high-purity material was produced by Cooper.

Cooper's initial procedure requires the electrolysis of a molten salt mixture of KBF_4 and KCl at a temperature of about 800°C. The electrolysis yields crystalline boron granules on an iron cathode while chlorine is generated at the walls of the graphite crucible. The crucible serves as the anode. The mixture can be electrolyzed until the boron and chlorine content is so low that the bath is largely KF. This causes a large voltage increase and a rise in the melting point of the bath. The boron product is removed from the cathode by washing in water and hydrochloric acid, and is dried at about 110°C.

In a second procedure B_2O_3 is added to the above bath. It is an important improvement. The electrolysis takes place about 800°C as before while small amounts of B_2O_3 are added periodically. Boron is produced as a very fine -325 mesh powder at the metal cathode while oxygen is generated at the graphite crucible walls. At these temperatures the oxygen readily reacts with the graphite to produce carbon dioxide. The operating life of the crucible, in part, is determined by the time required for the oxygen to reduce the cell wall thickness to the point of leakage.

The original cell design has been modified to provide a neutrally charged crucible and greatly increased crucible life with the insertion of flat graphite anodes. The anodes are cut smaller in length and width to cause an even distribution of current on the cathode. Electrolysis continues until the intervening space between electrodes is literally filled with boron. Anodes are readily replaced thereby greatly increasing cell crucible life. (See Fig. 1.) Note the smaller width and length with respect to the cathode.

Cooper and Schaefer have developed a procedure for essentially continuous operation of the $KCl-KBF_4$ bath previously described. Periodic, or continuous additions of BCl_3 to the bath replaces the boron electrodeposited on the cathode and the chlorine liberated at the anode, thereby keeping the bath at a nearly constant composition and negating the

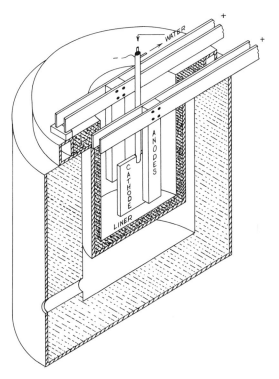

FIG. 1. Boron cell with flat anodes and cathode for improved current distribution.

necessity for frequent bath changes. The same procedure is used for reclaiming spent bath salts. This procedure is particularly applicable to the electrolysis of expensive isotopic materials on a large scale.

Cooper has also developed a method of forming tenacious coatings of boron up to 0.25 inch thick on metallic cathodes from a fused salt bath of $B_2O_3-KBF_4$. These coatings are especially suited for protection against high neutron radiation. The production procedure is similar to the other Cooper methods but the bath composition is quite different, requiring 15% B_2O_3 in KBF_4.

Nies has developed a cell system suitable for the production of electrolytic boron and borides whereby it is possible to remove the product from the molten bath without exposing it to the air before it has cooled. Two cells are used with one inverted over the other to serve as a cover chamber. After electrolysis the unit is inverted, the cover chamber becomes the cell and the former cell acts as a cooling chamber for the product which is now

TABLE 1. PHYSICAL PROPERTIES

Color – Black
Crystal forms – Tetragonal, α rhombohedral and β rhombohedral
Atomic number – 5
Atomic weight – 10.811
Isotopes – 10 and 11 (stable), 8, 9 and 12 (short half-lives)
Hardness – 9.3 (Mohs scale), 3300 Knoop (100g load)
Melting point – 2300°C
Boiling point – 2550°C
Electrical resistivity

Temperature °C	Resistivity, ohms-centimeter
− 150	40,000,000
− 10	4,000,000
0	3,000,000
27	650,000
100	40,000
170	3,000
320	40
520	1.2
600	0.2

Density – 2.34 g/cc
Atomic volume – 4.70 cc/g-atom
Index of refraction – 2.5 using Hg line 5790Å
Specific heat

Temperature °C	cal/g
− 191 to − 78	0.0071
− 76 to − 0	0.180
0–100	0.307
100	0.387
500	0.472
900	0.510

Ionization potentials in volts

I	8.296
II	23.98
III	37.75
IV	258.1
V	338

Heat of vaporization – 90,000 cal/mole
Neutron absorption

B^{10} 3850 barns
B^{11} 0.05 barns

Coefficient of linear expansion 1.1 to 8.3×10^{-6} per °C in 20 to 750° range

removed from the bath. When cool the cover cell and its product are removed and another unit is put in its place.

The Cooper processes do not require protective covers or atmospheres to attain high-purity boron.

Physical Properties

Some of the physical properties of boron are listed in Table 1.

Chemistry of Boron

The chemistry of boron is complex and unusual in many respects. Several of these complexities are emphasized in this section. Boron is an electropositive element of the third group of the Periodic Table. It exhibits an oxidation state of $+3$ in such compounds as BCl_3 and BI_3. These compounds readily hydrolyze in moist air to form HCl and $B(OH)_3$ or H_3BO_3. The weak base can form BPO_4 by reaction with H_3PO_4 or $B(HSO_4)_3$ by reaction with SO_3

$$B(OH)_3 + 3SO_3 \rightarrow B(HSO_4)_3.$$

The compound H_3BO_3 is also a very weak acid reacting with NaOH to form $Na_2B_4O_7$ or $NaBO_2$. This illustrates the amphoteric nature of boron. It is similar to aluminum in this respect.

Boron readily forms compounds similar to those of carbon and silicon, by forming multiple boron structures. Such compounds as SiB_3, SiB_6, B_4C, AlB_{12}, B_2H_6, B_5H_9 and $B_{10}H_{14}$ are examples. Boron has been reported to form almost spherical shaped icosahedral molecules of 10 boron and 2 carbon atoms with attached hydrogen atoms. A notable example is the benzene ring type structure of borazole, $B_3N_3H_6$. Several of the structures are illustrated and discussed in the references cited in this article.

Boron has an electrode potential that is relatively low but the element is not readily reduced to elemental form at the cathode in an aqueous media.

$$3H_2O + B \rightarrow H_3BO_3 + 3H^+ + 3e^-, E^\circ = 0.87$$

Boron is an excellent "getter" because of its great affinity for oxygen. It removes oxygen from various oxides in copper, brass, and aluminum. Often the result of the reaction can be seen when B_2O_3 appears at the surface of the particular melt. The generalized reaction might be written as follows:

$$3MO + 2B \rightarrow B_2O_3 + 3M$$

TABLE 2.   CHEMICAL PROPERTIES OF BORON

Heat of combustion with oxygen = 13.95 kcal/g or 25,150 BTU/lb
Reaction with:
    Fluorine – instantaneous at room temp.
    Chlorine – above 500°C
    Bromine – over 600°C
    Iodine – about 900°C
    Hydrochloric acid – none
    Hydrofluoric acid – none
    Nitric acid, hot, conc. – slow
    Oxygen – room temp. – slight, 1000°C – rapid
    Hydrogen iodide – explosive
    Hydrogen – above 840°C
    Nitrogen – bright red heat
    Sodium hydroxide – slow – over 500°C
    Boron nitride – none
    Metals – CARE! Over 900°C many metals react rapidly, and the reactions are exothermic.

Several chemical properties of boron are given in Table 2 which indicate the rather low degree of reactivity of the element.

Boron Compounds

Borax. Boron in its combined form, borax, $Na_2B_4O_7.10H_2O$, has been in use since early times. Early uses were as a mild antiseptic and cleaner because of its detergent and water-softening properties. Later it was used as a soldering flux and ceramic flux because of its ability to dissolve metal oxides. Characteristic colors resulting from fusion of the metal oxides can be used to identify many metallic ores in the field and in the laboratory. Borax is used to produce a heat-resistant borosilicate glass for the home and laboratory, familiar to many by the trade mark "Pyrex," and is the starting material for the preparation of other boron compounds.

Boric Acid and Boron Oxide. Boric acid is mildly antiseptic and is used widely as an eye wash. Its anhydride is used as a source of boron in the fused salt electrolysis method for the preparation of elemental boron. The anyhydride is also used to prepare boron trifluoride by reaction with calcium fluoride and sulfuric acid. Boric acid is used as a neutron absorber in the swimming-pool type nuclear reactors. It is also used in electroplating baths, such as those used for nickel deposition.

Boron Trifluoride. This gas is produced in large quantities for gas tube neutron radiation detectors for monitoring radiation levels in the earth's atmosphere and in space. Some organizations use these devices to ascertain the best underground level at which to blast to produce oil wells of high yield.

For the above uses the BF_3 is enriched to more than 90% isotopic $B^{10}F_3$. The U.S. Atomic Energy Commission has a plant at Model City, New York that separates $B^{10}F_3$ from $B^{11}F_3$ by dissociating a methyl ether complex in a fractionating column with a reflux ratio of 700 to 1. The B^{11} concentrates in the vapor while the B^{10} concentrates in the liquid.

The complex can be used to make $KB^{10}F_4$ and $KB^{11}F_4$. Fused salt electrolysis by the Cooper procedure provides elemental B^{10} or B^{11} powder.

Boron trifluoride is an important industrial

catalyst for many organic reactions, such as polymerization reactions, as in the production of butyl rubber from isobutene. It is also the source of the tetrafluoroborate ion, BF_4^-, which is used in the electroplating of nickel, lead and tin.

Boron forms many other useful metallic and inorganic compounds. Outstanding among these are the borides, carbides, silicides, nitride, and hydrides. Because of the difficulty of obtaining the borides in pure form by reduction methods, very little has been known about their properties until recently. Now that ample high-purity boron is available in quantity by the Cooper process, these compounds are made in pure form by direct combination of the elements. The borides of the refractory metals could become of great industrial importance and are being intensively studied. In general, they are characterized by high melting points—in excess of 2000°C (3632°F)—and great hardness, and in the case of borides of aluminum, AlB_{12}; silicon, SiB_6; titanium, TiB_2; zirconium, ZrB_2; and chromium, CrB_2; the resistance to scaling above 1000°C (1832°F) is quite good. The borides of tungsten, molybdenum, tantalum, and niobium, though not so resistant to high temperature in an oxidizing atmosphere, are exceedingly refractory, and are extremely hard. Chromium boride is currently being used in hardfacing operations for improving wear resistance, also for coating steel to render steel sections resistant to molten aluminum. Aluminum boride, AlB_{12}, has been used as a substitute for diamond dust for grinding and polishing. The Knoop hardness (100-g load) of aluminum boride has been determined to be 3,700. Boron carbide (2800 K_{100}) has been produced in quantity for a number of years; it has found extensive use as a polishing agent, for sandblast nozzles, etc. An impure form of calcium boride has also been marketed over a considerable period of time as a deoxidizing agent for copper. Pure calcium boride, CaB_6, is now being made and could be of interest in other directions. This compound is quite stable. It has a melting point of 2235°C (4055°F) and a Knoop hardness (100-g load) of about 2,500.

The borides can be substituted for elemental boron for the deoxidation or "killing" of steel, brass, copper and aluminium. They are more easily handled than the light elemental powder. Copper can be deoxidized with a 4% boron-copper alloy to produce a high-conductivity, low-oxygen metal with 103.5% of standard copper conductivity. The addition of AlB_{12} to aluminum will provide a very soft ductile metal.

The metallic borides of Group-IV metals, surprisingly, are better electrical conductors than their respective components, and it is to be expected that their thermal conductivities follow much the same pattern. Some of these compounds respond to conventional sintering and hot-pressing procedures, and in certain instances, the resulting shapes have considerable strength.

Boron forms a nitride having quite remarkable properties. This compound is a white powder having an average particle size of about 1μ. The melting point of boron nitride is about 3000°C (5432°F), and it withstands oxidation at temperatures up to about 650°C (1202°F). The true density is 2.20 g/cc, and the apparent density is 0.11 g/cc or 7 lb/cu ft. Electrical resistance is extremely high at all temperatures up to 2400°C (4352°F) at which point the material is not heated by high-frequency current. Boron nitride has a hexagonal plate structure like graphite and has been suggested as a lubricant. It has also been patented as a paint pigment. Boron nitride can be hot-pressed into various forms such as crucibles, etc. It has recently been subjected to pressures in excess of 1,000,000 psi at temperatures above 1650°C (3002°F) to yield a material as hard as diamond.

Boron Hydrides. The hydrides of boron are colorless solids, liquids, or gases and are easily oxidized, with consequent large energy liberation. These compounds have been extensively studied by government agencies because of desirable characteristics as rocket fuels. The highest jet velocities are attained with elements of low atomic weight, and, although hydrogen is probably the "tops" theoretically as a propellant fuel, it is extremely difficult to contain, and so must be combined with other elements, such as boron or lithium. It is generally agreed that, for many reasons, boron is the likeliest candidate for this role. For a propellant fuel of reasonably high bulk density, very high jet velocities may be expected from reacting boron hydride with fluorine oxide and water; boron hydride is a water-reaction fuel, being highly explosive when exposed to moist air or traces of water.

Applications and Importance of Boron and its Compounds

Boron. Boron provides unusually high energy and specific impulse values by direct reaction of elemental boron with fluorine. The reaction temperature is very high and the reaction product is gaseous boron trifluoride.

Boron Fibers. For structural purposes boron has been considered as a material difficult to utilize. Its hard and brittle properties make it difficult to roll or to work. In this respect it is much like glass. Glass, of course, is evident as structural material such as glass block, vacuum bell jars, glass pipe, glass tubing, etc. Glass can also be used as a reinforcing agent to strengthen other materials. For example, glass wool or glass cloth or loose glass fibers are added to plastic to form fiber glass boats, tanks, various types of containers, and high strength coatings. Boron can be used in a similar manner. It can be added to pure metals, alloys, or to other solids. While the host material such as the metals or alloys may have a tendency toward plastic flow, the addition of nonmetals such as boron give resistance to plastic flow and thereby add significant strength to the product. Fibers or whiskers of single crystal or ceramic crystal material are generally free from dislocation and other defects, permitting maximum strength. Whisker or fiber growth of various materials has been known for many years.

Initially, they were a curiosity and in many cases an undesired product. Investigation of glass fibers and iron fibers or whiskers disclosed that the fibers had unusually high strength. Single fibers are very limited in use. Random groups of fibers or cloth woven from fibers have shown a remarkable reinforcing effect.

An application that appears to be of great significance is the usage of fibers composed of boron and boron compounds such as boron carbide. The fibers or whiskers are grown from supersaturated vapors on temperature-controlled substrates by the vapor reaction methods described earlier. Several large companies are engaged in research and development in this area. The United States Government has sponsored much of the effort. The work is exciting, as evidenced by the fast-growing volume of government reports and journal articles. Boron wires of 0.004 inch on 0.0005 inch tungsten substrates averaging 2000 feet in length are available.

The recent F-111 series of U.S. military aircraft utilizing the variable-sweep wing feature uses boron filaments in its construction. Boron filament epoxy resin honeycombs are 30% lighter than equivalent aluminum structures.

Figs. 2, 3, and 4 illustrate boron fibers and some composites containing them.

Toxicity

Boron in the elemental form is not toxic. The finely divided powder is hard and abrasive, and may cause skin problems indirectly if the skin is rubbed after contact.

Trace amounts of boron seem necessary for

FIG. 2. Small solid rocket case from United Technology Center is made of boron filament and epoxy resin. Some 40 miles of filament were wound into the 6-in. diameter casing. *(Industrial Research)*

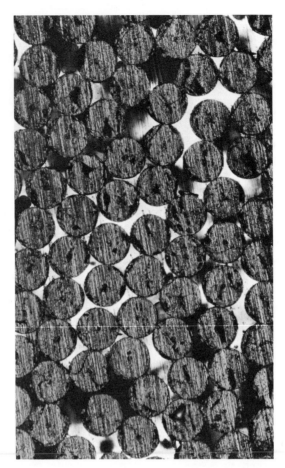

FIG. 3. A magnified view of boron composite developed at Texaco Experiment Inc. Dark circles are cross sections of close-packed boron fibers. *(Industrial Research)*

FIG. 4. Boron filament-resin composite undergoes flexing tests on specially built machine at Texaco. *(Industrial Research)*

good growth of plant life, but large amounts are toxic.

Boron accumulated in the body through absorbtion, ingestion, and inhalation of its compounds has an effect on the central nervous system. The symptoms are depression of circulation, vomiting, and diarrhea, followed by shock, coma and a body rash.

Boric acid doses of 15 to 20 g for an adult and 5 to 6 g for infants have proved to be fatal. The boron hydrides are toxic and explosive. The halides of boron are also toxic and must be handled with care. Their vapors are corrosive to the skin.

Elemental boron can not be classed as a poison, but the assimilation of its compounds has an accumulative poisonous effect.

References

1. Gould, R. F., Editor, "Borax to Boranes," No. 32, Advances in Chemistry Series, Washington, D.C., American Chemical Society, 1961.
2. Hampel, C. A., "Encyclopedia of Electrochemistry," "Boron Electrowinning" Chapter, New York, Reinhold Publishing Corp., 1964.
3. Hampel, C. A., "Rare Metals Handbook," "Boron" Chapter, New York, Reinhold Publishing Corp., 1961.
4. Medcalf, W. E., et al, "Metallurgy of Elemental and Compound Semiconductors," p. 381, Vol. 12, New York, Interscience Publishing Co., 1960.
5. Sax, N. I., "Handbook of Dangerous Materials," New York, Reinhold Publishing Corp., 1951.
6. Sitarik, J. P., and Ellis, W. C., "Preparation and Morphology of Boron Filamentary Crystals Grown by the Vapor-Liquid-Solid Mechanism," J. App. Physics, 37, No. 6, 2399 (May, 1966).
7. Sullenger, D. B., and Kennard, C. H. L., "Boron Crystals," Scientific American, 215, No. 1, 96 (July, 1966).
8. U.S. Dept. of Commerce, "Fiber-Reinforced Metals and Alloys," Washington, D.C., Review Report OTR-127, September, 1965.

JAMES C. SCHAEFER

BROMINE

Bromine and mercury share the distinction of being the only elements that are liquid at ordinary temperatures and pressures. Bromine is a dark, dense, red-brown liquid (sp. gr. >3) which vaporizes readily. Both liquid and vapor are very corrosive, and the vapor has an intensely irritating odor. The atomic number is 35. The element consists of two stable isotopes, Br^{79} and Br^{81}, present in a natural proportion, 50.57% and 49.43%, respectively, such that the atomic weight is 79.909. The liquid and vapor are diatomic (Br_2) over a wide range of temperature. The most stable valence states of bromine in its salts are -1 and $+5$, but positive valences of 1 and 3 are also known. Chemical properties of bromine are intermediate between those of chlorine and iodine (Group VIIB and Period 3 of Periodic Table). In some respects liquid bromine resembles an organic solvent, but it is a drastic oxidizing agent, stronger than iodine though weaker than chlorine.

Working independently, A. J. Balard in France and C. Löwig in Germany almost simultaneously discovered bromine in 1826. Balard, who was only 23 years old at the time of his investigations, was credited with the discovery. A thorough study of the chemical properties of the element and its compounds was published by Löwig in 1829. Balard suggested the name "muride" for the new element to the French Academy of Science. The Academy, in turn, proposed the name "brome" from the Greek word bromos meaning stench to indicate its strong irritating odor.

Occurrence

Bromine is the twenty-fifth element in order of abundance in nature. It is so active chemically that it never occurs free in nature, but is always found as a halide. Except for some rather rare silver salts, no natural mineral contains bromine as an essential constituent. There are salt deposits or brines in various parts of the world where bromine has been concentrated by evaporation of water from prehistoric seas or salt lakes. Average ocean water contains 67 mg of bromine per liter.

In the United States natural brines at Freeport, Pennsylvania, were first used as a source of bromine in 1846. Small scale recoveries were reported between 1870 and 1875 near Hartford, and Mason, West Virginia, and

Pomeroy, Ohio. Commercial extraction of bromine from raw ocean water was begun in 1934 near Wilmington, North Carolina. At present it is extracted commercially from the ocean, from underground brines in Michigan and Arkansas (0.05 to 0.50% Br), from saline basins such as Searles Lake, California (0.085%) and the Dead Sea, Palestine (0.56%), and from solid salt beds at Stassfurt, Germany.

Derivation

Bromine is ordinarily obtained from brines by displacement with chlorine and vaporization into a current of either air or steam. Steam is suitable when the raw brine is relatively rich in bromine (0.1% or more), but air is more economical when the source of bromine is as dilute as ocean water. When steam is used the vapor may be condensed directly; otherwise, the bromine must be trapped in an alkaline or reducing solution. In either case, stripping is necessary to remove chlorine.

The steaming-out method has been widely employed since the early German development of a continuous process and its further improvement in 1906 by Kubierschky. In the United States modified Kubierschky processes are used for recovering bromine from potassium chloride liquors at Searles Lake, from bitterns in California, and directly from brines.

The process in which air instead of steam is used for driving out bromine was developed in the United States in 1889, by H. H. Dow. In 1933 the process was applied to the ex-

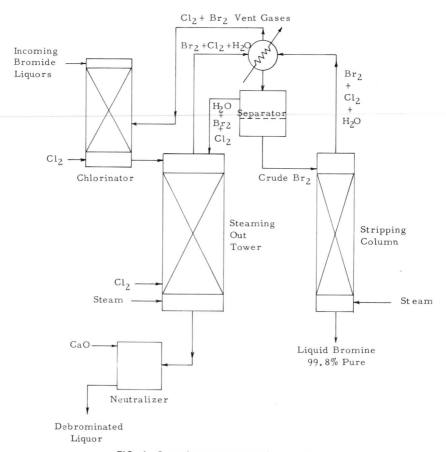

FIG. 1. Steaming out process for bromine.

traction of bromine from ocean water and a plant for the purpose was erected south of Wilmington, North Carolina. A larger plant was built at Freeport, Texas, during World War II and use of the Wilmington plant was discontinued in 1945. Other ocean water plants are operating at Hayle, Cornwall, Ahlwch, Wales, and Marseille, France.

Steaming-Out Process. A flowsheet of the steaming-out process is shown in Fig. 1. Raw brine preheated to about 90°C is treated with chlorine in a packed tower and then enters the steaming-out tower into which steam and additional chlorine are injected. The outgoing brine is neutralized and used to preheat raw brine.

From the top of the steaming-out tower the halogen-laden vapor passes into a condenser, and then into a gravity separator. From the separator, vent gases return to the chlorinator, the upper water layer containing Br_2 and Cl_2 flows to the steaming-out tower, and the lower crude bromine layer passes to the stripping column. Bromine from the stripping column is purified in a fractionating column from which liquid bromine of 99.8% purity is withdrawn as product.

Blowing-Out Process. As mentioned earlier, air is a more economical extracting agent than steam when the bromine source is as dilute as ocean water. In this process, the ocean water is acidified with sulfuric acid to a pH of 3.5, chlorinated with an excess of chlorine, dropped through a blowing-out tower and the free bromine and excess chlorine are removed in a countercurrent of air. The halogens are then absorbed from the air in a sodium carbonate solution. Bromine is liberated from this alkaline, sodium bromide-sodium bromate solution by treatment with sulfuric acid. The bromine is then steamed out and condensed as described previously.

A modification of the above process introduced in 1937 by The Dow Chemical Company involves replacement of the sodium carbonate absorption step by a sulfur dioxide reduction of the mixed halogens:

$$Br_2(Cl_2) + SO_2 + 2H_2O \rightarrow 2HBr(2HCl) + H_2SO_4$$

Bromine is separated by chlorination of the mixed acids in a steaming-out tower as already described. The hydrochloric-sulfuric

acid mixture remaining is used to acidify the incoming raw ocean water.

Physical Properties

The physical properties of bromine are intermediate between those of chlorine and iodine in most respects. They are summarized in Table 1.

TABLE 1. PHYSICAL PROPERTIES

Atomic number	35
Atomic weight	79.909
Isotopes, natural	79 (50.57%), 81 (49.43%)
Melting point	$-7.25 \pm 0.05°C$
Boiling point	58.8°C
Density, g/cc, 15°C	3.1396
20°C	3.1226
25°C	3.1055
30°C	3.0879
Index of refraction, 25°/D	1.6475
Vapor density vs air at 15°C	5.515
Viscosity, centipoise, 20°C	0.99
Surface tension, dyne/cm, 25°C	39.8
Heat capacity, cal/g	
Solid at $-23.15°C$	0.0886
Liquid at 25°C	0.113
Vapor at 83.228°C	0.0553
Heat of fusion, cal/g, $-7.25°C$	15.80
Heat of vaporization, cal/g, 59°C	44.8
Vapor pressure,	
mm Hg, $-48.7°C$	1
$-25.0°C$	10
$-8.0°C$	40
$-9.3°C$	100
41.0°C	400
58.8°C	760
Critical temperature, °C	311
Critical pressure, atm	102
Expansion coefficient, per °C, 20–30°C	0.0011
Compressibility coefficient, β (0–100 megabar) 20°C	62.5×10^{-6}
Electrical resistivity, ohm–cm, 25°C	6.5×10^{10}
Dielectric constant, 23°C (10^8 cycles/sec)	3.2
Solubility in H_2O,	
g/100 g solution, 0°C	2.31
25°C	3.35
53.6 °C	3.50
Thermal neutron absorption cross section, barns/atom	6.7 ± 0.3

At room temperature bromine is completely miscible with many of the common organic solvents such as carbon tetrachloride, perchloroethylene, carbon disulfide, acetic acid, benzene, and o-dichlorobenzene (slow bromination takes place in some of these cases). Miscibility is complete also with a few inorganic liquids such as titanium tetrachloride and phosphorus oxychloride. On the other hand, the solubility in 95% sulfuric acid is quite limited, being about 0.75 g per 100 g of solution at 25°C. The water solubility of bromine is increased in the presence of alkali halides, particularly potassium bromide. Presumably a complex polyhalide, KBr_3, is formed.

The solubilities of several alkali halides in liquid bromine are listed in Table 2.

TABLE 2. SOLUBILITIES OF ALKALI HALIDES IN LIQUID BROMINE
(g per 100 g of solution at 25°C)

Alkali Metal	Chloride	Bromide
Lithium	0.0037	0.005
Sodium	0.001	0.010
Potassium	0.0055	0.0185
Rubidium	0.015	0.058
Cesium	0.175	19.3

Chemical Properties

In reactivity bromine is similar to chlorine, though its normal oxidation potential is somewhat lower (−1.087 volts.) From the magnitude of this potential, as compared with oxidation potentials of other electrochemical reactions, it may be deduced that in general bromine is a stronger oxidant than ferric iron or dilute nitric acid, but weaker than oxygen or ceric sulfate. However, the reaction velocities must be considered. Reactions with bromine often proceed quite rapidly, in which cases bromine may be a more effective oxidant than oxygen.

Bromine attacks most metals; aluminum reacts with it vigorously, with the emission of light, and potassium reacts explosively. On the other hand, lead, nickel, and magnesium are not attacked by dry bromine and may be used as containers for the liquid. Even sodium does not react with dry bromine below 300°C. Iron and zinc, which scarcely react at all with dry bromine, are corroded rapidly if moisture is present. Platinum is relatively stable toward bromine in water or in hydrochloric acid. Tantalum is also resistant and bromine condensers are fabricated from it. Mercury is attacked and cannot be used in gages or other instruments that come into contact with the free halogen.

Under the influence of heat, catalysts, or an electrical discharge, bromine in the gaseous state unites directly with hydrogen:

$$H_2 + Br_2 \rightarrow 2HBr + 24{,}950 \text{ cal.}$$

This reaction takes place explosively if the gases are mixed in roughly stoichiometric proportions and ignited, but may be brought about smoothly by burning a jet of bromine vapor in an atmosphere of hydrogen.

Addition reactions take place between bromine and several of the nonmetals. Dry sulfur yields sulfur monobromide, S_2Br_2, while the related elements selenium and tellurium each yield two products: Se_2Br_2 and $SeBr_4$, and $TeBr_2$ (unstable) and $TeBr_4$. Reactions of bromine with phosphorus, producing PBr_3 and PBr_5, and with arsenic, producing $AsBr_3$, are violent and are best carried out by passing bromine vapor into a mixture of the element with some of its tribromide.

Bromine can be added to cold nitric oxide to form nitrosyl bromide, $NOBr$, and nitrosyl tribromide, $NOBr_3$. Apparently bromine does not form addition products with carbon monoxide or sulfur dioxide. Activated charcoal adsorbs bromine reversibly without reaction when moisture is absent. In the presence of moisture, the carbon is partially oxidized and hydrobromic acid is formed.

Solid polybromo complexes are produced by the addition of bromine to bromides of the higher alkali elements, such as cesium, and to the quaternary ammonium bromides. These addition compounds have rather limited solubility in water, but are quite soluble in liquid bromine.

Bromine hydrolyzes slightly in aqueous solution, producing hypobromous acid which is unstable:

$$Br_2 + H_2O \rightarrow HBrO + HBr$$
$$2HBrO \rightarrow 2HBr + O_2$$

The liberation of oxygen is accelerated by light and is responsible for the bleaching action of bromine water. Hypobromite solutions formed by neutralizing bromine water with alkali are also strong oxidants, capable of oxidizing ammonia to nitrogen, sulfur compounds to sulfates, and various metals to their higher valences. The hypobromite is also unstable, disproportionating to bromate and bromide.

In the organic field, bromine can be combined directly with alkenes to form dibromo addition products. This reaction is of importance in synthesis, and in many cases is sufficiently quantitative to be used for analytical purposes.

Substitution reactions in the organic field are of importance. Bromine replaces hydrogen attached to carbon, rapidly when the hydrogen is located ortho or para to a polar group in an aromatic compound, less easily in nonpolar aromatic compounds, and still less readily in aliphatic hydrocarbons.

Bromine can replace hydrogen on a nitrogen atom, but the resulting compound usually is unstable and decomposes. In the Hofmann reaction for preparing amines, an N-bromo derivative is formed but it is rearranged and hydrolyzed upon warming. With very little more difficulty than it displaces hydrogen, bromine can replace carboxyl and sulfonic acid groups in active positions. Thus, p-phenolsulfonic acid can be converted to tribromophenol, and anthranilic acid to tribromoaniline by simple bromination in aqueous solution.

Bromine water oxidizes aldose sugars to lactones, which subsequently hydrolyze to aldonic acids. Extensive use of bromine oxidation has been made in the classical studies on the structure of sugars.

Applications

The production of bromine amounts to several hundred million pounds annually.

The greatest use of bromine, one which consumes about 95% of the bromine produced, is in the manufacture of ethylene bromide, 1,2-dibromoethane (ethylene dibromide), for antiknock fluids for motor fuels. Commercial antiknock formulations based on tetraethyl and tetramethyl lead contain ethylene dibromide, as well as ethylene

dichloride, so that on combustion of the fuel, lead halides are formed which vaporize from the hot surfaces of the combustion chamber of the engine. This action prevents the accumulation of lead oxide in engines.

Lesser amounts of bromine are used to prepare a great variety of other compounds, organic and inorganic. A small proportion is sold as liquid bromine for use as a reagent for analytical and synthetic purposes. The usefulness of bromine in synthesis stems from the ease with which it can be added on, substituted into, and replaced in organic compounds. The dye industry uses bromine to modify the shades of indigo dyes and other colored compounds. Bromine is an excellent bleaching and sanitizing agent (water purification). Recent evidence indicates that bromine has some advantages over chlorine in swimming-pool applications, partly because of the differing stabilities and biocidal effectiveness of the haloamines produced when either halogen reacts with traces of ammonia in the water.

One small but interesting use of bromine is as a selective inorganic solvent. The solubilities of various alkali bromides and chlorides in liquid bromine are shown in Table 2.

The high solubility of cesium bromide makes possible a commercial process for its separation from the other alkali metal bromides, especially rubidium. The pure cesium bromide so obtained has been used in the manufacture of optical prisms highly transparent to infrared radiation, and in the preparation of pure cesium metal. The solubilities of other metallic bromides in liquid bromine have subsequently been studied, but no other striking solubility such as that observed for cesium bromide has been encountered.

Compounds and Their Uses

Inorganic

1. *Bromamines*. Bromamide, NH_2Br; bromimide, $NHBr_2$; and nitrogen bromide, NBr_3, can be prepared, but all are unstable and capable of violent decomposition.

2. *Bromides*. Alkali and alkaline earth bromides may be prepared directly from bromine and an appropriate carbonate or by

treating a corresponding hydroxide or carbonate with hydrobromic acid.

The bromides of the alkali and alkaline earth elements find usage in pharmacy because of their sedative actions, in photography for the preparation of silver bromide emulsions, and in the industrial drying of air as desiccants.

Anhydrous aluminum bromide is an effective catalyst for some types of bromination reactions.

Hydrogen bromide (hydrobromic acid), HBr, is a colorless, very irritating gas that fumes strongly in moist air. It is prepared commercially as described above.

Hydrobromic acid is an effective solvent for some ore minerals because of its high boiling point and strong reducing action. In respect to hydrogen-ion activity, hydrobromic acid is one of the strongest acids. With the bromides of several metals it forms complexes ($HFeBr_4$, amber; $HCuBr_3$, violet, etc.). Bromine is very soluble in strong aqueous hydrobromic acid.

An important use for hydrobromic acid is in the manufacture of inorganic bromides and several alkyl bromides.

Bromine Halides. Bromine and chlorine react reversibly in the liquid or vapor states to form bromine chloride. Bromine chloride is useful as a brominating agent in organic synthesis. A similar compound, iodine bromide, IBr, is formed from bromine and iodine. There is also evidence of a tribromo complex, IBr_3.

Fluorine reacts violently with bromine, forming various fluorides (BrF, BrF_3, and BrF_5) depending upon the proportions taken and other conditions. The tri- and pentafluorides are commercially available. They are strong fluorinating agents and are useful in the processing of uranium.

3. *Bromine Oxides, Acids, and Salts.* Because of their great instability, oxides of bromine were long considered incapable of existence. Since 1929, however, at least three oxides have been described, together with the methods by which they may be prepared and handled at low temperatures. Bromine monoxide, Br_2O, is obtained by the reaction: $HgO + 2Br_2 \rightarrow Br_2O + HgBr_2$, in carbon tetrachloride solution, or by thermal decomposition of the dioxide, BrO_2. Below

$-40°C$ bromine monoxide is stable; at -17 to $-18°C$ in dry air it melts with decomposition. Bromine dioxide is prepared by the action of atomic oxygen on bromine at liquid-air temperature, or by the electrolysis of bromine and oxygen under the same conditions. Higher oxides, Br_2O_5 and $(Br_3O_8)_n$, have been described.

Hypobromous and bromic acids are unstable and exist only in aqueous solutions; they are strong oxidizing agents.

4. *Bromates.* Bromates may be prepared by passing bromine into a warm solution of the appropriate alkali carbonate or alkaline earth hydroxide, bromide being formed simultaneously. The bromate is generally less soluble than the bromide, so that it may be crystallized out by cooling the solution. Alkali bromates may also be prepared by electrolytic oxidation of the bromides in the presence of a depolarizing ion such as dichromate.

The alkali and alkaline earth bromates are used as oxidizing agents, liberating oxygen when heated or bromine when treated with a bromide and acid. They are also used for the treatment of flour and as a "neutralizer" or oxidizer in certain hair wave preparations. Bromates are also used as primary standards in analytical chemistry.

5. *Unusual Inorganic Compounds.* A number of new or unusual inorganic compounds containing bromine have been described recently. Two which could not have been prepared at all a few years ago are technetium oxide tribromide, $TcOBr_3$, and potassium bromotechnetate, K_2TcBr_6.

The oxide tribromide, formed from technetium dioxide and bromine at $350°C$, sublimes at $400°C$. Potassium bromotechnetate is made by evaporation of the chloro analogue or of potassium pertechnetate with hydrobromic acid. Bromides and oxide bromides of rhenium have also been studied and the following compounds have been reported: $ReBr_3$, $ReBr_4$, $ReBr_5$, $ReOBr_4$, ReO_3Br, and K_2ReBr_6.

Sulfur bromide pentafluoride, $SBrF_5$, is prepared by addition of bromine to sulfur pentafluoride at $150–200°C$.

Other unusual inorganic compounds include: bromine(I) fluorosulfate, $BrOSO_2F$; bromine(III) fluorosulfate, $Br(OSO_2F)_3$;

$Br_2.3SO_3F_2$; bromochromic acid, $HCrO_3Br$; and boron dibromide azide, $(BBr_2N_3)_3$.

Tetrafluorobromates of the higher alkali metals result from the direct addition of fluorine to the alkali bromide at 15 to 250°C.

With graphite, bromine forms lamellar compounds by penetrating between the carbon planes. Two types of such compounds are known. In those with a bromine content up to that corresponding to the composition $C_{16}Br$ (Type I), the bromine has penetrated only between some of the carbon planes and the crystallographic order is two-dimensional. On introduction of further bromine, compounds (Type II) up to composition C_8Br are obtained in which there is one bromine layer for every two carbon layers; the crystallographic order is three-dimensional, and the distance between two carbon layers with an intercalated bromine layer is 3.70 Å.

Organic Compounds

The literature describes a great many organic bromine compounds used mainly in the synthesis of other compounds. Only those compounds that have some real commercial significance are considered here and are listed in the order of their commercial importance.

1. *Ethylene Bromide.* Ethylene bromide (ethylene dibromide, 1,2-dibromoethane), CH_2BrCH_2Br, is a clear, colorless liquid with a characteristic sweet odor. It is manufactured by reacting ethylene gas with bromine.

Ethylene bromide is poisonous, and breathing of the vapor should be avoided. The liquid causes skin lesions when there is prolonged contact.

Ethylene bromide is used as an ingredient of automobile and aircraft fuels, to aid in removing lead (derived from tetraethyl- or tetramethyl lead antiknock fluid) from the engine cylinders. The next most important use is as an active ingredient of grain fumigant formulations for insect control and of soil fumigants for the control of wireworms and nematodes.

2. *Methyl Bromide.* Methyl bromide (bromomethane), CH_3Br, is a colorless, practically odorless liquid or gas manufactured by reacting hydrobromic acid with methanol.

Methyl bromide presents a serious health hazard from a toxicity standpoint. Contact of the liquid with the skin for just seconds can cause itching and blistering. The upper safe limit for daily 8-hour exposure to the vapor in air is estimated to be between 20 and 40 ppm by volume. Exposure in concentrations greater than these can cause disorders of the central nervous system and even death.

The major use for methyl bromide is in the extermination of insect and rodent pests. The material is suitable for the fumigation of food commodities and establishments in which they are processed or stored, as well as for tobacco and many kinds of nursery stock.

3. *Bromochloropropane.* 1-Bromo-3-chloropropane (trimethylene chlorobromide), $CH_2BrCH_2CH_2Cl$, is a clear, colorless liquid, prepared by hydrobromination of allyl chloride. It is widely used as a soil fumigant for the control of nematodes and rootknot disease.

4. *Bromochloromethane.* Bromochloromethane (methylene chlorobromide), CH_2BrCl, is a clear, colorless liquid with a characteristic sweet odor. Common methods of preparation involve the partial replacement of chloride in methylene chloride (dichloromethane) by reaction with aluminum bromide, by treatment with bromine and aluminum, or by reaction with hydrogen bromide in the presence of an aluminum halide catalyst, followed by water-washing and distillation.

Bromochloromethane and bromodifluoromethane are used as fire-extinguisher fluids, where their effectiveness on a weight basis offers particular advantages for use in aircraft and portable extinguishers.

Other bromine compounds are incorporated into plastics to render the latter self-extinguishing. Some that have been found useful for formulation with polymers are pentabromochlorocyclohexane, vinyl bromide, tris (2, 3-dibromopropyl) phosphate, brominated diphenyloxide, and tetrabromoisopropylidenediphenol.

5. *Ethyl Bromide.* Ethyl bromide (bromomethane), CH_3CH_2Br, is a highly volatile, clear, colorless liquid, prepared by reaction of ethanol with hydrobromic acid or with an alkali bromide and sulfuric acid. During 1962, however, a method of preparation from the γ-radiation-induced reaction of ethylene and

hydrogen bromide was announced by The Dow Chemical Company. This appears to be the first commercial-scale synthesis process catalyzed by nuclear radiation. Cobalt-60 is used as the source.

Ethyl bromide is employed mainly as an ethylating agent in synthesis, particularly of pharmaceuticals.

6. *Dyes and Indicators*. Among the dyes that contain bromine, those of the indigo group have been in greatest demand. Dibromo- and tetrabromoindigo, being brighter in color and showing better light stability and covering power than indigo, have been found especially useful.

Eosin (tetrabromofluorescein) is known both as a dye and as an adsorption indicator. Eosin Y, the disodium salt, is used as a biological stain. Substances of interest mainly as acid-base indicators are bromophenol blue, bromocresol green, bromophenol red, bromocresol purple, bromothymol blue, and dibromoxylenol blue.

7. *Pharmaceuticals*. The action of bromine-containing pharmaceuticals depends in most cases upon specific properties of the compound, but in some others upon the liberation of bromide ion.

Merbromin (Mercurochrome, the disodium salt of 2, 7-dibromo-4-hydroxymercurifluorescein), $C_{20}H_8Br_2HgNa_2O_6$, is a rather widely used antibacterial. Bromoisovalum (2-bromoisovalerylurea or bromural), $C_6H_{11}BrN_2O_2$, is a central depressant and is used as a sedative or hypnotic. Carbromal (bromodiethylacetylurea), $C_7H_{13}BrN_2O_2$, is also a depressant.

Several compounds which contain both bromine and fluorine have been proposed as general anesthetics, being volatile, non-flammable liquids which can be administered by inhalation. Best known is halothane, 2-bromo-2-chloro-1,1,1-trifluoroethane, $CF_3CHBrCl$.

2,2,2-Tribromoethanol, CBr_3CH_2OH, in solution in amylene hydrate (*t*-amyl alcohol), sometimes known as bromoethol, is used rectally as an anesthetic.

Toxicological Safety and Biological Factors

Either liquid or gaseous bromine presents a serious health hazard. The liquid rapidly attacks the skin and other tissues to produce irritation and necrosis. Exposure to the vapors can cause painful irritation to the eyes and inflamation of the respiratory tract. The maximum concentration considered safe for an eight-hour exposure is less than 1 ppm. Even at this level, bromine can be detected by its odor. Exposure to a concentration of about 10 ppm can barely be tolerated for more than a few minutes. At a concentration level of 40–60 ppm exposure of 0.5 to 1 hour constitutes a danger to life. Fatality results on short exposure to concentrations of 500 to 1000 ppm.

Plants for the manufacture or use of bromine should be designed to provide rapid disposal of spilled liquid bromine and the rapid venting of vapors. Maximum safety precautions should be taken to prevent contact of bromine with the skin and eyes. Booklets describing the safe handling of bromine can be obtained from most major manufacturers of bromine.

The toxicity and safety factors related to bromine compounds are described in the previous sections about both inorganic and organic compounds.

Many bromine compounds have important physiological aspects and many are employed in medicine as sedatives, anesthetics, antiseptics, etc. These properties and applications are described in the sections about bromine compounds, where their effects on lower forms of life are also discussed.

References

1. Brauer, Georg, "Handbook of Preparative Inorganic Chemistry," Vol. 1, 2nd Ed., Part II, Section 5, New York, Academic Press, 1963.
2. Fleck, H. Ronald, "Synthetic Drugs," London, Clever-Hume Press, Ltd., 1955.
3. Fuson, Reynold C., "Reactions of Organic Compounds," New York, John Wiley and Sons, Inc., 1962.
4. Jolles, Z. E., "Bromine and Its Compounds," London, Ernest Benn Ltd., 1966.
5. Kolthoff, I. M., and V. A. Stenger," Volumetric Analysis," Vol. 2, Ch. 8 and 10, New York, Interscience Publishers, Inc., 1947.
6. Kolthoff, I. M., and P. Elving," Treatise on Analytical Chemistry," Part II, Vol. 7, New York, John Wiley and Sons, Inc., 1960.

7. Pascal, Paul, "Nouveau Traité De Chimie Minèrale," Vol. XVII, p. 337–447, Paris, Masson et Cie, EDITEURS, 1960.
8. Stenger, V. A., "Some Advances in the Inorganic Chemistry of Bromine," *Angew. Chem. Internat. Edit.,* V. **5**, No 3, 280–287 (1966).

G. B. WENGERT
AND P. F. REIGLER

C

CADMIUM

Cadmium in Group IIB, Period 5, of the Periodic Table is a soft, bluish white metal discovered in 1817 by F. Strohmeyer, a professor of metallurgy at Gottingen, Germany. While investigating some zinc carbonate from Salzgitter, Germany, Strohmeyer found that the compound, upon heating, was yellow in color instead of white, and he concluded from further tests that the color was due to a previously unknown oxide. Separating some of this metallic oxide from the zinc carbonate by careful precipitation with hydrogen sulfide, he subsequently reduced it to metal. Strohmeyer named the metal cadmium from "cadmia," a term for calamine (zinc carbonate).

At about the same time K. S. Hermann separated a similar sulfide from some Silesian zinc ore and sent it to Strohmeyer, who identified it as the sulfide of the same metal which he had just discovered.

Occurrence

Cadmium is a relatively rare element: its abundance in the lithosphere is estimated at about 0.5 parts per million in the earth's crust. No cadmium minerals have been found in commercial quantities, and no ore is mined solely for the recovery of cadmium. The most common mineral, greenockite (cadmium sulfide), occurs chiefly as a yellow stain or coating on zinc sulfide. Cadmium minerals are also found with lead and copper ores containing zinc, and it is generally accepted that the cadmium is associated with the zinc rather than the other metals.

Nearly all major zinc deposits contain cadmium in varying amounts, with the concentrates containing from less than 0.01% to a high of about 1%. Zinc concentrates containing as much as 1% are very unusual: the content averages less than 0.5%.

Production and Statistics

Primary cadmium is recovered entirely as a by-product from zinc, zinc-lead, zinc-copper, or complex ores containing these metals; hence, the volume of such ores smelted controls the amount of cadmium produced. The recovery of cadmium from secondary sources is relatively small.

The United States and world production of cadmium for the past five years as given by the U.S. Bureau of Mines are as follows:

	World Production lb	U.S. Production lb
1961	25,700,000	10,466,000
1962	26,300,000	11,137,000
1963	26,800,000	9,990,000
1964	28,900,000	10,458,000
1965	27,800,000	9,671,000

During the past five years the United States price of cadmium as quoted by major producers has varied from a low of $1.60 per pound (1962) to a high of $3.00 per pound (1963). The price as of September 1, 1967, was $2.65 per pound.

Recovery

The first commercial process for recovering cadmium was a crude separation during reduction of zinc in a retort. Roasted zinc ore, mixed with coal or coke, was charged to a retort, which was connected to a primary condenser and a secondary condenser or "prolong." The roasted zinc ore was reduced by externally applied heat, the zinc and cadmium were vaporized, and the bulk of the zinc and some of the cadmium were condensed in the first condenser. Most of the cadmium was not caught in the primary condenser, owing to its lower boiling point, but was condensed in the prolongs as "blue powder." The blue powder, containing 3 to 5% cadmium, was again reduced with coal or coke and redistilled to give fairly pure cadmium metal and some partially oxidized cadmium powder. The powder was returned for reduction and distillation. This process was very inefficient, giving low yields of metal, and the present emphasis in zinc-retort plants is on recovery from the roasting operations and from the zinc metal itself.

There are complete descriptions of cadmium-recovery processes given in the literature, e.g., Ref. 4, and only general methods are described here.

(1) *Horizontal Zinc-Retort Plants.* In the roasting of zinc concentrates to oxidize zinc and sulfur some of the cadmium is volatilized and collected as dust or fume, usually containing 3 to 5% cadmium, in baghouses and/ or electrostatic precipitators. The resulting calcines and dust are mixed with coal or coke and sodium or zinc chloride and passed over a sintering machine. Combustion of the fuel provides the necessary temperature in the bed to allow reaction of the chloride with cadmium, lead, and some other impurities; and these are volatilized and collected, usually in an electrostatic precipitator. The zinc is not appreciably affected at the sintering temperature and remains with the sinter.

When the cadmium content of the dust is comparatively low, it is often upgraded by refuming in either a kiln or reverberatory furnace.

The dust from sintering is leached with sulfuric acid, an oxidizing agent, and water. Any lead present is precipitated as lead sulfate, and some other impurities are separated by chemical means, leaving only cadmium and copper; these are fractionally precipitated by the addition of zinc dust. The prepared sponge is distilled in a horizontal batch-type retort, yielding cadmium blue powder, and residue.

(2) *Vertical Zinc-Retort Plants.* Cadmium may also be recovered directly from cadmium-bearing zinc by direct distillation. Employing the principles of rectification in this distillation, high-boiling impurities (such as lead) and low-boiling impurities (such as cadmium) can be separated from relatively impure zinc. Lead has a boiling point of 1740°C; zinc, 905°C; and cadmium 767°C. None of these elements forms constant boiling mixtures or stable compounds with each other that vaporize without dissociation; therefore, they lend themselves to separation by fractional distillation.

(3) *Electrolytic Plants.* In the electrolytic zinc process cadmium and copper are taken into solution with the zinc in the sulfuric acid leach of the roasted zinc ore. Zinc dust is added to precipitate many of the objectionable impurities. A limited amount of zinc dust is first added to give a high-copper precipitate, and then an excess of dust is added to the filtrate to yield a zincky, high-cadmium precipitate, which is the feed to the cadmium plant. This spongy precipitate is oxidized, dissolved in dilute sulfuric acid, and electrolyzed at 2.6 to 2.7 volts and 4 to 10 amp/sq ft. using aluminum cathodes and lead or "Duriron" anodes. Cathodes are stripped regularly, and the cadmium is washed, dried, melted in an iron pot under caustic soda or rosin to prevent excessive oxidation, and cast into desired shapes. About 40% of the cadmium produced is derived from electrolytic zinc plants.

Physical Constants

Atomic number	48
Atomic weight	112.40
Boiling point	767°C (1413°F)
Crystal structure	Close-packed hexagonal
Density at 20°C (68°F)	
g/cc	8.65
lb/cu in.	0.313
Electrical resistivity microhm-cm	
(solid) 0°C (32°F)	6.83
(liquid) 400°C (752°F)	33.7
(liquid) 700°C (1292°F)	35.8
Electrochemical equivalent	
Cd^{++}, mg/coulomb	0.5824
Electrode reduction potential	
Cd^{++} ($H_2 = 0.0$ volt)	0.40

Index of refraction

(liquid) 4360 Å	39
(solid) 6300 Å	1.13
Latent heat of fusion, cal/g	13.2
Latent heat of vaporization, cal/g	286.4

Linear coefficient of thermal expansion,

microinches/in/°C, 25°C (77°F)	29.8
321–540°C (610–1004°F)	150

Mechanical properties

Tensile strength, psi	10,000
Elongation, % in 1 inch	50
Brinell hardness	21
Modulus of elasticity, psi	8.0×10^6
Melting point	321°C (610°F)
Volume expansion on melting	5.1%

Nuclear data

Stable isotopes: (106, 108, 110, 111, 112, 113, 114, 116)	8

Thermal neutron cross section, 2200m/s

Absorption, barns	2500
Scattering, barns	7
Resonance absorption integral, barns	(not known)
Solidification shrinkage, %	4.74

Specific heat, cal/g/°C

(liquid) 321°C–700°C	0.0632
(solid) 25°C	0.055

Specific volume, cc/g

20°C (68°F)	0.1156
330°C (626°F)	0.1248

Surface tension, dyne/cm

330°C (626°F)	564
370°C (698°F)	608
420°C (788°F)	598
450°C (842°F)	611
500°C (932°F)	600

Thermal conductivity, cal/cm²/cm/°C/sec

20°C (68°F)	0.22
358°C (676°F)	0.105
435°C (815°F)	0.119
Valence	+2

Vapor pressure, mm Hg

394°C (741°F)	1.0
578°C (1072°F)	60
711°C (1312°F)	400
767°C (1413°F)	760

Viscosity, dyne/sec/cm², poise

349°C (660°F)	0.0144
603°C (1117°F)	0.0110

Chemical Properties

Cadmium is almost always divalent, the only two probable monovalent compounds being cadmium suboxide, Cd_2O, and cadmous chloride, Cd_2Cl_2.

Cadmium is unaffected by dry air but oxidizes readily in moist air with formation of a protective coating of oxides. The corrosion resistance of cadmium is good in rural atmospheres, but in industrial atmospheres (particularly where SO_2 or SO_3 is present) corrosion is rapid.

Most inorganic acids and some organic acids will dissolve cadmium, nitric acid being the best of the acid solvents. Unlike zinc, cadmium is not amphoteric and, hence, is not soluble in alkalis. Descriptions and characteristics of the more important cadmium compounds are given below.

Cadmium Sulfide, CdS. Cadmium sulfide is usually prepared by passing hydrogen sulfide through acid solutions of the salts, most commonly sulfates. The color of the precipitated compound varies from light yellow to brown, dependent on particle size. The precipitate may be amorphous or crystalline, the crystalline form being either alpha hexagonal or beta cubic. Cadmium sulfide is used as a pigment to color ceramics, paints, and plastics from light yellow to deep maroon where excellent color retention is required.

Cadmium Cyanide. Cadmium cyanide, $Cd(CN)_2$, is obtained as a white precipitate when potassium or sodium cyanide is added to a strong solution of a cadmium salt. A complex ion is formed when it is dissolved in an excess of the precipitating agent, and a solution of this complex ion is used as an electrolyte for electrodeposition of cadmium.

Cadmium Halides. The halides of cadmium can be readily made by dissolving the metal or oxide in the appropriate acid and evaporating to dryness in a nonoxidizing atmosphere. All of the halides are soluble in water, acids, and alcohols. There are minor uses of these salts on photography and lithography.

Cadmium Nitrate. Cadmium nitrate, $Cd(NO_3)_2$, is readily made by dissolving cadmium metal, oxide, or carbonate in nitric acid and evaporating to incipient crystallization. The white hygroscopic crystals are soluble in water, alcohol, and liquid ammonia.

Cadmium Oxide. Cadmium oxide, CdO, exists as cubic crystals and as a colorless amorphous powder. The crystals can vary in color from yellowish brown to dark red and are soluble in acids and alkalis. To make cadmium oxide, the metal is distilled in a retort and the vapor permitted to react with air and the product collected in a baghouse. There are many uses of the oxide, such as making plating solutions and electrodes of storage batteries.

Uses

The major use of cadmium is for plating articles to form a protective coating (mainly on iron and steel); most of this plating is done by electrodeposition. Cadmium is much easier to deposit evenly and smoothly than zinc, and such cadmium coatings have greater resistance to atmospheric and galvanic corrosion than do zinc coatings. Further, cadmium is resistent to alkalis whereas zinc is attacked by caustic solutions.

Although cadmium can be deposited from acid baths, such as sulfate or fluoborate, practically all commercial plating is done from cyanide baths. These baths are essentially solutions of cadmium oxide and sodium cyanide in water, and a typical formula is cadmium oxide, 32 gpl and sodium cyanide, 75 gpl.

The cadmium concentration is not critical and may be as much as 50% higher or lower and still obtain a good deposition. Brighteners are usually added to the bath, and there are a great many commercially available. Plating is done at room temperature with commercially pure cadmium anodes with current densities at the anodes up to 20 amp/sq ft and at the cathodes from 5 to 50 amp/sq ft. An important use for cadmium is in the nickel-cadmium storage battery. In one type of cell the negative plates comprise iron or nickel grids with sponge cadmium as the active agent, and the positive plates (also of iron or nickel grids) have a nickel oxide as the active ingredient. The electrolyte is an aqueous solution of potassium hydroxide. The nickel-cadmium battery has some important advantages: long service life, excellent shelf life, and a wide operating range: from -65 to $165°F$.

Cadmium is used in many alloys such as bearing metals, solders, electrical conductors, fusible metals, and jewelry. Cadmium-base bearing alloys are used in heavy-duty applications that operate at elevated temperatures.

There are two types: one containing about 1% nickel and the remainder cadmium, the other containing 0.7% silver and 0.6% copper with 98% or more of cadmium.

Alloys of silver and cadmium, along with varying proportions of copper, zinc, and sometimes other metals, are widely used for brazing. These series of alloys can be used to make satisfactory joints with both ferrous and nonferrous metals. Some of them have been successfully used with such difficult materials as tungsten, tungsten carbide, and molybdenum. Certain of these solders are used, with or without gold, in the jewelry trade.

Low-melting alloys, containing varying quantities of bismuth, lead, tin, and cadmium, are used in sprinkler systems, fire detection units, and similar applications as well as for low-temperature brazing and soldering. Some of these alloys are used for proof casting of materials where accurate casting is important.

Copper containing 0.7 to 1.0% cadmium is very ductile and has found wide use in telegraphic, telephonic, and power transmission wires since cadmium imparts good tensile strength, hardness, and high annealing temperature and does not seriously impair the conductivity. It is most useful as trolley wire where its high strength, high conductivity, and resistance to wear are of prime importance.

Cadmium absorbs low-energy (thermal) neutrons readily; and, when rods of cadmium are inserted in a nuclear reactor, this absorption of thermal neutrons provides a means for controlling the fission process. The rate of nuclear fission can be controlled to provide the desired energy by proper adjustment of the cadmium rods.

Graphite impregnated with cadmium is used in oilless bearings and bushing linings and for electrical purposes, chiefly brushes and contacts for controller switches.

In the electronics industry cadmium is used as a counter-electrode for selenium rectifiers and in television phosphors. High-purity, crystalline cadmium sulfide is being used in photovoltaic cells, radiation detection devices, infrared windows, and photosensitive devices. One of the intriguing uses is in solar cells for conversion of sunlight into electrical energy.

Cadmium sulfide and cadmium sulfoselenide are used extensively for pigments where

93

extreme color retention is required. These compounds are often extended with barium sulfate, in which case they are known as cadmium lithopones. Some of the commoner uses of these pigments are in durable machinery enamels and finishes, coated fabrics, plastics, baking enamels, and ceramic glazes. In certain formulations cadmium serves as a basic reaction stabilizer in PVC plastics.

Toxicity

Cadmium is one of the most toxic of metals. The main route of absorption of cadmium during industrial exposure is by inhalation and industrial processes which generate cadmium dust or fume should be well ventilated, preferably by local exhaust hoods. Workmen should wear respirators approved by the U.S. Bureau of Mines when exposures to excessive dust or fume are unavoidable. The recommended maximum atmospheric concentration of cadmium oxide fume (8-hour daily exposures) has been set at 0.1 mg per cubic meter by the American Conference of Governmental Industrial Hygienists.

Operations in which cadmium-containing materials are subjected to temperatures high enough to vaporize the metal, as in electric welding, are especially dangerous. A single exposure to high concentrations of freshly generated cadmium oxide fume can cause severe pulmonary irritation and even death. During the first few hours following exposure there may be no noticeable symptoms except for dryness of the throat and a tightness in the chest. These symptoms progress to coughing, shortness of breath, chest pain, and eventually to pneumonitis.

Repeated exposures to lower levels of cadmium fume or dust may cause emphysema with abnormal lung function and the excretion of a specific low molecular weight protein in the urine. Absorbed cadmium is excreted slowly from the body.

Acute illnesses from ingestion of cadmium leached from cadmium-plated containers by acid foods have been reported. Death from ingestion is rare, however, for cadmium acts as a violent emetic and usually not enough of the metal is absorbed to cause serious damage.

References

1. Atomic Energy Commission, "Liquid Metals Handbook," 2d Ed., Washington, D.C., Government Printing Office, 1952.
2. Dickinson, S. J., and Greene, G. U., "Encyclopedia of Chemical Technology," R. E. Kirk and D. F. Othmer, Editors, pp. 716–738, New York, Interscience Publishers, 1948.
3. McCutcheon, F. G., and Musgrave, J. R., "Rare Metals Handbook," C. A. Hampel, Editor, 2nd Ed., pp. 82–92, New York, Reinhold Publishing Corp., 1961.
4. Mathewson, C. H., "Zinc, The Metal, Its Alloys and Compounds," New York, Reinhold Publishing Corp., 1959.
5. Mentch, R. L., and Lansche, A. M., U.S. Bureau of Mines Information Circular No. 7881, 1958.

A. A. SMITH, JR.

CALCIUM

Calcium, symbol Ca, atomic number 20, atomic weight 40.08 is in Group IIA of the Periodic Table which contains the alkaline earth metals, calcium, strontium, barium, and radium. The last is known primarily in the form of its salts and, to date, has no metal application.

In the older chemistries, all the nonmetallic substances that were insoluble in water and unchanged by fire were called *earths*. Lime and magnesia showed alkaline reactions, hence they were termed *alkaline* earths. Calcium is derived from the Latin *calx* (lime); barium from the Greek *barys* (heavy); and strontium from Strontian, a town in Scotland. All three metals were first isolated by Davy, in 1808, by electrolysis of the fused chlorides.

Of the alkaline earth group, calcium has achieved the greatest use and tonnage. Calcium ranks fifth in the order of abundance of elements in the earth's crust, the percentage being estimated at 3.64; strontium is eighteenth, with a percentage of 0.03; and barium is nineteenth, with a percentage of 0.025.

In general, the metals are white and differ from each other by shades of color or casts. They are malleable, extrudable, and machinable, and may be made into rods, wire, or plate. They are less reactive than sodium and potassium, and they have higher melting and boiling points. Their common ores are the sulfates and carbonates, and they form analogous chlorides, peroxides, nitrates, chlorates (in all of which they are bivalent), true carbides, and acetylides. A typical acetylide is calcium carbide, CaC_2, which upon reaction with water gives acetylene. The volatilizable salts give intense flame colors, that of barium being green, calcium a brilliant crimson with a yellowish shade, and strontium a brilliant crimson without the yellow component. The nitrates, chlorides, and chlorates of strontium and barium compounds are used in pyrotechnics in the form of signals, flares, and fuses.

Occurrence

Calcium in compound form is one of the most widely distributed elements. It is present in the earth's crust as calcium carbonate (marble, chalk, limestone and calcite), calcium sulfate (anhydrite, $CaSO_4$, and gypsum, $CaSO_4 \cdot 2H_2O$), calcium fluoride (fluorspar or fluorite), calcium phosphate (apatite), and numerous silicates and aluminosilicates. Almost all natural waters, including sea water, contain either or both calcium carbonate and calcium sulfate. In addition, most natural salt deposits contain calcium in the form of the sulfate, carbonate or chloride.

Many organisms concentrate calcium compounds in their shells or skeletons and aggregations of these comprise important deposits of calcium compounds. For example, calcium carbonate is formed in the shells of oysters, clams and foraminifera, and in the skeletons of coral. Calcium phosphate is a major constituent of the bones of animals and deposits of fossil origin make up a large part of the phosphate rock in this country.

Derivation

During World War II the United States obtained its supply of calcium by the electrolysis of fused calcium chloride as a primary source, and in later years by thermal processes under high vacuum from lime reduced with aluminum. In operations involving the preparation of lead-calcium alloys, calcium carbide may serve as the source of calcium metal. Silicon has not been found useful as a reducing agent at 1200°C (2192°F), the temperature limit of the retorts employed. Operating details for the electrolytic produc-

tion of calcium in Europe are given by Mantell.

Pidgeon and Atkinson report the vapor pressure of calcium, above a reaction mass of calcium oxide and aluminum which form calcium and $CaO \cdot Al_2O_3$, to vary from 1.0 to 1.3 mm Hg from 1150–1200°C (2102–2192°F). It is suggested that the reaction proceeds by reduction of calcium oxide with aluminum vapor.

A method for the production of metallic calcium by thermal reduction of lime has been patented by Pidgeon and McCatty. Finely ground lime, containing not more than 3% impurities and not more than 1% magnesium oxide, is briquetted with a 5 to 20% excess of powdered aluminum as a reducing agent. The briquettes are heated in a vacuum of 10μ or better to about 1170°C (2138°F). A retort is used, so designed that the calcium vapor is condensed in a zone maintained at 740–680°C (1364–1256°F). The magnesium vapor is condensed in a zone maintained in the range of 350–275°C (662–527°F). A mixture of the two metals condenses in an intermediate zone where the temperature is 485–400°C (965–752°F). The reactions which take place when the briquettes are heated are described by:

$$5CaO + 2Al \rightarrow 3Ca + (CaO)_2Al_2O_3$$

$$3MgO + 2CaO + 2Al \rightarrow 3Mg + (CaO)_2Al_2O_3$$

TABLE 1. THERMAL REDUCTION BY ALUMINUM

Raw material	Calcined pure limestone (CaO), 200 mesh
Reducing agent	96 to 99% aluminum, 20 mesh
Temperature	1200°C (2192°F)
Pressure	20μ
Retort materials	28% Cr, 15% Ni, balance Fe
Retort size	10 in. diameter, 10 ft long, 1.1 in. thick
Calcium purity	Mg 0.50 to 1.0; Al 0.01 to 0.2; Mn 0.005 to 0.02; N under 0.02%; chlorides none; alkalies none; Ca 98–99%
Time of cycle	12 hr
Reaction	$6CaO + 2Al \rightarrow 3Ca + 3CaO \cdot Al_2O_3$

Manufacturing details of the production of calcium by the aluminum process are given in Table 1.

The Downs cell for the electrolysis of fused salt produces a sodium metal containing calcium. (See **Sodium**.) The calcium crystallizes out of solution and is filtered from the liquid sodium. This is a third source of calcium metal and calcium-sodium material.

The Ethyl Corporation has developed procedures for the recovery of calcium from sludges containing calcium and sodium and formed in electrolytic processes for the manufacture of sodium from a mixture of sodium chloride and calcium chloride, while simultaneously producing a higher alcohol from a lower one, by treatment with a lower aliphatic alcohol. The calcium freed by this process is recovered, washed, and dried.

Physical Properties

The tensile properties of calcium metal are greatly affected by impurities, and, in the pure forms, by methods of fabrication. Calcium metal work-hardens upon mechanical processing, as is shown by the values for yield point and ultimate strength as well as elongation and reduction in area in the as-rolled and annealed condition.

Bulk calcium is a soft, crystalline metal which is both ductile and malleable. It may readily be extruded on heating to 420–460°C (788–860°F). It exists in two allotropic crystalline forms—the alpha form below 464°C (867°F) and the beta form above 464°C.

Freshly cut surfaces of calcium are white, approximately the color of silver (See Fig. 1).

FIG. 1. Redistilled crystals of metallic calcium.

Fractured surfaces are more brilliant than steel. At relative humidities above 30% the metal tarnishes, with the formation of thin, bluish-gray films of oxide which are protective against further attack. Commercial calcium as a cast slab 2 in. (5.08 cm) thick, exposed to the atmosphere under average conditions, corrodes to depths of $\frac{1}{4}$ in. (0.635 cm) in 6 months' time.

The physical properties of massive calcium are presented in Table 2. There is some uncertainty as to their accuracy, however, because of the effect of certain impurities which are difficult to remove from the bulk metal. For example, less than 1 weight % of combined nitrogen reduces the melting point of calcium from its normal value of 851°C (1564°F) to as low as 780°C (1436°F). Other properties are also affected.

The heat capacity of the low-temperature (alpha) form of calcium is given in terms of calories per gram atom per degree centigrade by the following equation (T in °K):

$$C_p = 5.24 + 3.50 \times 10^{-3} \, T$$

For the high-temperature (beta) form, the corresponding equation is

$$C_p = 6.29 + 1.40 \times 10^{-3} \, T$$

Debye-Scherrer photographs are interpreted as showing that calcium exists in three allotropic modifications, viz., alpha calcium, face-centered cubic; beta calcium, hexagonal close-packed; and gamma calcium, body-centered cubic, the transition points lying at about 250 and 450°C (482 and 842°F). The observed lattice constants of the three modifications are closely related to those of the analogous modifications of strontium.

X-ray diffraction patterns of calcium samples of different purities show that 99.9 + % calcium exists in only two allotropic forms: face-centered cubic to 464°C (867°F) and body-centered cubic from 464°C to the melting point. The temperature dependence of the electrical resistivity of the 99.9 + % calcium is linear for both the face-centered cubic allotrope and for the body-centered cubic allotrope. Calcium is self-annealing at room temperature.

The energy of combustion is 15,806 joules/g. The corresponding standard heat of formation of the oxide, CaO, from the elements is

TABLE 2. PHYSICAL PROPERTIES OF CALCIUM

Atomic number	20
Atomic volume, cc/g-atom	25.9
Atomic weight	40.08
Boiling point	1482°C (2700°F)
Color	White, approximating silver
Compressibility	
At 30°C (86°F)	
0 atm pressure	5.885×10^{-6}
11,600 atm pressure	5.300×10^{-6}
At 20°C (68°F)	
99–493 atm pressure	5.8×10^{-6}
100–500 megabars/sq cm	5.7×10^{-6}
$\text{Compressibility} = -\dfrac{1}{\text{vol (cc)}} \times \dfrac{\varDelta \text{ vol (cc)}}{\varDelta \text{ pressure (atm)}}$	
Crystal structure	Face-centered cubic, a = 5.56 kX
Density, g/cc	
At 20°C (68°F)	1.54 (0.056 lb/cu in.)
At 450°C (842°F) alpha phase in extruded wire	1.48
At 480°C (896°F) beta phase	1.52
Elastic limit, psi	1,470
Electrical resistivity, microhm-cm	
At 0°C (32°F)	3.43
At 20°C (68°F)	4.6
At 21°C (70°F)	
As rolled	4.24–4.50
Annealed	4.04–4.11
Electrochemical equivalent (valence two),	
mg/coulomb	0.20762
coulomb/mg	4.81640
Electrolytic solution potential versus hydrogen, volts	−2.76
Electron configuration	2–8–8–2
Entropy, cal/°C/g-atom	
Solid [25°C (77°F)]	9.95
Gas [25°C (77°F)]	37.00
Erichsen value on 1/32-in. sheet	
As rolled	3.55–3.6
Annealed	11.1
Hardness number, cast slab	
Brinell (500-kg load)	17
Rockwell (15-kg load, 1/16-in. ball)	42 as rolled
Mohs	2
Heat capacity, cal/g/°C, (specific heat)	
Alpha phase [0–460°C (32–860°F)]	0.17
Beta phase [460–851°C (860–1564°F)]	0.19
liquid [851–1200°C (1564–2192°F)]	0.19
Heat of combustion, cal/g	151.9
Heat of fusion, kcal/g-atom	2.23
Heat of transition, kcal/g-atom	0.115
Heat of vaporization, kcal/g-atom 1482°C (2700°F)	36.7
Isotopes (stable)	40, 42, 43, 44, 46, 48
Mass magnetic susceptibility, cgs	$+1.10 \times 10^{-6}$
Melting point,	
°C	851
°F	1564
Minimum interatomic distance, kX	3.93
Modulus of elasticity, psi	$3–4 \times 10^6$

TABLE 2—*continued*

Specific heat, cal/g/°C	
−185–20°C (−301–68°F)	0.157
0–100°C (32–212°F)	0.149
460–851°C (752–1564°F)	0.19
Surface tension, dynes/cm	255
Temperature coefficient of electrical resistivity, per °C at 20°C (68°F)	0.00457
Tensile properties	
Yield strength, psi	
As rolled	12,300
Annealed	1,990
Ultimate strength, psi	
As rolled	16,700
Annealed	6,960
Elongation in 1 in., %	
As rolled	7
Annealed	51
Reduction in area, %	
As rolled	35
Annealed	58
Thermal conductivity, cal/sec/cm/°C, 20°	0.3, same order as that of sodium and other alkali metals
Thermal expansion, per °C	
Linear [0°–300°C (32–570°F)]	0.0000220
Cubic [0–21°C (32–70°F)]	0.000717
Thermal neutron absorption cross section, barns/atom	0.43
Transition temperature, °C alpha to beta	464 ± 4
Valence	2
Volume conductivity referred to standard copper, %	48.7

TABLE 3. ISOTOPES OF CALCIUM

Isotope	Half-life	Primary Radiations Type of Decay	Gamma Rays	Method of Preparation
Ca^{38}	0.66 sec	β^+	3.5 MeV	
Ca^{39}	1.0 sec	β^+ 6.1 MeV	(none)	Ca^{40} + gamma rays
Ca^{40}	Stable—96.97%			
Ca^{41}	1.1×10^5 yr	EC (100%)	(none)	Ca^{40} + neutrons
Ca^{42}	Stable—0.64%			
Ca^{43}	Stable—0.145%			
Ca^{44}	Stable—2.06%			
Ca^{45}	164 days	β^- 0.254 (100%)	(none)	Ca^{44} + neutrons
Ca^{46}	Stable—0.0033%			
Ca^{47}	4.7 days	β^- 1.94 (17%) 0.66 (83%)	1.29 (71%) 0.81 (5%) 0.50 (5%)	Ca^{46} + neutrons
Ca^{48}	Stable—0.185%			
Ca^{49}	8.8 min	β^- 2.1 (89%) ~1.0 (11%)	3.07 (89%) 4.04 (10%) 4.7 (0.8%)	Ca^{48} + neutrons

calculated to be -635.09 ± 0.89 kjoules/mole. X-ray examination of the combustion products shows only the lines of CaO.

Estimated surface tension values of the alkaline earth metals at their respective melting points, in ergs per square centimeter, are 195 for barium, 255 for calcium, and 165 for strontium.

For equal dimensions, the specific and relative resistances of calcium, in comparison with copper, aluminum, and sodium, follow:

	Specific Resistance, microhm-cm	Relative Resistance
International annealed copper standard	1.724	1.00
Calcium	4.53	2.63
Aluminum	2.83	1.64
Sodium	4.8	2.79

For equal weights and lengths, the relative resistance values are:

	Density, g/cc	Relative Resistance
Copper	8.92	1.00
Calcium	1.55	0.46
Aluminum	2.70	0.50
Sodium	0.97	0.30

Calcium has a number of isotopes whose half-lives and other data are detailed in Table 3.

Mechanical Properties

Distilled calcium shows an elongation of 53%, whereas extruded wire gives 61%, 98.5% calcium gives 30.5%, and impure materials (94 to 96%) show no elongation. The modulus of elasticity of distilled calcium varies between 32×10^5 and 38×10^5 psi. No creep is observed on loading calcium with less than 570 psi at room temperature. Crushing tests show complete recrystallization of calcium at 300°C (572°F), and above, during deformation. The pressure required for deformation decreases with the temperature and has a sharp break at 440°C (824°F), a little below the transformation temperature. Above

460°C (860°F), calcium deforms plastically under very small loads. Calcium wire can be easily extruded between 420 and 460°C (788 and 860°F). Values for mechanical properties are given in Table 2.

Calcium metal may be handled in a manner similar to magnesium and aluminum. It may be touched and may come in contact with the skin without danger. It can be machined in a lathe, turned into shapes, drilled, threaded, sawed, extruded, drawn into wire, pressed, and hammered into plates.

Calcium cannot be cast by the usual foundry methods, owing to rapid oxidation at the melting point, but melting and casting procedures employing protective fluxes give cast forms of the metal.

Chemical Properties

Calcium is not readily attacked by dry air or oxygen at room temperature, but in moist air a coating of calcium oxide rapidly forms on its surface. Water reacts with calcium to form $Ca(OH)_2$ with evolution of hydrogen. The element reacts when heated with oxygen, nitrogen, hydrogen, halogens, boron, sulfur, carbon and phosphorus to form binary compounds. It is attacked by acids to form salts.

Calcium is a good reducing agent and will react with the oxides or halides of most metals to form the corresponding metal.

In all of its compounds calcium is divalent.

Principal Compounds

Calcium carbonate, $CaCO_3$, is the most important calcium compound and the quantity mined and consumed is probably the largest of any raw material used by the chemical industry. Even greater tonnages are consumed in the steel industry as a fluxing agent and in the manufacture of cement, mortars, plasters, refractories and glass.

Limestone is calcium carbonate in an indistinctly crystalline and massive form. It is found throughout the United States. All varieties of calcium carbonate are almost insoluble in pure water but dissolve appreciably in the presence of carbon dioxide because of the formation of calcium hydrogen carbonate (bicarbonate):

$$CaCO_3 + H_2O + CO_2 \rightleftharpoons Ca^{++} + 2HCO_3^-$$

99

It is by this reaction that limestone is dissolved, often resulting in the formation of caves. Natural waters containing $CaCO_3$ are called hard waters. The action is reversible; and in many regions the underground waters, carrying large quantities of the carbonate, lose carbon dioxide on exposure in caves and deposit limestone. Travertime, used as a building stone, is a white concretionary calcium carbonate deposited by some springs when pressure on the water is suddenly released, permitting the rapid escape of CO_2.

For use in the chemical industry most calcium carbonate is first converted to lime, CaO, which is the raw material in the manufacture of sodium carbonate by the ammonia soda process, of calcium carbide, of calcium bisulfite used in the sulfite pulping process, and of a great variety of other chemicals and manufactured products.

Calcium oxide is commonly prepared by decomposing the carbonate in large vertical shaft kilns or rotary kilns at temperatures below 1200°C. Carbon dioxide is also formed by the reaction. Calcium oxide is a white solid, often called quicklime. It slakes or reacts with water to form calcium hydroxide, $Ca(OH)_2$, the form in which lime is most commonly used in the chemical industry.

Calcium fluoride, CaF_2, is used as a flux, but more important, is the source of hydrofluoric acid made by the action of sulfuric acid on fluorspar. Fluorinated organic compounds, such as the "Freons," used in the rapidly expanding aerosol industry, are made from HF.

Calcium bisulfate, $Ca(HSO_3)_2$, is made by the reaction of SO_2 with a slurry of $Ca(OH)_2$ at those paper mills which use it in the sulfite process for the separation of cellulose from wood. The wood in the form of chips is digested under pressure in a solution of calcium bisulfite whereby the lignin is solubilized to leave cellulose fibers that are converted into paper.

Calcium carbide, CaC_2 is made by heating a mixture of calcium oxide and carbon in large electric furnaces at a temperature of 1800 to 2100°C. The furnaces range from 30,000 to 50,000 kw in size and each produces 250 to 400 tons/day of calcium carbide. More than 99% of over one million tons produced annually in the United States is used for the generation of acetylene by the reaction: $CaC_2 + 2H_2O \rightarrow C_2H_2 + Ca(OH)_2$. Additional calcium carbide is made as an intermediate in the production of *calcium cyanamide,* $CaCN_2$, by the action of nitrogen on hot CaC_2: $CaC_2 + N_2 \rightarrow CaCN_2 + C$. This in turn is used to prepare calcium cyanide, hydrogen cyanide and melamine. Calcium cyanamide is also a nitrogen fertilizer and a source of ammonia since it reacts with water to form ammonia: $CaCN_2 + 3H_2O \rightarrow CaCO_3 + 2NH_3$.

Calcium phosphates occur abundantly in nature. Phosphate rock, which is substantially normal or tertiary calcium phosphate, $Ca_3(PO_4)_2$, and apatite, $Ca_5F(PO_4)_3$, are the principal minerals from which phosphate fertilizers and a host of phosphorus compounds are derived. About 40 million tons of phosphate rock are mined annually in the United States. In general two processes are used to convert these minerals to useful products. In one they are treated with sulfuric acid or phosphoric acid to form primary calcium phosphate, $Ca(H_2PO_4)_2$, which can be applied directly as a fertilizer or which can be converted to a variety of sodium phosphates by subsequent reaction with sodium carbonate. Orthophosphoric acid, H_3PO_4, is made by the use of additional sulfuric acid on the rock. In the other process the phosphate minerals are mixed with silica and carbon and reduced in an electric furnace to form elemental phosphorus. The latter is burned in air to produce phosphorus pentoxide, P_2O_5, which is then reacted with water to yield orthophosphoric acid.

Calcium chloride, $CaCl_2$, occurs in nature as tachhydrite, $CaCl_2 \cdot 2MgCl_2 \cdot 12H_2O$, and in some other minerals and also to the extent of about 0.15% in sea water. A considerable amount is removed from salt brines. It is chiefly obtained as a by-product of the ammonia soda and other chemical processes. Upon evaporation of its aqueous solution the hexahydrate, $CaCl_2 \cdot 6H_2O$, is obtained, and by partial dehydration it is converted into a porous mass which is used for drying gases and liquids. Calcium chloride is very soluble in water; for this reason it gives with ice an excellent freezing mixture. With the hexahydrate and crushed ice a temperature as low as −50°C can be reached. A solution of the salt is used as a refrigerating brine in cold-storage plants and in the manufacture of ice. Because of its deliquescent property it is sprinkled on roads to prevent ice formation and (in solution) in mines to decrease the danger of explosion from dust.

Anhydrous *calcium sulfate* occurs in nature as the mineral anhydrite, crystallized in rhombic prisms. The dihydrate or gypsum, $CaSO_4 \cdot 2H_2O$, however, is more common and plentiful. Three general groups of gypsum products—uncalcined, calcined building and calcined industrial—are sold. Uncalcined gypsum is used as a Portland cement retarder to prevent too rapid hardening, and as a soil corrector in agriculture. Calcined gypsum is employed in making tile, wallboard, lath, and various kinds of plasters. When gypsum is heated to about 125°C it loses three-fourths of its water of hydration and forms the hemi-hydrate, $2CaSO_4 \cdot H_2O$, or plaster of Paris. The resulting product is ground to a fine white powder. When this is mixed with water it forms a plastic mass which sets quickly to a coherent white solid consisting of small tangled crystals of more highly hydrated calcium sulfate.

Calcium hydride is formed when calcium metal combines with hydrogen gas. The reaction is reversible, and the hydrogen can be released by heating the hydride. Calcium hydride is stable at room temperature and is a useful source of hydrogen, since twice the volume of hydrogen is released when the hydride is slaked in water, as compared to that produced by a substantially equivalent weight of calcium metal. For hydrogen generation in isolated locations, calcium hydride offers attractive possibilities.

Applications

Calcium is more reactive chemically than barium or strontium, but considerably less reactive than sodium. Calcium is the cheapest of the alkaline earth metals but is more expensive than sodium; sodium is a fraction of the price of calcium, and the production of sodium is more than 100 times that of calcium. In organic synthesis, sodium is in a better competitive position, in metallurgical work, however, the low melting point and high vapor pressure of sodium are disadvantages in deoxidizing, reducing, degasifying, and alloy-ing, and the less volatile calcium is preferred. In addition, the end products of the sodium reactions are more volatile and of lower melting point than the corresponding end products of the calcium reactions. Calcium metal itself competes even in metallurgical work, with some of its own compounds, examples of which are calcium silicide, calcium boride, and calcium carbide, all of which are used as degasifiers, reductants, and sources of calcium for alloys. Often, however, in alloy work, examples of which are the nickel-chromium and nickel-chromium-iron materials for high-temperature service, these compounds may introduce undesirable materials from which the metallic calcium is free.

The metallurgical applications of calcium depend upon its reactivity at high temperatures with the formation of nitrides, silicides, and carbides such as Ca_2C (in contrast to acetylides like CaC_2), which are quite stable. At lower temperatures, stable hydrides, of which calcium hydride is typical, are formed. In the manufacture of electronic tubes the ability to fix residual gases as oxides, nitrides, and, to a lesser extent, hydrides, makes calcium a useful important "getter."

Calcium metal is employed as an alloying agent for aluminum and for bearing metals of the lead-calcium or lead-barium-calcium type; as an alloying agent and a deoxidizer for copper; as an alloying agent for the production of the age-hardening lead alloys for cable sheaths, battery plates, and related uses; as a modifying agent for magnesium and aluminum; as a debismuthizer for lead; as a controller for graphitic carbon in cast iron; as a carburizer and desulfurizer as well as a deoxidizer for numerous alloys, such as chromium-nickel, copper, iron, iron-nickel, nickel, nickel-cobalt, nickel-chromium-iron, nickel bronzes, steel, and tin bronzes; as an evacuating agent; as a reducing agent in the preparation of beryllium, chromium metal powder, hafnium, rare earth metals, scandium, yttrium, plutonium, thorium, uranium, titanium, vanadium, and zirconium; and as a separator for argon from nitrogen. Typical of these applications is the addition of 0.25% calcium to magnesium alloys to refine the grain structure, to reduce the tendency to take fire, and to modify the strengthening heat treatments. Other examples are the precipitation-hardening lead-calcium alloys. The solid solubility of calcium in lead is of the order of 0.1 % at the melting point and decreases rapidly with reduction of temperature so that precipitation hardening takes place, since at ordinary temperatures the solid solubility is of the order of 0.01%.

Details about the important use of calcium as a reducing agent in the preparation of the list of rare metals mentioned above are given in the entries about these metals in other parts of this book. In addition to its reducing power, the low vapor pressure and high melting point of calcium make it the preferred agent for this application.

Calcium Alloys

Among the alloys of calcium that are of commercial importance is calcium-silicon, made as an electric furnace product from lime, silica, and a carbonaceous reducing agent.

Calcium-silicon alloy is used as a deoxidizer and degasifier in the production of steel. It is also used in making high-tensile-strength gray irons.

In steelmaking, calcium-silicon alloy is used both as a furnace and a ladle addition. Both calcium and silicon are active deoxidizers, and their reaction products form a low-melting-point slag which frees itself readily from the metal, thus producing a clean steel. Calcium-silicon alloy also improves the fluidity of liquid steel. In open hearth practice this alloy is added in the ladle; in electric furnace practice it may be added either in the furnace or in the ladle.

In basic electric furnace practice the calcium-silicon alloy finds wide application for quick deoxidation of both metal bath and slag. It is usually used in crushed form, 2 in. or less in size.

In acid electric steelmaking, final additions of deoxidizing alloys are made primarily to prevent the evolution of gas and the formation of blowholes during solidification, although other effects, such as improved toughness, may also be obtained.

The amounts of calcium-silicon commonly used range from 1 to 6 lb/ton of steel, with 2 to 4 lb being the average.

Calcium-manganese-silicon alloy is sometimes used by steelmakers in place of calcium-silicon because it provides three active elements in proper balance to produce low-melting-point-reaction products which coalesce and become liberated easily from the molten metal. This alloy is a cleanser for oxides, gases, and nonmetallic impurities in steel. In addition to improving the cleanliness of steel, calcium-manganese-silicon alloy promotes fluidity, improves ductility, and helps prevent pinholes in steel castings.

The analyses of these alloys are given in Table 4. If the manufacturer of steel can use these materials without introduction of undesirable additions to the melts, the prices per pound of calcium show that the use of elemental calcium is entirely noncompetitive with these calcium alloys in the production of iron and steel or related metal products.

The constitutional diagrams of the alloys of calcium with aluminum, copper, hydrogen, gold, lead, magnesium, nickel, silicon, silver, tin, or zinc have been well studied and almost completely worked out, whereas those for the alloys with antimony, beryllium, bismuth, boron, cadmium, lithium, mercury, nitrogen, platinum, sodium, or thallium are either incomplete or fragmentary.

TABLE 4. ANALYSIS OF CALCIUM-SILICON AND CALCIUM-MANGANESE-SILICON ALLOYS

	Ca–Si	Ca–Mn–Si
Calcium (%)	30–33	16–20
Silicon (%)	60–65	53–59
Manganese (%)	–	14–18
Iron (%)	1.5–3	
Weight (lb/cu ft)	110	130

Biological and Biochemical Aspects

Calcium is an essential element in living organisms. It has been found necessary for continued miotic division in plants and it plays an important role in the metabolism of nitrogen in some plants where a deficiency of calcium leads to poor absorption of nitrogen. Lack of calcium in plant nutrition leads to a reduction in the number and size of the chloroplasts. The starch made by the chloroplasts is converted with difficulty into sugar, probably because of the fact that in calcium starvation the production of the starch-transforming enzyme, diatase, is greatly reduced.

Calcium in the soil is an important element in the maintenence of proper pH. Calcium carbonate combines with acids produced by root action, fermentation, and other biological and chemical processes. If these were not neutralized, the root hairs and feeding roots would be injured or killed and the plant would suffer from general starvation if not poisoning.

Calcium is the most abundant inorganic element in the higher animals and is located principally in the bones and teeth as a calcium phosphate mineral, apatite. Apatite is active metabolically in that there is a continuous exchange between it and the Ca^{++} and $HPO_4^=$ ions circulating in the blood. It is therefore a huge reservoir of calcium in the animal.

In addition, calcium is distributed throughout all tissues where it has special roles in controlling nerve impulse transmission, muscle action, blood clotting, and cell permeability. It is important in maintaining the proper Na^+/K^+ balance in cells. Calcium deficiency is exhibited by the onset of rickets, failure of the blood-clotting mechanism, and the nervous disorder, tetany, characterized by intermittent convulsive muscular contractions. Tetany is occasionally encountered when the diet is high in oxalic acid and other reagents which remove calcium from the body.

Parathormone controls the metabolism of calcium ion, but in turn, the production of parathormone by the parathyroid is adjusted by the level of calcium ion in the blood. Vitamin D greatly improves the absorbability of calcium ion and the value of this vitamin in treating rickets is based in part on this effect.

Abnormally large intakes of calcium ion can lead to some physiological disturbances, chiefly in the nature of excessive calcification of joints and the formation of calcium-containing solids in soft tissues. The most frequent evidence of this sort is kidney stones. Calcium compounds are not poisonous unless the anion present is toxic. Calcium oxide and calcium hydroxide are strongly alkaline and can cause skin and mucous tissue damage if permitted to remain in contact with these tissues.

References

1. Mantell, C. L., "Alkaline Earth Metals," in "Rare Metals Handbook," C. A. Hampel, Editor, 2nd Edition, pp. 15–31, New York, Reinhold Publishing Corp., 1961.
2. Mantell, C. L., "Industrial Electrochemistry," 3rd Edition, p. 535, New York, McGraw-Hill Book Company, Inc. 1950.
3. Mantell, C. L., and Hardy, C., "Calcium Metallurgy and Technology," New York, Reinhold Publishing Corp., 1945.
4. Pidgeon, L. M., and Atkinson, J. T. N., *Can Mining Met. Bull.,* No. 429, 14 (1948).
5. Pidgeon, L. M., and McCatty, S. A., U.S. Patent 2,464,767 (1948).

CHARLES L. MANTELL

CALIFORNIUM

Discovery

On February 9, 1950, S. G. Thompson, A. Ghiorso, K. Street and G. T. Seaborg performed a careful ion exchange separation of the products formed by the irradiation of microgram amounts of Cm^{242} with 35 MeV helium ions produced by the 60-inch cyclotron at the University of California, Berkeley.

A new radioactivity was found, which eluted just ahead of berkelium, in the position expected for element 98. This activity, which underwent decay, both by orbital electron capture and by alpha particle emission, was assigned to an isotope of mass number 245, atomic number 98, formed by the reaction:

$$_{96}Cm^{242} + {}_2He^4(35\ MeV) \rightarrow {}_{98}\square^{245} + {}_0n^1.$$

The new element was named *californium* (symbol Cf) for the state in which it was discovered.

Historical

Shortly after the discovery of californium, Thompson and coworkers investigated the coprecipitation behavior of trace concentration of Cf^{3+} in aqueous solution in the presence of powerful oxidizing and reducing agents; no evidence was found for the formation of higher or lower oxidation states.

It was not until 1958 that a sufficient amount of californium became available to carry out the first experiment with the pure element in concentrated form.

B. B. Cunnnigham and Thompson, working at the University of California's Radiation Laboratory in Berkeley, concentrated about 0.1 μg of Cf^{+3} on a 0.1 mm diameter bead of cation exchange resin in preparation for a measurement of the magnetic susceptibility of the ion. The molar susceptibility was found to be similar to that of Dy^{3+}, the rare earth analog of the Cf^{3+} ion.

Cunningham, Thompson and John G. Conway observed broad, weak absorptions at 7800 and 8300 Å in the spectrum of a solution containing 1.2 μgm of californium.

In 1961, in a collaborative experiment between the Berkeley and Livermore branches of the Radiation Laboratory, Conway, John B. Gruber, E. Kenneth Hulet, Richard J. Morrow and Ralph G. Gutmacher incorporated several micrograms of californium in a crystal of $LaCl_3$ weighing about one milligram. From the radiation induced fluorescence it was possible to identify 11 emission lines of Cf; five sharp lines observed in the violet and ultraviolet continuum were assigned to absorption by Cf^{+3}. Conway, Hulet and Morrow also observed 14 lines of the spark spectrum of californium between 3700 and 4400 Å, using 0.4 μgm of californium on a copper electrode.

In 1962 J. C. Wallman and Cunningham determined the crystal structures of $CfCl_3$ and CfOCl, using a few micrograms of californium containing several per cent of rare earth impurities.

The absorption spectrum of Cf^{3+} absorbed on sulfonic acid resin, and in the form of a single crystal of $CfCl_3$, weighing 0.2 μgm was determined in 1965, by J. L. Green, R. D. Baybarz and Cunningham.

The most prominent absorption lines for the absorbed californium were observed at 473 and $\sim$740 mμ; sixteen lines were observed in the absorption spectrum of the crystal, between 4304 and 8907 Å.

In a collaborative effort between the Lawrence Radiation Laboratory and the Argonne National Laboratory carried out in 1966, Conway, S. Fried, R. N. Latimer, R. McLaughlin, Gutmacher, T. Carnall and P. Fields used about 600 μgm of Cf^{252} to determine 21 absorption lines between 2800 and 16,000 Å in the spectrum of the aqueous tripositive ion.

The first crystallographic studies using highly purified californium were done in 1966 by J. L. Green and Cunningham who, determined the structures and lattice parameters of $CfCl_3$ and Cf_2O_3.

Prevalence

Since there are no natural sources of californium, the element must be prepared by nuclear synthesis; the known isotopes are listed in Table 1 below.

TABLE 1. ISOTOPES OF CALIFORNIUM

Mass no.	244	245	246	247	248	249
half-life	25 m	44 m	35.7 h	2.4 h	350 d	360 y
radiation	α	ϵ,α	α	ϵ	α,SF	α
Mass no.	250	251	252	253	254	
half-life	10y	800 y	2.55 y	19 d	60 d	
radiation	α,SF	α	α,SF	β^1	SF	

α, emission of a particle; ϵ, orbital electron capture; SF, spontaneous fission; m, minutes; h, hours; d, days; y, years.

A more detailed tabulation is given on page 751 in the article on **Transuranium Elements.**

The lighter isotopes of californium may be obtained by charged particle bombardments, the heavier ones by neutron irradiation. Fission reactors commonly provide the source of neutrons for the latter process, but heavy isotopes of californium have been recovered also from the debris of thermonuclear explosions. Although explosions provide high neutron fluxes only for microseconds, the extreme speed of neutron capture results in the formation of superheavy isotopes of uranium, plutonium or other heavy elements contained in the device. These heavy isotopes then undergo a sequence of β^- decays leading to the formation of elements of higher atomic number.

Various methods for the production of californium are illustrated in Fig. 1.

Regardless of the method of production, californium will constitute but a minute fraction of the product material. Separation from fission product and other elements is accomplished by an initial rough fractionation by precipitation methods, followed by careful purification by extraction or ion exchange processes.

(a) $_{96}Cm^{242} + _2He^4 \rightarrow _{98}Cf^{244} + 2_0n^1$
$_{96}Cm^{244} + _2He^4 \rightarrow _{98}Cf^{247} + _0n^1$
$_{92}U^{238} + _7N^{14} \rightarrow _{98}Cf^{248} + 3_0n^1$

(b) $\ldots Cf^{250} \rightarrow Cf^{251} \rightarrow Cf^{252} \rightarrow Cf^{253} \rightarrow Cf^{254} \quad Cf^{249} \rightarrow Cf^{250} \ldots$
$$\uparrow$$
$$Bk^{249} \rightarrow Bk^{250}$$
$$\uparrow$$
$Cm^{244} \rightarrow Cm^{245} \rightarrow Cm^{246} \rightarrow Cm^{247} \rightarrow Cm^{248} \rightarrow Cm^{249}$

(c) $_{92}U^{238} + 16_0n^1 \rightarrow _{92}U^{254} \rightarrow _{93}Np^{254} \rightarrow _{94}Pu^{254} \rightarrow \ldots$
$\ldots \rightarrow _{95}Am^{254} \rightarrow _{96}Cm^{254} \rightarrow _{97}Bk^{254} \rightarrow _{98}Cf^{254}$

FIG. 1. Production of californium. (a) charged particle reactions; (b) slow neutron irradiation; (c) thermonuclear explosion. $\rightarrow$, n, γ, reactions; $\uparrow, \beta^-$ decay.

Sources

Milligram quantities of Cf^{252} and fractional milligram amounts of Cf^{249} are available as the result of the prolonged neutron irradiation of plutonium, americium and curium. The heavier isotope is more difficult to work with because of the neutron activity associated with its decay by spontaneous fission.

Gram amounts of Cf^{252} may be expected to be available within a few years from the operation of the heavy isotopes production reactor at the Oak Ridge National Laboratory.

Physical and Chemical Properties

Reduction of californium to its metallic state has not yet been accomplished. From its relation to other elements of the $5f$ transition series it may be predicted that the metal can be prepared by the reduction of the trifluoride with barium. The metal will have a density of 14, will be readily soluble in dilute mineral acids, and will react rapidly with air or oxygen at 400-500°C.

Principal Compounds

Slightly soluble compounds include the hydroxide, $Cf(OH)_3$. and the trifluoride, CfF_3.

(1) *CfCl₃*. Emerald-green californium trichloride has been prepared by reacting Cf_2O_3 with HCl(g) at 500°C.

The trichloride exhibits a hexagonal structure, UCl_3 type, with a = 7.393 ± 0.040 Å, c = 4.090 ± 0.060 Å. The ionic radius of Cf^{3+}, calculated from the trichloride data, is 0.98 Å. The anhydrous trichloride melts at ~600°C. Its absorption spectrum has been investigated in the region from 4000-9000 Å.

(2) *Cf₂O₃*. The sesquioxide has been prepared by heating the sulfate in air to ca. 1200°C, followed by reduction with hydrogen at 500°C. The sesquioxide structure is monoclinic, Sm_2O_3 type, with a = 14.124 ± 0.020 Å, b = 3.591 ± 0.003 Å, c = 8.809 ± 0.013 Å, β = 100.31 ± 0.02 degrees.

Importance of Californium

The stability of the tripositive state of californium suggests that the oxidation-reduction properties of the elements belonging to the second half of the $5f$ transition series will resemble those of the elements comprising the first half of the $4f$ series. If this is indeed the case, element 102 may be expected to exhibit a divalent state under strongly reducing conditions.

The isotope of mass 252 may have important technological applications as indicated below.

Californium-252 is the highest weight isotope yet produced in gram quantities sufficient for the production of new elements.

Uses of Californium

The decay of Cf^{252} by spontaneous fission (partial half-life 66 y) makes the isotope a convenient and highly portable source of neutrons. Cf^{252} could be used for radiographic purposes or as a source of neutrons for neutron activation analysis of extraterrestrial surfaces or for logging in deep drilling operations.

Biological Effects of Californium

Similarly to other actinide elements californium in the body tends to accumulate in the skeletal system, where it causes damage to the red cell forming mechanism.

According to Handbook 69, 1959 edition, issued by the National Bureau of Standards, the maximum permissible burden of Cf^{252} in the skeletal system is 0.04 microcuries, in the whole body 0.3 microcuries; similar figures are given for Cf^{249}. In terms of mass, 0.04 μc corresponds to 6×10^{-5} micrograms of Cf^{252}, or 9×10^{-3} μgm of Cf^{249}.

References

1. Seaborg, G. T., "The Transuranium Elements," New Haven, Yale University Press, 328 p., 1958.
2. Katz, J. J., and Seaborg, G. T., "The Chemistry of the Actinide Elements," London, Methuen, 508 pp., 1957.
3. Seaborg, G. T., "Man-Made Transuranium Elements," Englewood Cliffs, N. J., Prentice-Hall, Inc., 120 pp., 1963.
4. Seaborg, Glenn T., *Chem. Eng. News*, **44**, 76, 1966.
5. Thompson S. G., and Muga, M. L., "*Intern. Conf. Peaceful Uses Atomic Energy*" 2nd, Geneva, **28**, 331, 1958.
6. Cunningham, B. B., *J. Chem. Ed.*, **36**, 32, 1959.
7. Green, J. L., UCRL-16516 Thesis, University of California, 1965.
8. Green, J. L., and Cunningham, B. B., *J. Inorg. Nucl. Chem. Letters*, in press.
9. Conway, J. G., Fried, S., Latimer, R. M., McLaughlin, R., Gutmacher, R. G., Carnall, W. L., and Fields, P., UCRL-16971, 1966.
10. Recent issues of *J. Inorg. Nucl. Chem.*, *J. Inorg. Chem.*, *J. Chem. Phys.*, *J. Opt. Soc. Am.*

B. B. CUNNINGHAM

CARBON

The element carbon, C, atomic number six, atomic weight 12.01115, is the first of five elements located in Group IVA of the Periodic Table, the other members being silicon, germanium, tin and lead.

Carbon is unique among the elements because it forms a vast number of compounds, more than the total of all other elements combined with the exception of hydrogen. It exists in three allotropic forms, namely, diamond, graphite and amorphous carbon. Diamond and graphite are naturally occurring crystalline solids possessing widely divergent properties, whereas amorphous carbon is a term applied to a comparatively large variety of carbonaceous substances not classified as either diamond or graphite.

Discovery

Carbon is of prehistoric knowledge as diamond and graphite. That diamonds were known at least as early as 1200 B.C. appears probable according to ancient Hindu writings. The earliest authentic reference to the diamond is ascribed to one Manilius near the First Century of our era. The name diamond derives from a corruption of the Greek word *adamas*, "the invincible."

The first recognition of graphite is obscured in antiquity. It was long confused with other minerals of similar appearance, chiefly molybdenite, MoS_2. One name for graphite is plumbago, like lead; and until modern times it was thought to contain lead. Scheele, in 1779, demonstrated that graphite oxidized to carbon dioxide proving its chemical constitution. The name graphite, which comes from the Greek verb *graphein*, "to write," originated with Werner in 1789.

Carbon as a reducing agent in the making of iron and other metals is also of prehistoric origin. Not until modern times, however, was the identity and role of carbon in such processes established and completely understood.

Prevalence

Carbon ranks nineteenth in the order of abundance of the elements comprising about 0.2% of the earth's outer crust. In the earth's atmosphere carbon is present in amounts up to 0.03% by volume as carbon dioxide. Though it is widely distributed in nature, mainly in the combined form, only minor amounts are found in the free or elemental state. It is present as a principal constituent of all animal and vegetable matter. Coal, petroleum and natural gas are also composed essentially of carbon. Various minerals, such as limestone, dolomite, and marble, as well as certain marine deposits such as oyster shells all contain carbon in the form of carbonates.

Carbon plays a vital role in what is known as the carbon or life cycle. Carbon dioxide from the air, together with water, is absorbed by plants and converted into carbohydrates in the process of photosynthesis. Animals consume the carbohydrates, returning the carbon dioxide to the atmosphere by the processes of respiration, excretion, fermentation and decay under bacterial action.

Sources and Derivation

Diamond. Though diamonds have been discovered on all the major continents, over 90% of the world's natural diamond production is from Africa. Other significant producers are the South American countries of Brazil, British Guiana and Venezuela, and most recently Siberia of the U.S.S.R.

Diamonds are most frequently found imbedded in "volcanic pipes" of a relatively soft, dark, basic peridotite rock called "blue ground" or "kimberlite," from which they are mined. While this is considered the primary source, diamonds are also found in alluvial deposits. To recover the diamonds from the blue ground or alluvial gravel, a series of gravity separations and flotation operations is first performed on the crushed ore to concentrate the heavier diamond. Final separation is accomplished on a grease table, the diamonds adhering to the grease. As found in nature, diamonds range widely in size, shape, color, purity, state of aggregation and crystal perfection. The largest known diamond weighs $3024\frac{3}{4}$ carats or a little over $1\frac{1}{4}$ pounds.

At least five basic varieties of diamond are recognized: (1) diamond proper; (2) macles; (3) boart; (4) ballas; and (5) carbonado. The term "diamond proper" includes single crystals and gem stones occurring in the octahedral (8-sided), dodecahedral (12-sided), and tetrahexahedral (24-sided) crystal habits. Gem diamonds are colorless or pale shades of pink, blue, yellow, green or brown, of good crystal soundness, with a minimum of flaws or inclusions. Macles, an industrially useful form, are triangular, pillow-shaped stones consisting of twin crystals. Boart, also called bort or bortz, refers to minutely crystalline, grey-to-black, translucent-to-opaque pieces of diamond used industrially. The term is also applied to diamond fragments useless as gem stones. Ballas is a name given to dense spherical masses of randomly oriented crystallites. It is extremely tough and hard, and therefore suited for industrial applications. Carbonado is a cryptocrystalline material composed of diamond crystallites, graphite and other impurities.

Diamonds have been produced synthetically since 1955 when the General Electric Company first announced the successful development of a reproducible process. In essence, the process involves the subjecting of a mixture of nondiamond form of carbon and a metal catalyst to temperatures high enough to melt the metal or metal-carbon mixture while the system is at a pressure where diamond is stable. Effective catalysts include Cr, Mn, Fe, Co, Ni, Ta and certain of the Group VIII metals. Synthetic diamonds are now being manufactured in the United States, Ireland, Sweden, Japan, the Republic of South Africa and the U.S.S.R. It is estimated that about 30% of the industrial diamonds used in the United States are now of the manufactured variety.

Graphite. Deposits of natural graphite are located in virtually all continents. Of the major producers, the Republic of Korea is currently the world's largest, followed by Austria, North Korea, the U.S.S.R., China, Mexico, Malagasy Republic (Madagascar), West Germany, Ceylon and Norway.

Natural graphites are classified into three physically distinct varieties based upon geological occurrence—lump (from vein deposits), amorphous (from metamorphosed coal beds) and crystalline flake (from layered metamorphosed rocks). Depending upon the nature of the deposit, both underground and surface methods are employed in mining the graphite. The purity of the deposits vary widely, and where necessary, the graphite bearing ores are generally beneficiated by flotation techniques.

Manufactured or synthetic graphite represents more than 70% of the total graphite consumption in the United States today. The various geometrical shapes which comprise the bulk of the manufactured graphite products are produced primarily from petroleum coke and a coal tar pitch binder. The raw materials are thoroughly mixed at about 150°C, cooled to about 100°C, formed by extrusion or molding into desired shapes, and baked to around 950°C in a nonoxidizing environment. Heating to temperatures of about 2800°C in special graphitizing furnaces converts the baked carbon body into a polycrystalline graphite article.

Pyrolytic graphite, another form of manufactured graphite, is deposited on surfaces when low molecular weight hydrocarbons are pyrolyzed at low pressures (4–6 mm Hg) in the temperature range of 1700–2500°C.

Fibrous forms of graphite—thread, yarn, felt and cloth—are produced by controlled carbonization of natural and synthetic organic fiber products followed by heating to temperatures of around 2500°C.

Amorphous Carbon. Natural organic matter, such as coal, petroleum, gas and timber, constitutes the primary source of amorphous carbon. All are in abundant supply in various countries throughout the world. Coal deposits are usually mined, although other special mining techniques, such as coal gasification by partial combustion, are sometimes employed to obtain the carbon values from the underground deposits. Petroleum and natural gas are recovered from subterranean deposits by drilling wells, while timber is derived from the forests.

The processes by which the various forms of amorphous carbon are obtained from these carboniferous materials generally involve some type of thermal decomposition or partial combustion. The so-called coking coals and mixtures thereof are converted to coke in beehive and slot-type ovens. Anthracite, a "hard" coal, is calcined to remove noncarbon constituents. Residual oils resulting from the refining of petroleum crudes are converted to petroleum coke by the delayed coking and fluid coking processes, both being forms of destructive distillation. The carbon blacks are produced by vapor phase decomposition of hydrocarbons in an open flame, in a partial combustion chamber or in a thermal decomposition chamber in the absence of air. They are classified, respectively, as lampblacks, furnace combustion blacks and thermal blacks. Charcoal, a generic term, is obtained from the destructive distillation of wood, sugar, blood and other carbonaceous materials. The so-called activated carbons are produced by gas (selective oxidation) or chemical treatment to create a very large surface area. Two distinct types are generally recognized: liquid phase or decolorizing carbons, and gas phase or vapor adsorbent carbons.

Physical Properties

The atomic weight of carbon is 12.011, its atomic number 6, and atomic radius (for single bonding) 0.77 Å. Six isotopes of carbon are known: C^{10}, C^{11}, C^{12}, C^{13}, C^{14} and C^{15}. Isotopes 12 and 13 are stable; the others are radioactive, having half-lives as follows; C^{10}, 20 sec.; C^{11}, 20.5 min.; C^{14}, about 5560 yrs.; and C^{15}, 2.4 sec. The isotope C^{12} is the current base to which the atomic weights of all the other elements of the Periodic Table are referred.

The thermal-neutron-absorption cross section (σ_a at 2200 m/sec) for carbon is 3.4 millibarns. The electronic configuration or orbital arrangement of electrons is $1s^2 2s^2 2p^2$, where the superscript indicates the number of electrons in that particular energy level.

Some physical properties of the allotropic crystalline forms of elemental carbon are given in Table 1. Since the amorphous forms of carbon are not capable of rigorous definition, a tabulation of corresponding physical property data is quite impossible. On the other hand, the specific classes or types of amorphous carbons, such as the carbon blacks, activated carbons and anthracite coals have been extensively characterized and the references should be consulted for specific information of this nature.

Specific mention must also be made with reference to the physical properties of the manufactured forms of polycrystalline graphite. In general, these properties are a function of the raw materials and the processing techniques employed; consequently, the range of physical properties attainable is very broad. Again, the references should be consulted for further information.

Of the two allotropic crystalline forms of elemental carbon, graphite is the more thermodynamically stable at atmosphere pressure. Diamond is transformed into graphite above 1500°C. Because of the formidable experimental difficulties associated with the extremely high temperatures and ultra high pressures required in the study of the carbon system, the phase diagram for carbon is incompletely known. Recent proposed diagrams of selected regions are shown in Fig. 1. At atmospheric

TABLE 1.   PROPERTIES OF THE GRYSTALLINE FORMS OF ELEMENTAL CARBON†

	Diamond	Natural Graphite
Density, g/ml	3.51	2.26
Melting point, °C	3700	—
Boiling point, °C	4200	4200
Sublimation point, °C	—	3620 ± 10
Mean coefficient of thermal expansion, per °C	$3\text{–}4.8 \times 10^{-7}$ @ 100°C	
a axis (< 383°C)	—	$-.15 \times 10^{-7}$
c axis (15–800°C)	—	$238 \quad \times 10^{-7}$
Thermal conductivity, cal/sec/cm/°C	1.27	
a axis	—	0.6
c axis	—	0.2
Specific resistance, ohm-cm	5×10^{14}	
a axis	—	$\sim 1 \times 10^{-4}$
c axis	—	~ 1
Specific heat, C_p, cal/mole/°C	1.462	2.038
Magnetic susceptibility, χ, emu/g	52×10^{-6}	$\sim -6.5 \times 10^{-6}$
a axis	—	$-22 \quad \times 10^{-6}$
c axis	—	-0.5×10^{-6}
Compressibility, cm²/kg	0.18×10^{-6}	$3 \quad \times 10^{-6}$
Young's Modulus, dyne/cm²	—	1.13×10^{15}
Shear Modulus, dyne/cm²	—	2.3×10^{10}
Hardness, Mohs	42	0.5–1.5
Refractive index	2.4173	1.93–2.07
Heat of formation, ΔH°_{298}, kcal/mole	0.4532	0
Free energy of formation, ΔF°_{298}, kcal/mole	0.6850	0
Entropy, S°_{289}, kcal/mole	0.5829	1.3609
Latent heat of vaporization @ b.p., kcal/mole	—	170

† Values listed are those measured at room temperature unless otherwise indicated.

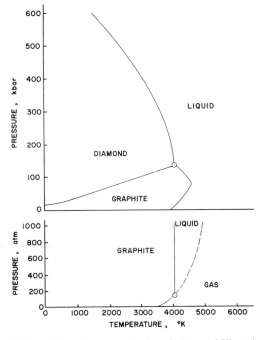

FIG. 1. Phase diagrams of carbon (1 kbar = 987 atm).

pressure, graphite sublimes at 3640 ± 25°K. The triple point (graphite-liquid-gas) is 4020 ± 50°K at 125 ± 15 atm. A second triple point (diamond-graphite-liquid) occurs at about 130 kbars at 4100°K. Regions involving metastable phases of either diamond or graphite have not been included in the figure.

The marked differences in the physical properties of diamond and graphite are readily understood from their crystallography and the nature of the interatomic forces within the crystals. The diamond crystal lattice consists of two interpenetrating face-centered cubic lattices so arranged that each carbon atom of one is surrounded by four carbon atoms belonging to the other (Fig. 2). Each carbon atom is covalently bonded to each of its four neighboring carbon atoms in the form of a tetrahedron. This type of carbon-to-carbon bonding is described in terms of the hybridization of one $2s$ and three $2p$ atomic orbitals of the carbon atom. Such bonds, termed sp^3 hybrids, are effectively localized, thereby

109

greatly restricting electron mobility within the crystal. The extreme hardness and the low electrical conductivity of diamond are consistent with this picture.

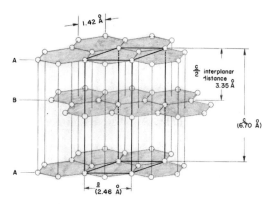

FIG. 3. Hexagonal form of graphite.

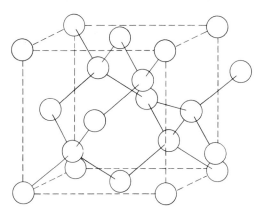

FIG. 2. Crystal structure of diamond.

The idealized crystal structure of graphite is hexagonal (Fig. 3), with the stacking arrangement of the parallel layers of carbon atoms in ABABAB....form; however, a small percent of the layer stacking in most natural graphites is rhombohedral (Fig. 4) wherein the stacking arrangement is ABCA-BCABC....Bonding between carbon atoms within the graphititic planes is different from that found in diamond, and results from a second type of combination of the atomic orbitals of the carbon atom known as trigonal or sp^2 hybridization. Only three of the bonding orbitals are effectively localized in this instance, leaving a fourth whose nature is such that the electrons are quite mobile within the layer of carbon atoms. Because the bonding electrons are all used in forming carbon-to-carbon bonds within the carbon layers, the layers themselves are held together only by weak van der Waals forces. The bonding energy between planes is only about 2% of that within the planes. These structural characteristics explain the highly anisotropic and widely divergent properties of graphite compared to diamond.

The arrangement of the carbon atoms in amorphous carbons cannot be rigorously defined. Evidence of varying degrees of order among the atoms in amorphous carbons is provided by x-ray diffraction methods. Thus, for example, it is well established that all

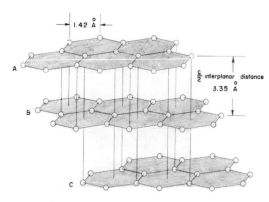

FIG. 4. Rhombohedral form of graphite.

carbon blacks exhibit a similar x-ray diffraction pattern relating to graphite. In carbon blacks, however, the ordering of the carbon atoms is two dimensional in contrast to three dimensional ordering in graphite. Regions of highly ordered structure can be found in most petroleum cokes and in anthracite coal.

Chemical Properties and Reactions

At room temperature, elemental carbon in any of its allotropic forms is relatively unreactive. It is insoluble in water, dilute acids and bases and in organic solvents. At elevated temperatures, however, it becomes highly reactive, combining directly with other elements such as oxygen and sulfur. When carbon reacts with oxygen or air, carbon monoxide or carbon dioxide are formed, depending upon the relative amounts of carbon and oxygen present in the reaction environment. With carbon in excess, carbon monoxide is formed:

$$2C + O_2 \rightarrow 2CO$$

With oxygen in excess, the reaction continues and carbon dioxide is formed:

$$2CO + O_2 \rightarrow 2CO_2 \quad \text{and}$$
$$C + O_2 \rightarrow CO_2$$

The temperature at which these reactions take place will vary greatly depending upon the form in which the carbon is present. Thus, while diamond does not oxidize in air until about 800°C, natural graphite oxidizes slowly above 450°C. Some forms of amorphous carbon may react with oxygen at temperatures even lower than 450°C because of their greater surface area and the presence of certain noncarbon elements and impurities.

Carbon reacts with water vapor to form carbon monoxide, carbon dioxide and hydrogen. The reaction rates and product compositions are dependent upon the form of the carbon employed and the reaction conditions. Diamond is virtually unreactive even at white heat, whereas graphite reacts at temperatures above 800°C. Certain forms of amorphous carbon will react at temperatures as low as 600°C.

Most metals react directly with elemental carbon to form the respective carbides. The temperature at which carbide formation takes place varies widely depending upon the metal involved. Cobalt forms the metastable carbide, Co_3C, at a temperature of 218°C, whereas hafnium carbide, HfC, is formed at 2000°C.

In reacting with oxides and oxygen-containing salts, carbon acts as a reducing agent. Depending on the temperature and other conditions of reaction, metal oxides are reduced to the free metal or converted to the carbide:

$$Me_xO_y + yC \rightarrow xME + yCO$$

The reduction of calcium phosphate rock with carbon in the presence of silica is the basis for the commercial process for the production of phosphorus:

$$Ca_3(PO_4)_2 + 3SiO_2 + 5C \rightarrow 3CaSiO_3 + 2P + 5CO$$

Certain chemical reactions of carbon are indigenous to the specific crystalline form of the element. Graphite, for example, forms a series of compounds known as lamellar compounds with a large number of salts, a few oxides, fluorine, chlorine, bromine, potassium, rubidium and cesium. Heating with a mixture of potassium chlorate and concentrated nitric acid converts graphite to graphite oxide. With hot oxidizing agents such as nitric acid and potassium nitrate, mellitic acid, $C_6(COOH)_6$, is formed.

The unique electronic band structure of the carbon atom is responsible for its ability to combine not only with itself but also with a large number of other elements, principally hydrogen and oxygen, to form the vast system of chemical compounds known as organic.

In bonds to carbon a unique concept of bonding is involved, namely, hybridization. Three basic types of hybridization of the bonding orbitals of the carbon atom are possible: the tetrahedral or sp^3 type; the trigonal or sp^2 type, and the digonal or sp type. Each type is stereospecific, or in other words, has directional properties. The first or tetrahedral type describes the nature of the bonding in organic molecules of the paraffin class as well as in diamond. The second or trigonal type describes the nature of the carbon-to-carbon double bonds in unsaturated organic compounds of the olefinic type. The third or digonal type describes the nature of the carbon-to-carbon triple bonds in unsaturated organic compounds of the acetylenic type. Such hybrid types form what is termed localized or σ type bonds. Still another type of bond is required in describing carbon bonding in organic molecules; namely, the π bond. This type of bond is used in describing the nature of the chemical bonding between carbon atoms in the so-called aromatic hydrocarbon series as well as in graphite. This versatility of the carbon atom with respect to bond formation serves to explain the prevalence and endless multiplicity of organic compounds, both natural and synthetic.

Principal Compounds

The principal industrial compounds of carbon are its oxides, carbon monoxide and carbon dioxide; the carbonates of calcium and magnesium; carbon disulfide; carbon tetrachloride;

and the carbides, notably silicon carbide, calcium carbide and the heavy metal carbides.

Carbon monoxide is an extremely poisonous, colorless, odorless, tasteless gas, stable at room temperature. Industrial quantities of carbon monoxide are derived from processes involving the partial combustion of a carbonaceous fuel or the water gas reaction. Blast furnace gas, methane partial-combustion gas and oil partial-combustion gas are examples of sources of carbon monoxide from partial-combustion processes. Industrial preparation of carbon monoxide by the water-gas reaction involves the passage of steam over a bed of hot coke or coal at 600 to 1000°C:

$$C + H_2O(g) \rightleftharpoons CO + H_2$$

The reaction is endothermic and air is alternated with steam to maintain the temperature above 600°C.

Two processes are used commercially to produce essentially pure carbon monoxide; one, based upon the absorption of carbon monoxide by an ammoniacal copper carbonate, copper acetate or copper formate solution; the other, based upon low-temperature condensation and fractionation. A primary use of the products from the water gas and partial-combustion gas processes is in the field of synthetic organic chemicals. Carbon monoxide is also used in the purification of such metals as nickel and iron through formation of the respective carbonyls.

Carbon dioxide is a colorless gas with a faintly pungent odor and acid taste. It is produced commercially by separation from flue gases resulting from the combustion of carbonaceous materials and as a by-product of synthetic ammonia production, fermentation and lime kiln operations. It is used in solid (dry ice), liquid and gaseous form in such widely diverse applications as carbonation of beverages, chemicals manufacture, fire extinguishing, food preservation and mining operations.

Calcium carbonate in the form of limestone is used extensively for fluxing and refining purposes in the metallurgy of iron and steel. In the form of sea shells, it constitutes a source of calcium oxide for the recovery of magnesium from sea water. Magnesium carbonate as dolomite, $(CaMg)(CO_3)_2$, and magnesite, $MgCO_3$, is used for the manufacture of refractories. Limestone and carbonates in general are decomposed thermally to the corresponding oxides and carbon dioxide. Carbonates are also decomposed by acids with evolution of CO_2.

Carbon disulfide, a low boiling, highly toxic and flammable organic solvent is made by the catalytic reaction of natural gas, CH_4, with sulfur vapor at 500–700°C. This catalytic process has all but displaced the time-honored process of reacting charcoal with sulfur in a retort. Carbon disulfide is used mainly in the manufacture of viscose rayon and cellophane, and as a raw material for the production of carbon tetrachloride.

Carbon forms compounds with the halogens according to the general formula CX_4, where X is fluorine, chlorine, bromine, iodine and mixtures thereof. By far the most important is carbon tetrachloride, a colorless, nonflammable, low boiling liquid (b.p. 76.4°C) manufactured by passing chlorine gas into carbon disulfide containing catalytic amounts of metal chloride such as $SbCl_3$. Carbon tetrachloride is commonly used as a dry cleaning fluid, in fire extinguishers and as an industrial solvent for fats, greases, waxes and other organic materials.

The metal carbides, an important class of carbon compounds, are formed by heating the metal or metal oxide with carbon or a carbonaceous material. Calcium carbide, produced by heating calcium oxide and coke in an electric arc furnace, has industrial importance as a source of acetylene. The carbides of titanium, hafnium, tantalum and tungsten are very refractory and find important use as cutting tools. Silicon carbide and boron carbide are extremely important compounds of carbon, inasmuch as they constitute the backbone of the entire abrasives industry. Silicon carbide and boron carbide are produced by reacting sand, SiO_2, and boric acid, respectively, with coke in a special type of electric furnacing operation.

Applications

Carbon is an indispensable element to industry. Industrial carbons are generally considered to include all forms of carbon used for industrial purposes excluding, however, natural graphite, diamonds and carbon used simply as a fuel or reductant. Within the scope of this definition, carbon ranks as the most important single product type in the inorganic and allied product field. Annual consumption of industrial carbon is estimated to be in the vicinity of four million tons.

Of minor volume tonnage-wise, a significant dollar volume (over $50 million) of industrial carbon is consumed annually as diamond, ballas, bort and carbonado. The largest volume is used in the form of grit and powder to make diamond-impregnated tools for sawing, shaping, drilling and grinding carbides, concrete, masonry, ceramics, stone, refractories, plastic and fiber. As single stones, diamonds are used as tools to dress conventional grinding wheels, as dies for wire drawing, and as phonograph needles, indenters, glass cutters and ruling tools. The significance of diamonds as gems is known universally.

Natural graphite is used for a wide variety of applications, the largest single use being foundry facings, which accounts for more than one-third the tonnage consumed. A second important application is in steelmaking where it is used as carbon raiser, in hot topping and as an ingot wash. Natural flake graphite finds extensive use in the manufacture of clay-graphite crucibles, retorts and other refractories. Minor amounts are used in the manufacture of lubricants and pencils. Total consumption of all forms of natural graphite amounts to about 60,000 tons, with an estimated value of over seven million dollars.

By far, the greatest single use of carbon is in the form of coke for the iron and steel industry where over 60 million tons are consumed annually. The major portion of this coke is used in the reduction of iron ore in blast furnaces.

Anthracite, coal coke, and petroleum coke are used extensively as reductants in electrothermal processes for producing ferroalloys, phosphorus, zinc, calcium carbide and silicon carbide. In combination with coal tar pitch, these same forms of carbon are also used in the manufacture of refractory carbon linings for blast furnaces, certain types of electric furnaces, aluminum reduction pots, and the like where high temperatures or unusual corrosion conditions prevail. So-called amorphous electrodes for use on ferroalloy, phosphorus and carbide furnaces are produced from these same carbon materials. Large quantities of petroleum coke are used in the form of anodes for the production of primary aluminum by the Hall process. Approximately 0.5–0.6 of a pound of carbon is consumed for each pound of aluminum produced.

Of the carbon blacks produced, the furnace combustion blacks are by far the most widely used. About 94% of the estimated 863,000 tons of carbon black consumed annually in the United States is in the form of furnace blacks for the rubber industry. Of this amount, about 90% goes into the manufacture of tires of all types. Outside the rubber industry, the other major applications for carbon blacks are in the printing ink, paint, paper and plastics industries. Minor amounts are used in the manufacture of dry cells and carbon brushes, and as insulation. This end use pattern has remained essentially unchanged over the past ten years.

The total annual consumption of activated carbons is growing, and for 1966 was estimated to be about 95,000 tons. The liquid phase or decolorizing type, which represents over 90% of the total activated carbon produced, is used mainly in decolorizing sugar solutions during the process of sugar refining, in water treatment and in the reclamation of dry cleaning solvents. Because of the increasing problems of water pollution by industrial wastes, considerable growth in this application is expected in the future. The largest single application for gas phase activated carbons is in the recovery of volatile organic solvents from air or vapor mixtures. Another large application is in the purification and separation of natural and industrial gases.

The manufactured forms of graphite find extensive use in a wide variety of applications, of a chemical, electrical, metallurgical, mechanical and physical nature. The largest single use is in the form of electrodes for electric open arc furnaces producing regular and alloy steels. Electrolytic anodes for electrolysis of brine to produce chlorine and caustic, and of molten salts to produce magnesium and sodium constitute another major use of manufactured graphite. Because of its excellent resistance to corrosion by many chemicals, particularly acids, alkalis, organics and inorganic compounds, graphite is used for process equipment in the chemical process, steel, food and petroleum industries. Corrosion resistance combined with a good thermal conductivity make it useful as a material of construction for heat exchangers and tower packings. Principal metallurgical uses for manufactured graphite are as molds, dies and crucibles. Important but lesser volume uses are those of moderator and reflector for nuclear reactors and rocket and missile components.

Principal applications for pyrographite and the fiber forms of manufactured graphite are found as components for rockets, missile and other aerospace vehicles.

Industrial carbons are vital to any modern industrial economy. The discovery of large new uses is not imminent, but many present uses are expanding rapidly, particularly in such industries as steel, aluminum and phosphorus.

Detection and Analysis

Carbon is usually determined chemically as carbon dioxide. The free element can be burned in oxygen or air, as can most of the combined forms of carbon. Metal carbonates can be decomposed by heat or by acids. The carbon dioxide formed or generated is first dried by passage over or through such drying agents as anhydrous $CaCl_2$, concentrated H_2SO_4, "Dehydrite" or "Anhydrone" and is then absorbed in caustic potash, soda-lime, or "Ascarite" and finally weighed.

Diamond can be identified by x-ray diffraction and petrographic analysis. Spectrographic analysis of natural diamond shows the presence of impurities, the more abundant of which are silicon, magnesium, aluminum, calcium, iron and copper, appearing in quantities up to 79 parts per million.

Natural graphite is best evaluated by means of the petrographic microscope and x-ray diffraction, coupled with an accurate chemical analysis. Industrial methods emphasize either carbon content or the incinerated ash, depending upon the ultimate application.

The carbon blacks are commonly evaluated on the basis of such properties as particle size, surface area, structure and surface chemistry. Test procedures for these proper-

ties are generally supplemented by performance evaluation tests in end uses.

The other forms of amorphous carbon are generally evaluated on the basis of properties peculiar to the intended application. End use performance evaluation tests are also used extensively to supplement specific physical and analytical testing.

Toxicology

No toxic effects appear to be associated with carbon in its elemental form. On the other hand, many of the more common carbon compounds exhibit strong toxicological effects. Principal among these are carbon monoxide, carbon dioxide, hydrogen cyanide and the alkali cyanides, carbon tetrachloride and carbon disulfide.

Carbon monoxide, an odorless gas, is extremely toxic, behaving as an asphyxiant. Compared to oxygen, it is not only more readily absorbed, but also more firmly bound by the hemoglobin of the blood. The capacity of the blood to carry oxygen to the vital parts of the body is thereby reduced, leading to possible brain damage, heart disease and pneumonia. Extended exposure to concentrations as low as 200 ppm can produce slight headache, while brief exposures to concentrations of the order of 5000–10,000 ppm can cause death. Carbon dioxide is less toxic and behaves chiefly as a simple asphyxiant and narcotic.

Hydrogen cyanide and the alkali cyanides are extremely toxic, functioning as protoplasmic poisons by inhibiting tissue oxidation. Extended exposure to 100–250 ppm of hydrogen cyanide is dangerous.

Acute exposure to the vapors of carbon tetrachloride can result in damage to both the liver and kidneys. Carbon disulfide is a powerful narcotic, but its chronic effects are the more serious. Excessive exposure can lead to permanent damage to the nervous system.

The toxicological properties of carbon compounds embraced within the field of organic chemicals are varied in both degree and kind. In general, the halogen, sulfur, phosphorus and nitrogen bearing organic compounds are the more toxic, with oxgyen bearing and pure hydrocarbons exhibiting less harmful effects.

References

1. Kirk, R. E., and Othmer, D. F., "Encyclopedia of Chemical Technology," Kirk-Othmer, Vol. 4, Second Edition, New York, Interscience Publishers, 1965.
2. Mellor, J. W., "A Comprehensive Treatise on Inorganic and Theoretical Chemistry," Vol. V, New York, Longmans, Green and Co., 1956.
3. Mantell, C. L., "Industrial Carbon," New York, D. Van Nostrand Co., Inc., 1928.
4. "Carbon," Chicago, Encyclopedia Britannica, 1963.
5. "Graphite," Chicago, Encyclopedia Britannica, 1963.
6. "Diamond," Chicago, Encyclopedia Britannica, 1963.
7. "Nuclear Graphite," R. E. Nightingale, Ed., New York, Academic Press, 1962.
8. Staff, Bureau of Mines, "Mineral Facts and Problems," Bulletin 630, Washington, Dept. of Interior, Bureau of Mines, 1965.
9. Staff, Bureau of Mines, "Minerals Yearbook," Vol. 1, "Metals and Minerals (Except Fuels)," Washington, Dept. of Interior, Bureau of Mines, 1964.
10. Cram, D. J., and Hammond, G. S., "Organic Chemistry," New York, McGraw-Hill Book Co., Inc., 1959.
11. "Chemistry and Physics of Carbon," P. L. Walker, Jr., Ed., New York, Marcel Dekker, Inc., 1965.
12. "Proceedings of the First and Second Conference on Carbon, Held at the University of Buffalo, Buffalo, New York, Nov. 1953 and June 1955," London, Pergamon Press, 1957.
13. "Proceedings of the Third Conference on Carbon, Held at the University of Buffalo, Buffalo, New York, June 1957," London, Pergamon Press, 1959.
14. "Industrial Carbon and Graphite," Conference Papers, London, September 24–26, 1957, London, Society of Chemical Industry, 1958.
15. "Proceedings of the Fourth Conference on Carbon, Held at the University of Buffalo, Buffalo, New York, June 1959," London, Pergamon Press, 1960.
16. "Proceedings of the Fifth Conference on Carbon, Held at Pennsylvania State University, University Park, Pennsylvania, June 1961," London, Pergamon Press, Vol. I (1962); Vol. II (1963).
17. "Encyclopedia of Science and Technology," Vol. 2, New York, McGraw-Hill Book Co., Inc., 1960.
18. Elkins, H. G., "The Chemistry of Industrial Toxicology," Second Edition, New York, John Wiley & Sons, Inc., 1963.

L. H. JUEL

CARBON-12 SCALE OF ATOMIC MASSES

The term "atomic weight" is a defined quantity. Thus we speak of the atomic weight of an element defined as the relative weight of that element with respect to that of an internationally agreed upon standard. As a result of long established usage, the term "atomic weight" seems still to be preferred to "atomic mass" by most chemists at present. All weights are relative, though precisely defined in terms of the force exerted on matter in a gravitational field in comparison to that of a standard. The amount of matter in a given weight is its mass.

For *nuclides*, a term suggested by Kohman and defined as "a species of atom and characterized by its nucleus, particularly by the number of protons and neutrons in its nucleus," the corresponding term *nuclidic mass* is used. Correspondingly, the nuclidic mass has a weight relative to that for the mass of an internationally agreed upon nuclide. Our use of the term "weight" when referring to mass follows the precedent of the IUPAC (International Union of Pure and Applied Chemistry) in its presentation of the Atomic Weight Table [see *J. Chem. Educ.* 3, 625 (1961)].

The Concept of Atomic Weight

The chemical method of determining the atomic weight of any element is, in many cases, dependent on a previous knowledge of the molecular weight of compounds in which the element is a constituent part. The determination of molecular weights is based fundamentally on Avogadro's hypothesis. The application of this hypothesis can yield only relative molecular weights and not absolute values; therefore, a defined standard is required on which one can base the atomic weights of other elements. Since hydrogen is the lightest element, it appeared best to choose this element as standard and assign the value of unity to its atomic weight. Prout's hypothesis that the elements were composed of a varying number of hydrogen atoms favored this choice. This would have been an adequate selection if the atomic or molecular weights alone were to be considered. But since these values must be used in connection with combining weights, oxygen serves as a better standard for comparison because of its abundance and reactivity. Since oxygen is a better working standard for chemically determined ratios, a scale based on oxygen gradually came to be preferred. It was natural to use an integral value for the atomic weight of this element. The choice of $O = 16$ had the fortunate coincidence of making nuclidic weights nearly identical with their mass numbers.

The Existence of Two Scales

The scale based on oxygen seemed to provide a satisfactory atomic weight scale. It remained a happy choice until it was discovered that some elements consisted of isotopic mixtures. The discovery of isotopes would not have altered the situation at all were it not for the fact that ordinary oxygen, the standard itself, was found to consist of a mixture of isotopes: O^{16}, O^{17}, and O^{18}, the latter two being discovered by Giauque and Johnston in 1929. The physicists, working with mass spectrometers in their study of isotopes, naturally chose for their standard system the oxygen nuclide of mass 16, while the chemists continued to use 16 for the atomic weight of the isotopic mixture.

The unit of the physical scale is called the "absolute mass unit" (amu) or "isotopic mass unit" and the unit of the chemical scale is called the "atomic weight unit" (awu). Atomic masses are given on the physical scale while atomic weights are given on the chemical scale. For isotopic elements it would be more rigorous to use the term "mean atomic mass or weight," but there is no evidence of confusion resulting from the shorter designation used by chemists. The unit of the physical scale is $\frac{1}{16}$ of the mass of O^{16} atom. The unit of the chemical scale is $\frac{1}{16}$ of the weight of the mean mass of an atom of natural oxygen and is therefore slightly greater than the physical unit.

The quantitative relationship between the two scales is established in the following manner:

Let $M_c(X)$ = atomic weight, on the chemical scale, of any natural element X

$M_c(O^*)$ = atomic weight, on the chemical scale, of natural oxygen

$M_p(X)$ = atomic mass, on the physical scale, of element X

$M_p(O^*)$ = atomic mass, on the physical scale, of natural oxygen

By definition of the chemical scale, $M_c(O^*) = 16$ exactly. The following relation exists among the above four quantities:

$$\frac{M_c(X)}{M_c(O^*)} = \frac{M_p(X)}{M_p(O^*)} \tag{1}$$

$M_p(O^*)$ is the average atomic mass of natural oxygen referred to O^{16}, and may be expressed in terms of mass, $M_{p,i}$, of each isotope and its abundance (atom fraction) A_i,

$$M_p(O^*) = <M_p(O^*)> = \sum_i A_i \times M_{p,i} \tag{2}$$

By definition, the conversion factor is

$$r = \frac{M_p(O^*)}{M_c(O^*)} = \frac{\text{physical mass (amu)}}{\text{chemical weight (awu)}} \tag{3}$$

Hence from (1)

$$M_c(X) = \frac{M_c(O^*)}{M_p(O^*)} M_p(X)$$
$$= \frac{1}{r} M_p(X) \tag{4}$$

The conversion factor, r, may also be defined in terms of the ratio of the units of atomic weight (chemical scale) to the units of atomic mass (physical scale).

$$r^* = \frac{\text{unit of the atomic weight}}{\text{unit of the atomic mass}} = \frac{\text{awu}}{\text{amu}} \tag{5}$$

The numerator and the denominator are magnitudes of the units when referred to the same reference base scale. We could say that the ratio is defined as a pure number. Thus, one may write for r and r^* the following identity

$$r = r^* \frac{\text{amu}}{\text{awu}}$$

The value of r can be calculated from a knowledge of the masses and the abundance ratios of oxygen nuclides O^{16}, O^{17}, and O^{18},

$$r = \frac{\text{mean atomic mass of natural oxygen}}{\text{atomic weight of natural oxygen}}$$

$$= \frac{A(O^{16})M(O^{16}) + A(O^{17})M(O^{17}) + A(O^{18})M(O^{18})}{16} > 1$$

Using values for the isotopic abundances and isotopic masses from the literature,

$$r = \frac{(99.7587)(16) + (0.0372)(17.004533) + (0.2039)(18.00487)}{16}$$

$$= 1.000273$$

The disparity between the chemical and the physical scales was further heightened when it was observed that the isotopic abundance of oxygen in nature varies from source to source. This led to the value of r varying between 1.000268 and 1.000278. In 1940 the IUPAC Commission on Atomic Weights adopted a value of 1.000275 for r corresponding to a "typical" natural oxygen. We thus note that the physical scale differs from the chemical scale by 275 ppm.

The Avogadro number, which was defined as the number of oxygen atoms in 16 grams of oxygen (now defined as the number of atoms in 12 grams of Carbon-12), also depends on what scale is chosen. So also do other properties which are functions of the mole, for example the Faraday constant, or the gas constant, R. The value based on one scale differs from the value based on the other scale by the factor r.

Proposals for Unification of the Two Scales

It is immediately clear that the key to the solution of the problem of two scales would be to agree on a single reference substance and assign a value to its mass. However, there are at least two requirements that this reference substance should meet. These are: (1) that its mass should be an invariant, and (2) that its mass should be intercomparable with the masses of other nuclidic species. Requirement (1) is clear in the light of what has already been discussed. Requirement (2) is closely related to the mass-spectroscopic method used by the physicists in mass determinations.

Of course, even if the indefiniteness of the chemical scale could have been removed by another better definition, we still would have been left with two lists of atomic weights and also two sets of values for those constants that are dependent on the mole. Proposals for the giving up on one scale in favor of the other met with objections, despite the fact that the adopted scale might have improvements over the discarded one. Many of these objections were well founded. To appreciate the seriousness of the problem, let us assume that the chemical scale was to be abandoned in favor of the physical scale. On the basis of this scale, $O^{16} = 16$ exactly, the atomic weight of natural oxygen would be 16.00440. This would mean a change of 275 ppm in the atomic weights and related values, an amount which cannot be regarded as negligible. The need would then arise for the immediate revision of all mass and related quantities reported in handbooks, scientific tables, and the great collection of reference works where relative masses on the discarded scale have been reported. It is well to note that the abandoning of the chemical scale would have involved the greater burden and difficulties involved in the revision process. It was on such grounds that the alternatives to abandoning either of the scales were sought, both by the chemists and the physicists.

At this time the necessity for giving up both the physical and the chemical scales and the need for adopting a "universal" scale were receiving more urgent attention. Several proposals were made. Among these a scale based on $H^1 = 1$ exactly was suggested. The great disadvantage of such a scale was that on this basis the masses (on the chemical scale) of all atoms would have had to be reduced by 7870 ppm. This, indeed, is too great a change to be ignored. Hence it was argued by some that a change of this magnitude might provide the spur for the total revision of all mass and related quantities. Another proposal was also put forward, urging the adoption of a scale based on F^{19}, with an assigned mass of 19 exactly [A. Labbauf, *J. Chem. Educ.*, **39**, 282 (1962)].

117

When the Commission on Atomic Weights of the IUPAC met in 1957 it was obvious that certain steps would need to be taken in order to clarify the entire situation. The ideas and suggestions that were proposed at that time aimed to solve the chemical atomic scale problem in such a manner as to avoid, if possible, the need for the great task of revision of the already existing chemical data. The suggestions that were put forward at that time were the following:

(1) to refer the scale of 16 (exactly) as the atomic weight of a defined mixture of oxygen isotopes;

(2) to adopt a defined ratio of the atomic weights on the chemical scale to those on the physical scale; and

(3) to define the chemical scale such that the mass of O^{16} will be $16/r$, where r is the conversion ratio discussed above and currently taken as 1.000275.

It should be noted that actually none of the above suggestions provided any means for the unification of the two scales. On the other hand, these suggestions and discussions served to emphasize the need for perhaps an entirely new scale instead of modifications of the existing ones. It appears that after the meeting in 1957, A. Olander and A. O. Nier had independently suggested the idea of using $C^{12} = 12$ exactly as a possible unified basis for atomic weights scale. O^{18} was suggested as another possibility by Olander. This idea of taking 12 exactly grams of isotopically pure carbon-12 as one mole had great appeal to both chemists and physicists. The reasons for this will be found in the original literature [A. Labbauf, *J. Chem. Educ.*, **39**, 282 (1962)].

Adoption and Use of Carbon-12 Unified Scale

The Commission on Atomic Weights of the International Union of Pure and Applied Chemistry (IUPAC) prior to the meeting of the Union in 1959, had proposed the adoption of a reference mass scale on C^{12} (carbon-12 isotope = 12 exactly) to which the atomic weights of all elements would refer and which would serve as a common scale for use by both chemists and physicists. In August, 1959, the IUPAC approved the recommendation for a unified atomic weight scale providing that similar action would be taken by the physicists.

TABLE 1. COMPARISON OF THE CHEMICAL SCALE, THE PHYSICAL SCALE, AND THE UNIFIED MASS SCALE BASED ON C¹²=12 (EXACTLY)

	1957 (or 1959) International table	1961 International table	Chemical scale†	Physical scale	Unified scale†
awu	—	—	1 exactly	1.000 275	0.999 957
Oxygen-16 unit (amu)	—	—	0.999 275	1 exactly	1.000 318
Carbon-12 unit (amu)	—	—	1.000 043	0.999 682	1 exactly
H¹	—	—	1.007 865	1.008 142	1.007 822
H (natural)	1.008 0	1.007 97	1.008 011	1.008 288¶	1.007 967
H²	—	—	2.014 181	2.014 735	2.014 094
C¹²	—	—	12.000 516	12.003 816	12 exactly
C (natural)	12.011	12.011 15	12.011 617	12.014 921¶	12.011 100
O¹⁶	—	—	15.995 601	16 exactly	15.994 912
O (natural)	16 exactly	15.999 4	16 exactly	16.004 400	15.999 312
H₂O	18.016 0‡	18.015 34§	18.016 022	18.020 976	18.015 247
CO₂	44.011 ‡	44.009 95§	44.011 618	44.023 721	44.009 726
CH₄	16.043 0‡	16.043 03§	16.043 661	16.048 073	16.042 971
C₂₀H₄₂	282.556‡	282.557 74§	282.568 809	282.646 516	282.556 663

† All the values in columns (4) and (6), except those that are based on definition, are calculated from the values based on the physical scale.
‡ Calculated by using the 1957 International Table for the Atomic Weights.
§ Calculated by using the 1961 International Table for the Atomic Weights.
¶ Calculated from isotopic masses and isotopic abundances.

The corresponding representative organization for physics, the International Union of Pure and Applied Physics (IUPAP), at its meeting in 1960, approved the adoption of the carbon-12 atomic weight scale, permitting the chemists to take final action at the meeting of the IUPAC held on August 2–5, 1961, in Montreal; the reference scale, based on C^{12} = 12 exactly, was formally adopted.

Having approved the adoption of the scale based on C^{12} = 12 exactly, the IUPAC recommended universal use of the new scale as of January 1, 1962. What does the adoption of this scale mean to the chemist? The new scale changes all chemical atomic weights by about 40 ppm, which is well within the limits of accuracy and precision of present-day chemical atomic weight determinations. However, these small changes still need to be taken into consideration whenever one is reporting critically selected physicochemical data or constants of the highest precision.

It might be stated that while carbon-12 as a reference standard does not operationally lend itself to techniques of chemical atomic weight determinations as satisfactorily as oxygen does, yet it has inherent advantages. These advantages result from the fact that the nuclidic mass of C^{12} can be very accurately related to the atomic weights of elements which in turn can be used as reference standards in the chemical atomic weight determinations.

A comparison of the atomic and molecular weights of some nuclides and substances in terms of the chemical, the physical, and the carbon-12 scales are made in the table in order to show what changes in molar properties can be expected. The recognized 1957 (or 1959) and 1961 International Atomic Weights are listed in the second and third columns of Table 1. The unit on the carbon-12 scale is represented by amu.

References

1. Giauque, W. F., and Johnston, H. L., *J. Am. Chem. Soc.*, **51**, 1436, 3528 (1929).
2. Wichers, E., *J. Am. Chem. Soc.*, **78**, 3235 (1956); **80**, 4121 (1958).
3. Wichers, E., *Physics Today*, **12**, 28 (1959).
4. Labbauf, A., *J. Chem. Educ.*, **39**, 282 (1962).

A. LABBAUF

CERIUM†

Cerium is one of the most fascinating elements of the Periodic Table, primarily because of its variable electronic structure. The energy of the inner $4f$ level is nearly the same as that of the outer or valence electrons, i.e., the $5d$ and $6s$ levels. Because of this, small amounts of energy are required to change the relative occupancy of these electronic levels thus giving rise to the dual valency states of cerium, trivalent ($4f^1$ configuration) and tetravalent (no electron in the $4f$ level). In solution the oxidation-reduction potential of the Ce^{+4}/Ce^{+3} couple varies from 1.28 to 1.87 v depending upon the kind of anion in solution and the anion concentration. In the elemental state, a pressure of about 7500 atm or a lowering of the temperature to about $110°K$ ($-163°C$) is sufficient to increase the number of valence electrons and to reduce the atomic volume by 12 to 16% (the amount depends upon temperature and pressure at which this is measured). Because of this valence change, cerium is the only material known today which has a solid-solid critical point, i.e., the termination of the phase boundary between two allotropic modifications. Furthermore, this valency change is thought to account for the unusual occurrence of liquid cerium being more dense than its solid form at the melting point under one atmosphere pressure.

In addition to these unusual scientific properties, cerium is also technologically important. Because of its dual valency, in many of its applications cerium may be used mixed together with the other rare earth elements (as a trivalent element); in other instances its utilization is based upon its tetravalent nature, and in some instances upon its ability to change its state of oxidation.

History[1], [2], [3], [4]

The element cerium, in the form of an oxide, was "discovered" in 1803 simultaneously and independently by Klaproth and by Berzelius and Hisinger. The name, ceria, which was proposed in honor of the newly-sighted asteroid Ceres, was nominated by Berzelius and Hisinger, and this is the name which was

† Work was performed in the Ames Laboratory of the U.S. Atomic Energy Commission. Contribution No. 1976.

accepted by the scientific community of the time. Thirty-six years later, however, Mosander showed that the oxide isolated by these researchers was composed of at least two oxides, for one of which he retained the name ceria and the second he called lanthana, which subsequently was shown to consist of not only lanthana, but also praseodymia and neodymia.

Metallic cerium was first isolated by Mosander in 1825 by reducing cerous chloride with sodium. It should be noted that the term cerium is used quite loosely, since Mosander's material contained other rare earths which had not yet been isolated and identified. In the succeeding years several other investigators prepared metallic cerium by a metallothermic reduction technique, but it was not until 1875, that Hillebrand and Norton prepared cerium by electrolysis of fused chlorides.

Today, these are the two most important methods used to prepare metallic cerium. Generally speaking, the metallothermic technique is used to prepare high-purity metal, and the electrolytic method to prepare many of the commercial cerium-based alloys. It should be noted, however, that high-purity cerium has been obtained by electrolysis of molten halides, but extensive use of this method is not evident.

The discovery of the electronic transformation in metallic cerium, wherein at least a greater portion of the $4f$ electron is transferred to the valence level, is contemporary history. [2],[4] A transformation in cerium, in which a large volume change (about 10 per cent) occurs, was observed by Bridgman (1948) at high pressure† and by Trombe and Föex (1943) at low temperature. The high-pressure x-ray data of Lawson and Tang (1949) and the low-temperature x-ray data of Schuch and Sturdivant (1950) revealed that the crystal structure of cerium remained unchanged upon undergoing this large volume change. On the bases of these x-ray data Zachariasen (1949) and Pauling (1950), working independently, suggested that the valence of metallic cerium changes from about 3 to about 4 when either cooled or compressed. [4]

Presently there is a great deal of research,

both experimental and theoretical, being carried out on metallic cerium to better characterize and understand its electronic behavior in the various polymorphic modifications.

Occurrence and Sources[1],[5]

Cerium is the most abundant element of the rare earth group. (See **Lanthanide Elements.**) It ranks 28th in the abundances of the 83 naturally occurring elements of the earth's lithosphere.

The more important minerals containing cerium are allanite (also known as orthite), bastnasite, cerite, and monazite. Allanite, which is a silicate containing rare earths, aluminium, calcium, and iron, is widely distributed in the Western United States and in many other parts of the world, primarily East Germany, Greenland, Malagasy Republic (Madagascar), U.S.S.R. and Scandinavia. Bastnasite, which is essentially a rare earth fluorocarbonate, is the second most important commercial source for cerium and the light rare earths. The major deposit of bastnasite is found in Southern California. Cerite, which is a calcium-iron-rare earth silicate, is principally found in Sweden. Although it is quite high in rare earth content, it is not abundant enough to be a primary source of the light rare earths. Monazite, which is the principal source of cerium, is a phosphate containing thorium and the light rare earths. It is widely distributed over the world. The most important deposits are located in Florida and Idaho-Montana in the United States, and also in Australia, Brazil, India, and South Africa. Deposits of lesser importance are found in Egypt, Malagasy Republic, and Malawi in Africa, Ceylon, Indonesia, Malaysia, and Republic of Korea in Asia, and Uruguay and Argentina in South America.

Derivation[1],[3],[5],[6]

Processing of Ores. [1],[3],[5] Allanite and cerite are treated with either hydrochloric or nitric acid to dissolve the rare earths. The rare earth solution is separated from the insoluble materials by filtering. The rare earths are recovered by precipitation as the oxalate. The separation of cerium from other rare earths is discussed in the next section.

---

† This transformation was observed at high pressure as early as 1927 by Bridgman using an electrical resistance technique, but the volume change was not determined until 20 years later.

Bastansite is concentrated by a flotation process to remove the quartz, barite, and calcite. The bastnasite, a fluorocarbonate, is then converted to the oxide by roasting.

Monazite is heated in sulfuric acid to convert the phosphate to a thorium-rare earth sulfate mixture. The thorium, yttrium and heavy rare earths are separated from the light rare earths by fractional precipitation with oxalic acid. An alternate method involves digestion of the monazite by using sodium hydroxide at elevated temperatures to give the insoluble rare earth hydroxide in a trisodium phosphate solution. Following filtration, the hydroxide is carefully neutralized to dissolve the light rare earths, leaving the thorium and the heavy rare earths as insolubles.

Separation from Rare Earth Mixtures. [1], [3], [5], [6] Cerium is easily separated chemically from the light rare earths by making use of its dual valence states (+3 and +4). The rare earth mixture obtained from the above ores is treated by any number of oxidizing agents to form the ceric ion, which may be precipitated at a low pH (the minimum pH required to precipitate the first trivalent rare earth is 6.3). Further purification is obtained by repeating the process.

Preparation of the Metal. [5], [6] After chemical separation from the remaining rare earths, the cerium is usually in the form of CeO_2. The ceric oxide is dissolved in hydrochloric acid in the presence of hydrogen peroxide, which is used to aid in the solution process. After solution has been completed, hydrofluoric acid is added to form the insoluble CeF_3. An alternate method for preparing the fluoride is to mix ammonium hydrogen fluoride with ceric oxide and heat in a flow of dry air to 130°C, hold for eight hours, and then heat to 450°C. The resultant trifluoride is mixed with calcium metal, and the mixture is loaded into a tantalum crucible. As the crucible and contents are heated in an argon atmosphere to 1400°C, the calcium reacts with cerous fluoride to form cerium metal and calcium fluoride. Since both cerium and calcium fluoride are molten at this temperature, the more dense cerium sinks to the bottom of the crucible and the immiscible calcium fluoride floats on the cerium. The cerium is mechanically separated from the tantalum and fluoride slag, and then slowly heated to 1500°C in a second tantalum crucible under a vacuum of 10^{-5} torr to remove the volatile calcium remaining in the cerium from the reduction step.

Anhydrous cerous chloride may be substituted for the fluoride. A variety of reducing agents, e.g., magnesium, lithium, sodium, etc., have also proved to be successful in preparing cerium in a manner similar to the process described above.

Cerium may also be prepared electrolytically using a mixture of cerium, calcium, sodium, and potassium chlorides. [12] A refractory metal such as molybdenum or tantalum serves as the cathode to collect the reduced cerium.

Allotropy [2], [4], [6], [7], [8]

The low-temperature (0–300°K) behavior of cerium is quite complex because of the existence of three allotropic modifications. The commonly accepted phase designation is that proposed by Trombe and Föex. The room-temperature modification at one atmosphere pressure is designated as γ-Ce. It is face-centered cubic, and has a cube edge equal to 5.16Å. Upon cooling to 250°K the γ-Ce starts transforming to β-Ce. The remaining γ-Ce, when cooled to 115°K, transforms to α-Ce, which is face-centered cubic, $a \simeq 4.85$Å. This latter transformation is essentially complete at 77°K. There is some evidence that β-Ce below 50°K transforms at least partially to α-Ce.

Upon warming the cerium, α-Ce transforms back to γ-Ce at 180°K. The β-Ce in the sample does not transform to γ-Ce until a temperature of 440°K is reached. Thus, by warming to only room temperature the sample consists of both β and γ modifications. By low-temperature cycling (298° to 77° or 4° and back to 298°K) the amount of β-Ce is increased, however, the maximum amount of β-Ce obtainable by cycling appears to be 60 to 75%.

In addition to these three allotropes, a fourth modification, δ-Ce exists above 726°C. The x-ray study by Spedding, Hanak, and Daane showed this modification to have a body-centered cubic structure, $a=4.11$Å.

High-pressure studies by a large number of American and Russian scientists indicate that at room temperature γ-Ce transforms directly to α-Ce at 7,700 atm. Any β-Ce present in the sample will transform at room temperature to γ-Ce under pressures of less than 3,000 atm.

High-temperature-high-pressure studies led to the discovery of the existence of a critical point between α- and γ- Ce. This was first observed by Ponyativiski in 1958, and consequently confirmed by other investigators.[2], [7] More recent studies by Jayaraman[8] on the effect of pressure on the γ-δ transformation and melting point show that the existence of this critical point has considerable influence on the shape of the melting curve as a function of temperature and pressure.

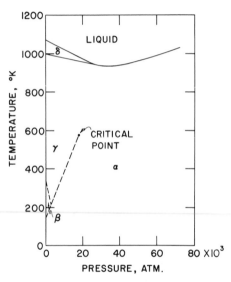

FIG. 1. Pressure-temperature diagram for cerium. The significance of the dashed and solid lines are noted in the text.

The temperature-pressure diagram of cerium, as composed from the results of about 25 different investigations, is shown in Fig. 1. Because of the large hysteresis for the β-γ, α-γ transformations, the phase boundaries are drawn as dashed lines to indicate that these are not necessarily the true equilibrium phase boundaries. The α-β boundary was calculated from thermodynamic considerations.[2] The γ-δ and δ-liquid boundaries are probably true equilibrium phase boundaries, and are so indicated by using solid lines. Two triple points, between α, β and γ and between γ, δ and liquid occur at −61°C (212°K) and 2900 atm, and 674°C (947°K) and 25,6000 atm, respectively.[2], [8] The critical point in solid cerium, the point above which γ- and α- cerium are identical, occurs at approximately 300°C (573°K) and 18,000 atm.[2], [8]

Electronic Structure[1], [3], [4], [5], [7]

The ground state configuration of cerium has recently been confirmed by spectral studies to be $4f^1\, 5d^1\, 6s^2$. It should be noted that this state corresponds to the isolated neutral cerium atom, and has no direct bearing on the electronic structure of metallic cerium or of cerium in its compounds. The excited $4f^2\, 6s^2$ lies fairly close to the ground state, and may well account for some confusion in the early literature regarding cerium's ground state configuration.

Cerium in ionic type compounds and solutions can exist as either the trivalent ion, which has one $4f$ electron, or the tetravalent ion, which has no $4f$ electron. This has been well documented by spectra, magnetic, and other physical and chemical property measurements made on these materials. Indeed, one of the more important oxidimetric analytical reagents, sulfatoceric (or nitratoceric or perchloratoceric) acid, makes use of the two valence states of cerium. The ceric ion, which is a strong oxidizing agent, is reduced to cerous ion during the titration.

There has been considerable debate concerning the electronic structure of the various allotropes of metallic cerium, especially α-Ce.[4] There is general agreement that β-Ce, γ-Ce, and δ-Ce contribute three electrons to the valence bands of these allotropes, presumably the $5d^1$ and $6s^2$ electrons. The $4f$ electron appears to be localized, giving rise to a magnetic moment which is very close to the theoretical moment calculated for the free ion containing one $4f$ electron. The γ-α transformation which involves a 10 to 16 per cent volume change was originally suggested to be accompanied by a transfer of the localized $4f$ electron in γ-Ce to the $5d$ band, giving rise to tetravalent α-Ce. Since then, other workers have suggested that about half of an electron per atom is transferred on going from γ-Ce to α-Ce. The most recent study,[4] in which all the available experimental data, such as magnetic susceptibility, metallic radii, Hall coefficients, and diffuse neutron scattering intensities, were examined, indicated that about 0.6 of an electron per atom is transferred to the valence band of α-Ce during the γ to α transformation.

Physical Properties[2], [5], [6], [7]

The physical properties of metallic cerium are listed in Tables 1 through 3. In Table 1 are presented the physical properties which are independent of the crystal structure. These include the atomic number, atomic weight, melting point, boiling point, heats of fusion and vaporization, and the ionization potentials.

TABLE 1. PHYSICAL PROPERTIES WHICH ARE INDEPENDENT OF CRYSTAL STRUCTURE (ALLOTROPIC MODIFICATION) [5],[6],[7]

Property	Value
Atomic number	58
Atomic weight, $C^{12} = 12$	140.12
Melting point, °C	798
Heat of fusion, kcal/g-atom	1.238
Vapor pressure,	
$\log P_{torr} = A/T + B$ A	-22991
B	9.396
Boiling point, °C	3257
Heat of sublimation, kcal/g-atom at 25°C	111.6
Ionization potentials, ev	
I	5.65
II	10.85
III	19.5
IV	36.7
Thermal neutron absorption cross section, barns	0.73

TABLE 2. TRANSFORMATION TEMPERATURES AND PRESSURES AND HEATS OF TRANSFORMATION [2], [7]

Trans.	Trans. Temp. at 1 Atm Press., °C	Trans. Temp. at 1 Atm Press., °K	Trans. Press. at 23°C (296°K), Atm	Heat of Trans., cal g-at
$\alpha \rightarrow \gamma$	-94	179	5680	648
$\gamma \rightarrow \alpha$	-157	116	7670	—
$\beta \rightarrow \gamma$	168	441	3020	13
$\gamma \rightarrow \beta$	-23	250	—	—
$\gamma \rightarrow \delta$	726	999	—	—

The transformation temperatures and pressures, and the heats of transformation are given in Table 2. Since hystereses are observed for the α-γ and β-γ transformations, the transformation temperatures and pressures are given for $\alpha \rightarrow \gamma$, $\gamma \rightarrow \alpha$, $\beta \rightarrow \gamma$, and $\gamma \rightarrow \beta$. The combined effect of pressure and temperature on the transformations is more easily visualized by examination of Fig. 1. The dashed lines in this figure represent the pseudoequilibrium values for the α-γ and β-γ phase boundries.

The properties which vary with the crystal structure (or the allotropic modification) are listed in Table 3. These include structural, thermodynamic, magnetic, transport, elastic, and mechanical properties. Little is known concerning β- and δ-Ce. For β-Ce the difficulty is that no specimen has yet been prepared which is free from the presence of α- and/or γ-Ce phases. For δ-Ce the high temperatures involved have limited the number of property measurements to only a few which are relatively easy to perform.

Cerium has 19 different isotopes, mass 129 and 131 through 148. Of these, only four are naturally occurring: 136, 138, 140, and 142, and their natural abundances are 0.19, 0.25, 88.48, and 11.07%, respectively.

Chemical Properties[1], [3], [5], [6], [9]

Cerium oxidizes very readily at room temperature especially in moist air. After europium, cerium is the most reactive of the rare earth metals. At temperatures below 300°C the oxidation proceeds at a controlled rate. Above this temperature the oxidation rate increases quite rapidly; indeed, ignition of cerium has been reported by some investigators.

In moist air at temperatures below 300°C, the cerium is oxidized to Ce_2O_3 (the hexagonal A-form) which is quite susceptible to hydration by water vapor to give $Ce(OH)_3$, or $Ce_2O_3 \cdot 3H_2O$ which destroys the protective Ce_2O_3 coating. Above 300°C, the Ce_2O_3 coating is, however, further oxidized to give CeO_2, which also causes flaking of the protective Ce_2O_3 coating. The oxidation of Ce_2O_3 proceeds at a much more rapid rate than the hydration of Ce_2O_3, and this accounts for the behavior at higher temperatures.

TABLE 3. PHYSICAL PROPERTIES WHICH ARE DEPENDENT ON CRYSTAL STRUCTURE (ALLOTROPIC MODIFICATION)[2], [5], [6], [7]

Property	α-Ce Value	α-Ce Temp., °C	α-Ce Press., atm	β-Ce at 25°C	γ-Ce at 25°C	δ-Ce at 768°C
Atomic volume, cc/mole	17.0	− 180	1	20.76	20.690	20.9
Crystal structure	fcc	—	—	hex	fcc	bcc
Lattice parameters						
a (Å)	4.84	− 180	1	3.673	5.1601	4.11
c (Å)	—	—	—	11.802	—	—
Density, g/cc	8.24	− 180	1	6.749	6.773	6.70
Metallic radius CN = 12†	1.71	− 180	1	1.826	1.824	1.84
Heat capacity, C_p		—				
cal/g-atom-deg	—	—	—	—	6.44	9.05
Electronic specific heat const.						
cal/g-atom-deg$^2 \times 10^4$	138	—	—	—	17.3	—
Debye temp., °K	118	—	—	—	138	—
Magnetic susceptibility,						
emu/g-atom $\times 10^6$	12500	− 253	1	—	2430	1030
Electric resistance, μ ohm-cm	34	− 249	1	—	75.3	123
Hall coefficient						
volt-cm/amp-Oe $\times 10^{12}$	0.45	25	7470	—	1.81	—
Thermal expansion,						
per °C $\times 10^6$	—	—	—	—	8.5	—
Thermal conductivity						
cal-cm/sec-cm^2-°C	—	—	—	—	0.026	—
Grüneisen constant	0.96	25	7470	—	0.51	—
Compressibility,						
cm^2/kg $\times 10^6$	3.74	25	8000	—	4.10	—
Young's modulus, kg/cm$^2 \times 10^{-6}$	0.196‡	25	1	—	0.306	—
Shear modulus, kg/cm$^2 \times 10^{-6}$	0.085‡	25	1	—	0.122	—
Poisson's ratio	0.14‡	25	1	—	0.248	—
Hardness, Vickers, kg/mm^2	—	—	—	—	24	—
Yield strength, kg/mm^2	—	—	—	—	9.3	—
Ultimate strength, kg/mm^2	—	—	—	—	10.4	—
Elongation, o/o	—	—	—	—	24	—

† CN means coordination number.
‡ Extrapolated from high-pressure data to zero pressure.

Cerium may be passivated at room temperature by dipping in a 2–5% nital (nitric acid in absolute alcohol), and removing the yellow deposit by swabbing with alcohol. This process is repeated until no further yellow deposit is formed on the surface of the metal when dipped into the nital solution. The cerium so treated is reported to retain its metallic luster for months.[5]

Cerium is readily attacked and dissolved by dilute and concentrated mineral acids. A 1:1 mixture of concentrated nitric acid and 48% hydrofluoric acid does not appear to attack cerium. Alkali solutions readily attack cerium.

Sodium nitrite solution appears to inhibit the corrosion of cerium by water at room temperature.[9]

Cerium reacts slowly at room temperature with the halogen gases to form the corresponding cerium trihalide. Above 200°C, cerium is reported to react very rapidly with these gases. At high temperatures in contact with sulfur, carbon, nitrogen, boron, and hydrogen, cerium will react to form a cerium metalloid compound. The stoichiometry of the compound depends upon the temperature and relative amounts of the materials present.

The pyrophoric nature of cerium is quite

evident by the shower of sparks emanating from the metal when filed, ground or machined. This behavior is observed in most cerium-base alloys. Indeed, the pyrophoric nature of iron-cerium alloys accounts for one of the most important uses of cerium, the lighter flint.

Principal Compounds[1], [3], [5], [6], [7]

Halides.[1], [3], [5], [6] The cerium trihalides ($CeCl_3$, $CeBr_3$, and CeI_3) are quite hygroscopic, and generally are found as hydrated salts. These halides are soluble in water. Cerium trifluoride is nonhygroscopic and is insoluble in water. Cerium tetrafluoride is the only stable halide of tetravalent cerium. Cerium trichloride and trifluoride are the salts generally used in the metal preparation processes. Subhalides of the stoichiometry CeX_2 are also known.

Oxides.[1], [3], [5], [6], [7] Cerium and oxygen form a whole series of related compounds between Ce_2O_3 and CeO_2. The number of compounds formed depends upon the temperature and oxygen pressure. When Ce_2O_3 is heated in air, it is oxidized to one of the intermediate phases and eventually to CeO_2. The sesquioxide is easily dissolved in mineral acids. The dioxide is much more slowly dissolved; the rate of dissolution is inversely proportional to the firing temperature. Cerium dioxide is technologically important as a polishing agent for glass and as an additive to various kinds of glass.

Other Salts.[1], [3], [5] Cerium hydroxide, sulfate, and carbonate are formed in the chemical separation of the rare earths from the other elements in their ores. The hydroxide is very insoluble and easily formed by neutralizing a cerous or ceric solution with ammonium hydroxide. The cerous hydroxide is easily oxidized, even by air, to ceric hydroxide. Cerous sulfate is moderately soluble in water, and its solubility decreases when the temperature of the solution is raised. Ceric sulfate, which is quite soluble in aqueous solutions, is a strong oxidizing agent. Cerous carbonate is readily formed by precipitation from most salt solutions. Ceric carbonate probably has not yet been prepared.

Metalloid Compounds.[1], [3], [5], [6], [7] Cerium reacts with hydrogen to form a dihydride which has the fluorite type structure.

This compound dissolves additional hydrogen atoms in the octahedral holes up to the CeH_3 stoichometry. As the hydrogen content increases beyond $CeH_{2.6}$, the electrical conductivity of the cerium-hydrogen alloys changes from metallic to semiconducting type conduction.

Cerium forms two carbides, Ce_2C_3 and CeC_2, both of which may be considered saline carbides because they contain C_2 groups or ions. Both carbides react with water to form hydrocarbons and hydrogen: the former yields a larger amount of hydrogen, but a smaller amount of acetylene, than the dicarbide.

Of the other metalloids (boron, silicon, nitrogen, phosphorus, sulfur, selenium, and tellurium) all form at least one compound with cerium. Most of the compounds have high melting points and are reasonably stable at room temperature. Silicon, sulfur, selenium, and tellurium form four or more compounds of varying stoichiometries with cerium; the structures of most of these compounds are quite complex.

Intermetallic Compounds.[5], [6], [7] With one exception cerium does not form intermetallic compounds with the elements which lie to the left of iron and its cogeners, ruthenium and osmium, the one exception being the compounds formed by cerium with the heavy lanthanide (Gd to Lu) and yttrium metals. This intermediate phase has the samarium type structure, a hexagonal close-packed lattice with the ABABCBCAC repeat unit,† and exists over a composition range of 5 to 10 atomic % in each case.

Cerium forms compounds with iron and its cogeners and all of elements to the right of these three. Except for iron and its cogeners, cerium forms at least four compounds with each of the elements.

Applications[1], [5], [6], [7], [10]

Commercially, ceric oxide is the most important form of cerium. There are also many other applications in which mixtures of cerium, lanthanum, neodymium, and other rare earths are used. These mixtures may be of the form of metallic alloys, mixed oxides or mixed

† This compares with an AB repeat unit for the normal hexagonal close-packed structure and for ABC for the face-centered cubic structure,

halides, etc. The economics are such that it is not practical to separate the cerium to use alone, since there is little, if any, improvement in the desired property or behavior by making such a separation. For example, cerium costs about $20 per 100-pound lot, but mischmetal (a cerium-rare earth alloy) only $3 per 100-pound lot.

Ceric Oxide.[1], [5], [6], [7], [10] Ceric oxide, CeO_2, is used to polish glass, especially precision optical glasses. It is superior to rouge, Fe_2O_3, in that it polishes glass much quicker. Furthermore, since CeO_2 can be recovered and reused, it is economically competitive with rouge. Because of its oxidizing power, cerium is used in glass which is subjected to α, γ, x-ray, light and electron radiation. The cerium decreases the rate of discoloration in glass, primarily by preventing divalent iron from forming, i.e., oxidizes Fe(II) to Fe(III). This is especially useful in color TV tubes, where electron radiation could cause the glass to discolor and destroy the color quality of the TV picture. Cerium dioxide is also used to opacify enamels, in photochromic glasses,† ceramic coatings, refractory oxides, phosphors, cathodes, capacitors and semiconductors, and as a catalyst.

Because of cerium's low nuclear cross section, CeO_2 is used as a diluent in uranium, plutonium or thorium oxide nuclear fuels.

Metallic Alloys.[5], [6], [7], [10] The most common form of cerium-rare earth alloys is known as mischmetal, and it contains about 50% Ce, 25% La, 18% Nd, 5% Pr, and 2% other rare earths. It is produced in tonnage quantities by the fused salt electrolysis of a mixture of anhydrous chloride of rare earth elements derived from monazite or bastnasite.[12] Mischmetal improves the malleability of cast iron by nodulizing the graphite. An increase in the high-temperature strength and creep resistance is noted by mischmetal additions to magnesium alloys. It is also reported to increase the strength of aluminum, the oxidation resistance of nickel and nickel alloys, and the hardness of copper with only a slight decrease in the electrical conductivity of the copper.

A 30% iron, 70% mischmetal is a common alloy used as lighter flints. The desirable

† Photochromic materials darken when light shines upon them, but become more transparent when the light is removed.

pyrophoric properties of this alloy are due primarily to the cerium.

Cerium is also used as a getter in vacuum tubes and as a diluent in plutonium nuclear fuels.

Mixed Forms.[1], [5], [6], [10] Mixed oxides and fluorides containing cerium are used as cores for carbon arcs. The rare earth mixture increases the intensity about tenfold while improving color balance of this white light.

The mixed ceric-rare earth oxides are also used as catalysts for cracking petroleum, as polishing materials and waterproofing agents, and fungicides in textile manufacturing.

Biological and Biochemical Nature[11]

Most of the biological, biochemical, pharmacological and toxicological studies on cerium have been carried out on small animals, such as mice, rats, and guinea pigs.

Oral administration of cerium or cerium compounds, unless the anion is toxic has very little or no effect. This is primarily due to the fact that very little cerium is absorbed by the body. Subcutaneous injection gives a greater absorption. The excretion of cerium, however, is slow. About 50% of the cerium absorbed is deposited in the liver and 25% in the skeleton, and the elimination half-lives are about 15 days and about 14 months, respectively. Cerium was found to produce granulomas from intradermal injections. Intraperitoneal administration of cerium in concentrations of 0.01, 0.1, and 1% in the diet for 90 days had no effect on the liver. Inhalation of the oxide and/or fluoride induces granulomas in the lung.

Cerous chloride and ceric ammonium nitrate stimulate gastric secretion in low doses but suppress it in high doses. Cerium, like all of the rare earths, decreases the blood pressure and serves as an anticoagulant agent.

The rare earths, including cerium, have a low acute toxicity rating.

References

1. Vickery, R. C., "Chemistry of the Lanthanides," New York, Academic Press, 1953.
2. Gschneidner, K. A., Jr., Elliott, R. O., and McDonald, R. R., *J. Phys. Chem. Solids*, **23**, 555 (1962).
3. Moeller, T., "The Chemistry of the Lanthanides," New York, Reinhold Publishing Corp., 1963.

4. Gschneidner, K. A., Jr., and Smoluchowski, R., *J. Less-Common Metals*, **5**, 374 (1963).
5. Love, B., and Kleber, V., "Technology of Scandium, Yttrium and the Rare Earth Metals," New York, Macmillan, 1963.
6. Spedding, F. H., and Daane, A. H., Eds., "The Rare Earths," New York, John Wiley and Sons, 1961.
7. Gschneidner, K. A., Jr., "Rare Earth Alloys," Princeton, New Jersey, Van Nostrand, 1961.
8. Jayaraman, A., *Phys. Rev.*, **137**, A179 (1965).
9. Lee, L., and Green, N. D., *Corrosion*, **20**, 145t (1964).
10. Mandle, R. M., and Mandle, H. H., "Progress in the Science and Technology of the Rare Earths," Eyring, L., Ed., Vol. 1, p. 416, New York, Pergamon Press, 1964.
11. Haley, T. J., *J. Pharmaceutical Sciences*, **54**, 663 (1965).
12. Hirschhorn, I. S., "Rare Earth Metal Electrowinning," "Encyclopedia of Electrochemistry," C. A. Hampel, Ed., pp. 1000–1003, New York, Reinhold Publishing Corp., 1964.

KARL A. GSCHNEIDNER, JR.

CESIUM

Discovery and History

Cesium is the heaviest of the naturally occurring alkali metals and is in Group IA of the Periodic Table. It was discovered in 1860 by Kirchhoff and Bunsen while examining the residues that were obtained by evaporation of the mineral waters from Kreuznach and Dürkheim. The new bright lines in the blue region were attributed to a new element—given the name cesium for the Latin *caesius*—sky blue. Extraction of cesium compounds by Bunsen involved concentration of the cesium and other impurities by evaporation of large volumes of the mineral water. The chloroplatinates of potassium, rubidium, and cesium were precipitated and fractionally crystallized repeatedly to obtain a concentrate of cesium and rubidium. The least-soluble fractions were converted to chlorides to effect the final separation of cesium from rubidium. (See **Rubidium**.)

Bunsen prepared chlorides, carbonates, tartrates and other salts of cesium. He studied the properties of these salts and, attempted to prepare cesium metal but was unsuccessful. The metal was first obtained by Setterburg in 1882 by electrolysis of a cesium cyanide-barium cyanide melt. He described its appearance and determined some of its properties, such as its ready fusibility, rapid ignition in air, and ability to violently decompose water into hydrogen.

Cesium had no significant industrial application until 1926 when the metal was used as a getter and an effective means for reducing the electron work function on coated tungsten filaments in radio tubes. The development of photosensing devices during the early thirties and the World War II period led to a small but constant demand for the rare metal.

Today, most of the cesium chemicals and

TABLE 1. CESIUM MINERALS

Property	Pollucite	Rhodizite
Chemical composition	$H_4Cs_4Al_4Si_9O_{27}$	$NaKLi_4Al_4Be_3B_{10}O_{27}$
Color	white or cream colored, rarely colorless	white to colorless
Hardness, Mohs	6.5	8.0
Appearance	translucent or opaque crystals or masses	transparent to translucent
Crystal structure	Cubic	Isometric, dodecahedral
Refractive index	1.522	1.693
Specific gravity	2.68–2.98	3.305–3.344
Associated minerals	lepidolite, petalite, and other lithium minerals in pegmatitic deposits	spodumene, tourmaline
% Cs_2O	10–35%	0–3% Cs and Rb substitute for K

metal are used in research on thermionic power conversion, magnetohydrodynamics, and ion propulsion. Current production of these materials is somewhat over 10,000 lb per year according to the Bureau of Mines statistics.

Occurrence

Cesium is widely distributed in the earth's crust at very low concentrations. Granites, sea water, and sedimentary rocks contain less than 5 ppm cesium. Mineral springs contain as much as 9 mg/l of cesium. Higher concentrations of cesium are found in certain potassium minerals such as the micas, beryl, feldspar, petalite. A cesium biotite from South Dakota contains 3.14% Cs_2O, and amazonite from the Ilmen Mountains in Russia contains 0.19% Cs_2O, for example. Lepidolite from Maine contains 0.3% Cs_2O. Carnallite, a double salt of potassium and magnesium chlorides, contain 0.001–0.004% Cs_2O. These last two sources have yielded commercial quantities of cesium.

Only two cesium minerals are known. These are pollucite, a cesium aluminum silicate, and rhodizite, a borate of aluminum, beryllium, sodium, and cesium. The physical properties of these two minerals are shown in Table 1.

Pollucite was first discovered in 1846 on the Isle of Elba where a few hundred grams of the mineral were obtained. Subsequent discoveries around 1900 in Maine and South Dakota, in the United States; Manitoba, Canada; Karibib area in Southwest Africa; and Bikita area

in Southern Rhodesia have made cesium-containing raw materials available at nominal cost.

The deposits at Bernic Lake, Manitoba have been estimated to contain more than 350,000 tons of pollucite averaging over 20% cesium. The Bikita, Southern Rhodesia deposit is estimated at 150,000 tons and the Karibib, S. W. Africa deposit at 50,000 tons. Most of the pollucite consumed by industrial users is obtained from these sources.

A former source of cesium was the mixed alkali metal carbonate, *Alkarb*, which was obtained as a by-product from the extraction of lithium from lepidolite in San Antonio, Texas. This material contained 2% cesium and 20–25% rubidium. Lithium is no longer extracted from lepidolite in the United States, and the supply of *Alkarb* has been exhausted.

The current use of brines as a source of potash and lithium may possibly lead to the eventual recovery of minor cesium and rubidium values from the process liquor. Reserves of this type are very large and are located in many areas of the world.

Carnallite deposits which are mined for their potassium and magnesium salts also contain minor amounts of rubidium and cesium. These extensive deposits represent another possible source for these elements if markets develop.

Derivation

The extraction of cesium from pollucite can be carried out by a number of methods. The preparation of pure cesium metal almost always involves the preparation of a cesium salt which has been carefully purified prior to its reduction to the elemental form. The physical and chemical properties of cesium metal require that special equipment be used in its manufacture.

The methods generally employed to extract cesium from pollucite can be placed in three categories:

1. Acid digestion, using H_2SO_4, HCl, HBr, or HF
2. Fusion or sintering with alkaline fluxes
3. Direct reduction of ore to cesium metal

In cases 1 and 2, cesium salts are extracted from the reaction mass and purification of

TABLE 2. COMPOSITION OF POLLUCITE MINERALS

	Isle of Elba	Oxford County, Maine	Bikita, U.S.S.R.	Bernic Lake, Manitoba
Cs_2O	34.07%	22.4%	29.0%	28.2%
Rb_2O	—	0.065	0.44	1.15
Na_2O	3.88	4.72	1.89	1.36
K_2O	—	0.24	0.24	1.0
Li_2O	—	0.2	0.2	0.35
Al_2O_3	15.97	14.0	15.9	16.8
SiO_2	44.03	53.8	48.1	48.7
Fe_2O_3	0.68	—	—	—
CaO	0.68	—	—	—
H_2O	2.40	—	—	—

these salts is then carried out prior to conversion to cesium metal.

The reaction between 14.4N sulfuric acid and -200 mesh pollucite at 120°C for 2–4 hours is capable of extracting over 90% of the cesium values. The hot acid solution of cesium alum is filtered to remove unreacted ore, then cooled to crystallize cesium alum. Fractional crystallization of the alum to remove the potassium, sodium, rubidium, and lithium impurities followed by aluminum and sulfate removal results in the formation of a pure cesium hydroxide or carbonate solution. From this, any cesium salts can be prepared, many of which are readily reduced to metal.

The Canadian Bureau of Mines developed a process whereby the cesium alum is decomposed by roasting with carbon, according to the following equation:

$$(1) \quad Cs_2SO_4 \cdot Al_2(SO_4)_3 \cdot 24H_2O + 3C + 3/2O_2$$
$$\rightarrow Cs_2SO_4 + Al_2O_3 + 24H_2O + 3SO_2$$
$$+ 3CO_2.$$

The roasted product is leached to give a solution of the sulfate. The solution is passed through a strong base anion exchanger such as "Dowex" 50W-X-8 to convert the sulfate to the chloride. The chloride can be recovered by crystallization and converted to cesium metal.

Reaction of pollucite with hot concentrated hydrochloric acid converts cesium to the chloride. The mixture of alkali metal and aluminum chloride is purified by the fractionation of cesium antimony chlorides, or cesium chlorostannate. Removal of the antimony or tin results in a pure cesium chloride.

Cesium recoveries of greater than 95% are obtained by sintering, -200 mesh pollucite, NaCl, and Na_2CO_3 in a weight ratio of 1/1.2/1.8 at 600–800°C for 1–2 hours. Leaching of the sintered mass produces an alkaline cesium chloride solution which can be purified by solvent extraction. The process, developed at Oak Ridge National Laboratories, utilizes 4-sec-butyl-2-(α-methylbenzyl) phenol (BAMBP) in a kerosene diluent. The use of four extraction and six scrub stages produces a pregnant organic that will yield a 98% recovery of cesium by stripping with hydrochloric acid solution. Purity of the cesium chloride is usually 99.97% plus. This method

can not only be used for extracting and purifying cesium from pollucite but also for the concentrating and removal of radioactive cesium isotopes generated in nuclear reactor wastes.

Another method utilizes hydrobromic acid for cesium dissolution from pollucite near the boiling point of the acid. Cesium bromide is precipitated by the addition of isopropyl alcohol and by cooling to 20°C. The cesium bromide is extracted by liquid bromine. The cesium tribromide solution is filtered to remove the other alkali bromides and the cesium bromide is then recovered by evaporation of the liquid bromine.

One of the earliest methods of extraction was to attack a water-pollucite slurry with concentrated hydrofluoric acid. The silicon in the ore was removed as the tetrafluoride at elevated temperatures. Sulfuric acid was added to the residue which was heated to remove excess hydrofluoric acid. The dry residue was leached with water, the leachant neutralized until it was weakly acidic, and then the heavy metals were precipitated with hydrogen sulfide. Evaporation of this purified liquor resulted in the crystallization of the cesium alums. Fractional crystallization, led to the removal of the alkali metal alum impurities in the crystallization liquors. Treatment of the purified cesium alum by conventional means can produce cesium carbonate or hydroxide.

The direct extraction of cesium metal from pollucite can be carried out by reduction of the ore with either lithium, potassium, sodium or calcium. Sodium is the preferred reductant. The ground ore and sodium are charged into a distillation system. The reaction takes place at 680–850°C when using sodium and the rate of reduction is inversely proportional to the temperature employed. The cesium metal so obtained will contain 3.5 to 7.5% sodium, 0.9 to 2.6% potassium, and 1.3 to 4.1% rubidium. This crude cesium metal is then fractionated through a column of stainless steel containing many theoretical plates. A product of 99.9% purity can be obtained.

A process for upgrading pollucite was developed by the U.S. Bureau of Mines utilizing a reverse flotation system to concentrate the silicate mineral. Undesirable minerals are air-frothed to the surface for removal.

Preparation of Cesium Metal

The early preparation of cesium metal involved the electrolysis of fused salts containing cesium. The properties of the metal necessitated unusual precautions that caused low yields. Later efforts involved the reduction of cesium oxide with magnesium. In the late Nineteenth Century, cesium aluminate was reduced with magnesium in a stream of hydrogen. Nearly theoretical yields were obtained.

The use of the direct extraction of cesium metal can be used very successfully. This route, described in the previous section, has been used commercially to prepare relatively large quantities of cesium metal. The efficiency of the direct extraction process is about 88%. The process can be adapted to prepare various cesium salts by amalgamating the metal and then carefully reacting the cesium amalgam with pure water to prepare cesium hydroxide and from this other compounds.

The most commonly employed methods for preparing quantities of very pure cesium metal involve the reduction of a pure salt by a suitable reducing agent. Cesium chloride or bromide can be reduced with calcium or lithium in an evacuated system at elevated temperatures. The nature of cesium metal requires that the system be constructed of stainless steel or nickel. The exclusion of oxygen and water vapor is the major problem of maintaining adequate purity. The most difficult metal impurity to remove is rubidium due to its similar physical and chemical properties. Oxygen is present in the metal as a dissolved oxide and can be easily picked up during the reduction and handling steps. The extreme reactivity of cesium necessitates considerable care during its preparation. The reaction is as follows:

$$(2) \quad 2CsCl + Ca \rightarrow CaCl_2 + 2Cs$$

The reactants are mixed after being carefully prepared and are charged to a reactor fitted with a condenser and a stainless steel or glass receiver. After evacuating the system, the reactor is heated under high vacuum. As the temperature rises to 250°C, gases are evolved. Toward the end of the run, the temperature will rise to about 650°C. The product can be further purified by successive

distillations. Yields of over 90% can be obtained.

Another method of cesium preparation is the electrolysis of pure cesium chloride at 670°C with a molten lead cathode which forms a Cs-Pb alloy. The cesium content in the lead can be raised to 3.6% Cs. It is easily separated from the lead by distillation.

Cesium can be prepared by a number of other less familiar routes. One of the methods used to prepare cesium inside of special electron tubes utilizes the reaction between cesium chromate and zirconium powder according to the reaction:

$$(3) \quad 2Cs_2CrO_4 + Zr \xrightarrow{\triangle} 4Cs + Zr(CrO_4)_2$$

This method satisfies a condition of being able to prepare the metal without the presence of gases that may dissolve in the metal causing contamination.

Very pure, gas-free cesium can be prepared by the thermal decomposition of cesium azide under high vacuum according to the equation:

$$(4) \quad 2CsN_3 \xrightarrow{\triangle} 2Cs + 3N_2$$

The reaction begins to take place at 200°C, and 10–12 hours are needed to insure decomposition. Upon complete evolution of N_2, the metal is distilled out of the reaction chamber. A yield of 90% can be obtained.

A method which has shown considerable promise is the Mathieu process. Cesium chloride vapor is reacted with heated calcium carbide under vacuum. Alkali metal is distilled from the reactor and condensed in a receiver while liquid calcium chloride remains at the bottom of the reaction chamber. The equation for the reaction is:

$$(5) \quad 2CsCl\ (g) + CaC_2 \xrightarrow{\triangle} CaCl_2 + 2C + 2Cs\ (g)$$

Other processes utilizing chemical reduction or displacement as the basic reaction require a reducing metal and high temperature. Sodium, calcium, aluminum, magnesium, molten iron, silicon, zirconium, titanium, hafnium, and thorium are reported in the literature to yield the alkali metal from carbonates, hydroxides, sulfates, oxides, halides, and chromates.

Thermal decomposition routes are possible by breaking down ferrocyanides, cyanides and hydrides under high temperature and vacuum.

Physical Properties

The physical properties of cesium, which are of greatest interest, are those which enable it to be used in the applications described in a later section. The low melting point (the lowest of the alkali metals), low density, large ionic radius, low electron work function, and highest position in the electromotive force series are among the properties which enable the metal to be used in the thermionic converter, ion engine, magnetohydrodynamic system of power generation, phototubes and other applications. Cesium has the lowest

TABLE 3. PHYSICAL PROPERTIES OF CESIUM

Atomic number	55
Atomic weight	132.905
Crystal form	body-centered cubic
Atomic radius	2.62 Å
Ionic radius	1.69 Å
Atomic volume	69.95 cc/g-atom @ 20°C
Lattice constant	a = 6.05 A @ − 173°C
Density, g/cc	
solid	1.90 @ 20°C
liquid	1.84 @ 28.5°C
Melting point	28.5°C
Boiling point	705°C
Latent heat of fusion	3.766 cal/g
Latent heat of vaporization	146 cal/g
Specific heat	0.052 cal/g/°C @ 20°C
	0.058 cal/g/°C @ 50°C
Vapor pressure, temperature for	°C
1 mm Hg	278
10 mm Hg	387
100 mm Hg	515
200 mm Hg	570
400 mm Hg	635
Thermal conductivity	0.044 cal/sec/°C/cm @ 28.5°C
Coefficient of linear thermal expansion	97×10^{-6} per °C from 0 to 26°C
Ionization potential of gaseous atoms	3.87 e
Electron work function	1.81 e
Electrical resistivity	20 microhm–cm @ 20°C
	22.2 ,, ,, ,, 27°C
	36.6 ,, ,, ,, 30°C
	37.0 ,, ,, ,, 37°C
Magnetic susceptibility	0.10×10^{-6} cgs units @ 18°C
Viscosity	0.6299 centipoises @ 43.4°C
	0.4753 centipoises @ 99.6°C
	0.4065 centipoises @ 140.5°C
	0.3750 centipoises @ 168°C
	0.3430 centipoises @ 211°C
Electrode potential $Cs \rightarrow Cs^+ + e^-$	3.02 volts
Thermal neutron absorption cross-section	29 barns
Important spectral lines	8943.50 Å
	8521.10 Å
	4593.18 Å
	4555.36 Å
Mohs hardness	0.2
Brinell hardness	0.015 kg/mm²

ionization potential of all the elements, and has the largest ionic radius.

The cesium-137 isotope has received wide attention in recent years. It is a product of the fission of uranium and along with strontium-90 is one of the most troublesome radioactive wastes to handle in the applications of atomic fission. Cesium-137 is a beta emitter with a half-life of 33 years. The only naturally occurring cesium isotope is cesium-133.

The physical properties of cesium are listed in Table 3.

Chemical Properties

Cesium is a very reactive metal, that has a slightly silvery-golden cast and is a liquid at 28.5°C. It will combine vigorously with oxygen and the halogens, the reactions being accompanied by spontaneous ignition. Reaction with elemental sulfur and phosphorus results in explosion. Cesium reacts very violently with water, giving off hydrogen, which ignites instantly. The reaction between cesium and oxygen can produce a variety of oxides, peroxides, or superoxides depending on the reaction conditions.

Cesium reacts with hydrogen and nitrogen to form cesium hydride and azide, respectively. Reaction of the metal with almost all the other elements is possible.

Due to its reactivity, cesium must be handled in sealed glass ampules with special break seals or in stainless steel cylinders.

Care must be exercised with a number of the salts due to their hygroscopic and corrosive nature.

Principal Compounds

Cesium Carbonate. Cesium carbonate occurs as a colorless crystalline powder. It is a very stable salt and can be heated to high temperatures without the loss of carbon dioxide. It is extremely hygroscopic and is quite soluble in alcohol. Cs_2CO_3 is usually made by passing carbon dioxide into a solution of hydroxide, and evaporating to dryness. Another route involves conversion of a salt such as the nitrate to the oxalate using an excess of oxalic acid and decomposing the oxalate to the carbonate with heat. Insoluble impurities can be removed by dissolving the decomposition product in water and filtering.

Cesium Aluminum Sulfate. This compound is one of the most useful salts to effect purification of cesium by fractional crystallization. It has the formula $CsAl(SO_4)_2 \cdot 12H_2O$. This is an ideal starting material for the preparation of cesium hydroxide or carbonate from which other various salts can be made.

Cesium Hydroxide. Cesium hydroxide is prepared by adding $Ba(OH)_2$ to an aqueous solution of cesium sulfate to the exact equivalence point. It is extremely soluble in water and is the strongest base known. It is extremely hydroscopic. Evaporation of an aqueous solution at 180°C results in the formation of $CsOH \cdot H_2O$. Dehydration at 400°C in vacuum produces CsOH.

Cesium Sulfate. Cesium sulfate forms rhombic or hexagonal colorless crystals usually obtained by precipitating aluminum hydroxide from a boiling solution of cesium aluminum sulfate. Evaporation of the filtrate after aluminum hydroxide removal causes crystallization of cesium sulfate.

Cesium Nitrate. Cesium nitrate forms hexagonal prisms when it crystallizes from aqueous solution. It is readily prepared from the chloride, hydroxide or carbonate. The fractional crystallization of cesium nitrate is sometimes used to eliminate the traces of Na, Li and K.

Cesium Chloride. Cesium chloride crystallizes from water in colorless cubic crystals. It is important as a primary salt for preparing other cesium compounds because many procedures utilize chloride extraction techniques by aqueous or fusion routes.

Applications

At present there are no uses of cesium that require large amounts of cesium salts. Cesium hydroxide has been recommended as an electrolyte in alkaline storage batteries for use in subzero climates. Cesium chloride has been used in the separation of organic constituents utilizing density gradient centrifugation as the separation method. Cesium carbonate has been used in specialty glasses. The iodide and bromide are used in some scintillation counters because they emit electrons when exposed to radiation. Cesium bromide spectrophotometers are used to measure the epitaxial film thickness of semiconductors. Certain cesium salts have been used as an antishock treatment after the administration of arsenical drugs.

Cesium metal has been getting a great amount of attention in recent years due to important advances in the utilization of the metal in electric power generation and in ion engines. Past uses of cesium have been numerous but none have required the consumption of very large quantities of the metal. One of the earliest uses of cesium was in the manufacture of photoelectric cells because of its property of being readily ionized by light energy.

The property of relative ease of ionization has resulted in the prototype production of a cesium vapor thermionic converter. This device if successful would revolutionize current concepts of power generation.

Cesium is also used in the magnetohydrodynamic system of power generation. A high-temperature ionized gas, containing cesium salts to increase the ionization or conductivity of the gas, is passed perpendicular to an intense magnetic field. The amount of power derived is a function of the velocity and degree of ionization of the plasma.

The use of cesium in the ion engine has received much publicity in its outer space applications. Its role as the rocket propellant is based on the fact that the cesium metal is vaporized and diffused through a heated porous plate to ionize the atoms and give them a positive charge. An electric field accelerates the ions to a velocity of 300,000 miles per hour and then they are exhausted through a nozzle to develop thrust.

The atomic clock utilizes cesium as the time measuring element based on the precise movement of its outer electron around its axis. The accuracy is five seconds in 300 years.

Cesium borohydride has been suggested as a possible solid fuel rocket propellant.

Semiconductors, ferroelectrics and piezoelectric crystals have been found among the salts of cesium. Some of these are the monosubstituted cesium-rubidium phosphates and arsenates when prepared under conditions favoring the crystallization to occur in the tetragonal system.

Toxicity

Cesium has been shown to have a pronounced physiological action on animals when administered in amounts equivalent to the potassium content in the diet of rats. Hyper-irritability including spasms have resulted, eventually leading to death in 10 to 17 days. Cesium metal can cause serious burns when it comes into contact with the skin. Its extreme reactivity with moisture and oxygen requires that it be handled with extreme care.

The toxicity of cesium compounds is generally of very minor importance except when cesium is combined with another toxic metal or radical. Such an example would be cesium cyanide or cesium gallium sulfate.

References

1. Brauer, G., "Handbook of Preparative Inorganic Chemistry," Volume 1, 2nd Edition, pp. 950–992, 1963.
2. Dean, K. C., Johnson, P. H., and Nichols, I. L., "Dissolution and Roasting Techniques for Extracting Cesium from Pollucite Ores," Washington, D.C., U.S. Bureau of Mines, RI-6387, 1964.
3. Eilertsen, E., "Cesium," a chapter from "Mineral Facts and Problems," 1965 Edition, Bulletin 630, Washington, D.C., Bureau of Mines.
4. Hampel, C. A., "Rare Metals Handbook," 2nd Edition, pp. 434–440, New York, Reinhold Publishing Corp., 1961.
5. Lam, H., and Foster, H. R., Jr., "Preparation of Cesium and Rubidium Metals," paper presented before the Division of Industrial and Engineering Chemistry, ACS Meeting, San Francisco, California, April 17, 1958.
6. Mellor, J. W., "Comprehensive Treatise on Inorganic and Theoretical Chemistry," Volume 11, Supplement 111, New York, Longmans Green & Co., 1963.
7. Moolenaar, R. J., "Cesium Metal—Its Production and Purification," *J. Metals*, **16**, 21–24 (January 1964).
8. ORNL—3452, "Chemical Technology Division Annual Progress Report for Period Ending May 31, 1963," Oak Ridge National Laboratory, pages 175–177, 189–192.
9. Parsons, H. W., Vizina, J. A., Simaid, R., and Smith, H. W., "Development of a Chemical Process for Production of Cesium Chloride from a Canadian Pollucite Ore," *Canadian Metallurgical Quarterly*, **2**, No. 1 (January–March 1963).
10. Perel'man, F. M., "Rubidium and Cesium," New York, Macmillan Co., 1965.

C. EDWARD MOSHEIM

CHLORINE

History

Chlorine was discovered in 1774 by K. W. Scheele, a Swedish chemist; he liberated this element for the first time by heating manganese dioxide with hydrogen chloride, HCl, an acid first made by alchemists in the 15th century and named "muriatic acid" by the French chemist Lavoisier (1787). Since the discovery was the outcome of a systematic search conducted along the guiding lines of the then prevailing phlogiston theory, the novel substance was considered as "dephlogisticated muriatic acid." Scheele noted its solubility in water, its bleaching action on organic matter and reactivity on metals, including gold.

A revolutionary advancement in chemical knowledge was to follow soon after the discovery of the voltaic pile (1800), which for the first time provided a source of continuous electric current at a voltage sufficient to electrolyze salts in ponderable quantities. To Sir Humphry F. Davy goes the merit of establishing the elementary nature of chlorine, to which he gave its present name, derived from Greek *chloros* = greenish-yellow.

The industrial exploitation of this newly available chemical was soon undertaken by Berthollet (1789) after finding that it can be fixed in stoichiometric amounts by an alkaline solution and that the latter is thereby imparted bleaching properties, which were immediately appreciated by the booming textile industry. Berthollet called his product "Eau de Javelle," from the place in Paris where it was fabricated. The process was brought to Glasgow by James Watt; here, in 1798, Charles Tennant replaced the alkali lye used by Berthollet with cheaper milk of lime; subsequently, on finding the possibility to absorb chlorine also in slaked lime, he gave origin to the industry of bleaching powder.

The industrial production of chlorine was initially achieved by adding sulfuric acid to a mixture of sodium chloride and manganese dioxide, so as to perform essentially the same reaction discovered by Scheele. A substantial economical improvement was reached about 1870 by Deacon's process, whereby chlorine is liberated from hydrogen chloride by treating the latter with atmospheric oxygen at about 450°C in the presence of a catalyst such as copper sulfate.

The invention of electromagnetic machines such as the dynamo for producing electric power on an industrial scale allowed the development of electrochemical processes that, at the turn of the past century, gradually displaced the other methods of chlorine production. Thus took its start the big chlorine and alkali industry that provides modern life with two of its most vital commodities. Impetus to the continuous progress of this industry is given by the ever increasing demand of chlorine, especially for the production of organic derivatives, such as plastics, solvents and insecticides.

Natural Occurrence

Chlorine abundance in the lithosphere, the ten-mile thick crust of the earth, is estimated about 0.045% by weight.[7] Due to its strong chemical affinity for the other elements, it never occurs in the free state, except as a minor constituent of the gaseous output from volcanic eruptions, which, however, are often quite rich in hydrogen chlorine. Under such conditions the presence of free chlorine can be easily explained as a consequence of thermal dissociation of chlorides at the high temperatures prevailing in the volcanic phenomenon.

Among the most common minerals consisting of chlorides are rock salt or halite, NaCl, sylvite, KCl, carnallite, $MgCl_2.KCl.6H_2O$. Beside being dispersed in the lithosphere, chlorine salts are also dissolved in the hydrosphere. Accordingly, the average chlorine content in sea water, as Cl^- ion, is nearly 2%, although local departures from this value can be quite marked in the several oceans. Since the mass ratio of hydrosphere to lithoshere is about 1:13, the overall chlorine abundance averages 0.19%.

In the hydrosphere as well as in the lithosphere sodium chloride, NaCl, is by far the most plentiful of alkali metal salts: hence its name of "common salt." The average concentration in sea water is approximately 2.6%.

Due to its unreplaceable function in human diet it is also known as "table salt" and the uneven distribution of its deposits over the earth's crust has played an essential role in conditioning the pattern of civilization in time and space. The occasional use of this commodity as a valuable currency is still reminded by the word "salary."[1]

Chlorine is a constituent of human body, averaging 0.1% by weight; it occurs as chloride and is almost totally combined with sodium. A small amount is secreted by the stomach as hydrochloric acid during digestion.

Chlorine Industry

Industrial chlorine production has been achieved for more than half a century by electrolysis of alkali metal chlorides and represents the most important development of electrochemical technology.[4,10] Well over 90% of this production is carried out by the electrolysis of sodium chloride solution, which yields caustic soda (sodium hydroxide or NaOH) as a co-product and thus forms the premise of the huge chlor-alkali or chlorine-caustic industry, which accounts for more than 2% of the electrical energy consumed in the United States. Indeed, as chemical raw materials, chlorine and caustic soda individually are exceeded only by salt, lime, sulfuric acid and soda ash, Na_2CO_3, in the quantities consumed.

In a minor proportion, chlorine is also manufactured by fused salt electrolysis of sodium chloride and magnesium chloride; in such cases it is to be considered as a co-product in the electrowinning of *sodium* and *magnesium*. (q.v.) Another minor fraction of the overall production is obtained by hydrochloric acid electrolysis, whereby chlorine is recovered from the excess of HCl made available as a by-product of chlorinated organic derivatives, such as polyvinyl chloride, PVC, which play a major role in establishing the ever increasing chlorine demand.

Sodium chloride or potassium chloride electrolysis in aqueous solutions can be achieved by making use of two different cell types, involving different processes, which have both reached a high degree of development: they are the diaphragm cell and the mercury cell process. In both of these the anodic reaction is the same and proceeds under equal conditions:

$$2Cl \rightarrow Cl_2 \text{ (gas)} + 2e^-$$

The chloride ion, Cl^-, gives up its excess negative charge (electron) with the consequent formation of free radicals Cl; these combine together by pairs to build up chlorine molecules that evolve in the gaseous state. The cathodic reaction, however, is accomplished in the diaphragm cell through quite different steps than in the mercury cell and establishes the main point of distinction between the two processes, which are briefly described hereunder in some of their most modern and outstanding examples.

Diaphragm process. The anode assembly includes a number of parallel rows of vertical graphite plates; a steel structure makes up the cathode and is formed by a set of double screens extending vertically between each pair of anode rows. The two elements forming a double screen are a fraction of an inch apart and are covered on their outer surfaces facing the anodes with a diaphragm, previously applied under a vacuum from a slurry of asbestos fibers. Each double screen thus builds up a narrow chamber or catholyte compartment, enveloped by the diaphragm, while the anodic compartment is confined between the diaphragm and the graphite anodes.

A typical modern diaphragm cell is shown in Fig. 1.

Sodium chloride brine at about 310 gpl is fed into the anolyte compartment and the effluent is continuously withdrawn from the catholyte compartment, into which it percolates through the diaphragm, while electrolysis proceeds. The catholyte, or cell liquor, contains the amount of sodium hydroxide produced by the cathodic reaction:

$$Na^+ + H_2O + e^- \rightarrow Na^+ + OH^- + \frac{1}{2}H_2(gas)$$

together with an unreacted residue of sodium chloride; a typical cell liquor concentration is 135 gpl of NaOH plus 150 gpl of NaCl. The function of the diaphragm is to prevent the evolving hydrogen from bringing about a mixing of the hydroxyl ions with the chlorine gas dissolved in the anolyte, which would form unwanted side reactions, with buildup of hypochlorous and chlorate ions and a consequent loss in chlorine and caustic production. This preventive function of the diaphragm would, however, not be sufficient to hinder the migration of the OH^- ions from

135

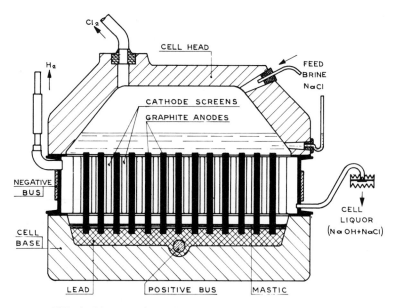

FIG. 1. Diagram of a typical modern diaphragm cell.

the cathode toward the anode, under the influence of the electric field. This is avoided by the "counterflow" action, by which the hydroxyl ions, as soon as formed, are obliged to percolate in a direction opposite to that of the electric field and at a velocity that, other conditions being equal, depends on flow rate and cell geometry; electric migration can thus be efficiently counteracted.

The biggest diaphragm cell model developed so far has a current capacity of 60,000 amps, corresponding to a daily production of 2 short tons of chlorine. Its average voltage is close to 4 v and its current efficiency is 96%.

Mercury cathode process. In this process there is no need for a diaphragm or for any "counterflow" device, since the alkali metal (sodium or potassium) is discharged on a cathode consisting of a flowing mercury layer and becomes dissolved in it, thus forming an amalgam that is continuously drained out of the electrolytic cell. Accordingly, the mercury cathode stream performs the function of a virtual diaphragm as well, in that the cathodic product is thereby impeded to diffuse back into the solution and bring about any side-reactions with chloride discharging at the anodes. The amalgam drains into a reaction vessel, called *decomposer* or *denuder,* where it is reacted with water so as to liberate its alkali

metal content, with production of caustic and hydrogen:

$$2Na \, (Hg) + 2H_2O \rightarrow 2NaOH \, (aq)$$
$$+ H_2 \, (gas) + Hg$$

The reaction would not be viable without the presence of a suitable catalyst, such as graphite, that performs as the positive metallic piece of a short-circuited battery, in which the mercury mass provides the negative pole and the caustic solution makes up the electrolyte. Hydrogen is thereby displaced from the water molecule, HOH, and replaced by sodium to form NaOH, as the consequence of an electromotive force that sets hydrogen free in the gaseous state, while its discharge is facilitated by the electrocatalytic material.

The caustic solution that can thus be obtained is characterized by a high-purity grade and a concentration that may reach 50% or more. Accordingly, the quality of this product is such as to require a little amount of post-treatment and only if further concentration is required to obtain solid (fused) caustic, whereas the diaphragm cell liquor must in any case be treated in multiple-stage evaporators to separate the salt and obtain a commercial-grade caustic product.

On the other hand, the average mercury cell voltage is 4.4 v, or 10% higher than in a diaphragm cell, with the same current efficiency of 96%. However, the 10% higher energy consumption per ton of chlorine thus required is under many circumstances more than offset by the advantage residing in no need for caustic finishing and in much less cell maintenance requirements. In several cases the most advantageous arrangement consists in combining the two processes tógether in particular if the starting raw material is provided by well brine; this is used to feed the diaphragm cell plant and the evaporated pure salt made available from cell liquor evaporation goes to resaturate the depleted brine outflowing from the mercury cells, so as to make it suitable for feeding this process again, without any need for further purification.

Modern mercury cells are rated for current capacities of 300,000 amps or more. A typical mercury cathode cell is illustrated in Fig. 2.

Production Figures. Chlorine production in the United States for the year 1967 was about 7.5 million tons, with an approximate 10% increase over the previous year. This corresponds to nearly one-half of the overall world production. At such an increase rate, the chlorine demand in the United States is more than doubling every ten years and will reach the target of 10 million tons by 1970.

Chlorine Institute. A Chlorine Institute[2] was founded in the United States in 1924, "to foster the industrial interests of those engaged in the chlorine industry; to promote a more comprehensive relationship between those engaged in the production and those engaged in the consumption of its products; and to engage in research work directed toward developing new uses and the more extended consumption of chlorine and its products."

Physical Properties

Chlorine (symbol Cl) is, at normal temperature and pressure, a greenish-yellow gas, characterized by a pungent and unpleasant odor. Its molecule is diatomic, so that the free state is usually designated by the symbol Cl_2. The atomic number 17 corresponds to the electronic configuration $1s^2 2s^2 2p^6 3s^2 3p^5$. The wide departure of the atomic weight (35.453) from an integer number is mostly due to the coexistence of the two isotopes Cl^{35} and Cl^{37}, which are present in the naturally occurring chlorine compounds in the per cent abundance of 75.4 and 24.6, respectively.

The chlorine gas density is nearly 2.5 times that of air. This explains why any amount released in the atmosphere tends to form a cloud hovering close to the ground and hard to dissipate.

The boiling point at standard pressure, 760 mm Hg, is $-34°C$; the liquefaction pressure at $25°C$ is 7.86 atm. These moderate values of boiling point and liquefaction pressure indicate that chlorine can be liquefied with relative ease and with great advantage for the purpose of storage and transportation,

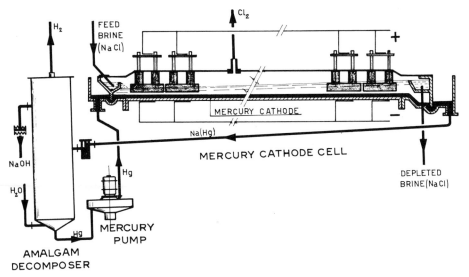

FIG. 2. Diagram of a typical modern mercury cathode cell.

TABLE 1. PROPERTIES OF CHLORINE IN LIQUID AND VAPOR STATE[12]

Temp., °C	Temp., °K	Press., atm abs	dP/dT, kg/m²·°K	Spec. vol., liquid, l/kg	Spec. vol., vap., l/kg	Density, liquid, kg/l	Density, vap., kg/m³	Evaporation heat, kcal/kg	Evaporation entropy, kcal/kg·°K	Enthalpy, liquid, kcal/kg	Enthalpy, vap., kcal/kg	Entropy, liquid, kcal/kg·°K	Entropy, vap., kcal/kg·°K
−70	203,16	0,1543	98,40	0,6042	1563	1,6552	0,6398	73,30	0,3608	83,86	157,16	0,9320	1,2928
−65	208,16	0,2104	127,0	0,6088	1174	1,6426	0,8519	72,67	0,3491	85,01	157,68	0,9376	1,2867
−60	213,16	0,2823	161,3	0,6135	894,4	1,6300	1,118	72,03	0,3379	86,15	158,18	0,9430	1,2809
−55	218,16	0,3728	202,1	0,6184	691,6	1,6172	1,446	71,40	0,3273	87,28	158,68	0,9482	1,2755
−50	223,16	0,4856	250,1	0,6233	541,8	1,6043	1,845	70,76	0,3171	88,41	159,17	0,9534	1,2705
−45	228,16	0,6242	305,6	0,6284	429,7	1,5913	2,327	70,11	0,3073	89,55	159,66	0,9584	1,2657
−40	233,16	0,7935	369,3	0,6336	344,9	1,5782	2,900	69,44	0,2978	90,69	160,13	0,9634	1,2612
−35	238,16	0,9949	441,6	0,6390	279,6	1,5649	3,577	68,75	0,2889	91,85	160,60	0,9683	1,2569
−30	243,16	1,236	523,1	0,6445	229,0	1,5518	4,367	68,06	0,2799	93,00	161,06	0,9730	1,2529
−25	248,16	1,520	614,2	0,6502	189,2	1,5380	5,286	67,35	0,2714	94,16	161,51	0,9778	1,2491
−20	253,16	1,852	715,2	0,6560	157,7	1,5244	6,342	66,60	0,2631	95,35	161,95	0,9824	1,2455
−15	258,16	2,237	826,3	0,6620	132,5	1,5105	7,549	65,89	0,2552	96,49	162,38	0,9870	1,2421
−10	263,16	2,680	948,0	0,6682	112,1	1,4965	8,922	65,14	0,2475	97,66	162,80	0,9914	1,2389
−5	268,16	3,186	1080,3	0,6746	95,51	1,4824	10,47	64,38	0,2401	98,83	163,21	0,9957	1,2358
0	273,16	3,762	1223,6	0,6812	81,89	1,4680	12,21	63,60	0,2328	100,00	163,60	1,0000	1,2328
5	278,16	4,412	1377,8	0,6880	70,64	1,4534	14,16	62,82	0,2258	101,16	163,98	1,0042	1,2300
10	283,16	5,142	1543,3	0,6951	61,26	1,4387	16,32	62,02	0,2190	102,33	164,35	1,0083	1,2273
15	288,16	5,958	1720,2	0,7024	53,40	1,4237	18,73	61,21	0,2124	103,49	164,70	1,0123	1,2247
20	293,16	6,864	1908,3	0,7100	46,77	1,4085	21,38	60,38	0,2060	104,66	165,04	1,0162	1,2222
25	298,16	7,868	2108,4	0,7179	41,14	1,3930	24,31	59,54	0,1997	105,83	165,37	1,0202	1,2199
30	303,16	8,973	2319,4	0,7261	36,35	1,3773	27,51	58,69	0,1936	106,98	165,67	1,0240	1,2176
35	308,16	10,19	2542,8	0,7346	32,22	1,3613	31,04	57,82	0,1876	108,14	165,96	1,0278	1,2153
40	313,16	11,52	2779,0	0,7435	28,66	1,3450	34,89	56,92	0,1818	109,31	166,23	1,0314	1,2131
45	318,16	12,97	3027,0	0,7529	25,57	1,3283	39,11	56,00	0,1760	110,48	166,48	1,0350	1,2110
50	323,16	14,55	3288,0	0,7627	22,88	1,3112	43,71	55,06	0,1704	111,65	166,71	1,0385	1,2089
55	328,16	16,26	3561,4	0,7729	20,52	1,2938	48,74	54,08	0,1648	112,83	166,91	1,0421	1,2069
60	333,16	18,11	3849,1	0,7837	18,44	1,2760	54,24	53,04	0,1592	114,05	167,09	1,0457	1,2049
65	338,16	20,11	4150,4	0,7951	16,60	1,2577	60,24	51,98	0,1537	115,26	167,24	1,0492	1,2029
70	343,16	22,27	4467,1	0,8073	14,97	1,2388	66,82	50,85	0,1482	116,50	167,35	1,0527	1,2009
75	348,16	24,58	4799,1	0,8201	13,51	1,2193	74,05	49,66	0,1426	117,77	167,43	1,0563	1,1989
80	353,16	27,07	5147,3	0,8339	12,20	1,1991	82,00	48,39	0,1370	119,08	167,47	1,0599	1,1969
85	358,16	29,73	5513,1	0,8487	11,01	1,1783	90,79	47,00	0,1312	120,47	167,47	1,0636	1,1948
90	363,16	32,58	5898,1	0,8646	9,944	1,1566	100,6	45,57	0,1255	121,87	167,44	1,0668	1,1923
95	368,16	35,64	6302,3	0,8820	8,970	1,1338	111,5	43,97	0,1194	123,40	167,37	1,0708	1,1902
100	373,16	38,89	6727,8	0,9010	8,082	1,1099	123,7	42,24	0,1132	125,00	167,24	1,0749	1,1881
105	378,16	42,37	7176,7	0,9221	7,265	1,0845	137,7	40,34	0,1067	126,68	167,02	1,0792	1,1859
110	383,16	46,07	7653,7	0,9456	6,508	1,0575	153,7	38,25	0,0998	128,47	166,72	1,0837	1,1835
115	388,16	50,02	8149,8	0,9725	5,814	1,0283	172,0	35,89	0,0925	130,43	166,32	1,0885	1,1810
120	393,16	54,23	8680,3	1,0039	5,169	0,9962	193,5	33,34	0,0848	132,47	165,81	1,0936	1,1784
125	398,16	58,70	9240,6	1,0415	4,570	0,9602	218,4	30,40	0,0764	134,78	165,18	1,0993	1,1757
130	403,16	63,47	9837,3	1,0890	4,001	0,9183	249,9	27,06	0,0671	137,36	164,42	1,1053	1,1724
135	408,16	65,55	10472	1,1541	3,453	0,8665	289,6	23,0	0,0564	140,2	163,2	1,1122	1,1686
140	413,16	73,93	11140	1,2624	2,842	0,7921	351,9	17,0	0,0412	144,2	161,2	1,1210	1,1622
144 (crit.)	417,16	78,53	11718	1,7631	1,763	0,5672	567,2	0	0	153,41	153,41	1,1432	1,1432

* Assuming for liquid chlorine at 0°C the enthalpy value $i_0 = 100$ kcal/kg
** Assuming for liquid chlorine at 0°C the entropy value $s_0 = 1$ kcal/kg·°K

(Reprinted by permission.)

138

since the density of liquid chlorine at 25°C is close to 1.4 g/cc as against 24.3 gpl in the gaseous state at liquefaction pressure and 2.93 gpl at atmospheric pressure. The thermodynamic properties, determined by several authors, have been critically revised by L. Ziegler,[12] who takes the following values for the critical constants, as a basis for the calculation of other characteristics.

Critical temperature 144.0°C

Critical pressure 78.525 atmosphere absolute (1 atm = 760 mm Hg)

Critical volume 1.763 liters per kilogram

Vapor pressures and heats of evaporation at several temperatures, together with densities, enthalpies and entropies for both liquid and vapor phases at equilibrium, are collected in Table 1.† Other properties for the aggregation states are given hereunder.

Gaseous Chlorine

Heat capacities. The heat capacity at constant volume and at 25°C, as determined by Ulich,[11] is 6.08 cal/mole/°C, or 0.086 kcal/kg/°C. The molar value is considerably higher than for other diatomic gases and closer to that predicted by the equipartition principle (6.93); this fact is in agreement with the tendency shown by chlorine to become more easily excited in its vibrational degree of freedom than other diatomic molecules.

In the temperature range between −70°C and +150°C the heat capacity at constant pressure may be expressed as a function of temperature, t by the equation:[12]

$$c_p = 0.11210 + 0.66094 \times 10^{-4}t - 0.14468 \times 10^{-6}t^2 \text{ (kcal/kg/°C)}$$

At 25°C, $c_p/c_v = 1.325$

Thermal expansion coefficient at atmospheric pressure. Within the temperature range from 0°C to 100°C the average value of α in the equation $V = V_0(1 + \alpha t)$ for the superheated vapor is 0.003817, as against the value $1/273 = 0.003663$ for ideal gases. The value of the specific volume, V, at 0°C and 1 atm is 0.3111 l/g to which corresponds the density, $\gamma = 3.214$ gpl.

Thermal conductivity at 0°C and 1 atm

† Similar data were published by Hulme and Tillmann[5], as well as by Kapoon and Martin.[6]

$= 19.3 \times 10^{-6}$ cal/cm/sec/°C according to Franck.[3]

Optical properties.[7] In the rarefied state, the gas presents an absorption band in the ultraviolet region, extending from 356 to 302 mμ. When the pressure is raised, the absorption band widens further, until it covers the wave length range between 465 and 263 mμ. The emission flame spectrum is continuous, whereas the spectrum excited by gaseous discharge under reduced pressure in a Geissler tube gives numerous lines, which show a particular intensity in the violet region. The spark spectrum is characterized by 10 lines in the region between 611 and 413 mμ.

The refractive index for white light versus air at 0°C and 760 mm Hg is 1.000772.

Magnetic properties.[7] Chlorine gas is slightly diamagnetic, with a susceptibility $\chi = -18.7 \times 10^{-10}$ (cgs)$_{em}$ units at 0°C and 760 mm.

Diffusion and solubility in water. The diffusion coefficient in water at 16°C is 1.098 cm^2/day. The solubilities at different temperatures under atmospheric pressure are given in Table 2. They indicate the amount of chlorine that disappears in the gas phase until

TABLE 2. SOLUBILITY OF CHLORINE IN WATER[7]

°C	gCl$_2$/100g H$_2$O	°C	gCl$_2$/100g H$_2$O
10	0.9972	50	0.3925
15	0.8495	60	0.3295
20	0.7293	70	0.2793
25	0.6413	80	0.2227
30	0.5723	90	0.127
40	0.4590	100	0.000

the latter reaches equilibrium with dissolved chlorine and its hydrolysis products, which form according to the reaction

$$Cl_2 + H_2O \rightleftharpoons HClO + H^+ + Cl^-$$

for which the reaction constant at 25°C is

$$K = \frac{(HClO)(H^+)(Cl^-)}{(Cl_2)_{aq}} = 4.66 \times 10^{-4}$$

Consequently, 1 liter of originally pure water, after attaining equilibrium conditions under 1 atm of chlorine gas at 25°, will contain, beside approximately 0.06 mole of free chlorine, also about 0.03 mole of hydrochloric acid and 0.03 mole of hypochlorous acid. Because of hydrolysis, the dependence of chlorine solubility on pressure does not obey Henry's law.

The solubility in saturated sodium chloride solution is 1/7 to 1/8 of that in water at same temperature and is further decreased by acidifying the solution. However, chlorine solubility is substantially higher in muriatic acid, and at 25°C approaches 10 gpl in 25% HCl; this fact is explained by assuming the existence of the compound, HCl_3.

When chlorinated water or brine are cooled down to near 0°C, crystals of hexahydrate, $Cl_2.6H_2O$, and octahydrate, $Cl_2.8H_2O$, are formed. In an open vessel, i.e., under atmospheric pressure, chlorine hydrate dissociates into gaseous chlorine and water vapor above $+9.6°C$ and into gaseous chlorine and ice below $-0.24°C$. Accordingly, chlorine solubility in pure water attains its maximum at $+9.6°C$ if chlorine hydrate is present as a solid phase.

The solubility of gaseous chlorine in organic liquids, notably chlorinated derivatives, is generally high. For instance, in carbon tetrachloride at 0°C and 1 atm press., chlorine solubility is 250 gpl.

Liquid Chlorine

In the liquid state chlorine is a pale-yellow substance, whose color intensity decreases with a lowering in temperature. The violet, ultraviolet and blue parts of the spectrum are easily absorbed.

An elegant laboratory experiment consists of liquefying chlorine using the same method by which Faraday attained this purpose for the first time. A V-shaped tube is sealed and turned upside down after filling one leg with chlorine hydrate crystals. This leg is dipped into lukewarm water, while the other is kept cool by melting ice. The hydrate decomposes and the dissociation pressure is sufficient to cause liquid chlorine to collect in the cold leg. In today's laboratories it is of course much more expeditious to obtain liquid chlorine by using a mixture of solid carbon dioxide and acetone to cool a stream of dry chlorine gas down to liquefaction temperature at atmospheric pressure ($-35°C$).

In modern industrial plants the chlorine gas from the electrolytic cells is liquefied at the daily rate of hundreds of tons, either by compression at several atmospheres while keeping the temperature close to the ambient value, or by deep cooling with "Freon," under pressures slightly above 1 atm.

Densities and specific volumes of liquid chlorine at different temperatures are listed in Table 1.

The *mean specific heat* at constant pressure and within the range from 0 to 24°C is 0.2262 cal/g.

The compressibility factor, that is, the per cent change in volume for each unit change in pressure, is higher than that of any other element in the liquid state. In Table 3 are listed the values at 20°C determined by Richards and Stull.[9]

TABLE 3. COMPRESSIBILITY FACTOR OF LIQUID CHLORINE AT 20°C

Pressure Range, bar	Compressibility factor, $\gamma = \%$ volume/bar
0–100	0.0116
100–200	0.0108
200–300	0.0100
300–400	0.0089
400–500	0.0083

The compressibility factor, γ, increases rapidly with temperature. Accordingly, the average values determined for several temperature ranges and for the lower pressure values are listed in Table 4.

TABLE 4.

Temperature range, °C	Compressibility factor, $\gamma = \%$ volume/bar
34–38	0.0225
63–67	0.0366
90–93	0.0637

The *thermal conductivity* at 25°C is about 49.5×10^{-5} cal/cm/sec/°C.

The *electrical conductivity* is in the order of 7×10^{-8} mho/cm. This low value classes chlorine among insulators, as predictable in consideration of its covalent bond.

The *dielectric constant*, ϵ, between -60 and $+8°C$, as measured by Linde, changes from 2.164 to 1.948.

The *magnetic susceptivity* at $-16°C$ is -0.59×10^{-6} (cgs)$_{em}$ units.

The *refractive index* of liquid chlorine is slightly smaller than that of water. For the D-line of sodium at $14°C$ its value is 1.367.

The *viscosity* changes considerably with temperature, in that it passes from 0.005 to 0.007 dynes-sec/cm^2 when the temperature varies between -33 and $-76°C$. These values are comparable with that of water at $20°C$, which is 0.01 dynes-sec/cm^2.

The *surface tension* ranges between 29.28 and 13.39 dynes/cm for temperatures between -49.5 and $+50°C$. (Water at $20°C$ has a surface tension of 72.8 dynes/cm.)

Liquid chlorine is a good solvent for a number of compounds, notably chlorides, such as CCl_4, $TiCl_4$, $SnCl_4$, $PbCl_4$, $POCl_3$, $AsCl_3$, SCl_2. Most of the oxygenated organic compounds, notably alcohols, are soluble, with formation of addition compounds.

Solid Chlorine

Solid chlorine consists of pale-yellow crystals belonging to the orthorombic system and iso-morphous with those of bromine and iodine. They present a strong birefrangence in parallel and normal directions to the principal axis.

The main physical constants of the solid state are the following:
Melting point $-100.98°C$
Heat of fusion 1531 cal/mole
Heat of sublimation 6980 cal/mole
Specific heat 2.31 cal/mole at $21.9°C$
             13.35 cal/mole at $159.8°K$
Density 2.1 g/cc

Chemical Properties and Compounds

Oxidation states. Chlorine is a nonmetal that occupies the second place, after fluorine, in the group of halogens (salt producers). Its proximity to the right corner of the Periodic Table points out its outstandingly electro-negative nature, that is, its marked electronic affiinty, or oxidizing power, which is next only to that of fluorine and oxygen and confers on

its chemical bond with most other elements the total or partial ionic character that is required to form stable compounds.[8]

With its electronegative value of 3, chlorine joins nitrogen in the third place on the electronegativity scale, after fluorine (e.v. = 4) and oxygen (e.v. = 3.5). The high oxidizing power of chlorine is reflected by the relatively high place occupied by the redox couple Cl_2/Cl^- in the electromotive force series, whereby its standard electrode potential at $25°C$ is $+1.36$ v. By definition, this is the open-circuit voltage measured between the poles of a galvanic cell made up of two half-cells, or electrodes, respectively consisting of a nonreactive piece of metal, such as platinum, in contact with a chlorine solution of unit activity saturated with chlorine gas at 1 atm pressure, and of another piece of platinum in contact with a solution of hydrogen ions of unit activity saturated with hydrogen gas at 1 atm pressure, the two solutions being in communication through a suitable liquid junction. Under such conditions, the chlorine electrode is positive versus the standard hydrogen electrode: this means that, if the equilibrium between the electrostatic and the electrochemical forces were upset by closing the circuit between the two metallic poles, the spontaneous passage of current thus resulting would be the outcome of an oxidation of hydrogen by chlorine, with formation of hydrochloric acid:

$$H_2 + Cl_2 \rightarrow 2H^+ + 2Cl^-$$

As a consequence of the fact that chlorine and nitrogen have the same electronegativity value, the molecule of nitrogen trichloride, NCl_3, is kept in a metastable equilibrium by a purely covalent bond; accordingly, this oily substance is so unstable that it can be made to decompose with explosive violence even by a moderate shock. On the other hand, al-though belonging to the same group, chlorine and fluorine are sufficiently apart on said scale to form the stable compounds, ClF and ClF_3, while the slight difference in electro-negativity between chlorine and oxygen allows them to form several compounds, most of which are unstable, due to the weakness in ionic character presented by such bonds.

The oxidation states that chlorine may

acquire, when combined with hydrogen and oxygen, range from -1 to $+7$, as follows:

-1 Cl^-, HCl
0 Cl_2
$+1$ $HClO$, Cl_2O
$+2$ no compound
$+3$ $ClO_2{}^-$, $HClO_2$
$+4$ ClO_2
$+5$ $ClO_3{}^-$, $HClO_3$
$+6$ no compound
$+7$ $ClO_4{}^-$, $HClO_4$, Cl_2O_7

It is noteworthy that chlorine differs markedly from its congener fluorine, in that the latter is too electronegative to combine with any other element in an oxidation state higher than -1. Consequently, whereas fluorine is the only halogen assuming a negative oxidation state to form compounds with oxygen, chlorine establishes in this respect a pattern of several positive oxidation states that is closely reproduced by its following congeners.

In the two extreme oxidation states, -1 and $+7$, the corresponding anions, Cl^- and $ClO_4{}^-$, acquire the same electronic structure as argon and neon, respectively, and thus show some of the stable characteristics proper to noble gases.

Metallic compounds. The greatest stability is shown by the oxidation state -1, in particular when the chemical bond structure is prevailingly ionic in character, as in alkali metal chlorides, LiCl, NaCl, KCl. In the molten state these salts are dissociated into alkali metal ions, Li^+, Na^+, K^+, and chloride ions, Cl^-, thus exhibiting electrolytic conductivity. The ionic dissociation of these chlorides, when dissolved in water, is almost complete, so that they are typical "strong electrolytes." Hydrogen chloride, HCl, is a colorless gas with a very pungent odor; it is very soluble in water, and its aqueous solution is called hydrochloric or muriatic acid. It is a strong acid, forming salts that are called *chlorides.* Metal chlorides are generally characterized by crystalline structure and high melting point (for example, NaCl, 800°C; KCl, 790°C; $FeCl_3$, 282°C).

Chloride complexes. Chloride has an outstanding capability of combining with metals also to form complex anions. Thus, the tetrachloromercurate ion, $HgCl_4{}^-$, is formed by adding mercurous chloride, Hg_2Cl_2, or mercuric chloride, $HgCl_2$, to a solution containing an alkali metal chloride, such as NaCl, whereby the solubility of both mercury salts is markedly increased. If hydrochloric acid or nitric acid are separately contacted with gold, no significant attack of this metal takes place. However, if gold is immersed in a mixture of both acids, called *aqua regia,* it will be readily dissolved, the rate of attack being promoted by the formation of the tetrachloroaurate ion, $AuCl_4^-$. Platinum is similarly attacked by aqua regia and dissolved as hexachloroplatinate ion, $PtCl_6{}^{--}$. An analogous dissolving action, through the mechanism of complex ion formation, is exerted on gold and platinum also by hot hydrochloric acid saturated with free chlorine.

Oxygen compounds. Hypochlorous acid, HClO, is formed from free chlorine dissolved in water, as the result of a hydrolysis process, whereby Cl atoms are partly reduced from the original state $+0$ in the free molecule, and partly oxidized with the consequent production of hydrochloric acid and hypochlorous acid:

$$Cl_2 + H_2O \rightleftarrows 2H^+ + Cl^- + ClO^-$$

The bleaching and sterilizing action of chlorine in water, so widely used for sanitation purposes, is due to this buildup of hypochlorous acid, which can easily react with organic matter by giving up its oxygen atom "in statu nascenti":

$$ClO^- \rightarrow Cl^- + O^*$$

If the solution to which chlorine is added contains as alkali, such as sodium hydroxide, the reaction may be written as follows:

$$Cl_2 + 2OH^- \rightarrow Cl^- + ClO^- + H_2O$$

The reaction product is a bleaching and sterilizing solution of sodium hypochlorite, NaClO, with a substantially higher concentration of "available chlorine" (i.e., chlorine capable of releasing an equivalent amount of atomic oxygen) than is possible to achieve with simply chlorinated water.

Bleaching powder is produced by passing chlorine gas over slaked lime, i.e., calcium hydroxide, so as to form a compound whose average hypochlorite content corresponds to the reaction

$$Ca(OH)_2 + Cl_2 \rightarrow Ca(ClO)Cl + H_2O$$

All these processes for the obtaining of hypochlorite must be conducted under carefully controlled conditions of temperature and reactant concentration, in order to prevent disproportionation of hypochlorite to the more stable chlorate:

$$3ClO^- \rightarrow ClO_3 + 2Cl^-$$

This reaction can be most simply achieved by electrolyzing a sodium chloride or a potassium chloride solution at relatively high temperature without taking any precaution to keep the hydroxide forming at the cathode separated from chlorine developing at the anode, as would be necessary if these two products were to be obtained separately.

Sodium hypochlorite can also be manufactured by straightforward electrolysis, without diaphragm, but under much more carefully controlled conditions than required by chlorates.

Calcium chlorate, $Ca(ClO_3)_2$, and sodium chlorate, $NaClO_3$, may be crystallized from their mother liquor and find use as weed killers. For the fabrication of matches and fireworks potassium chlorate, $KClO_3$, is preferred to sodium chlorate, because it is less deliquescent, although more expensive.

Perchlorates, such as $KClO_4$, can be made by disproportionation of the corresponding chlorates, when brought to the melting point:

$$4KClO_3 \rightarrow 3KClO_4 + KCl$$

A more convenient way, however, is to electrolyze a chlorate solution, by use of an anodic material, such as platinum, presenting a sufficiently high overvoltage to oxygen discharge, so as to allow the anodic oxidation of chlorate ion to perchlorate ion:

$$ClO_3^- + OH^- \rightarrow ClO_4^- + \frac{1}{2}H_2 + e^-$$

Perchlorates are more stable and therefore less hazardous than chlorates. However, any contact with easily ignitable matter, such as organic substances, must be carefully avoided in order to prevent an immediate danger of fire and explosion.

Perchloric acid can be separated by distillation under reduced pressure from an acidified perchlorate solution. It distills and crystallizes as monohydrate acid, $HClO_4.H_2O$.

As to the three chlorine oxides listed above, the monoxide, Cl_2O, is a yellow gas condensing at about 4°C; it can be obtained by passing chlorine over mercuric oxide, HgO. Chlorine dioxide, ClO_2, is the only known compound of chlorine in the oxidation state + 4. It develops as a reddish-yellow gas when a strong acid is added to a solid chlorate, with the tendency to decompose into chlorine and oxygen with an explosive reaction rate, which renders any such procedure very dangerous. However, if the reaction is carried out in aqueous solution, the produced chlorine dioxide remains dissolved and finds an important application in modern pulp bleaching, by virtue of its milder and more selective action on the wood fibers than that exhibited by hypochlorite. When dissolved in an alkaline solution, chlorine dioxide disproportionates into chlorate and chlorite ions:

$$2ClO_2 + 2OH^- \rightarrow ClO_3^- + ClO_2^- + H_2O$$

Chlorite ions, however, are very unstable in that they tend in turn to disproportionate into chloride and chlorate ions.

Chlorine heptoxide, Cl_2O_7, is the anhydride of perchloric acid and is obtained by dehydration of the latter by phosphorus pentoxide. It separates as an oily liquid that decomposes with explosive violence.

Compounds with nonmetals and metalloids. In most other chlorine compounds the covalent bond character prevails and the intermolecular forces of attraction are comparatively weak, with correspondingly low boiling points and melting points.

A typical example is offered by carbon tetrachloride, CCl_4, melting at − 23°C and boiling at 77°C.

Organic Chlorine Compounds. The high electronegativity value of chlorine enables it to form very stable compounds with a host of saturated and unsaturated hydrocarbons, as well as with more complex organic substances; of these, more than two thousand are described by Huntress.[6]

The economic importance of many among such products can hardly be overestimated, because of their peculiar properties, as solvents, CCl_4 cleaning agents, $CHCl = CCl_2$, insecticides, such as gammexane and DDT and plastics; among the latter, a particular mention is deserved by PVC, i.e., the polymer of vinyl chloride, $CH_2 = CHCl$.

Chlorination of organic compounds may involve reactions of addition to the unsaturated bonds, substitution of hydrogen and replacement of groups, all such processes being of a highly exothermic nature. The chlorinating agent may be not only chlorine gas as such, but also hydrochloric acid or hypochlorous acid. The reaction must often be promoted by suitable catalysts, many of which are halogen (chlorine) carriers. When chain mechanisms are to be favored, the activation energy for the reaction can be usefully provided by light (photohalogenation) or nuclear energy. Preparation and properties of some among the most important organic chlorine compounds are described by Sconce.[10]

Chlorine Handling

Physiological Response and Toxicity. Chlorine gas has a characteristic, pungent odor with a detectability threshold of a few parts per million in air.

Liquid chlorine in contact with eyes, skin or clothing may cause severe burns; as soon as it is released in the atmosphere, it vaporizes with irritating effects and a suffocating action, which were exploited in World War I by using it as a war gas. The physiological response to the presence of any amount of chlorine gas in air may be evaluated from the following data published by the Bureau of Mines (Technical Paper No. 248). Concentration values are given in parts per million by volume.

Least detectable odor	ppm 3.5
Least amount required to cause irritation of throat	ppm 15.1
Least amount required to cause coughing	ppm 30.2
Least amount required to cause slight symptoms of poisoning after several hours exposure	ppm 1.0
Maximum amount that can be breathed for one hour without serious effects	ppm 4.0
Amounts dangerous in 30 minutes to one hour	ppm 40–60
Amount likely to be fatal after a few deep breaths	ppm 1000

Consequently, chlorine must be considered as a hazardous chemical, to be handled in accordance with ICC pertinent regulations and specifications. When dealing with liquid chlorine containers, whatever their size, a suitable gas mask should be at hand, in order that proper action may be taken to control any sudden and accidental escape of chlorine gas into the atmosphere.

Storage and Shipment. Chlorine is always stored in the liquid state. Big chlorine manufacturing plants are provided with liquefaction equipment also when the whole production is to be captively used at site. In such case, part of it is stored after liquefaction and used as a fly-wheel to provide for any momentary peak or decline in demand from the processing plant sections. The storage tanks are connected with the utilization gas header through a vaporizer.

Before liquefaction, chlorine is thoroughly dried, so as not to be corrosive against the steel containers in which it is stored or shipped.

Cylinders for chlorine transportation are of seamless construction and have a capacity ranging from 1 to 150 pounds. Ton containers are of welded construction and in their maximum size have a loaded weight of 3700 pounds. Tank cars may hold up to 55 tons and tank barges as much as 600 tons. All types of containers used in transportation are subject to the regulations and specifications of the United States Coast Guard or the Interstate Commerce Commission.

References

1. Bloch, M. R., "The social influence of salt," *Scien. Amer.*, **209**, No. 1, 110 (July 1963).
2. Chlorine Institute Pamphlets, Drawings and Miscellaneous Publications, The Chlorine Institute, Inc., 342 Madison Ave., New York, N.Y. 10017.
3. Frank, F. U., *Z. Elektrochemie*, **55**, 636 (1951).
4. Hampel, C. A., Ed., "Encyclopedia of Electrochemistry," New York, Reinhold Publishing Corp., 1964. Entries bearing *Chlorine Industry* and *Chlorine Production* headings; *Chlorates*; *Perchlorates*; *Hydrochloric Acid Electrolysis*; *Sodium, Electrolytic Production*.
5. Hulme, R. E., and Tillmann, A. B., *Chem. Eng.*, **56**, 99 (Jan. 1949).
6. Huntress, E. M., "Organic Chlorine Compounds," New York, John Wiley and Sons, Inc., 1948.

6a. Kapoor, R. M., and Martin, J. J., "Thermodynamic Properties of Chlorine," Engineering Research Institute Publications, Ann Arbor, University of Michigan Press, 1957.

7. Meyer, R. J., "Gmelins Handbuch der anorganischen Chemie—Chlor," Berlin, Verlag Chemie G.M.B.H., 1927.

8. Pauling, L., "General Chemistry," San Francisco, W. H. Freeman and Company, 1959.

9. Richards, Th. W., and Stull, D. R., *J. Am. Chem. Soc.*, **26**, 408 (1904).

10. Sconce, J. S., Ed., "Chlorine," New York, Reinhold Publishing Corp., 1962.

11. Ulich, H., *Lehrb. phys. Chem.*, 5 Aufl., Dresden u. Leipzig (1948).

12. Ziegler, L., *Chem. Ing. Tech.*, **22**, 229 (1950).

ORONZIO DE NORA AND
PATRIZIO GALLONE

CHROMIUM

Chromium is element 24 in the Periodic Table occurring in the subgroup of Group VI that contains molybdenum and tungsten. It is a hard, blue-white metal crystallizing in the cubic system. The mineral, chromite, is its only important source.

Vauquelin discovered chromium in 1797 in a new red lead mineral known as crocoite ($PbCrO_4$) from Siberia. The name chromium is derived from the Greek word "chromos" meaning color because chromium compounds are highly colored. A year later Vauquelin claimed to have isolated chromium by heating Cr_2O_3 with charcoal. Moissan, in 1893, reduced chromic oxide with coal in the electric furnace, and in 1898, Goldschmidt obtained carbon-free chromium by reducing Cr_2O_3 with aluminum.

Chromium ores were first used about 1800 to produce chemicals for the tanning and pigment industries. They were used as refractories in 1879, and they became metallurgically important in 1910.

Chromium is never found in the free state in nature, and most ores consist of the mineral, chromite. The ideal formula for this ore is FeO–Cr_2O_3 containing 68% Cr_2O_3 and 32% FeO, but the actual composition of the higher grade ores varies between 42–56% Cr_2O_3 and 10–26% FeO with varying amounts of magnesia, alumina and silica also present.

The chief sources of chromite are the U.S.S.R., Union of South Africa, the Philippines, and Southern Rhodesia, in that order.

Chromite is an insoluble mineral with the following properties:

Fracture	Brittle, uneven
Mohs hardness	5.5
Specific gravity	4.1–4.9
Color	Black to brownish-black
Magnetism	May be weakly magnetic
Softening points	1260–1425°C
Chemical properties	Neutral, insoluble in most slags

Most chromium ores are hand sorted but can be beneficiated to give a concentrate with about 50% Cr_2O_3, but this treatment does not improve the chromium-to-iron ratios.

Chromium ores are divided into three groups: (1) metallurgical, (2) refractory, and (3) chemical. About 52% of the ore used in the United States is metallurgical, 32% refractory, and 16% chemical grade.

The metallurgical grade must be hard and lumpy, contain a minimum of 48% Cr_2O_3, and have a chromium to iron ratio of 3:1.

Ores for use as refractories must be high in Cr_2O_3 plus Al_2O_3 and low in iron. Magnesium oxide in excess is added to the ores to form magnesium silicates on firing.

Chemical ore should be low in SiO_2 and Al_2O_3 and high in Cr_2O_3, but the specifications for this grade are not as rigid as for the other two grades and depend on price, availability and past experience.

Derivation

There are two classes of chromium available to industry: (1) ferrochromium and (2) chromium metal. Ferrochromium is produced by the direct reduction of the ore and will be discussed later. Chromium metal is produced electrolytically or by the reduction of chromium compounds, generally Cr_2O_3 produced from the ore by processing to remove iron and other impurities.

Commercial chromium metal has been prepared in large amounts by the reduction of Cr_2O_3 by aluminum.

$$Cr_2O_3 + 2Al \rightarrow 2Cr + Al_2O_3$$

The oxide mixed with aluminum powder is

ignited in a refractory-lined container by means of barium peroxide and magnesium powder. The reaction is exothermic and sustains itself, and produces a 97–99% chromium metal containing aluminum, iron, and silicon as the chief impurities. The metal contains about 0.03% carbon, 0.02% sulfur, and 0.045% nitrogen.

A silicon reduction of Cr_2O_3 also produces chromium metal:

$$2Cr_2O_3 + 3Si \;\rightarrow\; 4Cr + 3SiO_2$$

This reaction is not self-sustaining and is carried out in an electric arc furnace. The product is similar to that from the aluminothermic process, but the aluminum content is lower and the silicon may run as high as 0.8%.

Chromium metal may also be produced by the reduction of Cr_2O_3 with carbon at low pressures:

$$Cr_2O_3 + 3C \;\rightarrow\; 2Cr + 3CO$$

The finely divided oxide and carbon are thoroughly mixed, briquetted, and heated to 1275–1400°C in a refractory vessel. A minimum pressure of about 280 to 315 μ is required for a reduction at 1400°C and low pressures cause chromium volatilization. The product obtained contains 0.015% carbon, 0.001% nitrogen, 0.04% oxygen, about 0.02% silicon, and less than 0.03% iron.

There are two commercial processes used for the electrowinning of chromium: (1) chrome-alum electrolytes and (2) chromic acid electrolytes.

The flowsheet (Fig. 1) of the Union Carbide

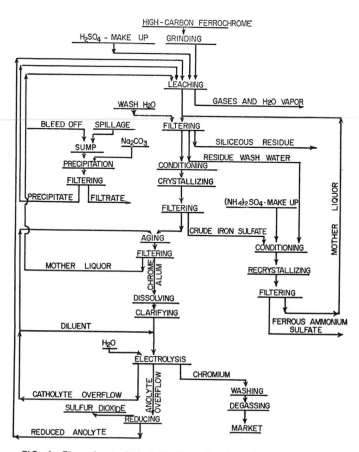

FIG. 1. Flow sheet of Marietta Plant for electrolytic chromium.

Corporation plant at Marietta, Ohio, is typical of the chrome-alum type plants and shows this process from the high-carbon ferrochrome starting material to the chromium metal.

Although chrome-alum can be prepared from leached chromite ore, the large number of steps necessary to produce a sufficiently pure electrolyte renders this process costly from both operating and construction viewpoints so that it is not used. Instead, a commercially available intermediate product, high-carbon ferrochrome, has been found to be the cheapest source of chromium and is used as the starting material.

High-carbon ferrochrome, crushed and sized to twenty mesh, is slowly fed to a brick-lined, lead-protected steel tank in which it is leached by a mixture of reduced anolyte, chrome-alum mother liquor and make-up sulfuric acid. The tank is equipped with a heating coil to keep the temperature near the boiling point and with a condenser to control the spray. Leaching plus digestion time is 48 hours. After leaching, the slurry is transferred to a holding tank and cooled to 80°C by the addition of cold mother liquor from the ferrous ammonium sulfate circuit and the silica and undissolved solids are filtered from the solution. The chromium in the filtrate is then converted to the non-alum forming condition by holding for several hours at elevated temperature. The temperature of the liquid is then lowered to about 5°C and the crude iron sulfate crystals that form are separated from the mother liquor by an acid-proof drum vacuum filter. The crude iron sulfate is dissolved by the liquor resulting from washing the leach residue. Ammonium sulfate is added to the solution which is conditioned at elevated temperatures for several hours. The ferrous ammonium sulfate is recovered and sold as fertilizer or for other purposes.

The mother liquor freed from the crude iron sulfate is clarified in an acid-proof filter press and then aged. Aging and crystallization take place at about 30°C and about 80% of the chromium is stripped as ammonium-chromium alum. The crystal slurry is filtered and washed and the filtrate is pumped to the leach circuit. The washed chromium-alum crystals are dissolved in hot water and filtered to produce cell feed.

Successful cell operation depends on close pH control of the catholyte and the presence of divalent chromium at the cathode. The sulfuric acid and chromic acid that form at the anode are prevented from mixing with the catholyte by diaphragms of limited porosity fitted into the cells. A description of the cells is given by Bacon in Ref. 1.

The flow of the catholyte through the diaphragm into the anolyte compartment controls the pH and the sulfuric acid content of the anolyte is held at 250 to 300 gpl by the addition of water.

The cathodes are removed from the cells on a 72-hour cycle, treated with hot water to remove adhering salts and the brittle deposit of chromium ($\frac{1}{8}$–$\frac{1}{2}$ inch thick) is stripped by hand.

The material thus obtained is crushed by rolls and washed with hot water. It is then placed in stainless steel cans and heated to dry and dehydrogenate it. For a more complete description of this process, see Ref. 2.

Typical cell operating data are given in Table 1.

TABLE 1.   CELL OPERATING DATA

Cathode current density	70 amp/ft²
Cell potential	4.2 volts
Current efficiency	45%
Electrical consumption	8.4 KWH/lb
pH	2.1–2.4
Catholyte temperature	53 ± 1°C
Time of deposition	72 hours
Cathode material	Type 316 stainless steel
Anode material	1–99 Ag–Pb

The current efficiency of 45% includes low efficiencies which always prevail during the start-up of a cell. The 2.1–2.4 pH also results in lower current efficiencies but provides a safe operating latitude.

The metal, after dehydrogenation, contains percentagewise 99.8 chromium, 0.14 iron, 0.01 carbon, nil silicon, phosphorus, aluminum, and manganese, 0.001 copper, 0.002 lead, 0.50 oxygen, 0.004 hydrogen, and <0.01 nitrogen.

Another way of producing electrolytic chromium is from a chromic acid bath.[3]

The cell conditions for the process are as follows:

Bath composition	300 gpl CrO_3, 4 gpl sulfate ion
Temperature	84–87°C
Current density	880 amp/ft^2
Current efficiency	6.7%
Plating time	80–90 hours
Production rate	1000 g/wk

The current efficiency of this process is low because (1) hydrogen evolution at the cathode increases the pH resulting in the precipitation of $Cr(OH)_3$ and $Cr(OH)_2$; and (2) it is inherently low as six electrons are required to reduce hexavalent ions to chromium metal.

The plating variables of this process are influenced by:

1. Higher operating temperatures (87°C) which enable the oxygen content of the metal to be reduced to 0.01%.
2. The ratio CrO_3/SO_2 should be below 100 to obtain low oxygen metal.
3. Current efficiencies above 8% are associated with high oxygen contents.
4. Better current efficiencies are obtained at low current densities.

The metal thus has lower iron and oxygen than that from the chrome-alum process. It contains 0.02% oxygen, 0.0025% nitrogen and 0.009% hydrogen, and the latter can be further lowered by the dehydrogenation treatment.

If ductile metal is desired, consideration must be given to the removal of oxygen from the metal obtained by both processes. There are four methods used to remove oxygen: (1) the hydrogen reduction method in which the electrolytic metal is heated to about 1500°C in a stream of pure, dry hydrogen. This method lowers the oxygen content to <0.005% and the nitrogen content to <0.001%; (2) the iodide purification process in which the impure chromium and iodine are sealed in an evacuated bulb containing an electrically heated wire. The bulb is heated to the temperature of formation of chromous iodide (about 900°C) which diffuses to the hot wire (1000–1300C°) where it decomposes and deposits chromium. The iodine which is freed then forms additional chromous iodide. The metal so produced analyzes 0.0008% oxygen, 0.003% nitrogen, 0.00008% hydrogen, and

0.001% carbon with other impurities being very low; (3) the calcium refining process in which the chromium is reacted with calcium vapor at about 1000°C in a titanium-lined bomb. The bomb containing the charge is first evacuated and then heated to temperature. A pressure to 20μ is maintained while heating until the calcium vapor reaches the cold end of the bomb and condenses. The resulting chromium metal contains 0.027% oxygen, 0.0018% nitrogen, 0.008% carbon, 0.012% sulfur, and 0.015% iron; (4) heating in a vacuum in the presence of a small amount of carbon which removes the oxygen as carbon monoxide.

Physical Properties

The physical properties of chromium are given in Table 2.[3-7]

Chemical Properties

Chromium is characterized chemically by the several valences it exhibits, chiefly 2, 3 and 6, although it may be 4 and 5 in chromium phenyl compounds and probably zero in chromium carbonyl, $Cr(CO)_6$; the intense and varied colors of its compounds; and the two forms in which the metal exists: active and passive. In the active form the metal reacts readily with dilute acids (with evolution of hydrogen) to form blue solutions of chromous, Cr^{++}, salts which absorb oxygen rapidly from the air and change to green solutions of chromic, Cr^{+++}, salts. If the metal is treated with oxidizing agents, such as nitric, chromic, phosphoric, chloric and perchloric acids, a thin oxide layer forms on the surface which passivates the metal so that it is then unreactive toward dilute acids. Halogen acids and halide salts must be absent to maintain the passive condition in acidic solutions. This passive film is responsible largely for the fine corrosion resistance of chromium and its alloys.

The dominant factors in the chemistry of chromium are the chromic compounds, including chromic oxide, Cr_2O_3, in which chromium has a $+3$ valence, and the chromates and dichromates, including chromium trioxide, CrO_3, in which the valence is $+6$. Depending on conditions, the chromic compounds are green or blue or violet, the

TABLE 2   PHYSICAL PROPERTIES

Atomic number	24
Atomic weight	51.996
Electronic structure	$(1s)^2$, $(2s)^2(2p)^6$, $(3s)^2(3p)^6(3d)^5$, $(4s)^1$
Isotopes	50 (4.31%), 52 (83.76%), 53 (9.55%), 54 (2.386%)[2]
Crystal structure, 20°C	Body-centered cubic, $a_0 = 2.8844–2.8848$ Å
Density, 20°C	7.19 g/cc
Melting point	1875°C
Boiling point	2199°C
Heat of fusion	3.2–3.5 kcal/mole

Heat content solid and liquid chromium — H_t-H_{298}
- 400°K = 595 cal/mole
- 1000°K = 4640
- 2000°K = 14,220
- 3000°K = 29,090

Heat content for gaseous chromium — H_t-H_{298}
- 400°K = 505
- 1000°K = 3480
- 2000°K = 8765
- 3000°K = 15,400
- 4000°K = 23,335
- 5000°K = 43,435
- 8000°K = 69,600

Vapor pressure	$\log P_{atm} = -20{,}473/_t + 7467$
Entropy	5.58 cal/g-atom
Latent heat of vaporization at b.p.	76.635 kcal/mole
Specific heat	5.55 cal/mole or 0.11 cal/g/°C
Linear coefficient of thermal expansion, 20°C	6.2×10^6
Thermal conductivity, 20°C	0.16 cgs units
Electrical resistivity, 20°C	12.9 microhm-cm
Magnetic susceptibility, 20°C	3.6×10^{-6} emu
Total emissivity at 100°C nonoxidizing atmos.	0.08

Reflectivity, λ Å

λ Å	3000	5000	10,000	40,000
%R	67	70	63	88

Refractive index	$\mu = 1.64–3.28$; $\lambda = 2{,}570–6{,}082$
Standard electrode potential valence	0 to $+3$; 0.71 volt
Valence	$+2$, $+3$, and $+6$
Superconductivity	0.08°K
Electrochemical equivalent (hexavalent)	0.08983 mg/coulomb
Electrochemical equivalent (trivalent)	0.17965 mg/coulomb
Thermal neutron absorption cross section	3.1 barns

chromates are usually yellow, although the insoluble silver chromate is red, and the dichromates are orange-red or red. The chromic ion also forms many coordination compounds having a coordination number of 6. The $+3$ and $+6$ chromium compounds are oxidizing agents and are in general stable in both solid and solution form, unless a reducing agent is present. The interesting chemistry of chromium compounds is treated extensively in many inorganic chemistry books; see also Refs. 3 and 5.

Elemental chromium reacts with anhydrous halogens, HCl and HF. Aqueous solutions of hydrohalogens will dissolve chromium, as will sulfuric acid. It is not affected by phosphoric acid, fuming nitric acid or aqua regia at room temperature. At 600–700°C chromium is attacked by alkali hydroxides, at 600–700°C sulfides are formed when it is exposed to sulfur vapor or hydrogen sulfide, and it also reacts with SO_2 in this temperature range. Oxidation of the metal occurs at about 1000°C in carbon monoxide, and it is attacked by phosphorus at about 800°C. Ammonia reacts with chromium at 850°C to form a nitride, and hot nitric oxide forms both a nitride and an oxide with chromium.

149

Chromium has a high oxidation resistance at elevated temperatures due to the formation of a tight oxide film on its surface.

Passivated chromium is resistant to acetic, benzoic, butyric, carbonic, citric, fatty, hydrobromic, hydroiodic, lactic, nitric, oleic, oxalic, palmitic, phosphoric, picric, salicylic, stearic, and tartaric acids. It is also resistant to acetone, air, methyl and ethyl alcohols, aluminum chloride and sulfate, ammonia, ammonium chloride, barium chloride, beer, benzyl chloride, calcium chloride, carbon dioxide, disulfide and tetrachloride, dry chlorine, chlorobenzene, chloroform, copper sulfate, ferric and ferrous chlorides, foodstuffs, formaldehyde, fruit products, glue, hydrogen sulfide, magnesium chloride, milk, mineral oils, motor fuels, crude petroleum products, phenols, photographic solutions, printing inks, sodium carbonate, chloride, hydroxide and sulfate, sugar, sulfur, sulfur dioxide, chlorinated, distilled and rain water, and zinc chloride and sulfate.

The first and second ionization potentials of chromium are 6.74 and 16.6 volts, respectively.

Chromium Compounds

The principal industrial compounds of chromium are sodium chromate and dichromate, potassium chromate and dichromate, chromium trioxide, basic chromic sulfate, and chromic oxide.

The first two compounds mentioned are produced by roasting chrome ore with soda ash or soda ash and lime.

The ore is crushed and ground to 90–98% through 200 mesh. It is then mixed with the soda ash and roasted at 1100–1150°C in oil-fired rotary kilns. The reaction is:

$$2Cr_2O_3 + 4Na_2CO_3 + 3O_2 \rightarrow 4Na_2CrO_4 + 4CO_2$$

The time of passage through the kiln is about 4 hours and the rate of oxidation increases with temperature, but to avoid a sticky charge, there is a limit on the maximum temperature.

The kiln product passes through a rotary cooler and the product is leached to dissolve the sodium chromate.

If the sodium chromate solution contains large amounts of sodium aluminate, the alumina is removed by treatment with sodium dichromate solution at a pH of about 9:

$$Na_2Al_2O_4 + Na_2Cr_2O_7 + 3H_2O \rightarrow Al_2O_3 \cdot 3H_2O + 2Na_2CrO_4$$

Sodium dichromate is made from the chromate by the following reaction:

$$2Na_2CrO_4 + H_2SO_4 \rightarrow Na_2Cr_2O_7 + Na_2SO_4 + H_2O$$

The Na_2SO_4 settles out and is removed.

Carbon dioxide under pressure can be used in place of H_2SO_4 in which case Na_2CO_3 is formed instead of Na_2SO_4. The hot concentrated sodium dichromate solution is filtered and cooled to 35°C to obtain crystals of the dihydrate which are dried in a rotary steam drier to remove free water and then screened and packed.

These salts are used in leather tanning, the textile industry, for passifying the surfaces of metals, as catalysts and in organic oxidations.

Potassium chromate is made in the same manner as the sodium salt but using K_2CO_3 instead of Na_2CO_3.

It is more economical, however, to make potassium dichromate from sodium dichromate rather than from the potassium chromate:

$$Na_2Cr_2O_7 + 2KCl \rightarrow K_2Cr_2O_7 + 2NaCl$$

The dichromate crystallizes out on cooling the hot solution and is separated from the NaCl.

Chromium trioxide which is used in chromium plating is prepared from sodium dichromate by the following reaction:

$$Na_2Cr_2O_7 + 2H_2SO_4 \rightarrow 2CrO_3 + 2NaHSO_4 + H_2O$$

The process consists of mixing sodium dichromate dihydrate with a slight excess of 66°Be H_2SO_4 in a steel tank or cast iron container, externally heated and provided with an agitator. The temperature is varied to just above the melting point of CrO_3 (197°C) where the solid phase has disappeared and the water evaporated. The agitation is then stopped and the mixture separates into a supernatant layer of $NaHSO_4$ and a lower layer of molten CrO_3. The layer of bisulfate is drawn off and goes to waste. The CrO_3 must not be overheated or held molten too long as the molten oxide decomposes with a loss of oxygen and the formation of lower oxides of chromium which contaminate solutions of the finished product.

Basic chromic sulfate used in leather tanning is prepared by reducing sodium dichromate by a carbohydrate or SO_2.

When commercial glucose is used the reaction is:

$$4Na_2Cr_2O_7 + 12H_2SO_4$$
$$+ C_6H_{12}O_6 + 26H_2O \rightarrow$$
$$8[Cr(OH)(H_2O)_5]SO_4 + 4Na_2SO_4 + 6CO_2$$

On using SO_2 as a reducing agent the reaction is:

$$Na_2Cr_2O_7 + 3SO_2 + 11H_2O \rightarrow$$
$$2[Cr(OH)(H_2O)_5]SO_4 + Na_2SO_4$$

Chromic oxide, Cr_2O_3, is used as a green pigment and as a starting material for aluminothermic chromium metal. It is prepared from sodium dichromate by reduction with sulfur if pigment grade is required and with carbon if starting material is desired. The reactions are:

$$Na_2Cr_2O_7 + S \rightarrow Na_2SO_4 + Cr_2O_3$$
$$Na_2Cr_2O_7 + C \rightarrow Na_2CO_3 + Cr_2O_3 + CO$$

The mixtures are ignited in a furnace or kiln, leached, filtered and washed, dried and pulverized. The product is usually in excess of 99% Cr_2O_3.

Chromic oxide is used as a pigment when chemical and heat resistance are required. It is also used as a ceramic color, for coloring cement, for green granules for asphalt roofing, in camouflage paints and in the production of chromium metal and Al-Cr master alloys.

Metallurgy

The consolidation of chromium metal may be carried out by powder metallurgy techniques or by arc melting in an inert atmosphere.

In powder metal consolidation, the metal is ball milled using chromium plated balls, then the powder is compressed at 20–30 tons/in.^{2} with or without a wax binder. The compacts are then heated to 300°C to remove the binder and then sintered at 1450 to 1550°C in a slow stream of purified hydrogen, helium or argon.

Very refractory crucibles such as pure zirconia or beryllia or alumina coated with thoria must be used when vacuum arc melting chromium. Under proper conditions of melting, the nitrogen in chromium-base alloys can be lowered to 0.01% or less and with the proper control, carbon deoxidation can be used to obtain metal with 0.01% oxygen and carbon. Chromium volatilization is the chief drawback of this process. Chromium may be arc-melted into a water-cooled copper mold in an inert atmosphere and in this case, no refractory material comes in contact with the molten metal. Scavengers such as yttrium or other rare earth elements may be added during melting, and it has been claimed that the workability and mechanical properties are improved by such additions.

Chromium when sufficiently pure, is ductile enough at elevated temperatures to be rolled, forged or extruded. On heating at 800 to 850°C in an inert atmosphere, arc-melted ingots have been forged and swaged. Light reductions must be made until the initial cast structure is broken down, after which heavier reductions can be made and rolling as low as 500°C accomplished. The metal may be extruded at 1100°C to break down the cast structure. The metal is usually sheathed with stainless steel or steel to protect it against contamination during hot working and the sheath removed by an acid treatment on completion of the working.

Chromium resembles cast steel in machinability, and machining is best accomplished using cobalt-base, high-speed steels at fast speeds and slow feed. Milling and drilling the metal are difficult.

Mechanical Properties

The mechanical properties of chromium are governed by metal purity, prior mechanical history, grain size, strain rate and surface condition. The metal should contain less than 0.2% oxygen, less than 0.01% nitrogen, below 0.01% carbon, below 0.15% silicon, and 4–18 ppm hydrogen to assure good tensile ductility. The ductility of chromium is decreased and its hardness increased by cold working.

As the temperature is raised from room to 700°C, the Brinell hardness of forged as-cast chromium decreases from 125 to 70. Arc-melted metal as-cast shows a minimum BHN of 50 at 300°C.

TABLE 3. MECHANICAL PROPERTIES AT VARIOUS TEMPERATURES

Temp. C°	Ultimate Strength, psi	Yield Point, psi	Proportional Limit, psi	Young's Modulus, psi	Elongation, %	Red. of area, %
Room	12,000	—	—	36×10^6	0	0
200	33,900	—	—	—	0	0
300	22,400	19,000	1,700	42×10^6	3	4
350	28,600	—	15,300	24.4×10^6	6	8
400	32,600	20,300	19,100	32.9×10^6	51	89
500	—	—	—	—	30	75
600	35,100	—	10,000	29×10^6	42	81
700	29,500	—	—	—	33	85
800	26,100	—	14,000	37×10^6	47	92

It has been claimed that the tensile strength of electrolytic chromium lies between 15,000 and 80,000 psi and Young's modulus between 12×10^6 and 33×10^6 psi depending on the density. Sintered chromium compacts show a decrease in tensile strength from 13,500 psi at 20°C to 10,200 psi at 900°C with a maximum elongation of 5% at 900°C.

Some tensile test results on swaged, arc-cast electrolytic metal recrystallized at 1200°C in hydrogen and tested at a strain rate of 0.017 in./in./min at the Bureau of Mines are given in Table 3.

Impact values of not over 1.5 ft-lb are obtained on unnotched samples of arc-cast metal at room temperature. At 400°C, this value is increased to 118 ft-lb.

Bend tests are generally used to determine the ductility of chromium. Using sintered electrolytic chromium samples, 2.5 × 0.5 × 0.5-inch in dimensions, the ductile-to-brittle transition temperature is found to be between 25 and 50°C. The impurities present, degree of working, and heat treatment alter this temperature range.

Chromium Coatings

Chromium surfaces are produced on other metals by decorative or hard electroplating and chromizing. Decorative plate varies in thickness between 0.00001 and 0.00002 inch and is usually deposited over a layer of electrodeposited nickel. "Hard" plating is used because of its wear resistance and low coefficient of friction.

For decorative and hard chromium plating, solutions of CrO_3 are exclusively used. A small amount of another ion (sulfate) is necessary to cause chromium deposition and H_2SO_4 in the ratio CrO_3/H_2SO_4 of 100/1 by weight is used but this ratio may vary.

Typical bath compositions used only as guides (for the best performance the current literature and proprietary processes should be examined) are

	Dilute bath (No. 1)	Concentrated bath (No. 2)
CrO_3, gpl	250	400
H_2SO_4, gpl	2.5	4

The current density and temperature are related for bright plating.

Unlike most plating baths, chromium plating employs anodes of a metal different from that being plated. Anodes are of Pb-Sb or Pb-Sn alloy.

The current efficiency is very low for the reasons given on page 148.

There are several methods used in modern chromizing. In one method, chromium is deposited on the surface to be plated from the gas phase and then the coating diffused in. In another process, a chromium layer is fused on the surface to be coated and diffused in, and, in a third process, chromium is electron beam deposited on the surface and diffused into the metal. Salt bath chromizing using $CrCl_2$ has been tried.

Ferrochromium

The various grades of ferrochromium are the alloys most used for adding chromium to steels.

The high-carbon ferrochromiums vary from 50 to 70% chromium, 5 to 9% carbon, and

1–12% silicon with 0.03% max. sulfur. Low-carbon ferrochromium varies from 65–73% chromium, 0.025 to 2% carbon, and 0.02–1% silicon. There is also a "Simplex" low-carbon ferrochromium varying in the ranges 68–72% chromium, 0.01–0.02% carbon, and ∼ 2% silicon. There are also proprietary exothermic ferrochromium mixtures which give off heat when added to a steel bath, thus causing less of a temperature drop in the molten steel and increased solution rate.

To produce high-carbon ferrochromium coke and chromite are fed into the top of an open-top submerged-arc furnace and the molten alloy is collected at the furnace bottom and cast into chills. After cooling, it is broken into lumps and graded. It is used to produce steels in which both chromium and carbon may be present or where blowing the bath with oxygen to reduce the carbon content is feasible.

Low-carbon ferrochromium is made by the silicon reduction of chromite in a two-stage process. First, a high-silicon ferrochromium, practically carbon free, is made in a submerged-arc furnace. This product is then treated with a synthetic slag containing Cr_2O_3 in an open-arc furnace. Another method of producing this material, which is said to be less costly, is by oxygen top-blowing high-carbon metal. This grade of ferrochromium is used in the production of steels in which the presence of carbon is harmful.

A very low-carbon ferrochromium is made by heating high-carbon ferrochromium with ground quartzite or by oxidizing high-carbon ferrochromium in a vacuum with the removal of carbon as carbon monoxide.

Chromium Alloys

Phase diagrams of chromium with other metals are given in Hanson's book, "The Constitution of Binary Alloys," and in the "Metals Handbook" published by the American Society for Metals.

Although pure chromium has been produced in the form of ingots, rod, sheet, and wire, its use as metal is limited due to its low ductility at ordinary temperatures. Most pure chromium is used for alloying purposes such as in the production of nickel-chromium or other nonferrous alloys. The chief use of ferrochromium is as an addition agent to steel.

Chromium is added in amounts up to 3% to low alloy steels to improve mechanical properties, increase hardenability, and improve atmospheric corrosion resistance. It is used in combination with molybdenum, nickel, manganese, and vanadium in steels for high-strength applications.

Air hardening steels containing 5–6% chromium are used in the oil industry because of their increased corrosion and oxidation. Martensitic steels containing 0.30% carbon and 12–14% chromium are used in cutlery manufacture while high-carbon 16–18% chromium steels are used as special tool and die steels. The greatest use of the ferritic or nonhardenable chromium steels (14.0–18.0% chromium, 0.12% carbon max.) is for equipment in the nitric acid industry and for decorative trim for buildings and automobiles. A 23–27% chromium steel is available as a good oxidation-resistant alloy.

Nickel or nickel plus manganese are added to high-chromium steels to make them austenitic with improved corrosion and oxidation resistance. These steels cannot be hardened by heat treatment.

Chromium is added to cobalt-base alloys in amounts up to 25% to give corrosion resistance and hardness. Cobalt-chromium-tungsten combinations are used for cutting tools and hard facing.

Nickel-base alloys with up to 20% chromium have high heat and electrical resistance.

Chromium is added to niobium-base alloys to impart improved strength and oxidation resistance.

It is also used in the so-called "superalloys" for high-temperature applications.

Chromium Refractories

Chrome refractories are neutral or sometimes considered basic in character. This important group of refractories is made from mixtures of magnesite and chrome ore. Magnesite consists chiefly of periclase or crystalline magnesia, MgO, and the chrome ore consists of several spinels, such as $FeCr_2O_4$ or $FeO·Cr_2O_3$ and $MgAl_2O_4$ or $MgO·Al_2O_3$.

Turkish chrome ore was used for the first chrome refractories in the United States. Since domestic sources have never been adequate or suitable, ores from Greece, South Africa, and the Philippines have been used.

In one method for making refractory brick, a mixture of chrome ore and magnesite is fused in an arc furnace and cast into brick. The chemical analysis is 62.5% MgO, 18.5% Cr_2O_3, 6% Al_2O_3, 11% FeO, 1.0% SiO_2, 0.8% CaO. The bricks so formed have high transverse strengths at elevated temperatures. The bricks are high density with low voids and their slag resistance at high temperatures is also high.

Typical applications include roofs of open hearths with high oxygen-input hearths, lower sidewalls of vacuum degassing vessels, and the sidewalls of electric furnaces and copper converters.

Toxicology of Chromium

Pure metallic chromium, chromite, and trivalent compounds do not produce any serious damage to body tissue. The toxic action of chromium is confined to the hexavalent compounds. These compounds exert an irritative, corrosive, and possibly toxic action on the human body. Under certain conditions the hexavalent compounds cause denaturation and precipitation of tissue proteins. Intimate contact, as in industrial exposure, will affect primarily the skin and respiratory tract. Skin contact may result in chrome ulcers and dermatitis. Inhalation of chromate dust or chromic acid mist may cause ulceration and perforation of the nasal septum as well as chronic irritation or congestion of the respiratory passages. There is increasing evidence that the incidence of cancer of the respiratory tract is abnormally high among workmen exposed to hexavalent chromium dusts in chromium refining. The maximum allowable concentration of dusts and mists in the air measured as CrO_3 has been stated to be 0.1 mg/cu m of air for daily 8-hr exposure.

References

1. Bacon, F. E., "Encyclopedia of Chemical Process Equipment," W. J. Mead, Ed., New York, Reinhold Publishing Corporation, 1964.
2. Bacon, F. E., "Encyclopedia of Electrochemistry," C. A. Hampel, Ed., New York, Reinhold Publishing Corporation, 1964.
3. Hampel, C. A., "Rare Metals Handbook," New York, Reinhold Publishing Corporation, 1961.
4. Sully, A. H., "Chromium," London, Butterworths Scientific Publications, 1954.
5. Udy, M. J., "Chromium," New York, Reinhold Publishing Corporation, 1956.
6. Bacon, F. E., "Chromium," Chicago, Illinois, "Encyclopedia Britannica," 1962.
7. Bacon, F. E., "Encyclopedia of Chemical Technology," Kirk-Othmer, Vol. 5, Second Edition, New York, Interscience Publishers, 1965.
8. Bacon, F. E., "Encyclopedia of Engineering Materials and Processes," H. R. Clauser, Ed., New York, Reinhold Publishing Corporation, 1963.

F. E. BACON

COBALT

H. C. Hoover records in his translation of "De Re Metallica" by Agricola that the word "cobalt" (German *Kobalt*, is from the Greek word *cobalos*, mine. Its German form signified a mischievous spirit (gnomes and goblins) and was used by the German miners in Saxony to designate certain ores which injured their hands and feet; these ores were later found to contain arsenical cobalt.

Spectrographic analysis of blue glass statuettes and pottery found in Egypt and Babylonia as far back as 1450 B.C. reveals that a cobalt-base coloring agent was used. Cobalt salts impart a blue color to ceramics, and when combined with nickel, chromium or manganese compounds, all shades of blue and green are obtained.

Brandt in 1735 discovered the element cobalt, and in 1780 Bergman studied the properties of this new metal.

Prior to the close of the Nineteenth Century, the world output of cobalt was derived from Germany, Hungary and Norway. In 1864 Garnier discovered the oxidized ores of New Caledonia which were developed in 1874. The next discovery in 1903 was the rich silver-cobalt ores of Ontario, Canada, which produced 16 tons of cobalt in 1904.

Union Minière du Haut Katanga in the Belgian Congo initiated in 1920 the extraction of cobalt from copper-cobalt ores and is now the leading producer of cobalt.

Occurrence

Cobalt is not one of the abundant elements but is widely diffused in rocks, sea and mineral

TABLE 1. OCCURRENCE AND SOME PROPERTIES OF COBALT MINERALS

Mineral	Formula	Co	Cu	S	As	Sp gr	Occurrence
		\multicolumn{4}{}{Per cent element}			
Carrollite	$CuS \cdot Co_2S_3$	38.0	20.5	41.5	—	4.84	N'Kana, Rhodesia
Linnaeite	Co_3S_4	57.9	—	42.1	—	4.90	Cobalt varies from 31–40% depending on iron, nickel, or copper present; Belgian Congo and Missouri
Smaltite	$CoAs_2$	28.2	—	—	71.8	6.50	Germany, Canada, French Morocco
Skutterudite	$CoAs_3$	20.8	—	—	79.2	6.79	Morocco, Norway
Cobaltite	$CoAsS$	35.5	—	19.3	45.2	6.3	Canada, Burma, Australia
Asbolite	$CoO_2 \cdot MnO_2 \cdot 4H_2O$	35.0	—	—	—	1.1	New Caledonia, Northern Rhodesia; cobalt varies from 4–35%
Heterogenite	$CoO \cdot 2Co_2O_3 \cdot 6H_2O$	57.3	—	—	25.0	3.0	Belgian Congo
Erythrite	$3CoO \cdot As_2O_5 \cdot 8H_2O$	29.5	—	—	25.0	3.0	Canada, Germany, Morocco

waters, coal, meteorites, the sun and stellar atmospheres, soils, plants and animals. The igneous rocks of the earth's crust contain only 0.0023%, as compared with 0.008% for nickel.

Relatively little cobalt ore is mined for the cobalt content, and most of the metal is recovered as a by-product of ores treated for their copper or nickel content.

Table 1 lists the principal cobalt minerals.

Concentration

The ores of cobalt contain very low concentrations of cobalt associated with other metals and, therefore require concentration as described for the following typical ores.

Chalcopyrite-Cobaltite Ores. These sulfide ores are found in the Blackbird district, Idaho, and contain 0.4 to 1% cobalt, 1 to 2% copper, 10 to 15% iron, 0.5–1.5% arsenic, and 3 to 13% sulfur. The ore is ground for differential flotation. A copper concentrate is floated at pH 9, and the underflow activated for the separation of iron and the flotation of cobalt. The cleaned concentrate averages 17.5% cobalt, 20% iron, 1.0% nickel and 0.50% copper.

Copper-Cobalt Oxidized and Sulfide Ores. The cobalt-bearing ores of Union Minière du Haut Katanga[1] in the Belgian Congo are of three types which require separate treatment:

(1) oxide copper containing a minor amount of cobalt; (2) cobalt-copper oxide ore; and (3) mixed ore which contains copper-cobalt oxides and sulfides.

Copper-Cobalt Sulfide Ores. The ores of Rhokana Corporation, Ltd., Zambia, are mined at N'Kana and contain the minerals chalcopyrite, chalcocite, and carrollite. The ore, averaging (by %) 3 copper and 0.14 cobalt is concentrated by (1) floating the copper in a high lime circuit with minimum additions of frothing and collecting agents, and (2) by increasing the addition of flotation reagents to produce a cobalt concentrate containing 25% copper, 3.5–4% cobalt.

Arsenide Ores. Ores containing cobalt arsenides, oxides and other metals occur in Morocco, Canada and the United States.

Moroccan ores occur in the southern part of Morocco at Bou-Azzer and Aghbar. High-grade ore is hand sorted; lower grade material is concentrated by gravity on air shaking and Wilfey tables. Cobalt oxides are magnetic; the arsenides nonmagnetic. For oxide-arsenide ores, an oxidizing roast is used to remove most of the arsenic as As_2O_3 and to leave the rest as arsenate which is magnetic. Magnetic beneficiation yields 93% of the cobalt and nickel, and 91% of the gold.

Canadian cobalt arsenides occur in the Cobalt-Gowganda area of northern Ontario.

These ores are silver bearing and are concentrated by hand sorting, tabling or flotation or by a combination of these methods. Concentrates contain 5–12% cobalt and 100–2,500 oz per ton of silver.

Extractive Metallurgy

The extraction of cobalt from cobalt-bearing materials is essentially a chemical process except where a pyrometallurgical treatment is economical for the reduction of arsenide and sulfide minerals to speiss or matte which is roasted to oxide to render soluble in acid.

The principal extraction processes are briefly as follows:

Cobalt from Oxidized Ores. The Musonoi ore deposit of Union Minière du Haut Katanga is an oxidized copper deposit containing 0.5 to 10% cobalt. High-grade ore and concentrate are processed in an electric furnace to yield two liquid metal layers and slag.

The top layer, "the white alloy," contains, in %, 15 copper, 44 cobalt, 1.5 silicon, and 39 iron; the bottom layer, "the red alloy," 89 copper and 4.5 iron. They are shotted and pulverized for dissolving in sulfuric acid solution for the recovery of copper and cobalt.

Katanga produces electrolytic cobalt at the Jadotville-Shituru plant from copper concentrate which also contains cobalt oxide. The solution from the copper electrolysis contains ferrousferric sulfate ion which is used to dissolve the copper-cobalt ores. The enriched cobalt-copper solution is treated for removal of iron and copper. The cobalt is precipitated with milk of lime at pH 8.0, and the cobalt hydroxide is dissolved in the cobalt spent electrolyte to form the feed to the cobalt electrolytic cells. The cobalt is deposited on mild steel cathodes at 37 amp/sq ft. The cobalt is stripped from the cathode plates, washed and refined in a 1,600 KVA Héroult furnace. The finished cobalt analyzes (by %) 99 cobalt, 0.5 nickel, 0.1 carbon, 0.15 iron, 0.02 copper, and 0.02 manganese.

Arsenical Cobalt Ores. Ore or concentrate with coke, iron scrap or ore, limestone or silica, as required, are smelted in a Traylor blast furnace. Arsenic fume is collected in a Cottrell precipitator for further refining.

Speiss, matte, and bullion are tapped together into pots to separate into layers.

The speiss and matte are ground to -100 mesh for roasting to eliminate arsenic and sulfur and to oxidize the iron. The roasted material is dissolved in sulfuric acid to convert all metals to water-soluble sulfates. After removal of silver, iron, arsenic and copper, the solution containing cobalt and nickel is subjected to oxidation by sodium hypochlorite to yield first, pure cobaltic hydroxide, $Co(OH)_3$, and then mixed cobaltic and nickelic hydroxides, $Co(OH)_3$ and $Ni(OH)_3$, which are recirculated.

The cobaltic hydroxide is filter pressed, converted to oxide and washed. The washed oxide is mixed with charcoal, reduced to metal fines at 1000°C, refined in an electric furnace and granulated in water.

Physical Properties

Cobalt is a hard, magnetic metal, silvery white on fracture and closely resembling nickel and iron in appearance. Its atomic number is 27 and its atomic weight is 58.94. An isotope, cobalt 60, formed by atomic irradiation, is competing with radium as a gamma-ray source. The naturally occurring element is composed of 0.2% of isotope 57 and 99.8% of isotope 59.

Cobalt is one of the three ferromagnetic elements, along with iron and nickel, with a permeability approximately two-thirds that of iron, but, when alloyed with iron, nickel, and other metals, exceptional magnetic properties have been developed.

The properties of cobalt are more structure sensitive than those of most other elements, because, in addition to the usual effects of impurities, cobalt tends to exist as a mixture of two allotropes over a wide range of temperatures, the beta form predominating below about 400°C (752°F) and the alpha above that temperature. However, the transformation of beta to alpha and vice versa is sluggish and probably accounts for most of the wide variation in the reported data on physical properties.

For this reason, values have been preferred which are known to refer to either hexagonal or cubic cobalt rather than to the more usual mixture of the two forms.

The self-diffusion in cobalt has been

TABLE 2. PHYSICAL PROPERTIES OF COBALT
(Most Accepted Values)

Atomic number	27
Atomic weight	58.9332
Isotopes	57, 59, 60 (artificial)
Density, g/cc	8.90 (0.321 lb/cu in.)
Melting point	1493°C (2720°F)
Boiling point at 760 mm Hg	3100°C (5610°F)
Latent heat of fusion, cal/g	62
Latent heat of vaporization, cal/g	1,500
Lattice constants	
Alpha, face-centered cubic	$a_o = 3.5370$ Å
Beta, hexagonal close-packed	$a_o = 2.5017$ Å
	$c = 4.0614$ Å
Transformation temperature, beta to alpha	$417° \pm 7°$C ($783° \pm 13°$F)
Volume expansion on transformation from hexagonal close packed to face-centered cubic	approx. 0.3%
Heat of transformation, cal/mole	60
Curie point	1121°C (2050°F)
Specific heat, cal/g/°C	
15–100°C (59–212°F)	0.1056
Liquid	0.141
Coefficient of thermal expansion, 40°C (104°F)	13.36×10^{-6}
Electrical resistance, 0°C, microhm-cm	5.68
Volume conductivity at 20°C (reference copper)	27.6%
Velocity of sound	
m/sec	4,724
ft/sec	15,500
Thermal conductivity	
0–100°C, cal/sec/sq cm/°C/cm	0.165
32–212°F, Btu/hr/sq ft/°F/in.	479
Hardness	
Cast, Brinell	124
Electrodeposited, Brinell	300
Tensile strength, psi	
Cast	35,000
Annealed	40,000
Wire	100,000
Compressive strength, cast, psi	120,000
Yield point, psi	42,000
Young's modulus, psi, tension	30,000,000
Modulus of elasticity in shear	11,100,000

HIGH TEMPERATURE PROPERTIES

Rupture strength, 100 hr at 649°C (1200°F)	12,500 psi
at 816°C (1500°F)	3,000 psi
Creep 99.6% cobalt, 100 hr at 500°C (930°F); 12,000 psi, 2.7% elongation	
Creep at 1000°C (1832°F) for 1% strain in 24 hr:	
99.97% cobalt sintered and swaged	13,900 psi
Vacuum melted	6,700 psi

Tensile properties	Ultimate, psi	Yield, psi	Red. of Area, %
Arc melted electrolytic			
At room temperature	57,500	43,000	3
At 927°C (1700°F)	12,400	8,100	12

measured with divergent results. The constant in the Arrhenius equation has been found to be 0.37 and 0.032, respectively, with the activation energies of 67,000 and 61,900 cal, respectively.

By a method not sensitive to surface preparation, the equation $D = 0.83e^{-67,700/RT}$ sq cm/sec has been obtained for self-diffusion in 99.9 + % cobalt; for dilute cobalt diffusing in nickel, $D_{Ni}^{Co} = 1.46e^{-68,300/RT}$ sq cm/sec.

The self-diffusion of cobalt in cobaltous oxide over a range of compositions has been measured and the following diffusion coefficients established:

At 1000°C (1832°F)
$$D = 2.6 \times 10^{-9} (PO_2)^{0.35} \text{ sq cm/sec}$$
At 1150°C (2102°F)
$$D = 9.0 \times 10^{-9} (PO_2)^{0.30} \text{ sq cm/sec}$$
At 1350°C (2462°F)
$$D = 5.1 \times 10^{-8} (PO_2)^{0.28} \text{ sq cm/sec}$$

The surface energy has been calculated to be 234 ergs/sq cm for the liquid-to-solid interface.

The most accepted values for the physical properties of cobalt are listed in Table 2.

Chemical Properties

The chemical properties of cobalt are intermediate between those of iron and nickel. Most compounds of cobalt have a valency of +2 or +3. The simple cobaltous ion, Co^{+2}, is quite basic and not subject to hydrolysis in aqueous solutions. The simple cobaltic ion, Co^{+3}, is a powerful oxidizing agent and cannot exist as such in an aqueous media. The cobaltous ion in the complexed state is unstable, being readily oxidized to the cobaltic form by ordinary oxidants. Many cobaltic complex ions are quite stable in aqueous media.

Finely divided cobalt is pyrophoric, whereas large pieces are not attacked by air or water at temperatures below 300°C (570°F). Cobalt combines with the halogens to form the respective halides and with most of the other metalloids when heated or in the molten state. Cobalt does not combine readily with nitrogen, but decomposes ammonia at elevated temperature to form a nitride. It reacts with carbon monoxide above 225°C (435°F) to form Co_2C.

Electrochemical Properties. In the electro-motive series cobalt occupies a position between iron and nickel.

For a valence of +2, the electrochemical equivalent of cobalt is 0.3054 mg per absolute coulomb (1.099 g/amp-hr or 0.0388 oz/amp-hr.)

The electrode potential of cobalt has been reported as 0.237–0.278 volts for $Co \rightarrow Co^{++}$, and 1.8 volts for $Co^{++} \rightarrow Co^{+++}$. The standard electrode potential at 25°C can be taken as +0.278 volts. The hydrogen overvoltage, or minimum voltage for the first visible appearance of hydrogen, with a cobalt electrode in NH_2SO_4 at 20° was found by Harkins to be 0.22 volt.

Corrosion and Oxidation Resistance. Corrosion-rate data reported by Young[2, 3] for cobalt in aqueous media at 25°C are given in Table 3.

TABLE 3.

Reagent	Corrosion Rate, mg/dm²/day
5 vol. % CH_3COOH	12.5
5 vol. % NH_4OH	5.3
5 vol. % H_2SO_4	56.8
10 vol. % $NaOH$	5.6
1:1 HF	178.6
Conc. HF	101.5
1:1 H_3PO_4	65.1
Conc H_3PO_4	7.4
5 vol. % H_2NNH_2	7.8
H_2O	1.1

Cobalt is severely attacked by concentrated nitric acid at room temperature, but becomes passive at about −11°C (+12°F). Cobalt is more resistant to air-free 5% sulfuric acid at 25°C than iron. In the presence of air it corrodes rapidly.

Cobalt cannot be rated as an oxidation-resistant metal. Scaling and oxidation rates of unalloyed cobalt in air are 25 times those of nickel. Cobalt in the hexagonal form (cold-worked specimen), oxidizes more rapidly than in the cubic form (annealed specimen) and both forms are less resistant than iron, titanium and beryllium at 76 mm Hg of O_2 and 400°C (750°F).

Simple Compounds of Cobalt

Most of the simple compounds of cobalt are bivalent and confined to oxides, sulfates, sulfides, fluorides and acetates. The stable cobalt complexes are predominately in the trivalent state.

Acetate. Cobaltous acetate, $(CoC_2H_3O_2)_2 \cdot 4H_2O$, can be prepared by dissolving cobalt carbonate in acetic acid. Cobaltic acetate may be prepared by the oxidation of a cobaltous salt in acetic acid.

Cobaltous acetate is used as a bleaching agent and drier for varnishes and laquers, in anodizing, and in inks.

Antimonides. Three antimonides, CoSb, $CoSb_2$ and $CoSb_3$, have been reported.

Arsenides. Two compounds of arsenic and cobalt exist at room temperature, Co_2As and CoAs.

Carbides. The carbide-forming tendency of cobalt is less than that of iron; the metal is largely dissolved in solid solution above $1300°C$. In steel only Co_3C is formed. The carbides, Co_3C, Co_2C and CoC_2, have been reported. Above $225°C$, carbon monoxide reacts readily with cobalt to form Co_2C and the deposition of elemental carbon.

Carbonates. Cobaltous carbonate, $CoCO_3$, is found in nature as sphaerocobaltite. The precipitate formed when an alkaline carbonate is added to a cobaltous solution is a basic carbonate, and is the carbonate formed in industrial processes for the recovery of cobalt when soda ash or lime are added to a cobalt salt.

Carbonyls. Dicobalt octacarbonyl, $Co_2(CO)_8$, (also called cobalt tetracarbonyl) is prepared by treatment of finely divided cobalt with carbon monoxide at a pressure of 100 atmospheres and a temperature of $200°C$.

The cobalt carbonyls present no great health hazard because of their low vapor pressure and because the vapors are unstable when mixed with air. The volatile hydride and nitrosyl are more toxic.

Cobalt carbonyls are of greatest importance in catalyzing the Oxo reaction as noted under "Catalysts."

Citrate. Cobaltous citrate, $Co(C_6H_5O_7)$. $2H_2O$, is a light rose-red amorphous powder. It is used in the medicinal field for vitamin preparations and therapeutic agents.

Ferrites. Cobaltous ferrite, $CoO.Fe_2O_3$, is of interest as a constituent in the magnetically-soft ferrites which have high permeability, low coercive force, low magnetic saturation, and high resistivity.

Formates. Cobaltous formate, $Co(O.CHO)_2$ is a pink salt existing in the dihydrate state.

Fluosilicate. Cobaltous fluosilicate, $CoSiF_6$. $6H_2O$, is used in the ceramic field and a possible source of fluorine in dental preparations.

Halides.

Bromide–Cobaltous bromide, $Co\ Br_2$, is produced by the action of hydrobromic acid on cobaltous hydroxide or carbonate, or of bromine on cobalt.

Chlorides–An aqueous solution of cobaltous chloride is obtained by dissolving the metal, oxide, hydroxide or carbonate in HCl. Concentration of the solution gives the pink hexahydrate, and dehydration yields the blue anhydrous salt.

Papers impregnated with $CoCl_2.6H_2O$ make cobalt chloride useful as an indicator of humidity and moisture. Cobalt thiocyanate has also been recommended for this purpose.

Fluorides–Cobaltous fluoride, CoF_2, is prepared by dehydrating the tetrahydrate, obtained by dissolving cobalt hydroxide in hydrofluoric acid. Elemental fluorine reacts on cobalt at temperatures above $450°C$ ($840°F$) to form a mixture of cobaltous and cobaltic fluorides. Ammine complexes can be prepared from the hydrate.

Hydrated cobaltic fluoride, $CoF_3.7H_2O$, is prepared by electrolytic oxidation of cobaltous fluoride in hydrofluoric acid. Anhydrous cobaltic fluoride reacts with bromine, iodine, sulfur, phosphorus, arsenic, carbon, and silicon, fluorinating them and being reduced to the cobaltous state.

Iodides–Cobaltous iodide is made by heating powdered cobalt in a stream of hydrogen iodide at $400–450°C$ to give a black crystalline α-form which yields a pink solution in water. This compound sublimes in vacuo mainly as the black form, but partly as an isomeric anhydrous yellow modification (β-cobalt iodide) which gives a colorless aqueous solution. By its change in color, cobaltous iodide is a most sensitive halide for determining water in organic solvents.

Hydroxides. When an alkali hydroxide is added to a solution of a cobaltous salt, cobaltous hydroxide, $Co(OH)_2$, is formed.

Cobaltous hydroxide is oxidized slowly by air and rapidly by strong oxidizing agents to a hydrated form of cobaltic oxide, Co_2O_3.

159

H_2O. One of the most important industrial separations of cobalt from nickel is based on the fact that in neutral solutions cobalt oxidizes more readily than nickel—following the addition of sodium hypochlorite, for instance—and that the oxidized compounds hydrolyzes and precipitates, leaving nickel in solution.

Linoresinates, Naphthenates, Octoates. Cobalt is marketed in the form of linoresinates, naphthenates, and octoates, both as liquids, which contain about 6% Co, and as solids with about the following cobalt contents: 8 to 9% for the linoleate, 10.5 to 11% for the naphthenate, 2 to 9% for the fused resinates, and 8 to 9% for the linoresinate. These compounds are used as driers in paint and varnish formulations.

Nitrates. When dilute nitic acid is added to cobalt metal, oxide, hydroxide or carbonate, an aqueous solution of cobaltous nitrate is formed which, on evaporation, yields red crystals of the hexahydrate, $Co(NO_3)_2.6H_2O$. This compound is exceedingly hygroscopic and is readily soluble in many organic solvents.

Cobalt reacts with ammonia gas at 470°C to form a cobalt nitride, Co_4N_2 which decomposes at 600°C.

Oxalates. Cobaltous oxalate, $Co(C_2O_4)_2$, is usually found as the pink dihydrate, but the tetrahydrate and anhydrous states exist. It is almost insoluble in water but soluble in concentrated ammonia.

Oxides. Cobalt has less affinity for oxygen than has iron but more than nickel. Like iron, cobalt has three well-known oxides: the monoxide or cobaltous oxide, CoO, cobaltic oxide, Co_2O_3, and cobaltosic oxide, Co_3O_4.

Cobaltous oxide is the final product formed when the carbonate or the other oxides are calcined at high temperature, in a neutral or slightly reducing atmosphere. Pure cobaltous oxide is a difficult substance to prepare, since it readily takes up oxygen to reform a higher oxide. The gray oxide of commerce, which is used for most metallurgical and chemical applications, generally contains 76% Co and is essentially CoO with a little Co_3O_4 present.

Cobaltic oxide, Co_2O_3, is formed when cobalt compounds are heated at a low temperature in the presence of an excess of air.

Cobaltosic oxide, Co_3O_4, a stable black oxide, is formed when cobalt compounds, such as the carbonate or the hydrated sesquioxide, are heated in air at temperatures above approximately 265°C and not exceeding 800°C. Black oxide is used by some pottery manufacturers and powder metallurgists. It is readily reduced to metal by carbon, carbon monoxide or hydrogen.

Phosphates. Anhydrous cobaltous phosphate, $Co_3(PO_4)_2$, can be prepared by heating cobaltous salts with phosphoric acid or phosphates. The hydrated salt, $Co_3(PO_4)_2.8H_2O$, which contains 33.5% Co, is marketed as an amorphous powder; being brilliant deep lavender, it is used in artists' colors, plastic resins, and for ceramic pigments.

Phosphides. A study of the Co-P system indicates the probable existence of three cobalt phosphides, Co_2P, CoP and CoP_3. These have not been isolated.

Selenides. Six cobalt selenides have been described: Co_2Se, CoSe, Co_5Se_6, Co_3Se_4, Co_2Se_3, and $CoSe_2$. Only two have been verified by x-ray investigation, they are CoSe and $CoSe_2$.

Silicates. The orthosilicate of cobalt, $2CoO.SiO_2$, can be obtained by direct heating of cobalt oxide and silica. An intense blue is obtained from the compound, $CoO.SiO_2$, which is made by the solution of cobalt oxide in melts containing aluminosilicates and borates such as those present in pottery fluxes and glazes. The silicate color is known in the pottery industry as mazarine blue or royal blue.

Silicides. There are a number of cobalt silicides, of which five have been studied in research on insoluble anodes: Co_2Si (19.23% Si), Co_3Si_2 (24.09%), CoSi (32.25%), $CoSi_2$ (48.77%), and $CoSi_3$ (58.82%). The silicon-rich silicides are highly resistant to attack by strong mineral acids, either hot or cold, while the cobalt-rich silicides have high resistance to strong alkali solutions, hot or cold.

These compounds can be prepared electrothermally from CoO and SiO_2, or they can be formed by melting the elements Co and Si together. CoSi has also been prepared by heating SiC and CoO.

Sulfates. When cobalt oxide, hydroxide or carbonate is dissolved in dilute sulfuric acid, an aqueous solution of cobaltous sulfate is obtained which crystallizes as pink heptahydrate, $CoSO_4.7H_2O$, the commercial form of cobalt sulfate.

Oxidation of a solution of cobaltous sulfate in dilute sulfuric acid, either electrolytically or with ozone or fluorine, yields hydrated cobaltic sulfate, $Co_2(SO_4)_3.18H_2O$.

Sulfides. The affinity of cobalt for sulfur is greater than that of iron but less than nickel. Cobalt combines with sulfur to form ordinary cobaltous sulfide, CoS, two others which are probably cobaltous, CoS_2 and Co_3S_4, and a cobaltic compound, Co_2S_3.CoS, which is the common black precipitate formed when H_2S is passed into an alkaline or ammonical cobalt solution.

Tellurides. The compounds, $CoTe$ and $CoTe_2$, have been investigated.[4]

Cobalt Complexes

Cobalt, particularly the trivalent ion, is one of the most prolific complex-formers known. The important donor atoms (in order of decreasing tendency to complex) are nitrogen, carbon in the cyanides, oxygen, sulfur, and the halogens. The most numerous are the complexes of ammonia and amines. Divalent cobalt exhibits a coordination number of either four or six, while that of the trivalent ion is invariably six.

Trivalent cobalt forms an immense number of complexes, most of which are quite stable. In these complexes, cobalt takes on enough electrons to complete its electron shell by forming coordinate covalent linkages with the donor atoms. According to the hybridization theory, the six $3d$ electrons of the cobaltic ion become paired, leaving vacant two orbitals in the $3d$ shell, one in the $4s$ shell, and three in the $4p$ shell. Each orbital is capable of accepting an electron pair from a donor atom. Since these six orbitals are of very nearly the same energy levels, they are able to hybridize and form six equivalent bonds with donor atoms.

A large number of chelate compounds have also been studied in which a polyfunctional donor molecule, e.g., ethylenediamine, spans adjacent positions in the coordination sphere. These compounds are capable of existing as optical isomers. They have unusual oxygen-carrying properties; some have the ability to absorb and release oxygen so readily that they have been used to purify oxygen. Cobalt tetrine, the cobalt salt of disodium ethylene-diaminetetraacetate, $CoNa_2(C_{10}H_{12}O_8N_2)$.$H_2O$(13.5% Co), is used in support of other chelating compounds in medicinal and tree-spraying preparations.

Cobalt in Catalysts

The removal of sulfur from crude oils is carried out in catalytic hydrogenation units and of the many catalysts the most important are cobalt-molybdena-alumina (CMA) and tungsten-nickel sulfide.

CMA catalyst consists of 3 to 3.5% cobalt (as CoO) and 10% molybdenum (as MoO_3) on gamma alumina. The catalyst has a long life and can be regenerated in situ, using an air-stream mixture containing 1 to 2% oxygen and a temperature of 595°C maximum for 1 to 3 days.

The Oxo reaction or hydroformylation of olefins with carbon monoxide and hydrogen is effected in the presence of a cobalt catalyst to produce aldehydes.

Complete fluorination of a hydrocarbon is obtained by passing it over a higher metal fluoride of CoF_3, MnF_3 and AgF_2. Cobaltic fluoride is most advantageous as it is easy to handle and has a suitable heat of formation.

Cobalt catalysts have commercial possibilities in the fields of polymerization, oxidation, dehydration, hydrogen sulfide production, nitrile synthesis, amination of olefins and decomposition of acetylene.

Radioactive Cobalt

Of ten known isotopes of cobalt, only cobalt-59 is stable and is found in nature. The well known cobalt radioisotope cobalt-60 has a 5.2-year half-life and decays by the emission of beta radiation accompanied by gamma rays.

Cobalt-60 is produced from cobalt-59 by neutron bombardment of cobalt metal placed inside a nuclear fission reactor. The equation of the reaction in the reactor is $_{27}Co^{59} + o^{n1} \rightarrow {}_{27}Co^{60}$.

Co^{60} has the units of atoms/cc but a more useful unit is the curie, a unit of power defined as 3.70×10^{10} atomic disintegrations/ sec. Each disintegration releases energy which is different for different isotopes. For cobalt-60, 1 curie equals 0.015 watts/g. Theoretically, it should be possible to obtain 1140 curies/g or 17.1 watts/g of cobalt. Practically this is not achieved, and the specific activity of cobalt varies from 1 to 100 curies/g depending on the neutron flux level in the reactor.

Cobalt-60 and other isotopes have been used in chemical, physical, and biological research. Minute quantities of isotopes are used for tracing complex reactions and processes. Isotopes having half-lives ranging from hours to years are highly sensitive, only $10^{-16} - 10^{-19}$ g of radioactive element being necessary for analysis.

Cobalt isotopes are utilized in the study of metal plating, corrosion prevention, catalysis, degassing, tracer techniques for determining wear, etc.

Metabolism in animals can be determined by tracing intake of food in the form of elements, and inorganic and organic compounds; intake and incorporation of food into various regions of the body; breakdown of food and excretion of waste.

Cobalt-60, as well as other isotopes, generates radiation which causes chemical change by producing ionized molecules or free radicals which in turn react to produce new molecules.

Cobalt-60 is used as a concentrated source of gamma rays for distant therapy treatment of malignancies. It is also used in implantation therapy in three categories: (1) intracavitary, (2) interstitial, and (3) external.

Applications

The United States is the largest consumer of cobalt in the world and is largely dependent on imported supplies to satisfy its demands. Very little cobalt metal is used as such. Some 80% of the cobalt consumed is used in the manufacture of alloys, and the remainder in the form of compounds is used in pigments, salts, driers and ceramic frits.

About 20% of all cobalt consumed enters into several kinds of permanent and soft magnets. Among them are (1) steels containing 30 to 50% cobalt with smaller amounts of tungsten, chromium, vanadium and nickel; (2) ternary alloys containing typically 45% nickel, 25% cobalt, and 30% iron, the "Perminvars;" (3) the "Alnico" type containing 14–30% nickel, 6–12% aluminum, 5–35% cobalt, and balance iron; (4) the "Supermedur" type containing 49% cobalt,

49% iron and 2% vanadium; (5) the cobalt-platinum variety, with the 50–50 atomic % ratio having the best magnetic properties; and (6) the oxide type, comprised of cobalt oxide and iron or manganese oxide.

In the category of alloys cobalt is an essential constituent of tungsten tool steels, the "high-speed steels." Several ferrous alloys containing nickel, cobalt, chromium, tungsten and molybdenum are important for corrosion and oxidation resistance and are used in gas turbines and valve stem tips for aircraft engines, for example.

Cobalt is a major constituent of several important nonferrous alloys containing 20 to 65% cobalt which have excellent wear resistance and are oxidation and corrosion resistant under extreme corrosion media and elevated temperature conditions. Among them are the "stellites," cobalt-chromium base alloys to which tungsten, molybdenum and carbon are added to produce cutting tools superior to high-speed tools steels. Others are applied as dental and surgical alloys, e.g., "Vitallium," that are not attacked by body fluids; as hard-facing alloys; and as high-strength alloys at elevated temperatures for jet engines and ordnance requirements.

Cobalt powder is used to manufacture sintered alloys. While not a major tonnage use for cobalt, probably the most important items in this category are the tungsten carbide-cobalt alloys that permit the valuable cutting and abrasive properties of tungsten carbide to be utilized. The cobalt acts as a binder for the tungsten carbide particles in these cemented carbides.

Cobalt can be electroplated but is seldom used alone as an electrodeposited coating since nickel and chromium are cheaper and provide better oxidation resistance. However, cobalt-nickel and cobalt-tungsten alloys electrodeposited from appropriate baths are of commercial interest.

Several applications of cobalt compounds have been mentioned in the section describing them as well as in the sections on catalysts and feeds. The largest application of cobalt chemicals is in the field of driers in paints and varnishes of various sorts, where cobalt naphthenate, resinate, oleate, etc. have been found to be exceptionally useful.

The annual consumption of cobalt in the

United States is about 10 million pounds of contained cobalt in metallic and nonmetallic forms. Its current price is $1.85/lb (1967).

Cobalt in Biochemical Sciences

Animal Nutrition. The importance of trace elements in the feeding of ruminants has been well known for many years. In many agricultural regions, it was found that flocks living all year round in the same feeding area wasted rapidly away but could be revitalized by sending them to another region to avoid the disease known as "pining."

In 1933 it was proved that active trace elements were most important and of these cobalt is the one of most importance. Its effectiveness has been proven by the results obtained in Australia, New Zealand, Scotland and Kenya, which show the rapid and beneficial action of cobalt on the health of animals suffering from deficiency diseases.

Cobalt in the form of chloride, sulfate, phosphate or nitrate is either mixed with the fertilizers spread on the fields or added directly to the feed or to the salt-block licks.

A method developed in Australia to administer cobalt to ruminants comprises feeding a pellet consisting of a mixture of kaolin and cobalt oxide. The pellet remains in the rumen and the animal's system draws upon it for the cobalt which it requires.

Humans. For the treatment of anemia, cobalt salts are used alone or with salts of other elements, such as iron or manganese. Vitamin B_{12} has a complex organic molecule containing cobalt.

Cobalt Toxicity

Cobalt when added with lime to acid podzolic and peat soils has been found to increase crop yields and the quality of such crops as wheat, barley, flax and sugar beets. Without lime cobalt has had little effect and may be harmful. Evidence indicates that minute quantities of cobalt may be detrimental to higher plant life, particularly in water and sand cultures. Cobalt toxicity is characterized by a chlorosis similar to that induced by lack of iron. Plants can tolerate higher concentrations of metal ions in soils than in water or sand cultures.

Growing cattle can consume up to 50 mg cobalt per 100 lb body weight without ill effects. Sheep can tolerate up to 160 mg daily per 100 lb weight for at least eight weeks without harmful effects. Higher dosages are injurous. Most investigators believe that cobalt deficiency in ruminants is essentially a deficiency of vitamin B_{12}.

There is no evidence that cobalt encountered by man under normal conditions in his foodstuffs or industrial products is deleterious to his health.

References

1. "Cobalt Monograph," 35 Rue des Colonies, Brussels, Belgium, Centre D' Information du Cobalt, 1960.
2. "Cobalt," Quarterly Publication on Cobalt and Its Uses, 35 Rue des Colonies, Brussels, Belgium, Centre D' Information du Cobalt, No. 1 (1938), No. 33 (1966).
3. "Gmelins Handbuch der Anorganische Chemie, System No. 58, Cobalt," 8th Ed., Part A and Part B, Berlin, Verlag Chemie, G.m.b.h., 1932.
4. Mellor, J. W., "A Comprehensive Treatise on Inorganic and Theoretical Chemistry," Vol. 14, London, Longmans, Green and Co., 1935.
5. "Metals Handbook," Vol. I, "Properties and Selection of Metals," 8th Ed., Cleveland, American Society for Metals, 1961.
6. Perrault, R., "Le Cobalt," Paris, Dunod, 1946.
7. Whittemore, C. R., Chapter on "Cobalt," "Rare Metals Handbook," Hampel, C. A., Editor, New York, Reinhold Publishing Corp., 1961.
8. Young, R. S., "Cobalt," New York, Reinhold Publishing Corp., 1948.
9. Young, R. S., "Cobalt, Its Chemistry, Metallurgy and Uses," American Chemical Society Monograph 149, New York, Reinhold Publishing Corp., 1960.

CARL R. WHITTEMORE

COPPER

History

The discovery of copper dates from prehistoric times; it has been mined for more than 6,000 years. Gold was probably the first metal to attract man's attention because of its sparkling yellow color, and iron in the form of meteorites may have been used before copper in some localities, but there is evidence that every ancient metal culture was actually introduced by the use of the red metal. The early age of copper probably had its greatest development in Egypt. The most important copper-ore deposits of antiquity were in Sinai, Syria, Afghanistan, Cyprus, Macedonia, Iberia and Central Europe. European copper mines of the Bronze Age are known in Austria, Germany, France, Spain, Portugal, Greece, and the Tyrol. In Britain the copper mines were developed by the Romans in 43 A.D. In the Americas copper was probably used as early as 200 A.D. The metal was first produced in the English-speaking American Colonies in 1709 at Simsbury, Connecticut. However, production in the United States did not exceed a few hundred tons a year until the discovery of the Michigan ore deposits in the early 1840's and the development of the Montana, Arizona, and Utah ore bodies from 1860 to 1906. The smelter output from domestic mines increased from 750 tons in 1850 to 30,000 tons in 1880. In 1966 the United States produced more than 1.4 million tons of primary metal, and the world production exceeded $5\frac{1}{2}$ million tons. This expansion occurred as a result of the development of electrical power and expansion of the brass and bronze industry.

The world copper industry of today is confronted with many technical and economic problems; one of the most challenging of these is preventing the loss of markets to substitute materials such as aluminum, steel, and plastics.

Occurrence

Copper is widely distributed in many parts of the world—chiefly as mineral combinations with iron, sulfur, carbon and oxygen. Some 165 copper minerals have been identified, but only about a dozen are commercially important, and six minerals are the source of over 95% of the copper that is being mined. Copper minerals are conveniently divided into three groups. Primary or hypogene minerals, deposited at considerable depth in the earth by processes related to igneous activity are represented by compositions such as bornite, chalcopyrite, enargite and similar combinations. The second group is composed of oxidized copper minerals which are commonly formed by the weathering of copper sulfides

exposed to erosion. Cuprite, malachite, azurite, and chrysocolla are the principal representatives of this group of the supergene zones of copper deposits. The third group is that of the secondary sulfides which generally have been formed by copper leached from sulfides exposed near the earth's surface. The metal is carried downward and is precipitated near water level. Chalcocite and covellite are members of this group, and other copper-bearing sulfides are occasionally placed in this category. Native copper deposits, containing uncombined copper, at one time occurred in numerous localities, but now are found in commercial tonnages only in the state of Michigan. The principal copper minerals are listed in Table 1. As the source of the world's total production of copper, chalcocite represents about one-half, chalcopyrite one-quarter, enargite 3%, other sulfides 1%, native copper about 6%, and the oxidized minerals approximately 15%. Of the latter, malachite is the most abundant.

TABLE 1. CHIEF COPPER ORE MINERALS

Name	Chemical Formula	% Copper	Specific Gravity
Native copper	Cu	100	8.9
Sulfides			
Bornite	Cu_5FeS_4	63.3	5.1
Chalcocite	Cu_2S	79.8	5.6
Chalcopyrite	$CuFeS_2$	34.5	4.2
Covellite	CuS	66.4	5.0
Enargite	$Cu_3As_5S_4$	48.3	4.4
Tennantite	$Cu_3As_2S_7$	57.0	4.9
Tetrahedrite	$Cu_8Sb_2S_7$	52.1	4.9
Oxides			
Antlerite	$Cu_3SO_4(OH)_4$	54.0	3.4
Atacamite	$CuCl_2\cdot3Cu(OH)_2$	59.4	3.7
Azurite	$2CuCO_3\cdot Cu(OH)_2$	55.1	3.8
Brochantite	$Cu_4SO_4(OH)_6$	56.2	3.9
Chrysocolla	$CuSiO_3\cdot2H_2O$	36.0	2.2
Cuprite	Cu_2O	88.8	6.0
Malachite	$CuCO_3\cdot Cu(OH)_2$	57.3	4.0
Tenorite	CuO	79.8	6.0

Open-pit and underground methods are used in mining various types of copper deposits. Open-pit mining accounts for about 75% of the copper mined in the United States. This method permits the use of large-scale equipment and can be economically employed for deposits with a copper content of less than 1%. It is ideally suited for disseminated deposits close to the surface. Underground mining on the other hand, is generally suited to mining deep, vein-type deposits, and the copper content of the ore so mined must, in most cases, be higher than for open-pit mining because the costs tend to be greater.

Production

The world production of new copper in 1964 was about 5½ million tons. The leading countries were: the United States, 23%; Russia, 14%; Zambia, 13%; Chile 12%; Canada, 9%; Congo, 6%. The "Minerals Yearbook" lists fifty countries with some copper production. In the United States the primary copper industry is composed of about 200 companies engaged in the production and sale of the metal. The mining, smelting, refining, fabricating, and marketing are controlled by a few large vertically integrated companies. Twenty-five mines produce 97% of the domestic copper output; the five largest produce 47%, and 10 mines furnish 72%. Kennecott Copper Corp., Phelps Dodge Corp., and the Anaconda Company usually account for about two-thirds of the annual domestic mine production.

Most of the copper mined in the United States is produced in five Western States (Arizona, Utah, Montana, New Mexico, and Nevada), and about 85% of the remainder is obtained from Michigan and Tennessee. The concentrating and smelting facilities are situated near the mines, and some "custom" plants treat ore purchased from prospectors and small producers. There are eight primary smelters in Arizona, three in Michigan, and one each in Nevada, New Mexico, Montana, New Jersey, Tennessee, Texas, Utah, and Washington. Chile has six smelters, and there are two in Peru. Mexico has two operating smelters. Canada has three in Ontario, two in Quebec, and one in Manitoba. There are about 30 smelters in other parts of the world.

Collection and treatment of secondary materials, including "junk," is an important part of the copper industry. Scrap is collected in almost every community, and tonnage of copper recovered in this manner each year in the United States totals almost one million tons. New scrap is generated in manufacturing articles from primary metal or alloys and consists of defective finished or semi-finished articles, clippings, punchings, turnings, borings, skimmings, drosses, and slags. If consumed in the plant of generation, the material is referred to as "home" or "runaround" scrap. Old scrap is the term given to "junk"— articles that have been discarded after serving a useful purpose. Such articles may be worn out, obsolete or damaged and include thousands of different items. Old scrap is generally sold to secondary refiners, brass and bronze ingot makers, and the brass mills.

Average annual prices of copper in the United States have ranged from a low of 5.67 ¢/lb in 1932 to a high of 41.88 ¢ in 1956. Increased consumption and labor strikes forced the price to 46 ¢/lb in February, 1956, the highest in 90 years. The price in early 1967 was 38 ¢/lb.

Extraction and Refining

Copper is extracted from its ores by either hydrometallurgical or pyrometallurgical processes. In the former the ore, usually consisting of oxidized minerals, is leached without prior concentration with a solvent such as sulfuric acid or a mixture of sulfuric acid and ferric sulfate. The procedures used vary according to the nature of the deposit. Leaching in place is carried out on bodies that contain sulfide minerals which have been shattered so that air and water have had an opportunity to react and change some of the minerals to water-soluble sulfates. The leach solution is accumulated in drainage tunnels in the lower levels of the mine and is eventually pumped to the surface for treatment.

Copper-bearing material which is too low-grade to be processed profitably by any other method, but which must be removed to mine profit-grade ore, is often treated by heap leaching. The as-mined ore is piled on an area having proper drainage to catch basins, and leach solutions are directed through the piles to dissolve soluble compounds formed by weathering.

However, most of the leaching is done on ore which has been mined and crushed to the optimum degree and placed in vats to be brought in contact with the solvent. Where the ore particles are finely divided, dissolution is accelerated with mechanical agitation of a pulp suspension, but for larger particles the solution is allowed to percolate through a fixed bed of the ore. When agitation is employed, reaction times are in hours, whereas percolation procedures require days. Copper is recovered from leach solutions by precipitation with scrap or sponge iron to give cement copper or by electrolysis with insoluble anodes.

Professor Frank Forward and the Sherritt-Gordon Mines, Ltd., are largely responsible for the newest hydrometallurgical process for treating sulfide ores to recover copper sulfides, nickel and cobalt. The finely ground sulfide concentrates are treated in a two-stage countercurrent ammoniacal leaching system at a temperature of 175–195°F and at pressures from 100–125 psig. The copper, nickel and cobalt are dissolved while the sulfur forms ammonium sulfates and thiosulfates. The iron is oxidized to an insoluble hydrate and is filtered off with insoluble siliceous minerals. The filtered pregnant solution is boiled at 230°F to precipitate copper preferentially in reactions such as:

$$Cu^{+2} + S_3O_6^{-2} + 2H_2O \rightarrow$$
$$CuS(c) + 4H^+ + 2SO_4^{-2}$$
$$Cu^{2+} + S_2O_3^{-2} + H_2O \rightarrow$$
$$CuS(c) + 2H^+ + SO_4^{-2}$$

Metallic copper is extracted from the CuS by conventional smelting procedures.

Most of the ores treated by smelting or pyrometallurgical processes are first subjected to concentration, primarily by the flotation process, in which the finely ground ore is agitated in water with air or other gases in the presence of small amounts of surface-active chemicals. A froth, to which is attached the ore mineral, is separated from the gangue to give a concentrate assaying from 20–50% copper. Some plants use a combination of leaching and concentration. The concentrate may receive a partial oxidizing roast to remove some of the sulfur or it may be smelted directly in a large reverberatory furnace fired with natural gas, oil, or pulverized coal. In the reverberatory furnace the concentrate or calcine from roasting reacts with fluxes of silica or iron oxide and limestone at temperatures great enough to produce two molten products: a "matte" of copper, iron, sulfur, oxygen, gold, silver, platinum metals,

selenium, tellurium and nickel, and waste slag that is primarily a silicate of iron. Because these two liquid phases form two separate layers in the furnace, the matte and slag are easily separated by tapping the furnace at regular intervals.

The molten matte (at a temperature of 1100–1200°C) is then blown with air in a converter similar to the Bessemer process for making steel. In the latter process only a few percent of the charged material is oxidized, very little slag is formed, and the operation is complete in less than fifteen minutes. Moreover, the iron and its impurities are in liquid solution during the blowing period. In the copper converter more than half the material is oxidized, and it is carried out in two distinct stages. The initial oxidation produces mainly iron oxides which combine with siliceous flux to form a slag which is sparingly soluble in the remaining matte. When most of the iron has been removed from the matte, the slag is decanted from the converter, and a second blowing period is started to oxidize the remaining sulfur (roughly 20% of the liquid matte) to produce "blister copper," assaying 98 +% copper plus precious metals, selenium, tellurium and nickel. During the second stage of copper converting the metallic copper formed is only slightly soluble in the matte and its density is greater than that of the sulfide. As a result, the copper segregates to the bottom of the vessel where it could be oxidized if the converter were bottom blown as in the case of the Bessemer process. To prevent this from occurring the copper converter is side blown in such a way that air is contacting the sulfide-rich matte instead of the copper-rich layer on the bottom. Converting time runs into several hours, and the copper content of the slag is great enough (around 5%) that it is put back into the matte smelters for retreatment.

The molten blister copper is transferred to a refining furnace for oxidation and adjustment of the oxygen content to about 0.05% by green poles or by gaseous reduction of cuprous oxide which is dissolved in the molten metal. It is then cast into anodes weighing from 500 to 750 lb for electrorefining. In this operation the anodes are suspended in an electrolyte of copper sulfate and sulfuric acid and electrolyzed at a current density of 15 to

20 amp/ft² to produce copper cathodes of 99.98% purity. The refined cathode copper is usually remelted and cast into cakes, wire bars, billets and other shapes suitable for fabrication. Some of the impurities in the anode copper, such as nickel, dissolve in the electrolyte without plating out at the cathode; but others like gold, silver, tellurium, and selenium do not dissolve, but fall to the bottom of the tank as a "slime" which is treated to recover the metals.

In addition to copper there are recovered as byproducts from the copper extraction processes important quantities of gold, silver, sulfuric acid, molybdenum, selenium, tellurium, arsenic, and the platinum group metals. About 25% of the molybdenum produced is obtained from copper ores; 93% of the selenium, 76% of the tellurium, 32% of the United States gold production and 28% of the silver are derived from the processing of copper ores.

Physical Properties

Copper is the first element of Group IB of the Periodic Table. It is one of the few common metals which find their greatest commercial application in the pure form rather than in alloys. Some of its properties are listed in Table 2, and Table 3 presents some thermodynamic properties of copper and some of its compounds.

Chemical Properties

Cuprous (Cu^+) and cupric (Cu^{++}) compounds are quite numerous, and the Cu^{+++} form occurs in only a few unstable compounds. The excellent corrosion resistance of the metal is due not only to its inherent relative nobility but also to the formation of a protective film. The green coating produced by weathering is hydrated copper carbonate, mixed with basic copper sulfate in industrial atmospheres. In dry climates, and especially when heated,

TABLE 2. PHYSICAL PROPERTIES OF COPPER

Atomic number	29
Atomic weight	63.54
Melting point	1083°C
Boiling point	2582°C
Crystal structure	face-centered cubic, a = 3.615 Å
Density	8.94 g/cc at 20°C
Elastic modulus in tension	17,000,000 psi (annealed)
Poisson's ratio	0.33
Tensile strength	32,000–37,000 psi (annealed)
	55,000–61,000 psi (drawn)
Yield strength	4,600–12,000 psi (0.5% extension of annealed)
	50,000–55,000 psi (0.5% extension of drawn)
Elongation, % in 2 in.	46 (annealed)
Reduction of area, %	48 (annealed)
Electrical conductivity	101.8% (annealed)
Thermal conductivity	0.934 cal/sq cm/cm thickness/°C/sec at 20°C
Linear coefficient of thermal expansion	0.0000165 at 20°C
Brinell hardness number	43 (annealed); 103 (hard rolled)
Magnetic susceptibility, cgs units × 10⁻⁶	− 0.097 (− 253°C); − 0.080 (18°C)
	− 0.077 (1080°C); − 0.054 (1090°C)
Surface tension	1104 dynes/cm at 1150°C
Viscosity	0.0341 cgs units at 1145°C
Velocity of sound	12,700 ft/sec at 20°C
Solidification shrinkage	4.92 %
Hall effect	− 5.24 × 10⁻⁴ volts; 3000 to 8116 gausses
Emissivity, 90 at 1125°C	11.8 (7,000Å), 20.5 (6,000Å),
	38.7 (5,000Å)
Minimum creep rate at 204°C	5,000 psi, 0.042 %/1,000 hr
	6,700 psi, 0.10 %/1,000 hr
	9,000 psi, 0.21 %/1,000 hr

copper receives a coating of black CuO. The stable oxide at high temperatures in air is red Cu₂O.

Although it is easy to oxidize metallic copper to the +1 state in the presence of various precipitating and complexing agents, the +2 state is the more stable in aqueous solution. In the absence of such agents, oxidation in solution produces cupric copper, and unipositive copper is unstable with respect to the transformation:

$$2Cu^+ \rightarrow Cu^\circ + Cu^{+2}$$

for which the equilibrium constant at 25°C is 1.2×10^6. Reduction of dipositive copper ions normally yields the metal; the unipositive state is produced only if suitable precipitants or complexing groups are present. The Cu^{+2} ion equilibrium concentration is always about a million times the square of that of the Cu^+ ion. Hence, although insoluble cuprous compounds such as the chloride, bromide, iodide, oxide, and sulfide are common, water-soluble materials exist only in the presence of complexing groups like chloride or cyanide ion, ammonia, and acetonitrite. In the presence of these groups the cuprous form of copper is more stable than the cupric.

At elevated temperatures binary cupric compounds decompose to give cuprous compounds. CuO and CuS are good examples of this. It is well known that many minerals formed at high temperatures contain only unipositive copper. The nature of the univalent copper species has received considerable attention because copper halides are associated in the vapor state. There appears to be no evidence for the species Cu_2^{+2}. Cuprous oxide, Cu_2O, is diamagnetic, insoluble in water or alkaline solutions, but is converted by

TABLE 3. THERMODYNAMIC PROPERTIES OF COPPER AND SOME OF ITS COMPOUNDS

Cu(c): $S°_{298} = 7.97$; m.p. $= 1357°K$; $\Delta H_M = 3,120$; $C_p = 5.41 + 1.50 \times 10^{-3}T$ (298–1357°K);
$\quad H_T - H_{298} = -1,680 + 5.41T + 0.75 \times 10^{-3}T^2$ (298–1357°K)
Cu(l): $C_p = 7.50$; $H_T - H_{298} = -20 + 7.50T$ (1357–1600°K); b.p. $= 2855°K$; $\Delta H_v = 72,800$
Cu(g): $C_p = 2.86 + 1.06 \times 10^{-3}T$ (2000–5000°K); $S°_{298} = 39.74$; $H_T - H_{298} = 2.86 + 0.53 \times 10^{-3}T$
Vapor pressure of Cu(l): 0.001 atm at 1602°C; 0.01 atm at 1844°C;
$\qquad\qquad$ 0.1 atm at 2162°C; 0.5 atm at 2450°C.
Cu₂(g): $S°_{298} = 57.0$
Cu⁺(aq): $S°_{298} = 9.4$
Cu²⁺(aq): $S°_{298} = -26.5$
CuBr(c): $\Delta H°_{298} = -25,450$; $S°_{298} = 22.97$; $C_p = 12.80 + 1.58 \times 10^3 T$; m.p. $= 761°K$
$\quad \Delta H_M = 2,300$; b.p. $= 1591°K$; $\Delta H_v = 33,400$
CuBr₂(c): $\Delta H_{298} = -33,200$; $S°_{298} = 33$; decomposes at 600°K, pressure Br₂ is 1 atm
CuCO₃(c): $\Delta H°_{298} = -142,800$; $S°_{298} = 17.7$; decomposes upon heating
CuCl(c): $\Delta H°_{298} = -32,600$; $S°_{298} = 20.8$; m.p. $= 703°K$;
$\quad \Delta H_M = 2,620$; $C_p = 5.87 + 19.20 \times 10^{-3}T$ (298–703°K);
$\quad H_T - H_{298} = -2,605 + 5.87T + 9.60 \times 10^{-3}T^2$ (298–703°K)
CuCl(l): $C_p = 15.80$; $H_T - H_{298} = -2,220 + 15.80T$ (703–1200°K); $S°_{298} = 20.8$;
$\quad$ b.p. $= 1763°K$; $\Delta H_v = 11,918$
CuCl₂(c): $\Delta H°_{298} = -53,400$; $S°_{298} = 27$;
$\quad C_p = 15.42 + 12.0 \times 10^{-3}T$; $H_T - H_{298} = -5,131 + 15.42T + 6.00 \times 10^{-3}T^{-2}$;
$\quad$ decomposes, pressure Cl₂ is 1 atm at 810°K
CuCl₂·2H₂O(c): $\Delta H°_{298} = -193,000$
CuCl₂⁻(aq): $\Delta H°_{298} = -65,800$; $\Delta F°_{298} = -58,100$
CuCl₂·CuO(c): $\Delta H°_{298} = -85,300$
CuCl₂·3CuO(c): $\Delta H°_{298} = -154,900$
CuCl₂·3CuO·4H₂O: $\Delta H°_{298} = -450,000$
CuFe₂O₄(c): $S°_{298} = 33.7$
CuF(c): $S°_{298} = 15.5$
CuF(g): $C_p = 8.73 + 0.14 \times 10^{-3}T - 0.74 \times 10^5 T^{-2}$; $\Delta H°_{298} = 44,000$; $S°_{298} = 54.1$;
$\quad H_T - H_{298} = 8.73T + 0.07 \times 10^{-3}T^2 + 0.74 \times 10^5 T^{-1} - 2,857$
CuF₂(c): $\Delta H°_{298} = -126,900$
CuF₂·2H₂O(c): $\Delta H°_{298} = -274,500$

TABLE 3—*continued*

CuI(c): $\Delta H^\circ_{298} = -16,500$; $S^\circ_{298} = 23.1$;
$\quad\quad C_p = 12.1 + 2.86 \times 10^{-3}T$; $H_T - H_{298} = -3,733 + 12.1T + 1.43 \times 10^{-3}T^2$;
$\quad\quad$ m.p. $= 861^\circ K$; $\Delta H_M = 2,600$; b.p. $= 1480^\circ K$; $\Delta H_v = 31,100$

CuO(c): $\Delta H^\circ_{298} = -37,500$; $S^\circ_{298} = 10.19$
$\quad\quad C_p = 9.27 + 4.80 \times 10^{-3}T$; $H_T - H_{298} = -2,977 + 9.27T + 2.40 \times 10^{-3}T^2$;
$\quad\quad$ m.p. $= 1720^\circ K$; $\Delta H_M = 2,820$;
$\quad\quad$ decomposes at high temperatures to Cu_2O and O_2

Cu$_2$O(c): $\Delta H^\circ_{298} = -40,800$; $S^\circ_{298} = 22.44$;
$\quad\quad C_p = 14.90 + 5.70 \times 10^{-3}T$; $H_T - H_{298} = -4,696 + 14.90T + 2.85 \times 10^{-3}T^2$;
$\quad\quad$ m.p. $= 1502^\circ K$; $\Delta H_M = 13,400$

CuSO$_4$(c): $\Delta H^\circ_{298} = -184,000$; $S^\circ_{298} = 26.8$: $C_p = 24.7$; decomposes upon heating to $CuO\cdot CuSO_4$

CuSO$_4\cdot$H$_2$O(c): $\Delta H^\circ_{298} = -259,000$; $S^\circ_{298} = -35.8$

CuSO$_4\cdot$3H$_2$O(c): $\Delta H^\circ_{298} = -402,300$; $S^\circ_{298} = 53.8$

CuSO $\cdot$5H$_2$O(c): $\Delta H^\circ_{298} = -544,500$; $S^\circ_{298} = 73.0$

CuS$_2$O$_6\cdot$5H$_2$O(c): $\Delta H^\circ_{298} = -611,500$

Cu$_2$SO$_4$(c): $\Delta H^\circ_{298} = -179,200$

CuSO$_4\cdot$4NH$_3$(c): $\Delta H^\circ_{298} = -300,200$

CuSO$_4\cdot$3CuO$\cdot$4H$_2$O(c): $\Delta H^\circ_{298} = -592,600$

Cu(NO$_3$)$_2$(c): $\Delta H^\circ_{298} = -73.4$

Cu$_3$N(c): $\Delta H^\circ_{298} = 17,800$; decomposes at $740^\circ K$

CuN(c): $\Delta H^\circ_{298} = -60,230$; $S^\circ_{298} = 39.68$

Cu$_2$Se(c): $\Delta H^\circ_{298} = 14,500$; $C_p = 21.2$; transition at $383^\circ K$;
$\quad\quad \Delta H_{Tr} = 1,160$; $H_T - H_{298} = 20.2T - 4,775$

CuAl$_2$(c): $\Delta H^\circ_{298} = 9,500$; $C_p = 16.01 + 5.32 \times 10^{-3}T$;
$\quad\quad H_T - H_{298} = 16.01T + 2.66 \times 10^{-3}T^2 - 5,010$

Cu$_3$Sb(c): $\Delta H^\circ_{298} = 2,500$; $C_p = 21.97 + 9.0 \times 10^{-3}T$;
$\quad\quad H_T - H_{298} = 21.97T + 4.50 \times 10^{-3}T^2 - 6,897$

---

acids such as nitric or sulfuric to the cupric salt. The color of Cu_2O may vary from yellow to red, depending upon particle size.

While the $+2$ oxidation state of copper is common and stable in solution, the dipositive state is stabilized in certain instances by complex formation. Anhydrous cupric fluoride crystallizes with a fluorite-type lattice and is ionic, but anhydrous cupric bromide and chloride have chain structures involving halogen bridges and are largely covalent. The fluoride is difficulty soluble in water, but the chloride and bromide are readily soluble. In concentrated solutions, the latter two exist at least in part as halo complexes:

$$[CuX_3]^- \text{ or } [CuX_4]^{-2} \text{ (X = F, Cl, or Br)}$$

On dilution these revert to aquo complexes:

$$[CuX_3(H_2O)]^-, [Cu(H_2O)_4]^{+2}$$

Because copper possesses all of the factors favoring true complex formation involving covalent bonds, a wide variety of coordination compounds can be prepared exhibiting coordination numbers of two and four. Beside those already mentioned, there occur thiosulfates: $[Cu(S_2O_3)]^{-1}$; thiourea (tu) compounds of the type $[Cu(tu)_3]X$, ammines such as $[Cu(NH_3)_n]^+$ (with n usually 2, but also 1 or 3): and the cyano complexes $[Cu(CN)_n]^{1-n}$ (with $n = 2$, 3 or 4). Carbon monoxide is readily absorbed by solutions of cuprous chloride in ammonia or hydrochloric acid to form $Cu(CO)Cl$. $CuCl\cdot C_2H_4$ and similar compounds are formed with ethylene and other hydrocarbons.

Cuprous chloride is used extensively as a catalyst, desulfurizing agent, and decolorizing agent in the petroleum industry. It catalyzes the formation of chlorine in the reaction between oxygen and hydrogen chloride. Cupric chloride is used as an ingredient of isomerization and cracking catalysts; it is also used as a mordant in the dyeing and printing of textiles, as an oxidizing agent for aniline dyestuffs, and in laundry marking inks. Basic cupric chlorides make up part of some commercial fungicidal preparations used for crop spraying and dusting.

Cuprous oxide is used in antifouling paints for steel and wood exposed to sea water and as a fungicide. The compound is incorporated in some brazing pastes as a reducing agent and in the manufacture of ruby-red glass and red glazes on ceramics. Many rectifiers of alternating current depend upon cuprous oxide for their performance.

Cupric nitrate is used in light-sensitive reproductive papers, as a burnishing reagent for iron and for coloring copper black, zinc brown, and for giving copper an antique finish.

Cupric fluoride has found use as an opacifier in enamels, glasses, and ceramics. It is an ingredient of welding and brazing fluxes and is added to cast iron to improve strength and wearing qualities.

Many other compounds are suitable as fungicides, among them are: copper naphthenate, copper resinate, copper-zinc chromate.

Cupric oxide is a black, covalent compound which is difficultly soluble in water but dissolves in acids. Precipitation of aqueous cupric salt solutions with alkali produces a blue hydrate which is changed to the oxide by boiling the suspension.

Copper sulfate, $CuSO_4 \cdot 5H_2O$, is the most important industrial compound of copper. It is used as a soil additive to prevent copper deficiencies in crops and animals and to improve crop yields. It serves also as a fungicide or in making other copper-bearing fungicides such as "Bordeaux mixture," a mixture of $CaSO_4$ and $Cu(OH)_2$ which results from the interaction of lime and copper sulfate. Cupric acetoarsenite, "Paris green," and cupric arsenite, "Scheele's green," are used as wood preservatives and as larvicides for mosquito control.

Electroplating

Copper is electroplated on many parts as an undercoat for nickel and chromium, as a stop-off against carburizing, for color effects, and for other special purposes. Nearly all zinc alloy die castings which are to be bright-nickel plated are first given an electroplate of copper to protect the castings from dissolving in the acid, nickel sulfate solutions used. Steel wire is copper plated to make high-strength, electrical cable, and some steel parts receive a copper plate and a buffing to smooth the pieces prior to nickel and chromium plating.

The properties of copper plate depend on plating conditions. Small concentrations of addition agents cause large changes in brightness, smoothness, hardness, and strength. Variations in current density and temperature also affect some solutions to a marked degree.

The solutions used commercially for copper electroplating are: (1) *cyanide*—containing 25 to 150 gpl of sodium cyanide; 15 to 100 gpl copper cyanide; 15 to 30 gpl sodium carbonate; and 6 to 40 gpl of free sodium cyanide; cyanide plating is carried out at temperatures of 100–150°F at cathode current densities of from 5 to 50 amp per sq ft; (2) *sulfate*—assaying 150 to 250 gpl of copper sulfate and 45 to 110 gpl sulfuric acid; operating temperatures are from 70 to 100°F at cathode current densities of 20 to 40 amp per sq ft; (3) *fluoborate*—is suited for operation with higher current densities than are practical for any other copper plating bath and has 224 to 448 gpl copper fluoborate, 15 to 30 gpl fluoboric acid, 15 to 30 gpl boric acid; cathode current densities vary from 20 to 60 amp per sq ft, and temperatures vary from 70 to 100°F; (4) *pyrophosphate*—is prepared with sodium or potassium pyrophosphate to give 150 to 250 gpl of phosphate ions; copper ions are present to the extent of 22 to 38 gpl, oxalate ions, 15 to 30 gpl, nitrate ions 5 to 10 gpl, and ammonia 1 to 3 gpl; cathode current densities range from 10 to 75 amp per sq ft, and temperatures from 122 to 140°F.

Alloys of Copper

The 83 metals and metalloids permit the formation of the following number of copper alloy systems: 82 binaries, 3,321 ternaries, 88,560 quaternaries and 1,749,060 quinaries. The latest compilation reveals that 55% of the copper binary systems have been investigated, but work has been reported on only 5% of the ternaries, 2% of the quaternaries and $2 \times 10^{-4}\%$ of the quinaries.

A large number of commercial alloys contain small percentages of copper, but many industrially important alloys contain copper as the principal element. These materials are used because of high electrical and thermal conductivity, malleability, machinability, corrosion resistance, strength, pleasing color, ease of soldering and welding, and ability to be plated or lacquered to give an attractive finish. Alloying often solves the problem of improving some of the basic properties of copper, especially strength. Two main groups of copper-base materials are recognized: those suitable for producing wrought products and those mainly employed for castings. The electrical conductivity of the wrought alloys varies from 5% (IACS) for the silicon bronzes and nickel silver to 101% for electrolytic tough pitch copper. The tensile strengths change by alloying from about 35,000 psi for annealed copper to 215,000 psi for beryllium copper strip.

Temperatures as low as $-300°F$ do not embrittle copper alloys, but impart a slight gain in strength and toughness. In high-temperature uses, cupro-nickel and aluminum bronzes exhibit good oxidation resistance. Most copper alloys soften between 400 and 800°F, depending upon the amount of cold work during fabrication and composition.

The simple brasses (Cu + Zn) were originally developed partly because they were cheaper than unalloyed copper, but they also offer increased cold formability as the zinc content increases to about 30%. Adding more zinc than this to copper decreases the formability due to the appearance of the relatively brittle beta phase. Cartridge brass is extensively used for cold drawing, wire upsetting, and bending operations. Red brass, gilding, and commercial bronze are not as strong, but permit successive operations without intermediate annealing. Alloys commonly specified for hot forming are the coppers, brasses, and leaded brasses with less than 63% copper, aluminum-silicon bronzes, naval brass, and cupro-nickel. Two-phase alloys of leaded brasses, such as forging brass or architectural bronze, are used for die-pressed forgings and extrusions.

Components for automobiles, refrigerators and air-conditioning equipment, decorative elements, hardware, camera parts, valves and hundreds of parts made on high-speed automatic screw machines are of free cutting brass rod. Tubular parts to be machined and lightly cold-formed may be made of leaded brass with 0.5% Pb. If they are only to be machined, the lead content can be 1.5% because the lead dissolves only very minutely in copper, and most of it is finely dispersed throughout the alloy matrix, acting as a lubricant for the cutting tool.

Copper alloy castings are used wherever superior electrical conductivity, corrosion resistance, and good bearing surface qualities are desired. Compositions of the casting alloys may differ from comparable wrought alloys since casting permits a wider choice in the use of alloying elements because hot and cold working properties are not important. Similarly, the tolerance for impurities is normally greater in casting than in their wrought counterparts. All copper alloys can be successfully sand-cast, the most economical casting method with the greatest flexibility for size and shape. Yellow brass is best die-cast, and the pieces generally weigh less than two pounds.

Castings weighing from a few ounces to twenty-five tons are being made by the centrifugal process from virtually all copper alloys. For plaster-mold casting, silicon brasses and bronzes, low-nickel bronzes, yellow brasses, aluminum bronzes and manganese bronzes are best suited. Such plaster castings can be made up to several hundred pounds in weight. Many of the copper casting alloys are sold under various trade names or SAE and AMS designations, as well as ASTM numbers.

Most of the casting copper alloys containing tin, lead or zinc have moderate tensile and yield strengths, low to medium hardness, and high elongation. The aluminum and manganese bronzes, silicon brasses and bronzes, and

TABLE 4. USES OF METALLIC COPPER IN THE UNITED STATES

Use	% of Total
Electrical equipment	19
Light and power industry	18
Building construction	16
Industrial equipment and supplies	10
Motor vehicles	9
Communication	6
Military	6
Household appliances	3
Railroad and marine	3
Electronics	3
Scientific	2
Miscellaneous	5

some nickel silvers are used for applications requiring higher strengths. Manganese bronzes are specified for marine propellers and fittings, pinions, ball bearing races, worm gears, and architectural work. A wide range of properties is obtainable with the various cast aluminum bronze alloys by varying the aluminum content and by heat treating. The aluminum bronzes are corrosion resistant to many solutions and also have a high fatigue limit.

Table 4 shows the use pattern of copper in the United States as compiled by the Bureau of Mines.

Biochemical Behavior of Copper*

The activity of copper in plant metabolism manifests itself in two forms: synthesis of chlorophyll and activity of enzymes. In leaves, most of the copper occurs in close association with chlorophyll, but little is known of its role in chlorophyll synthesis, other than that its presence is required.

Copper is a definite constituent of several enzymes catalyzing oxidation-reduction reactions (oxidases), in which the activity is believed to be due to the shuttling of copper between the $+1$ and $+2$ oxidation states. Ascorbic acid oxidase catalyzes the reaction between oxygen and ascorbic acid to give dehydroascorbic acid. This oxidase occurs widely in plants, particularly in cucurbits and beans. Tryosinase, also known as polyphenol oxidase or catechol oxidase, occurs in potatoes, spinach, mushrooms, and other plants. It catalyzes the air oxidation of monophenols to ortho diphenols, and the oxidation of catechol to dark-colored compounds known as melanins. Laccase also catalyzes the oxidation of phenols, and is fairly widely distributed. The cytochrome enzymes (see below) are also found in plants.

Traces of copper are required for the growth and reproduction of lower plant forms, such as algae and fungi, although larger amounts are toxic.

The effects of copper deficiency in plants are varied and include: die-back, inability to produce seed, chlorosis, and reduced photosynthetic activity. On the other hand, excesses of copper in the soil are toxic, as is the application of soluble copper salts to foliage.

It is for this reason that copper fungicides are formulated with a relatively insoluble copper compound. Their toxicity to fungi arises from the fact that the latter produce compounds, primarily hydroxy- and amino-acids, which can dissolve the copper compounds from the fungicide.

Copper is also a necessary trace element in animal metabolism. The human adult requirement is 2 mg per day, and the adult human body contains 100–150 mg of copper, the greatest concentrations existing in the liver and bones. Blood contains a number of copper proteins, and copper is known to be necessary for the synthesis of hemoglobin, although there is no copper in the hemoglobin molecule.

Copper in plasma is mainly present in the blue protein ceruloplasmin, which is thought to be responsible for the transport of copper in the body. Copper has been shown to be a constituent of some of the cytochrome enzymes. These proteins are the catalysts for the main respiratory reaction chains, involving transfer of electrons from various carbohydrates to oxygen.

Copper is also required for the synthesis of a number of enzymes, and is involved in the glycolysis or breakdown of sugars.

The blue copper protein hemocyanin occurs in the blood of certain lower forms of animal life. This compound performs the oxygen-carrying function for these species. This protein is believed to be a polypeptide containing $+1$ copper. It is not, however, as efficient an oxygen carrier as hemoglobin. The enzyme tryosinase is found in many animals, being mainly responsible for skin pigmentation and for hardening of fresh tissue in molting species.

Copper is also found in bacteria: in the diphtheria bacillus copper is necessary for the production of toxins.

Anemia can be induced in animals on a low copper diet, such as milk, and appears to be due to an impaired ability of the body to absorb iron. This, however, is rare, because of the widespread occurrence of copper in foods. In some places, e.g., Australia and Holland, diseases of cattle and sheep, involving diarrhea, anemia and nervous disorders, can be traced either to a lack of copper in the diet, or to excessive amount of molybdenum, which inhibits the storage of copper in the liver.

Ingestion of copper sulfate by humans causes vomiting, cramps, convulsions, and as little as 27 g of the compound may cause death. An important part of the toxicity of copper to both plants and animals is probably due to its combination with thiol groups of certain enzymes, thereby inactivating them. The effects of chronic exposure to copper in animals are cirrhosis of the liver, failure of growth, and jaundice.

*by R. R. GRINSTEAD

References

1. American Society For Metals, "Metals Handbook," Vol. 1, 8th Edition, Metal Park, Ohio, 1961.
2. Butts, A., "Copper," ACS Monograph 122, New York, Reinhold Publishing Corporation, 1954.
3. Elliot, R. P., "Constitution of Binary Alloys," New York, McGraw-Hill Book Company, 1965.
4. Florkin, M., and Stotz, E. N., "Comprehensive Biochemistry," **8,** Part 2, New York, Elsevier, 1963.
5. Hampel, Clifford A., "The Encyclopedia of Electrochemistry," New York, Reinhold Publishing Corp., 1964.
6. Kelley, K. K., and King, E. G., "Contributions To the Data on Theoretical Metallurgy XIV Entropies of the Elements and Inorganic Compounds," Washington, D.C., Bureau of Mines Bulletin 592 (1961).
7. McElroy, W. D., and Glass, B., "Symposium on Copper Metabolism," Baltimore, Johns Hopkins Press, 1950.
8. Moeller, T., "Inorganic Chemistry," New York, John Wiley and Sons, Inc., 1954.
9. Monier-Williams, G. W., "Trace Elements in Food," New York, John Wiley and Sons, Inc., 1950.
10. Newton, J., and Wilson, C. L., "The Metallurgy of Copper," New York, John Wiley and Sons, Inc., 1942.
11. Wicks, C. D., and Block, F. E., "Thermodynamic Properties of 65 Elements," Washington, D.C., Bureau of Mines Bulletin 605 (1963).
12. Wideman, F. L., "Copper—Mineral Facts and Problems," Washington, D.C., Bureau of Mines Bulletin 630, 1965 Edition.

E. A. PERETTI

CURIUM

Discovery

In the summer of 1944 G. T. Seaborg, R. A. James and A. Ghiorso, working at the Manhattan Project's Metallurgical Laboratory in Chicago, performed a careful chemical fractionation on a sample of plutonium which had been irradiated with 32 MeV helium ions at the University of California's 60-inch cyclotron at Berkeley.

A new radioactivity was found which emitted 4.7 MeV alpha particles and was chemically separable from neptunium and plutonium.

Both nuclear and chemical evidence indicated that the activity should be ascribed to an isotope of a new element, atomic number 96, produced by the reaction:

$$_{94}Pu^{239} + _{2}He^{4}(32\ MeV) \rightarrow _{96}\boxed{}^{242} + _{0}n^{1}$$

In tribute to the brilliant pioneering achievements of Pierre and Marie Curie in the field of radioactivity the new element was given the name *curium* (symbol, Cm).

The discovery of element 96 preceded that of element 95 by some months. The latter was first identified in plutonium which had been subjected to prolonged neutron irradiation.

Historical

In a series of tests of the coprecipitation behavior of the 4.7 MeV alpha activity, Seaborg, James and Ghiorso demonstrated that unlike neptunium and plutonium, curium was not oxidized beyond the 3+ state even in the presence of such a powerful oxidizing agent as peroxydisulfate.

This observation was of profound importance in the subsequent search for still higher transuranium elements, for it was anticipated correctly that the chemistry of these elements, like that of curium and the rare earths would be dominated by great stability of the 3+ state.

Both curium and its rare earth analog, gadolinium, honor the names of pioneers of science, the latter the Eighteenth Century initiator of rare earth chemistry, J. Gadolin.

Visible amounts of curium were not isolated until 1947, when L. B. Werner and I. Perlman, working at the University of California's

Radiation Laboratory in Berkeley, obtained about 30 μgm of the curium isotope of mass 242 as the pure hydroxide.

Additional advances in curium chemistry became possible with these increased amounts of material. W. W. T. Crane, J. C. Wallmann and B. B. Cunningham in 1950 measured the magnetic susceptibility of microgram samples of curium trifluoride and found it to be of about the same magnitude as gadolinium trifluoride; the result provided direct experimental evidence for assigning a $5f^7$ electronic configuration to Cm^{+3}. In the following year these same workers prepared curium in its elemental form (a silvery metal) for the first time, while J. G. Conway, M. F. Moore and Crane, also working at the Radiation Laboratory in Berkeley, obtained more than 200 lines in the arc and spark spectra of the element.

Early efforts to investigate the crystallography of curium compounds were hampered by the intense radioactivity of the isotope of mass 242 which rapidly destroyed lattice order in crystalline solids. Some success in this area was realized by F. H. Ellinger of the Los Alamos Scientific Laboratories by working rapidly with freshly crystallized samples.

The more stable isotope, Cm^{244}, gradually became available as the result of several years exposure of comparatively large amounts of plutonium to the intense neutron fluxes produced by nuclear reactor facilities.

Using the 18-year alpha-emitting isotope of mass 244, L. B. Asprey and Ellinger, in collaboration with S. Fried and W. H. Zachariasen of the Argonne National Laboratory, showed in 1955 that curium exhibited a tetrapositive state in some solids. X-ray diffraction methods were used to identify both a dioxide and a tetrafluoride.

The ground state electronic configurations of the neutral gaseous atom of curium was determined in 1959 by J. C. Hubbs, R. Marrus and J. O. Winocur at Berkeley using the atomic beam resonance method. The configuration was shown to be $5f^76d7s^2$ analogous to the $4f^75d6s^2$ configuration of neutral gadolinium, but attention was called to the greater importance of jj coupling in the $5f$ as compared with the $4f$ transition series.

The crystal structure and melting point of curium metal were determined in 1964 by B. B. Cunningham and J. C. Wallmann.

The paramagnetic resonance spectrum of the Cm^{+3} ion incorporated in crystalline matrices of $LaCl_3$ or lanthanum ethyl sulfate was observed by M. Abraham, B. R. Judd and H. H. Wickman in 1963. The single line resonance, obtained at liquid helium temperatures, was shown to be entirely different from the seven-line spectrum of Gd^{+3} (an impurity in the lanthanum used in earlier work) which had been mistakenly ascribed to Cm^{+3}.

Prevalence

The known isotopes of curium are listed in Table 1 below.

A more detailed tabulation is given on page 749 in the article on **Transuranium Elements**.

The half-life of the most stable isotope, Cm^{247}, is so short in comparison with the age of the earth that any primordial curium must long since have disappeared from the natural environment.

Infinitesimal amounts of curium undoubtedly exist in natural deposits of uranium, owing to a sequence of neutron captures and β^- decays sustained by the very low flux of neutrons which is naturally present in radioactive ores; however the presence of curium has not been detected in natural sources.

Curium has been produced mainly by the exposure of lower atomic number elements to the very intense neutron fluxes provided by fission reactors. The series of neutron captures and β^- decays leading to the

TABLE 1. ISOTOPES OF CURIUM

Mass no.	238	239	240	241	242	243	244	245	246	247	248	249
Half-life	2.5 h	~ 3 h	26.8 d	35 d	163 d	32 y	18.1 y	9320 y	5480 y	1.67×10^7 y	4.7×10^5 y	65 m
Radiation	ϵ, α	ϵ	α	α	α	α	α	α	α	α	α	β^-

formation of Cm^{244} and other isotopes is indicated in Fig. 1 below.

The capture and decay sequences shown in Fig. 1 are greatly outweighed by heavy element fission; prolonged neutron irradiation of the heavy elements with thermal neutrons results principally in the formation of

3.5% smaller metallic radius, and evolves about 20 kcal less heat on dissolution in mineral acids.

Except for its heat of solution the known properties of curium fall within the range exhibited by the metals of the normally trivalent rare earths.

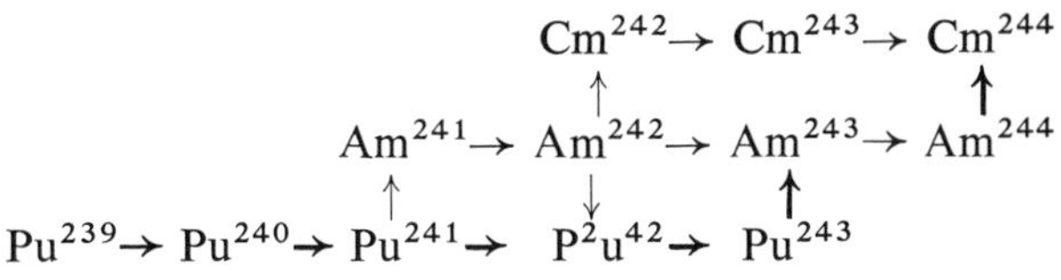

$$
\begin{array}{ccc}
Cm^{242} \rightarrow & Cm^{243} \rightarrow & Cm^{244} \\
\uparrow & & \uparrow \\
Am^{241} \rightarrow Am^{242} \rightarrow & Am^{243} \rightarrow & Am^{244} \\
\uparrow & \downarrow & \uparrow \\
Pu^{239} \rightarrow Pu^{240} \rightarrow Pu^{241} \rightarrow & P^2u^{42} \rightarrow & Pu^{243}
\end{array}
$$

$\rightarrow$ (n,γ) reaction (neutron capture)
$\uparrow$ β^- decay
$\downarrow$ electron capture

heavier arrows indicate principal path to Cm^{244}

FIG. 1.   Buildup of heavier elements by the irradiation of Pu^{239} with thermal neutrons.

elements of atomic number in the range from 31-65.

Both Cm^{242} and Cm^{244} are available in multigram quantities; the much more stable isotope Cm^{248} has been produced only in fractional milligram amounts.

Other methods for obtaining curium isotopes are charged particle bombardments and thermonuclear explosions. The former is used to make the lighter isotopes, as, for example

$$_{94}Pu^{239} + {}_2He^4(50\ MeV) \rightarrow {}_{96}Cm^{238} + 5_0n^1$$

Thermonuclear explosions create intense neutron fluxes for very brief periods of time (microseconds). Because of the rapidity of the neutron capture process, superheavy isotopes may be created which then undergo a series of β^- decays:

$$_{92}U^{238} + 8_0n^1 \rightarrow U^{246} \xrightarrow{\beta^-} {}_{93}Np^{246} \xrightarrow{\beta^-} {}_{94}Pu^{246}$$

$$\xleftarrow{\beta^-} {}_{95}Am^{246} \xrightarrow{\beta^-} {}_{96}Cm^{246}$$

Physical Properties of Curium

The known physical properties of curium metal are given in Table 2 above.

Curium is similar to gadolinium, its rare earth analog, in melting point and effective magnetic moment, but possesses a more complex crystal structure (double as compared with simple hexagonal close packing), has a

TABLE 2.   PHYSICAL PROPERTIES OF CURIUM

Color—silvery		
Crystal structure	d.h.c.p.,	a = 3.496 ± 0.003Å
		c = 11.331 ± 0.005Å
Density (calculated from crystal structure)		13.51 g/cc
Atomic volume		18.07 cc/mole
Metallic radius (CN 12)		1.74 ± 0.01Å
Melting point		1340 ± 40°C
Boiling point		?
Magnetic susceptibility		12,200 × 10⁻⁶ cgs units per mole at 25°C
Effective magnetic moment		8.0 ± 0.1 BM (150-300°K)
Heat evolved on solution in mineral acids		140 ± 3 kcal/mole

Chemical Properties of Curium Metal

Curium is a chemically reactive metal, somewhat more electropositive than aluminum.

Its reactions in various chemical environments are summarized in Table 3 below:

Important Compounds of Curium

Slightly soluble compounds useful for the quantitative precipitation of curium from solution include the hydroxide, $Cm(OH)_3$, fluoride, $CmF_3 \cdot \frac{1}{2}H_2O$ and oxalate, $Cm_2(C_2O_4)_3$; the solubility products of these compounds

TABLE 3. REACTIONS OF CURIUM METAL

Environment	Temperature, °C	Reaction
air	25	stable for days after quick initial tarnish
air	600	oxidized to Cm_2O_3
free halogens, X_2	400–600	forms CmF_4 with F_2, CmX_3 with other halogens
gaseous hydrogen halides	500	forms trihalides CmX_3
dilute acids		evolves H_2 with formation of Cm^{+3}(aq)

are roughly 10^{-21}, 10^{-13}, and 10^{-28}, respectively.

The more important binary compounds are the oxides and halides listed below:

1. CmO_2. The black dioxide may be obtained by decomposing curium(III) oxalate in an oxygen-ozone atmosphere at 300°C and cooling in the gas stream. The dioxide crystallizes in the cubic fluorite-type structure, $a = 5.372 \pm 0.003Å$.

2. Cm_2O_3. The faint yellow sesquioxide is formed by heating the dioxide in vacuum. Below 600°C the sesquioxide exhibits the cubic Mn_2O_3 type structure, $a = 11.00Å$; at higher temperatures the hexagonal modification, $a = 3.80 \pm 0.02Å$, $c = 6.00 \pm 0.03Å$, is obtained.

3. CmF_4. The monoclinic tetrafluoride, isostructural with UF_4, has been prepared by treating the trifluoride with fluorine at 400°C.

4. CmF_3. Treatment of Cm_2O_3 with dry HF gas at 500° converts the oxide to the hexagonal trifluoride, $a = 4.041 \pm 0.001Å$, $c = 7.179 \pm 0.002Å$. A hydrated fluoride, $CmF_3 \cdot \frac{1}{2}H_2O$, precipitates when HF is added to aqueous solutions of Cm^{+3}. The hydrate is converted to the anhydrous compound by drying in $HF_{(g)}$ at 300-500°C.

5. $CmCl_3$. The anhydrous trichloride is readily prepared by reacting the sesquioxide with either $CCl_{4(g)}$ or dry $HCl_{(g)}$ at around 550°C. This compound forms hexagonal crystals, UCl_3 structure type, with $a = 7.380 \pm 0.001Å$, $c = 4.185 \pm 0.001Å$. The trichloride is strongly hygroscopic and must be handled in a dry atmosphere.

6. $CmBr_3$. Orthorhombic curium tribromide, $a = 4.048 \pm 0.002Å$, $b = 12.66 \pm 0.01Å$, $c = 9.124 \pm 0.007Å$, is isostructural with $PuBr_3$. It has been prepared by treating $CmCl_3$ with a large excess of NH_4Br and subliming off the excess ammonium bromide at 400-450°C.

7. CmI_3. Prepared from $CmCl_3$ and NH_4I in a manner similar to that used for the preparation of $CmBr_3$, the triiodide has a hexagonal structure, BiI_3 type, with $a = 7.44 \pm 0.09Å$, $c = 20.4 \pm 0.10Å$.

Most compounds of trivalent curium exhibit a faint yellow color due to extension into the visible region of the spectrum of an absorption band which peaks at about 3950Å. Other absorption peaks occur at 3800, 3715 and 2800Å. Molar absorptivities are in the range from 10 to 50.

Uses of Curium

Both Cm^{242} and Cm^{244} are useful for the thermoelectric generation of power for the operation of instruments at remote terrestrial locations or in space vehicles. A power package utilizing the isotope of mass 244 can maintain a nearly constant output for many years.

Biological Action of Curium

Curium absorbed into the body tends to accumulate in the bone. The shorter-lived isotopes are extremely toxic owing principally to the destruction of radiation of the red cell-forming mechanism. The maximum permissible body burden of Cm^{244} in a human being is $0.002\mu gm$.

References

1. Seaborg, G. T., "The Transuranium Elements," New Haven, Yale University Press, 328 pp., 1958.

2. Katz, J. J., and Seaborg, G. T., "The Chemistry of the Actinide Elements," London, Methuen, 508 pp., 1957.
3. Seaborg, G. T., "Man-Made Transuranium Elements," Englewood Cliffs, N. J., Prentice-Hall, Inc., 120 pp., 1963.
4. "Noveau Traite de Chemie Minerale," published under the direction of Paul Pascal, Volume XV, Paris, Masson et Cie, 1962.
5. Hubbs, J. C., Marrus, R., and Winocur, J., *Phys. Rev.*, **114**, 586 (1959).
6. Abraham, M., Judd, B. R., and Wickman, H. H., *Phys. Rev.*, **130**, 611 (1963).
7. Cunningham, B. B., and Wallmann, J. C., *J. Inorg. Nucl. Chem.*, **26**, 271 (1964).
8. Recent issues of *Inorg. Chem.* and *J. Inorg. Nucl. Chem.*

B. B. CUNNINGHAM

D

DYSPROSIUM

Dysprosium, atomic number 66, is a relatively abundant element of the lanthanide series. (See **Lanthanide Elements.**) Although little in demand at present, its sesquioxide, Dy_2O_3, could be derived at a rate exceeding 20,000 pounds per annum directly (and with little additional effort or expense) from the current (1967) commercial production of yttrium oxide by ion exchange.

History[1,2,3]

The element was discovered in 1886 by Lecoq de Boisbaudran and was named dysprosium after the Greek word *dysprositos*, meaning hard to get at. Neither the oxide nor the metal was available in good quality until the development of adequate ion-exchange separation and metallographic reduction techniques by Spedding and co-workers about the middle of the 20th Century.

Occurrence and Sources[1,4]

Dysprosium is the most abundant of the heavier (yttrium group) lanthanide elements and is approximately as abundant as arsenic, hafnium, and uranium. It is listed 49th in order of abundance among the elements of the earth's crust and estimated to be more plentiful than boron, tantalum, bromine, antimony, mercury, and many other familiar elements. Of the 15 lanthanides, only six (cerium, praseodymium, neodymium, samarium, and gadolinium) outrank it.

The more important mineral sources of dysprosium include xenotime, gadolinite, euxenite, samarskite, fergusonite, blomstrandine, polycrase, loparite, and yttroparisite. Xenotime occurs in Norway, Sweden, Brazil, Malaysia, Korea, Switzerland, and the United States (Colorado and North and South Carolina). Gadolinite occurs in Norway, Sweden, Malagasy Republic (Madagascar), and the United States (Arizona, Colorado, and Texas). Euxenite is found in Australia, Brazil, Canada, Finland, Madagascar, Norway, and the United States (Idaho and North Carolina); fergusonite in Greenland, Norway, Sweden, and the United States (North and South Carolina and Texas); samarskite in Madagascar, North Carolina, and Ontario; blomstrandine in Norway; polycrase in Norway, Sweden, and North and South Carolina; loparite and yttroparisite in Russia. Of these minerals, xenotime and gadolinite are the most easily opened by chemical action, and yield directly the cleanest rare earth concentrates. Because it is processed commercially for uranium, thorium, and yttrium, euxenite is a prime source of dysprosium. Because monazite is commonly processed for its thorium, cerium, and lanthanum values, it is also an important source of yttrium and other lanthanides including dysprosium. Dysprosium and other lanthanide elements occur in minute amounts in many common rocks and minerals including apatite.

In yttrium-rich oxide concentrates isolated by chemical means from minerals such as xenotime, the dysprosia content often exceeds 10%, so that dysprosium is the major by-product of the commercial production of pure yttrium.

Derivation[1-3]

Processing of Ores.[1, 3, 4] After physical concentration, finely ground xenotime—essentially $(Y)PO_4$—is heated with excess 95% sulfuric acid to obtain a paste of yttrium and rare earth sulfates in sulfuric and phosphoric acids, and the sulfates are leached from unreacted mineral, silica, etc., with cold water. The pregnant liquor is filtered and fed directly into the ion exchange system used to isolate yttrium and the individual rare earths.

Pulverized gadolinite (ostensibly $Be_2Fe(Y)_2 Si_2O_{10}$) is attacked by hot, concentrated nitric and hydrochloric acids, and the dissolved beryllium, iron, yttrium, and various rare earths are diluted and filtered free from the silicaceous residue. Oxalic acid is added next to precipitate yttrium and the rare earths, leaving behind the berryllium and iron; and the oxalate precipitate is roasted to a mixture of yttrium and rare earth oxides at about 800°C. It is expedient to redissolve the oxide mixture in hydrochloric acid and to filter the solution (to reduce the silica content) before proceeding with the isolation of yttrium and the individual lanthanides. Gadolinite can also be attacked by caustic fusion. The sodium silicate formed is leached away with water, and the residue of mixed yttrium and lanthanide hydroxides is taken into solution by treatment with dilute acid.

Euxenite, samarskite, fergusonite, blomstrandine, polycrase, and loparite are generically either niobate-tantalate or niobate-titanate minerals of a complex and refractory nature. They are sometimes treated with hydrofluoric acid to solubilize the niobium, tantalum, and titanium values, leaving an insoluble yttrium and rare earth fluoride residue. This is decomposed subsequently by treatment with hot concentrated sulfuric acid, and the resulting sulfates are dissolved in cold water. The refractory minerals also have been opened successfully by direct chlorination procedures and by other means.

Separation of Rare Earth Mixtures.[1, 3-5] Dysprosium is separated from its mixtures by displacement ion exchange techniques. An yttrium-rich concentrate, containing from 6 to 18% Dy_2O_3, is dissolved in dilute mineral acid; and the tripositive cations are sorbed on an appropriate cation exchange system, and eluted a distance equal to one-fourth the length of the sorbed band with 0.015M ammonium ethylenediaminetetraacetate (EDTA) solution at pH 8.4-8.5 over cation resin pretreated with 1M $CuSO_4$-1M H_2SO_4 solution. The leading one-tenth of the partially developed chromatogram (containing all the lutetium, ytterbium, thulium, and erbium values) is diverted from the system at this point. Elution of the remaining charge is then continued either over cupric or zinc state resin beds until the sorbed band of yttrium and rare earth cations has been displaced a total of two band lengths. Then the solution issuing from the system is collected in a series of appropriate fractions which are treated separately with oxalic acid. The insoluble dysprosium, yttrium, and other rare earth oxalates formed are filtered off, decomposed to the corresponding oxides by roasting at 800-900°C, and analyzed carefully. Excellent yields of both yttrium and dysprosium oxides are obtained if proper care is taken in designing the ion exchange system. As long as the market for Y_2O_3 exceeds the demand for Dy_2O_3 by a factor of 8 or 10, prices of Y_2O_3 and Dy_2O_3 should be comparable.

Preparation of the Metal[2,4,5]

Metallic dysprosium is prepared from its sequioxide by the following reactions:

$$Dy_2O_3 + 6(NH_4)HF_2 \xrightarrow{heat} 2DyF_3 + 6NH_4F + 3H_2O$$

$$2DyF_3 + 3Ca \xrightarrow{heat} 2Dy + 3CaF_2.$$

The reduction to metal is carried out in tantalum or tungsten containers in an inert atmosphere (argon) above the melting point of dysprosium metal, 1407°C. At this temperature CaF_2 is also molten so that the metal and slag form individual layers which can be parted after cooling to room temperature. The metallic product contains a small amount of tantalum or tungsten due to the appreciable solubilities of these metals in elemental dysprosium at its melting point.

Physical Properties[4-6]

The more significant properties of metallic dysprosium are compiled in Table 1.

Chemical Properties[1,3-6,8]

Dysprosium metal is relatively stable in air at room temperature, in fact, the corrosion rate is only 59 mil/year at 400°C and 1110 mil/year at 600°C. This behavior is due to the similar densities of the metal and the sesquioxide (8.559 and 7.81), and the fact that Dy_2O_3 does not react with moist air to form

TABLE 1. PHYSICAL PROPERTIES OF DYSPROSIUM METAL

Atomic number		66
Atomic weight, C-12 = 12.0000		162.50
Atomic volume cc/g-atom		19.032
Allotropic modification, (orthorhombic below 86²K)	$b/a =$	1.732
Transformation temperature, a-β, °C		1384
Ionic radius trivalent ion, Å		0.908
Structure, a		Hcp
Lattice constants, Å	$a_o =$	3.5903
	$c_o =$	5.6475
Density, g/cc		8.559
Metallic radius, Å		1.773
Melting point, °C		1407
Heat of fusion, kcal/g-atom		3.8
Vapor pressure, log $P_{torr} = A/T + B$	$A =$	−15,090
	$B =$	8.822
Heat capacity, cal/g-atom/°C	$C_{p298} =$	6.73
	$C_{p1773} =$	9.02
Entropy of metal, eu	$S_{298} =$	17.9
	$S_{1773} =$	31.1
Boiling point, °C		2335
Heat of sublimation, kcal/g-atom at 25°C		71.2
Heat of combustion, kcal/g-atom		222.92
Coefficient of linear thermal expansion $\times$ 10⁶, per°C		10.0
Thermal conductivity at 28°C, cal/sec/cm²/°C/cm		115
Cohesive energy, kcal/mole		71.5
Debye temperature, °K		186
Susceptibility at 25°C, emu/g-atom $\times$ 10⁶		99,800
Effective magnetic moment. Bohr magnetons		10.64
Curie temperature, °K		85
Néel temperature, °K		178.5
Grüneisen constant		1.35
Young's modulus, kg/cm² $\times$ 10⁶		0.644
Shear modulus, kg/cm² $\times$ 10⁻⁶		0.259
Poisson's ratio		0.243
Compressibility, cm²/kg $\times$ 10⁶		2.552
Hardness, (DPH)		42
Tensile strength, psi $\times$ 10⁻³	70° F	35.7
	400° F	30.8
Yield strength, psi $\times$ 10⁻³	70° F	32.6
	400° F	20.8
Elongation, %	70° F	6
	400° F	8.3
Ultimate compressive strength, psi $\times$ 10⁻³		73.8
Impact strength, Izod, ft-lb		1.6
Electrical resistivity at 25°C, μ ohm-cm		56
Temperature coefficient of resistivity, per°C $\times$ 10³		1.19
Thermal neutron absorption cross section, barns/atom		1100
cm²/g		4.1

the hydroxide as is the case with cerium-group rare earth oxides. Elemental dysprosium is readily attacked and dissolved with the evolution of hydrogen by dilute and concentrated mineral acids, yet a 1:1 mixture of nitric acid and 48% hydrofluoric acid does not greatly affect the metal.

Dysprosium reacts slowly with the halogen gases at room temperature forming trihalides; above 200°C the reaction is vigorous. At high temperatures dysprosium also combines with oxygen, sulfur, nitrogen, carbon, boron, hydrogen, and water, forming Dy_2O_3; DyS, Dy_5S_7, Dy_2S_3 and DyS_2; DyN; Dy_3C, Dy_2C_3 and DyC_2; DyB_2, DyB_4, DyB_6 and DyB_{12}; DyH_2 and DyH_3; and Dy_2O_3; respectively. $DyAg_2$, $DyAu_2$, $DyBe_{13}$, Dy_6Zn_{23}, $DyGa$, $DyGa_2$, $DyIn$, $DyIn_3$, Dy_3In, $DyTl$, $DyTl_3$, $DySi_2$, $DyGe$, $DyGe_3$, DyP, $DyAs$, $DySb$, $DyBi$, $DySe$, Dy_2Se_3, $CrDy_4Se_7$, $MnDy_4Se_7$ $FeDy_4Se_7$, $DyTe$, $DyTe_2$, Dy_3Te_4, $DyPo$, $DyMn_2$, $DyPt$, $DyPt_2$, and $DyPt_3$ have also been prepared by direct combination of the elements.

Halides.[1, 3-5] Anhydrous dysprosium trifluoride is readily prepared by the reactions:

$$Dy_2O_3 + 6HF \xrightarrow{\text{heat}} 2DyF_3 + 3H_2O$$

$$Dy_2O_3 + 6(NH_4)HF_2 \xrightarrow{\text{heat}} 2DyF_3 + 3H_2O + 6NH_4F.$$

The latter reaction is generally preferred for the preparation of high-purity DyF_3. The anhydrous trichloride, tribromide, and triiodide may be prepared by careful dehydration of the corresponding hydrated trihalides at relatively low temperatures and pressures in a hydrogen halide atmosphere. $DyOX$ is a common hydrolysis product observed if the temperature is raised too rapidly during the dehydration.

Subhalides having the stoichiometries $DyCl_2$ and $DyCl_{2.11}$ are known, but Dy^{+2} apparently does not exist in aqueous solutions.

Oxides.[1, 3-6] Dy_2O_3, the only oxide of the element known, is obtained by burning the metal in air and by thermally decomposing a variety of dysprosium compounds in air, including the hydroxide, carbonate, tricarballylate, and oxalate, all of which are insoluble in water, and the nitrate and acetate which are. The oxide is attacked readily by most common mineral acids and many water-soluble hydrated dysprosium salts have been prepared, for example, $DyCl_3 \cdot 6H_2O$, $DyBr_3 \cdot 6H_2O$, $Dy(NO_3)_3 \cdot 5H_2O$, $Dy_2(SO_4)_3 \cdot 8H_2O$, $Dy_2(SeO_{43}) \cdot 8H_2O$, $Dy(BrO_3)_3 \cdot 9H_2O$, $Dy(CH_3COO)_3 \cdot 4H_2O$, and $Dy(C_2H_5OSO_3)_3 \cdot 9H_2O$.

Other Salts.[1, 3, 4] The water-insoluble (hydrated) hydroxide, fluoride, carbonate, oxalate, and tricarballylate are frequently formed in chemical separation of the rare earths as a group from other elements. The complex salts (or mixed oxides) $DyAlO_3$, $DyCrO_3$, $DyFeO_3$, $DyScO_3$, $DyBO_3$, $DyPO_4$, $DyCrO_4$, $DyVO_4$, $DyAsO_4$, $DyNbO_4$, $DyTaO_4$, Dy_3NbO_7, Dy_3TaO_7, Dy_2MoO_6, Dy_2WO_6, $Dy_2Ti_2O_7$, $Dy_2Ru_2O_7$, $Dy_3Al_5O_{12}$, $Dy_3Fe_5O_{12}$, and $Dy_2Ga_5O_{11}$ have also been prepared (generally by fusion of appropriate oxide mixtures). Dy_2S_3, Dy_2Se_3, and Dy_2Te_3, as well as Dy_2O_2S, Dy_2O_2Se, and Dy_2O_2Te, have been prepared and characterized.

Valency.[3] Only the tripositive ion of dysprosium is encountered in aqueous media.

Applications[1,4-6,9]

Dysprosium has been recommended as a possible consumable poison in reactor fuels and has been used in metallic foil form to measure neutron flux. These applications are related to the high cross section of dysprosium for thermal neutrons (1100 barns) much of which is due to the 28.2% Dy^{164} content (2700 barns) of natural dysprosium. Dysprosium has also been employed as a fluorescence activator in some phosphors.

Biological and Biochemical Nature[10]

Dysprosium has a low acute toxicity rating, but soluble salts injected intravenously cause some degeneration of the liver and spleen.

References

1. Vickery, R. C., "Chemistry of the Lanthanides," New York, Academic Press, 1953.
2. Daane, A. H., Dennison, D. H., and Spedding, F. H., *J. Am. Chem. Soc., 75,* 2272 (1953).
3. Moeller, T., "The Chemistry of the Lanthanides," New York, Reinhold Publishing Corp., 1963.
4. Love, B., and Kleber, E. V., "Technology of Scandium, Ytterbium and the Rare Earth Metals," New York, Macmillan, 1963.
5. Spedding, F. H., and Daane, A. H., Ed., "The Rare Earths," New York, John Wiley and Sons, 1961.
6. Gschneidner, K. A., Jr., "Rare Earth Alloys" Princeton, New Jersey, Van Nostrand, 1961.
7. Hall, H. T., Barnett, J. D., and Merrill, L., *Science, 139,* 111 (1963); Stager, R. A., and Drickamer, H. S., *Science, 139,* 1284 (1963); Souers, P. C., and Jura, G., *Science, 140,* 481 (1963); Hall, H. T., and Merrill, L., *Inorg. Chem., 2,* 618 (1963); Jayaraman, A., *Phys. Rev., 135,* A1056 (1964); and Stephens, D. R., *J. Phys. Chem. Solids, 26,* 943 (1965).

8. Love, B., and Kleber, E. V., *Materials in Design Eng.*, **52**, [5], 134 (1960); and Lee, L., and Green, N. D., *Corrosion*, **20**, 145t (1964).
9. Mandle, R. M., and Mandle, H. H., "Progress in the Science and Technology of the Rare Earths," Eyring, L., Ed., Vol. 1, p. 416, New York, Pergamon Press, 1964.
10. Haley, T. J., *J. Pharmaceutical Sciences*, **54**, 663 (1965).

JACK E. POWELL

E

EINSTEINIUM

Einsteinium (element 99) is the seventh of the man-made transuranium elements, and the tenth member of the actinide series. Its electron configuration is predicted to be $5f^{11} 7s^2$ outside the radon core. Since elements 99 and 100, fermium, were discovered at the same time, their discoveries will be described together. These elements have, perhaps, the most dramatic histories of all the elements in the Periodic Table.

Discovery of Elements 99 and 100

During 1949, the preceding two elements, berkelium (97) and californium (98), were synthesized in minute amounts at the University of California Radiation Laboratory, Berkeley (UCRL), by bombarding americium (95) and curium (96) with helium ions, accelerated in the cyclotron. At that time, curium was the highest element available in weighable amounts, and helium ions were the heaviest bombarding particles available. It was clear that the synthesis of elements beyond californium could be achieved by two methods: exposing heavy elements to a very high neutron flux, or bombarding them with heavier ions, such as carbon or nitrogen. The Materials Testing Reactor (MTR) in Idaho, came into operation during 1952, and provided a neutron flux an order of magnitude higher than previously available. Plutonium samples were placed in this reactor for periods of a few months to several years. At the same time, techniques for accelerating useful beams of heavy ions were being developed in several laboratories. These developments ensured the eventual synthesis of elements 99 and 100, but the first observation of these elements came unexpectedly, from a quite unrelated experiment—the explosion of the first thermonuclear device ("Mike") in the Pacific during November 1952.

Samples of debris were collected by drone aircraft flying through the cloud, and analyzed at Argonne National Laboratory (ANL) and Los Alamos Scientific Laboratory (LASL). These samples proved to contain very heavy and previously unknown plutonium isotopes with masses 244 and 246, formed by the instantaneous capture of 6 and 8 neutrons, respectively, in uranium-238 present in the device, and subsequent beta decay of U^{244} and U^{246}. These observations demonstrated that the brief but very intense neutron burst from a thermonuclear explosion can be as effective in producing new heavy nuclides as several years irradiation in a high-flux reactor, and led to a search for heavier products in the debris. Among the new activities detected at ANL and UCRL were alpha-emitters of 6.6 and 7.1 MeV energy, which were shown by elution from cation exchange columns with ammonium citrate solution to behave chemically as expected for isotopes of elements 99 and 100, by analogy with their rare earth analogues, holmium and erbium. Subsequently, larger quantities of these products were obtained by working up hundreds of pounds of coral from the Pacific atoll, and the 6.6 and 7.1 MeV alpha-emitters were ascribed to the nuclides 99^{253} and 100^{255} with half-lives of 20 days and 20 hours, respectively. The 20-hour activity was observed several weeks after the explosion because it was supported by a 40-day parent, 99^{255}.

For security reasons, these observations, in late 1952 and early 1953, could not be published in the open literature. The first publication concerning element 99, from

UCRL in 1954, reported the production of a 7.3-minute isotope, produced by bombarding uranium-238 with nitrogen ions in the 60-inch Berkeley cyclotron. This was tentatively ascribed to 99^{247}, but more recent experiments indicate that it was probably the mass 246 isotope.

Shortly afterwards, also in 1954, groups at ANL and UCRL reported the detection of elements 99 and 100 in plutonium samples which had been exposed to the intense neutron flux of the MTR reactor. Again, the final identification was by elution order from a cation column with ammonium citrate solution. The major element 99 activity detected was the 20-day, 6.6 MeV alpha-emitter, 99^{253}, but the element 100 fraction contained mainly a 3-hour, 7.2 MeV alpha-emitter, which was ascribed to 100^{254}.

The full story of the discovery of elements 99 and 100 was finally published in mid-1955 by a combined group of authors from ANL, UCRL, and LASL. Element 99 was named einsteinium (symbol originally E, but now changed to Es), in honor of Albert Einstein, and element 100 was named fermium (symbol Fm) in honor of Enrico Fermi.

Isotopes of Einsteinium

Table 1 shows the known isotopes of einsteinium, their half-lives, decay properties, and methods of preparation (as of the end of 1966).

The most readily available isotope is 20-day Es^{253}, which is being produced in microgram quantities at the present time by neutron irradiations of plutonium. However, its short half-life precludes the accumulation of large stocks, and its high specific alpha activity limits its use for chemical studies above the tracer scale.

The 276-day ground-state isomer of Es^{254} is produced in much lower yield than Es^{253}, but it should be possible to accumulate it in microgram amounts.

Chemical Properties of Einsteinium

To date, tracer studies using Es^{253} (e.g., coprecipitation solvent extraction, and ion exchange experiments) have shown that the chemical properties of einsteinium are typical of a heavy trivalent actinide element:— generally similar to the rare earths, but

TABLE 1. ISOTOPES OF EINSTEINIUM

Mass No.	Half-life	Modes of Decay	Preparation
245	75 s	(EC), α	$Pu^{240} + B^{10}$ / $Np^{237} + C^{12}$
246	7.3 min.	EC, α	$U^{238} + N^{14}$
248	25 min.	EC, α	$Cf^{249} + d$
249	2 h	EC, α	$Bk^{249} + \alpha$ / $Cf^{249} + d$
250	8 h	EC	$Cf^{249} + \alpha$
251	1.5 d	EC, α	$Bk^{249} + \alpha$
252	~140.d	α	
253	20.7 d	α	multiple neutron capture (reactor or explosion). $Cf^{252} + d$
254	276 d	α	multiple neutron capture (reactor)
254m	39.3 h	β^-, α	
255	39.8 d	β^-, α	multiple neutron capture (reactor or explosion).

m = metastable nuclear isomer, EC = orbital electron capture, α = alpha decay, or helium ion as bombarding particle, β = negative beta decay, and d = deuteron.

See also the tabulation on pages 753 in the article on **Transuranium Elements.**

showing the characteristic effects of the $5f$ electron shell in complex ion formation. All attempts to produce oxidation states other than $3+$ by oxidation or reduction in aqueous solution have failed.

When microgram amounts of Es^{254} become available, it should be possible, by ultra-microchemical techniques, to make limited studies of solid einsteinium compounds, perhaps the metallic state, and to carry out chemical experiments at macro concentrations.

References

1. Hyde, E. K., Perlman, I., and Seaborg, G. T., "Nuclear Properties of the Heavy Elements," Vol. II, "Detailed Radioactivity Properties," New York, Prentice Hall, 1964.
2. Seaborg, G. T., "The Transuranium Elements," New Haven, Yale University Press, 1958.

JOHN MILSTED

ELECTRODE POTENTIALS OF THE ELEMENTS

Metallic elements, placed in contact with an electrolyte containing an ion of the metal in a definite state of oxidation, tend to develop an electrical potential characteristic of the equilibrium between the metal and its ion. This electrical potential is measurable by comparison with that of a reference electrode. Nonmetallic elements can also develop a characteristic electrical potential when equilibrated with one of their ions, both the element and the ion being in contact with a catalytically active but chemically inert metallic conductor (usually platinum or platinized platinum). For aqueous electrolytes, the reference electrode commonly used is the standard hydrogen electrode (SHE) of platinized platinum in contact with an aqueous solution of hydrogen ion H^+ at unit activity (e.g., approx. 1 molar HC1) saturated with hydrogen gas H_2 under 1 atm. fugacity (approx. 1 atm. pressure). The schematic diagram of the SHE is $(Pt)H_2/H^+$. This electrode is assigned the standard potential, $V°$ (SHE) = 0, and the isothermal temperature coefficient, $(dV°/dT)_{iso}$ (SHE) = 0, at all temperatures. Other common reference electrodes are: the saturated calomel electrode (SCE): Hg/Hg_2Cl_2, KCl satd., for which $V = +0.245$ v $- 0.0007(t - 25)$ at $t°C$; the sea water silver-silver chloride electrode: $Ag/AgCl$, Cl^- (sea water), $V = +0.245$ v $- 0.0006 (t - 25)$; and the saturated copper-copper sulfate electrode: $Cu/CuSO_4$ satd., $V = +0.30$ v $- 0.0001(t - 25)$. For the generic electrode M/M^{z+}, the electrode potential, $V(M/M^{z+})$ is defined as the open-circuit potential difference, $V'' - V'$, of the isothermal cell

$$(V')Cu'/SHE//M^{z+}/M/Cu''(V'') \quad (A)$$

where $//$ means that the liquid junction potential has been eliminated or minimized, e.g., by the use of salt bridges. The isothermal temperature coefficient, $(dV/dT)_{iso}$ (M/M^{z+}), is equal to $d(V'' - V')/dT$ for the isothermal cell [the second coefficient $(d^2V/dT^2)_{iso}$ is $d^2(V'' - V')/dT^2$]. The thermal temperature coefficient, $(dV/dT)_{th} = (dV/dT)_{iso} + 0.871$ mv/°C, where the latter constant is the thermal temperature coefficient of the SHE.

The potentials and isothermal temperature coefficients listed in Table 1 are given for the elements and their ions in their standard states of unit activity in aqueous medium [the second coefficients (S.C.), where known, are given in parentheses]. For nonstandard electrodes, the equilibrium potential V is given by the Nernst equation (at $T°K$)

$$V = V° + (RT/zF) \ln (Ox)/(Red) \quad (1)$$

where R is the gas constant (86.17 microvolt-faradays per degree mole) and $\mathbf{F}$ is the faraday (96,487 ampere-seconds). (Ox) and (Red) denote the activities or activity products of the electromotively active oxidized and reduced forms of the element that appear in the balanced expression for the electrode reaction. For example, for the electrode $Mn^{++}/MnO_4^-,H^+$, $V° = +1.51$ v, the balanced equation can be written by supplying one H_2O for every oxygen, disposing of the excess hydrogens as H^+, and supplying electrons to balance the charge, i.e.,

$$Mn^{++} + 4H_2O = MnO_4^- + 8H^+ + 5e^-. \quad (2)$$

The Nernst equation then takes the form

$$V = +1.51v + \frac{0.05916v}{5} \log \frac{(MnO_4^-)(H^+)^8}{(Mn^{++})(H_2O)^4} \quad (3)$$

at 25°C.

In alkaline solutions, supply one H_2O for every oxygen, and dispose of the excess hydrogens as $H_2O - OH^-$, e.g. for the electrode, $H_2PO_2^-/HPO_3^{--}$, OH^-, $V° = -1.565v$, supply one H_2O for the excess oxygen atom of the phosphite, and dispose of the three resultant excess hydrogen atoms as $3 (H_2O - OH^-)$. Rearrange to give the balanced equation

$$H_2PO_2^- + 3OH^- = HPO_3^{--} + 2H_2O + 2e^- \quad (4)$$

which yields the Nernst equation

$$V = -1.565v + \frac{0.05916v}{2} \log \frac{(HPO_3^{--})(H_2O)^2}{(H_2PO_2^-)(OH^-)^3} \quad (5)$$

TABLE 1. STANDARD ELECTRODE POTENTIALS OF THE ELEMENTS AND ISOTHERMAL TEMPERATURE COEFFICIENTS AT 25°C, VERSUS THE STANDARD HYDROGEN ELECTRODE

[I.U.P.A.C.-Gibbs-Stockholm Sign Convention. The second temperature coefficient (S.C.), where known, is given in parentheses in microvolts per degree C^2].

Electrode	$V°$, volts	$(dV°/dT)_{iso}$, mv/deg C	Electrode	$V°$, volts	$(dV°/dT)_{iso}$, mv/deg C
Actinium			$Br^-/Br_2(aq)$	+1.087	−0.478
Ac/Ac^{+++}	−2.6	—	$Br_2(1)/BrO_3^-$, H^+	+1.52	−0.418
					(S.C. +1.871)
Aluminum			**Cadmium**		
$Al/Al(OH)_3$, OH^-	−2.30	−0.93	$Cd/Cd(OH)_2$, OH^-	−0.809	−1.014
Al/Al^{+++}	−1.662	+0.504	Cd/Cd^{++}	−0.4029	−0.093
					(S.C. +2.2)
Americium			**Calcium**		
Am/Am^{+++}	−2.320	+0.089	$Ca/Ca(OH)_2$, OH^-	−3.02	−0.965
			Ca/Ca^{++}	−2.866	−0.175
Antimony					
Sb/SbO_2^-, OH^-	−0.66	—	**Carbon**		
$Sb/SbH_3(g)$, H^+	−0.510	−0.06	C/CO_3^{--}, OH^-	−0.7667	−1.232
Sb/Sb_2O_3, H^+	+0.152	−0.375	$C/CH_4(g)$, H^+	+0.1316	−0.209
					(S.C. −0.266)
Arsenic			$C/CO_2(g)$, H^+	+0.2073	−0.853
As/AsO_2^-, OH^-	−0.675	—	$C/CO(g)$, H^+	+0.5178	−1.310
$As/AsH_3(g)$, H^+	−0.607	−0.05	C/CCl_4, H^+, Cl^-	+1.18	−0.645
$As/HAsO_2(aq)$, H^+	+0.2476	−0.510			(S.C. −5.934)
Astatine			**Cerium**		
At_2/AtO^-, OH^-	0.0	—	$Ce/Ce(OH)_3$, OH^-	−2.87	—
At_2/At^-	+0.2	—	Ce/Ce^{+++}	−2.483	+0.101
$At_2/HAtO$, H^+	+0.7	—	Ce^{+++}/Ce^{+4}	+1.61	—
Barium			**Cesium**		
Ba/Ba^{++}	−2.906	−0.395	Cs/Cs^+	−2.923	−1.197
$Ba/Ba(OH)_2$, OH^-	−2.81	−0.93			
			Chlorine		
Berkelium			Cl^-/ClO^-, OH^-	+0.89	−1.079
Bk^{+++}/Bk^{+4}	+1.6	—	ClO_3^-/ClO_4^-, H^+	+1.19	−0.41
			$HClO_2/ClO_3^-$, H^+	+1.21	−0.25
Beryllium			Cl_2/Cl^-	+1.3595	−1.260
Be/BeO, OH^-	−2.613	−1.172			(S.C. −5.454)
		(S.C. −6.596)	$Cl_2/HClO$, H^+	+1.63	−0.14
Be/Be^{++}	−1.847	+0.565	$HClO/HClO_2$, H^+	+1.645	−0.55
Bismuth					
Bi/Bi_2O_3, OH^-	−0.46	−1.214	**Chromium**		
		(S.C. −6.828)	$Cr/Cr(OH)_3(cryst)$, OH^-	−1.48	−0.98
Bi/BiO^+, H^+	+0.320	—	Cr/CrO_2, OH^- ..	−1.27	—
			Cr/Cr^{+++}	−0.744	+0.468
Boron			Cr^{++}/Cr^{+++}	−0.408	—
$B/H_2BO_3^-$, OH^-	−1.79	−1.147	$Cr^{+++}/Cr_2O_7^{--}$, H^+	+1.33	−1.263
$B/H_3BO_3(aq)$, H^+	−0.8698	−0.481			
			Cobalt		
Bromine			$Co/Co(OH)_2$, OH^-	−0.73	−1.064
Br^-/BrO_3^-, OH^-	+0.61	−1.287	Co/Co^{++}	−0.277	+0.06
		(S.C. −6.748)	$Co(OH)_2/Co(OH)_3$, OH^-	+0.17	−0.80
$Br^-/Br_2(1)$	+1.0652	−0.629	Co^{++}/Co^{+++}	+1.808	—
		(S.C. −6.210)			

TABLE 1– *continued*

Electrode	$V°$, volts	$(dV°/dT)_{iso}$, mv/deg C	Electrode	$V°$, volts	$(dV°/dT)_{iso}$, mv/deg C
Columbium (see **Niobium**)			**Hydrogen**		
Copper			$H(g)/H_2O$, OH^-	-2.9345	-0.323
Cu/Cu_2O, OH^-	-0.358	-1.326			(S.C. -7.050)
		(S.C. -6.828)	H^-/H_2	-2.25	-1.57
$Cu_2O/Cu(OH)_2$, OH^-	-0.080	-0.725	$H(g)/H^+$	-2.1065	$+0.511$
Cu/Cu^{++}	$+0.337$	$+0.008$			(S.C. $+0.221$)
Cu/Cu^+	$+0.521$	-0.058	$H_2(g)/H_2O$, OH^-	-0.82806	-0.8342
					(S.C. -7.272)
Dysprosium			$D_2(g)/D^+$	-0.0034	—
$Dy/Dy(OH)_3$, OH^-	-2.78	—	$H_2(g)/H^+$ (SHE)	0.0000	0.000
Dy/Dy^{+++}	-2.353	$+0.154$		(def.)	(S.C. 0.000)
					(def.)
Erbium					
$Er/Er(OH)_3$, OH^-	-2.75	—	**Indium**		
Er/Er^{+++}	-2.296	$+0.166$	$In/In(OH)_3$, OH^-	-1.00	-0.97
			In/In^{+++}	-0.343	$+0.40$
Europium					
$Eu/Eu(OH)_3$, OH^-	-2.83	—	**Iodine**		
Eu/Eu^{+++}	-2.407	$+0.137$	I^-/IO^-, OH^-	$+0.485$	—
Eu^{++}/Eu^{+++}	-0.429	—	I_2/I^-	$+0.5355$	-0.148
					(S.C. -5.965)
Fluorine			I_2/IO_3^-,$/H^+$	$+1.195$	-0.364
F^-/F_2O, H^+	$+2.15$	-1.184			(S.C. $+1.813$)
$F_2(g)/F^-$	$+2.87$	-1.830	I_2/HIO, H^+	$+1.45$	$+0.42$
		(S.C. -5.339)	IO_3^-/H_5IO_6, H^+	$+1.601$	—
$F_2(g)/HF$, H^+	$+3.06$	-0.60			
			Iridium		
Gadolinium			Ir/Ir_2O_3, OH^-	$+0.098$	—
$Gd/Gd(OH)_3$, OH^-	-2.82	—			
Gd/Gd^{+++}	-2.397	$+0.147$	**Iron**		
			$Fe/Fe(OH)_2$, OH^-	-0.877	-1.06
Gallium			$Fe(OH)_2/Fe(OH)_3$, OH^-	-0.56	-0.96
$Ga/H_2GaO_3^-$, OH^-	-1.219	—	Fe/Fe^{++}	-0.4402	$+0.052$
Ga/Ga^{+++}	-0.529	$+0.67$	$Fe(OH)_3/FeO_4^{--}$, OH^-	$+0.72$	-1.62
			Fe^{++}/Fe^{+++}	$+0.771$	$+1.188$
Germanium			Fe^{+++}/FeO_4^{--}, H^+	$+2.20$	-0.85
$Ge/HGeO_2^-$, OH^-	-1.03	-1.29			
Ge/GeO_2, H^+	-0.15	-0.335	**Lanthanum**		
			$La/La(OH)_3$, OH^-	-2.90	-0.95
Gold			La/La^{+++}	-2.522	$+0.085$
$Au/Au(OH)_3$(cryst), H^+	$+1.45$	-0.206			
Au/Au^{+++}	$+1.498$	—	**Lead**		
Au/Au^+	$+1.691$	—	Pb/PbO, OH^-	-0.580	-1.163
					(S.C. -6.841)
Hafnium					
$Hf/HfO(OH)_2$, OH^-	-2.50	—	$Pb/PbSO_4$, H^+, SO_4^{--}	-0.3588	-1.015
Hf/Hf^{+4}	-1.70	—			(S.C. -1.555)
			Pb/Pb^{++}	-0.126	-0.451
Holmium			PbO_2/PbO, OH^-	$+0.247$	-1.194
$Ho/Ho(OH)_3$, OH^-	-2.77	—	PbO_2/Pb^{++}, H^+	$+1.455$	-0.238
Ho/Ho^{+++}	-2.319	$+0.161$	$PbO_2/PbSO_4$, H^+, SO_4^{--}	$+1.682$	$+0.326$
					(S.C. $+2.516$)

TABLE 1-*continued*

Electrode	$V°$, volts	$(dV°/dT)_{iso}$, mv/deg C	Electrode	$V°$, volts	$(dV°/dT)_{iso}$, mv/deg C
Lithium			**Niobium (Columbium)**		
Li/Li^+	-3.045	-0.534	Nb/Nb^{+++}	-1.099	—
			$Nb/Nb_2O_5, H^+$	-0.644	-0.39
Lutetium					
$Lu/Lu(OH)_3, OH^-$	-2.72	—	**Nitrogen**		
Lu/Lu^{+++}	-2.255	$+0.193$	$N_2/NH_4OH, OH^-$	-0.7361	-1.462
			$N_2/NO_3^-, OH^-$	$+0.2521$	-1.348
Magnesium			$N_2/NH_4^+, H^+$	$+0.2746$	-0.618
$Mg/Mg(OH)_2, OH^-$	-2.690	-0.945	$N_2/NO_2^-, OH^-$	$+0.4156$	-1.407
		(S.C. -6.079)	$N_2/HNO_3, H^+$	$+1.2457$	-0.347
Mg/Mg^{++}	-2.363	$+0.103$	$N_2/N_2O_4, H^+$	$+1.356$	-0.460
			$N_2/HNO_2, H^+$	$+1.4535$	-0.372
Manganese			$N_2/NO, H^+$	$+1.678$	-0.910
$Mn/Mn(OH)_2, OH^-$	-1.55	-1.079	$N_2/N_2O, H^+$	$+1.766$	-0.462
Mn/Mn^{++}	-1.180	-0.08			
$MnO_2/Mn(OH)_2, OH^-$	-0.05	-1.329	**Osmium**		
$Mn(OH)_2/Mn(OH)_3$,			$Os/HOsO_5^-, OH^-$	$+0.015$	—
OH^-	$+0.15$	-0.903	$Os/OsO_4, H^+$	$+0.85$	-0.433
$MnO_4^{--}/MnO_4^-, H^+$	$+0.564$	—			
$MnO_2/MnO_4^-, OH^-$	$+0.588$	-1.778	**Oxygen**		
$MnO_2/Mn^{++}, H^+$	$+1.23$	-0.661	$O_2/H_2O, OH^-$	$+0.401$	-1.680
Mn^{++}/Mn^{+++}	$+1.51$	$+1.23$			(S.C. -6.719)
$Mn^{++}/MnO_4^-, H^+$	$+1.51$	-0.66	$O_2/H_2O_2, H^+$	$+0.6824$	-1.033
$MnO_2/MnO_4^-, H^+$	$+1.695$	-0.666	$O_2/H_2O, H^+$	$+1.229$	-0.846
					(S.C. $+0.552$)
Mercury			$H_2O_2 H_2O, H^+$	$+1.776$	-0.658
$Hg/HgO, OH^-$	$+0.098$	-1.120			
		(S.C. -6.775)	**Palladium**		
$Hg/Hg_2Cl_2, Cl^-$	$+0.2676$	-0.317	$Pd/Pd(OH)_2, OH^-$	$+0.07$	-1.064
		(S.C. -5.664)	Pd/Pd^{++}	$+0.987$	—
Hg/Hg_2^{++}	$+0.788$	—			
Hg_2^{++}/Hg^{++}	$+0.920$	—	**Phosphorus**		
			$P/H_2PO_2^-, OH^-$	-2.05	—
Molybdenum			$H_2PO_2^-/HPO_3^{--}, OH^-$	-1.565	—
$Mo/MoO_4^{--}, OH^-$	-1.05	-1.36	$HPO_3^{--}/PO_4^{---}, OH^-$	-1.12	-0.49
Mo/Mo^{+++}	-0.20	—	$P/H_3PO_2, H^+$	-0.508	-0.42
			$H_3PO_2/H_3PO_3, H^+$	-0.499	-0.36
Neodymium			$H_3PO_3/H_3PO_4, H^+$	-0.276	-0.36
$Nd/Nd(OH)_3, OH^-$	-2.84	—	$P/PH_3(g), H^+$	-0.063	-0.104
Nd/Nd^{+++}	-2.431	$+0.124$			
			Platinum		
Neptunium			$Pt/Pt(OH)_2, OH^-$	$+0.15$	-1.144
Np/Np^{+++}	-1.856	-0.054	$Pt/Pt(OH)_2, H^+$	$+0.98$	-0.310
Np^{+++}/Np^{+4}	$+0.147$	$+1.36$	$PtO_2/Pt(OH)_2, H^+$	$+1.1$	—
$Np^{+4}/NpO_2^+, H^+$	$+0.75$	-3.13	Pt/Pt^{++}	$+1.2$	—
NpO_2^+/NpO_2^{++}	$+1.15$	$+0.58$			
			Plutonium		
Nickel			$Pu/Pu(OH)_3, OH^-$	-2.42	—
$Ni/Ni(OH)_2, OH^-$	-0.72	-1.04	Pu/Pu^{+++}	-2.031	$+0.06$
Ni/Ni^{++}	-0.250	$+0.06$	$Pu(OH)_3/Pu(OH)_4, OH^-$	-0.963	—
$NiO_2/Ni(OH)_2, OH^-$	$+0.490$	—	Pu^{+++}/Pu^{+4}	$+0.97$	$+1.40$
$Ni/NiO_2, H^+$	$+1.678$	—	$Pu^{+4}/PuO_2^{++}, H^+$	$+1.04$	-1.56

TABLE 1–*continued*

Electrode	$V°$, volts	$(dV°/dT)_{iso}$, mv/deg C	Electrode	$V°$, volts	$(dV°/dT)_{iso}$, mv/deg C
Polonium			SeO_3^{--}/SeO_4^{--}, OH^-	+0.05	−1.187
Po/H_2Po, H^+	−1.0	—	Se/H_2SeO_3, H^+	+0.740	−0.520
Po/PoO_3^{--}, OH^-	−0.49	—	H_2SeO_3/SeO_4^{--}, H^+	+1.15	+0.553
Po/Po^{++}	+0.65	−0.43			
Po^{++}/PoO_2, H^+	+0.80	−0.26	**Silicon**		
PoO_2/PoO_3, H^+	+1.5	—	Si/SiO_3^{--}, OH^-	−1.697	—
			Si/SiO_2, H^+	−0.857	−0.374
Potassium					(S.C. +0.594)
K/K^+	−2.925	−1.080	$Si/SiH_4(g)$, H^+	+0.102	−0.197
					(S.C. −0.302)
Praseodymium					
$Pr/Pr(OH)_3$, OH^-	−2.85	−0.92	**Silver**		
Pr/Pr^{+++}	−2.462	+0.115	$Ag/AgCl$, Cl^-	+0.2222	−0.658
Pr^{+++}/Pr^{+4}	+2.86	—			(S.C. −5.744)
			Ag/Ag_2O, OH^-	+0.345	−1.337
Promethium					(S.C. −6.718)
$Pm/Pm(OH)_3$, OH^-	−2.84	—	Ag_2O/AgO, OH^-	+0.607	−1.117
Pm/Pm^{+++}	−2.423	+0.120	AgO/Ag_2O_3, OH^-	+0.739	—
			Ag/Ag^+	+0.7991	−1.000
Protactinium					(S.C. −0.924)
Pa/PaO_2^+, H^+	−1.0	—	Ag^+/Ag^{++}	+1.980	—
Radium			**Sodium**		
Ra/Ra^{++}	−2.916	−0.59	Na/Na^+	−2.714	−0.772
Rhenium			**Strontium**		
Re/ReO_2, H^+	+0.2513	—	Sr/Sr^{++}	−2.888	−0.191
Re/ReO_4^-, H^+	+0.362	−0.51	$Sr/Sr(OH)_2$, OH^-	−2.88	−0.96
Rhodium			**Sulfur**		
Rh/Rh^{+++}	+0.80	—	S/S^{--}, OH^-	−0.447	−0.93
Rh/Rh_2O_3, H^+	+0.87	−0.40	S/H_2S, H^+	+0.142	−0.209
		(S.C. +0.50)	S/SO_4^{--}, H^+	+0.3572	−0.168
					(S.C. +1.278)
Rubidium			S/H_2SO_3, H^+	+0.450	−0.66
Rb/Rb^+	−2.925	−1.245	$SO_4^{--}/S_2O_8^{--}$, H^+	+2.01	−1.26
Ruthenium			**Tantalum**		
Ru/Ru^{++}	+0.45	—	Ta/Ta_2O_5, H^+	−0.812	−0.377
Ru/RuO_2, H^+	+0.788	−0.418			(S.C. +0.514)
Samarium			**Technetium**		
$Sm/Sm(OH)_3$, OH^-	−2.83	—	Tc/Tc^{++}	+0.4	—
Sm/Sm^{+++}	−2.414	+0.136	Te^{++}/TcO_2, H^+	+0.6	—
			TcO_2/TcO_4^-, H^+	+0.7	—
Scandium					
$Sc/Sc(OH)_3$, OH^-	−2.61	—	**Tellurium**		
Sc/Sc^{+++}	−2.077	+0.25	Te/Te^{--}, OH^-	−1.143	—
			Te/H_2Te, H^+	−0.718	+0.280
Selenium			Te/TeO_2, H^+	+0.529	−0.370
Se/Se^{--}, OH^-	−0.92	−0.89			(S.C. +0.453)
Se/H_2Se, H^+	−0.399	−0.028	TeO_2/H_6TeO_6, H^+	+1.02	+0.13
Se/SeO_3^{--}, OH^-	−0.366	−1.318			

189

Electrode	$V°$, volts	$(dV°/dT)_{iso}$, mv/deg C	Electrode	$V°$, volts	$(dV°/dT)_{iso}$, mv/deg C
Terbium			**Uranium**		
$Tb/Tb(OH)_3$, OH^-	-2.79	—	U/UO_2, OH^-	-2.39	-1.220
Tb/Tb^{+++}	-2.391	$+0.146$	$U(OH)_4/UO_4^{--}$, OH^-	-1.618	—
			U/U^{+++}	-1.789	-0.07
Thallium			U^{+++}/U^{+4}	-0.607	$+1.40$
$Tl/TlOH$, OH^-	-0.343	-0.868	U^{+4}/UO_2^{++}, H^+	$+0.330$	-1.27
Tl/Tl^+	-0.3363	-1.327 (S.C. -0.85)			
$TlOH/Tl(OH)_3$, OH^-	-0.05	-0.940	**Vanadium**		
Tl^+/Tl^{+++}	$+1.25$	$+0.89$	V/V^{++}	-1.186	—
			V^{++}/V^{+++}	-0.256	—
Thorium			V^{+++}/VO^{++}, H^+	$+0.359$	—
$Th/Th(OH)_4$, OH^-	-2.48	-0.99	$VO^{++}/V(OH)_4^+$, H^+	$+1.00$	—
Th/Th^{+4}	-1.899	$+0.28$			
			Xenon		
Thulium			Xe/XeO_3, H^+	$+1.8$	—
$Tm/Tm(OH)_3$, OH^-	-2.74	—	XeO_3/H_4XeO_6, H^+	$+3.0$	—
Tm/Tm^{+++}	-2.278	$+0.179$			
			Ytterbium		
Tin			$Yb/Yb(OH)_3$, OH^-	-2.73	—
$HSnO_2^-/Sn(OH)_6^{--}$, OH^-	-0.93	—	Yb/Yb^{+++}	-2.267	$+0.188$
$Sn/HSnO_2^-$, OH^-	-0.909	—	**Yttrium**		
Sn/Sn^{++}	-0.136	-0.282	$Y/Y(OH)_3$, OH^-	-2.81	-0.95
Sn^{++}/Sn^{+4}	$+0.15$	—	Y/Y^{+++}	-2.372	$+0.18$
Titanium			**Zinc**		
Ti/Ti^{++}	-1.628	—	$Zn/Zn(OH)_2$, OH^-	-1.245	-1.002 (S.C. -5.978
Ti^{++}/Ti^{+++}	-0.369	—			
Ti^{+++}/TiO^{++}, H^+	$+0.099$	—	Zn/Zn^{++}	-0.7628	$+0.091$ (S.C. $+3.84$
Tungsten			**Zirconium**		
W/WO_4^{--}, OH^-	-1.05	-1.36	Zr/H_2ZrO_3, OH^-	-2.36	-1.11
$W/WO_3(c)$, H^+	-0.090	-0.400 (S.C. $+0.480$)	Zr/Zr^{+4}	-1.529	—

Two sign conventions have been used in the tabulation of electrode potential data of the elements. In Table 1, the potentials are presented according to the internationally accepted I.U.P.A.C.-Gibbs-Stockholm sign convention, in which the electrode potential is given the same algebraic sign as the observed d-c polarity of the electrode in the SHE//Electrode cell, e.g., Zn/Zn^{++}, $V° = -0.76$ v. The negative sign means that Zn is the $(-)$ terminal of the hydrogen-zinc cell. In the alternative "oxidation potential" convention, the oxidation potential of the Zn/Zn^{++} couple is listed as $+0.76$ v, where the positive value signifies that zinc is a more powerful reducing agent than hydrogen. The two sign conventions, although divergent in their mode of presentation, refer to the same fundamental scientific fact, i.e., zinc as an element is more anodic than hydrogen, therefore it is a stronger reducing agent, it has a stronger tendency to undergo oxidation by loss of electrons, and to produce a negative potential in the external circuit, than does hydrogen.

In every electrode potential, an element appears in an oxidized form in which it can act as oxidizing agent, e.g., Zn^{++}, H^+, O_2, F_2, and in a reduced form in which it can act as a reducing agent, e.g., Zn, H_2, H_2O, F^-. The more positive the electrode potential (in the I.U.P.A.C.-Gibbs-Stockholm convention) the stronger the oxidizing power of the oxidizing agent; the more negative the potential, the stronger the reducing power of the reducing agent. In general, any oxidizing agent can react with a reducing agent having a less positive or more negative potential, but not vice-versa, e.g., H^+ can attack Na, Zn, Fe or Pb, but not Cu or Ag; Cu^{++} can react with Zn, Br_2 with I^-, but Na^+ does not react with Zn; Zn^{++} does not react with Cu, Br_2 cannot react with Cl^-; and F^- cannot reduce any oxidizing agent in the Table. Electrode potentials can be used to construct oxidation chains such as those of iron in acidic medium

$$\text{Fe} \xrightarrow{-0.44} \text{Fe}^{++} \xrightarrow{+0.77} \text{Fe}^{+++}$$
$$\xrightarrow{+2.20} \text{FeO}_4^{--}$$

or in alkaline medium

$$\text{Fe} \xrightarrow{-0.88} \text{Fe (OH)}_2 \xrightarrow{-0.56} \text{Fe (OH)}_3$$
$$\xrightarrow{+0.72} \text{FeO}_4^{--}$$

which serve to define the domains of stability of the various oxidation states. When an inversion occurs in the potential sequence, e.g.,

$$\text{Cu} \xrightarrow{+0.521} \text{Cu}^+ \xrightarrow{+0.153} \text{Cu}^{++}$$
$$\xrightarrow{+0.337}$$

the intermediate species, Cu^+ in this instance, is unstable and disproportionates to Cu and Cu^{++} so that the observed potential is that of Cu/Cu^{++}. The unstable cuprous ion potentials have been computed from free energy data. In alkaline medium, the normal sequence reappears

$$\text{Cu} \xrightarrow{-0.358} \text{Cu}_2\text{O} \xrightarrow{-0.080} \text{Cu (OH)}_2$$

and the copper-I oxide has a narrow band of stability. Potential-pH diagrams, pioneered by Pourbaix, describe in graphical form these domains of stability over the entire acid-base range.

Electrode potentials provide thermodynamic information as follows: for the anodic (oxidation) half-cell reaction: $\text{Red} = \text{Ox} + ze^-$, $\triangle G°$ (oxidation) $= +zFV°$; $\triangle H°$ (oxidation) $= +zFV° - zFT(dV°/dT)_{iso}$; for the cathodic (reduction) half-cell reaction (coupled with the counter reaction of the SHE): $\text{Ox} + (z/2)H_2 = \text{Red} + zH^+$, $\triangle S°$ (reduction) $= +zF(dV°/dT)_{iso}$; $\triangle Cp°$ (reduction) $= +zFT(d^2V°/dT^2)_{iso}$. The energy conversion factor 1 volt-faraday $= 96,487$ joules $= 23,061$ calories is convenient for this purpose.

The voltage of any cell formed from two different elements is given by the algebraic difference of their electrode potentials, the element with the more negative potential being the $(-)$ terminal or anode of the cell. The standard potential at $t°C$, referred to SHE at the same temperature, can be computed from the entries in Table 1 by means of the expression: $V°(t°C) = V°(25°C) + 10^{-3} (dV°/dT)_{iso} \cdot (t-25) + \frac{1}{2} \cdot 10^{-6}(S.C.) \cdot (t-25)^2$.

The electrode potentials provide a convenient way of representing an important chemical property of the elements, namely their reactivity, or more specifically, their anodicity or cathodicity (i.e., their reducing power or oxidizing power, respectively). With the hydrogen electrode potential selected as zero, the scales of cathodicity and anodicity extend to almost equal voltages in both directions, from the extreme cathodicity of fluorine, with its high oxidizing power at $+2.87$ volts, to the extreme anodicity of lithium, with its high reducing power, at -3.05 volts. The cathodic elements after fluorine are easily recognized in order of decreasing oxidizing power; chlorine at $+1.35$ v, oxygen at $+1.23$ v, bromine at $+1.07$ v, iodine at $+0.53$ v, astatine at $+0.2$ v, sulfur at $+0.14$ v, selenium at -0.40 v, tellurium at -0.7 v, polonium at -1.0 v (in acidic medium). The anodic elements after lithium can also be recognized in order of decreasing reducing power: potassium at -2.93 v, barium, strontium and calcium at -2.9 v, sodium at -2.71 v, the: lanthanide and actinide metals between -2.6 and -2.0 v, magnesium at -2.36 v, aluminum at -1.66 v (when not masked by passivity), zinc at -0.76 v, iron and cadmium at -0.4 v, tin and lead at -0.1 v, copper at $+0.34$ v, silver at $+0.80$ v, platinum at $+1.2$ v, gold at $+1.5$ v (in acidic medium).

191

These potential values give directly the Gibbs free energy of oxidation of the anodic elements by hydrogen ions, and, with the reversed sign, the free energy of reduction of the cathodic elements by hydrogen gas, in volt-faradays per gram-equivalent. (1 vF = 23.06 kcal.).

For example, consider the zinc electrode: Zn/Zn^{++}, $V° = -0.7628$ v, $(dV°/dT)_{iso} = +0.091$ mv/°C, S.C. $= +3.84$ $\mu v/(°C)^2$. For the *oxidation* of one mole (two equivalents) of zinc by hydrogen ions

$$Zn + 2H^+ = Zn^{++} + H_2 \qquad (6)$$

at 25°C, $\triangle G° = (+2F)$ $(-0.7628v) = -1.5256$ volt-faradays $= -35.18$ kilocalories, $\triangle S° = (-2F)$ $(+0.091$ mv/deg$) = -0.182$ mvF/deg $= -4.20$ cal/deg, $\triangle H° = \triangle G° + T\triangle S° = -36.43$ kilocalories, $\triangle Cp° = (-2F)$ $(298°K)$ $(+3.84$ $\mu v/deg^2) = -2.29$ mvF/deg $= -52.8$ cal/deg. Consider, again, the acid oxygen electrode: O_2/H_2O, H^+, $V° = +1.229$ v, $(dV°/dT)_{iso} = -0.846$ mv/°C, S.C. $= +0.552$ $\mu v/(°C)^2$. For the *reduction* of one mole (four equivalents) of oxygen by hydrogen gas

$$O_2 + 4H^+ + 4e^- = 2H_2O \qquad (7a)$$
$$2H_2 = 4H^+ + 4e^- \qquad (7b)$$
$$\overline{O_2 + 2H_2 = 2H_2O} \qquad (7c)$$

the thermodynamic properties are given with reversed signs for reductions, so that $\triangle G° = (-4F)(+1.229v) = -4.916$ volt-faradays $= -113.4$ kilocalories, $\triangle S° = (+4F)$ $(-0.846$ mv/deg$) = -3.384$ mvF/deg $= -78.0$ cal/deg, $\triangle H° = \triangle G° + T\triangle S° = -136.7$ kilocalories, $\triangle C_p° = (+4F)$ $(298°K)$ $(+0.552$ $\mu v/deg^2) = +0.658$ mvF/deg $= +15.2$ cal/deg. For the alkaline oxygen electrode: O_2/H_2O, OH^-, $V° = +0.401$ v, $(dV°/dT)_{iso} = -1.680$ mv/°C, S.C. $= -6.719$ $\mu v/(°C)^2$, the thermodynamic quantities calculated from the potential and the temperature coefficient refer to the reduction of oxygen in alkali by the hydrogen gas of the acid SHE

$$O_2 + 2H_2O + 4e^- = 4OH^- \qquad (8a)$$
$$2H_2 = 4H^+ + 4e^- \qquad (8b)$$
$$\overline{O_2 + 2H_2 + 2H_2O = 4OH^- + 4H^+} \qquad (8c)$$

For reaction (8c), $\triangle G° = (-4F)$ $(+0.401v) = -1.604$ volt-faradays $= -37.0$ kilocalor-

ies, $\triangle S° = (+4F)$ $(-1.680$ mv/deg$) = -6.72$ mvF/deg $= -155.0$ cal/deg, $\triangle H° = \triangle G° + T\triangle S° = -83.2$ kilocalories, $\triangle C_p° = (+4F)$ $(298°K)$ $(-6.719$ $\mu v/deg^2) = -8.013$ mvF/deg $= -184.8$ cal/deg. For the reduction of oxygen by hydrogen gas in alkaline medium, it is necessary to change the alkaline oxygen electrode potential from the acid SHE reference, to the alkaline hydrogen electrode H_2/H_2O, OH^- reference, whose potential and temperature coefficient are listed in Table 1. Since the shift in pH affects the oxygen and hydrogen electrodes in the same way, the final result of the calculation in this instance coincides with that given above for the reduction of oxygen by hydrogen in acid.

The potentials of the elements constitute a useful summary of quantitative information regarding the reactivities of the elements. The more than 260 potentials listed in the present table permit in principle the calculation of free energy changes of over 30,000 possible reactions between the elements and their ions. The temperature coefficients give access to the free energies of oxidation, relative to hydrogen, within the ordinary temperature range of aqueous solutions, i.e., from 0° to 100°C. They also permit the calculation of enthalpies (heats) and entropies of reaction, as outlined above. In conclusion the electrode potentials table of the elements provides one of the most succinct and versatile keys to a knowledge of the reactivities and thermodynamic properties of the chemical elements.

References

1. Christiansen, J. A., "I.U.P.A.C.-Stockholm Conventions," *J. Am. Chem. Soc.*, **82**, 5517 (1960).
2. de Bethune, A. J., and Light, T. S., "Signs of Electrode Potentials," *J. Chem. Education*, **34**, 433 (1957).
3. de Bethune, A. J., Light, T. S., Swendeman, N. A., and Salvi, G. R., "Temperature Coefficients of Electrode Potentials, I," *J. Electrochem. Soc.*, **106**, 616 (1959); "II," *ibid*, **108**, 672 (1961).
4. de Bethune, A. J., and Swendeman-Loud, N. A., "Table of Standard Electrode Potentials and Temperature Coefficients at 25°C," in "Encyclopedia of Electrochemistry," C. A. Hampel, Ed., pp. 414–426, New York, Reinhold, 1964.

5. de Bethune, A. J. and Swendeman-Loud, N. A., "Standard Aqueous Electrode Potentials," C. A. Hampel, Pub., 8501 Harding Ave., Skokie, Illinois 60076, 1964.
6. Gibbs, J. Willard, "Thermodynamics, Vol. I," pub. 1878, reprinted New Haven, Yale University Press, 1949.
7. Latimer, W. M., "Oxidation Potentials," New York, Prentice-Hall, 2nd Edition, 1952.
8. Nernst, Walter, *Z. physik. Chem.*, **4**, 129 (1889); *Ber.*, **30**, 1547 (1897); "Theoretische Chemie," 2nd Edition, Stuttgart, Enke, 1898.
9. Petrocelli, J. V., "Electromotive Series," in "Encyclopedia of Electrochemistry," C. A. Hampel, Ed., pp. 511–514, New York, Reinhold, 1964.
10. Pitzer, K. S., and Brewer, L., "Lewis and Randall's Thermodynamics," 2nd Edition, New York, McGraw-Hill, 1961.
11. Pourbaix, M., et al., "Atlas of Electrochemical Equilibria," London, Pergamon, 1966.
12. Rossini, F. D., et al., "Chemical Thermodynamic Properties," National Bureau of Standards, Circular 500, 1952.

ANDRE J. DE BETHUNE

ELECTRONIC CONFIGURATION

The arrangements of electrons around the nucleus of an atom is called the "electronic configuration" of the atom. Since the electronic cloud is highly dynamic, the arrangement cannot be a static one with each electron occupying a definite physical position with respect to the nucleus and the other electrons. Instead, the situation of each electron is identified in terms of four quantum numbers which designate its quantized energy with respect to the other components of the atom. These quantum numbers may be roughly described as follows:

(1) *Principal:* designated by n and of positive integral value: 1, 2, 3, 4---. This number indicates very roughly the average position of the electron with respect to the nucleus. The smaller the principal quantum number, the closer the average distance between the electron and the nucleus, and correspondingly, the stronger the attraction tends to be. Very crudely, the electronic cloud of an atom may be imagined as composed of concentric spheres of electrons around the nucleus, increasing in energy with increasing radius as the value of n increases.

(2) *Orbital:* designated by l and having some integral value 0, 1, 2, 3--- up to $(n-1)$. Each electron is confined to a certain region within the principal quantum level, in the sense that at any given instant the electron is probably somewhere within that region. Such a region is called an "orbital." Orbitals may differ in their shape, which is specified by the orbital quantum number. Approximate shapes of the different kinds of orbitals are shown in Fig. 1. The values of l equal to 0, 1, 2, and 3 correspond to what are called s, p, d, and f orbitals, respectively.

(3) *Orbital magnetic:* designated by m_l and having any integral value, 0 to $\pm l$. An electron moving around a nucleus is a charge in motion. Like all charges in motion, it creates an electromagnetic field capable of interacting with an external field. If there are more than one orbital of a certain kind (same value of l) within a given principal quantum level, these must be oriented differently. When the atom is placed in an external magnetic field, the energies of the different possible orientations are quantized, as represented by the vector of the magnetic moment of each orbital in the direction of the external field. Thus m_l can have only certain values, corresponding to the restricted number of similar type orbitals. The number of orbitals is given by $2l + 1$, which is the number of m_l values possible if m_l can equal 0 up to $\pm l$.

(4) *Spin magnetic:* designated by m_s, and of value either $+\frac{1}{2}$ or $-\frac{1}{2}$. Each electron independent of its translational motion, acts as a magnet. The m_s value $+\frac{1}{2}$ represents an electron magnet of poles opposed to another electron of value $-\frac{1}{2}$. The electrons are said to possess "spin" to give them these properties of a magnet. "Parallel" and "opposed" spins correspond to parallel and opposed magnets.

A given principal quantum level, or "energy shell" of an atom may then include several types of orbitals. Where $n = 1$, l can only be 0, corresponding to an s orbital. The number of orbitals of s type is given by $2l + 1$ which is one. Only one s orbital can occur in any principal quantum level.

When $n = 2$, l can be either 0 or 1. The value 0 corresponds to an s orbital. The value 1 corresponds to a p orbital. The number of similar p orbitals is given by $2l + 1 = 3$. The second principal quantum level thus consists

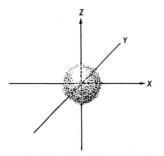

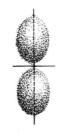

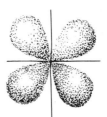

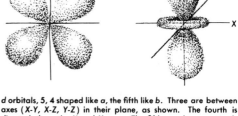

s orbital, 1, spherically symmetrical about the origin (nucleus).

p orbitals, 3, one directed along each axis (X, Y, and Z). Taken together, the 3 p orbitals are spherically symmetrical about the origin (nucleus).

d orbitals, 5, 4 shaped like a, the fifth like b. Three are between axes (X-Y, X-Z, Y-Z) in their plane, as shown. The fourth is directed along the X and Y axes. The fifth, as shown, extends along the Z axis. A doughnut-shaped ring is perpendicular to its center, in the X-Y plane. Taken together, the 5 d orbitals are spherically symmetrical about the origin (nucleus).

FIG. 1. (From "Inorganic Chemistry," R. T. Sanderson, Reinhold Publishing Corp., 1967)

of four orbitals, one s and three of p type.

When $n = 3$, l can have values of 0, 1, or 2. The values of 0 and 1 lead to one s orbital and the p orbitals as before. When $l = 2$, the orbitals are called d orbitals. There are $2l + 1 = 5$ of them. The third principal quantum level thus consists of one s, three p, and five d orbitals, for a total of nine.

When $n = 4$, l can have the values of 0, 1, 2, and 3. The first three values correspond to the $s, p,$ and d orbitals, nine altogether, as before. When $l = 3$, the orbitals are called f. Their number is $2l + 1 = 7$, giving a total for the fourth principal quantum level of sixteen orbitals.

In theory, higher principal quantum levels can contain additional orbitals, but in practice, none do. Sixteen, consisting of one s, three p, five d, and seven f orbitals, is the maximum number in any shell of any atom.

An important empirical principle of wave mechanics is that stated by Pauli and called the "exclusion principle": No two electrons of the same atom can have the identical four quantum numbers. Since each orbital is specifically designated by its values for n, l, and m_l, electrons occupying the same orbital must differ in m_s value. This value can only be $+\frac{1}{2}$ or $-\frac{1}{2}$, which means that no orbital can accommodate more than 2 electrons, and then only if their spins (magnets) are opposed. This establishes the capacity of each principal quantum level at twice the number of orbitals. The number of orbitals (through $n = 4$) is

given by n^2: 1, 4, 9, 16. Therefore, the shell capacity is $2n^2$: 2, 8, 18, 32.

In the building up of atoms by feeding electrons one by one into the region surrounding the nucleus, each electron occupies the most stable position left available to it. When given a choice of orbitals within a given principal quantum level, the electron enters that type of available orbital that penetrates closest to the nucleus and is therefore most stable. The order of decreasing penetration and decreasing stability is $s > p > d > f$. When several orbitals of equal energy are available, the electron tends to occupy a vacant orbital if possible rather than overcome the repulsion to become paired with another electron. A set of similar orbitals accommodates one electron in each, all of parallel spins, before pairing begins.

On the basis of these rules, the Pauli exclusion principle, spectroscopic data, and a knowledge of the general chemistry of the elements, all of the chemical elements have been assigned electronic configurations which appear to describe atomic structure with a minimum of ambiguity. The only significant source of controversy arises in the heavier elements, especially the transuranium elements, where the energies of $6d$ and $5f$ orbitals are so nearly alike that any specific assignment of electrons must remain somewhat uncertain.

The spectroscopic designation of electronic configuration involves giving the principal

TABLE 1. ELECTRONIC CONFIGURATIONS OF THE ELEMENTS

n =	1	2	3	4	5	6	7	n =	1	2	3	4	5	6	7
H	1							I	2	8	18	18	7		
He	2							Xe	2	8	18	18	8		
Li	2	1						Cs	2	8	18	18	8	1	
Be	2	2						Ba	2	8	18	18	8	2	
B	2	3						La	2	8	18	18	9	2	
C	2	4						Ce	2	8	18	19	9	2	
N	2	5						Pr	2	8	18	21	8	2	
O	2	6						Nd	2	8	18	22	8	2	
F	2	7						Pm	2	8	18	23	8	2	
Ne	2	8						Sm	2	8	18	24	8	2	
Na	2	8	1					Eu	2	8	18	25	8	2	
Mg	2	8	2					Gd	2	8	18	25	9	2	
Al	2	8	3					Tb	2	8	18	27	8	2	
Si	2	8	4					Dy	2	8	18	28	8	2	
P	2	8	5					Ho	2	8	18	29	8	2	
S	2	8	6					Er	2	8	18	30	8	2	
Cl	2	8	7					Tm	2	8	18	31	8	2	
Ar	2	8	8					Yb	2	8	18	32	8	2	
K	2	8	8	1				Lu	2	8	18	32	9	2	
Ca	2	8	8	2				Hf	2	8	18	32	10	2	
Sc	2	8	9	2				Ta	2	8	18	32	11	2	
Ti	2	8	10	2				W	2	8	18	32	12	2	
V	2	8	11	2				Re	2	8	18	32	13	2	
Cr	2	8	13	1				Os	2	8	18	32	14	2	
Mn	2	8	13	2				Ir	2	8	18	32	17	0	
Fe	2	8	14	2				Pt	2	8	18	32	17	1	
Co	2	8	15	2				Au	2	8	18	32	18	1	
Ni	2	8	16	2				Hg	2	8	18	32	18	2	
Cu	2	8	18	1				Tl	2	8	18	32	18	3	
Zn	2	8	18	2				Pb	2	8	18	32	18	4	
Ga	2	8	18	3				Bi	2	8	18	32	18	5	
Ge	2	8	18	4				Po	2	8	18	32	18	6	
As	2	8	18	5				At	2	8	18	32	18	7	
Se	2	8	18	6				Rn	2	8	18	32	18	8	
Br	2	8	18	7				Fr	2	8	18	32	18	8	1
Kr	2	8	18	8				Ra	2	8	18	32	18	8	2
Rb	2	8	18	8	1			Ac	2	8	18	32	18	9	2
Sr	2	8	18	8	2			Th	2	8	18	32	18	10	2
Y	2	8	18	9	2			Pa	2	8	18	32	20	9	2
Zr	2	8	18	10	2			U	2	8	18	32	21	9	2
Nb	2	8	18	11	2			Np	2	8	18	32	22	9	2
Mo	2	8	18	13	1			Pu	2	8	18	32	24	8	2
Tc	2	8	18	13	2			Am	2	8	18	32	25	8	2
Ru	2	8	18	15	1			Cm	2	8	18	32	25	9	2
Rh	2	8	18	16	1			Bk	2	8	18	32	26	9	2
Pd	2	8	18	18	0			Cf	2	8	18	32	28	8	2
Ag	2	8	18	18	1			Es	2	8	18	32	29	8	2
Cd	2	8	18	18	2			Fm	2	8	18	32	30	8	2
In	2	8	18	18	3			Md	2	8	18	32	31	8	2
Sn	2	8	18	18	4			No	2	8	18	32	32	8	2
Sb	2	8	18	18	5			Lr	2	8	18	32	32	9	2
Te	2	8	18	18	6										

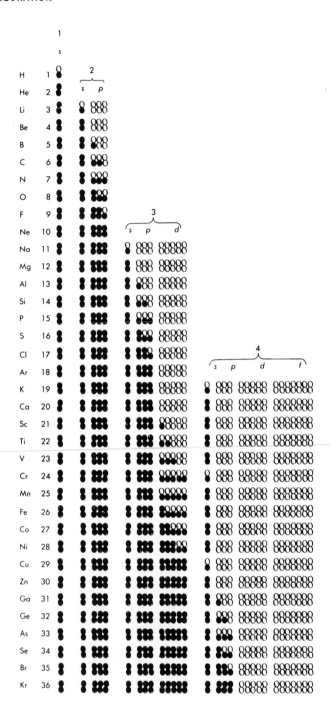

FIG. 2. Electronic configuration of the elements. (*Note:* Exact arrangement in "lanthanides" and "actinides" is uncertain.) (From "Inorganic Chemistry," R. T. Sanderson, Reinhold Publishing Corp., 1967)

		1	2		3			4				5			
		s	s	p	s	p	d	s	p	d	f	s	p	d	f
Rb	37														
Sr	38														
Y	39														
Zr	40														
Nb	41														
Mo	42														
Tc	43														
Ru	44														
Rh	45														
Pd	46														
Ag	47														
Cd	48														
In	49														
Sn	50														
Sb	51														
Te	52														
I	53														
Xe	54														
Cs	55														
Ba	56														
La	57														
Ce	58														
Pr	59														
Nd	60														
Pm	61														
Sm	62														
Eu	63														
Gd	64														
Tb	65														
Dy	66														
Ho	67														
Er	68														
Tm	69														
Yb	70														
Lu	71														
Hf	72														

(For elements Cs–Hf, an additional shell 6 is shown with sub-shells s, p, d.)

FIG. 2 *contd.*

		1	2		3			4				5				6		
		s	s	p	s	p	d	s	p	d	f	s	p	d	f	s	p	d
Ta	73																	
W	74																	
Re	75																	
Os	76																	
Ir	77																	
Pt	78																	
Au	79																	
Hg	80																	
Tl	81																	
Pb	82																	
Bi	83																	
Po	84																	
At	85																	
Rn	86																	
Fr	87																	
Ra	88																	
Ac	89																	
Th	90																	
Pa	91																	
U	92																	
Np	93																	
Pu	94																	
Am	95																	
Cm	96																	
Bk	97																	
Cf	98																	
E	99																	
Fm	100																	
Mv	101																	

(Column at far right: 7 s, 8 s)

FIG. 2 *contd.*

quantum number of each shell, followed by the orbital type (*s, p, d,* or *f*), with a superscript number (if greater than 1) to tell how many electrons are present in orbitals of that type. For hydrogen, $1s$ means there is one electron in the *s* orbital of principal quantum level $n = 1$. For carbon, $1s^2$, $2s^2$, $2p^2$ means that the $1s$ orbital has its full complement of 2 electrons, as does also the $2s$ orbital. Two additional electrons occupy $2p$ orbitals, which are *p* orbitals of principal quantum level $n = 2$. The thirty electrons of zinc are distributed as follows: $1s^2$, $2s^2$, $2p^6$, $3s^2$, $3p^6$, $3d^{10}$, $4s^2$.

Within any given principal quantum level, the *s* orbital always fills before *p* orbitals are occupied, and these in turn become filled before *d* orbitals are occupied. The *f* orbitals accept electrons only after the *d* orbitals are full. Consequently if the total number of electrons in a principal quantum level is given, detailed spectroscopic designation is unnecessary. For example, the electronic configuration of zinc could be simplified as 2–8–18–2. One knows, for any principal level, that the first 2 electrons *must* be in an *s* orbital, the next 6 in *p* orbitals, the next 10 in *d* orbitals, and any beyond 18 therefore in *f* orbitals.

With only a few exceptions, each element has an electronic configuration exactly like that of the element one lower in atomic number, with then one additional ("differentiating") electron. The exceptions occur principally where a slight rearrangement can produce an especially symmetrical array that is energetically favorable. A set of three *p* orbitals, or five *d* orbitals, or seven *f* orbitals, all are spherically symmetrical with respect to the nucleus. This symmetry is lacking when the set is only partly filled with electrons, unless it happens to be exactly half-filled, with one electron in each orbital of the set. For example, an atom of chromium would normally have four electrons in its five 3*d* orbitals, and two electrons in the 4*s* orbital. However, it gains stability by transfer of one of the 4*s* electrons into the fifth 3*d* orbital, completing the half-filled set. Similarly, an atom of copper would be expected to have 9 electrons in its 3*d* orbitals and two in its 4*s* orbital. Transfer of one of the 4*s* electrons to the remaining 3*d* vacancy would restore spherical symmetry to the five 3*d* orbitals, which occurs because it also is energetically favorable.

The filling of successive principal quantum levels gives a periodicity to atomic structure as atomic number is increased. This periodicity of electronic configuration underlies the periodic law (which see). It is complicated, however, by an apparent overlapping of adjacent principal quantum levels, such that the most stable orbital of the next higher principal level seems more stable than the least stable orbitals of the level being filled. Specifically, the 4*s* orbital appears more stable than the 3*d*, the 5*s* more stable than the 4*d*, and the 6*s* more stable than the 5*d* or the 4*f*. In other words, the elements build up in this order of orbital filling. (No such overlap is evident in any given element, where, for example, 4*s* electrons are less stable than 3*d*.) As a consequence of this "overlap," no outermost shell ever contains more than 8 electrons (2 in the first shell). The ninth electron always starts a new outermost shell.

The electronic configurations of the chemical elements are tabulated in condensed form in Table 1, and represented more graphically in Fig. 2. All the physical and chemical properties of all the chemical elements are the consequences of their atomic structure as revealed in these electronic configurations. (See Periodic Law and Table.)

References

1. Herzberg, G., "Atomic Spectra and Atomic Structure," New York, Dover, 1944.
2. Hochstrasser, R. M., "Behavior of Electrons in Atoms," New York, Benjamin, 1964.
3. Rich, R., "Periodic Correlations," New York, Benjamin, 1965.
4. Semat, H., "Introduction to Atomic Physics," New York, Rinehart, 1946.

R. T. SANDERSON

ELECTRONEGATIVITY

All atoms (except those of helium) that have fewer than 8 electrons in their highest principal quantum level have low-energy orbital vacancies capable of accommodating electrons from outside the atom. The existence of these vacancies is evidence that within these regions the nuclear charge can exert a significant attraction for such electrons, even though as a whole the atom is electrically neutral. This attraction is called "electronegativity." To the extent that the initially neutral atom may be able to acquire electrons from outside, it will acquire also their negative charge. The word "electronegativity" means "tendency to become negatively charged."

The concept of electronegativity is an extremely useful one in chemistry, because all chemical bonding (q.v.) originates with attractions of nuclei for electrons. In a single covalent bond, for example, one pair of electrons is mutually attracted to two atomic nuclei. The properties of the bond, and therefore of the compound, are significantly dependent on the relative strengths of these attractions. If the two atoms are initially of the same electronegativity—attract electrons equally—then the bond will be symmetrical and have relatively little effect on the other parts of each atom, since half share of two electrons is not very different from full control of one electron. But if the two atoms are initially unlike in electronegativity, the bond will not be symmetrical because more than half share of the electron pair will be acquired by the atom initially higher in its attraction for electrons. This atom thus becomes partially negative, leaving the other partially positive, and significantly altering the nature of any other bonds these same atoms may form. The extreme limit of uneven sharing would be reached if the electron pair should spend all its time with one nucleus and none with the other. The atoms would thus acquire integral negative and positive charge, becoming ions. The electrostatic attraction between oppositely charged ions is conventionally considered to provide the bonding force, called "ionic bonding," in compounds of elements widely different in electronegativity. In general, then, the direction and approximate extent of covalent bond polarity is suggested by the relative electronegativities of the elements forming the bond.

Unfortunately, electronegativity is much easier to picture qualitatively than to evaluate quantitatively. Without being precisely defined, it cannot be exactly measured, and a precise definition is lacking. Nevertheless, *relative* values are of greatest practical importance. Such values have been determined by a wide variety of methods. For example, electronegativities have been derived from ionization energies and electron affinities, from heats of reaction and bond energies, from measurements of the relative compactness of electronic clouds, from calculations of the effective nuclear charge at the surface of the atom, from work functions of metals, from force constants determined by infrared spectroscopy, and by various other methods. When adjusted to the same arbitrary scale the different values show surprisingly good agreement, with only a few minor discrepancies that are still controversial. The general order of increasing electronegativities, scaled from about 1 to 4, is Cs, Rb, K, Na, Li, Ba, Sr, Ca, Mg, Be, Al, Cd, Si, B, Zn, In, Hg, Tl, Pb, Sn, Bi, P, Sb, H, Ge, Te, C, I, As, S, Se, N, Br, Cl, O, and F. Reliable values for the transitional elements are not yet available but they would probably come between calcium and aluminum. A comparison of electronegativities obtained by three different methods is given in Table 1.

The agreement among these diverse evaluations suggests that the quality of electronegativity is so profoundly involved with the whole atomic structure that a qualitative concept is the best to be expected pending the development of deeper understanding. This agreement also suggests, and an overwhelming body of experimental evidence supports this suggestion, that these electronegativity values do indeed represent significant differences among the elements that can be usefully employed toward an interpretation of their properties and those of their compounds.

Table 2 shows graphically how electronegativities vary over the periodic system. The values given here for the transitional and inner transitional elements are somewhat tentative estimates based on atomization energies of their compounds and the assumption that electronegativity increases consistently across any given period. Possible ligand field effects and differences among oxidation states were not used in these estimates.

The most useful practical application of electronegativities is to a quantitative estimation of the relative condition of combined atoms. Much of chemistry becomes intelligible if one recognizes that the contribution made by an atom to the properties of its compound depends at least as much on the condition of that atom in the compound as it does on which element it is. The best available index of the condition of a combined atom is its partial charge, which results from initial atomic electronegativities in the following way.

The electrons involved in a covalent bond must, in effect, be equally attracted to both nuclei. When these two atoms are initially unlike in electronegativity, their bonding orbitals must of necessity be different in energy. Therefore the process of forming the bond must provide some mechanism by which these energies can be equalized. Such a mechanism can be based on the fact that the electronegativity of an atom must decrease as the atom begins to acquire an electron and increases as it begins to lose an electron. An atom of fluorine has a very high electronegativity but a fluoride ion has none. An atom of calcium has relatively little attraction for electrons but a calcium ion attracts them strongly. Consequently, the energies of the bonding orbitals can be equalized through an equalization of electronegativity, which in

TABLE 1. COMPARISON OF ELECTRONEGATIVITIES FROM DIFFERENT METHODS

(all in Pauling scale: Relative compactness
Pauling Type
Allred-Rochow)

Main group elements (values listed as: Relative compactness / Pauling Type / Allred-Rochow):

	M1	M2	M2'	M3	M4	M5	M6	M7	M8
1				H 2.31 / 2.2 / 2.2					He
2	Li 0.86 / 1.0 / 1.0	Be 1.61 / 1.5 / 1.6		B 1.88 / 2.0 / 2.0	C 2.47 / 2.60 / 2.6	N 2.93 / 3.05 / 3.0	O 3.46 / 3.50 / 3.4	F 3.92 / 3.90 / 4.0	Ne
3	Na 0.85 / 0.9 / 0.9	Mg 1.42 / 1.2 / 1.3		Al 1.54 / 1.5 / 1.6	Si 1.74 / 1.90 / 1.9	P 2.16 / 2.15 / 2.2	S 2.66 / 2.60 / 2.6	Cl 3.28 / 3.15 / 3.2	Ar
4	K 0.74 / 0.8 / 0.8	Ca 1.06 / 1.0 / 1.0	Zn 1.86 / 1.6 / 1.7	Ga 2.10 / 1.6 / 1.8	Ge 2.31 / 1.90 / 2.0	As 2.53 / 2.10 / 2.2	Se 2.76 / 2.55 / 2.6	Br 2.96 / 2.95 / 3.0	Kr
5	Rb 0.70 / 0.8 / 0.8	Sr 0.96 / 1.0 / 1.0	Cd 1.73 / 1.7 / 1.7	In 1.88 / 1.7 / 1.8	Sn 2.02 / 1.90 / 2.0	Sb 2.19 / 2.05 / 2.1	Te 2.34 / 2.40	I 2.50 / 2.65 / 2.7	Xe
6	Cs 0.69 / 0.7 / 0.8	Ba 0.93 / 0.9 / 0.9	Hg 1.92 / 1.9 / 2.0	Tl 1.96 / 1.9 / 2.0	Pb 2.01 / 1.8 / 2.3	Bi 2.06 / 1.8 / 2.0	Po 2.0	At 2.2	Rn
7	Fr	Ra							

Transition elements (values listed as: Relative compactness / Pauling Type / Allred-Rochow):

	T3	T4	T5	T6	T7	T8	T9	T10	T11
4	Sc 1.09 / 1.3 / 1.20	Ti 1.13 / 1.5 / 1.32	V 1.24 / 1.6 / 1.45	Cr 1.35 / 1.6 / 1.56	Mn 1.44 / 1.5 / 1.60	Fe 1.47 / 1.8 / 1.64	Co 1.47 / 1.8 / 1.70	Ni 1.47 / 1.8 / 1.75	Cu 1.74 / 1.9 / 1.75
5	Y 0.98 / 1.2 / 1.11	Zr 1.00 / 1.4 / 1.22	Nb 1.12 / 1.6 / 1.23	Mo 1.24 / 1.8 / 1.30	Tc 1.33 / 1.9 / 1.35	Ru 1.40 / 2.2 / 1.42	Rh 1.47 / 2.2 / 1.45	Pd 1.57 / 2.2 / 1.35	Ag 1.72 / 1.9 / 1.42
6	La 0.92 / 1.1 / 1.08 ; Lu 0.96 / 1.2 / 1.14	Hf 0.98 / 1.3 / 1.23	Ta 1.04 / 1.5 / 1.33	W 1.13 / 1.7 / 1.40	Re 1.19 / 1.9 / 1.45	Os 1.26 / 2.2 / 1.52	Ir 1.33 / 2.2 / 1.55	Pt 1.36 / 2.2 / 1.44	Au 1.72 / 2.4 / 1.42
7	Ac 1.1 ; Lw	104							

Lanthanides (values listed as: Relative compactness / Pauling Type / Allred-Rochow):

6	Ce 0.92 / 1.1 / 1.06	Pr 0.92 / 1.1 / 1.07	Nd 0.93 / 1.1 / 1.07	Pm 0.94 / 1.1 / 1.07	Sm 0.94 / 1.1 / 1.07	Eu 0.94 / 1.1 / 1.01	Gd 0.94 / 1.1 / 1.11	Tb 0.94 / 1.2 / 1.10	Dy 0.94 / 1.2 / 1.10	Ho 0.96 / 1.2 / 1.10	Er 0.96 / 1.2 / 1.11	Tm 0.96 / 1.2 / 1.11	Yb 0.96 / 1.2 / 1.05

Actinides:

7	Th 1.3	Pa 1.5	U 1.7 / 1.4	Np 1.3	Pu 1.3	Am	Cm	Bk	Cf	Es	Fm	Md	No

(From "Inorganic Chemistry," R. T. Sanderson, Reinhold Publishing Corp., 1967)

TABLE 2. ELECTRONEGATIVITIES OF THE ELEMENTS (RELATIVE COMPACTNESS SCALE)

M1	M2	M2	M3	M4	M5	M6	M7	M8
1				H 3.55				He
2	Li 0.74	Be 2.39		B 2.84	C 3.79	N 4.49	O 5.21	F 5.75	Ne
3	Na 0.70	Mg 1.99		Al 2.25	Si 2.62	P 3.34	S 4.11	Cl 4.93	Ar
4	K 0.41	Ca 1.22	Zn 2.84	Ga 3.23	Ge 3.59	As 3.91	Se 4.25	Br 4.53	Kr 4.81
5	Rb 0.33	Sr 1.00	Cd 2.59	In 2.86	Sn 3.10	Sb 3.37	Te 3.62	I 3.84	Xe 4.06
6	Cs 0.29	Ba 0.78	Hg 2.93	Tl 3.02	Pb 3.08	Bi 3.16	Po	At	Rn
7	Fr	Ra							

	T3	T4	T5	T6	T7	T8	T9	T10	T11
4	Sc (1.30)	Ti 1.40	V 1.60	Cr 1.88	Mn 2.07	Fe 2.10	Co 2.10	Ni 2.10	Cu 2.60
5	Y (1.05)	Zr 1.10	Nb (1.36)	Mo 1.62	Tc (1.80)	Ru (1.95)	Rh (2.10)	Pd 2.29	Ag 2.57
6	La (0.88) Lu (1.00)	Hf 1.05	Ta (1.21)	W 1.39	Re (1.53)	Os (1.67)	Ir (1.78)	Pt 1.91	Au 2.57
7	Ac Lw	104							

6	Ce (0.90)	Pr (0.91)	Nd (0.92)	Pm (0.93)	Sm (0.94)	Eu (0.95)	Gd (0.96)	Tb (0.97)	Dy (0.97)	Ho (0.98)	Er (0.98)	Tm (0.99)	Yb (0.99)
7	Th	Pa	U	Np	Pu	Am	Cm	Bk	Cf	Es	Fm	Md	No

(From "Inorganic Chemistry," R. T. Sanderson, Reinhold Publishing Corp., 1967)

turn can result from uneven sharing of the bonding electrons. When the bonding electrons spend more than half-time more closely associated with the nucleus of the atom that initially attracted them more, they reduce its electronegativity, at the same time imparting a partial negative charge. By spending less than half-time more closely associated with the initially less electronegative atom, they leave it with net partial positive charge and correspondingly a higher electronegativity. The final state is one of even attraction through uneven sharing.

Such adjustment is postulated by the

"Principle of Electronegativity Equalization," which may be stated: When two or more atoms initially different in electronegativity unite, their electronegativities become equalized in the compound. The intermediate electronegativity in the compound is taken as the geometric mean of the electronegativities of all the atoms before combination. An estimate of the relative condition of a combined atom with respect to partial charge can be based on the assumption that the charge changes linearly with electronegativity. Assignment of a particular ionicity to a particular bond (arbitrarily, 75% to Na-F) then permits calculation of the change in electronegativity per unit charge for any element of known electronegativity. The relative partial charge on any combined atom is then defined and estimated as the ratio of the electronegativity change undergone in forming the compound to the electronegativity change that would correspond to the gain or loss of one electron. The sign of the charge is negative if the electronegativity of the element has decreased on combination, and positive if it has increased.

The partial charge distribution in any compound composed of elements of known electronegativity can thus easily be estimated. Such information provides many valuable insights that contribute toward a fundamental understanding of chemistry.

References

1. Allred, A. L., and Rochow, E. G., *J. Inorg. Nucl. Chem.*, **5**, 264, 269 (1958).
2. Hinze, J., and Jaffe, H. H., *J. Am. Chem. Soc.*, **84**, 540 (1962).
3. Hinze, J., Whitehead, N. A., and Jaffe, H. H., *J. Am. Chem. Soc.*, **85**, 148 (1963).
4. Pauling, L., "Nature of the Chemical Bond," 3rd Ed., Ithaca, Cornell Univ. Press, 1960.
5. Sanderson, R. T., "Inorganic Chemistry," New York, Reinhold Publishing Corp., 1967.
6. Sanderson, R. T., "Chemical Periodicity," New York, Reinhold Publishing Corp., 1960.

R. T. SANDERSON

ERBIUM

Erbium, atomic number 68, atomic weight 167.26, is one of the metallic elements. It is the eleventh member of the lanthanide rare earth series (see **Lutetium** and **Lanthanide Elements**) and, therefore, in the condensed state of matter has 11 electrons in its $4f$ subshell. These $4f$ electrons play almost no part in the valency forces of the atom but do give rise to sharp absorption bands in the visible and ultraviolet regions of the spectrum. As a result of this property, it was one of the early rare earths to be discovered.

Isotopes

The naturally occurring stable isotopes of erbium and their per cent abundances are Er^{162} (0.136%), Er^{164} (1.56%), Er^{166} (33.41%) Er^{167} (22.94%), Er^{168} (27.07%) and Er^{170} (14.88%). In addition to the naturally occurring isotopes, at least nine radioactive isotopes have been prepared and studied.

History

In 1794, J. Gadolin discovered a new element in a heavy black mineral (gadolinite) which he had found near Ytterby, Sweden. He obtained about 38% of the new oxide from the mineral. This new oxide was called yttria. This same oxide was isolated from a number of other minerals. In 1842, C. G. Mosander found that this oxide was complex and that it could be resolved into three fractions—the most basic one which he called yttria, the least basic one, erbia, and the intermediate one, terbia. All of these rare earth oxides were named after the town of Ytterby, Sweden, near where the first mineral was found. Yttria was white and gave colorless salts, erbia was orange-yellow and gave colorless salts, while terbia was white and gave rose-colored salts. Mosander's results were confirmed by several other chemists, but during this early period of rare earth chemistry, the names erbia and terbia became confused so that Mosander's terbia became erbia after 1860 and his erbia was known as terbia after 1877. (Also see **Lutetium**.) Mosander's intermediate fraction, now called erbia, was later shown to be complex and resolved into a mixture of five oxides: erbia, rose-colored; scandia, white; holmia, tan; thulia, white; and ytterbia, white. By 1905, G. Urbain and C. James had independently succeeded in isolating fairly pure erbia. The metallic form of the element was produced in a powdered form mixed with KCl by W.

Klemm and H. Bommer in 1934. They reduced the anhydrous chloride with potassium vapor.

During the late 1940's and the early 1950's separation methods were developed at the Ames Laboratory of the Atomic Energy Commission, which carried out these fractionation processes automatically. The methods utilized the then new synthetic ion exchange resins and took advantage of the tendency of the rare earth ions to form chelate complexes. (See articles on **Cerium, Thulium** and **Lutetium** for more details). Many kilograms of 99.99% Er_2O_3 were prepared. At the present time, a number of industries are using ion exchange techniques to prepare pure erbia, and it can be obtained in high purity in up to ton quantities if desired. A recent quotation listed erbium oxide 99.99% pure for as low as $90 per pound.

Highly pure individual rare earths at reasonable prices have not been available commercially for a sufficient time to allow large scale industrial uses to be developed. It is already clear that they will play an important role in laser development, in the electronics industry (garnets) and in some sensing instruments. However, to date the most important use of the heavy rare earths is as powerful tools used by scientists in obtaining a better understanding of chemical, physical and metallurgical principles and in obtaining a clearer picture of the nature of matter. The fact that rare earth atoms all exist in a trivalent state where the radii diminish slightly as one progresses across the series, permits a scientist to prepare a series of compounds where only a few variables change, usually in a predictable manner, from compound to compound. With such information, he can check his theories or explanations of why matter behaves as it does. It should be pointed out that, while the trivalent ions in aqueous solutions are encased in a water envelope and, therefore, are very similar as one progresses across the series, this is not true for the anhydrous compounds or the metals. In the latter cases, the differences across the series are as great as they are in other series of the Periodic Table, for example, among copper, silver and gold or in the alkali metal group. Nevertheless, the properties change in a regular manner for several members of the series before there is

an abrupt change in properties and even these abrupt changes can be valuable in correlating the changes with some factor which occurs in the structure of the rare earths at that point in the series.

Occurrence

The rare earths are not really rare in that they are found in the parts per million range widely distributed throughout the earth's crust. They always occur as mixtures of all the rare earths, and these mixtures are frequently found concentrated in numerous minerals. The relative abundance of the rare earths varies from mineral to mineral, but in general the heavy rare earths are always present in minor amounts. (See articles on **Lanthanide Elements, Holmium, Thulium,** and **Lutetium** for types of minerals and the methods of breaking them up and separating them.) It is estimated that erbium occurs in the earth's crust to about 24 parts in ten million. Erbium is more abundant, therefore, than bromine, iodine, antimony, mercury and cadmium.

Erbium Metal Preparation

The preparation of erbium metal in massive quantities is usually accomplished by the reduction of erbium chloride or erbium fluoride by an alkali or alkaline earth metal. Since erbium very closely resembles, in many ways, holmium, it can be prepared and purified in the same manner as described in the article on **Holmium**.

Physical Properties

Erbium is highly electropositive and will, therefore, react readily with acids. It has a silvery metallic luster and at room temperatures is not attacked by atmospheric gases. Even at higher temperatures, a massive sample of high-purity metal will oxidize very slowly in air. However, as with other highly electropositive metals, finely divided erbium can be ignited readily and will burn white hot. Average values (January, 1967) of the physical properties of erbium metal are listed in Table I. Since a number of these properties are very sensitive to the presence of small amounts of impurities, particularly oxygen, nitrogen, carbon and the halides, it should be expected

TABLE 1. PHYSICAL PROPERTIES OF ERBIUM METAL

Melting point	1522°C
Vapor pressure, 1520°C	0.4mm
Boiling point	2510°C
Density	9.045 g/cc
Crystal structure	Hexagonal close-packed
	a = 3.559 c = 5.595
Atomic volume	18.49 cc/mole
Metallic radius, Coordination #12	1.758Å
Heat of fusion	4.757 kcal/mole
Heat of sublimation, 25°C	74.5 ± 7.6 kcal/mole
C_p, 25°C	6.73 cal/mole-deg
Grüneisen constant	0.88
Debye temperature	163°K
Thermal conductivity	0.023 ± 0.002 cal/sec/cm/°C
Linear coefficient of expansion	9.2×10^{-6}/°C (25°C)
	11.5×10^{-6}/°C (400°C)
Compressibility	2.39×10^{-6}cm²/kg
Young's modulus	7.33×10^{11} dynes/cm²
Shear modulus	2.96×10^{11} dynes/cm²
Poisson's ratio	0.238
Hardness, Vickers Diamond Pyramid	44
Electrical resistivity, 4°K	5 microhm-cm
77°K	43 microhm-cm
298°K	87 microhm-cm
1273°K	205 microhm-cm
Coefficient of resistivity, 298°K	0.16 microhm-cm/°K
Yield strength, 0.2% offset	42,300 psi
Ultimate strength	42,400 psi
Thermal neutron cross section, barns	166

that some of these values will change slightly as purer metal is prepared and measured.

Magnetic and Electrical Properties

The magnetic behavior of erbium is mainly due to the unpaired electrons in its $4f$ shell. It has an effective magnetic moment of 9.9 Bohr magnetons at room temperature. Upon cooling below room temperature, erbium changes from paramagnetic to antiferromagnetic at about 84°K and to ferromagnetic at 19.6°K. The antiferromagnetic structure is complex and has been shown to have a single axis of magnetic moment aligned parallel to the c axis between 53.5 and 84°K in which the z component of the moment varies sinusoidally in successive planes along the c axis. In this structure, there is no order among the x-y components of the moment. Between 19.5°K and 53.5°K, the x-y components begin to order possibly in a screw-type structure.

Erbium has a high electrical resistivity compared with other metals. At room temperature, its resistivity is 87 microhm-cm compared with 1.67 for copper. The resistivity of erbium is anisotropic and at room temperature is 1.74 times higher along the a axis than it is along the c axis.

Chemical Properties

The only valency that has been observed for erbium in aqueous solutions or in its salts is $+3$. The Er^{+3} ion gives rose-colored solutions, and salts of erbium are usually colored a light shade of red. A slightly oxygen-deficient oxide of erbium with the formula $ErO_{1.489}$ has been observed which is black in color.

Erbium forms a water-soluble fluoride, hydroxide, carbonate, oxalate and phosphate. The chloride, bromide, iodide, nitrate, sulfate and acetate are soluble and form hydrated salts. The anhydrous halides can be prepared in the manner analogous to that described under **Holmium**. Some of the physical

205

TABLE 2. SOME PHYSICAL PROPERTIES OF ERBIUM OXIDE AND HALIDES

Property	Er_2O_3	ErF_3	$ErCl_3$	$ErBr_3$	ErI_3
Melting point	(2350°C)†	1140°C	776°C	925	1000°C
Boiling point	(3000°C)	(2230°C)	1500°C	(1460°C)	(1280°C)
Structure	Cubic	Orthorhombic‡ a = 6.354	Monoclinic		Hexagonal a = 7.451
Lattice constants Å	a = 10.547	b = 6.848 c = 4.380			c = 20.78
Density, g/cc	8.66	7.81			3.28
ΔH formation, kcal/mole, 25°C	− 453.6	(− 392)	− 229.1	(− 205)	− 162
ΔH fusion, kcal/mole		8	7.8	10	10
ΔH vaporization, kcal/mole		60	44	43	40

† Figures in parentheses are estimates by R. E. Thoma, 1965, ORNL 3804.
‡ Hexagonal above 1100°C.

properties of the sesquioxide and anhydrous halides of erbium are given in Table 2.

Melting and Fabrication

Although the vapor pressure of erbium is moderately high at its melting point (see Table I), it can be arc melted on a water-cooled copper hearth under an argon atmosphere or arc cast into ingots, both consumably or nonconsumably. Erbium can also be electron beam-melted. However, because of its high vapor pressure, volatization is rapid in vacuum. Casting by induction or resistance heating can be carried out in tantalum or tungsten crucibles with some contamination from the crucibles. However, the maximum contamination which would occur if the metal were not superheated would be about 0.50 at. % tantalum or 0.10 at.% tungsten, respectively. Since these are equilibrium values in the neighborhood of the casting temperature, lesser contamination can be achieved if the melting is done in about two minutes. Erbium can be hot rolled, swaged or extruded if protected from atmospheric corrosion. Cold rolling of erbium in the "as cast" condition results in edge cracking after about 10% reduction in thickness. However, a greater reduction can be achieved by cold rolling if the metal is initially hot rolled. Since the single crystals of erbium metal are highly anisotropic, polycrystalline samples are very likely to exhibit preferred orientation. It is difficult to grow single crystals of erbium by the Bridgman technique since a crystal transformation is expected to take place slightly below the melting point. So far, the only evidence for this transition has been from alloy studies. Single crystals can, however, be grown by the strain anneal technique.

Alloying Behavior

One of the basic rules of alloying is that solid solution is unlikely unless the atomic radii of the two elements are within a few per cent of each other. For this reason, it is easy to see why erbium has very low solubility for the alkali or alkaline earth metals which have a much larger radius or with the elements in Groups IB through VIIB, Group VIII or Group IIIA, whose radii are much smaller. Since erbium is similar in radius to the other rare earth metals, it forms continuous solid solutions with rare earth metals which have the same structure and extensive solid solutions with those with different crystal structure. Two exceptions are europium and ytterbium which have very limited solubility in erbium, probably due again to the large difference in radii. Intermediate phases with the structure of samarium metal have been observed when erbium is alloyed with rare earths lower in atomic number than samarium. Erbium also forms intermediate phases with elements in Groups IB, IIB, VIIB, VIII and Groups IIIA through VIIA. The compounds formed between erbium and these elements are usually brittle.

Toxicity

The toxicity of various erbium salts has been studied. When inhaled, taken orally, or injected into the blood stream in massive amounts, erbium salts can cause serious damage. However, the conclusion of the investigators is to classify the rare earths as having a low acute toxicity rating. Since their effect in low concentrations on humans over long periods of time has not been determined, these materials should be handled with reasonable care.

References

1. Mellor, J. W., "Treatise on Inorganic and Theoretical Chemistry," Vol. 5, pp. 480–709 New York, Longmans, Green and Company, 1946. (Early work.)
2. Weeks, Mary Elvira, "Discovery of the Elements," Easton, Pennsylvania, Mack Printing Company, 1945.
3. Yost, Don N., Russell, H., and Garner, C. S., "The Rare-Earth Elements and Their Compounds," New York, John Wiley & Sons, Inc., 1947.
4. Spedding, F. H., and Daane, A. H., Editors, "The Rare Earths," New York and London, John Wiley & Sons, Inc., 1961.
5. Gschneidner, Karl A., Jr., "Rare Earth Alloys," Princeton, N.J., D. Van Nostrand Company, Inc., 1961.
6. Eyring, LeRoy, Editor, "Progress in the Science and Technology of the Rare Earths," Vol. 1, New York, Pergamon Press, 1964.
7. Trombe, F., Loriers, J., Gaume-Mahn, Mme. F., and La Blanchetais, Mlle. Henry, "Elements des Terres Rares (Ou Lanthanides) Scandium, Yttrium," Vol. I, Vol. II, Paris, Masson et Cie, 1960.
8. Topp, N. E., "Chemistry of the Rare-Earth Elements." New York, Elsevier Publishing Company, 1965.
9. Moeller, Therald, "The Chemistry of the Lanthanides," New York, Reinhold Publishing Company, 1963.
10. "Rare Earths," *Chem. Eng. News*, May 10, 1965 (special report on uses).
11. Haley, T. J., "Pharmacology and Toxicology of the Rare Earth Elements," *J. Pharm. Sci.*, **54**, 5 (1965).

F. H. SPEDDING AND
B. J. BEAUDRY

EUROPIUM

Europium, atomic number 63, is one of the group of 15 elements in Group III of the Periodic Table having atomic numbers from 57 to 71 and known as the rare earth metals, or as lanthanons or lanthanides. (See **Lanthanide Elements.**) Its discovery is generally credited to Demarcay who obtained the earth in pure form in 1901 by fractional crystallization of the double magnesium nitrates, although as early as 1892 Boisbaudran had obtained basic fractions from samarium-gadolinium concentrates having spark spectral lines not accounted for by samarium or gadolinium and subsequently shown to belong to europium. The scarcity and complex chemistry of europium undoubtedly accounted for its late discovery, coming over 15 years after the isolation of samarium. The name, of course, is taken from Europe.

The rare earths as a group constitute about 0.008% of the earth's crust and europium generally comprises from 0.05 to 0.2% of the rare earth mixture. The principal commercial ores from which rare earths are extracted are monazite and xenotime, each being rare earth phosphates, and bastnasite, a rare earth fluocarbonate.

The lanthanides as a group are characterized by the successive filling-in of the well-shielded $4f$ electron shell while maintaining (ideally) the same $5d^16s^2$ outer electronic configuration in each element. Europium, the seventh number of the series, thus has the assigned electronic configuration $4f^65d^16s^2$, although the probable configuration is $4f^76s^2$ for the neutral atom and $4f^76s^25p^6$ for the Eu^{3+} ion. These configurations account for the observed oxidation states of $2+$ as well as $3+$. The tripositive state is the more stable of the two species in aqueous solution.

Elemental europium is a metal having a density of 5.24 g/cc. It has a metallic luster when freshly cut, but tarnishes rapidly in air, quickly forming an oxide coating. It is active chemically as evidenced by its rapid attack by dilute acids and even by water at room temperature. Europium has 5 stable isotopes with atomic masses 151 through 155. The thermal neutron cross sections of these range from 420 to 13,000 barns, while the natural mixture has a thermal neutron absorption of

4600 barns. The five-membered chain of absorbing isotopes makes europium desirable for nuclear control rods.

Occurrence and Extraction

Monazite and bastnasite are the two most abundant rare earth bearing ores. Monazite, a rare earth-thorium orthophosphate is found in many countries such as India, Brazil, Australia, and the United States, occurring as placer deposits on the beaches as the result of weathering and gravity concentration (specific gravity, 5.2). It also occurs in massive lodes, the largest of which is in South Africa. Domestic sources of monazite are located in Idaho, the Carolinas, and Florida where commercial mining for ilmenite, rutile, zircon, and staurolite produces monazite as a by-product. The heavy mineral content of these deposits generally averages less than 10% with the monazite being less than 0.01%. Thorium also is found in monazite, ranging from 4–9% ThO_2 and accounts for monazite's radioactivity. Bastnasite is a rare earth fluocarbonate, the largest deposit being located in the Mountain Pass region of southeastern California. Unlike monazite, the thorium and heavier yttrium earths in bastnasite are essentially less than 1%. Both ores are beneficiated by flotation to about 95% of the desired mineral constituents and contain after beneficiation 50 to 70% equivalent rare earth oxide, of which the europium (Eu_2O_3) ranges from about 0.05 to 0.15%. Associated minerals such as xenotime may increase the europium value by as much as 20–30%, depending on the amount present.

Both monazite and bastnasite may be opened by sulfuric acid attack. In the case of monazite, the ore concentrate is reacted with sulfuric acid at temperatures of 120 to 170°C. The exothermic reaction increases the temperature to 250°C, converting the rare earths to anhydrous sulfates, and the thorium to a soluble phosphate. The reaction mass is then added to cold water which solubilizes the thorium and rare earth sulfates. The thorium is separated by precipitating the rare earth-sodium sulfate double salts. These are converted to rare earth hydrated oxides by heating with sodium hydroxide. The cerium in the hydrated oxide upon drying in air oxidizes to the tetravalent state permitting a basicity separation. Treatment with either hydrochloric or nitric acid solubilizes most of the rare earths other than cerium which remains as ceric hydrated oxide (ceric hydroxide). The mixture of rare earths, minus the cerium, is referred to as "didymium." Monazite may also be cracked by boiling with concentrated sodium hydroxide which converts the thorium and the rare earths to hydrated oxides which are washed free of the soluble trisodium phosphate. The cerium is oxidized to the Ce(IV) state by drying the hydrated oxide, or by treatment with Cl_2 in the presence of NaOH. After oxidation, the didymium fraction again is separated by leaching with HCl or HNO_3.

The solution of soluble didymium salts remaining after cerium separation may be used as feed for ion exchange, solvent extraction, or fractional crystallization to separate and purify the individual rare earths. Although any of these methods may be used to purify europium, they generally are used only to obtain europium-rich fractions from which the europium is then separated by taking advantage of the relative ease of reduction to the divalent state. Thus Marsh developed techniques whereby europium was reduced by contacting a dilute acetate solution with sodium amalgam, after which the europium was recovered from the amalgam by treating with dilute sulfuric acid. The over-all method, however, is cumbersome (because of the relatively high weight of mercury necessary) and present commercial practice employs the method devised by H. N. McCoy, or solvent extraction. In the solvent extraction method, rare earth concentrates are extracted into di(2-ethyl-hexyl) phosphoric acid and then separated by countercurrent methods in which the distribution coefficients are controlled by adjusting the acidity.

In a method developed by McCoy, the Eu(III) species is reduced with zinc in the presence of barium ions and sulfate ions. $EuSO_4$ which is isomorphous with $BaSO_4$ coprecipitates and is recovered by filtration, thus effecting a separation from the trivalent rare earths which largely remain in solution. Treatment of the barium europium sulfate cake with nitric acid or hydrogen peroxide oxidizes the Eu(II) to Eu(III) which is resolubilized. Repetition of this process several times upgrades the europium content to about 50% of the total rare earth oxides from which it can be recovered in over 99.9% purity by precipitating $EuCl_2 \cdot 2H_2O$ from concentrated HCl, in which it is relatively insoluble.

Bastnasite, like monazite, may be opened by either acid or basic attack. The resulting rare earth sulfates or rare earth hydroxides are processed in a manner similar to that when derived from monazite. A recent method of separating europium from bastnasite developed by the Colorado School of Mines for Molybdenum Corporation of America involves preliminary roasting of the bastnasite concentrate to oxidize the cerium. The didymium fraction is then solubilized by leaching with hydrochloric acid. The soluble didymium chloride solution is extracted after pH adjustment with di(2-ethyl-hexyl) phosphoric acid which concentrates the europium into fractions which are then processed by a modification of McCoy's method to produce pure Eu_2O_3.

Other methods of producing high-purity $(99.9^+\%)$ Eu_2O_3 involve basicity separations and ion exchange. Thus Bronaugh showed that europium in the reduced state is soluble in a basic system, especially ammonium hydroxide. The trivalent rare earths precipitate as the hydrous oxides, leaving europium in solution from which it can be recovered by precipitation as europium oxalate by addition of oxalic acid. Calcination of the oxalate yields Eu_2O_3. Purities of over 99.9% have been obtained by this method, but the slow filtration and difficulty of washing the precipitated hydrous oxides limits its commercial use. Cation exchange separation techniques have also produced high purity Eu_2O_3. The rare earths are loaded on a cation exchange resin and eluted with a chelating agent such as ethylenediamine tetraacetic acid. However, the separation is relatively poor because of the close separation factor between gadolinium and europium and excessive elution times are necessary.

Europium Metal

Although most of the rare earth metals may be prepared by the metallothermic reduction of their trihalides with calcium, europium as well as samarium and ytterbium cannot be prepared by this method because reduction stops at the dihalide. However, as a result of the relatively high vapor pressure of europium compared to that of lanthanum, a method was devised by Daane and co-workers in which lanthanum turnings in 10% excess are mixed with Eu_2O_3 and the charge heated in a tantalum crucible under high vacuum. The reduced metal volatilizes and is collected as a bright crystalline condensate on the walls of the upper part of the crucible. Because of the high reactivity of europium in finely divided form, it must be handled in an inert atmosphere, and considerable care must be exercised in removing and storing it. Cerium may also be used as the reducing agent.

Physical Properties

At room temperature europium crystallizes in the body-centered cubic form having a lattice constant $a_0 = 4.582$ Å. The bcc form exists up to the melting point at 826°C. The density is 5.245 g/cc. Europium metal, like ytterbium, is quite soft, the approximate hardness (DPH kg/sq mm) being 20 as compared to 55 for gadolinium. Europium boils at 1439°C and has a heat of vaporization of 42 kcal/mole. The abnormally low melting and boiling points in comparison with the

TABLE 1. PHYSICAL PROPERTIES OF EUROPIUM

Symbol	Eu
Atomic number	63
Atomic weight	151.96
Density	5.245 g/cc
Melting point	826°C
Heat of fusion	2.0 kcal/mole
Boiling point	1439°C
Heat of vaporization, 25°C	42 kcal/mole
Vapor pressure, 733–903°K	$\text{Log } P_{mm\ Hg} = 8.160 - \dfrac{8982}{T}$
Specific heat, 25°C	6.4 cal/mole °C
Heat of combustion, 25°C	217.0 kcal/g-atom
Heat of sublimation, 25°C	43.11 kcal/mole
Debye temperature	70–120°K
Thermal neutron absorption cross section	4600 barns
Thermal expansion coefficient	$32 \times 10^{-6}/°C$
Electrical resistivity	81 microhm-cm

other rare earths are attributed to the bivalency of europium in the metallic state. Table 1 lists the physical properties.

Chemical Properties

Europium is the most reactive of the rare earth metals and in many respects more closely resembles the alkaline earth metals than the other rare earths. It will reduce the oxides of many metals including iron, manganese, chromium, silicon, tin, lead, and zirconium. It burns readily in air and may ignite spontaneously in finely divided form. It reacts slowly with water at room temperature, first forming a yellow water soluble compound, $Eu(OH)_2$, which then oxidizes to white insoluble hydrous europic oxide. The metal is soluble in liquid ammonia, giving a blue solution.

Many compounds such as nitrides, sulfides, carbides, etc., may be formed by the direct union of europium with the corresponding nonmetal, usually at high temperatures. Hydrides are formed by exposure of the metal to hydrogen at 300°C forming a brittle amorphous solid.

Analysis

Europium may be determined by several different methods, among them volumetric, polarographic, spectrophotometric, and spectrographic. The volumetric method depends on the reduction to the divalent state in a Jones reductor. Because the europous ion is not very stable, the europium is not determined directly by titration with an oxidant, but rather is passed into a solution of ferric chloride or standard iodine solution and the ferrous ion or excess iodine is determined by an appropriate method. As little as 0.1% europium in rare earths material may be determined.

The polarographic method is considerably more sensitive than the volumetric method and allows the determination of europium in other rare earths at concentrations as low as 0.003%. Zinc, however, interferes and must be removed. The method is based on the relatively low potential, about -0.67 volt relative to the saturated calomel electrode, for the reaction $Eu^{+3} + e \rightarrow Eu^{+2}$. The diffusion

current is proportional to the europium ion concentration in the range of 1.1 to 11.8 millimoles/liter.

The rare earths as a group are characterized by sharp absorption bands in the visible and ultraviolet regions of the spectrum and, therefore, may be determined spectrophotometrically. For europium the sharp peak at 394 mμ is generally used. Samarium, dysprosium, and holmium interfere, and suitable corrections must be applied if these are present. Europous ion has a strong absorption band at 248 mμ, but it is of little use analytically because of its ease of oxidation.

Europium in other rare earths and other rare earths in europium may be determined by emission spectrography using the d-c arc technique. By using the matrix material as its own internal standard, variations in arc temperatures are largely overcome. For europium in other rare earths and other rare earths in europium, the method is useful in the range of 0.005–1.0%.

Principal Compounds

The principal compounds of europium are the trivalent oxide, hydrous oxide, oxalate, nitrate, chloride, and sulfate. The divalent salts, because of their instability, are of little value commercially, but use is made of them in separating and purifying europium.

The oxide, Eu_2O_3, is the most important salt. It is insoluble in water, but soluble in mineral acids. It is usually prepared by the calcination of the oxalate, but may also be prepared by calcining the carbonate, hydrous oxide, or nitrate.

Europium oxalate, $Eu_2(C_2O_4)_3 \cdot 10H_2O$, is precipitated from aqueous salt solutions by the addition of oxalic acid or ammonium oxalate. It is virtually insoluble in water, but the solubility increases in acid solutions. Calcination of the oxalate gives the oxide.

Europium carbonate, $Eu_2(CO_3)_3 \cdot 3H_2O$, precipitates when solutions of soluble europium salts are treated with solutions of alkali bicarbonates saturated with carbon dioxide. Use of normal alkali carbonate gives mixtures of normal, basic, and double salts.

Europium chloride, $EuCl_3 \cdot 6H_2O$, is formed by dissolving the oxide, hydrous oxide, or carbonate in hydrochloric acid. The anhydrous salt is prepared by heating the hydrated salt in a stream of dry hydrogen chloride. The water-insoluble oxychloride is formed by heating the hydrated salt in air. As discussed earlier, divalent europium chloride may be prepared by reducing a solution of the trivalent salt with zinc. The divalent salt, $EuCl_2 \cdot 2HCl$, precipitates in concentrated hydrochloric acid.

Europium fluoride, $EuF_3 \cdot 3H_2O$, forms as a gelatinous precipitate when hydrofluoric acid is added to an aqueous solution of a europium salt. It can also be prepared by treating the oxalate, hydrous oxide, or carbonate with HF. The fluoride is insoluble in water or acid. The oxyfluoride is formed by heating the hydrated fluoride in an atmosphere of air. Anhydrous EuF_3 is prepared by heating Eu_2O_3 in a current of HF.

Europium nitrate, $Eu(NO_3)_3 \cdot 6H_2O$, is prepared by dissolving the metal, oxide, hydrous oxide, or carbonate in nitric acid. It is very soluble in water. On heating, the nitrate first dissolves in its own water of crystallization, then goes through a series of basic nitrates, and finally reverts to the oxide.

Europium sulfate, $Eu_2(SO_4)_3 \cdot 8H_2O$, can be prepared similarly to the chloride and nitrates by dissolving the metal, oxide, hydrous oxide, or carbonate in sulfuric acid. It can also be prepared by adding a soluble sulfate to a concentrated solution of the chloride or nitrate inasmuch as it is much less soluble than these compounds. Contrary to normal behavior, the solubility of the sulfate decreases with increasing temperature.

Importance and Uses

Up until 1964 europium was used primarily as a neutron absorbing component of control rods in nuclear reactors. Even here the use was limited due to the high cost, and total consumption was less than 50 lb/year. The real impact on the rare earth industry came in June of 1964 when General Telephone and Electronics Corporation announced the development of a new red phosphor for color television: europium-activated yttrium orthovanadate, to replace the silver-activated zinc-cadmium sulfide. Because the brightness of the vanadate phosphor increased linearly with the beam current density while the sulfide was sublinear, the resulting brightness was 40% greater and the emission color a definite red as opposed to a more orange-red color for the sulfide.

Yttrium orthovanadate, YVO_4, is a white body and crystallizes in the tetragonal system with a zircon structure. The vanadium atoms are tetrahedrally coordinated with oxygen atoms, while each yttrium ion is surrounded by eight oxygen atoms arranged in two groups of four equidistant atoms. The tripositive europium ion having the same valence as the yttrium ion has an ionic radius (1.13Å) comparable to that of of yttrium (1.06Å). This makes it possible to admix the oxides and fire at more than 1000°C to synthesize YVO_4 in such a manner that europium ions can be substituted for yttrium ions in the matrix. The phosphor usually contains 19 parts yttrium ions to 1 part europium ion, or about 5 atom-%. The light emitted from the cathodoluminescent spectrum of YVO_4:Eu is a narrow band peaking at 619 nanometers. Other host materials such as gadolinium, lanthanum, and lutetium may be substituted for yttrium in the orthovanadate to obtain relative emission intensities, and spectral output. A chemical blend of yttrium oxide and europium oxide has been reported to give a more orange-red emission and as yet has not found acceptance. Moreover, since it requires about twice as much yttrium and europium as the vanadate, it may be less attractive economically. The purities of europium, yttrium, and vanadium required in the phosphor preparations exceeds 99.9%. Most rare earth impurities in excess of 100 ppm appear to be deleterious, as are non-rare earths, such as calcium, uranium, thorium, zirconium, etc.

Consumption of europium and yttrium has increased in relation to the phenomenal growth of the color television industry. In 1964, the rare earth industry produced and sold approximately 1000 lb; in 1965, 8000 lb; and in 1966, 15,000 lb of Eu_2O_3. Production may reach as much as 25,000 lb in 1967, along with 250,000 lb of yttrium oxide. More than 95% of this amount will be sold to the television industry as a phosphor compound.

Principal producers of europium oxides are American Potash and Chemical Corporation, Goldschmidt, and Molybdenum Corporation. As early as 1955, europium oxide 99.9% sold for $2500/lb. The current price range (1967) is about $700 per pound and may well level off at some value between $500–700 per pound. At projected requirements, along with improved technology, there appear to be ample reserves to meet any future demands in electronic or nuclear applications.

Safety

The toxicity of europium is unknown. Care must be exercised in handling the metal due to its reactivity, particularly with respect to spontaneous ignition in finely divided form.

References

1. Eyring, L., Ed., "Progress in the Science and Technology of the Rare Earths," Vol. 1, New York, The MacMillan Co., 1964.
2. Gibson, J. A., and Harvey, G. S., "Properties of the Rare Earth Metals and Compounds," Technical Report AFML-TR-65-430, pp. 71, 185–203 (Battelle Memorial Institute), Air Force Materials Laboratory, Wright-Patterson Air Force Base, Ohio, 1966.
3. Kremers, H. E., in Hampel, C.A., Ed., "Rare Metals Handbook," Chapter 19, 2nd Edition, New York, Reinhold Publishing Corp., 1961.
4. Moeller, T., "The Chemistry of the Lanthanides," New York, Reinhold Publishing Corp., 1963.
5. Spedding, F. H., and Daane, A. H., "The Rare Earths," New York, John Wiley & Sons, Inc., 1961.
6. Topp, N. E., "The Chemistry of the Rare Earth Elements," New York, Elsevier Publishing Company, 1964.
7. Vickery, R. C., "The Chemistry of the Lanthanons," London, Academic Press, Inc., 1953.
8. Woyski, M. M., and Harris, R. E., in Kolthoff, I. M., and Elving, P. J., Eds., "Treatise on Analytical Chemistry," Part 2, Vol. 8, New York, Interscience Publishers, 1963.
9. Yost, D. M., Russell, H., and Garner, C. S., "The Rare Earth Elements and Their Compounds," New York, John Wiley & Sons, Inc., 1947.
10. Color-Television Phosphor-Screen Application Symposium, Electrochemical Society, 127th Meeting, San Francisco, May 9–13, 1965, *Electrochem. Tech.*, **4,** 3–42 (1966).

G. L. THOMPSON

F

FERMIUM

Fermium (element 100) is the eighth of the man-made transuranium elements, and the eleventh member of the actinide series. Its electron configuration is predicted as $5f^{12} 7s^2$, outside the radon core.

Element 100 was discovered at the same time as element 99 (einsteinium) in 1952, and its discovery is described in the article on **Einsteinium** (q.v.). It was named in honor of Enrico Fermi, in recognition of his outstanding contributions to nuclear physics, including the first controlled release of nuclear energy.

During 1953 and early 1954, while the discovery of elements 99 and 100 was withheld from publication, a group at the Nobel Institute for Physics in Stockholm bombarded uranium-238 with oxygen-16 ions, and isolated a 30-minute alpha emitter which they tentatively ascribed to 100^{250}, without claiming discovery of the element. This isotope has since been identified positively, and the 30-minute half life has been confirmed, although the true particle energy (7.43 MeV) is somewhat less than that reported by the Swedish group (7.7 MeV).

Isotopes of Fermium

Table 1 shows the known isotopes of fermium, their half-lives, decay properties, and methods of preparation (as of the end of 1966). The most readily available isotopes are 3-hour Fm^{254} and 20-hour Fm^{255}, which can be separated from heavy element samples after intense neutron irradiation. Einsteinium-253 is the best target material for this purpose. Since these isotopes of fermium are supported by longer lived einsteinium parents, 39-hour Es^{254} and 40-day Es^{255}, further fermium fractions can be separated from the irradiated

TABLE 1. ISOTOPES OF FERMIUM

Mass No.	Half-life	Modes of Decay	Preparation
244	4.5 s	α	
245	3.3 ms	SF	
246	1.6 s	α	
247†	35 s	α	$Pu^{239} + C^{12}$
247†	9.2 s	α	
248	0.6 min.	α	$Pu^{240} + C^{12}$
249	2.5 min.	α	$U^{238} + O^{16}$
250	30 min.	α	$Cf^{249} + \alpha$
251	7 h	EC, α	$Cf^{249} + \alpha$
252	25 h	α, SF	$Cf^{249-252} + \alpha$
253	3.0 d	EC, α	$Cf^{252} + \alpha$
254	3.24 h	α, SF	multiple neutron capture (reactor) $Cf^{252} + \alpha$
225	20.0 h	α, SF	multiple neutron capture (reactor or explosion).
256	2.7 h	SF, α	$\begin{cases} Fm^{255} + n \\ Md^{256} \text{ EC decay.} \end{cases}$
257	97 d	α, SF	multiple neutron capture (reactor or explosion). $Cf^{252} + HI$

†Fm^{247} apparently has two nuclear isomers, but it is not known which represents the metastable state.
EC = orbital electron capture, α = alpha decay, or helium ion as bombarding particle, SF = spontaneous fission and HI = heavy ion (B^{11}, C^{12}, C^{13}).

A more detailed tabulation is given on page 754 in the article **Transuranium Elements.**

material periodically. The short half-lives of these isotopes limit their use to the tracer scale. The 97-day isotope, Fm^{257}, would be much more useful for chemical studies, but it is only produced in very small yield in the highest neutron fluxes available. There seems little hope that it will become available in weighable quantities in the foreseeable future.

Spontaneous fission is a competing mode of decay in several fermium isotopes, particularly those of even mass number, and in Fm^{256} it becomes the major mode of decay. Recent attempts to observe Fm^{258} in reactor neutron irradiation, and in underground thermonuclear explosions, have failed, and it must be concluded that Fm^{258} has a very short half-life for spontaneous fission, probably less than 10 seconds. This severely limits the possibility of making elements above fermium by reactor neutron irradiation.

Chemical Properties of Fermium

Tracer-scale studies have shown that fermium has chemical properties typical of a heavy trivalent actinide element, very similar to those of californium and einsteinium. No oxidation state other than $3+$ has been observed.

References

1. Hyde, E. K., Perlman, I., and Seaborg, G. T., "Nuclear Properties of the Heavy Elements," Vol. II, "Detailed Radioactivity Properties," New York, Prentice-Hall, 1964.
2. Seaborg, G. T., "The Transuranium Elements," New Haven, Yale University Press, 1958.

JOHN MILSTED

FLUORINE

The considerable reactivity of the ninth element in the Periodic Table, fluorine, hindered its original preparation, makes its preparation and handling difficult even today, and yet confers on it uniquely interesting and valuable chemical properties. The history of the element dates back to the Eighteenth Century; Scheele prepared crude hydrofluoric acid in 1771 and named it "fluoric acid" (from the Latin "fluo," flow), and Davy in 1813 recognized that this compound contained a new element for which the name "fluorine" was suggested by Ampere. Numerous unsuccessful attempts to isolate the element were made first by Davy and then by Henri Moissan, culminating in 1886 with its successful preparation by the latter chemist. Moissan's method, still the only one practic-

able, involved the electrolysis of anhydrous hydrogen fluoride containing dissolved potassium fluoride. However, the corrosion of Moissan's apparatus, consisting of a platinum cell with platinum electrodes, was so severe that the weight loss of platinum exceeded the weight of fluorine produced! These problems were not overcome until 1939–45, when the need for large quantities of elementary fluorine as part of the atomic energy program led to it becoming a readily available chemical for industrial and research purposes.

Occurrence

In terms of abundance fluorine is not a scarce element. Although such estimates are often of dubious reliability, the usual orders place fluorine thirteenth in the list of elements, in order of relative abundance, so that it is more abundant than chlorine. Despite this and its wide distribution, fluorine does not commonly occur in deposits sufficiently rich for commercial development and only three minerals are of importance, namely, cryolite, $3NaF \cdot AlF_3$; fluorspar, CaF_2; and fluorapatite, $CaF_2 \cdot 3Ca_3(PO_4)_2$. Cryolite, or Greenland spar, is not a common mineral, and commercial deposits occur only in Greenland. Exports of the ore approximate 50,000 short tons annually, but the ore reserves were considered sufficient in 1953 for only 15–25 years operation. Cryolite has numerous industrial applications, the most important being in the aluminum industry, and it is now manufactured synthetically from fluorspar. Fluorspar is the most important fluorine mineral in commerce, and workable deposits are found in many countries with the United States, Mexico, U.S.S.R., China and Europe being principal producers. Annual world production is of the order of 2 million tons, with the world's reserves estimated at 75 million tons. The principal uses of fluorspar are in the steel industry, in the manufacture of hydrofluoric acid and cryolite, and in the ceramics industry. In contrast to the high fluorine content of fluorspar, fluorapatite has only 3.3–3.8% of fluorine. It occurs in massive form as phosphate rock deposits in the United States, the U.S.S.R., North Africa, and islands of the Pacific and West Indies. It is, of course, used principally by the phosphate fertilizer industry and at present it is not economically feasible to recover the fluorine by-products, chiefly fluosilicic acid and its salts, in any large amounts. As the reserves of fluorspar dwindle, greater amounts of fluorine will be recovered by the phosphate industry.

Preparation

The electrochemical method of Moissan is still the basis of all convenient preparations of fluorine, the electrolytes being solutions of potassium fluoride in anhydrous hydrogen fluoride. The potassium fluoride is necessary to make the solution electrically conducting since pure hydrogen fluoride is a non-conductor. The electrode processes can therefore be given as:

Anode: $F^- - e \rightarrow F$; $2F \rightarrow F_2$
Cathode: $H^+ + e \rightarrow H$; $2H \rightarrow H_2$

The hydrogen fluoride is therefore consumed, and must be occasionally replenished to maintain the electrolyte composition. Mixtures of various composition have been used over the past 70 years, but at the present time, all fluorine is produced using an electrolyte of approximate composition $KF \cdot 2HF$. The reasons are two-fold: (a) at this composition, the electrolyte has a melting point of about 70°C which does not vary greatly with minor composition changes, and (b) at this composition, the partial pressure of hydrogen fluoride over the electrolyte is very low, and therefore the concentration of HF in the fluorine and hydrogen produced is also low. The only other composition which meets this latter requirement is $KF \cdot HF$, but such an electrolyte has an inconveniently high melting point of ca 250°C.

In view of the highly corrosive nature of hydrogen fluoride, particularly at higher temperatures, it is not surprising that severe corrosion problems have been encountered throughout the development of fluorine technology, and that much developmental work has been done in the selection of suitable electrode materials and in the design of the cell. The arrangement of the components of a fluorine cell is described in detail in Ref. 3. The constructional material now used for most cell components is mild steel, with the cell body acting as cathode. The anode in modern commercial fluorine cells is un-graphitized carbon, and the skirt which divides the cell into anode (F_2) and cathode (H_2) compartments, is made of Monel metal. Such a laboratory cell would operate at 10–60 amps, producing 6–40 g of fluorine per hour. On the industrial scale, the fluorine cell has essentially the same features; thus, a 4–6 KA cell may be roughly 6 ft long by 3 ft wide and 2 ft, 6 in. deep, holds about 2000 lb of electrolyte, and be fitted with up to 24 carbon anodes. The fluorine produced electrolytically always contains 4–8% of hydrogen fluoride which can be removed by passage over dry sodium fluoride, resulting in the formation of the compound $NaF \cdot HF$. Fluorine of 99.5% purity can thus be readily obtained. Reliable estimates of the total production of fluorine are not available, but in the United States alone, it is certainly in excess of 1000 tons per year.

The use of laboratory-scale fluorine generators is not common in North America, with the availability of cylinders of the compressed gas, usually containing 6 lb of fluorine at 400 lb per square inch pressure. Although this avoids the dangers inherent in the operation of the electrolytic generator, considerable care must be exercised in handling the compressed gas. The cylinder must be securely fastened behind a suitable barricade, and opened by means of remote-controlled valves. The components of the high pressure side of the line should be of stainless steel nickel or Monel metal, and all parts must be thoroughly cleaned, degreased and dried. The equipment is then treated with increasing concentrations of fluorine gas, so that any impurities may be burned out without the simultaneous ignition of the metal equipment. The need for all operators to wear safety clothing, for there to be adequate ventilation, an alarm system, and readily available safety showers cannot be over-emphasized.

Despite the many dangers involved, fluorine in the liquid state is also transported in the United States over long distances in tonnage quantities. Containers have been developed which hold as much as $2\frac{1}{4}$ tons of liquid fluorine.

Physical Properties

The available data are presented in Table 1. At ordinary temperature and pressure, fluorine is a yellow gas, somewhat paler in color than

TABLE 1. PHYSICAL PROPERTIES

Atomic weight	18.9984
Isotopes	19
Melting point (°C)	−219.62
(°K)	53.54
Boiling point (°C)	−188.14
(°K)	85.02
Density, liquid at b.p.	1.108 g/cc
Density, gas, 0°C, 1 atm	1.696 g/l
Critical temperature (°K)	144
Critical pressure	808.5 psi
Heat of fusion at m.p.	372 cal/mole
Entropy of fusion, e.u.	6.75
Heat of vaporization at b.p.	1564 ± 3 cal/mole
Entropy of vaporization, e.u.	18.6
Heat capacity, liquid, 20.01°K, C_p	2.240 cal/mole/deg
Heat capacity, liquid, 20.01°K, C_v	2.203 cal/mole/deg
Thermal conductivity, gas, 0°C, 1 atm	5.92×10^{-5} cal/cm/deg/sec
Viscosity, gas, 0°C, 1 atm	0.0218 centipoise
Surface tension, 81.0°K	14.6 dynes/cm
Ionization potential	101.8 kcal/g-atom
Electron affinity	79.5 kcal/g-atom
Oxidation potential: $2F^- \rightleftharpoons F_2 + 2e$, E°	−2.87 v
Interatomic distance in molecule, Å	1.435
Dissociation energy	37.7 ± 0.2 kcal/mole
Nuclear spin	1/2

chlorine. It has a sharp, pungent odor which is very characteristic and is detectable in very low concentrations. Fluorine is highly toxic, but because it can be so readily detected, inhalation in seriously toxic quanties is unlikely. With a critical temperature of 144°K, fluorine is a "permanent gas." Among other data in Table 1 worth special comment is the very low dissociation energy of fluorine, 37.7 kcal/mole; this is very much less than the value of 58 kcal/mole for the dissociation energy of the chlorine molecule, and accounts in part for the high reactivity of fluorine. Fluorine is the most electronegative of all elements, this being reflected in its oxidation potential, and also in its electronegativity of 4.0, the highest value in the Pauling scale. The oxidation potential of −2.87v is a reflection of the dissociation energy (very small for fluorine), the energy liberated in the conversion of F to F⁻ (i.e., the electron affinity which is smaller than the value of 87 kcal/atom for chlorine), and the hydration energy of the F⁻ ion. This last term, equal to 122 kcal/mole, is appreciably larger than for other halide ions (for Cl⁻, the hydration energy is 89 kcal/mole).

Chemical Properties

The electronic configuration of fluorine is $1s^2 2s^2 2p^5$; with seven electrons in its outer electronic shell, the chemistry of fluorine is dominated by its tendency to complete the octet of electrons. This may be achieved either by formation of the fluoride ion, F⁻, or by participation in formation of a single electron pair bond. The oxidation state of fluorine is always −1.

Fluorine is the most powerful oxidizing agent known, and under suitable conditions reacts readily with most inorganic and organic substances. Although such reactions are usually highly exothermic, it is frequently necessary to supply an initial amount of energy in order to start the reaction (i.e., for many fluorination reactions, the activation energy is relatively high). Thus, the direct reaction of gaseous hydrogen and fluorine is very exothermic, liberating 64 kcal per mole of HF. However, reaction between equimolar quantities of the two gases usually requires initiation by raising the temperature, or by providing a suitable catalyst, such as water vapor, or even the walls of the reaction vessel.

All metals react with fluorine at sufficiently high temperatures. For many metals in the massive form at ordinary temperatures, protective fluoride coatings are rapidly formed which restrict further reaction. However, for reactive metals such as the alkali and alkaline earth metals, the fluoride coating offers no resistance to further fluorination and the reactions of such metals with fluorine are violent and highly exothermic. Even in cases where a protective fluoride coating is formed at ordinary temperatures, it may readily volatilize when the temperature is raised, allowing the massive metal to burn vigorously in the stream of fluorine. This is particularly true for metals such as uranium, tungsten, titanium, and vanadium. Other metals, of which copper, aluminum, and nickel are the best examples, form fluoride coatings of low volatility and hence offer greater resistance to fluorine. Fortunately, these are the principal construction materials, but even with these, sufficiently high temperatures will cause volatilization of the fluoride coating and ignition of the massive metal. As an illustration of both the reactivity of fluorine and of the problems inherent in the handling of high pressure fluorine, the effect of small traces of grease or other organic matter on the valve of a cylinder of compressed fluorine can be mentioned. Under ordinary temperature conditions, the metal of the valve and cylinder is covered with a protective fluoride coating. However, grease or other organic matter usually ignites spontaneously in contact with gaseous fluorine, and the heat of this reaction volatilizes the fluoride coating and can result in the disastrous ignition of the metal valve and cylinder in the escaping fluorine.

Most nonmetals such as boron, silicon, amorphous carbon, phosphorus, arsenic, sulfur and selenium inflame in fluorine. Bromine and iodine react readily although less violently at room temperature, and chlorine at 200°C. Oxygen and fluorine do not combine except in an electric discharge and nitrogen is also unreactive with fluorine.

Other than krypton, xenon and radon, the inert gases are unaffected by fluorine.

The reaction of fluorine with water is complex, giving hydrofluoric acid and oxygen as the principal products, with hydrogen peroxide, oxygen difluoride, OF_2, and ozone also being formed in varying but small amounts, according to the conditions. With an alkaline solution, (e.g., 2% aqueous sodium hydroxide), fluorine gives a good yield of oxygen difluoride. Provided hydrofluoric acid is absent, fluorine does not have any effect on glass at ordinary temperatures; borosilicate glass and quartz are virtually unaffected by several hours exposure to fluorine at 200–250°C, although soda glass is less resistant.

All organic compounds, except carbon tetrafluoride, react immediately with fluorine, with either inflammation or explosion unless precautions are taken. Many such reactions can be controlled to some extent, for example, by dilution of the fluorine with nitrogen. Fluorocarbons, C_nF_{2n+2}, containing C–C bonds which are still reactive to fluorine can thus be obtained, although thermodynamically, carbon tetrafluoride is the only carbon compound with any intrinsic stability with respect to fluorine.

Of the numerous methods devised for the analytical determination of fluorine, the majority require the initial conversion to, and separation of, the fluorine as fluosilicic acid, H_2SiF_6. The fluorine can then be detected by a variety of methods, including precipitation as calcium fluoride, lead chlorofluoride, or triphenyltin fluoride, or by titration with thorium nitrate. Colorimetric and electrical methods have also been described.

Elementary fluorine is not an important industrial chemical, particularly in terms of its total annual production. By far the greater part is used in the atomic energy field for the preparation of hexafluorides of uranium, neptunium and plutonium. The gaseous diffusion of uranium hexafluoride is the basis of one of the principal methods of separating the isotopes of uranium. In addition, the volatilities of the above hexafluorides are utilized in the recovery treatment of fuel elements from nuclear reactors. A limited amount of fluorine is being used as an oxidizer in rocket-fuel mixtures, and it is probable that this use will increase as the technical problems are solved. Fluorine is also used in the manufacture of sulfur hexafluoride, which is an efficient insulator in high-voltage apparatus, and of chlorine trifluoride, a powerful fluorinating agent.

Inorganic Fluorides

The most important inorganic fluoride is hydrogen fluoride, commonly encountered as its aqueous solution, hydrofluoric acid. The manufacture of hydrogen fluoride uses the greater part of the total world production of fluorspar. Concentrated sulfuric acid of preferably 99% strength is distilled with powdered, high-purity fluorspar in steel retorts at 200–350°C. Reactors 40 ft long and 6 ft in diameter, with a capacity of 6 tons of 80% hydrofluoric acid per day are successfully operated. After scrubbing to remove dust and sulfuric acid spray, the gas from the retort is condensed to give the crude acid. The purity can be improved by distillation although small samples of very pure hydrogen fluoride are best obtained by heating dry potassium hydrogen fluoride in a metal vessel.

Anhydrous hydrogen fluoride is a colorless, fuming liquid, with a melting point of $-83°C$ and a boiling point of $19.5°C$. Measurements of the density of the gas indicate the presence of polymers $(HF)_x$ with x dependent on the pressure. Electron diffraction studies of the vapor show it to contain zigzag polymers, probably up to H_5F_5. In the solid, the tetragonal unit cell contains infinite zigzag chains with the F-H-F distance equal to 2.7 Å.

Hydrogen fluoride is therefore very different from the other hydrogen halides which exist as monomeric units in both gaseous and solid states, and which have very much lower boiling points (e.g., HCl boils at $-85°C$). These differences are due to the hydrogen bonding in hydrogen fluoride resulting from the electrostatic interaction between hydrogen and the very electronegative fluorine atoms. Hydrogen fluoride has a dielectric constant of 83.6 at 0°C and behaves as an ionizing solvent with properties somewhat similar to water. It is miscible in all proportions with water in which it behaves as a weak acid, in contrast to hydrogen chloride. Concentrated aqueous solutions of hydrogen fluoride contain the HF_2^- ion as well as F^-.

The best known chemical property of hydrogen fluoride is its reaction with silica. This varies to some extent according to the form of the silica, fused quartz being attacked least readily. Anhydrous hydrogen fluoride produces silicon tetrafluoride from silica, while aqueous hydrofluoric acid gives fluosilicic acid, H_2SiF_6. Depending on the refractory nature of either the substance or the products of reaction and the temperature, hydrogen fluoride combines with or reacts with any substance that contains a negative element or group of elements other than fluorine. Thus, with oxides and hydroxides of metals, the reaction products are water and the metal fluorides. Hydrogen fluoride reacts vigorously with chlorides, bromides and iodides to liberate the hydrogen halides. In some cases the addition of a catalyst, frequently antimony pentachloride, is desirable. Hydrogen fluoride also reacts with all metals below hydrogen in the electrochemical series, except those that form insoluble protective fluoride coatings, such as aluminum and magnesium. With organic compounds, it acts as a fluorinating agent, a dehydrating agent, an excellent catalyst for condensation reactions, a polymerizing agent, and a hydrolysis catalyst. In many cases, use is made of the solubility of both organic and inorganic substances in hydrogen fluoride to give conducting solutions. Hydrogen fluoride is used extensively as a catalyst in the low-temperature alkylation of paraffin hydrocarbons to give highly-branched chain compounds for high-octane aviation fuel. Considerable quantities of hydrogen fluoride are used in the atomic energy program for the preparation of fluorine, and of uranium tetrafluoride. It is also used extensively to convert chlorinated organic compounds to chlorofluorocarbons.

Of the numerous inorganic compounds of fluorine, only a few of the more important can be mentioned here. In general, a distinction can be made between the nonvolatile inorganic fluorides and the volatile fluorides. The former class consists of the fluorides of metals in oxidation states up to (III) or perhaps (IV). Volatile fluorides are formed by most nonmetals, and by the metals in the higher oxidation states (e.g., (V) and (VI)). The nonvolatile fluorides can be classified structurally into two related subdivisions. (a) The first is based on ionic lattices containing F^- and M^{n+} ions. The alkali metal fluorides are typical examples. Because of the small size of the F^- ion (radius -1.36 Å), these salts have very high lattice energies and are characterized by considerable thermal stability and relative inertness. Other typical examples are the lower fluorides of many transition metals, e.g., FeF_2, NiF_2, CuF_2, etc. (b) The second is based on nonvolatile fluorides whose structures can be regarded as infinite, three-dimensional, fluorine-bridged polymers. Aluminum fluoride, AlF_3, is an excellent example. Each aluminum atom is octahedrally surrounded by six fluorine atoms and the total structure has very considerable stability. Fluorides such as TiF_4 and SnF_4 are other examples. The distinction between these two subdivisions is by no means a clear-cut one, but is nevertheless useful.

Typical of the volatile fluorides are boron trifluoride, silicon tetrafluoride, phosphorus pentafluoride, the halogen fluorides, and metal fluorides such as VF_5, WF_6, and UF_6. These are essentially covalent compounds, with low melting and boiling points, existing usually as discrete neutral molecules, or sometimes as covalent polymeric species. The central atom is always in a high, often the highest possible, oxidation state, and there is therefore only a small electronegativity difference between it and fluorine.

Of the methods available for the preparation of anhydrous inorganic fluorides, the most generally applicable involves the action of fluorine on an element or almost any of its compounds, occasionally at room temperature but more commonly at elevated temperatures. Such fluorinations yield higher or the highest fluorides, e.g., SF_6, PbF_4, AgF_2. Other common methods are: (a) the action of HF on a metallic oxide, hydroxide or carbonate, to give, for example, AgF or NH_4HF_2; (b) precipitation of an insoluble fluoride, e.g., CaF_2, PbF_2, or SmF_2; (c) reduction of a higher fluoride with hydrogen or organic matter to give a lower fluoride, e.g., TiF_3, or WF_4; and (d) methods involving the use of other fluorides as fluorinating agents, e.g., halogen fluorides used to prepare AuF_3, TlF_3 or UF_6.

Aluminum fluoride, AlF_3, and its related compound, Na_3AlF_6, are important nonvolatile fluorides. Aluminum fluoride is a white solid, which melts or sublimes above 1000°C, and which is unaffected by water. It is prepared by the reaction of either aqueous hydrofluoric acid or gaseous hydrogen fluoride with hydrated alumina. It is used to some extent in the ceramics industry, but Na_3Alf_6 is of much greater importance. This is prepared industrially, to supplement the limited natural supply of cryolite, by the reaction of aqueous hydrofluoric acid with hydrated alumina and alkali.

$$Al_2O_3 \cdot 3H_2O + 12HF + 6NaOH \rightarrow$$
$$2Na_3AlF_6 + 12H_2O$$

The molten Na_3AlF_6, containing dissolved aluminum oxide, is the electrolyte used in the production of aluminum metal.

Boron trifluoride is an important industrial catalyst for many organic reactions, and can be prepared by several methods. One process involves the treatment of boric acid with fluosulfonic acid, and others consist of the treatment of borax with hydrofluoric acid, or of boric acid with ammonium fluoride, followed by treatment with fuming sulfuric acid to liberate the boron trifluoride. It is a colorless gas, boiling at -100.3°C, which fumes in air due to rapid hydrolysis. Boron trifluoride forms numerous molecular complexes with organic compounds capable of donating a pair of electrons, e.g., ethers, alcohols, and organic acids. The BF_3 molecule can act as an electron-pair acceptor towards the F^- ion to give the tetrafluoroborate anion BF_4^-, derived from the parent acid, HBF_4. The acid is known only in aqueous solution but numerous tetrafluoroborates of metals are known as stable salts. Some, such as those of tin and lead, find industrial use in electrodeposition baths. Boron trifluoride is especially useful as a catalyst in the polymerization of olefins to oils, fuels, and high polymers, the polymerization of isobutene catalyzed by BF_3 having been extensively studied.

The fluorides of sulfur illustrate excellently the variety of reactivities found in fluorine chemistry. The hexaflouride, SF_6, the highest fluoride of sulfur, is the main product of fluorination of the element. It boils at -64°C, is odorless and nontoxic, and is extremely inert, being without action on water, fused caustic potash, and ignited copper oxide. Decomposition can be achieved with boiling sodium to give sodium sulfide and sodium fluoride, and with some red-hot metals. It is interesting that thermodynamic calculations show that SF_6 should undergo hydrolysis with water. The lack of such reaction indicates that the activation energy must be extremely high. Because of its chemical inertness, high dielectric strength and high molecular weight, it is used as a gaseous insulator in high-voltage generators and other electrical equipment. The most convenient preparation of sulfur tetrafluoride involves the reaction of SCl_2 with sodium fluoride in acetonitrile at 70–80°C. In contrast to the hexafluoride, sulfur tetrafluoride is very reactive although its fluorinating action is quite selective. It is a colorless toxic gas which condenses to a liquid boiling at −37°C. Sulfur tetrafluoride is now available commercially and is used in the preparation of partially fluorinated organic compounds. Lower fluorides of sulfur are represented by SF_2 and S_2F_2, whose existence has been questioned for many years. Recently, the preparation and high reactivity of S_2F_2 have been confirmed but there is still doubt as to the existence of SF_2. The change in behavior from SF_6 to S_2F_2 emphasizes one aspect of fluorine chemistry.

The halogens form a series of binary compounds with fluorine of which chlorine trifluoride and bromine trifluoride are the most important. Other well-characterized derivatives are ClF, BrF_5, IF_5, and IF_7. These halogen fluorides are all prepared by direct combination, the product obtained depending on the conditions used. Chlorine trifluoride, the only halogen fluoride of any industrial importance, is prepared from fluorine and chlorine at 300°C. The halogen fluorides are covalent substances, readily condensed to highly reactive liquids whose boiling points range from −100°C for ClF, to 12°C for ClF_3, to 125°C for BrF_3. Since all these compounds contain fluorine combined with a halogen in a high positive oxidation state, they are very powerful oxidizing and fluorinating agents, and are among the most reactive compounds known. Chlorine trifluoride is used in the production of uranium

hexafluoride and to a smaller extent in the fluorocarbon industry.

Organic Fluorides

A vast area of chemistry, closely related to "classical" organic chemistry, is being rapidly developed in the study of partially or fully fluorinated organic compounds. The enormous variety of types ranges from the fully fluorinated "perfluorocarbons," through partially fluorinated derivatives containing in addition to fluorine, other atoms such as hydrogen, chlorine, bromine and iodine also bonded to carbon, to derivatives containing functional groups and heterocyclic ring systems attached to fluorocarbon groups. The general chemistry is dominated by three factors: (a) the small size of flourine relative to other halogens introduces no steric factor when hydrogen in hydrocarbons is replaced by fluorine; on the other hand, the fluorine atoms more effectively shield the carbon skeleton from chemical attack; (b) the C-F bond has considerable strength, the bond energy being of the order of 105–115 kcal/mole, in comparison with 75–80 kcal/mole for the C-Cl bond; and (c) the high electronegativity influences the polarity of organic compounds.

The most noticeable general effect accompanying the replacement of hydrogen by fluorine is an increase in thermal and chemical stability.

The principal methods of preparation of fluorocarbon compounds include the use of alkali metal fluorides, antimony trifluoride or pentafluoride, or hydrogen fluoride, in reactions with chlorine-containing organic compounds. Alternatively, fluorinations of hydrocarbons are performed with reactive metal fluorides, particularly AgF_2 and CoF_3, or halogen fluorides, notably ClF_3. With the latter fluorinating agent, both chlorine and fluorine are usually introduced into the organic compound. The direct fluorination of organic compounds with elementary fluorine is usually a more difficult process to control than the above reactions, but suitable fluorinations in the vapor phase have been performed. The process of electrolytic fluorination, involving the electrolysis of a dilute solution of an appropriate compound in anhydrous hydrogen fluoride, is one of the very few methods of preparing highly fluorinated compounds containing functional groups.

Although numerous fully fluorinated organic compounds are known, only two or three are of any great importance as yet. Tetrafluoroethylene, $CF_2 = CF_2$, and perfluoropropene, $CF_3CF = CF_2$, are the starting materials for fluorinated polymers, and perfluorobenzene is the parent compound of the fully fluorinated aromatic compounds. Tetrafluoroethylene is made from the reaction of chloroform with hydrogen fluoride to give CF_2CClH, which on pyrolysis at 600–800°C gives $CF_2 = CF_2$. Polymerization to polytetrafluoroethylene, $(CF_2CF_2)_n$, occurs exothermally in the presence of a polymerization-initiating catalyst such as ammonium persulfate. Polytetrafluoroethylene, known commercially as "Teflon" in North America and as "Fluon" in Britain, is characterized by a very high softening point in excess of 300°C; there is no true melting point. Teflon is a white solid with a waxy feel, which has outstanding resistance to solvents and to chemical attack, very low water absorption, and excellent electrical insulating properties. Because of its low free surface energy, Teflon has an exceptionally low coefficient of friction. This combination of highly desirable properties, (chemical resistance, thermal stability, insulating properties, etc.) makes Teflon a very valuable polymer. It now finds use in the insulation of electric equipment, as gaskets and seals in many chemical process operations, in bearings and packings for sleeves in valves, and to some extent in packaging. The anti-stick property of Teflon has also become important; extensive use has been made of Telflon in coating frying pans, items used in handling bakery doughs, and many types of industrial rollers.

A very similar polymer is obtained from trifluorochloroethylene, $CF_2 = CFCl$, and additionally a polymer of tetrafluoroethylene and perfluoropropene is now marketed. The former does not have quite the same thermal and chemical inertness as polytetrafluoroethylene but is nevertheless a very valuable and highly stable polymer.

Partially fluorinated organic compounds, of which CF_2Cl_2, CF_3Cl and CF_3H are perhaps the best examples, are manufactured on a large scale for use as refrigerants, and as aerosol propellants. Such applications utilize the stability and chemical inertness, non-toxicity, and noninflammability of these compounds, which are at present the most important industrial organic compounds of fluorine. It is also worth noting that several organic fluorine compounds, such as $CF_3CClBrH$ and $CF_3CH_2OCH = CH_2$, possess valuable anesthetic properties and are finding increasing use.

Physiological Properties

Fluorine is a highly toxic gas, for which the recommended maximum allowable concentration for a daily 8 hour exposure is 0.1 ppm. It can in fact be detected by its smell in a concentration of 3 ppm, while an atmosphere containing 50 ppm is intolerable. The inhalation of high concentrations of fluorine would cause asphyxia and subsequently would result in severe lung congestion. High fluorine concentrations on the skin produce thermal-type burns, but at lower concentrations chemical-type burns result resembling those produced by hydrofluoric acid.

Hydrogen fluoride gas in a concentration of 40 ppm can cause severe toxic symptoms in 1 minute, while 2–3 ppm is considered to be the maximum concentration allowable for continuous exposure. For comparison, the corresponding figures for hydrogen cyanide are 40 ppm and 10 ppm, respectively. The vapor or the liquid (anhydrous or aqueous solution) vigorously attacks the skin, producing slowly healing sores. Inhalation of the vapor constricts the breathing, and causes coughing and irritation of the throat.

All inorganic fluorides which have an appreciable solubility in water are toxic when ingested in quite small amounts. Less than 1 gram of sodium fluoride constitutes a fatal dose. Somewhat smaller quantities taken over a prolonged period produce fluorosis. In extreme cases, symptoms include hypercalcification of bones, and a permanent stiffness of the spinal column, with joints becoming stiff and painful. An indication of a much milder excess of fluoride is mottling of the teeth, wherein affected teeth take on a characteristic brown stain, and with severe mottling may become pitted. The usual source of such small amounts of fluoride is drinking water, and it is now well-established that drinking waters must contain in excess of 2 ppm to produce even very mild mottling, and that severe mottling requires in excess of 12–14 ppm. It is also unambiguously established that maintenance of the fluoride content of drinking waters at 1 ppm causes a very substantial reduction in dental caries.

The question of the physiological properties of organic fluorides is a complex one, due to the great variety of structures possible. It is now known that saturated fluorocarbons are neither toxic nor narcotic. In contrast, monofluoroacetates are very toxic and the free monofluoroacetic acid is responsible for the high toxicity of a number of tropical plants. The monofluorophosphoric esters are "nerve gases," with the most potent compound being the di-isopropyl ester, $(iso\text{-}C_3H_7O)_2POF$. Among other classes of fluorinated organic compounds, the toxicity and physiological effects vary considerably and have attracted much study.

References

1. Simons, J. H., Editor, "Fluorine Chemistry," New York, Academic Press Inc., Vol. 1, 1950, and subsequent volumes.
2. Stacey, M., Tatlow, J. C., and Sharpe, A. G., Editors, "Advances in Fluorine Chemistry," London, Butterworths, Vol. 1, 1960, and subsequent volumes.
3. Rudge, A. J., "The Manufacture and Use of Fluorine and its Compounds," London, Oxford University Press, 1962.

HOWARD C. CLARK

FRANCIUM

Francium, the element with atomic number 87, is the heaviest member of the alkali family of elements. In its chemical properties francium most closely resembles cesium. Owing to its great nuclear instability, all its isotopes have very short half-lives for radioactive decay, and consequently all our knowledge of the chemical properties of this element comes from radiochemical techniques. No weighable quantity of the element can be prepared or isolated.

The element was discovered in 1939 by the Frenchwoman, Marguerite Perey, who established the presence of a 21-minute radioisotope with properties of a heavy alkali element among the decay products of actinium. Actinium, element 89, was isolated by Debierne in 1899 soon after the Curies' discovery of polonium and radium. Much later it was established that actinium is a member of the decay chain of the rare uranium isotope, U^{235}. Actinium decays chiefly by beta-emission to produce thorium of mass 227, but Mlle. Perey showed that actinium also undergoes α-decay in about one per cent of its radioactive decay events. By the laws of α transformation, this must produce an isotope of element 87 with mass number 223. (These genetic relationships are shown in Fig. 1.) Mlle. Perey isolated this product, determined its radiochemical and nuclear properties, and proved its genetic relationship to actinium. She chose the name actinium-K to accord with the system of nomenclature in use at that time for the natural radioactivities. She later proposed the name francium for the element. It is now known that 21-minute Fr^{223} is the only isotope of element 87 occurring in nature.

Nuclear properties of numerous other isotopes of francium which have been made by nuclear reactions of artificial transmutation are summarized in Table 1. The heavy elements, thorium or uranium, under bom-

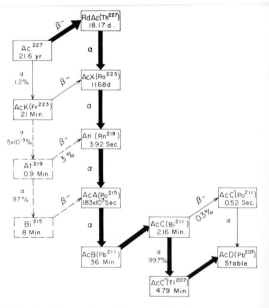

FIG. 1. Decay of actinium and its daughter products. The main decay path is shown in bold arrows. Actinium-K (Fr 223) is shown at the left.

bardment with protons of energy 100 MeV or higher undergo complex spallation reactions leading to the production of francium isotopes. The isotopes below mass number 215 can also be made by reactions induced in lighter target elements bombarded with complex nuclear projectiles such as accelerated ions of carbon, nitrogen, or neon. Such ions are available from cyclotrons or from specially designed linear accelerators. Some suitable target and projectile combinations are Pb + B, Tl + C, and Au + O. The complete fusion of target and projectile nuclei is the main first step in these nuclear reactions for bombardment energies of the order of 100 MeV and francium isotopes are the chief result of this nuclear fusion.

From a glance at Table 1, it is clear that no isotope of greater stability than actinium-K is known. Francium-212 has a half-life only slightly shorter and as a consequence this isotope has frequently been used as a tracer isotope in a study of the properties of the element. Isotopes not listed in the table are certain to be even more unstable. This great instability of francium can be understood in terms of systematic trends in nuclear binding. There is a periodicity in the properties of nuclei resulting from the quantum properties of nuclear binding, just as there is a periodicity in the characteristics of the chemical elements resulting from quantum properties of electron binding. In the nuclear case, the element lead is particularly stable because of a closed configuration of 82 protons and 126 neutrons. The extra neutrons and protons in elements beyond lead are not so tightly bound. This decrease in binding is reflected in an increase in the potential energy for α decay, the radioactive process in which a helium nucleus is spotaneously ejected from the nucleus. The probability for α-decay is very high for those few francium isotopes which would be stable or nearly stable toward other forms of radioactive decay. In the absence of α decay, francium would have the isotope 219 as its sole beta-stable isotope.

The radiochemistry of francium has been investigated with the following purposes in mind:

TABLE 1. ISOTOPES OF FRANCIUM

Isotope	Half-life	Type of Radioactive Decay	Energy of Radiation
Fr^{203}	0.7 sec	α	7.13 MeV
Fr^{204}	3.3 sec	α	6.97
Fr^{204} (isomer)	2.2 sec	α	7.03
Fr^{205}	3.7 sec	α	6.92
Fr^{206}	16 sec	α	6.79
Fr^{207}	15 sec	α	6.77
Fr^{208}	60 sec	α	6.65
Fr^{209}	52 sec	α	6.65
Fr^{210}	3.2 min	α	6.55
Fr^{211}	3.0 min	α	6.55
Fr^{212}	19 min	α	6.41 (21%) 6.38 (23%) 6.34 (12%) 6.26 (40%)
Fr^{213}	34 sec	α	6.77
Fr^{218}	0.005 sec	α	7.85
Fr^{219}	0.02 sec	α	7.30
Fr^{220}	27.5 sec	α	6.69
Fr^{221}	4.8 min	α	6.33 (84%) 6.12 (16%)
Fr^{222}	15 min	β^-	2.05
Fr^{223} (Ac-K)	21 min	β^- (99+%) α (0.005%)	1.15 5.34
Fr^{224}	~2 min	β^-	—

(1) The development of procedures for the separation of actinium-K (Fr^{223}) from actinium sources as a preliminary step to the investigation of the radiochemical or nuclear properties of this isotope.

(2) The quantitative removal of actinium-K from an actinium source followed by the quantitative measurement of the francium radioactivity as a method of assay of the strength of the actinium source. This application is of some importance owing to the difficulty of calibration of actinium sources by other methods.

(3) The development of procedures for the isolation of the element from bombarded targets, usually for the purpose of a study of nuclear radiations of particular isotopes.

(4) The study of the comparative properties of francium and the other alkali elements.

Research workers in laboratories without nuclear particle accelerators can obtain francium in only one way, namely, by having a supply of actinium which can serve as a "cow" for the continuous replenishment of the 21-minute isotope, Fr^{223}. A millicurie strength supply of actinium is necessary for most experiments. A consideration of Fig. 1 will show that an actinium source in equilibrium with all its daughter products is a complex mixture of radioactivities. Hence, a chemical procedure for the rapid isolation of francium must be based on a few highly specific chemical steps or on several steps which one-by-one eliminate the contaminants, the most troublesome of which is usually Tl^{207}. However, another approach can be used. If the actinium mother source is first radiochemically purified from its Th^{227} and Ra^{223} daughter products, it will be relatively free of those radioactivities for a period of days. The Fr^{223} daughter isotope on the other hand grows back to its equilibrium amount within a couple of hours. Since monovalent francium is easily separated from trivalent actinium, a single-step procedure can serve for the rapid isolation of a francium solution for experimental studies.

Chemical Properties

The chemical properties of francium are summarized in the following paragraphs.

Francium exists in aqueous solution as a large singly-charged ion with small tendency to form complex ions. Like other alkali elements, francium remains in solution when other elements are precipitated as hydroxides, carbonates, fluorides, sulfides, chromates, etc. This small tendency to coprecipitate makes it possible to devise a separation procedure in which all foreign cations or radioactive contaminants are removed by the successive precipitation of a series of insoluble scavenger precipitates, following which the radiations of francium are observed in the residual solution.

Francium will coprecipitate with certain insoluble salts. Notable among these are alkali perchlorates, iodates, chloroplatinates, cobaltinitrites, and salts of heteropoly acids such as cesium silicotungstate.

From many standpoints, one of the most useful compounds for the coprecipitation of francium is silicotungstic acid. This carrier is to be distinguished from its cesium salt. Silicotungstic acid forms an easily filterable precipitate in solutions saturated with hydrochloric acid and carries down with it any francium ions in solution. This coprecipitation is highly specific for francium and cesium. This carrier compound has the favorable property that it can be instantly dissolved in water. The francium can then be separated from the silicotungstic acid carrier by adsorbing it on a short column of cation exchange resin. After a water rinse of the columns, the francium can be desorbed immediately with concentrated hydrochloric acid.

Very few organic solvents immiscible with water are effective for the extraction of francium from aqueous solution, but there are some exceptions. One of the most effective is a benzene or nitrobenzene solution of the sodium salt of tetraphenyl boron. At a pH of nine, 99% of the francium can be extracted in a single contact.

Francium is readily adsorbed on synthetic cation exchange resins such as the sulfonic acid cation exchangers of the polystyrene-divinylbenzene and phenol-formaldehyde types. Adsorption occurs from neutral or slightly acidic solution. Desorption occurs at higher acid strengths. Control of acidity and other factors allows a clear separation of francium from most other elements. The alkali metal ions can be separated from each other by this technique, but the separation of cesium and francium is partial at best in the time limit set by the short francium lifetime. Inorganic cation exchangers such as zirconium molybdate, zirconium phosphate, zirconium phosphomolybdate, and similar materials, are highly specific adsorbants for the alkali elements compared to most other elements. Under controlled conditions they can also be used to separate the alkali elements from each other. Here again, however the separation of francium and cesium is difficult.

An ion-sieve effect in a synthetic ultramarine has been employed in one rapid procedure for the separation of Fr^{223} from an actinium source. Actinium-227 is strongly adsorbed by the ultramarine preparation and at any time that a new supply of Fr^{223} is required the equilibrium amount can be immediately eluted with a small amount of dilute NH_4Cl solution.

In the carrier-free condition, simple salts of francium are quite volatile at temperatures of a few hundred degrees Centigrade.

These chemical properties have been ex-ploited in the development of many extraction and purification procedures to accomplish the purposes mentioned above.

References

1. Perey, M., "Francium," Tome III, Nouveau Traite' de Chimie Minerale, Paris, Masson et Cie, 1957.
2. Hyde, E. K., "The Radiochemistry of Francium," National Academy of Sciences—National Research Council Report, NAS-NRC-3003 (1960) available from Superintendent of Documents, Washington, D.C., U.S.A.
3. Sedlet, J., "Francium," pp. 501–520 in Vol. 6, Part II of "Treatise on Analytical Chemistry," I. M. Kolthoff, P. J. Elving, E. B. Sandell, Eds., New York, Interscience Publishers, 1964.
4. Lavrukhina, A. K., Posdnyakov, A. A., and Rodin, S. S., "Chemical Properties of Francium," Pergamon Press, *International Journal of Applied Radiation and Isotopes*, **9**, 34–48 (1960).

EARL K. HYDE

G

GADOLINIUM

Gadolinium, atomic number 64, is one of the group of 15 elements having atomic numbers from 57 to 71, and known as the rare earth metals, or as lanthanons or lanthanides. (See **Lanthanide Elements**.) These fall in Group III of the Periodic Table and are characterized by the successive filling-in of the well-shielded, $4f$ electron shell while maintaining (ideally) the same $5d^1 6s^2$ outer electronic configuration in each element. Gadolinium has seven $4f$ electrons and the configuration $4f^7 5d^1 6s^2$. It thus occupies a position in the middle of the lanthanon series having a half-completed $4f$ shell. It exhibits only one valence state, $+3$, in contrast to adjacent members of the series, particularly samarium and europium preceding and terbium immediately following it. Certain properties of gadolinium show irregularities when compared to other lanthanons. For example, plots of the crystal radii of the trivalent lanthanon ions or the molecular volumes of trivalent lanthanon compounds as a function of atomic number show a "break" in the curve at gadolinium. This has been related to the high stability of its half-filled $4f$ shell. Another consequence of this structure is the ferromagnetism of gadolinium below about 16°C.

The discovery of gadolinium is generally credited to the Swiss chemist, Marignac, who isolated the element from Mosander's yttria in 1880. It was independently discovered in 1885 by Boisbaudran who isolated the element from Mosander's "didymia," a mixture of rare earths from which the cerium and lanthanum had been extracted. It was named in honor of the Swedish chemist, Gadolin. Elemental gadolinium is a metal resembling steel. It is active chemically as evidenced by its reaction with dilute acids to give the corresponding nitrates, chlorides, etc., and also by the fact that it will burn in air at about 150–200°C to form Gd_2O_3. Gadolinium compounds are colorless showing absorption bands only in the ultraviolet.

Gadolinium has 6 naturally occurring isotopes: 152, 154, 155, 156, 157, and 158 which have respective natural abundances of 0.2, 2.86, 15.61, 20.59, 16.42, and 23.45%. All are stable. The natural mixture has a thermal neutron absorption cross section of 46,000 barns, making it one of the strongest neutron absorbers known. This makes it useful for shielding nuclear reactors.

Occurrence and Extraction

The two most important ores from which rare earths are extracted are monazite and bastnasite. Monazite is a rare earth-thorium orthophosphate forming light brown to red monoclinic crystals having a specific gravity of 5.0–5.5 and a hardness of 5–5.5 on the Mohs scale. The mineral usually concentrates as a sand in beach placers in such countries as India, Brazil, Ceylon, Australia, and the southeastern United States. It also occurs in massive lodes, the largest of which is the van Rhynsdorp region of South Africa. Monazite contains 5–9% ThO_2 and thus is radioactive. Bastnasite is a rare earth fluocarbonate, but in contrast to monozite contains only about 0.1% thorium.

Both ores after beneficiation contain from 50 to 70% equivalent rare earth oxide of which the gadolinium as Gd_2O_3 is about 2–3% in monazite and about 0.2–0.5% in bastnasite. The ores generally are cracked by acid attack (H_2SO_4 or HCl) which converts the rare earth values to the soluble sulfates or chlorides. In the case of monazite a mixture of sand and sulfuric acid is heated to a temperature of from 120 to 170°C in cast iron pots fitted with cast iron covers and heavy anchor stirrers. The reaction is exothermic and the temperature rises to about 200 to 250°C. After reaction the mixture is added to cold water to dissolve the anhydrous rare earth sulfates. Thorium is then removed by addition of sodium pyrophosphate or by fractionally precipitating basic thorium salts. After thorium removal, the rare earths may be recovered by treatment with sodium hydroxide. If the rare earth hydroxide is dried, the cerium is oxidized to $Ce(OH)_4$ which then may be leached with hydrochloric or nitric acids to solubilize the rare earths other than cerium (didymium). Fractional crystallization of the didymium ammonium or magnesium nitrates may be used to separate lanthanum and the other components of didymium, but as the series is ascended recovery by this method becomes increasingly more difficult. However, gadolinium can be recovered by continued crystallization of the double magnesium nitrates. Commercially, crystallization is only used for obtaining concentrates containing the middle rare earths (Sm–Eu–Gd) which are then separated into their components by ion exchange methods.

Large samarium-gadolinium concentrates also are obtained by solvent extraction as a by-product of europium processing.

Derivation of Metal

Gadolinium metal may be prepared by a number of methods; however, there are two which are most widely used. For the preparation of relatively small amounts of very high-purity metal, calcium reduction of anhydrous gadolinium halides (usually $GdCl_3$ or GdF_3) is used. A mixture of pure $GdCl_3$ and Ca (excess) is heated in a tantalum crucible in an atmosphere of argon to a temperature of about 1450°C. After cooling, the brittle slag is broken away from the metal. The small amount of calcium impurity may be decreased by heating to 1400–1450°C under vacuum to volatilize the calcium. Large scale production is usually carried out by the electrolysis of fused $GdCl_3$ with NaCl or KCl in an iron pot which serves as the anode. Graphite cathodes are used and the pot is externally heated until

fusion begins. The temperature is kept above the melting point of the metal so that it collects at the bottom of the pot and can be removed easily. Another electrolysis method involves the use of fused $GdCl_3$ with a molten cadmium cathode. An alloy is formed from which cadmium is distilled.

Sponge metal can be prepared by contacting molten $GdCl_3$ with a reducing metal vapor at a temperature lower than the melting point of gadolinium. It can thus be vacuum melted in the presence of reducing compounds, such as carbon monoxide and carbon dioxide, and the oxides of many metals such as iron, manganese, vanadium, tantalum, silicon, boron, titanium, and others.

Physical Properties

Gadolinium metal resembles steel in appearance. At room temperature it crystallizes in the hexagonal close-packed form (α-Gd) having the respective lattice constants, $a_0 = 3.636$ Å and $c_0 = 5.782$ Å. The metallic radius is 1.802 Å and the density is 7.886 g/cc. On heating, α-Gd undergoes at 1262°C an allotropic transformation to β-Gd having a body-centered cubic structure. It melts at 1312°C

TABLE 1. PHYSICAL PROPERTIES OF GADOLINIUM

Symbol	Gd
Atomic number	64
Atomic weight	157.25
Density	7.886 g/cc
Melting point	1312°C
Heat of fusion	2.1 kcal/g-atom
Boiling point	3000°C
Heat of vaporization, 25°C	72 kcal/g-atom
Heat of sublimation, 25°C	81.22 kcal/g-atom
Vapor pressure,	$\text{Log } P_{mmHg} =$
1620–2097°K	$8.517 - \dfrac{19,600}{T}$
Specific heat, 25°C	8.8 cal/mole/°C
Heat of combustion	216.97 kcal/g-atom
Coefficient of linear thermal expansion	8.6×10^{-6}/°C (25–950°C)
Thermal conductivity, 28°C	0.021 cal/cm²/sec/ deg/cm
Electrical resistivity, 25°C	134.0 microhm-cm
Thermal neutron absorption cross section	46,000 barns
Modulus of elasticity	8.15×10^6 psi
Poisson's ratio	0.259

and boils at 3000°C. The heats of fusion and vaporization are 2.1 kcal/g-atom and 72 kcal/g-atom, respectively. Physical properties are listed in Table 1.

Chemical Properties

Gadolinium, as a result of its half-filled $4f$ shell, exhibits only one valence state, $3+$. The metal is an active reducing agent, decomposing the oxides of many metals including iron, manganese, chromium, silicon, tin, lead, and zirconium, as well as reducing carbon monoxide and carbon tetrachloride. The electrode potential for the reaction $Gd \rightarrow Gd^{3+} + 3e$ in aqueous solution is $+2.2$ volts. Gadolinium reacts vigorously with dilute acids, but is not appreciably attacked by strong bases, nor is it appreciably attacked by boiling water. It forms many compounds such as sulfides, nitrides, carbides, hydrides, and silicides by direct union with other elements, usually at high temperature. The metal burns above 200°C in halogen vapors and also in air at temperatures between 150–180°C if in a form such as sponge or powder exposing relatively large surface areas. In machining operations, hot chips have been known to ignite. The large heat of formation of Gd_2O_3 (217 kcal/mole) accelerates the reaction once combustion commences.

Analysis

The analysis of gadolinium is carried out by instrumental methods exclusively as there are no wet chemical methods suitable for analysis of gadolinium in the presence of other lanthanons. The two methods most commonly used are spectrographic and spectrophotometric. Other methods such as atomic absorption and neutron activation are also used in some instances, although the use is not yet as widespread. The spectrophotometric method involves the use of acid solutions such as the chloride, nitrate, or perchlorates. Gadolinium solutions show absorption bands only in the ultraviolet region, namely, a group of sharp bands in the 270–280 mμ region. Most of the other lanthanons also have minor bands in this region and make detection of gadolinium difficult. The presence of greater than 2–3% cerium necessitates its prior removal. The detection of other lanthanon impurities in gadolinium is easier, as most of them have

major bands in the region where gadolinium has none. This is especially true for the elements adjacent to gadolinium in the Periodic Table (Sm, Eu, Tb) which normally are the major impurities in ion exchange separations. The detection of individual lanthanons in gadolinium can be carried down to a level of 0.1% or less. The use of concentrated solutions can decrease the limit to 0.01% or less in certain cases. The method is very convenient for following the progress of an ion exchange separation.

The d-c arc spectrographic method is used widely for the determination of trace amounts of lanthanons in gadolinium or the presence of gadolinium in other individual lanthanons. The method can generally be depended upon for analysis of an element down to the range of 10 ppm and, in many cases, less. The lanthanons exhibit very complex spectrograms with many lines. When analyzing quite pure materials, this trouble is considerably reduced as lines free from interference are easier to detect. The following abbreviated table shows useful lines for the analysis of gadolinium in some lanthanons and vice versa.

Matrix	Impurity	Standard Line, Å	Analytical Line, Å	Range, %
Gd_2O_3	Y	3321.706	3327.875	0.032–1.0
	Nd	3391.705	4012.250	0.05–1.0
	Sm	3637.742	3634.271	0.004–1.0
	Eu	4437.45	4435.53	0.02–1.0
	Tb	3321.706	3324.40	0.021–1.0
La_2O_3	Gd	3397.71	3350.482	0.007–1.0
Sm_2O_3	Gd	3028.478	3027.61	0.013–1.0
Eu_2O_3	Gd	3012.380	3010.139	0.002–0.5
Tb_4O_7	Gd	3085.502	3100.508	0.022–1.0

X-ray fluorescence methods are also of value, in some cases being useful down to the range of 0.01–0.05% for impurities. This method is much quicker than the spectrographic method and is reasonably accurate within certain impurity ranges, but it is not as accurate as the spectrographic method for the detection of trace amounts.

Principal Compounds

The principal compounds of gadolinium are the oxide, hydrous oxide, oxalate, nitrate, chloride, fluoride, sulfate, carbonate, and sulfide. Many other compounds, such as the nitrides, hydrides, borides, selenides, phosphates, and a number of others, including complex compounds, are known and have been used in research or commercially. The classical methods of individual lanthanon concentration and purification utilized many different compounds such as double salts with ammonium, ammonium or magnesium nitrates, and the potassium or sodium sulfate, acetylacetonate, bromate, dimethyl phosphate, and the ethyl sulfate. These compounds are essentially no longer in use being superseded by ion exchange and solvent extraction in the separation of individual lanthanons.

The oxide, Gd_2O_3, is formed by calcination of such salts as the hydrous oxide, carbonate, oxalate, nitrate, and sulfate. The oxide is a very stable compound except for a slight tendency to absorb moisture and carbon dioxide from the air. It is a convenient compound to use for the preparation of many other salts by solid state reactions at elevated temperatures or by dissolving in acids. Gd_2O_3 is virtually insoluble in water ($K_{sp} = 1.8 \times 10^{-23}$).

Gadolinium oxalate, $Gd_2(C_2O_4)_3 \cdot 10H_2O$, is precipitated from aqueous salt solutions by the addition of oxalic acid or ammonium oxalate. It is used extensively as an intermediate for the production of purified gadolinium oxide and also in some analyses. The oxalate is virtually insoluble in water, less than 0.01 gpl at 25°C. The solubility in acids such as HCl increases somewhat, being about 0.94 gpl in 1.0 N HCl and about 1.9 gpl in 6.0 N HCl at 25°C. Thermal conversion of the oxalate to the oxide takes place through one or more carbonate intermediates at about 800°C.

Gadolinium carbonate, $Gd_2(CO_3)_3 \cdot 13H_2O$ can be prepared by precipitation from solution with alkali bicarbonate saturated with carbon dioxide or by hydrolysis of a solution of the trichloroacetate. The use of normal alkali carbonates forms a mixture of normal gadolinium carbonate and double and basic carbonates. Heating a slurry of the normal carbonate results in the loss of CO_2 with the resultant formation of basic gadolinium carbonate, $GdOHCO_3$. The carbonate is insoluble in water, but readily soluble in most acids. Thermal decomposition to the oxide is complete at about 800°C.

Gadolinium chloride, $GdCl_3 \cdot 6H_2O$, is conveniently formed by dissolving the oxide, hydrous oxide, or carbonate in HCl, followed by evaporation to a syrup and cooling. It is very soluble in water. The anhydrous chloride is prepared by heating the oxide or hydrous oxide with ammonium chloride and subliming the excess ammonium chloride or by reaction of the oxide with carbon and chlorine or carbon tetrachloride at elevated temperatures. Heating the hydrated chloride in air results in extensive formation of the insoluble oxychloride.

Gadolinium fluoride, $GdF_3 \cdot H_2O$, precipitates as a gelatinous precipitate when hydrofluoric acid or sodium fluoride is added to a gadolinium solution. It can also be prepared by reaction of HF with the oxalate, hydrous oxide, or carbonate. The fluoride is insoluble in water and acids. Dehydration is accomplished below 500°C in air with some formation of the oxyfluoride. The oxyfluoride formation is avoided by using an atmosphere of HF during dehydration.

Gadolinium hydrous oxide (hydroxide), $Gd(OH)_3$, forms as a gelatinous precipitate by the addition of alkali or ammonium hydroxide to a solution of a soluble gadolinium salt. The gelatinous nature can be avoided by reacting a salt such as the double sulfate, oxalate, or fluoride with an alkali hydroxide. The solubility in water is very low, being 1.6×10^{-6} moles/liter at 25°C. The oxide is formed by thermal decomposition at 350–400°C.

Gadolinium nitrate, $Gd(NO_3)_3 \cdot 6H_2O$, is prepared by dissolving the oxide, hydrous oxide, or carbonate in HNO_3 followed by evaporation to a syrup and cooling. It is very soluble in water and shows some solubility in alcohols, ketones, and esters. Its extractability in tributylphosphate is well known and is the basis of commercial solvent extraction processes for the separation of lanthanon mixtures. Before the advent of ion exchange and solvent extraction, fractional crystallization schemes using the double nitrates with ammonium or magnesium were common separation methods. The anhydrous nitrate can be prepared by reaction of the oxide with liquid nitrogen tetroxide at 150°C under pressure. The hydrates or anhydrous nitrates can be thermally decomposed to the oxide.

Gadolinium sulfate, $Gd_2(SO_4)_3 \cdot 8H_2O$, is

formed by dissolving the oxide, hydrous oxide, or carbonate in sulfuric acid and crystallized by evaporation or by the addition of sulfuric acid to a concentrated solution of the chloride or nitrate. The sulfate shows decreasing solubility in water with an increase in temperature. The solubility in water is approximately 2.33 g/100 g H_2O at 20°C and 1.77 g/100 g H_2O at 40°C. The addition of alkali or ammonium sulfate to a solution of a soluble gadolinium salt results in the precipitation of the double sulfate which is only slightly soluble in acids. Thermal decomposition of the sulfate to the oxide can be achieved at about 1000°C following the formation of intermediate basic sulfate salts.

Gadolinium sulfides, GdS_2 and Gd_2S_3, cannot be prepared by precipitation from solution with such agents as ammonium or alkali sulfides inasmuch as the hydrous oxide precipitates under these conditions. The sulfides are prepared by heating the oxide, carbonate, sulfate, or chloride with substances such as sulfur, carbon disulfide, hydrogen sulfide, and ammonium sulfides. The sulfides are water insoluble and decompose in acids with the liberation of hydrogen sulfide.

Importance and Uses

A number of uses for gadolinium have been found ; however, because of its relative scarcity and high cost, the uses have not been of the magnitude of those related to such lanthanons as lanthanum and cerium. These factors, however, are not necessarily a deterrent to future expanded markets when the recent large scale use developed for the even more scarce and costlier europium in phosphors for color television is considered.

The use of gadolinium as shielding in nuclear applications due to its high thermal neutron absorption cross section, 46,000 barns, has been mentioned. Unfortunately, it has a very fast burnout rate due to the fact that it has only two absorbing isotopes which are present in low concentrations. Therefore, its use is limited as a control rod material. In contrast, the use of europium, although about five times as expensive as gadolinium, is suitable under high flux conditions because of its chain of five absorbing isotopes in high concentration.

The largest single use of gadolinium is as a partial substitute for yttrium in yttrium-iron garnets where it stabilizes the characteristics of the garnet with respect to temperature. These are used in microwave filters where their high efficiency in filtering out "noise" allows detection of signals at very low intensity levels. Another use which has already been developed to the commercial stage is in thermoelectric generating devices employing gadolinium selenide. Gadolinium has shown to be useful as an activator in a number of phosphors. Also, a solid solution of neodymium and gadolinium oxides has exhibited properties useful as a thermionic emitter. A number of catalytic uses such as the polymerization of ethylene, the decarboxylation of oxaloacetic acid, and the conversion of orthohydrogen to parahydrogen have been reported.

In the field of nonferrous alloys, gadolinium has been effective for the deoxidation of molten titanium. However, the cost has prevented large scale use.

The capacity of the industry for producing gadolinium far exceeds the demand. Estimated annual production by the industry of gadolinium metal is 200 lb. The cost of 99% metal is approximately $300/lb. The production of all gadolinium salts, based on the oxide, is estimated to be 8000 lb/yr. The costs of 99% and 99.9% grades of gadolinium oxide are about $80 and $90/lb respectively.

Safety

The toxicity of gadolinium is unknown. Some care must be exercised in machining the metal to prevent hot chips from igniting.

References

1. Eyring, L., Ed., "Progress in the Science and Technology of the Rare Earths," Vol. 1, New York, The Macmillan Co., 1964.
2. Gibson, J. A., and Harvey, G. S., "Properties of the Rare Earth Metals and Compounds," Technical Report AFML-TR-65-430, p. 71, 185–203, (Battelle Memorial Institute), Air Force Materials Laboratory, Wright-Patterson Air Force Base, Ohio, 1966.
3. Kremers, H. E., in Hampel, C. A., Ed., "Rare Metals Handbook," Chapter 19, 2nd Edition, New York, Reinhold Publishing Corp., 1961.

4. Moeller, T., "The Chemistry of the Lanthanides," New York, Reinhold Publishing Corp., 1963.
5. Spedding, F. H., and Daane, A. H., "The Rare Earths," New York, John Wiley & Sons, Inc., 1961.
6. Topp, N. E., "The Chemistry of the Rare Earth Elements," New York, Elsevier Publishing Company, 1964.
7. Vickery, R. C., "The Chemistry of the Lanthanons," London, Academic Press, Inc., 1953.
8. Woyski, M. M., and Harris, R. E., in Kolthoff and Elving, Eds., "Treatise on Analytical Chemistry," Part 2, Vol. 8, New York, Interscience Publishers, 1963.
9. Yost, D. M., Russell, H., and Garner, C. S., "The Rare Earth Elements and Their Compounds," New York, John Wiley & Sons, Inc., 1947.

N. J. GOETZINGER

GALLIUM

Discovery and Occurrence

Gallium was discovered in 1875 by the French chemist, Lecoq de Boisbaudran. Spectroscopic examination of concentrates from a Pyrenean zinc blende revealed emission lines whose positions corresponded to those predicted for "eka-aluminum," a missing element between aluminum and indium in Mendeléev's periodic scheme of the elements. Boisbaudran subsequently prepared this new element by electrolysis of caustic solutions and observed some of its properties. He named it gallium from the Latin *Gallia* in honor of his fatherland.

A close analog of aluminum, gallium is widespread in the earth's crust. It occurs almost entirely as the hydrated oxide in reconstituted minerals and comprises a rather constant proportion of all aluminum-bearing ores. In zinc and germanium ores gallium may occur as the sulfide. Its most concentrated deposits (0.5–1%) have been found with South African germanite.

Gallium has been found concentrated up to 1% in flue dust as a result of the volatility of gallium suboxide that forms by reduction of the sesquioxide by carbonaceous matter. It has also been reported in concentrations up to 0.5% in coal ash, although its occurrence in such material is spotty. Gallium is not present in significant amounts in the sea or other natural waters because of the very low solubility of the oxide at near neutral pH.

Production

There are no minerals sufficiently rich in gallium to be processed economically for the gallium alone. Consequently, commercial production is always carried out in conjunction with some other refining operation. Although there was some early processing of South African germanite for both germanium and gallium, this source has been exhausted and gallium is presently produced as a by-product of the aluminum and zinc industries. It occurs in a fairly constant proportion of 0.005 to 0.01% in both monohydrate and trihydrate bauxite deposits all over the world. Occurrence with zinc appears to be limited to the Missouri-Oklahoma-Kansas area of the United States, where it occurs to the extent of about 0.005%.

In aluminous minerals gallium occurs as the hydrated oxide incorporated in bauxite, clay, laterite, etc. In all phases of the commercial Bayer process for refining of aluminum oxide for use in the production of aluminum the gallium undergoes the same reactions as the aluminum. In that process the ore is digested with hot caustic solution to extract most of the aluminum as sodium aluminate. The gallium accompanies the aluminum into solution as sodium gallate. When this liquor is cooled and seeded, much of the aluminum and a little of the gallium co-precipitate. Since the gallium is somewhat more acidic, however, it concentrates in the supernatant liquor. Unless it is removed it will build up to such a concentration that, by mass action considerations, it begins to go into the precipitated alumia at the same rate as it is replenished from the fresh ore. The maximum concentration that is achieved in the liquor depends on operating parameters of the particular plant, as well as on the source of the bauxite. In the best case it is still less than 0.2 gram per liter of solution.

Various methods have been employed to obtain the gallium values from Bayer liquor. The concentration is too low for the metal to be recovered in pure form immediately by electrolysis, since the re-solution rate in the electrolyte is faster than the deposition rate. A method employed in France to get around this problem was to electrolyze the gallium into an agitated mercury cathode from which it could be recovered subsequently by a caustic digest and re-electrolyzed in a pure state.

The character of domestic bauxites precludes the use of the mercury process in the United States. A more common practice is to concentrate the gallium in the liquor to the point where electrolytic recovery is possible. Hudson[1] describes two processes for doing this. Both involve precipitation of the major part of the remaining aluminum; in the first, as calcium aluminate by the addition of lime, and in the second, as alumina hydrate by careful neutralization with carbon dioxide. Concentrates containing 1 gram per liter of gallium that result from these processes can be electrolyzed economically. Generally, a stainless steel cell is used, with stainless steel anodes and cathodes.

Thompson[2] describes one method of obtaining gallium from zinc ores. For the production of zinc this sulfide ore is air roast-ed to convert it to oxide which is then leached with sulfuric acid to form zinc sulfate solution. In purifying this solution for subsequent zinc recovery the excess acid is carefully neutralized to precipitate iron and aluminum. This "iron mud" also contains most of the gallium, amounting to about 0.07%. The gallium and much of the aluminum are extracted from the filter cake with caustic. This solution is again neutralized to precipitate the gallium and aluminum hydrated oxides. One more extraction is performed, this time with hydrochloric acid to dissolve the gallium and some of the aluminum. The acidic solution is extracted with ether to separate the gallium chloride. The extract is treated with caustic to precipitate remaining traces of iron, then the resulting alkaline solution is electrolyzed for recovery of the gallium.

Physical Properties

Some of the physical properties of gallium are given in the following table:

As a solid, gallium strongly resembles zinc, showing a bluish luster and a semibrittle

TABLE 1. PHYSICAL PROPERTIES

Symbol	Ga
Atomic weight	69.72 (60.2% Ga-69; 39.8% Ga-71)
Crystal structure	pseudotetragonal
	($a = 4.5167$, $b = 4.5107$, $c = 7.6448$)
Specific gravity, 29.6° (solid)	5.904
29.8° (liquid)	6.095
Surface tension, 30°	735 dynes/cm
Viscosity, 100°	1.60 centipoises
500°	0.81
1000°	0.59
Melting point	29.78°C
Latent heat of fusion	19.16 cal/g
Boiling point	2403°C
Latent heat of vaporization	1014 cal/g
Vapor pressure, 900°C	0.0001 mm
1000	0.0008
1100	0.0059
1200	0.0309
1500	1.41
Specific heat, 29–127°C	0.0977 cal/g/°C
Coefficient of linear thermal expansion (average)	1.8×10^{-5}
Thermal conductivity, 30°C	0.08 cal/sec/cm/°C
Electrical resistivity (solid) a axis	17.5 microhm-cm
b „	8.20
c „	55.3

fracture. The liquid metal, when free of oxide, is almost indistinguishable in appearance from mercury. However, the surface film that forms immediately on contact with air prevents it from coalescing. This rapid oxidation limits the number of applications that could be envisioned for a metal that is liquid near room temperature. The adherence of this oxide to most surfaces gives the appearance of wetting. Oxide-free gallium does not wet any surface, however, until the actual onset of alloying or chemical reaction with the surface.

Gallium has a very unusual crystal structure. It is pseudotetragonal, with a very open lattice. The average nearest neighbor distance in the solid is greater than that in the liquid, and the metal expands more than 3% on freezing. Bismuth is the only other element that exhibits this property. The anisotropy of both the electrical conductivity (see Table 1) and the thermal conductivity is greater for gallium than for any other metal.

Gallium can be maintained liquid indefinitely at temperatures considerably below its normal freezing point. Occasionally, it can be held at liquid nitrogen temperature ($77°K$) for short periods without freezing. The unusual crystal structure of gallium is perhaps responsible for the inability of dust particles, oxide, container walls, etc., to nucleate crystallization of this super-cooled liquid, since nucleation requires some conformity between the structure of the nucleus and the crystal. Speculation in the early literature that the supercooling behavior of gallium is related to the purity of the material has not been verified.

Chemical Properties

To a large extent gallium's chemical properties are as expected from its position in Group IIIA of the Periodic Table. It is normally trivalent. It forms stable compounds with the halides and chalcogenides, and with phosphorus, arsenic, and antimony in Group VA. It dissolves in, but does not react with, bismuth. A nitride, GaN, can be prepared but it is unstable at high temperatures.

The gallium halides can be prepared by direct reaction of the elements but, because of the vigor of these reactions, preparation from the corresponding hydrogen halides is preferred. Gallium fluoride can be prepared by evaporation and dehydration of aqueous gallium fluoride solutions. The other halides require nonaqueous synthesis.

Gallium phosphide, arsenide and antimonide are very interesting semiconductor compounds whose methods of preparation is dictated more by requirements of purity and crystal perfection peculiar to semiconductor technology than by simplicity, economy, etc. These materials will be discussed in another section.

Gallium forms a stable oxide and all of the other chalcogenides and the halides, with the exception of the fluoride, hydrolyze in water to form a hydrated gallium oxide. In the case of the halides this reaction is extremely vigorous. The reaction rate of the chalcogenides with water decreases from the sulfide to the telluride. The latter is attacked only superficially in hot water.

Gallium sesquioxide is the most common gallium compound. It precipitates in a hydrated form during neutralization of either acidic or basic solutions. The only crystalline oxide hydrate is the monohydrate, $Ga_2O_3 \cdot H_2O$. In this respect gallium differs from aluminum, which forms both mono- and trihydrates. "Gallium hydroxide," which would be equivalent to $Ga_2O_3 \cdot 3H_2O$, is therefore a misnomer, but it is found in the literature.

Calcination of gallium monohydrate to high temperatures yields beta-Ga_2O_3. This oxide is isomorphous with theta-alumina. The corundum analog of Ga_2O_3, alpha-gallia, is a metastable phase that is passed through on calcination to the high-temperature stable form.

An interesting behavior of gallium is the ease with which it forms the relatively volatile suboxide, Ga_2O. This compound forms by reduction of the trivalent oxide by any of a variety of reducing agents. Gallium becomes clean in appearance and coalesces readily when heated above red heat in vacuum because of the reduction of the oxide skin to volatile suboxide by the underlying metal. Erroneous weights can result during a conventional gravimetric determination of gallium as the oxide because of reduction of the product by carbonaceous filter paper residue and attendant loss of the volatile suboxide.

Gallium also forms lower valent halides. The monohalides such as GaCl, can exist in the vapor state. However, there is considerable doubt that they can exist as condensed phases. The dichloride, $GaCl_2$, is a stable liquid or solid (m.p. 170°C) in the absence of oxidizing agents. The other dihalides probably exist but little is known about them.

Most of the other chemical properties of gallium are very similar to those of aluminum. An important exception is the absence of a carbide. Gallium atoms are too large compared to carbon for stability of a salt-like carbide analog of Al_3C_3. There are also differences in stability of the corresponding gallium and aluminum fluoride coordination compounds. Screening of the nucleus by the large electron cloud reduces the stability of the gallium analog of cryolite, Na_3GaF_6, in favor of the four-fold coordinated compound, $NaGaF_4$.

High-purity gallium is attacked only slowly by individual mineral acids. It dissolves in aqua regia or caustic and in concentrated $HCl-H_2O_2$ mixtures. Reaction with the milder reagents is facilitated by having it in contact with a more noble metal, such as a platinum wire or crucible, to promote electrolytic dissolution.

An important difference between the chemistry of gallium and that of the other elements with which it usually occurs is the high solubility of gallium chloride in organic ethers. The partition of $GaCl_3$ between ether and strongly acidic aqueous solutions so strongly favors the ether that separation is almost quantitative. (After three successive extractions with equal volumes of isopropyl ether, only one part in a billion of the gallium remains in the aqueous layer.) Of the few other elements that transfer substantially to the ether, i.e., antimony, arsenic, gold, and iron, only iron normally occurs with gallium and this can be retained in the aqueous layer by reducing it to the ferrous state.

Ether extraction is employed in many laboratory separations of gallium and in some processes for its commercial production.

Purification of Gallium

Almost all current uses of gallium require material of extreme purity and a substantial part of the cost of producing gallium is in the purification of the crude primary metal. The impurities found dissolved in primary gallium are principally those metals that are more noble than gallium and plate out with it in the electrolytic cell. Because of the high hydrogen overvoltage on gallium, however, some aluminum and possibly some sodium, which are present to a very large excess in the electrolyte, are also deposited with it even though they normally would not plate out of aqueous solutions.

The impurities in primary gallium can be grouped into three categories, depending on the method of their removal: (1) those that are retained mechanically in the dross, (2) those that can be removed by extraction with acid, and (3) those removed by fractional crystallization.

Considerable dross forms on the surface of primary gallium and on the cathode. It contains iron and similar elements that plate out of aqueous solutions but have very low solubility in the gallium, as well as reaction products from attack of the gallium or electrolyte on the cathode itself. There can be organic matter in this dross as well, particularly if bauxite was the source of feed. This is probably the result of electromigration of charged organic colloids to the electrodes. Dross is generally separated by hand, dissolved in caustic, and the solution reelectrolyzed.

The principal impurities removed by acid extraction are zinc and iron. The purity of intermediate grades of gallium is largely determined by their zinc content. Since the solubility of iron in gallium is extremely low at room temperature it is present chiefly as particulate matter that was not separated mechanically.

Fractional crystallization is universally employed to upgrade the purity of gallium after acid cleaning. Practices by different gallium producers differ in the manner in which crystallization is nucleated, the size of the crystals that are produced, fraction of metal frozen per crystallization, number of crystallizations, recycling schedule of the liquid, etc. No peritectic impurities have been observed in gallium; hence, there is no benefit from rejecting the first fraction to freeze. Silver, lead, copper, gold, and zinc concentrate strongly in the last portion to freeze.

Probably, elements that do not show a pronounced tendency to segregate during freezing, such as iron, aluminum, magnesium, silicon, and calcium, have migrated to exposed surfaces where they were oxidized and became incorporated in the oxide skin, or they were not truly dissolved in the gallium.

Gallium of 99.9999% purity is being produced in the United States and abroad. The residual impurities are not positively identified. Spectroscopic analysis shows only traces of aluminum, silicon, magnesium, iron and calcium, but it has not been convincingly demonstrated that these are present in the gallium and do not come from the background during analysis.

Handling Gallium Metal

Because of the high cost of refining gallium the applications that have evolved employ only small amounts of material—typically grams rather than pounds. Practices have been developed for manipulating these small quantities, bearing in mind that in most cases contamination must be avoided.

The low melting point of gallium precludes sawing by conventional techniques because it melts back away from the saw and a ragged cut results. Spark cutting and string sawing are generally unsuccessful since the molten metal fills in behind the electrode or string and solidifies. Fig. 1 illustrates a means by which solid gallium can be cut easily without contamination. The cutting wheel of a commercial abrasive, glass cut-off saw is replaced by a thin "Teflon" disc. This disc melts its way through the solid gallium from the heat of friction to give a smooth, clean "cut." The bar pictured was cut in a matter of seconds.

Gallium is most easily transferred in the molten state. The only contamination encountered in this operation is the formation of a thin oxide skin. It is easier to remove this skin by pouring the liquid out from under it than to try to prevent its formation by working in an inert atmosphere.

Because of the strong tendency for gallium to supercool below its normal freezing point it must be "seeded" with a solid crystal to initiate solidification. This is accomplished by simply touching the surface of the supercooled liquid with a point of the crystal. Fig. 2 shows a large single crystal that was grown from a supercooled melt with the use of a starting seed.

Since gallium is perhaps the purest metal that can be obtained commercially there has been considerable interest in determining some of its fundamental properties when in a monocrystalline, strain-free form. Fig. 3 illustrates a means of growing a single crystal

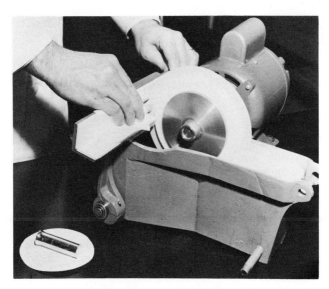

FIG. 1. Sectioning a gallium crystal with a teflon "saw."
(Courtesy Aluminum Company of America)

FIG. 2. Single crystal of gallium grown from a starting seed.
(Courtesy Aluminum Company of America)

of gallium with smooth faces oriented along any desired crystallographic axis. The mold is of machined lucite. Both arms and the communicating passage between are filled with liquid gallium, then the entire assembly is immersed in a constant temperature bath held at a few tenths of a degree below the normal freezing point. A small seed crystal, appropriately oriented, is brought into contact with the gallium surface through a thin layer of dilute hydrochloric acid to remove the oxide film. Solidification is thus initiated and the crystallographic orientation of the seed is maintained as the solid-liquid interface proceeds down one side, across the bottom, and up the other side of the mold. Fig. 3 also shows an oriented single crystal that was grown in this manner.

Uses of Gallium

When gallium first became available, it appeared that its chemistry was uninteresting and that there were few applications of its compounds where cheaper materials would not serve as well. In the metallic form, on the other hand, gallium seemed to offer properties not found in any other material. It is relatively inert, nontoxic, and with a melting point only slightly above room temperature and a boiling point of 2403°C it has one of the widest liquid ranges of any metal. It is not surprising,

therefore, that the first uses that were envisioned for this unusual element exploited these properties. There were half-serious attempts to use it as the thermometric fluid in high-temperature thermometers of otherwise conventional design. It was considered as a liquid sealant in high-vacuum systems, as a heat-transfer medium in high-temperature engines, such as nuclear reactors, and as a component of dental alloys. Either because of cost considerations or unrealistic demands on the material none of these applications became commercial.

It is somewhat paradoxical that the rather substantial uses of gallium that eventually evolved were based not on the unique physical properties of the metal but on the specific chemistry of some of its compounds. The first significant use of gallium, and in fact the application that justified the first commercial production, was in the spectroscopic analysis of uranium oxide in conjunction with operations of the Atomic Energy Commission. Gallium oxide is added together with graphite to the powdered sample and, in the high temperature of the arc, the vigorous evolution of the volatile gallium suboxide that is formed carries impurities into the vapor and greatly enhances the sensitivity of their detection.

The application of gallium that has received the most attention, and possibly promises the

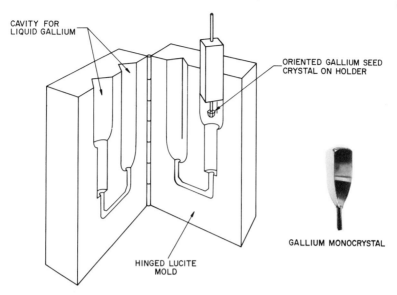

CAVITY FOR LIQUID GALLIUM

ORIENTED GALLIUM SEED CRYSTAL ON HOLDER

GALLIUM MONOCRYSTAL

HINGED LUCITE MOLD

FIG. 3. Apparatus for growing an oriented monocrystal of gallium.
(Courtesy IBM Corporation)

largest market, is in the production of semiconducting compounds. For many years this technology was dominated by the elemental semiconductors, silicon and germanium. In 1952, German workers reported the achievement of semiconduction in compounds between elements in Group III and Group V of the Periodic Table, bordering the Group IV semiconductors. Of these, compounds of gallium with antimony, arsenic or phosphorus are the most important. The characteristic semiconductor behavior exhibited by gallium antimonide and gallium arsenide is being utilized in various electronic devices to perform functions that were previously in the domain of silicon, germanium, or conventional vacuum tubes. Among these are voltage rectification and amplification, and magnetic field and temperature sensing. New phenomena are observed in some of the gallium compound semiconductors that had no counterpart in the elemental semiconductors or conventional devices. Among these are semiconductor "lasing" and microwave generation in gallium arsenide and electroluminescent light emission in gallium arsenide (infrared) and gallium phosphide (visible.)

Recent reports indicate that gallium compounds such as magnesium gallate, $MgGa_2O_4$, containing divalent impurities such as Mn^{+2}, will find a place among the growing list of commercial ultraviolet activated powder phosphors.

For some years to come the uses of gallium will probably be restricted to these and similar applications where the importance of some specific phenomenon justifies the relatively high cost of the material.

References

1. Hudson, L. K., *J. Metals*, **17**, 948–51 (1965).
2. Thompson, A. P., "Rare Metals Handbook," Clifford A. Hampel, Editor, 2nd Ed., pp. 178–187, New York, Reinhold Publishing Corp., 1961.

L. M. FOSTER

GERMANIUM

In his report on "The Periodic Law of the Chemical Elements," Mendeleev predicted the existence of several unknown elements. Among them was one which was supposed to be just below silicon and for that reason he called it eka-silicon. In 1886 Winkler discovered this missing element in the mineral argyrodite and called it germanium.

Occurrence

Estimates of the abundance of germanium in the earth's crust range from 10^{-11} to 10^{-3} weight %. Accordingly it is considered to be a rare element. Among the known minerals of importance are argyrodite, $4Ag_2S \cdot GeS_2$; germanite, $7CuS.FeS.GeS_2$; canfieldite, $4Ag_2S.$ $(Sn,Ge)S_2$; and réniérite, $(Cu,Ge,Fe,Zn,As)S$. Of these only the germanite deposits in Tsumeb (southwest Africa) and the réniérite deposits of Katanga (Congo) which contain from 5 to 8% Ge are of major industrial significance. Trace amounts of germanium, up to 0.3% are reported in many sulfide and oxide minerals and coal. It is commercially extracted from zinc blende ores in the United States and from coal ash in England.

Recovery

The first step in extracting germanium from germanite and réniérite is the treatment of the powdered mineral with a mixture of HNO_3 and H_2SO_4. After evaporation of the excess acid the residue is treated with HCl whereupon $GeCl_4$ is distilled away in a stream of Cl_2. In an alternate method the mineral is treated with a concentrated sodium hydroxide solution; the mixture is then heated to dryness and the formed thiogermanate is extracted with hot water. After purification of the water solution GeO_2 is precipitated by neutralization with ammonia. The oxide is dissolved in HCl and then $GeCl_4$ is separated by distillation.

In the United States germanium is recovered as a by-product from zinc blende ores (Kansas-Missouri-Oklahoma). The ore is concentrated by flotation and converted to ZnO by roasting. Germanium and other metallic impurities are separated as volatile chlorides by heating the crude oxide with sodium chloride and coal. From the condensed vapors $GeCl_4$ is isolated by fractional distillation.

In England germanium is recovered by smelting coal ash and flue dust with sodium carbonate, copper oxide, lime and coal dust. The resulting regulus is converted to the chlorides which are then subjected to fractional distillation.

The crude $GeCl_4$ obtained by the various processes contains arsenic and boron as main impurities. Purification is accomplished in an oxidizing medium ($8N$ HCl and Cl_2) by fractional distillation in quartz stills. For the production of high-purity germanium, $GeCl_4$ is hydrolized to GeO_2 with doubly distilled water. Final reduction to Ge is commercially performed with H_2 in silica tube furnaces. Germanium thus obtained is up to 99.9999% pure and by chemical standards a very high-purity material.

Purification and Controlled Doping

Germanium used for electronic devices must be "transistor grade," i.e., with an impurity content of the order of one part in 10^{10}. This degree of purity is obtained by "zone refining," a technique based on the fact that impurities generally exhibit different solubilities in the solid (C_S) and in the melt (C_L). With the exception of boron, which is effectively removed during the fractional distillation of the chlorides, the commonly encountered impurities in Ge are more soluble in the melt than in the solid, i.e., the impurity distribution coefficient $k = C_S/C_L < 1$. Thus, effective removal of impurities from Ge is obtained by traversing a molten zone along the impure ingot. The impurities are carried along in the molten zone. After repeated passes of a molten zone the impurities are essentially found at the one end of the ingot. The rest of the ingot is of extremely high purity.

The successful use of Ge in solid state electronics depends largely on the uniform incorporation of trace amounts of specified impurities (doping) at well specified concentration levels into single crystals of high-purity material. These "donor" or "acceptor" impurities (see below) are either added to the melt from which the single crystal is grown or alternately incorporated into monocrystalline Ge by solid state diffusion.

Single Crystal Growth

Germanium single crystals up to a few inches in diameter are commercially prepared from the melt. The Czochralski technique is the most commonly employed. A seed crystal is contacted with the melt under an inert atmosphere (H_2, He, N_2) and then lifted (under rotation) at rates up to several inches per hour. The degree of perfection of the resulting single crystals (regarding dislocation density, twinning, impurity distribution, etc.) depends largely on the control of the experimental parameters (temperature stability, seeding conditions, uniformity of rotation and pulling rates, etc.).

TABLE 1. PROPERTIES OF GERMANIUM

Atomic number	32
Atomic radius, Å	1.37
Atomic volume, cc/g-atom	13.5
Atomic weight	72.59
Band gap, at 0°K, ev	0.75
Boiling point, °C	~ 2900
Covalent radius, Å	1.22
Crystalline structure	diamond (type A_4)
Debye temperature, °K	362
Density at 25°C, g/cc	5.323
Density of intrinsic electrons at 300°K, per cc	2.4×10^{13}
Dielectric constant, ε	15.7
Electrode potential, E_0,v	
$Ge + 5OH^- \rightarrow HGeO_3^- + 2H_2O + 4e$	-1.0
$Ge + 2H_2O \rightarrow GeO_2 + 4H + 4e$	-0.15
Electron drift mobility, cm²/v-sec	3800
Electronegativity	1.8
Hardness, Mohs' scale	6
Hole drift mobility, cm²/v-sec	1900
Ionic radius Ge^{2+}, Å	0.93
Ionic radius Ge^{4+}, Å	0.53
Isotopic distribution, % natural abundance	
Ge^{70}	20.51
Ge^{72}	27.43
Ge^{73}	7.76
Ge^{74}	36.54
Ge^{76}	7.76
Latent heat of fusion, cal/g-atom	7300
Latent heat of vaporization, cal/g-atom	78,000
Melting point, °C	934
Polarizability of Ge^{4+}, cc	0.14×10^{-24}
Refractive index, n_0	3.994
Resistivity, ohm-cm	47
Specific heat, cal/g/°C	0.074
Specific magnetic susceptibility at 20°C	0.122×10^{-6}
Thermal conductivity, cal/sec/cm/°C	0.15
Valence electrons	4 ($4s^2$, $4p^2$)
Vapor pressure at 27°C, atm	1×10^{-9}
Work function, eV	4.5

The preparation of large single crystals from the vapor phase (vapor transport methods) and of monocrystalline films by evaporation techniques, widely employed with other semiconductors (notably silicon), are not particularly advantageous in the case of germanium. Polycrystalline Ge films used as resistors are prepared by various deposition techniques from the vapor phase.

Physical and Chemical Properties

Germanium is a silvery-white, brittle semiconductor with the diamond structure. It is opaque to ultraviolet and visible light but transparent in the infrared. Its physical constants are listed in Table 1.

The chemical characteristics of germanium reflect its position (Group IV) in the periodic system of the chemical elements. It is below carbon and silicon and above tin and lead, having properties somewhere in between those of metals and insulators.

Germanium is stable at room temperature and reacts with air or oxygen and chlorine at elevated temperatures. It is also stable at room temperature in water, hydrochloric acid,

TABLE 2. PROPERTIES OF GERMANIUM (IV) HALIDES

Compound	Mol. wt.	Density, g/cc	Melting Point, °C	Boiling Point, °C	Soluble in	State at room temperature
GeF_4	148.60	6.65×10^{-3}	subl. -37	—	—	colorless gas
$GeCl_4$	214.43	1.879(1)	-49.5	83.1	alcohol, ether	colorless liquid
$GeBr_4$	392.26	3.132 (2)	26.1	186.5	alcohol, ether, benzene	grey-white crystals
GeI_4	580.28	4.322 (3)	144.0	dec. 440	CS_2, CCl_4, benzene	yellow crystals

(1) at 20°C
(2) at 29°C
(3) at 26°C

sulfuric acid and sodium hydroxide solutions provided they do not contain dissolved oxygen It is readily attacked by nitric acid and "aqua regia." Germanium and most of its compounds are considered nontoxic. Ill effects caused by inhalation of $GeCl_4$ are due to its hydrolysis in the lungs which leads to the formation of HCl, thus causing internal bleeding.

Germanium Compounds

The reactivity of germanium with other elements and the stability of its compounds reflect its position between Si and Sn in Group IV of the periodic system. It forms divalent and tetravalent compounds of which only the latter are very stable. All divalent compounds, with the exception of GeS, are unstable.

Among the compounds of germanium only those most commonly encountered are discussed. Organogermanium compounds, of which more than 1000 are known, are not included.

Germanium Halides.

All halides are known for divalent and tetravalent Ge. Their physical and chemical properties (with the exception of GeF_2) have been extensively studied.

Ge (II) halides, GeF_2, $GeCl_2$, $GeBr_2$ and GeI_2, can be obtained by passing vapor of the respective Ge (IV) halides over Ge at elevated temperatures. The compounds form colorless-to-yellow solids which readily disproportionate at high temperatures to the tetravalent halide and elemental Ge. They are dissolved by their corresponding Ge (IV) compounds and are only slightly soluble in alcohol or chloroform.

Ge (IV) halides. Some of the properties of the tetravalent germanium halides are summarized in Table 2.

$GeCl_4$ is the most important of all Ge compounds. It is formed as an intermediate compound in most extraction and purification processes of Ge. It is obtained by reaction of Cl_2 with elemental Ge or during the dissolution of GeO_2 by HCl. $GeCl_4$ is insoluble in concentrated HCl but is soluble in carbon disulfide, chloroform, benzene and ether. Upon reduction with H_2 at 1000°C in a quartz reactor a condensate, tentatively identified as GeCl, has been observed.

Mixed halides. $GeCl_3F$, $GeCl_2F_2$, and $GeClF_3$ have been obtained by reaction of SbF_3 with $GeCl_4$ in the presence of $SbCl_5$. Halides of complex composition like $GeClBr_2I$ have been isolated from mixtures of $GeCl_4$, $GeBr_4$ and GeI_4. Complex Ge (IV) halides like $K_2[GeF_6]$ are precipitated by the addition of KF to a solution of GeO_2 in HF. The acid, H_2GeF_6, is obtained by the reaction of GeF_4 with H_2O: $3GeF_4 + 2H_2O \rightarrow GeO_2 + 2H_2GeF_6$.

Germanium Oxides.

Ge (II) oxide. GeO is formed by heating a mixture of GeO_2 and Ge to 850°C in a stream of N_2: $GeO_2 + Ge \rightarrow 2GeO$. Since GeO sublimes at 650°C, this reaction is of considerable importance. By heating in vacuum it makes possible the removal of GeO_2 from Ge surfaces leading to oxygen-free "clean" surfaces.

GeO can also be obtained by reacting Ge with CO_2 at about 800°C: $Ge + CO_2 \rightarrow GeO + CO$. It is obtained as a black powder which is readily oxidized. It can be obtained from aqueous solutions in hydrated form as a

TABLE 3. PROPERTIES OF GERMANIUM DIOXIDE

Crystal System	Crystal Type	Density, g/cc	Solubility in H_2O, g/100 ml at 25°C	Solubility in HF	Refractive index
tetragonal	rutile	6.239 (1)	insoluble	insoluble	2.05–2.10
hexagonal	quartz	4.703 (2)	0.447	diss. as H_2GeF_6	1.735
amorphous	glass	3.637 (3)	0.518	—	1.607

(1) at 20°C
(2) at 18°C
(3) at 20°C

yellow precipitate. GeO is attacked by HCl at 175°C forming $GeHCl_3$, germanium chloroform.

Ge (IV) oxide. GeO_2 appears in two crystalline and one amorphous modification (see Table 3). It is prepared directly from the elements, by hydrolysis of Ge (IV) halides, by oxidation of GeS and from germanate solutions. The resulting product is always the water-soluble hexagonal modification. This solubility of GeO_2 in H_2O and the fact that Ge is not attacked by H_2O free of dissolved oxygen make possible the preparation of oxide-free Ge surfaces.

Tetragonal water-insoluble GeO_2 is obtained from hexagonal GeO_2 by heating to 350°C in H_2O under pressure. The phase transformation is reportedly slow if very pure materials are used. Both types of GeO_2 melt at about 1100°C and form a clear glass which devitrifies to (hexagonal) crystalline GeO_2. Aqueous solutions of GeO_2 are acidic due to the formation of metagermanic acid, H_2GeO_3 Ortho- and metagermanates are obtained by melting a mixture of GeO_2 and metal oxides. Heteropoly acids form upon addition of tungstic acid to aqueous solutions of germanates, e.g., $H_8[Ge(W_2O_7)_6].28 H_2O$. Germanium dioxide in the form of stable gel forms upon hydrolysis of $Ge(C_2H_5)_4$.

Germanium Sulfides.

Ge (II) sulfide. GeS in the form of black crystals of metallic luster (m.p. 530°C) is obtained when heating Ge to 700°C in a stream of H_2S. An amorphous red modification of GeS forms when H_2S is added to solutions containing $GeCl_2$. GeS is the most stable known divalent Ge compound.

Ge (IV) sulfide. Crystalline white GeS_2 (m.p. 800°C) forms upon sublimation of GeS in the presence of sulfur vapor. An amorphous modification is obtained by precipitation from strong acidic solutions of GeO_2 with H_2S. GeS_2 is only slightly soluble in H_2O but dissolves readily in ammonia and ammonium sulfide under formation of thiogermanates, $[GeS_3]^{--}$.

Germanium Hydrides (germanes).

Germanium forms hydrides of the general formula Ge_nH_{2n+2} (see Table 4). Ge (IV) hydrides are less stable than the corresponding carbon and silicon compounds. They decompose readily, forming H_2 and Ge. GeH_4 is obtained by reacting Mg_2Ge and NH_4Br in liquid ammonia. It is also formed upon electrolysis of a solution of GeO_2 in H_2SO_4 on lead electrodes. Pure GeH_4 forms in ether from $LiAlH_4$ and $GeCl_4$. GeH_4 is oxidized to GeO_2 with O_2 and decomposes at elevated temperatures, forming a germanium mirror.

TABLE 4. PROPERTIES OF GERMANIUM HYDRIDES

Name	Formula	Mol. Wt.	Melting Point, °C	Boiling Point, °C	Decomposition Temperature, °C
germane	GeH_4	76.63	−165	−90	∼350
digermane	Ge_2H_6	151.25	−109	29	∼210 (200 mm Hg)
trigermane	Ge_3H_8	225.86	−105.6	110.5	∼190 (200 mm Hg)

Polygermanes of the general formula Ge_nH_{2n+2} are obtained by reacting Mg_2Ge with dilute HCl in a hydrogen atmosphere. $Ge(H_2)_x$ is formed as a yellow powder when CaGe is treated with HCl. Germanium hydrides form a large number of derivatives in which one or more hydrogen atoms are replaced by alkaline metals, halides and organic groups.

Uses

Germanium is very extensively used in solid state electronics because of its semiconductive properties. It finds application as an alloying constituent in metallurgy. Its addition to beryllium results in increasing ductility. Ge-Cu alloys are golden colored and of high chemical resistivity. It is also used in several brazing alloys. Germanium in the form of GeO_2 is an important constituent of industrial glasses because of its infrared transmission and high refractive index.

Polymer germanium compounds—equivalent to the silicones—have found no commercial application but remain the subject of intensive investigations.

The world production of germanium for the period 1960 to 1964 is estimated at about 75,000 kg per year. The quoted price of "transistor grade" polycrystalline Ge (40 ohm-cm) in 1967 was $270/kg. In the United States the element is supplied by American Zinc, Lead Smelting Co., Fairmont, Ill., Sylvania Electric Products Co., Towanda, Pa., and others.

Semiconducting Nature of Germanium

Germanium like carbon, has four valence electrons $(4s^2, 4p^2)$, which by orbital hybridization form four (sp^3) equivalent covalent bonds of a tetrahedral configuration. The bond angles are $109°28'$. As a result of this spatial bond distribution Ge crystallizes in the diamond structure, in which each atom has four tetrahedrally arranged nearest neighbors.

In crystalline Ge the total number of valence electrons is just sufficient to fill all sp^3 bonding orbitals. Consequently electrical conductivity in Ge results from the excitation of valence electrons from their bonding positions (valence energy band) to their antibonding positions (conduction energy band).

In this excitation process electron deficiencies are created in the valence band which constitute positive electrical carriers referred to as "holes." Both electrons and holes contribute to the conduction of electricity. The energy required for the excitation of carriers represents the "forbidden energy gap" (E_g) between the top of the valence energy band and the bottom of the conduction energy band.

The exponential increase of conductivity with increasing temperature, a characteristic feature of semiconductors, reflects in the case of germanium the exponential temperature dependence of the charge carrier concentration. The mobility of the carriers in Ge is only a weak function of temperature.

Pure germanium at room temperature has a charge carrier concentration of about 2×10^{13} per cc (by comparison aluminum has about 10^{22} conduction electrons per cc). Correspondingly, the room temperature intrinsic conductivity of Ge is about 2×10^{-2} ohm^{-1} cm^{-1} (the conductivity of aluminum is about 10^6 ohm^{-1} cm^{-1}, that of Al_2O_3 is about 10^{-13} ohm^{-1} cm^{-1}). The electrical characteristics of Ge are substantially influenced by the presence of impurities. For example, an atom of Group V (say, arsenic) has five valence electrons, one more than a germanium atom. This extra electron must enter the conduction band without, of course, the generation of a hole. The Group V atom is called a donor (D) and releases the extra electron according to: $D \leftrightharpoons D^+ + n$. The positive charge associated with the donor atom is localized and not free to move. On the other hand, if a Group III element (say, boron) substitutes for germanium, an electron deficiency is brought about in the crystal, leading directly to the formation of holes in the valence band. The electron deficient atoms are called acceptors (A) and are ionized according to: $A \leftrightharpoons A^- + p$. Here again the negative ion (A^-) is localized and not free to conduct. The excess carrier concentration is, of course, determined by the concentration of impurities. At the same time, however, the concentration of carriers due to intrinsic excitation increases exponentially with temperature. Thus, at sufficiently high temperatures the intrinsic carrier concentration exceeds the concentration of carriers due to impurities and the semiconductor is rendered intrinsic.

The electrical characteristics of germanium may also be influenced by crystal imperfections. Defects such as vacancies, dislocations, grain boundaries, etc., lead to perturbations in the bonding configuration and thus often result in changes in the charge carrier concentration. Crystal imperfections further affect the electrical conductivity of germanium by increasing the carrier scattering and, thus, decreasing the mobility of the charge carriers.

The Role of Germanium in Solid State Science and Technology

Germanium has played by far the most significant role in the development of solid state electronics beginning with the discovery of the transistor in 1948. It lends itself more readily than any other semiconductor to extreme purification, high crystalline perfection and controlled doping. Furthermore, its surfaces can be prepared and characterized with high degree of precision. As a result one might safely state that it is the most studied and best understood of all elements.

The discovery of the transistor action pointed the way to numerous solid state electronic phenomena which formed the basis for a new science and technology of solid state electronics. It became at once apparent that extremely high purities, both chemical and crystalline, were essential. Thus, zone refining was first applied successfully on germanium in the early 1950's leading to crystalline germanium with a purity of one part in 10^{10}, a level which was never achieved previously. At the same time single crystal growth techniques were developed or perfected leading to germanium single crystals of crystalline perfection never achieved in other solids. It was in germanium single crystals that edge dislocations were first observed in 1952. This observation led to the confirmation of the dislocation theory formulated some years earlier, and provided new criteria for the perfection of crystals.

The availability of extremely pure germanium crystals with a high degree of crystalline perfection made possible a number of fundamental measurements. Cyclotron resonance, a means for determining the effective mass of charge carriers, was first observed in germanium single crystals. A variety of optical and magneto-optical measurements made possible the determination of fundamental parameters necessary for understanding and determining the band structure of solids. With measurements performed on germanium crystals many theoretical considerations regarding the solid state were confirmed or rejected. In addition, x-ray diffraction theories pertaining to lattice defects were submitted to experimental testing employing germanium single crystals of controlled crystalline perfection.

Germanium has served further as the basic material for the study of solid state diffusion phenomena, the solid melt interface and the incorporation and distribution of impurities upon solidification from the melt.

Another significant aspect of germanium has been its surface characteristics. Its high purity and crystalline perfection combined with its covalent nature and four-fold coordination led to the preparation of highly characterized surfaces. The property of germanium dioxide to react with germanium to form volatile germanium monoxide has been of basic importance in achieving the preparation and study of oxide-free surfaces. Furthermore, the solubility of germanium dioxide in water allowed the preparation of oxide-free surfaces in aqueous solutions and thus the realization of fundamental electrochemical studies. Numerous physical and chemical surface experiments of far-reaching fundamental significance were performed for the first time on germanium surfaces.

References

1. "Gmelin: Handbuch der Anorganischen Chemie;" "Germanium," Vol. 45, Berlin, Deutsche Chemische Gesellschaft, Verlag Chemie, 1958.
2. Germanium Information Brochure, Germanium Information Center, Kansas City, Mo., Midwest Research Institute, 1967.
3. Sidgwick, N, V., "Chemical Elements and Their Compounds," Vol. 1, London, Oxford University Press, 1950.
4. Pascal, Paul, "Nouveau Traité de Chimie Minérale," Vol. 8, Paris, Masson et Cie., Editeurs, 1965.
5. Corey, Richard Clarke, "Occurrence and Determination of Germanium in Coal Ash from Power Plants," Washington, U.S. Govt. Print. Office, 1959.

6. Hannay, N. B., "Semiconductors," New York, Reinhold Publishing Corporation, 1959.
7. Johnson, Otto H., *Chem. Rev.*, **51**, 431 (1952).

AUGUST F. WITT AND
HARRY C. GATOS

GOLD

Gold, symbol Au from the Latin *aurum*, has the atomic number of 79 and the atomic weight of 196.967 and is located in Group IB of the Periodic Table. It is one of the most indestructible and heaviest (density = 19.32 g/cc) metals known and has been mined, used and treasured by man since before the beginnings of recorded history. Probably the first metal discovered by man, gold and the search for it have been among the major factors in exploration, conquest, and the growth of civilization.

Archaeological studies have shown that the goldsmith's art dates from at least 4000 B.C. in Mesopotamia and that it then spread throughout the whole group of ancient civilizations around the eastern Mediterranean, including Egypt. It also arose in the New World in the pre-Columbian cultures of Peru and Mexico, as well as in the Asian civilizations. The earliest written records of all nations mention gold and its uses and value.

More recently, alchemy, based on the search for the Philosopher's Stone which would convert base metals to gold, contributed to chemistry, medicine and metallurgy.

Occurrence

Gold is widely distributed throughout the world, normally in very low concentration and generally in native form as metal. It is usually alloyed with silver and often contains small amounts of copper.

The only compounds of gold found in nature are the tellurides, typically calaverite, $AuTe_2$; petzite, $(AuAg)_2Te$; sylvanite, $(AuAg)Te_2$; and several other tellurides of variable composition.

Gold is found in native form in both lode and alluvial deposits. In the largest gold reefs in the world, the Witwatersrand and the Orange Free State in the Union of South Africa, the gold is present as veins and stringers in a quartz matrix accompanied with pyrite and quartz sand. The presence of gold in the quartz veins suggests that the gold was originally deposited from solution. Many pyrite and pyrrhotite minerals contain gold from which the metal is recovered during the extraction of copper, silver, lead, zinc and nickel.

In certain geographic areas erosion of primary deposits over the centuries has freed native gold resulting in nuggets and flakes being found in the sand and gravel of river beds. The discovery of such deposits has stimulated the famous "Gold Rushes."

Gold is present in sea water, the concentration being dependent upon depth and geographic location. An average estimate places the concentration at 0.014 microgram per liter. While this is a very low concentration, it may be conservatively estimated that the oceans contain 70 million tons of gold in solution. In addition to this, off-shore exploration of the continental shelf indicates that gold is present on the ocean floor. Conservative estimates suggest these deposits to contain ten billion tons of gold. At present there is no practical method of recovering either the gold in solution or that from the ocean floor. Considering the vast quantities of strategic elements present in the ocean, it seems probable that gold may someday become a by-product of ocean mining.

Distribution

Gold is found in nearly every country and has been produced in at least seventy-five countries since 1952. The leading gold-producing country since 1905 has been the Republic of South Africa. The Witwatersrand in the Transvaal and similar deposits in the Orange Free State produced about 73% of the total world output in 1965.

Domestic production for 1965 was 1.705 million ounces of which 6% was recovered by placer mining, 54% from gold and silver ores, and 40% as base-metal refining by-product.

The Homestake mine in South Dakota is the leading domestic producer, treating in 1965 about 2.03 million tons of ore by cyanidation and amalgamation. The average recovered grade was valued at $10.88 per ton. The second largest producer, the Utah Copper mine at Bingham, Utah recovers gold as a by-product of treating copper ore.*

Most of the placer mine production is from bucketline dredging in Alaska and California. The Homestake and Utah Copper mines produced about 62% of the domestic production in 1965.

TABLE 1. AVERAGE PRODUCTION BY CONTINENT (1965)

	Troy ozs.
North America	
Canada	3,587,168
Central America and West Indies	426,363
United States	1,705,190
South America	763,000
USSR	6,100,000
Asia	1,165,000
Africa	
Republic of South Africa	32,130,000
Australia	877,139

Recovery

Lode gold may be recovered by smelting, amalgamation, flotation, or cyanidation; very often a combination of several of these methods is required.

The most important is the cyanidation process which utilizes the principle that gold dissolves in dilute alkaline cyanide solutions in the presence of air. The ground ore is treated with an 0.01 to 0.05% calcium or sodium cyanide solution in which the pH is controlled by the addition of lime. The gold dissolves as $Au(CN)_2$ from which it is recovered by precipitation with zinc dust, aluminum or electrolysis.

Gold is recovered from placer deposits by a combination of physical and chemical procedures. The free gold is released from the rock by grinding the crushed ore which is then subjected to water washing, the difference in density between gold, 19.3, and quartz rock at 2.5 being sufficient to effect hydraulic separation. In order to recover flakes of gold trapped in the ground ore, mercury is added and the mixture of ore, mercury and water (called pulp) is passed over copper plates coated with mercury. The gold amalgam adheres to these plates effecting a separation from the gangue.

* See Editor's Note on page 250.

The gold amalgam is recovered by scraping the copper plates, squeezing out the excess mercury and heating in retorts. The mercury is recovered by distillation. The gold and silver left in the retort is upgraded by chemical treatment.

Refining of Gold

Metal recovered by the preceding methods usually contains silver, copper and other base metals, plus traces of platinum group metals. Melting and oxidizing is used to slag off most of the base metals. Silver, if present, alloys with the gold. The gold-silver alloy is cast into anodes for electrolytic refining. The electrolyte is gold chloride containing 5–10% free HCl. A current of about 70 amp/sq ft at 65° is normally used. To prevent silver chloride buildup on the anode, an a-c current is superimposed on the d-c; this effectively breaks up the silver chloride and permits gold alloys containing as much as 50% silver to be electrorefined. Copper, palladium and platinum go into solution as chlorides; most other metals remain in the silver chloride slimes. The gold deposited on the cathode is normally 99.95% pure.

An important refining process used to upgrade gold to 99.5% purity is the "Miller" process involving the bubbling of chlorine gas through the molten impure gold. In this process, the base metals either volatilize or slag off as chlorides. Silver is converted to chloride, which at this temperature remains molten and may be removed by decantation.

There are many chemical methods of precipitating gold which are applicable to refining of scrap and bullion, precipitation with reducing agents such as SO_2 and ferrous sulfate being most common.

Physical Properties

The density of gold, 19.32 g/cc, is exceeded only by that of iridium, rhenium, osmium, platinum and neptunium among the elements. Gold is the third best electrical and thermal conductor, being exceeded only by the other elements of Group IB, copper and silver. Specific data on its physical properties are listed in Table 2.

Massive gold is deep yellow in color. Gold is the most ductile and most malleable of all metals and may be rolled or beaten to films

TABLE 2. PHYSICAL PROPERTIES

Atomic number	79
Atomic weight, $C^{12} = 12.00000$	196.967
Naturally occurring isotopes	197
Radioactive isotopes, half-life	
≤ 187	4.3 minutes
186	15 minutes
188	4.5 minutes
189	42 minutes
190	39 minutes
191	3.2 minutes
192	4.8 hours
193m	3.9 seconds
193	15.8 hours
194	39 hours
195m	30.6 seconds
195	200 days
196m	10 hours
196	5.55 days
197m	7.2 seconds
198	64.8 hours
199	3.15 days
200	48 minutes
201	26 minutes
202	~ 25 seconds
203	55 seconds
Distance closest approach,† d, at 25°C, Angstrom units	2.884
Crystal structure	FCC
Lattice constant, a, at 25°C, Angstrom units	4.0786
Thermal neutron capture cross section, barns	98.8
Electronic configuration (ground state)	$5d^{10}\ 6s$
Chemical valence	1,3
Oxidation potential‡	
Reaction: $Au \rightarrow Au^{+++} + 3e(1)$	
$Au \rightarrow Au^{+} \quad + 1e(2)$	
E° ox, volts (1)	−1.50
(2)	−1.68
Mass susceptibility, X 10^6 cgs units	−0.15
First ionization potential, electron volts	9.22
Second ionization potential, electron volts	20.5
Thermionic work function, electron volts	4.25
X-ray emission, Angstrom units $K\alpha_1$	0.1802
$K\alpha_2$	0.1851
$L\alpha_1$	1.2764
$L\alpha_2$	1.2878
Commercially accepted density§ at 20°C, g/cc	19.32
Melting point, °C	1063
Boiling point, °C	2808
Vapor pressure	
temperature, °C	torr.
953	10^{-6}
1038	10^{-5}
1140	10^{-4}
1260	10^{-3}
1403	10^{-2}
1574	10^{-1}
1786	1

TABLE 2. PHYSICAL PROPERTIES-*continued*

2055	10^1
2412	10^2
Specific heat at 25°C, cal/g	0.03077
Thermal conductivity, 0–100°C, cal-cm/cm²/sec/°C	0.74
Linear coefficient of thermal expansion, 100°C, micro-in./in. °C	14.16×10^{-6}
Electrical resistivity at 0°C, microhm-cm	2.06
Temperature coefficient of electrical resistance 0–100°C/°C	0.004
Thermal EMF vs NBS Pt 27 (U.S. Standard)	
temperature, °C	millivolts
100	+0.92
500	+6.40
800	+12.35
Reflectance, %	
0.400 μ evaporated	38.7
0.450 μ	38.7
0.500 μ	47.7
0.550 μ	81.7
0.600 μ	91.9
0.650 μ	95.5
0.700 μ	97.0
Spectral emissivity	
at 6500 Å ‖ solid	0.14
liquid	0.22
Total emissivity	
at 100°C	0.02
500°C	0.03
Tensile strength (0.020″-dia. wire)	
annealed 300°C, psi	18,000–20,000
60% cold worked, psi	30,000–32,000
Elongation, % in 2″ (0.020″-dia. wire)	
at 20°C, psi, annealed 300°C	39–45
60% cold worked	4
Hardness (0.020″-dia. wire ¶)	
at 20°C, DPN, annealed 300°C	25–27
60% cold worked	55–60
as cast	33–35
Young's Modulus	
at 20°C, psi, static	11.2×10^6
Poisson's ratio	0.42

† Calculated from the lattice constant, a, using the equation $d = a\dfrac{\sqrt{2}}{2}$.

‡ Values referred to the hydrogen-hydrogen ion couple as zero are for unit activities and temperature of 25°C.
§ Theoretical density at 25°C is 19.28. This value is calculated from the lattice constant and the atomic weight, both cited above, using Avogadro's number $= 6.02296 \times 10^{23}$.
‖ Near melting point.
¶ Except "as cast," on rod.

less than five millionths of an inch thick. Gold leaf produced by beating between skins to a thickness of about 1000Å transmits green light, but appears yellow by reflected light. Gold films produced by vacuum-evaporation are used as interference filters. A commercial application for evaporated gold films is the production of automobile glass and window glass where good visibility is required with a substantial reduction of infrared transmission. The reflectivity of gold in the infrared region is about 97%, which makes gold an excellent radiant heat shield for heat-sensitive components.

Chemical Properties

Gold is number 97 in the Periodic Table, Group IB. The atomic weight is 196.967 (Carbon-12). Gold has valences of $+1$ and $+3$, and forms aurous and auric series of compounds.

The oxidation-reduction potentials of gold are:

$$Au \rightarrow Au^+ + e^- \qquad -1.68 \text{ volts}$$
$$Au^+ \rightarrow Au^{+3} + 2e^- \qquad -1.29$$
$$Au + 4Cl \rightarrow [AuCl_4] + 3e^- \qquad -1.0$$
$$Au + 4OH^- \rightarrow [AuO_2] + 2H_2O$$
$$+ 3e^- \qquad -0.5$$

Gold is chemically very inert. Gold does not react with oxygen, sulfur or selenium, but does react with molten tellurium to form an intermetallic compound. At 25°C the solubility of gold in mercury is about 0.7% gold by weight, the value increasing with temperature. All compounds of gold are readily reduced to metal.

The halogens react directly with gold at elevated temperatures; however, the reaction with fluorine is very slow even at 600°C.

Chlorine, bromine and iodine all react at room temperature in the presence of moisture to form the corresponding halide.

Gold is insoluble in the single halogen acids, but is readily attacked if oxidizing agents capable of releasing nascent halogen are present, with the exception of HF. The common solvent for gold is a mixture of nitric and hydrochloric acids, aqua regia, which yields chloroauric acid, $HAuCl_4$.

Gold is not attacked by cold or hot phosphoric, or sulfuric acids. Nitric acid attacks gold only slightly and if the gold is completely free of silver and copper, the attack is negligible.

Gold is not attacked by fused alkali hydroxides in the absence of oxidizing agents.

Alkaline cyanides dissolve gold in the presence of oxygen; gold may also be dissolved in cyanides by making it anodic.

The only single acid which dissolves gold is selenic acid at about 225°C, but the reaction has no commercial importance.

Gold Compounds of Commercial Importance

Gold chloride; tetrachloro-
auric (III) acid hydrate $\qquad HAuCl_4 \cdot \times H_2O$

Gold cyanide; aurous (I)
cyanide $\qquad AuCN$
Gold hydroxide; auryl (III)
hydroxide $\qquad AuO(OH)$
Gold bromide; tetrabromo-
auric (III) acid $\qquad HAuBr_4 \cdot \times H_2O$
Potassium gold cyanide;
potassium dicyonoaurate
(I) $\qquad KAu(CN)_2$
Sodium gold cyanide; sod-
ium dicyonoaurate (I) $\qquad NaAu(CN)_2$

By far the greatest bulk item in gold salt sales is the potassium and sodium gold cyanides which form the basis of nearly all of the gold electroplating solutions.

There are a number of complex organic compounds of gold which form the basis of the gold compositions used in the decorative arts. These compounds are usually sold as proprietory blends with combinations of fluxes and other metals. These compositions known as "Liquid Bright," "Liquid Gold," etc., are designed to be painted, sprayed or silk-screened onto ceramics, glass, enamel, high-temperature plastic, etc., and subjected to thermal decomposition. These compounds decompose leaving a film of gold on the fired item. Recently, gold organic compositions have been developed that can be fired as low as 250°C, enabling gold films to be applied to plastics for printed circuits, infrared reflectors, and fuel cell electrode supports.

Colloidal Gold

Gold compounds are readily reduced to metal. If the reduction takes place in a dilute aqueous medium, a gold colloid results. The color of this product is dependent upon particle size, which in turn is a function of concentration, temperature and pH. Generally low pH favors large particle size which exhibits a blue color, whereas, high pH produces smaller particle sizes which exhibit shades of red or pink. The particle size varies from 10 to 100 millimicrons. The collodial gold carries a negative charge.

The best known gold sol, "Cassius Purple," is formed by the reduction of gold chloride with stannous chloride. In this reaction, the gold is reduced to metal at the same time the tin is oxidized to $H_2Sn(OH)_6$ which acts as a protective colloid preventing coagulation of the gold. The reaction is very sensitive and is used to detect traces of gold as low as 0.1 ppm.

Gold colloids are used to color ceramic enamels and glass. One part of "Cassius Purple" in 50,000 parts of glass produces a beautiful ruby red color.

Colloidal gold is also used as a nucleating agent in photosensitive glasses.

Major Alloys

Gold is rarely used in its pure form mainly due to its softness. While gold may be electrodeposited readily in pure form, most electrodeposits contain small amounts of other metals, such as cobalt, nickel or silver, to provide wear resistance, and color modification. Nearly all gold alloys other than those used in purely functional applications are expressed by the karat system in which the weight per cent of gold is expressed as 24ths. Thus, 18 Kt, 14 Kt and 10 Kt are, respectively, 75.00, 58.33 and 41.67% gold. The number of karat gold alloys is very large; every jewelry manufacturer has his own alloys which provide desired work properties with color for a particular item. A few typical gold alloys for 14 Kt items are shown below:

Color of Alloy

	White	*Yellow*	*Red*	*Green*
Gold, %	58.33	58.33	58.33	58.33
Copper, %	17.00	25.58	27.96	6.50
Silver, %		13.33	6.54	35.00
Zinc, %	7.67	2.76	7.17	.17
Nickel, %	17.00			

Gold alloys find extensive use in dentistry where advantage is taken of the high corrosion resistance for oral fluids plus the mechanical properties and the ease of soldering and casting.

Due to the high intrinsic value of gold alloys, it is often customary to bond thin gold alloys to base-metal stock, thereby providing the desirable properties of the precious metal with the strength of the basis metal; this process is called cladding. Such combinations are available in almost every conceivable configuration.

If the clad stock is to serve a functional application, it is known as clad stock. If used in jewelry, it is often referred to as gold-filled

and is usually designated on a ratio basis such as 1/10 14 Kt, etc., meaning a 14 Kt alloy bonded to a suitable base metal in the ratio of a minimum of 10% of the weight of the article as 14 Kt gold alloy. No article having a karat gold surface of less than 5% of the total weight can be marked "gold filled."

Uses

One property of gold that distinguishes it from all other metals is its universal status as a monetary standard. Gold has been used as a medium of exchange since 3000 B.C. In the late 1700's it became the world monetary standard. Its price today is fixed in the United States at $35.00 per troy ounce, and the world price does not vary far from this figure.

All transactions in gold starting at the mine are subject to government regulations that require all gold bullion and gold coins to be delivered to a United States Treasury institution. Licenses are issued by the Treasury Department permitting purchases, sales, imports and exports of gold for use in the arts and industries.

Most of the world production is absorbed by governments. Some metal is used in coinage, but the chief use is for backing currency and to settle international trade balances. Probably over one-half of the total world production is in government vaults or central banks. It may also be assumed that considerable quantities are hoarded by private individuals. The major nonmonetary uses are both decorative and functional. The net industrial consumption in 1965 was 5,276,000 troy ounces. The decorative uses include jewelry, religious items, coloring of glass, decorating ceramics, and bookbinding.

Functional applications have more than doubled since 1960, mainly in electronics and space applications. It is estimated that over 1.0 million ounces of gold were consumed in 1965 for the electrodeposition of gold on electronic components, including heat shields, diodes, printed circuits, tube pins and plugs. Most of the electroplated applications are under 0.00005" thick. While this is very thin, the gold film gives excellent infrared reflectivity, corrosion resistance, solderability and low noise contact reliability. One troy ounce of gold covers 68.3 sq ft of surface to a thickness of 0.0001".

Other functional applications include dental alloys for bridges and inlays; in these, gold is usually alloyed with platinum or palladium for increased corrosion resistance and hardness. The use of gold in dentistry dates back to Egypt. Mummies of pharaohs who lived several thousand years ago contain gold bridgework and fillings. Today some 600,000 troy ounces of gold are used annually in dentistry.

Spinnerets for certain synthetic fiber production are made of gold which is usually alloyed with platinum group metals. Other applications are: electrical contact alloys, infrared reflectors, chemical equipment, photography, brazing alloys, and atomic energy.

Gold in Medicine

Gold is used in the treatment of arthritis, generally being administered intramuscularly as a soluble salt, such as disodium aurothiomalate.

Collodial suspensions of radioactive isotope Au^{198} have been used in treating several forms of cancer.

Gold sodium thiosulfate was used in the treatment of tuberculosis prior to the discovery of antibiotics.

Gold leaf is being used experimentally for surgical dressings due to its ability, when electrostatically charged, to conform intimately to surface contours of depressions in tissues, etc. This development was reported by Drs. J. P. Gallagher and C. F. Geschickter of Washington, D.C. in 1964.

References

1. Wise, Edmund M., "Gold: Recovery, Properties and Applications," New York, D. Van Nostrand Co., Inc., 1964.
2. Kolthof, I. M., and Elving, P. J., "Treatise on Analytical Chemistry," Part II, Vol. 4, New York, Interscience Publishers, 1966.
3. "Engelhard Industries Technical Bulletin," Vol. VI, No. 3, December 1965, Research & Development Division, Engelhard Industries, Newark 5, New Jersey.
4. "Minerals Yearbook," 1964, Vol. 1, Washington, D.C., U.S. Department of Interior, Bureau of Mines, 1965.
5. "Mineral Facts and Problems," 1965 Edition, Bulletin 630, Washington, D.C., U.S. Department of Interior, Bureau of Mines, 1965.
6. Industrial Research, Vol. 8, No. 3, 42ff, March 1966, Industrial Research Inc., Beverly Shores, Ind.
7. Jewelers' Circular-Keystone, CXXXVII, No. 9, Part II (June, 1967). (Editor's Note: This special issue contains 29 articles, 206 pages, covering the many facets of the technology, history and applications of gold.)

HAROLD W. ROBINSON

Editor's Note: The second largest gold mine in the United States is now the Carlin, Nevada mine of Carlin Gold Mining Co. owned by Newmont Mining Corp., which produced its first gold ingot in May 1965, as reported by S. W. Matthews, Nat. Geographic Mag., 133, No. 5, 668-679 (May 1968). This article includes color illustrations and flowsheet of the operations at Carlin, as well as recent data on gold production in this country.

HAFNIUM

Hafnium is a strong ductile metal located in Group IVB of the Periodic Table below zirconium, above thorium and between lutetium (which has the highest atomic number of the lanthanide group of elements) and tantalum. Its atomic number is 72 and its atomic weight 178.49. Probably the most noted characteristic of hafnium is its remarkably close chemical similarity to zirconium. Even though their atomic numbers differ greatly (72 and 40) this similarity results from their closely identical atomic radii (1.442 Å for Hf and 1.452 Å for Zr) caused by the lanthanide contraction among elements 57–71. Of all the elements in the Periodic Table hafnium and zirconium are the most difficult to separate.

Discovery and History

This association and similarity of hafnium and zirconium influenced the late discovery of hafnium in 1922 after zirconium had been discovered over 130 years earlier in 1789. The presence of from 0.5 to several per cent Hf in zirconium ores and minerals (the average is 2% in the most prevalent mineral, zircon) long escaped the notice of chemists.

Coster and de (or von) Hevesy working at the University of Copenhagen used x-ray spectra to identify hafnium, element number 72, in zirconium-containing minerals following a suggestion of Bohr. They named it hafnium after the Latin "Hafnia," the word for Copenhagen. Their claim of discovery was disputed by Urbain of France, who named element 72 celtium. A heated controversy arose whose details are discussed by Martin and Pizzolato and by Wilson and Staehle (see References). In any event, Coster and de Hevesy were soon given credit for discovery of hafnium and this name was retained.

After some 25 years as little more than a laboratory curiosity, hafnium came into prominence when it was found that hafnium-free zirconium would make a most suitable structural material for nuclear reactors, due to its corrosion resistance and its low thermal neutron absorption cross section of 0.18 barns. However, zirconium containing 2% Hf, as derived from natural sources without hafnium separation, has a cross section of 2.5 barns, due to the high cross section of 105 barns for hafnium. Processes for the drastic reduction of the Hf content of zirconium were worked out, the most widely used being the liquid-liquid extraction method, and hafnium became available as a by-product.

In 1950 Admiral H. G. Rickover of the U.S. Navy decided to use zirconium in the *Nautilus* reactor and in 1951 he further decided to use hafnium for the control rod material in the same reactor. This decision resulted in hafnium becoming a readily available metal when several plants were constructed for the production first of low-hafnium zirconium and subsequently of hafnium metal. Research and development studies were undertaken to determine the properties and modes of processing and handling both metals. As a result information about hafnium has increased greatly since the early 1950's.

Occurrence

Hafnium is prevalent to the extent of about 4 g/ton in the earth's crust. There are no minerals containing hafnium independently of zirconium and hafnium always occurs in zirconium minerals in the average ratio of

Hf/Hf + Zr = 0.02. Some few scarce minerals, usually altered zircons, contain more than 2% Hf, referred to Zr, but the principal commercial sources of hafnium are the minerals zircon, $(Zr,Hf)SiO_4$, and baddeleyite, $(Zr,Hf)O_2$, which are processed primarily for their zirconium content.

The only commercial source of an altered zircon appears to be a by-product of columbite and tin mining operations in Nigeria. This material contains 70% zircon with a hafnium content of 3.5–5.0% HfO_2.

Zircon is worldwide in occurrence. The largest amount comes from Australia, followed by India and Brazil; the latter nation also has immense deposits of baddeleyite. Beach sands of Australia, India and the United States (Florida, Oregon, South Carolina) also contain large quantities of zircon.

After the zircon of beach sands is mined by dredging or strip mining it is washed and concentrated by gravity methods. The concentrates are dried and passed over electrostatic and magnetic separators, the zircon remaining with the tailings.

Extraction and Separation

Zircon, zirconium silicate, is the chief source of both hafnium and zirconium. Since hafnium-free zirconium is required for use in nuclear reactors, the largest application for that metal, the separated hafnium is the source of all hafnium produced. The steps used to effect the separation of the Hf from Zr are identical to those described in the article on **Zirconium**.

Zircon ore concentrates are blended with coke and fed to an electric arc furnace operated at about 3500°C to form a mixture of hafnium and zirconium carbides or carbonitrides (the product contains nitrogen as well as carbon). This mixture is fed to a vertical tower where fixed-bed chlorination is conducted by passage of chlorine gas into the tower. The mixed $HfCl_4$ and $ZrCl_4$ formed sublime and pass to a water-cooled condenser where they turn into solid particles containing 2 to 8% $HfCl_4$.

While several methods have been proposed for the separation of hafnium and zirconium, the one used almost exclusively on a commercial scale is based on the liquid-liquid extraction process using methyl isobutyl ketone to extract a hafnium thiocyante complex. The mixed Hf and Zr chlorides are reacted with an aqueous solution of ammonium thiocyanate to form oxychlorides that complex with thiocyanate ions. The solvent preferentially extracts the hafnyl chloride, $HfOCl_2$, from the aqueous solution while the water solution preferentially retains the zirconyl chloride. Zirconium extracted with the hafnium (about 2% of the Hf + Zr content) is stripped from the organic phase with HCl and the hafnium is stripped from the organic phase with H_2SO_4, the solvent being recycled.

The 99% hafnium raffinate is then treated with NH_4OH to precipitate $Hf(OH)_4$. This is calcined to HfO_2 in a kiln at 650°C, the oxide is mixed with carbon and formed into pellets, and the pellets chlorinated in a fixed-bed chlorinator to produce $HfCl_4$. The latter is purified by passage as a sublimed vapor through a fused salt bath containing 10% NaCl–10% KCl–80% $HfCl_4$ and held at 370°C. This scrubbing removes chiefly aluminum and iron as well as lowering the content of most other metals (except zirconium) present in the $HfCl_4$ feed.

Hafnium Metal Production

Almost all hafnium metal produced is made by the reduction of $HfCl_4$ with magnesium (Kroll process) or with sodium, the magnesium method being the most widely used. High-purity $HfCl_4$ is sublimed and passed into the upper part of an electrically-heated furnace which contains a pool of molten magnesium in the lower portion. It reacts according to the equation:

$$2Mg + HfCl_4 \longrightarrow Hf + 2MgCl_4.$$

The hafnium is formed as a sponge that is then heated under vacuum to distill off the magnesium chloride and the excess magnesium added to the reduction furnace.

During the reduction stage and the subsequent consolidation steps, great pains are taken to maintain an inert atmosphere or vacuum condition to prevent contamination of the hafnium and adverse effects of such contamination on the properties of the metal.

Ductile massive metal is made from the

hafnium sponge by consumable electrode arc melting in an atmosphere of argon or helium or under a vacuum, or by electron beam melting (a high-vacuum operation). The latter is also a purifying process. In one commercial operation the hafnium sponge is electrolytically refined before being consolidated by melting so as to reduce the content of nonmetallic and some metallic impurities. A feasible process consists of depositing hafnium crystals on a cathode in a molten electrolyte of 95% NaCl–5% KCl at a current density of 175 amp/sq ft, a voltage of 0.3 and a temperature of 840°C. The product is then arc melted under vacuum or in an inert atmosphere.

Hafnium magnesium-reduced sponge can be purified by the iodide process, a bithermal, closed-cycle system in which the metal iodide is simultaneously synthesized and decomposed. In one chamber sponge held at 600°C reacts with iodine vapor to form HfI_4 vapor and in another chamber the HfI_4 vapor is decomposed on a hafnium wire filament maintained at about 1600°C by resistance heating. High-purity hafnium deposits on the wire, liberating iodine for recycle; it is often called crystal bar hafnium.

Physical Properties

Hafnium is a strong ductile metal with a brilliant luster whose density, 13.29 g/cc, and melting point, 2230°C, are among the highest dozen such values for all metals.

The physical properties of hafnium are listed in Table 1. Insofar as possible the values given refer to hafnium of lowest content of other elements, including zirconium. Such material is usually iodide hafnium.

Also listed in Table 1 are some mechanical properties; the latter are to be regarded as typical since considerable variation occurs depending on source of metal, heat treatment, mechanical working, etc. Many of the physical and mechanical properties of hafnium are affected markedly by the presence of interstitial impurities, such as oxygen, nitrogen and carbon.

Thomas and Hayes and Martin and Pizzolato present many additional detailed values showing effects of the different sources and treatments on the mechanical properties of hafnium.

Chemical Properties

The chemical properties of hafnium resemble closely those of zirconium, as mentioned previously. Not only are the atomic radii almost identical, 1.442 Å for Hf and 1.454 Å for Zr, but the valence electrons are also similar, $5d^2\ 6s^2$ for Hf and $4d^2\ 5s^2$ for Zr.

In aqueous solutions hafnium is always tetravalent. The electrode potential for the reaction: $Hf = Hf^{+4} + 4e^-$ is -1.70 volts and that for the reaction: $Zr = Zr^{+4} + 4e^-$ is -1.529 volts. It has been observed that in the molten LiCl–KCl eutectic at 450 and 550°C hafnium ion exists only in the tetravalent state. The standard electrode potentials against a Pt(II)/Pt(0) reference electrode in molten LiCl–KCl eutectic are -1.88 volts at 450°C and -1.92 volts at 550°C for the Hf(IV)/Hf(0) couple.

Hafnium is a reactive metal at high temperatures, but is extremely stable at room temperature. Like a score or so of other metals with high melting points, such as zirconium, titanium and tantalum, the resistance to chemical attack of hafnium is due to a thin tenacious layer of metal oxide on the surface of the metal. Only as this is penetrated by reactants as the temperature is increased is the metal affected. Thus, only at temperatures of a few hundred degrees centigrade does hafnium begin to react appreciably with water, oxygen, nitrogen and hydrogen. Actually, it has excellent corrosion resistance for its chief application as a control rod material in nuclear reactors. It withstands pressurized water and steam at 400°C and is not affected by radiation.

Finely divided hafnium is pyrophoric and can ignite spontaneously in air, a potential hazard when machining the metal or when handling hot sponge hafnium. The massive metal begins to react slowly with air or oxygen at about 400°C, the rate increasing with rising temperature as a parabolic function. However, hafnium can be hot worked in air at about 900°C for a short duration. The reaction product in air and oxygen is HfO_2.

Hafnium begins to react with nitrogen at about 900°C to form hafnium nitride, HfN. It also combines directly when heated with carbon to yield hafnium carbide, HfC; with boron to form hafnium boride, HfB; with

TABLE 1. PHYSICAL PROPERTIES OF HAFNIUM

Atomic number	72
Atomic weight	178.49
Atomic volume, cc/g-atom	13.37
Atomic diameter, for coordination number 8, Å	3.078
Covalent radius, Å	1.442
Isotopes, natural (% abundance)	174 (0.18)
	176 (5.15)
	177 (18.39)
	178 (27.08)
	179 (13.78)
	180 (35.44)
Crystal structure	
Lattice constants, Å	alpha, close-packed
	hexagonal
	a=3.197
	c=5.057
	c/a=1.582
	beta, body-centered
	cubic
	a=3.50
Transition temperature, °C	1760
Density, g/cc	13.29
Melting point, °C	2230
Boiling point, °C	5200
Specific heat, C_p, 25°C, cal/mole/°C	6.24
Thermal conductivity, 50°C, cal/sec/cm/°C	0.0533
Coefficient of linear thermal expansion, 0–1000°C, per °C	5.9×10^{-6}
Latent heat of fusion, kcal/g-atom	5.8
Latent heat of vaporization, kcal/g-atom	72
Vapor pressure, atm	
2430°K	10^{-8}
2610°K	10^{-7}
2820°K	10^{-6}
3360°K	10^{-4}
4170°K	10^{-2}
4740°K	10^{-1}
5500°K	1
Electrical resistivity, 20°C, microhm-cm	35.5
Temperature coefficient of electrical resistivity, 0°C, per °C	3.82×10^{-3}
Magnetic susceptibility, 25°C, emu/g	0.42×10^{-6}
Hall effect, 25°C, volt-cm/amp-gauss	-0.16×10^{-13}
Spectral emissivity, 1750–2300°K, $\epsilon_{0.65\mu}$	0.40
Electron emission, 1900°K, ma/sq cm	4.80
2000°K	26.2
2100°K	123
2200°K	485
Work function, electron volts	3.5
Surface tension, melting point, ergs/sq cm	1500
Thermal neutron absorption cross section, barns/atom	105

Mechanical Properties

Modulus of elasticity, psi	20,000,000
Tensile strength, 25°C, psi	58,000
Elongation, % in 2 in.	31
Hardness, Rockwell B	95

sulfur to form HfS_2; and with silicon to form $HfSi_2$. The halogens react directly with hafnium to yield the corresponding tetrahalide compounds.

Hafnium absorbs hydrogen at a rapid rate at 700°C to give the composition $HfH_{1.86}$. The composition of $HfH_{2.10}$ is obtained with thermal recycling to 500°C in hydrogen followed by slow cooling in hydrogen at 1 atm to room temperature.

In aqueous solutions hafnium is soluble in hydrofluoric acid and in concentrated sulfuric acid, is resistant to dilute HCl and to dilute H_2SO_4, and is unaffected by HNO_3 in all concentrations. In the case of HNO_3 a protective oxide film forms on the metal. Aqua regia dissolves hafnium. With the addition of even small amounts of a soluble fluoride salt the reaction with other acids becomes rapid.

Hafnium is very resistant to alkalis and even boiling or concentrated NaOH solutions do not attack the metal. Blumenthal gives more detailed chemistry background for hafnium.

Principal Compounds

Hafnium tetrachloride, $HfCl_4$, an important intermediate in the production of hafnium metal, is made by the chlorination of HfO_2 in the presence of carbon by the reaction: $HfO_2 + 2Cl_2 + 2C \rightarrow HfCl_4 + 2CO$. It is also made by the chlorination of hafnium carbide. It sublimes at 317°C where its sublimation pressure is 1 atm. Like all except a very few hafnium compounds, $HfCl_4$ is unstable in water and rapidly hydrolyzes to form the oyxchloride, $HfOCl_2$.

Hafnium oxide, HfO_2, m.p. 2775°C, density 9.86 g/cc, is a refractory oxide with attractive properties whose high cost is the chief drawback to wider usage as a high-temperature material. One recent development may increase its use as a reactor control rod material. A new family of ceramic products comprised of compounds of HfO_2 and oxides of selected rare earths, such as dysprosium, erbium and holmium, called rare earth polyhafnates, is available. These materials have high thermal neutron absorption values and good stability under long reactor exposures. Other ceramic applications of hafnia systems are in special optical glasses and in glazes.

Hafnium carbide, nitride and boride have some of the highest melting points known among compounds: 3900°C for HfC, 3300°C for HfN, and 3250°C for HfB. The last two compounds are highly conductive at high temperatures. These properties will undoubtedly lead to applications in high-temperature technology, and much work is now being conducted on many systems and mixtures containing these compounds to determine their properties and areas of use.

Fabrication of Hafnium Metal

Hafnium can be fabricated by the same techniques that are used on zirconium and titanium and with the same precautions to prevent pickup of deleterious contamination. Since hafnium does not deform as readily as zirconium, higher temperatures are required for forging and rolling.

Hafnium can be rolled hot in the temperature range of 900–930°C and forged at 900–1000°C with only minor scaling and loss of metal. It can be cold rolled, swaged, hammered, drawn into wire or rod, extruded and machined.

The metal must be melted under argon or helium or in a vacuum in either nonconsumable or consumable electrode arc furnaces. Annealing during fabrication also should be done under vacuum to prevent atmospheric contamination of the hafnium. Thoroughly cleaned metal can be welded by fusion welding under an inert atmosphere.

Applications of Hafnium Metal

The chief use of hafnium metal is that of a control rod material for nuclear reactors, where its value is fully proved as a long-life, high burn-up material. It is readily available as a by-product in the production of low-hafnium zirconium required for atomic reactors, has excellent mechanical properties, is very corrosion resistant, is not affected adversely by radiation, and can be used without cladding in the reactor. For this use, so-called crystal bar hafnium which contains 1 or 2% Zr is fabricated into desired shapes.

The metal is also being used to a small extent as a component of alloys with other refractory metals, such as tungsten, tantalum and columbium. Not only does the HfO_2 formed on exposure to air help form oxidation resistant surfaces, but HfC precipitates at crystal boundaries tend to lock slippage planes and prevent high temperature creep.

The high melting point and high electron emission of hafnium suggest uses in radio tubes, incandescent lamps and rectifiers and as a cathode in x-ray tubes. Jewelry applications might take advantage of the density, tarnish resistance and beautiful luster of hafnium.

Biological and Biochemical Aspects

There appears to be no evidence of any biochemical or biological activity of hafnium in living organisms. Further, the metal is nontoxic, as are its compounds, unless the latter hydrolyze to yield acidic solutions or vapors.

References

1. Martin, D. R., and Pizzolato, P. J., "Hafnium," chapter in "Rare Metals Handbook," C. A. Hampel, Editor, pp. 198–219, 2nd Edition, New York, Reinhold Publishing Corp., 1961.
2. Thomas, D. E., and Hayes, E. T., Editors, "The Metallurgy of Hafnium," Washington, D.C., U.S. Atomic Energy Commission, 1960. (Obtainable from U.S. Government Printing Office.)
3. Wilson, W. H., and Staehle, R. W., "History of Hafnium," *ibid*, pp. 1–7.
4. Guccione, E., "Here's Hafnium: Hardest Element to Isolate," (with flowsheet), *Chem. Eng.*, **70**, 128–130 (Feb. 18, 1963).
5. McClain, J. H., and Shelton, S. M., "Zirconium and Hafnium Separation," Vol. 1, p. 64, "Reactor Handbook," New York, Interscience Publishers, Inc., 1960.
6. Siebert, M. E., "Hafnium, Electrolytic Preparation," in "Encyclopedia of Electrochemistry," C. A. Hampel, Editor, pp. 692–693, New York, Reinhold Publishing Corp., 1964.
7. Baker, D. H., Jr., and Henrie, T. A., "Electrorefining in Molten Salts," *ibid*, pp. 568–572.
8. Blumenthal, W. B., "The Chemical Behavior of Zirconium," Princeton, N.J., D. Van Nostrand Company, Inc., 1958.
9. "Zr,Hf,Ti Newsletter," an abstract of literature, published periodically since 1966 by Amax Specialty Metals, Inc., P.O. Box 32, Akron, N.Y. 14001.

CLIFFORD A. HAMPEL

HELIUM

Helium, chemical symbol He, or, more completely, He^4, is the second element (atomic number 2) in the periodic chart of the elements, and is the first and lightest member of the rare, noble, or inert gas group having zero valence. (See **Noble Gases**.) It is a gas at ordinary temperatures and pressures and is colorless, odorless, tasteless, and nontoxic. Like all noble gases, its molecule is monatomic, so its atomic and molecular weights are equal, being 4.0026 on the carbon-12 scale.

He^4, containing approximately 0.1 ppm of the light isotope He^3, is obtained from natural gas by a low-temperature separation process. He^4 derived from air contains 1 ppm He^3. Because air contains only 5 ppm He^4, large-scale production of helium from the atmosphere is not attractive economically.

Discovery

P. J. C. Janssen and J. Norman Lockyer shared the honor of discovering helium in the sun's chromosphere by spectroscopic observations in 1868. Janssen studied the sun during the total solar eclipse of August 18 that year. Lockyer's most detailed studies were later, without an eclipse, but Lockyer was responsible for classifying the lines and identifying the elements responsible for them. Lockyer observed a bright yellow line near the Fraunhofer D line—he later called the new line D_3 to distinguish it from the D_1 and D_2 doublet of sodium at 5890 and 5896 Å. D_3 was later shown to have a wavelength of 5876 Å.

Lockyer and his friend Frankland performed many experiments with hydrogen, thinking that the D_3 line was due to some type of hydrogen not present on earth. Their work was unsuccessful, and Lockyer became convinced that they were dealing with a new element. Just when he coined the name "helium" (from the Greek word "helios," meaning sun) is uncertain, but more evidence for the new element was slow in developing. Lockyer apparently became unconvinced later, however, and wrote, even as late as 1889: "D_3 . . . is a fine vapor of hydrogen!"

Proof came on March 26, 1895, when Ramsay found the elusive helium in a sample of cleveite, a variety of uraninite. He treated cleveite with sulfuric acid, and, after removing nitrogen and oxygen, examined its spectrum. He found the argon he was looking for, but he also saw the yellow D_3 line of helium. Ten years later helium was found in natural gas by Cady and McFarland at the University of Kansas, in gas from a shallow well drilled at Dexter, Kansas, in 1903. Their results were not published until 1907.

Occurrence

Because the source of the sun's energy is the thermonuclear conversion of hydrogen to helium through the carbon cycle, helium is present in the chromosphere of the sun and in the atmospheres of all stars deriving their energy by this reaction. This process is responsible for it being second only to hydrogen as the most abundant element in the universe. The sun's composition is approximately 80/20 hydrogen/helium, with about 1% of heavier elements. Helium is present in minute quantities in gases from fumaroles and mineral springs. The earth's atmosphere contains 5.2 ppm He^4 at sea level and the concentration is essentially constant to a height of 15 miles. At a height of 600 miles there is a "layer" where the concentration of helium atoms is unusually high, compared with other elements at this level. The presence of helium in samples of sea water taken from a depth of 3400 meters at a station in the Pacific Ocean was reported in 1964. The gas is present in excess of its normal solubility in sea water and in relation to concentrations of the other noble gases. The excess helium is attributed to an influx from sediments where it is produced by the natural radioactive decay of members of the uranium and thorium series. Low concentrations of the light isotope He^3 have been found in meteorites and have been observed in the atmospheres of stars.

The only occurrences of helium that are of commercial value—as large-scale sources of the gas—are in a few natural gas deposits. Natural gases in the Texas and Oklahoma Panhandles and in Kansas contain large reserves of helium. Helium contents of these gases fall into two ranges of concentration—from ~ 0.4 to 0.9% and from ~ 1.8 to 2.3%. Isolated natural gas fields, where the helium concentration approaches 9%, with the remainder being principally nitrogen, are in the northwestern corner of New Mexico and in eastern Arizona. These reserves are small and have limited value as long-range sources of helium.

Origin on Earth

It is now generally accepted that terrestrial helium is formed by the natural decay of alpha-emitting radioactive minerals in the earth's crust. Alpha particles are helium nuclei, and each particle readily gains the two electrons necessary to become a neutral helium atom. The amount of helium contained in the known reserves is so great that it is almost inconceivable that the gas could have originated by this process. Calculations show that one cubic mile of the earth's crust produces only 0.5 cubic feet of helium per year. When all facts are considered—the quite uniform distribution of radium and other alpha emitters in the earth's crust, the total volume of the earth's crust, and the 4.7 billion years that the earth has existed—the process can account not only for the total reserves of helium, but also for the continuing loss to the atmosphere by diffusion. Because helium-bearing natural gases are not associated with highly radioactive minerals, the presence of helium in these gases may be assumed to be due to its production by radiodecay in other geologic formations, and its subsequent migration to areas where the gas becomes trapped and mixed with hydrocarbon-rich gas.

Production of Helium

The United States Government began its efforts in helium production during World War I following a suggestion by Sir Richard Threlfall that barrage balloons filled with non-flammable helium would offer protection against Germany's hydrogen-filled Zeppelins and low-flying aircraft which were bombing Allied ships and British cities. The suggestion was a bold one because at that time only a few cubic feet of the unique gas had ever been obtained.[†] By the time World War I was over in 1918, three small experimental plants had produced about 200,000 cu ft of 92% helium under Navy sponsorship. Later this helium was used in the world's first helium-filled airship—the Navy's nonrigid C–7. Its maiden

† This work was done by C. W. Seibel, then a graduate student at Kansas University.

flight was on December 7, 1921, from Hampton Roads, Virginia, to Bolling Field, District of Columbia.

Until World War II helium requirements were limited to lighter-than-air ships, weather balloons, diving operations, and medical applications. A survey made to assess possible wartime requirements showed that new plants were needed to augment the 20 million cu ft per year capacity of the Bureau of Mines plant at Amarillo, Texas. The Exell plant near Masterson, Texas, was completed in 1943, and soon thereafter plants were built at Otis and Cunningham, Kansas, and Shiprock, New Mexico. Their total annual capacity was about 140 million cu ft.

Helium use slackened after World War II but increased sharply in the period 1950–1960 as new uses for helium were found in developing the early ICBM's and space boosters. Helium was in short supply periodically until the Bureau's Keyes plant in the Oklahoma Panhandle began production in mid-1959.

Production Process

Helium is extracted from natural gas by subjecting the entire gas stream to conditions of low temperature and sufficiently high pressure that the hydrocarbons, nitrogen, and other gases are nearly all liquefied and thus may be physically separated from the helium. The helium remains a gas throughout the process. Small helium losses occur by solution in the hydrocarbon-rich liquid phases. The process is divided into two separate operations: "extraction" refers to the physical separation of a "crude helium" product from the original gas, and "purification" is the process of subjecting the crude helium, under pressure, to successively lower temperatures to liquefy more of the nitrogen, and thus purify the helium further. Remaining impurities are removed by adsorption on activated charcoal at liquid nitrogen temperature and the helium finally obtained is usually better than 99.995% pure. It is designated "Grade A" helium.†

The production process at the Keyes plant may be taken as a specific example. Natural

† The average impurities, in ppm, in helium produced at the Bureau of Mines plants, are as follows: Ne 10–15, N_2 1–5, H_2O 1–3, O_2 0.2–0.6, CO_2 0.0–0.1, H_2 0.0–0.1, and Ar 0.0–0.1.

gas at 450 psig and containing 2.1% helium, is stripped of its carbon dioxide and water by a monoethanolamine-diethylene glycol scrubbing column and bauxite drying agent. The gas is then cooled to $-250°F$, still at 450 psig. After liquefaction occurs, the pressure is dropped to 225 psig to reduce the amount of helium lost by solution in the liquid and the vapor phase (crude helium) is then extracted. The crude helium is about 79/21 helium/nitrogen, and may contain 0.1% methane and a few ppm hydrogen. The hydrogen is removed by adding oxygen and passing the crude helium through a palladium catalyst. The crude helium is then compressed to 2750 psig and purification is accomplished in three additional steps, all at the same pressure: (1) The crude helium is cooled to $-320°F$ and the resulting phase separation increases the helium content to 98.2%. (2) This 98.2% helium is cooled to $-340°F$ by reducing the pressure on a bath of liquid nitrogen surrounding the containing vessel. The resulting gas phase is 99.5% helium. (3) Final purification is effected by passing the 99.5% stream through a bed of activated coconut charcoal at $-320°F$.

An auxiliary liquid nitrogen cycle provides refrigeration for both the extraction and the purification processes, and all cold streams, gas and liquid, are heat-exchanged with warm incoming streams to conserve refrigeration. The hydrocarbon-rich natural gas liquids condensed in the extraction process are vaporized as they return through the heat exchangers and are returned to the gas supplier for sale as fuel.

A number of variations are employed at the several Bureau, commercial, and conservation plants, but the basic low-temperature or cryogenic process is essentially the same.

A small experimental plant in Canada has been reported which separates helium by diffusion, using a barrier material of high-silica glass. In 1921, when various means were considered for recovering helium, Bureau engineers knew that helium could be separated from natural gas by diffusion through high-silica glass and other permeable barriers or semipermeable membranes and at that time negotiated a contract with the Massachusetts Institute of Technology to evaluate the practicality of the diffusion process. The studies concluded that the cryogenic process was better, and it was used. Recently, studies by Du Pont, Linde, and others indicate that the diffusion process may be suitable, but its successful competition with the cryogenic process has not as of 1967 been demonstrated. The method may be excellent for purification.

Production Data

As of August, 1967, 14 helium plants were in operation in the United States and Canada. Fig. 1 shows the location and ownership of

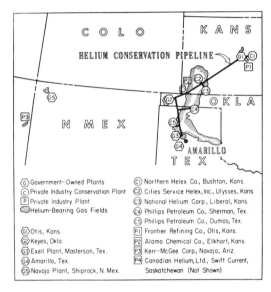

Government-Owned Plants — (G)
Private Industry Conservation Plant — (C)
Private Industry Plant — [P]
Helium-Bearing Gas Fields

(G1) Otis, Kans.
(G2) Keyes, Okla.
(G3) Exell Plant, Masterson, Tex.
(G4) Amarillo, Tex.
(G5) Navajo Plant, Shiprock, N. Mex.

(C1) Northern Helex Co., Bushton, Kans.
(C2) Cities Service Helex, Inc., Ulysses, Kans.
(C3) National Helium Corp., Liberal, Kans.
(C4) Phillips Petroleum Co., Sherman, Tex.
(C5) Phillips Petroleum Co., Dumas, Tex.

[P1] Frontier Refining Co., Otis, Kans.
[P2] Alamo Chemical Co., Elkhart, Kans.
[P3] Kerr-McGee Corp., Navajo, Ariz.
[P4] Canadian Helium, Ltd., Swift Current, Saskatchewan (Not Shown)

FIG. 1. Helium production facilities in the United States.

the United States plants and identifies the single plant in Canada. In addition, International Helium Corporation is building a plant at Wood Mountain, Saskatchewan, which is scheduled for completion in 1967. Also, Arizona Helium Co. is to start construction (1967) of a plant in eastern Arizona, and the capacity of the plant at Swift Current, Saskatchewan was recently tripled; the enlarged plant began operations in mid-1967.

The Bureau of Mines recovers 750 million cu ft of helium per year from natural gas at its five plants (G1-G5, Fig. 1). The Exell and Keyes plants produce 300 million each, the Navajo plant 75, and the Amarillo and Otis plants 45 and 30, respectively. The product is of "Grade A" purity. The Otis plant dis-

continued this grade in 1965; it now produces crude helium only.

Tables 1 and 2 give the total production of helium on the United States and Canada for

TABLE 1.

Helium production for selected years, 1918–1960 (millions of cu ft at 14.7 psia and 70°F).

Calendar Year	Total Production†
1918	0.2
1921‡	2.1
1925	9.4
1930	10.6
1935	8.4
1940	11.6
1943	116.3‡
1944	126.9§
1945	94.7
1950	81.4
1955	220.7
1960	642.0

† These are the *total* production figures for the United States and Canada during the years shown, except for a small experimental plant in Canada which operated intermittently from 1917 to 1920, and the Girdler Corporation's two plants in the United States which produced about 10 million cu ft during 1927–1937.
‡ No production in 1919 and 1920, except for 60,000 cu ft at the Canadian plant.
§ Increase due to demand for helium during World War II for use in Navy blimps.

a few years during the period 1918 to the present. Table 2 shows approximate production of the four private plants (P1-P4, Fig. 1) and the five helium conservation plants (C1-C5, Fig. 1). The private plants have been built since 1960 and supply helium to non-Government users. The five conservation plants extract helium and sell it to the Bureau of Mines under long term contracts for storage. (See page 264). Little is known of helium production in Eastern Europe, but it is certain that helium is recovered in the U.S.S.R. for scientific and industrial use. It is reported that a plant in France produces helium from air as a by-product in the liquefaction of air.

Isotopes

Heavier isotopes of masses 5, 6, 7, and 8 have been reported. The atomic wt of He[5] is 5.0123. It is very unstable, with a half-life of

TABLE 2.

Helium production (U.S. and Canada), including Government and commercial plants, and helium extracted by conservation plants, for 1962–1966 (millions of cu ft at 14.7 psia and 70°F).

Calendar Year	From Bureau Plants		From Commercial Plants	From Conservation Plants	Total
1962	680.9	35.7†	29.0	2.2	747.8
1963	774.2	0.0	35.0	1420.0	2,229.2
1964	784.5	0.7†	50.0	3193.1	4,028.3
1965	757.4	20.7†	66.0	3549.6	4,393.7
1966	769.2	93.2†	149.0	3692.7	4,704.1

† Produced in previous years and withdrawn from storage during the current year for use.

TABLE 3. PHYSICAL PROPERTIES OF He^4

Boiling point at 1 atm, °K	4.216
Melting point at 25 atm, °K	1.0
Critical temp, °K	5.2
Critical pressure, atm	2.26
Critical density, g/cc	0.0693
Density at 0°C and 1 atm, gpl	0.1785
Density of vapor at b.p., gpl	17.0
Latent heat of vaporization of liquid at normal b.p., cal/g	4.9
Latent heat of fusion of solid at m.p. (at 25 atm), cal/g-mole	1.0
Heat capacity, C_p, at 25°C and 1 atm, cal/°K/g-mole	4.968
Ratio of specific heats, C_p/C_v, 0 to 20°C	1.63
Viscosity at 20°C and 1 atm, micropoise	196.1
Thermal conductivity at 0°C, cal/cm/sec/°C	0.000339
Solubility in water†, ml gas (STP)/g H_2O at 20°C	0.0088
Expansion factor, from liquid at 4.2°K, 1 atm, to gas at 0°C, 1 atm	699.7
Joule-Thomson inversion temp at 1 atm, °K	32–50
Atomic diameter, Å	2.56
First ionization potential, electron volts	24.58
Second ionization potential, electron volts	54.40
First resonance potential, electron volts	20.91
Metastable potential, electron volts	19.77
Compressibility factor at 70°F and 1 atm	1.00049
Dielectric constant at 25°C, 1 atm	1.0000639
Refractive index at 0°C, 1 atm	1.000036

† At one atmosphere partial pressure.

2×10^{-21} second. He^6 (atomic wt 6.0197) is radioactive with a half-life of 0.8 second, and decays by emitting a 3.5-MeV beta ray. He^7 and He^8 are produced in certain nuclear reactions and are more appropriately called "hyperfragments." The half-life of He^7 is less than 10^{-8} second. It emits a 10-MeV beta ray and a 0.5-MeV gamma ray. The existence of He^8 was predicted in 1960 and confirmed in 1966. Its half-life is about 0.03 seconds.

Physical Properties

Table 3 summarizes some principal properties. Though the data are not shown in the table for every case, it is interesting to compare some of the properties of helium with those of other gases. Thermal conductivity of helium is higher than that of any other gas except hydrogen; it is less soluble in water than any other gas, and its solubility in other liquids is low; its rate of diffusion or permeation through solids is about 65% that of hydrogen, but is three times greater than that of air, a property which makes helium especially useful for leak detection; the index of refraction of helium is so close to unity that a light wave is distorted less when it enters an atmosphere of helium that it is upon entering any other gas. Although its density is almost twice that of hydrogen, it has about 98% of the lifting power of hydrogen. One thousand cu ft of helium lifts 65.8 lbs at sea level.

The ionization potential given in the table is that required to remove the first electron. Helium may absorb energy without becoming ionized; the first resonance potential is the energy required to raise the atom from its ground level to the first energy level above ground. It also has higher energy states from which the excited atom may return to the ground state or to some intermediate energy state. Helium also possesses "metastable levels," from which direct return to the normal state is impossible. Consequently, these have a much longer life than do normal energy states. All the "helium group" gases possess metastable states, and thus it is possible for them to become ionized in an electrical discharge where the voltage is lower than the ionizational potential. Helium is a nearly ideal gas, and follows the ideal gas law closely.

The specific heat of helium gas is unusually high. To vaporize one liter of liquid helium requires 2.48 BTU. This same energy will heat the resultant vapor only $4°K$. Heating the vapor from $4.2°K$ to room temperature requires 180 BTU. Density of the vapor at the normal boiling point—the vapor in equilibrium with liquid helium—is also very high, so the vapor expands greatly on heating to room temperature. As a safety precaution, vessels filled with helium gas at $5–10°K$ should be treated as though they contained liquid because of the great increase in pressure that results from warming these containers to room temperature. Helium, unlike most gases, heats upon free expansion at usual temperatures (has a negative Joule-Thomson coefficient). When cooled to a sufficiently low temperature, it cools upon expanding. This is the Joule-Thomson inversion temperature, and is not accurately known (see Table 3).

Chemical Properties

This information would be perhaps more appropriately included in a discussion of atomic spectra or energy states. Because the species considered are really compounds, however unstable, they illustrate the chemical properties of helium.

Rutherford and Royds demonstrated in 1907 that alpha particles are helium nuclei. Thus, broadly, *all* nuclear reactions involving alpha particles may be considered as properties of helium, and any source of alpha particles is a source of helium. Many nuclear reactions involving different isotopes of helium as reactant or product are reported.

Helium has a valence of zero and the statement is generally made that it will not combine with any other element. Some have said that helium has a *very weak tendency* to combine with certain other elements. Xenon is also an inert gas, and the discovery in 1962 of easily-produced stable fluorides of xenon and radon has caused new inquiry into the chemical properties of helium. Unusual techniques are now being studied for the preparation of a difluoride of helium. Most promising of these is a technique based on nuclear transmutation.

At extreme conditions—high temperatures, low pressures and ionizing conditions, such as are obtained in plasmas and glow and spark discharges (under conditions for the production of spectra)—combinations of helium with other elements have been observed. Species such as HeNe and the molecular ions He_2^+ and He_2^{++} have been studied. The molecule He_2 exists under these conditions and has a large number of band systems.

In the fluorescence spectrum of mercury vapor to which a rare gas is added, diffuse bands have been observed, apparently formed by a mercury atom and a rare gas atom. The band of HgHe does not, however, show any structure and the molecule is apparently held together by polarization forces only. The species $HgHe_{10}$ and WHe_2 have also been reported. HeH^+ and HeD^+ ions have been observed in the ionizing conditions used in mass spectroscopy. Most of these species are not stable at ordinary temperatures and pressures. Though clathrates and hydrates have been reported for some of the inert gases, none containing helium have been announced as of August 1967.

Liquid Helium

Helium was first liquefied by Kamerlingh Onnes in 1908 in his now-famous low-temperature laboratory in Leiden, Holland. He attempted to produce solid helium the same day by reducing the pressure in equilibrium with the liquid to lower the boiling point. Though he reduced the temperature to approximately 0.8°K, he did not produce the solid. The phase diagram for helium (Fig. 2) shows why he failed. Helium does not have a

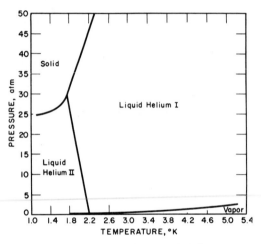

FIG. 2. Phase diagram of He4.

triple point where the vapor, liquid and solid phases are in equilibrium at a single temperature and pressure. The figure shows that a pressure of 25 atmospheres is required at 1–1.5°K to produce the solid.

Gaseous helium does not exhibit any properties unexpected for a gas of low density, but liquid helium does. Helium liquefies at 1 atmosphere at 4.2°K. The liquid is called "Helium I" to distinguish it from a second form. Its "gas-like" index of refraction (value is 1.026) makes the surface of the liquid so difficult to see that floats of "Styrofoam" are often used to mark the surface during demonstrations of the liquid in apparatus permitting visual inspection. The liquid is colorless, has very low viscosity, and a density 1/8th that of water. This density is only one-fourth the

value expected from classical physics; thus, the atomic volume of the liquid is four times the expected value. This "wide spacing" of the atoms cannot be explained classically, and is considered to be a direct result of the quantum nature of the liquid. Because helium contains an even number of particles in its nucleus (2 protons and 2 neutrons) it was expected earlier that it would represent a close approach to the "hard core" atom of classical physics. This, however, is not the case and the liquid displays phenomena explained only by quantum mechanics. The liquid is called a "quantum fluid," as it exhibits atomic properties on a macroscopic scale; probably because the boiling point is so close to absolute zero that the atomic properties are not masked by random molecular motion that occurs at warmer temperatures. Quantum characteristics are particularly evident in liquid Helium II, in the phenomenon of "superfluidity" (see page 263).

An interesting property that occurs at Helium I temperatures, although it does not directly involve the helium itself, is that of "superconductivity." This is sometimes called the "frictionless" or "superfluid" flow of electrons. It is the ability of some materials, when cooled to a sufficiently low temperature, to permit the flow of electrical current without offering any resistance whatsoever. The phenomenon was discovered by Kamerlingh Onnes in 1911, while working with columns of mercury a fraction of a millimeter in diameter. It usually occurs at temperatures higher than the helium liquefaction temperature of 4.2°K; lead, for example, becomes superconducting at 7.3° K (its "transition" temperature), so a lead "wire" of small cross section immersed in Helium I will permit a large current flow, limited only by the "threshold magnetic field" of the superconductor. In the "Persistent Current" experiment superconductivity is demonstrated by maintaining a current flow of several amperes in a lead ring at 4.2°K in liquid helium. The current is induced in the ring by external means. The exciting source is then removed and the current flows unabated in the ring as long as it is kept at the low temperature. The experiment has been performed in several laboratories; in one case the current flow continued for several years before the lead ring was allowed to warm above its transition temperature.

Superconductors are now used to increase the field strengths of magnets and in many cases to allow a reduction in the physical size of the magnet. Superconducting transformers, dynamos, and gyroscopes have been built.

As the boiling point of Helium I is lowered, usually by evacuating the system, a unique transition occurs at 2.19°K—a liquid, called Helium II, is formed, with new and far more unusual properties than Helium I. The temperature at which this transition occurs is called the "lambda" point—from the shape of the plot of C_s (the specific heat of the liquid in equilibrium with its saturated vapor) versus temperature. The plot resembles the Greek letter "lambda" from about 1.5 to 2.5°K. The transition marks the boundary between classical and quantum fluids.

Liquid Helium I contracts with lowering temperature till the lambda point is reached; at this transition temperature the liquid suddenly expands. The rate of expansion decreases as the temperature is lowered below the lambda point, and at about 1°K the expansion ceases entirely and the normal contraction displayed by Helium I returns.

The most unusual property of Helium II is that of "superfluidity," which is often demonstrated as follows: an open beaker or cup is placed in a system containing the liquid, wherein the cup, liquid and container are all below the lambda point. When the cup is lowered so that its bottom touches the surface of the liquid, the liquid helium flows up the outer surface of the cup, over the lip and down the inner surface. The flow continues until the surface of the liquid in the container is level with that outside—without the lip of the cup having been immersed in the liquid. If now the cup is lifted free of the liquid, the reverse process occurs, with the flow of liquid continuing until the cup is empty, the liquid helium forming droplets on the bottom of the cup. The liquid flows in an extremely thin layer, or film, only 3×10^{-6} cm thick. The film is called the "Rollin film," after B. V. Rollin, who first studied and characterized it. The rate of transport of helium in the film is almost completely independent of the nature of the cup material or the height of the cup. Helium II is thus called a "superfluid" and

the phenomenon is termed "superfluidity."

Helium II has an extremely high thermal conductivity, several hundred times that of copper or silver at room temperature. This is easily observed in the behavior of the surface of Helium I as it is being cooled. Helium I exhibits the usual boiling of a cryogenic fluid due to heat input into the system. When the temperature reaches the lambda point the boiling stops immediately and the liquid is very quiescent. The high thermal conductivity of Helium II will not permit the temperature differential necessary to cause normal boiling, and heat input into the system causes evaporation of helium *directly from the surface* of the liquid.

It is possible to establish a temperature differential in Helium II, and when this is done the system responds in a number of interesting ways. In the "Fountain Effect" there is produced a jet of superfluid helium several cms high; in the "Mechanocaloric Effect" a difference in liquid level is produced. Descriptions of the phenomena are given in texts on liquid helium.

Materials that are good heat conductors are usually good electrical conductors; however, helium has no free electrons and is an electrical insulator. It transmits heat by virtue of its quantum-mechanical character—equations describing the rate of heat transfer in Helium II are similar to those used in acoustics for travel of sound in air. Hence, the transfer of heat in Helium II is called "second sound." The velocity is about 20 meters per second at 1.8°K.

The viscosity of Helium I can be measured by conventional methods; it is 25.5 micropoise at 2.2°K—compared with that of water at 20°C, 10,000 micropoise. The measurement of viscosity of the superfluid Helium II, though, is another matter. The method employed by Andronikashvili, that of using an oscillating twisting motion of a series of parallel plates, which caused the liquid helium to "pick up" the motion of the oscillating discs, enabled him to measure the viscosity of Helium I easily, but he found that in Helium II, the liquid did not pick up *any* motion. The liquid acted as though it had *zero* viscosity (by other methods it has been found to be $<10^{-5}$ micropoise). The superfluid flows rapidly through channels only 10^{-5} or 10^{-6} cm wide.

Solid Helium

Solid helium was produced by W. H. Keesom in 1926 by raising the pressure of the system to 25 atmospheres at a temperature of about 1°K. There was no surface demarcation between the solid and the liquid during the experiment, as the refractive indices of the two phases are nearly equal. The solid has a sharp melting point, however, and is now known to be crystalline. It is transparent and is an almost invisible solid.

Helium 3

Of the "unusual" isotopes of helium, He^3, atomic weight 3.01603 (carbon-12 scale), is by far the most important. It is a stable isotope with 2 protons and 1 neutron in the nucleus. Its concentrations in He^4 derived from the atmosphere and from natural gases were mentioned previously. He^3 has been recently found to exist in stellar atmospheres. The properties of He^3 are so unlike those of He^4 that a 50/50 mixture of the two isotopes, when liquefied, separates into two immiscible phases below 0.8°K. Mixtures of He^3 and He^4, both gas and liquid, have become of great interest in recent years in theoretical physics, because each isotope follows different quantum statistics. Liquid He^3, unlike liquid He^4, does not have a lambda point and accompanying anomalous phase change. It does not exhibit superfluidity. A recent calculation, however, shows that between 0.008 and 0.0001°K it should exhibit this phenomenon. Peshkov reported a slight increase in the heat capacity of liquid He^3 at 0.0055°K, and suggested that this is due to a superfluid phase transition. His work, however, has not yet been generally accepted. Temperatures around 0.00002°K have been produced, using elaborate apparatus, so this question is being studied by repeating the experiment at still lower temperatures. It is certain, however, that the properties of superfluid He^3 would not be identical with those of superfluid He^4 (Helium II).

Helium-3 is available in high purity at a price of about $100 per liter at STP†, from the AEC. It is produced in nuclear reactors by the bombardment of Li^6 with neutrons to produce He^4 and tritium, H^3. The tritium is

† Standard temperature and pressure (0°C and 1 atm).

separated from the mixture and decays with a half-life of 12.5 years to produce He^3. The resulting He^3 contains small concentrations of tritium, which is a disadvantage for some research purposes. Though sophisticated procedures reducing the tritium content to $2 \times 10^{-10}\%$ have been developed, there is interest in acquiring He^3 from a natural gas source, because the isotope so derived would contain no tritium. There are several possible ways to do this. The "heat-flush" method might be used for separation because He^4 exhibits superfluidity below the lambda point, whereas He^3 does not. Thermal diffusion is a standard technique for performing the separation. Recently-developed gas centrifuges may lead ultimately to a practical separation.

One of the greatest practical uses of He^3 is as the circulating medium in refrigerators to maintain constant temperature in the region 0.3 to 3°K. This use is due to its lower boiling point (3.195°K) and because it is not a superfluid at these temperatures. A very new use is in He^3-dilution refrigerators for the range 0.004 to 0.1°K.

Helium Conservation Program

A $47.5 million-per-year helium conservation program authorized by Congress in 1960 and implemented in 1961 by four long-term helium purchase contracts gives good assurance of a continuing helium supply beyond the year 2000. The plants, financed, built and operated by private industry, recover helium which would otherwise be lost uselessly to the atmosphere when helium-bearing gas is used as fuel. Each plant extracts, from natural gas containing 0.4–0.7% helium, a crude helium product, nominally 50 to 80% helium, and 50 to 20% nitrogen, and delivers it to a 425-mile Bureau of Mines pipeline system for transportation and underground storage in the Government-owned Cliffside gas field about 15 miles northwest of Amarillo, Texas.

About 3.6 billion cu ft of helium are purchased annually, and over the 25-year life span of the program 62.5 billion cu ft of helium will be acquired. The stored helium will be used to supplement the volume available from the presently declining reserves of helium-bearing natural gas. Wastage of helium in fuel gas is continuing at the rate of about 4 billion cu ft per year because many helium-containing gases are marketed as fuel. About half of this volume could be saved for future use at costs comparable to those in the present program. Fig. 1 shows the location and ownership of the 5 conservation plants and the location of the pipeline. Production data for the plants are included in Table 2.

Shipments

Helium is shipped as a compressed gas in cylinders, railway tank cars, and automotive semitrailers. Liquid helium is shipped in dewars and in special vacuum-insulated, over-the-road semitrailers.

A "standard" cylinder contains 213 cu ft of helium (14.7 psia and 70°F) at 2200 psig. Tank cars are made of multiple, forged steel tubes and have a net weight of about 240,000 pounds. When filled to an average capacity of 275,000 cu ft (at pressures to 4,000 psig) they weigh only 2,900 pounds more. The Federal Government owns the only tank cars (239) used for helium transportation. Semitrailers have from 20 to 30% of the capacity of tank cars. They are hauled by truck-tractors or transported "piggy-back" on railway flatcars.

Dewars contain from 25 to 7,000 liters of helium. They are usually flown to destination, but may be transported by truck. The capacity of some semitrailers in liquid helium transportation service is 10,000 gallons each, which is equivalent to about one million cu ft of gaseous helium.

No shipments of liquid helium are made from Bureau of Mines plants. Most of the helium produced by Kansas Refined Helium Co. and Alamo Chemical Co. is shipped as a liquid for freight economy even though the end use is primarily for helium gas. Kerr-McGee Corporation sells much of its production as liquid helium. Refer to Fig. 1 for locations of these plants. Several private companies liquefy helium purchased from the Bureau and sell it for end use as a liquid.

The Bureau of Mines sells Grade A helium at $35 per 1000 cu ft, measured at 14.7 psia and 70°F, f.o.b. its plants. The price is set to defray the cost of producing and conserving helium. Private plants sell helium for less than this, as they are not concerned with conservation costs.

Uses

A list of the current uses of helium (gas and liquid) is given in Table 4. Uses are listed in order of decreasing volume for each main classification and for each subheading. Some low-volume uses are very important.

Total volume of helium used in the U.S. and Canada during 1966 is estimated at 960 million cu ft. About 20 million cu ft was exported for low-temperature research, leak detection, chromatographic analysis, and metallurgy. The U.S. Government, through its agencies and contractors, uses about 80% of the total. Private and commercial uses account for the remainder. Bureau of Mines long-range projections indicate that the annual volume of helium used will double to about 2 billion cu ft by the year 2000. Present indications, however, are that helium use in 1967 may drop 20 to 30% as a result of a slackened pace in United States space programs.

Helium has a combination of 5 well-defined properties which are responsible for its long list of uses. These are (1) low density, (2) low boiling point, (3) low solubility, (4) chemical inertness, and (5) high thermal conductivity. In Table 4 the property primarily responsible for each use is indicated, where applicable, by the above numbers in parentheses.

Current Research

The Bureau of Mines Helium Research Center, in Amarillo, Texas, engages in a modest program of helium research. Projects include experimental measurements of the heat capacity of liquid helium; determination of the PVT† relationships of helium and mixtures of helium with other gases; critical evaluations of published data relating to helium in an effort to establish the "best data" for helium; experimental measurement of enthalpy of helium-nitrogen mixtures over a wide range of temperature and pressure; viscosity, dielectric constant and diffusion coefficient data for mixtures of helium with other gases and phase behavior of mixtures of helium-hydrogen and helium-neon at conditions of 10,000 psia and to 10°K. A study of the lifetime of metastable helium in the 2^3s state is in progress.

† pressure-volume-temperature.

TABLE 4.

Estimated use of helium (gas and liquid) during 1966, in U.S., Canada, and countries of import shown as percentage of total of estimated 960 million cu ft. Numbers in parentheses refer to properties (page 265). Use is specifically for gas, unless LHe (liquid He⁴) is noted.

Use and Property	% of Total
1. Launch vehicles and rockets (NASA† and Air Force programs)	56
a. As an "ullage" medium, to displace fuels and oxidizers withdrawn from storage tanks or forced into the combustion chambers by helium pressure (2,3,4)	
b. To purge fuel and oxidizer systems in ground-support work for launch (2,3,4)	
c. LHe—to precool liquid-hydrogen-fueled space vehicles, to improve engine efficiency (2)	
2. Metallurgical applications (4)	14
a. In shielded-arc welding of magnesium, titanium, aluminum, copper, stainless steel, and other metals	
b. To provide an inert atmosphere for growing crystals of germanium and silicon in transistor and diode manufacture; in furnaces for metal treating, and in production of titanium and other metals	
c. To sparge dissolved gases from molten metals during purification	
3. Nuclear and atomic energy applications (AEC‡ programs)	12
a. As a heat-transfer, protective atmosphere, and coolant medium for nuclear reactors (4, 5)	
b. As artificially accelerated projectiles for nuclear reactions (alpha particles and helium ions)	
c. LHe and LHe³—for bubble chambers§	
4. Miscellaneous	6
a. For detecting leaks in high-vacuum equipment and pressure containers	
b. In analytical chemistry, as a carrier gas in chromatography (2, 4)	
c. LHe—to provide an environment for superconducting apparatus of all types—magnets, dynamos, transformers, gyroscopes, etc. (2)	
d. In mixtures with other gases, especially neon, for lasers	
e. For gas-lubricated bearings in high-speed gyroscopes and for rotation of mirror systems in ultra-high-speed photography (1)	
f. In luminous signs, of "neon" type, for advertising	
g. In optical instruments, to fill space between lenses (4)	
h. In geological dating	
i. To provide an inert environment for preservation of historical documents (4)	
5. As a lifting gas (1, 4)	5
a. Weather balloons, in meteorological research	
b. Research balloons, for astronomical and astrophysical studies, such as high-altitude telescopic photographs of the sun, etc.	
c. A few commercially owned nonrigid airships	
d. "Kite-type" balloons to move timber in logging operations	
e. Toy balloons, including larger balloons for advertising	
f. A few balloons for sport flying	
6. Aerodynamic and space research	4
a. In wind tunnels and shock tubes to study design of airfoils, etc. (1)	
b. LHe—for cooling masers and lasers for communications with space vehicles, and in radio astronomy (2)	
c. LHe—to produce high vacuum systems by "cryopumping"¶ techniques for space simulation chambers (2)	
7. Low-temperature research (1)	2
a. LHe, LHe³, and mixtures—in He³-dilution refrigerators for 0.004 to 0.1°K and in research aimed at reaching absolute zero	

TABLE 4—*continued*

---

    b. LHe³—to provide refrigeration in the region 0.3 to 3°K for any purpose where this temperature is needed (such as the storage of free radicals)

    c. LHe and LHe³—in theoretical studies of the liquid state, to explain superfluidity and to provide fundamental information on systems following Bose and Fermi statistics

8. Medical applications   1

    a. In mixtures with oxygen, as a breathing atmosphere, in the treatment of asthma and respiratory diseases, and in the recovery room for "easy" breathing   (3, 4)

    b. To dilute flammable gaseous anesthetics to reduce fire hazard in operating rooms (4)

    c. In mixtures with oxygen, as a breathing atmosphere, in space and oceanographic programs   (3, 4)

    d. Same as c, but for caisson workers and divers to prevent the "bends"   (3, 4)

    e. LHe—to quick-freeze living cells to promote their viability in cancer and other medical research   (2)

---

† National Aeronautics and Space Administration.
‡ Atomic Energy Commission.
§ LHe³ has been recently used in an experimental bubble chamber 5 inches in diameter and 1 cm deep. It contained 100 cc of the isotope, which cost $25,000.
¶ A procedure in which an evacuated system is cooled with liquid helium, thereby freezing residual gas in the system and lowering the pressure significantly. Systems can be evacuated to 10^{-12} torr by the method.

Low-temperature physicists in this country and in Europe are studying the behavior of liquid helium to develop a better fundamental understanding of the quantum liquid, and to explain superfluidity and superconductivity. Studies of quantized vortices in rotating Helium II are throwing light on the phenomena. Mixtures of He^3 and He^4 are interesting for theoretical study, particularly in the liquid state. Work is in progress on superconductivity, which does not directly concern helium but requires liquid helium to obtain the necessary low temperatures. The possible development of superconducting transmission lines for both direct and alternating current is being studied. Measurement of properties of solid helium is of current interest also and research on metastable helium is continuing—probably because of its long-range potential as a rocket fuel. Metastable helium would release 820,000 BTU/lb in returning to its normal state. The corresponding I_{sp}† is 4,420, which compares with 274 for presently-used storable propellants such as nitrogen tetroxide-unsymmetrical dimethylhydrazine. Storage of free radicals at low-temperatures continues to be an active field and there is renewed interest in rigid lighter-than-air craft to transport booster engines for

† "Specific Impulse", a term denoting the energy available for rocket propulsion.

NASA from the point of manufacture to Cape Kennedy. A lot of research and development work is being done to provide breathing mixtures for advancing undersea technology, such as the Navy's Sea Lab experiments. Helium may ultimately play an important role in permitting man to colonize the sea.

References

1. Allen, J. F., "Superfluid Helium," New York, Academic Press, 1966.
2. Atkins, K. R., "Liquid Helium," London, Cambridge Univ. Press, 1959.
3. Birmingham, B. W., Editor "Liquid Helium Technology," Washington, D.C. U.S. Government Printing Office, April, 1968.
4. Careri, G., "Liquid Helium," course 21 of the International School of Physics, Varenna, Italy, Academic Press, New York, 1963.
5. Cook, G. A., "Argon, Helium, and the Rare Gases," in two volumes, New York, Interscience Publishers, 1961.
6. Deaton, W. M., and Haynes, R. D., "Helium Production at the Bureau of Mines Keyes, Okla., Plant," Bureau of Mines Information Circular No. 8018, 1961.
7. Keesom, W. H., "Helium," New York, Elsevier Publishing Co., 1942.
8. Lane, C. T., "Superfluid Physics," New York, McGraw-Hill Pub. Co., 1962.
9. Lifshits, E. M., and Andronikashvili, E. L., "A Supplement to 'Helium'," New York, Consultants Bureau, 1959.

10. Lockyer, T. M., and Lockyer, W. L., "Life and Work of Sir Norman Lockyer," London, MacMillan, 1928.
11. Travers, M. W., "A Life of Sir William Ramsay," London, Edward Arnold, 1956.
12. Vance, R. W., and Duke, W. M., "Applied Cryogenic Engineering," Chapter 12, New York, John Wiley and Sons, 1962.

L. W. BRANDT

HOLMIUM

Holmium, atomic number 67, atomic weight 164.93, is one of the metallic elements. It is the tenth member of the lanthanide rare earth series (see **Lutetium**) and, therefore, in the condensed state of matter has 10 electrons in its $4f$ subshell. These $4f$ electrons play almost no part in the valency forces of the atom but do give rise to sharp absorption bands in the visible and ultraviolet regions of the spectrum. As a result of this property, it was one of the early rare earths to be discovered. Incidentally, its spectrum is closely related to that of promethium, atomic number 61, the missing member of the naturally occurring rare earths. Both elements possess the same type of absorption multiplets except in holmium the multiplets are inverted. This follows from the fact that various coupling of the angular momenta of the electrons of an incomplete subshell gives rise to different energy states, and these states can also be calculated from the number of holes in the subshell. Promethium has four electrons in the $4f$ subshell and, therefore, ten holes, while holmium has 10 electrons and four holes.

Isotopes

There is only one naturally occurring isotope of holmium: Ho^{165}. This element is of considerable interest to nuclear spectroscopists because it is already a pure isotope and it has one of the highest nuclear moments of the rare earth series. Over 25 radioactive isotopes and isomers have been prepared and identified. Eight of them have half-lives longer than an hour.

History

The element was discovered in erbia by J. L. Soret and M. Delafontaine in 1878 by means of its spectrum. Soret named the new element X. P. T. Cleve, by 1879, had independently shown that Marignac's erbia was a mixture of at least three oxides, those of erbium, holmium and thulium. He named one fraction holmia after his native city, Stockholm. This fraction was later found to have the same spectrum as X. Cleve's holmia, however, was shown to be complex by L. deBoisbaudran in 1886 and to contain dysprosia. Holmia was not isolated into a reasonably pure compound until 1911 following the work of O. Homberg and others. Between 1911 and 1945, a great deal of work was done on fractionating processes to separate pure holmium from the other rare earths. These processes were laborious, gave only limited quantities of the holmia material, and even then the oxides were not very pure according to present standards.

The metallic form of the element was produced in a powder form mixed with KCl by W. Klemm and H. Bommer in 1934. They reduced the anhydrous chloride with potassium vapor.

During the late 1940's and early 1950's, separation methods were developed at the Ames Laboratory of the Atomic Energy Commission, which carried out these fractionation processes automatically. The methods utilized the then new synthetic ion exchange resins and took advantage of the tendency of the rare earth ions to form chelate complexes. (See articles on **Thulium** and **Lutetium** for more detail.) Many kilograms of 99.99% Ho_2O_3 were prepared. At the present time, a number of industries are using ion exchange techniques to prepare pure holmium, and it can be obtained in high purity in commercial quantities if desired. A recent quotation listed holmium oxide 99.99% pure for $150 per pound.

Occurrence

The rare earths are widely distributed throughout the earth's crust in extremely low concentrations. They also occur concentrated in numerous minerals but always as mixtures of all the rare earths, along with lanthanum, yttrium, thorium and other elements. The amount of a given rare earth varies greatly from mineral to mineral, but the heavy rare earths are usually present in low concentrations. Further, it is a general rule that the rare earths with an even number of electrons in their $4f$ subshell are much less abundant than the neighbors with an odd number of electrons which appear on either side of them in the series.

Holmium is one of the less abundant of the rare earths; however, it has been estimated to be present in the earth's crust to about 12 parts in ten million. It is, therefore, more abundant than antimony, mercury, iodine or bismuth.

The more important sources of holmium are the yttrium-rich minerals—xenotime, gadolinite, euxenite and fergusonite, to mention a few. In these minerals, holmium is present to about 1%. However, holmium also occurs as a trace impurity in many minerals such as apatite, bastnasite and monazite, where it is present from 0.001 to 0.1%. Monazite and some of the other rare earth minerals are processed extensively for cerium, lanthanum, thorium and yttrium, and the by-products of some of these processes are the principle sources of holmium at the present time.

Since the same minerals are used as sources for all the rare earths, the physical concentration, breaking up of the minerals and the separation of the individual rare earths are the same for all the elements and will not be repeated here. (See **Thulium, Dysprosium** and **Lanthanide Elements**.)

Holmium Metal

The preparation of holmium metal in massive quantities is usually accomplished by the reduction of anhydrous $HoCl_3$ or HoF_3 by an alkali or alkaline earth metal. A typical procedure for the preparation of high-purity holmium metal would be to react Ho_2O_3 with NH_4HF_2 to form HoF_3 via the following reaction:

$$Ho_2O_3 + 6NH_4HF_2 \text{ (10\% excess is added)} \rightarrow 2HoF_3 + (6NH_3 \cdot 6HF) + 3H_2O.$$

This reaction is carried out by heating the weighed quantities in a platinum boat at 130°C for eight hours with dry air flowing over the boat. The gaseous reaction products and excess NH_4HF_2 are then removed by heating very slowly to 350°C and holding for two hours at this temperature. It is very important that all the H_2O be swept out

before all the NH_4HF_2 is exhausted, since any water remaining will produce HoOF as a by-product, and the oxygen will end up in the metal after the reduction. HoF_3 prepared in this way will usually contain 100–200 ppm oxygen and a small amount of nitrogen as occluded NH_3. The latter is removed and the HoF_3 consolidated by vacuum melting in a tantalum crucible.

The HoF_3 is then reduced according to the following equation: $2HoF_3 + 3Ca \rightarrow 3CaF_2 + 2Ho$. This reaction is carried out by placing the HoF_3 on top of calcium metal in a tantalum crucible and heating under an atmosphere of pure argon to a temperature above the melting point of holmium. After the reaction products are cool, the slag (CaF_2) which has floated to the top can be removed and the holmium reheated in a vacuum to distill away the remaining calcium metal and fluoride. The vacuum-cast holmium will contain about 0.3% Ta which can be removed by distillation of the holmium. Other impurities, such as oxygen, nitrogen, and carbon, can also be lowered by distillation. To carry out the distillation, the tantalum crucible is fitted with a cylinder of thinner tantalum which acts as a condenser. The crucible is heated to 1500°C while the condenser is maintained at 800–900°C by radiation cooling. No additional cooling is necessary or desirable, since a cold condenser results in a powdered highly pyrophoric metal. A higher degree of purification is obtained if the crucible temperature is kept below the melting point of the holmium (sublimation).

Another method of preparing holmium which results in a high purity metal starts with the chloride. After $HoCl_3$ has been purified by distillation, it is remelted and the molten chloride reduced with lithium vapor. The resulting holmium metal crystallizes in the molten $HoCl_3$-LiCl salt. When the reaction is complete, the LiCl and any excess $HoCl_3$ is removed from the holmium metal crystallites by distillation. The entire reduction and separation of products is carried out in a sealed bomb.

Physical Properties

Holmium is a soft, silver-colored metal which to the present time has few industrial uses. However, due to its unusual magnetic behavior and as a member of the rare earth series, holmium has been of great interest to the research scientist, since it is an ideal metal upon which to test theories of magnetism and of the alloying behavior of metals. Holmium is highly electropositive and will, therefore, react readily with acids. At room temperature, the metal is not appreciably attacked by atmospheric gases and, even at elevated temperatures, a massive sample of high-purity metal will oxidize slowly. However, as with most electropositive metals, finely divided holmium can be ignited and will burn white-hot.

In spite of the apparent inertness of the massive samples, the rare earths are among the world's best "getters" for the nonmetallic atoms and holmium is no exception, especially when really hot. The hot metal slowly deteriorates in a 10^{-5}mm vacuum since the metal reacts with water vapor, CO_2, NH_3, hydrocarbons, and the oxygen, nitrogen, carbon, and even hydrogen, end up in the metal.

Apparatus should be well baked out before the metal is heated, since the hot metal will clean up the apparatus and it should be emphasized that the hot metal will react with almost any container material with which it comes in contact.

The values of the physical constants of the metal are sensitive to the impurities in the metal. Some properties, such as electrical resistivity, are very sensitive, while others, like density, are insensitive.

The latest average values (January 1, 1967) of some of the physical constants are listed in Table 1, but it should be kept in mind that some of these values will change slightly as purer metal is produced and measured.

Magnetic and Electrical Properties

The unpaired electrons in the $4f$ shell of holmium account for its high magnetic moment. Holmium is paramagnetic with an effective magnetic moment of 11.2 Bohr magnetons. Two magnetic transitions have been observed in holmium below room temperature. At 132°K, it transforms from the

TABLE 1. PHYSICAL PROPERTIES OF HOLMIUM METAL

Melting point	1470°C
Vapor pressure, 1470°C	0.55 mm
Boiling point	2720°C
Density	8.78 g/cc
Crystal structure	Hexagonal close-packed
Lattice constants	$a = 3.578$ $c = 5.626$
Atomic volume	18.78 cc/mole
Metallic radius, Coordination #12	1.767Å
Heat of fusion	2.9 kcal/mole
C_P, 25°C	6.83 cal/mole/deg
Heat of sublimation, 25°C	71.7 kcal/mole
Debye temperature	161°K
Grüneisen constant	0.80
Thermal conductivity	0.106 watts/cm/deg/C
Coefficient of thermal expansion	$9.5 \times 10^{-6}/°C$ (400°C)
Compressibility	2.47×10^{-6} cm²/kg
Young's modulus	6.71×10^{11} dynes/cm²
Shear modulus	2.67×10^{11} dynes/cm²
Poisson's ratio	0.255
Hardness, Vickers Diamond Pyramid	42 kg/mm²
Electrical resistivity, 4°K	7 microhm-cm
77°K	36 microhm-cm
298°K	81 microhm-cm
1273°K	195 microhm-cm
Coefficient of resistivity, 298°K	0.15 microhm-cm/°K
Yield strength, 0.2% offset	32,100 psi
Ultimate strength	37,500 psi
Thermal neutron cross section, barns	64

paramagnetic to a complex antiferromagnetic structure. The observed neutron diffraction patterns can be explained on the basis of a helical spin arrangement where the magnetic moments are parallel within each hexagonal layer but rotate in successive planes along the c axis. The amount of rotation decreases with decreasing temperature. At 20°K, the antiferromagnetic alignment changes to ferromagnetic with the aid of a magnetic field. The magnetic properties of holmium are anisotropic in both the para and antiferromagnetic regions with the c axis the direction of hard magnetization.

The electrical resistivity of polycrystalline holmium at room temperature is 81 microhm-cm compared with 1.67 for copper. The anisotropy in magnetic properties is reflected in the electrical resistivity. The resistivity along the a axis is 1.70 times greater than along the c axis.

Chemical Properties

The only valence that has been observed for holmium in aqueous solution, in salts or in fused salt-metal systems, is +3. The tripositive ion has a radius in the neighborhood of 0.894Å. The actual value depends on the method used for determining ionic radii. Its solutions are brownish-yellow and it forms salts with various shades of tan or orange. Due to the ion's incomplete $4f$ subshell, it is highly paramagnetic and forms salts with high magnetic moments. As would be expected from the highly colorful salts of holmium, the tripositive ion has extremely well-defined absorption bands peaking at very specific wavelengths. The most significant absorption bands occur at wavelengths of 2870, 3611, 4508, 5370 and 6404 angstroms.

Holmium forms a water-insoluble fluoride, hydroxide, carbonate, oxalate, and phosphate, while the chloride, bromide, iodide, nitrate, sulfate and acetate are soluble. On evaporation of these solutions, hydrated salts are formed such as $HoCl_3 \cdot 6H_2O$. These salts cannot be dehydrated directly, since on heating they give basic compounds such as HoOCl. Some of the physical properties of the sesquioxide and anhydrous halides of holmium are given in Table 2.

The sesquioxide, Ho_2O_3, can be formed by direct combination of the elements or by thermal decompositions of the oxalate, hydroxide, carbonate, sulfate, nitrate, or many other oxygen containing salts. The oxide is basic and will absorb H_2O and CO_2 slowly from the atmosphere. It will dissolve in strong mineral acids and slowly in weak acids.

The anhydrous fluoride can be prepared by precipitation from aqueous solution followed by dehydration in an HF atmosphere, or by the reaction of anhydrous HF with the oxide at 600–800°C. The reaction of Ho_2O_3 with NH_4HF_2 described more fully above is also used.

The anhydrous chloride can be prepared by dehydration of the hydrated chloride in

TABLE 2. SOME PHYSICAL PROPERTIES OF HOLMIUM OXIDE AND HALIDES

Property	Ho_2O_3	HoF_3	$HoCl_3$	$HoBr_3$	HoI_3
Melting point	(2350°C)†	1143°C	720°C	914°C	1010°C
Boiling point	(3000°C)	(2230°C)	1510°C	(1470°C)	(1300°C)
Structure	Cubic	Orthorhombic‡	Monoclinic		
Lattice		6.404Å			
constants	10.607Å	6.875Å			
		4.379Å			
Density, g/cc	8.41	7.64			3.204
ΔH formation, kcal/mole, 25°C	−449.50	(−395)	−233	(−207)	−164
ΔH fusion, kcal/mole		8	7	10	10
ΔH vaporization, kcal/mole		60	44	43	41

† Figures in parentheses are estimates (R. E. Thoma, 1965, ORNL 3804).
‡ Hexagonal above 1100°C.

an HCl atmosphere or by reacting Ho_2O_3 with NH_4Cl. $HoCl_3$ can be readily purified by vacuum sublimation.

The bromide can be prepared by reacting the oxide with NH_4Br or dehydration of the bromide hydrate in the presence of NH_4Br followed by vacuum sublimation to purify the bromide. The iodide can best be formed by reacting the metal with NH_4I or reacting $HoCl_3$ with a mixture of gaseous HI and H_2 at 600°C.

Melting, Fabrication and Alloy Behavior

The melting, fabrication and alloy behavior of holmium is very similar to that for erbium and details concerning these properties will be found under **Erbium.**

Toxicity

The toxicity of various holmium salts has been studied. When inhaled, taken orally, or injected into the blood stream in massive amounts, holmium salts can cause serious damage. However, the conclusion of the investigators is to classify the rare earths as having a low acute toxicity rating. Since their effect in low concentrations on humans over long periods of time has not been determined, these materials should be handled with reasonable care.

References

1. Mellor, J. W., "Treatise on Inorganic and Theoretical Chemistry," Vol. 5, pp. 480–709, New York, Longmans, Green and Company, 1946. (Early work.)
2. Weeks, Mary Elvira, "Discovery of the Elements," Easton, Pennsylvania, Mack Printing Company, 1945.
3. Yost, Don N., Russell, H., and Garner, C. S., "The Rare-Earth Elements and Their Compounds," New York, John Wiley & Sons, Inc., 1947.
4. Spedding, F. H., and Daane, A. H., Editors, "The Rare Earths," New York and London, John Wiley & Sons, Inc., 1961.
5. Gscheindner, Karl A., Jr., "Rare Earth Alloys," Princeton, N.J., D. Van Nostrand Company, Inc., 1961.
6. Eyring, LeRoy, Editor, "Progress in the Science and Technology of the Rare Earths," Vol. 1, Pergamon Press, New York, 1964.
7. Trombe, F., Loriers, J., Gaume-Mahn, Mme. F., and La Blanchetais, Mlle. Henry, "Elements des Terres Rares (Ou Lanthanides) Scandium, Yttrium," Vol. I, Vol. II, Paris, Masson et Cie, 1960.
8. Topp, N. E., "Chemistry of the Rare-Earth Elements," New York, Elsevier Publishing Company, 1965.
9. Moeller, Therald, "The Chemistry of the Lanthanides," New York, Reinhold Publishing Company, 1963.
10. "Rare Earths," *Chem. Eng. News*, May 10, 1965 (special report on uses).
11. Haley, T. J., "Pharmacology and Toxicology of the Rare Earth Elements," *J. Pharm. Sci.*, **54,** 5 (1965).

F. H. SPEDDING AND
B. J. BEAUDRY

HYDROGEN

Hydrogen, the lightest of all the known chemical elements, with an atomic weight of 1.008, has been known to exist for centuries. However its true nature began to slowly emerge about the 16th Century when F. B. Paracelsus first described a gaseous product when iron was dissolved in sulfuric acid. He described this gaseous product as "an air which bursts forth like the wind." Subsequently others reported this gas in various ways, but always in terms of "inflammable air" which would not support the combustion of other substances. However, confusion soon arose between a number of other "inflammable airs" as they were discovered, such as methane, carbon monoxide, hydrocarbons, hydrogen sulfide, carbon dioxide and others. Even as late as 1783, Priestly, the discoverer of oxygen, referred to hydrogen as "inflammable air." But to Henry Cavendish (1766) goes the credit for first discovering the true properties of hydrogen, as well as several methods for its preparation. He further determined the composition of water. In 1783 Lavoisier named the gas "hydrogen" meaning "water former."

Hydrogen, in the free elemental state, occurs in relatively small quantities compared to many other elements. The earth's immediate atmosphere has been shown to contain traces of hydrogen ranging from 1 part in 15000 to 1 part in a million. This ratio of hydrogen to air increases with altitude. The escape of the lighter hydrogen through the more dense air is shown to be very rapid, so that shortly after an appearance of hydrogen in a particular geographic location, it disappears into the upper atmosphere and outer space. Hydrogen gas has been detected in volcanic gases, in gases associated with certain salt beds, in a few meteorites, and near a few isolated industrial installations which discharge hydrogen to the atmosphere. Hydrogen in vast quantities is present on the sun where it is heated to incandescence. Because of the gigantic movements of this complex incandescent mass of ionized particles, mammoth effects are manifest in numerous terrestrial phenomena, such as those related especially to radio and electromagnetic type behaviours.

When chemically combined hydrogen is considered, then hydrogen becomes one of the more abundant of the elements occurring in nature. One ninth of the weight of all the water in the earth's crust, in the oceans, and in the atmosphere is hydrogen. The natural abundance rating of hydrogen is ninth in percentage composition by weight. The percentage of all the known atoms that are due to hydrogen has been estimated at 15.4%. Hydrogen when combined with carbon, oxygen, nitrogen, and other elements is one of the chief constituents of animal and vegetable matter. The whole field of organic chemistry has millions of known compounds of which the vast majority contain combined hydrogen. This vast number of organic compounds, ranging from the simple hydrocarbon like methane, CH_4, to the gigantic protein-like virus molecules, contains tremendous numbers of hydrogen atoms.

Kinds of Hydrogen

Ordinary hydrogen is not just a simple gaseous system as may well be supposed from its atomic properties and extreme lightness. There are in fact three known isotopes of hydrogen possessing mass numbers of 1, 2, and 3. The isotopes of mass 1 and 2 form the naturally occurring variety. Hydrogen of mass number of 3 must be made artificially by bombardment of other species. These isotopes have been named protium, deuterium, and tritium for the mass numbers 1, 2, and 3, respectively. The chemical properties of these

three forms are practically identical with the natural isotopic mixture. Tritium has one property unshared by the other two, namely, radioactivity. It is a beta emitter. These various isotopes react with oxygen to give water in similar type chemical reactions. The waters produced have the formulae H_2O, D_2O, T_2O, and separately are called protium oxide or light water, deuterium oxide or heavy water and tritium oxide, respectively. These oxides are chemically identical except for properties that might be dependent on atomic masses, such as bond energies. The molecular weights of these oxides are, respectively, 18, 20, and 22. The various possible mixed isotopic hydrogen water species are generally also present in mixtures of these oxides. The relative amounts of deuterium to light hydrogen in naturally occurring water has been reported variously as being one deuterium atom to 4,500–6,500 protium atoms. There is a growing certainty that the 6,500 value is the most nearly correct one. This occurrence ratio seems remarkably constant, not only in the naturally occurring waters, but in other natural sources such as petroleum, hydrates, and organic matter.

To further complicate the hydrogen systems is the phenomena of ortho and para nuclear behavior. If the angular momentum of a hydrogen nucleus is $\pm 1/2$ (expressed in $h/2\pi$ units), then the two hydrogen nuclei in combination to produce the hydrogen molecule are able to combine in two ways, either with their spins additive or with their spins opposed. The molecules with their spins additive, and consequently with their total nuclear spin equal to unity, are said to be the symmetrical ortho form and possess the odd quantum states 1, 3, 5, etc. The molecules with their nuclear spins opposed are the antisymmetric para form, and possess the even quantum states 0, 2, 4, etc., and a total nuclear spin equal to zero.

Since for hydrogen, the para forms occupy only the even rotational energy levels and the ortho form occupies only the odd levels, the ratio of the functions for the even- and odd-numbered rotational quantum numbers, J, gives the ratios of the concentrations, 1:3, of ordinary hydrogen due to the para and ortho forms, respectively, which vary with the temperature. At 20°K the percentage of para is 99.82% and of ortho 0.18; while at a temperature sufficiently high, where the number of odd terms equal the number of even terms, the proportions of para- to the ortho-hydrogen in ordinary hydrogen systems will be constant at 1 to 3. However, as the temperature is decreased (as $T \to 0°K$) the energy of all molecules must decrease. To do so, the energy must decrease, level by level, to the lowest level where $J = 0$. But $J = 0$ is an even number; so all forms must tend to crowd into this lowest quantum level of $J = 0$. Ortho-hydrogen has its lowest quantum level at $J = 1$; and thus for the ortho form to attain the $J = 0$ level it must change its nuclear spin from odd to even values. Below 20°K this reversible conversion of o-H_2 to p-H_2 does take place, but there is an appreciable reluctance of o-H_2 to do so. The rate of conversion of the o-H_2 into p-H_2 can be catalyzed by certain forms of charcoal, by some metals, salts, metal oxides and substances possessing paramagnetic moments. The conversion can be followed by methods involving measurements of vapor pressure, thermal and electrical property changes, conductivity, and heterogeneous adsorption, etc.

By allowing ordinary hydrogen to stand at temperatures as near 0°K as possible in the presence of one of these reversible conversion catalysts for a sufficiently long period of time, the ortho form will practically completely change to the para form. Very pure samples of the para-hydrogen have been prepared, but only when sufficient time and precise experimentation were employed. Many of the properties of the pure para have been determined. But when it comes to the preparation of samples of the pure ortho-hydrogen, the picture is different. Low temperatures give para; and any temperature above these lowest temperatures produces an equilibrium mixture of both forms. At high temperature there is always a 1:3 para-to-ortho mixture. So for years it was thought that pure ortho could not be obtained. However, in 1958, Cunningham, Chapin and Johnson discovered that pure ortho-hydrogen could be prepared by selective adsorption processes. They found that the surface of alumina would selectively adsorb the ortho form in preference to the para at 20°K. Mixed isotopic molecules such as HD, HTO, and DTO do not show ortho and para behaviour. Ortho and para forms of hydrogen do show differences in their total energies and their heat capacities.

Production of Hydrogen

The various forms of hydrogen, ordinary, protium, deuterium or tritium can be prepared in identical manners. The methods of producing hydrogen gas are numerous, and the choice of the one to use depends frequently on its eventual use. Industrial preparations are often quite different from preparations for chemical laboratory use. Further, the gas prepared by many of the methods is impure due to the presence of varying amounts of various other gases. Often these impurifying gases do not need to be removed because their presence would not affect the ultimate use of the hydrogen. However, pure hydrogen can be obtained by purification methods dictated by the nature of the impurity.

In the laboratory hydrogen is usually prepared by displacement reactions. The hydrogen in compounds like acids, water, and certain bases, is replaced with more reactive elements capable of forming positive cations in the replacement compound. Many of the metals are active enough to replace the hydrogen in acids. Some of the most active of the metals will replace the hydrogen in cold water as well as hot water. Certain nonmetals, like white-hot carbon or silicon, can replace the hydrogen in water in the form of steam. This latter preparation is primarily an industrial one.

A common laboratory method uses mossy zinc. When the zinc is placed in nonoxidizing acids, hydrogen gas is evolved. Hydrochloric acid reacts with zinc to yield hydrogen according to the equation

$$Zn + 2HCl \to ZnCl_2 + H_2$$

This is typical of the type of reactions when the metals replace the hydrogen from acids. The ranking of the metals that will liberate hydrogen from nonoxidizing acids is shown in the so-called "electrochemical" (replacement) series. This is an arrangement of the metals in the order of their decreasing ability to displace the hydrogen in acids. The alkali metals, lithium, cesium, rubidium, potassium, are the most reactive of the metals, and so they top the list. They are so reactive in hydrogen replacement that they will replace the hydrogen from cold water with such vigor that the heat of reaction often will cause the hydrogen to burst into flame. The metals grade down in the series as their displacement tendency lessens. The cut-off point in the series between the metals that do and those that do not liberate hydrogen is designated by hydrogen. The metals below hydrogen in the series will not react with these acids. The acids themselves generally must not be oxidizing acids. Such acids, like nitric and hot concentrated sulfuric acid, usually end up by oxidizing the hydrogen to water and liberating a gas other than hydrogen. Many of the more active metals like aluminum and zinc when heated in dilute sodium hydroxide will liberate the one remaining hydrogen in the base, as:

$$2Al + 6NaOH \rightarrow 2Na_3AlO_3 + 3H_2$$
$$Zn + 2NaOH \rightarrow Na_2ZnO_2 + H_2.$$

A patented process whereby hydrogen is liberated from sodium hydroxide, called the "Silical Process," according to the equation

$$Si + 2NaOH + H_2O \rightarrow Na_2SiO_3 + 2H_2$$

is a satisfactory process, but the yield begins to fall off after about 80% completion. However, the addition of some calcium hydroxide to the reacting mixture increases the yield of hydrogen, thus making the reaction more economical. The preparation of hydrogen by using sodium hydroxide had use in World War II where it served as a mobile source of hydrogen for filling war observation balloons right at the battle front. Another source of hydrogen is the reaction of calcium hydride with water:

$$CaH_2 + 2H_2O \rightarrow Ca(OH)_2 + 2H_2.$$

This is not a very economical method.

Electrolysis of water will produce hydrogen and oxygen in fair degree of purity. This method is of importance in the industrial production of oxygen and hydrogen, but it can also serve as a laboratory preparation. It is especially important in regions where electric power is unusually cheap. An electric current is passed through water, containing an electrolyte, usually dilute sulfuric acid, between electrodes housed in separated compartments to prevent the gaseous products from mixing. The reaction is

$$2H_2O \xrightarrow[\text{elec.}]{\text{[acid]}} 2H_2 + O_2$$

From this equation it can be seen that the volumes of the products are two volumes of hydrogen to one of oxygen. However, the weight of gaseous products show that for every 4 parts by weight hydrogen formed there are 32 parts by weight of oxygen. If these weights are calculated back to the composition of the water, then water is one-ninth by weight of hydrogen to eight-ninths by weight of oxygen. If this electrolysis was carried out under about 300 atmospheres of pressure, the purity of the gases produced approaches 99.9%. Electrolysis of water solutions of sodium chloride or sodium hydroxide can be used to prepare hydrogen. Chlorine is formed along with hydrogen from the electrolysis of the salt solution. This method is the principal source for industrial chlorine. The electrolysis of a potassium or sodium hydroxide solution produces oxygen as a product in addition to hydrogen.

The demand for pure hydrogen as a raw material for the manufacture of hydrogen compounds is, to a large extent, met by obtaining hydrogen from the "water gas reaction" or from variations of this method in which high carbon content materials like coal, lignite, or coke are heated to a white heat. Steam is then passed over this white-hot fuel bed, and carbon monoxide and hydrogen are evolved. The heat is furnished by first burning a portion of the original fuel bed until the whole system is heated to the correct temperature range between 1000-1100°C. As the reaction proceeds: $C + H_2O(\text{steam}) \xrightarrow{1000°C} CO + H_2$, the temperature of the fuel bed cools down because the reaction is highly endothermic. This temperature behavior limits the actual reaction time to not more than 6 minutes. When the temperature has decreased to about 960°C the steam is cut off and the fuel allowed to burn and reheat the system again to the operating temperature. The reaction cycle is repeated. Production by this method is thus a batch cyclic process. The carbon monoxide produced is oxidized to CO_2 and absorbed out by passing through water, leaving a relatively pure hydrogen with CO and N_2 trace impurities. Water gas, because of its combustible components, makes a fuel of fair heating efficiency. Many industries, and even municipalities, have used it for industrial and domestic heating.

The by-product coke oven serves as a source of additional industrial hydrogen. Bituminous coal is subjected to destructive distillation in retorts at high temperature. Because air is excluded during the heating process very little complete combustion of the constituents of the coal occurs. Rather at this high temperature the compounds present in the coal are thermally broken down to simpler ones and eventually gaseous molecules are formed and evolved. The gaseous products are separated by distillation leaving the nonvolatile residue behind as coke. Among the volatile products are found ammonia, hydrogen, hydrocarbon gases, tar, carbon monoxide, carbon dioxide, and nitrogen. A ton of bituminous coal produces on the average about 10,000 cu ft of coke oven gas, of which about 5,000 cu ft is hydrogen. This hydrogen may be purified from its co-gases, and it furnishes over a fourth of the world's production of hydrogen.

Physical Properties

Hydrogen, the lightest element known, is only one-sixteenth as heavy as oxygen and less than one-fourteenth as heavy as air. One liter of hydrogen gas weighs 0.08987 grams at 0°C and 1 atmosphere pressure. It is so light that it can be poured upward through the air, from one container to another. It has no color, taste, or odor when samples of it are pure. However, as hydrogen is evolved from reactions of acids on certain metals, like iron, the escaping gas often has a distinct odor, often times offensive. This odor is due to impurities within the metal which are gaseous by-products of the overall reaction. These by-products are often poisonous. Hydrogen dissolves to a limited extent in water. At standard pressure and room temperature about 2 ml of hydrogen will dissolve in 100 ml of water. This solubility is slightly less than the solubility of oxygen in water under the same conditions. Some physical

TABLE 1. PHYSICAL PROPERTIES OF HYDROGEN

Atomic number	1
Atomic weight	1.00797
Melting point, 1 atm	−259.1°C
Triple point, 1 atm	−259.1°C
Boiling point, 1 atm	−252.7°C
Critical temperature	−240°C
Critical pressure	12.8 atm
Critical density	31.2 g/l
Density, gas, 0°C, 1 atm	0.0899 g/l
liquid, −253°C	70.8 g/l
solid, −262°C	76.0 g/l
Specific gravity, air = 1.0	0.0695
Specific heat, C_p, 0–200°C	3.44 cal/g/°C
C_v, 0–200°C	2.46 cal/g/°C
C_p/C_v, 0–200°C	1.40
Heat of combustion, gross	33.940 cal/g
Latent heat of vaporization, −253°C	107 cal/g
Latent heat of fusion, −259°C	13.89 cal/g
Thermal expansion coefficient	0.00356/°C
Thermal conductivity, 0°C	0.00038 cal/cm²/sec/°C/cm
Viscosity, 15°C, 1 atm	0.0087 centipoise
Minimum ignition temperature	574°C
Thermal neutron absorption cross section	0.332 barns
Dielectric constant at 2×10^6 cycles/sec	1.000264
Velocity of sound, 0°C	1269.5 m/sec
Diffusion coefficient, into air, 0°C	0.634 cm²/sec

properties of hydrogen are listed in Table 1. Certain metals, like palladium and platinum, (especially when finely divided) have the capacity of rapidly adsorbing large quantities of hydrogen. Over 800–900 ml of hydrogen can be adsorbed in 1 ml of finely powdered palladium. This adsorption process is similar in many ways to the process of dissolving solutes in solvents, but differs in that the hydrogen is caught on the surface of the metal substrate to a depth of one-to-many atoms or molecules thick. An interesting change occurs in the hydrogen molecules upon being adsorbed. The hydrogen is changed from the diatomic to the monatomic condition by the time the molecules become located on the metal surface. In this monatomic state it is in a highly activated or energized state, and consequently it is chemically highly reactive. If given the correct conditions it is immediately oxidized to water with oxygen of air. Ordinary hydrogen and oxygen mixtures need to be ignited before interaction.

Atomic hydrogen, once called "nascent" hydrogen, comes from the dissociation of ordinary hydrogen diatomic molecules into its constituent atoms. Increasing the energy of each molecule sufficiently to exceed the bond energy dissociates the molecules into separate atoms. The energy of the H-H bond, 103.2 kcal per mole, is large enough to cause the molecules to be very stable. Thus the separated hydrogen atoms, when formed, are extremely activated. Hydrogen dissociation can be accomplished by other methods in addition to diffusion into metals like palladium. Atomic hydrogen can be prepared by passing ordinary hydrogen through an electric discharge. Hydrogen atoms are also generated in small, but important amounts, in chemical reactions that are initiated and/or propagated through complicated mechanisms involving multiple steps. The initiating energy could be light, heat, high-energy particles, etc. Generally however, due to the high bond energy, hydrogen molecules do not become involved in the primary initiation steps in such mechanisms, but rather they propagate the reaction chains by replacement of one of the hydrogen atoms in H_2 by other atom types like halogen. It requires light of a wave length of 2776Å to furnish sufficient energy to break the bond in the hydrogen molecule.

Second only to helium, hydrogen is the most difficult of all gases to be liquefied. The boiling point of liquid normal hydrogen is $20.40 \pm 0.2°K$. Upon rapid evaporation of the liquid, the temperature of the residual liquid rapidly decreases and eventually begins to solidify to a snow-white solid which melts at 13.95°K. The critical temperature of liquid hydrogen is 33.2°K with an accompanying critical pressure of 12.8 atmospheres. Hydrogen has its triple point at 13.95°K, and this triple point is also its melting point. The solubility of ordinary hydrogen measured in cc of gas per liter of solvent in water is 19.9; in benzene 75.6; in alcohol 89.4; in acetone 76.4; and in ethyl alcohol 89.4.

An interesting property of hydrogen, demonstrating its extreme lightness, is the increase in the pitch of reed instruments, including the human voice larynx, when the surrounding air is replaced by this extremely light gas, hydrogen. The frequency of vibration of such reeds varies inversely as the density of surrounding gas. This produces an increase in the pitch of the sound emitted and the sounds are practically unrecognizable until the air eventually returns to again bathe the vibrating reed. This gas, because of its extreme lightness, has been used for inflating heavier than air craft, such as balloons, dirigibles, and even toy balloons. This use is practically nonexistent at present because of the extreme combustibility of hydrogen in the presence of oxygen. The lifting power of 500,000 cu ft of hydrogen at 0°C and 760 mm has been estimated at nearly 38,000 pounds. Hydrogen gas has a density of 0.08995 gpl at 0°C, 760 mm in a latitude 45° at sea level, and one gram will occupy 11.117 liters at STP. Liquid hydrogen has a density of 0.07 g/cc at −253°C, while the density of the solid is 0.076 g/cc at −262°C.

Chemical Properties

Many of the more active metals react directly with hydrogen. The Group IIA metals, especially beryllium and magnesium, react so violently with hydrogen that they burst into visible flame. The alkali metals are less energetic in their direct union with hydrogen. Most metals react best when finely divided or gaseous. Many of these hydrides of the lighter metals are white, solid crystalline substances, with a great reactivity toward water in the following manner:

$$Ca + H_2 \rightarrow CaH_2 \text{ (calcium hydride)}$$
$$CaH_2 + 2H_2O \rightarrow Ca(OH)_2 + 2H_2$$

The metal hydrides are vigorous reducing agents due, in part at least, to the ionic nature of compounds in which the hydride ion carries a negative one charge. In these hydrides the bonding electron has actually transferred to the hydrogen from the metal. Hydrides of nonmetals are nonionic and are covalently bonded. Such hydrides are easily volatilized liquids. Many of the nonmetals and metalloids form hydrides: especially those in the Groups IIIA, IVA, VA, VIA, and VIIA of the Periodic Table. Some of the heavier metals (Pb, Sb, Bi, Pt) bond to hydrogen forming hydrides with chemical properties somewhat similar to the non-metallic hydrides. These heavier metal hydrides are covalent and generally gaseous. The halogen hydrides are strong acid formers in polar solvents while the hydrogen compounds of Group VIA, H_2O, H_2S, etc., form much weaker acids in such solvents. Non-stoichiometric hydrides are often formed with members of the transition group metals. The thorium and cerium hydrides seem to possess the greatest hydrogen content, while the least hydrogen is found combined with Pt, Ti, Zr, V, Ta, and the rare earth metals. These latter hydrides possess some metallic properties. They are usually interstitial compounds wherein the very small hydrogen atoms are found filling the holes of the lattice of the metal. Thus solid solutions are often formed between the parent metal and its hydride. The exact bonding linkage in these interstitial compounds is still under investigation.

Hydrogen gas is capable of forming many types of compounds with nitrogen. Ammonia, NH_3, is made industrially by direct union of the nitrogen gas obtained by the most economical methods available. The reaction requires a catalyst. Methly alcohol, CH_3OH; formaldehyde, HCHO; and many other compounds are also formed by synthetic processes. Especially in the petroleum industry in the rapidly developing area of petrochemicals, hydrogen is united with or abstracted from many organic chemical compounds formed in various stages of the overall refining process. Such synthetic reactions involving hydrogen are called hydroforming. The value of the list of substances formed, and those being almost daily discovered resulting from hydroforming, represents a gigantic, profitable industrial operation.

Synthetic ammonia was first produced on an industrial scale during World War I in Germany to supplement the ammonia production from by-product coke production. The Haber synthesis of ammonia requires the direct union of hydrogen and nitrogen in the presence of a catalyst:

$$3H_2 + N_2 \rightleftarrows 2NH_3 + 22{,}000 \text{ calories}$$

The ammonia so produced was eventually converted to the oxides of nitrogen and then into nitric acid. The nitric acid was needed to make military explosives. Soon similar methods, possibly with modifications, had been developed in many countries. By the time of World War II, the Haber process was the principal source of ammonia and nitric acid in the industrial world.

The reaction which was first proposed by F. Haber in 1915 is a reversible one and is highly exothermic. At equilibrium the ammonia percentage ranges from 15.3 at 200°C to 0.05 at 600°C under 1 atmosphere of pressure.

Since the Haber reaction is exothermic, the yield of ammonia will be increased by a low reaction temperature. Accordingly it is run at 400 to 600°C. Temperatures less than this range cause the reaction rate to be too slow to be practical. Still lower temperatures may eventually be employed provided more efficient catalysts are developed. Many substances have been used as catalysts; such as mixtures of the oxides of potassium, iron and aluminum, as well as mixtures of iron and molybdenum, and various individual metals like molybdenum, osmium, uranium, tungsten, iron. The energy of activation of the homogenous uncatalyzed Haber reaction is about 80,000 cal/mole. But this energy requirement is lowered in the heterogenous reaction to 32-40 kcal with molybdenum and to 39 kcal with tungsten as catalysts. Much of the ammonia produced is then converted by catalytic oxidation with oxygen to water and the oxides of nitrogen and eventually to nitric acid. This catalytic process, generally called the "Oswald process" for producing nitric acid, is so successful that the problem of procurement of nitric acid in commercial amounts is now solved.

In the production of the hydrohalogen acids, several methods are used involving direct union of hydrogen with the halogen, or by involving the exchange reaction with a nonvolatile acid. The preparation of hydrohalogen acids by exchange reaction requires a halogen salt reacting with a nonvolatile, nonoxidizing acid. HBr and HI require the acid to be H_3PO_4, if pure acids are desired. Concentrated H_2SO_4 can be used with NaCl and NaF to give HCl and HF. With NaBr and NaI the H_2SO_4 is a strong enough oxidant to produce free halogen along with some HBr or even less amounts of HI. HF can be prepared in similar manners, but because of its extreme chemical reactivity it must be prepared under special conditions including inert reactors (lead) and added precautionary measures to prevent health hazards and extreme reactivity. Hydrofluoric acid forms a weak acid in water, but the other three hydrohalogen acids are among the strongest acids in aqueous media.

The Bonding of Hydrogen

The bonding in hydrogen and hydrogen-containing molecules represents the three bond types in which the hydrogen atom's single electron and the hydrogen molecule's two electrons can participate. The hydrogen atom has a structure consisting of a nucleus surrounded by a $1s$ electron. This is the atomic structure of the protium, deuterium or tritium atoms. This $1s$ electron is basic in the bond formation of the three bond types, namely, (1) bonding through loss of the $1s$ electron, (2) bonding through the acceptance of electrons from another atom to form an electron pair, and (3) the procurement of an extra electron to give a $1s^2$ structure as in the negative hydride ion, H^-.

When the $1s$ electron of a hydrogen atom is lost to another atom (bond type 1), a bare proton, or the H^+ ion remains. This H^+ ion is about 10^{-6} times the radius of ordinary atoms. The mass of H^+ ion is essentially the same as an H-atom, but it has a charge of a positive one. The large ratio of charge to

mass in such a small volume, makes its polarizing effect on electron clouds surrounding other neighboring atoms so large that opposite ionic-like charges are established. This separation of charges then gives rise to ionic bonds or to dipole attractions. To remove the electron from a hydrogen atom in the gas phase requires about 313 kcal/mole which is so large a requirement that seldom can the H^+ ion form outside of solutions of protonic solvents which can solvate the hydrogen ion. The solvation process then furnishes the extra energy for the solvates to form. Approximately 268 kcal/mole of H^+ ions are required for the process of solvation to be complete. Water, concentrated H_2SO_4 and liquid ammonia are typical of protonic solvents. Such solvents undergo self-ionization within their pure liquid states.

The solvated hydrogen ion or hydronium ion, is the acidic species in water solutions of acids. The concentration of the H_3O^+ is often expressed in units of pH invented in 1909 by S. P. Sorenson. Sorenson defined pH as $pH = -\log_{10}C_{H+}$. C_{H+}, here, is now replaced by the symbol $[H_3^+O]$ where the concentration of the hydrated proton is measured in moles per liter. Applying this to pure water which undergoes the self-ionization as: $H_2O +$

$H_2O \rightleftarrows H_3O^+ + (OH)^-$, the ion product is $[H_3^+O] \times [OH^-] = 10^{-14}$ at 25°C, and since one H_3O^+ is produced for each OH^- then $[H_3^+O] = [OH^-] = 10^{-7}$ moles per liter. From this value the pH of pure water is 7. Solutions of lower pH are acid; those of higher pH are basic. Strong acids, because they are assumed to be 100% ionized, lower the pH of their water solutions toward zero. Strong bases raise the pH of their water solutions toward 14.

The bonding of hydrogen in hydride formation represents H^- ion coordination with metallic ions. These bonds show variations in bond strengths. The geometric arrangement of these various complexes varies with the periodic group to which the metal belongs. For instance, $Na(BH_4)....Al(BH_4)_3$ are tetrahedral.

Hydrogen forms many bonds with many elements, including itself, by the sharing of its electron with an electron from another atom. The $1s$ electron with its + or − spin can pair off with an electron of another atom possessing the opposite spin. The stable electron pair acts as the bonding agent between the two atoms. This is the typical normal covalent bond. The $1s$ orbital of the hydrogen atom is now full at $1s^2$, and the orbital of the shared electron is also full. Such electron pair normal covalent bonds are numerous in the field of organic chemistry. Methane, CH_4, and CH_3CH_3 are good examples of this type of bonding. Small inorganic molecules often are bonded by the shared pair as in ammonia and HCl. A majority of the bond energy of HCl is probably due to n.covalent shared pair bonding.

The molecule of H_2 is probably a mixed bonded structure. Each of the hydrogens contribute their $1s$ to the pair and a covalent bond results. But because of resonance between the possible bond structures, the two electrons could, and do, find themselves at times on the same hydrogen atom at the same time. Then ionic bonds are formed between the electron deficient atom which is positive, and the other atom, with the extra transferred electron, is negative. Thus in such a homonuclear molecule as H_2, the bonding is not pure one class or another.

Another bonding method that the proton can undergo is coordinate covalent bonding. Here the H^+ ion with its $1s$ shell completely empty can accept an already formed electron pair from another atom. This establishes a new electron pair bond, very similar to a normal covalent pairing, but different in its method of formation. When the proton becomes solvated in water it shares an electron pair from an oxygen in a water molecule to form H_3O^+

$$H^+ + :\overset{..}{\underset{H}{O}}:H \underset{\leftarrow}{\overset{\rightarrow}{\rightleftharpoons}} H^+:\overset{..}{\underset{H}{O}}:H = H_3O^+$$

This is the method of coordination.

Hydrogen Addition Interactions

In addition to uses of hydrogen as described in a previous section on the chemical properties, there are a large number of reactions peculiar to industrial processes. The hydrogen addition to or subtraction from many types of molecules comprises the basis of a large economical portion of industrial enterprises.

Hydrogen reacts with multiple bonded molecules to produce saturated molecules. Such hydrogenation reactions usually require a catalyst along with careful temperature and pressure control to make the process efficient. Mineral, plant, or animal oils are all subject to hydrogenation in various industrial operations.

Petroleum (mineral) oils in the presence of catalysts like copper or nickel, or metallic mixtures, react by opening the double or triple bonds and adding hydrogen across these bonds. This multiple bond saturation changes the physical and chemical properties. The viscosity and boiling points increase. Very viscous or hard oils are produced which can then be processed into lubricants, or can be tailor-made to fit specialized specifications. Finely pulverized coal can be hydrogenated to produce a variety of hydrocarbons. In Europe this reaction is used to produce motor fuel.

Methanol is produced commercially by the hydrogen interaction with carbon monoxide by the reaction:

$$CO + 2H_2 \rightarrow CH_3OH; \Delta H = -24,620 \text{ cal}$$

A temperature of 300°C with metallic copper and mixed oxides of zinc, chromium, manganese and aluminum produces methanol with a purity approaching 99%. By similar reactions, various aliphatic amines are catalytically hydrogenated to produce nitriles:

$$RCN + 2H_2 \rightarrow RCH_2NH_2.$$

The hydrogenation of edible oils and fats is performed by essentially the same type chemistry. Soybean, fish, whale, peanut, cottonseed, hog, and beef oil or fat upon hydrogenation produce the edible fats that are becoming so important to diets.

For a brief but thorough review on the kinetic theory of hydrogenation reactions see Basolo and Pearson, Ref. 2.

The Hydrogen Bond

A very unusual bond, involving hydrogen atoms, is frequently found where a single atom of hydrogen apparently is bonded between two electronegative atoms. Oxygen atoms commonly are found participating in a bond where the hydrogen atom is bonded between two oxygens. Fluorine forms these peculiar bonds with hydrogen as a bridge. Such bonds are found in HF and in the $(FHF)^-$ anion of KHF_2. The bond energy of the hydrogen bond is of the order of 5-6 kcal/mole while most chemical bonds have energies of 30 to 100 kcal/mole. Hydroxyl and carbonyl groups are often involved in such hydrogen bonds, and thus become of special importance in many organic and biological compounds and reactions.

The bond is usually represented as —O---H—O— or --F---H---F--. The importance of hydrogen bonds lies in their ability to tie up electronegative atoms in unexpected rings, chains or matrix of bonded structures not normally anticipated from the graphical formula. Although the energy of the bond is about 5 kcal/mole, it is sufficient to cause these unusual structures to be present. Ice shows such hydrogen bonding, especially if the ice is cooled to low temperatures. The water molecules form a nearly complete coordination lattice structure with the hydrogen bonds well formed and maintained. Many liquids are molecular associations of several molecules held together by hydrogen bonds.

Deuterium

Deuterium, often called heavy hydrogen, is an isotope of hydrogen with an atomic mass of 2 and an atomic number of one. The nucleus of the deuterium atom contains a neutron in addition to the single proton, characteristic of all forms of hydrogen. This heavy isotope of hydrogen was forecast in 1920 by Rutherford. In 1932 Urey, Brickwedde, and Murphy found spectral proof of deuterium in the last liquid hydrogen left after the careful fractionation of a very large amount of total liquid hydrogen. The occurrence ratio of protium to deuterium was found to lie between about 4,000 to 6,000 to one. This ratio remains constant in all naturally found sources of bound hydrogen, as in water and hydrogen compounds as well as any free unbounded hydrogen.

Many methods of preparation were developed in addition to the separation by extraction of the protium from natural hydrogen gas. The continued long-time electrolysis of water splits the light water molecules apart first, and the deuterated oxygen is concentrated in the residual liquid. This method became one of the most prevalently used techniques. However, ordinary diffusion processes and thermally induced diffusions became highly successful separations, giving yields of high degree of purity. The methods of analysis involve density measurements of the waters, or the measuring of the cooling rates of a hot wire. The isotopes of hydrogen, like all other cases of isotopes, undergo chemical reactions that are practically identical. However, in some reactions where the bond energies involved in bonds either breaking or forming, slight differences are observed in chemical processes that depend on the bond strength. The energy states of deuterium are the same as for protium except where zero point energy is concerned. Deuterium reacts like hydrogen in its basic chemistry, but deuterium will exchange practically instantly with hydrogen when provided the correct interaction conditions. Mixtures of D_2O in H_2O immediately form HDO, and similar type of replacement reactions will occur when the correct type of hydrogen containing solutes are dissolved in H_2O–D_2O mixtures or in pure D_2O. Hydrogen attached directly to carbon atoms is but slowly if at all replaced by deuterium.

Solubilities in heavy water, D_2O, show slight differences when compared to the same solutes dissolved in light water. Organic solutes, especially, show small differences in their solubility in D_2O compared to H_2O. These molecular properties are reflected in some of the following comparative values (Table 2).

Tritium

Tritium with a mass number of 3 is the heaviest of the three isotopes of hydrogen. The tritium atom has the one electron external to the nucleus, similar to the other hydrogen isotopes, but its nucleus contains 2 neutrons in addition to the single proton common to all forms of hydrogen. It is believed not to be a normal constituent of the earth or the earth environment. Calculations of tritium content in naturally occurring hydrogen give estimations of less than 1 part of tritium to 10^{17} parts

TABLE 2. PROPERTIES OF D_2O AND H_2O COMPARED

Property	D_2O	H_2O
Max. density	11.22°C	4.08°C
Freezing point	3.8°C	0.0°C
Boiling point, 1 atm	101.4°C	100.00°C
ΔH vaporization, kcal/mole	11.10	10.7
Critical temperature	371.5°C	374.2°C
Density, 20°C/20°C, g/cc	1.10726	0.9998
Molecular volume, cc/mole, 20°C	18.092	18.016
Specific heat, liq., cal/g/°C	1.028	1.018
ΔH fusion, kcal/mole	1.523	1.435
Dielectric constant, 0°C	80.7	81.5
Dipole moment, 25°C, C_6H_6	1.78	1.76
Dipole moment, 25°C, dioxane	1.87	1.86
Crystal structure, ice	Same for both	

HDO has not been reported as separated pure from H_2O–D_2O mixtures but it undoubtedly exists. Its calculated boiling point is reported as 100.76°C. Ionic mobilities are in general smaller in D_2O than in H_2O.

of ordinary hydrogen. Tritium is formed in the incandescent hot-particle mass around the sun, and probably in outer space by cosmic ray and nuclear bombardment in induced nuclear reactions. It has a time of half-life of 12.4 years and could be the precursor of helium, mass-number 3. Tritium can be made by nuclear bombardment of deuterium with other hydrogen species, or by thermal neutrons reacting with lithium, mass number 6, in nuclear reactors. It is available from commercial suppliers in solutions.

Its principal use is in tagging other atoms or reactions in order to follow mechanism pathways or to identify and analyze products. These hydrogen atoms, whose mass is three times the protium (hydrogen, mass 1) can be made to replace lighter hydrogen in many compounds and thus render the new molecule radioactive, and their presence and concentration can be monitored with beta-particle detecting devices.

References

1. Andrews, Frank C., "Equilibrium Statistical Mechanics," Chapters 9, 10, 11, New York, John Wiley and Sons, Inc., 1963.
2. Basolo, F., and Pearson, R. G., "Mechanisms of Inorganic Reactions," pp. 342–350, New York, John Wiley and Sons, Inc., 1960.
3. Briscoe, H. T., "General Chemistry for Colleges," 4th Edition, Chapter 8, and pp. 471–477, New York, Houghton Mifflin Company, 1949.
4. Farkas, A., "Orthohydrogen, Parahydrogen and Heavy Hydrogen," London, Cambridge, at the University Press, 1935. Contains practically complete bibliography up to 1935.
5. Glasstone, Samuel, "Recent Advances in General Chemistry," Chapters III and IV, Philadelphia, P. Blakiston's Son and Co., Inc., 1936.
6. Laidler, K. J., "Chemical Kinetics," First Edition, p. 170, New York, McGraw-Hill Co., Inc., 1950.
7. Mellor, J. W., "Modern Inorganic Chemistry," Chapters III, VI, IX, XI, XIII, XXVIII, New York, Longmans, Green and Co., 1925.
8. Pauling, Linus, "Nature of the Chemical Bond," pp. 36–43, Ithaca, N.Y., Cornell University Press, 1943.
9. Sidgwick, N. V., "The Chemical Elements and Their Compounds," Vol. I, Group (Chapter) I, pp. 658, 708–718, Oxford at the Clarendon Press, 1950.
10. Urey, H. C., Brickwedde, F. G., and Murphy, G. M., *Phys. Rev.*, **39**, 864 (1932); *ibid*, **40**, 1 (1932); Washburn, E. W. and Urey, H. C., *Proc. Nat. Acad.*, **18**, 496 (1932); Pegram, G. B., and Huffman, J., and Urey, H. C., *Phys. Rev.*, **49**, 883 (1936).

A. C. ANDREWS

I

INDIUM

Indium was discovered in 1863 by F. Reich and T. Richter at the Freiburg School of Mines, while they were checking local zinc ores with a spectrograph for thallium. The new metallic element was named "indium" from the characteristic indigo blue lines of its spectrum.

Occurrence

Indium does not occur in the native state. It is widely distributed in nature, although generally in low concentrations. The earth's crust has been estimated to contain 0.1 ppm of indium, about the same abundance as silver. It is found in many ores including those of iron, lead, copper, tin and particularly zinc. Most ores contain less than 0.001% indium; many less than 0.0001%. Like many of the rarer metals indium becomes concentrated in by-products during recovery of the major metals. Indium is most frequently associated with zinc, and is usually recovered commercially from zinc residues and smelter slags.

The occurrence of indium has been reported in several countries, including Canada, Finland, Germany, Italy, Japan, Peru, Sweden, United States and the U.S.S.R.

Production

In the United States, the American Smelting and Refining Co., Perth Amboy, N.J. began production about 1940. The Anaconda Company also began producing indium about 1940, but discontinued production after 1960, and resumed small scale production in 1966. Several other United States firms have produced indium in small quantities in the past, but have discontinued production because of high recovery costs. United States reserves of indium, obtainable as a by-product of zinc production, are estimated to be in the order of ten million troy ounces.

In Canada, Cominco Ltd., Trail, B.C., is the only indium producer. This company began its production on a laboratory basis in 1941 and has been producing the metal commercially since 1950. Potential output of this company is in the order of one million troy ounces of indium annually. A potential new producer could come from the indium showings in the tin-zinc mineralization at Mount Pleasant, N. B. However, no production planning has been reported.

Cerro Corp., Oroya, Peru started producing indium in 1945, discontinued production in 1951 and resumed production in 1966. In recent years Japan has become an important producer of indium. The four primary Japanese producers are: Mitsui Metal Mining and Smelting Co., Mitsubishi Metal Mining Co., Ltd., Toho Co., Ltd., and Nippon Mining Co., Ltd. Production of indium has also been reported in Belgium (Societe Belgochimie), Germany (Duisberger Kupferhutte, Duisberg; and Unterharzer Berg und Huttenwerke, G.m.b.H., Goslar), Holland (N.V. Billiton Maatschappij) and the U.S.S.R. (Konstantinowka).

Japan is the only country for which recent production figures are available; Japanese production in 1965 was double that in 1961. Total indium production capacity in Japan is reported to be in the order of 400,000 troy ounces annually, considerably in excess of the 1965 primary production of 280,000 troy ounces. The Japanese production in recent years is shown in Table 1.

In other countries, production has been adjusted to marketing activity. Scattered

TABLE 1. PRIMARY INDIUM PRODUCTION IN JAPAN (Troy Ounces)

1961	139,100	1964	231,800
1962	150,700	1965	280,000
1963	150,700		

production makes reliable statistics impossible to obtain. Total annual production of such countries in recent years, outside of the Soviet sphere, has been estimated in the range of 1.0–1.5 million troy ounces, with one-half marketed in the United States and one-half in Europe.

United States Price History

Indium was first quoted by *Engineering and Mining Journal* Metal and Mineral Markets in September, 1930, at a price of $15/gram (equivalent to $466/troy oz) for 99% indium. The quoted price was reduced gradually as the demand developed and additional supplies became available, reaching $2.25/troy oz for 99.9% grade in December, 1945. Both labor costs and prices have increased since then, and the current quotation (May 1967) for the standard grade (99.97%) is: sticks, 30–90 oz lots, $2.75/troy oz; ingot, 100 oz lots, $2.30/troy oz; lots over 10,000 oz, $2.00/troy oz. High-purity grades (99.999% and 99.9999%) are available at higher prices.

Extraction Metallurgy

As mentioned previously, indium is usually recovered from metallurgical residues. Typical recovery processes are outlined in the following:

Anaconda Company Process. The Anaconda Company has patented a process for recovering indium from zinc calcine or zinc oxide fume. The calcine or fume is leached with dilute sulfuric acid, dissolving most of the zinc and leaving the indium in the insoluble residue. The residue is leached with stronger acid to dissolve the indium, which is precipitated as the hydroxide or sulfite by adding zinc oxide or sodium sulfite or bisulfite to the clarified solution. The precipitate is purified and the indium recovered as a sponge by adding zinc. The sponge may be purified further to remove sulfate and residual heavy metals, and the indium is recovered electrolytically.

American Smelting and Refining Company Processes. The American Smelting and Refining Company (Asarco) has patented two processes for the recovery of indium. In the earlier patent indium is recovered from residues by leaching with acid and precipitating it as the phosphate. Indium phosphate is converted to the hydroxide with strong caustic and the hydroxide heated to form the oxide which is reduced with hydrogen to indium metal. This metal may be refined further by electrolysis.

Another patent assigned to Asarco describes a process for recovering indium from crude zinc-lead metal. The molten metal is treated with lead chloride and sodium chloride, forming a slag which contains the indium as chloride. The chloride slag is leached with a dilute sulfuric acid, and the indium is precipitated with zinc dust. The indium-zinc sponge is melted, the zinc removed with chlorine and the crude indium is refined electrolytically.

German Process. In the processing of Rammelsburg ores, the indium finally reports in the lead residue from zinc distillation. The lead residue is cupelled and indium remains in the litharge, which is leached with dilute sulfuric acid, and crude indium is recovered by sponging with zinc slabs. The crude indium is dissolved in sulfuric acid and purified. Refined indium with a purity exceeding 99.99% is recovered from the purified solution by sponging with aluminum strips.

Cerro Corporation Process. In the lead-zinc operations of Cerro Corporation at Oroya, Peru, indium is recovered by treating a tin-indium dross from the drossing of lead bullion. The tin-indium dross is reduced to metal, a mixture of zinc and lead chloride added to the molten metal and indium is removed as the chloride in the slag. After wet grinding with sulfuric and hydrochloric acid, the pulp is removed and the filtrate purified by cementation with strips of indium. Indium with a purity of 99.8% is recovered as a sponge, using zinc rods.

Japanese Processes. Mitsui Metal Mining and Smelting Company, the principal Japanese producer, recovers indium from certain flue dusts from various operations. Standard grades (99.97 and 99.99%) are produced by leaching the flue dust with sulfuric acid and refining electrolytically. Distillation of standard grade indium yields the high-purity grades (5/9 and 6/9). Toho Company Limited, the second ranking Japanese producer, reduces the residue from its zinc leaching plant to produce pig iron, which is treated further to yield electrolytic iron powder. Indium is recovered, along with zinc and cadmium, from electric furnace flue dust.

Mitsubishi Metal Mining Company, Ltd. recovers indium as a by-product of electrolytic tin production. Spent tin electrolyte, in which indium has been concentrated as an impurity, is treated to form indium hydroxide. Standard grade indium is produced from the hydroxide using chemical purification and electrolytic refining in a chloride electrolyte. Additional chemical purification followed by electrolysis yields high-purity grades (5/9 and 6/9).

Nippon Mining Company Ltd. reportedly recovers indium from zinc distillation residue, but process details are not known, except that electrolysis in a hydrochloric acid bath is used in the production of standard grade metal.

Russian Process. One process for recovery of indium from hydrometallurgical lead operation residue, particularly suitable for use in lead-zinc operations, and developed at VNII Tsvetmet, was published recently. The lead cake starting material is mixed with spent zinc electrolyte. The mixture is heated in a furnace to sulfatize the solids and then distill off surplus sulfuric acid. The solids are acid leached at 70–80°C. After filtration and copper removal, the indium-containing filtrate is treated with zinc oxide dross to give a precipitate containing about 2.2% indium, 17% zinc, 2.6% iron, and 1.9% arsenic as the major metal components. The precipitate is filtered and treated with sulfuric acid and the acid solution is extracted with alkyl phosphoric acids. The organic phase is separated and re-extracted with hydrochloric acid. The hydrochloric acid extract is cemented with either aluminum or zinc to give an indium sponge which is briquetted and electrolytically refined in an amalgam cell. The cathode is briquetted and melted in a vacuum to produce indium of 99.99–99.999% purity.

Cominco Ltd. Process. In the lead-zinc operations of Cominco Ltd. at Trail, B.C., indium concentrates in the dross retreatment furnace (D.R.F.) slag, a by-product of the lead smelting operations. This complex material contains lead, tin and copper as major constituents, along with 2.5 to 3% indium. Copper is removed from the ground D.R.F. slag as a marketable flotation concentrate. The flotation tailing is sintered, then smelted with coke and limestone in an electric furnace. The electric furnace bullion is parted electrolytically, producing a marketable lead-tin alloy containing approximately 10% tin, and leaving the indium in the anode slime. Recovery of indium from the anode slime involves roasting the slime with sulfuric acid, followed by leaching with water, purifying the leach solution first electrolytically then by cementation with indium sheets, recovering the indium by sponging with zinc or aluminum, and refining electrolytically.

This process yields standard grade (99.97+%) indium which is sufficiently pure for use in bearings and alloys but not for use in the electronics industry. High-Purity Grade 59, which is used principally in the manufacture of solid state electronic devices, is made by additional pyrometallurgical treatment followed by electrolysis. High-Purity Grade 69, which is used in the production of intermetallic compound semiconductors, is made from High-Purity Grade 59 indium by carefully-controlled electrolysis, followed by a special vacuum treatment. Typical impurity analyses of the three grades of indium produced by Cominco are shown in Table 2.

TABLE 2. COMINCO BRAND INDIUM
Typical Impurity Analyses (parts per million)

Grade	Standard	High Purity Grade 59	High Purity Grade 69
Purity (%)	99.97+	99.999	99.9999
Impurities (ppm)			
Lead	30	2	< 0.1
Tin	20	2	< 0.1
Cadmium	40	1	< 0.1
Thallium	1	1	< 0.1
Copper	1	1	< 0.1

Physical Properties

Indium is a silvery-white metal with a brilliant metallic lustre. It is softer than lead (it can be scratched with the fingernail), malleable, ductile, and crystalline. When the pure metal is bent, it gives a high-pitched "cry" similar to tin. Indium is less volatile than zinc or cadmium, but will vaporize when heated in hydrogen or in a vacuum. General properties and constants are listed in Table 3.

Structurally indium is a weak metal. It is abnormally soft, highly plastic, and can be deformed almost indefinitely under compression. It remains soft at liquid nitrogen temperatures. The softness also imparts an interesting cold flow phenomenon. Freshly exposed indium surfaces cold-weld with great ease. Its elongation is abnormally low because indium does not work harden. Some mechanical properties are shown in Table 4, along with those of lead, tin, and cadmium for comparison.

Chemical Properties

Indium is associated with boron, aluminum, gallium and thallium in Subgroup IIIA of

TABLE 3. PHYSICAL PROPERTIES OF INDIUM

Atomic number		49
Atomic weight		114.82
Stable isotopes	113	4.23%
	115	95.77%
Thermal neutron cross section		
absorption, barns		190 ± 10
scattering, barns		2.2 ± 0.5
Valence		Commonly 3, also 2 and 1
Crystal structure		Face-centered tetragonal
		$a_o = 4.583$ Å, $c_o = 4.936$ Å
Closest approach of atom		3.24 Å
Atomic volume, cc/g-atom		15.7
Density, g/cc at 20°C		7.31
Melting point, °C		156.6
Boiling point, °C		2075
Vapor pressure		
Constants for the equation		$A = -12,860$
		$B = 10.71$
$\log p_{mm} = \dfrac{A}{T} + B + C \log T$		$C = -0.7$
Applicable temperature range, °K		430–2350
Specific heat (mean), cal/g/°C, 0–100°C		0.058
Heat of fusion, cal/g		6.8
Volume change during melting, %		2.5
Heat of vaporization, cal/g at bp		484.0
Coefficient of linear expansion $\times 10^6$, 0–100°C		24.8
Thermal conductivity, cal/cm-°C-sec, 0–100°C		0.17
Surface tension, dynes/cm		602–0.10 T
Electrical resistivity, ohm-cm		
3.38°K		Superconducting
0°C		8.4×10^{-6}
22°C		8.8×10^{-6}
156.6°C		29.0×10^{-6}
300°C		36.0×10^{-6}
600°C		44.0×10^{-6}
Highest known $\rho_{298}/\rho_{4.2}$		1.7×10^4
Temperature coefficient of resistivity $\times 10^3$, 0–100°C		4.7
Standard electrode potential, volt		-0.34
Electrochemical equivalent, mg/coulomb		0.39641
Magnetism		Diamagnetic

TABLE 4. MECHANICAL PROPERTIES† OF PURE METALS

	Indium	Lead	Tin	Cadmium
Brinnell hardness	0.9	3.9	5.2	20.7
Tensile strength, psi	380§	2410	1770	10,000
Elongation, % in 1 inch	22	32	37	42
Reduction in area, %	87	74	81	76
Compressive strength, psi‡	310	2050	2070	13,300
Modulus of elasticity, psi	1.57×10^6			

† Tests conducted on the metals as annealed 1 week at 100–130°C
‡ True compressive strength at 10% true strain
§ Other reported values: 430 psi (99.9% indium); 388 psi (99.97 + %indium)

the Periodic Table. In this subgroup the chemical properties are largely determined by the behavior of the incomplete outer electron shell consisting of 2 s electrons and 1 p electron. Thus, principal valences of one and three may be anticipated. The common valence state is three, particularly in aqueous solutions. Compounds in the bivalent state are unstable, generally disproportionating on heating. The ionization potentials for the three valence electrons are reported to be 5.76 ($5p$), 18.79 ($5s$), and 27.91 ($5s$) volts.

The standard potential of the reaction $In^\circ \rightarrow In^{+3} + 3e$ is approximately -0.34 volt. Thus indium is slightly more noble than cadmium. In common with some other elements, indium metal surfaces passivate with ease. The resulting relative slowness of chemical reaction gives indium an apparent nobility greater than would be predicted by its thermodynamic properties.

Indium dissolves slowly in cold dilute mineral acids and more readily in hot dilute or concentrated acid. Massive metal is not perceptibly attacked by boiling water or alkalis, but finely divided indium (sponge or powder) forms the hydroxide on contact with water.

As in all branches of sciences, our knowledge of the chemistry of indium is by no means complete and continuing research activities are being carried out in many institutions. One of the areas being more actively pursued is the coordination chemistry.

Compounds

Some of the representative compounds will be discussed briefly.

Indium trisulfate, $In_2(SO_4)_3$, may be obtained by neutralizing the hydroxide or carbonate with sulfuric acid or by dissolving the metal or oxide in warm sulfuric acid. The sulfate is a white, crystalline, slightly deliquescent solid, readily soluble in water. In addition to the normal anhydrous sulfate, basic sulfate, acid sulfate, and hydrate have all been reported.

Indium trichloride, $InCl_3$, is readily obtained by the direct union of the elements or by the action of hydrochloric acid on the metal. Like the trichlorides of iron, aluminum, and other elements with valences above two, the molecular nature of indium trichloride is displayed by its high vapor pressure, subliming at temperatures below 400°C. The trichloride is a white crystalline solid, very deliquescent, and soluble in water.

Indium trioxide, In_2O_3, may be obtained by burning the metal or, more readily by calcining the hydroxide, carbonate, nitrate or other salts. At comparatively low temperatures a pale-yellow amorphous oxide is formed which is converted to the crystalline form by heating at higher temperatures. The amorphous form is readily soluble in acids, but the crystalline variety is relatively insoluble. The trioxide is isomorphous with hematite, Fe_2O_3, and can substitute for the latter compound in double oxides or ferrites such as magnetite. Indium oxide can readily be reduced with hydrogen.

Indium trisulfide, In_2S_3, may be prepared by heating the metal with sulfur or by passing hydrogen sulfide into an aqueous indium salt solution of low acidity. Its color may vary from yellow through red to brown. The color and crystal structure of this compound appear to be related to the rate of formation which, in turn, depends on the solution from which it is precipitated by hydrogen sulfide. From a chloride solution a yellow product of small particle size or disordered structure is obtained This is suggestive of rapid crystal growth. From a sulfate solution, however, the red colored product that is formed exhibits a well-defined structure when examined by x-ray diffraction. A less rapid crystal growth is suggested in this case.

Indium monoiodide, InI, may be cited as being representative of the monovalent compounds of indium. It is a stable reddish solid, having a density of 5.31 g/cc at room temperatures, a melting point of 351°C and a boiling point of about 713°C. It can be readily prepared in two ways. (1) Indium metal is reacted with hydroiodic acid to give indium tri-iodide, InI_3, which is separated, dried, and reacted with more metallic indium to form the monoiodide, InI. (2) Alternately, indium may be reacted directly with elemental iodine in essentially stoichiometric proportion to form the monoiodide. Other monovalent indium compounds may be prepared in similar fashion.

Organo-indium compounds such as indium triethyl, $In(C_2H_5)_3$, indium trimethyl, $In(CH_3)_3$, and indium triphenyl, $In(C_6H_5)_3$, have all been prepared by essentially conventional routes. One method is to react indium with mercury diphenyl to form indium triphenyl, and the mercury is conveniently separated from indium triphenyl by distillation. A second method is to react indium trichloride with materials such as lithium phenyl, LiC_6H_5. A third method is by way of Grignard reagent preparation. The Grignard route needs some modification, however, because the indium compounds form strong coordination adducts with ether and the coordination bonds are very difficult to break. Either a long-chain ether or benzene may be used as the solvent to overcome this difficulty. Care should be exercised in handling the organo-indiums. Indium triethyl and indium trimethyl, when free from solvent, are spontaneously flammable on contact with air.

Indium forms compounds with both metallic and nonmetallic elements including selenium, tellurium, antimony, phosphorus, nitrogen, sulfur, oxygen, and the halogens. Most of these compounds, including indium phosphide, arsenide, atimonide, oxide, sulfide, selenide and telluride, are semiconductors.

Electrochemistry

The tendency of indium to form covalent bonds is one of the more important properties influencing its electrochemical behavior. The low conductivity of solutions of indium salts is an indication of this tendency. In some electrolytes, such as the sulfate, the fluoride and the perchlorate, the electrode reactions require moderately high activation energies, while in others, such as the chloride, the bromide and certain organic acid solutions the reactions are reversible. Electrolytic refining in a chloride medium, using soluble crude indium anodes and indium cathodes, is a common practice.

The electrochemical properties of indium may be studied by polarography. Data obtained from this source can be very useful in interpreting process data and developing electrochemical processes for the recovery of this metal. The half-wave potential of indium ion in an aqueous halide electrolyte is about −0.55 volt, measured against a standard calomel electrode.

Corrosion Resistance

Pure indium is resistant to corrosion in air at room temperatures, but at higher temperatures it oxidized rapidly to the trioxide. Salt spray corrosion tests showed a gain in weight corresponding to 2 mdd (mg/sq dm/day) for pure indium. A hard yellow film (the color of indium trioxide) was found partially covering the specimens.

Indium resists attack of organic acids formed by the decomposition of lubricating oils under operating conditions. Its use in bearings is based in part on this property.

Fabrication Techniques

Indium can readily be cast, rolled or extruded. Massive metal can be melted in open pots without excessive oxidation, but finely divided indium, such as sponge or crystals, is reactive and should be melted under a cover of caustic soda, paraffin, purified kerosene or other suitable material to prevent oxidation.

Indium has been successfully plated on a number of metals, including lead, zinc, copper, cadmium, tin, gold, silver, and iron.

An undercoat is often used with iron. The most common commercial electrolytes are the cyanide and the sulfate, but the fluoborate and the sulfamate are also used. (After plating, indium can be diffused into the base metal by heating, thus improving the coating). Indium can be deposited on cold surfaces by evaporation in a vacuum. Techniques have been developed for codeposition of indium alloys, including those with lead, cadmium, zinc, tin, copper, antimony, lead-tin and copper-tin.

Indium forms alloys with a wide variety of metals. Generally, the addition of a small amount of indium has the effect of hardening strengthening and increasing the corrosion resistance of the metal with which it is alloyed.

Uses

Reliable statistics on the uses of indium are difficult to obtain, due in major degree to fast changing markets. A general estimate of the 1965–66 market is that approximately 25% of the non-Soviet production goes into automobile bearings, 45% into germanium electronic device manufacture, 20% into specialty brazing and solder alloys, and the remaining 10% into other uses, including plating solutions, nuclear reactor control rod alloys, electroluminescent devices, and III–V compound semiconductors. This market distribution is very different from that of 1960, and is expected to change again in future years.

Bearings. The first major commercial use of indium was in the production of bearings and this application continues to be a major consumer of Standard Grade (99.97%) metal. The addition of indium to bearings improves strength and hardness, increases corrosion resistance and gives improved wettability with a resultant improvement in antiseizure properties. A typical bearing, as manufactured by Vandervell Products Limited, London, England, consists of a steel backed shell of lead-bronze with an indium overlay. This type of bearing is used in substantial quantities by European automobile manufacturers. Other types of indium-containing bearings find application in piston-type aircraft engines and in heavy-duty truck engines.

Germanium Electronic Device Manufacture.

The major use of indium in the semiconductor industry is in the manufacture of alloy junction germanium transistors, diodes, and rectifiers. In this application, indium acts as a doping agent in the formation of p-type germanium. A typical pnp transistor is formed by alloying discs or spheres of indium into each side of a wafer of n-type germanium. On cooling, the germanium in the alloyed area recrystallizes as p-type, giving a p-n-p junction. The stringent requirements by the semiconductor industry led to the development of higher purity grades of indium and to methods of fabricating indium and its alloys into preformed shapes of very close dimensional tolerance. A wide range of products including discs, spheres, squares, rectangles and washers is now available, all manufactured to very close dimensional and mass tolerance and with carefully controlled chemical compositions.

Alloys. Indium is capable of forming alloys with a wide range of metals. The major uses of these alloys are as solders, brazing alloys and forming alloys. Alloys are available having melting temperatures ranging from 118°C for the indium-tin eutectic solders, through the lead-indium-silver solders melting at approximately 300°C to the copper-silver-indium and copper-gold-indium brazing type alloys with a melting range of 700 to 800°C. Some of the more common trade designations of indium-containing alloys and general properties are given in Table 5.

Plating. The electrolytic properties of the ion In^{+++} offer many interesting plating applications. This ion can be complexed to varying degrees with different anions, in particular, those with coordination numbers of 4 and 6. As a result, by adjusting anion variety (Cl^-, CN^-, etc.), anion concentration, pH, etc., the polarization potential may be controlled and codeposition of alloys achieved.

III-V Compounds. During the past 15 years considerable research work has been carried out on the class of semiconductors known as III-V compounds. These compounds comprise two elements, one each from groups III-A and V-A of the Periodic Table, but in general exclude thallium and bismuth. The indium compounds with phosphorus, arsenic and antimony have all received attention. Cominco 69 grade indium, the highest purity

TABLE 5.   MORE COMMON TRADE NAME INDIUM-CONTAINING ALLOYS

Trade Name	Manufacturer	Major Components other than Indium	Applications
Cerrolow	Cerro Corp.	Bi, Pb, Sn, Cd	Forming alloys (controlled expansion)
Incuro	Western Gold and	Au, Cu	Vacuum tube brazes and
Incusil	Platinum Co.	Ag, Cu	hermetic seals
Indalloy	Indium Corp. of America	Pb, Sn, Ag	Low melting point solders

indium commercially available today, was developed for the preparation of these compounds. Of the three indium compounds, indium antimonide has been considered the most interesting because of its high electron mobility at liquid nitrogen (77°K) temperatures. When the total carrier concentration in this compound is less than 10^{14} cm^{-3}, electron mobilities in excess of 1×10^6 cm^2/volt-sec have been observed for n-type material, and hole mobilities in excess of 2×10^4 cm^2/volt-sec for p-type material. Such properties could lead to much improved solid-state device performance. To date, however, the only use which has been developed for the three indium compound semiconductors is in infrared detectors. A basic limitation is the fact that at room temperature indium antimonide of high purity is intrinsic. Thus, a cryogenic environment is required to develop optimum parameters. There is no indication at present that indium phosphide or arsenide will replace germanium or silicon in semiconductor device manufacture, although such possibilities have been suggested by optimists.

Electroluminescence. Electroluminescent panels, utilizing indium oxide, have been developed by the General Electric Company of the United States.

Minor Uses. Among the minor uses of indium, its value as a temperature standard may be mentioned. Indium is also used in laboratories as a glass sealing material. Although indium does not wet glass, excellent seals may be made in the presence of a judicious amount of oxygen, not enough to form an interference pattern.

Industrial Hygiene and Toxicity

Experience following more than 20 years of industrial history and specifically at Cominco Ltd. where many employees have worked with indium continuously for periods up to and exceeding ten years in processes ranging from pyrometallurgical operations involving temperatures up to and exceeding 1000°C, through preparation of alloys, compound semiconductors and chemical compounds, indicates there is no significant toxicity or health hazard associated with industrial use of this element. Experience over some 10 years of industries employing indium solder in semiconductor device fabrication, work which is of a delicate and repetitive nature usually employing female labor, has been without incident with respect to general health or skin irritation.

References

1. Ludwick, M.T., "Indium," New York, The Indium Corporation of America, 1959.
2. Mills, J. R., King, R. A., and White, C. E. T., "Rare Metals Handbook," Hampel, C. A., Editor, New York, Reinhold Publishing Corp., 1961.
3. Schroeder, H. J., "Mineral Facts and Problems," pp. 441–445, Washington, D.C., U.S. Bureau of Mines, 1965 Edition.

S. C. LIANG
R. A. KING
C. E. T. WHITE

IODINE

Discovery

Iodine was discovered in May 1811 by the French chemist, Bernard Courtois, who manufactured potassium nitrate for Napoleon's armies. In Courtois' process calcium nitrate, isolated from nitre beds, was converted to potassium nitrate by means of potash from wood ashes. In order to conserve potash, much of the nitrate was converted to sodium nitrate by means of crude ash which was obtained from kelp (seaweed ashes). While washing the kelp with sulfuric acid to destroy certain impurities, Courtois noticed violet fumes which condensed and corroded his copper equipment. He found that solutions made strongly acid gave a black powdered precipitate which on heating also yielded a violet-colored vapor. Properties of this new substance were investigated by F. Clement and J. B. Desormes and later by J. L. Gay-Lussac who first recognized it as a new element and named it after the Greek word for violet. In August, 1814, Gay-Lussac published the results of his investigations in his famous "Memoire sur l'Iode."

Since its discovery, iodine has been a major factor in the advance of chemical technology. Its importance in the development of synthetic organic chemistry is exemplified by Hofmann's researches on the reactions of alkyl halides with ammonia and the amines (1850) and the Williamson (1851), Wurtz (1855), and Grignard (1900) reactions. One of the most useful tools in analytical chemistry, iodine analysis has acquired a special name of its own, "iodometry." The availability of radioactive isotope I^{131} is today aiding in the elucidation of reactions in which iodine and its compounds have found use, either as catalysts or as reagents.

Occurrence

Iodine, according to the United States Geological Survey, is the 47th most abundant element in the earth's crust, counting the rare earths as a single element. It is widely distributed in nature, occurring in rocks, soils, and underground brines in small quantities (20–50 ppm), while seawater contains about 0.05 ppm. Less than a dozen minerals in which iodine is an essential constituent have been found; lautarite, anhydrous calcium iodate, is probably the most important of these since it is the form in which iodine is found in the Chilean nitrate deposits.

Despite the low concentration of iodine in seawater, some seaweeds, notably those of the brown variety such as Laminaria family and the Fucus are able to extract and accumulate up to 0.45% iodine on a dry basis.

Iodine Production

The total world production of iodine in 1966 is estimated at about 10 million pounds. Chile supplies about 50%, Japan about 40% and the rest of the world including the United States the remaining 10%. The United States, one of the largest consumers, uses over 3,000,000 pounds a year, of which about 30% is supplied from domestic sources. Imports of iodine into the United States for the five years ending in 1965 averaged 2,880,000 pounds which was a 55% increase over the preceding five year period. Most of the iodine consumed goes into the production of potassium iodide.

Extraction from Nitrate Deposits. The major world source of iodine is the Chilean nitrate deposits. The large deposits were first reported in 1840, and the first iodine was exported in 1868. The nitrate ore, or "caliche," contains between 0.05 to 0.3% iodine. The form in which iodine is found in the nitrate deposits is calcium iodate (lautarite.) It is possible that some is present as one or both of the double salts of sodium iodate with sodium sulfate. The iodate salts dissolve with sodium

TABLE 1. UNITED STATES CONSUMPTION OF CRUDE IODINE, 1964

Chemical	No. of Plants	Crude Iodine Consumed Pounds	% of Total
Resublimed iodine	8	160,000	5
Potassium iodide	12	1,285,000	41
Other inorganic compounds	22	946,000	30
Organic compounds	25	737,000	24
Total	43†	3,128,000	100

† Plants producing more than one product are counted only once in total.

nitrate when the caliche ore is leached with hot water for the recovery of the latter substance. The leach solutions are filtered and cooled to precipitate most of the nitrate salts. The iodates are allowed to build up in the leach solutions which are recycled until a reasonable concentration is obtained before being drawn off and treated with sodium bisulfite to precipitate the free iodine.

$$2NaIO_3 + 5NaHSO_3 \longrightarrow I_2 + 3NaHSO_4 + 2Na_2SO_4 + H_2O$$

The amount of bisulfite added must be carefully controlled since excess will reduce the iodine to iodide. The free iodine is purified by sublimation in retorts.

Extraction from Natural Brines. The major domestic source of crude iodine is from natural brines underlying much of Michigan. The brines are pumped from a subterranean sandstone basin at a depth of some 5000 feet. The Michigan brines contain about 30–50 ppm iodine as iodide salts in addition to other salts which are the source of several commercial products. In the Dow process, hot brine is acidified with HCl and oxidized with chlorine to liberate the elemental iodine. The acidified, chlorinated brine is then passed over a packed desorption tower where a stream of air desorbs the iodine from the brine and carries it to the HI absorber tower. In the HI tower water and sulfur dioxide are fed to reduce and absorb the iodine as an HI/H_2SO_4 solution. The more concentrated HI/H_2SO_4 solution is continuously drawn off, stored momentarily, then forwarded to a precipitator where the addition of gaseous chlorine precipitates elemental iodine from the solution. The precipitated iodine is melted under concentrated sulfuric acid and drawn off in liquid states at as high as 99.8% purity.

Iodine is also recovered from brine associated with natural gas. In the processing of the brine, the natural gas is removed first, and later used as a heat source for the sublimation step. There are three alternative methods. The first consists of adding iron and copper sulfates to the brine to produce copper iodide. This is then oxidized to crude iodine. The second method depends on the addition of sulfuric acid to the brine to produce chlorine gas. Sodium nitrate is added and the resulting crude iodine is absorbed by inactive carbon.

This is then dissolved in hot caustic and treated with sodium nitrate and chlorine to precipitate refined iodine. The third method is the electrolysis of a mixture of brine and sulfuric acid to produce crude iodine which is absorbed on activated carbon. Recent ion-exchange techniques have been reported to give a new, more economical extraction process for producing iodine with exceptionally high purity.

Extraction from Ashes of Seaweed. The first commercial source of iodine was the ashes of seaweed or kelp where it was first discovered. Although the Chilean nitrates and brine production account for most of the world's supply, seaweed still continues to be an important local source of iodine in Japan, France, Scotland and eastern Russia. The stages in the preparation are: drying and burning the seaweed, leaching of the ash, release of the iodine by chemical reaction, and purification. After concentrating the leaching solution, sulfuric acid is added to decompose any sulfite and sulfide. Manganese dioxide added to the acidified solution releases iodine which is vaporized and purified by sublimation.

Physical Properties

Iodine having the highest atomic weight 126.9044 of the common halogens (excluding astatine) begins to exhibit some metallic-like properties. It exists as a bluish-black solid with a metallic luster and is classified as a semiconductor of electricity. Its physical properties are listed in Table 2.

Of the common halogens, iodine is the least soluble in water with 0.0162 parts soluble in 100 parts water at 0°C and 0.45 parts in 100 parts at 100°C. There are no known hydrates of iodine. The solubility of iodine in aqueous solutions is increased markedly by introducing iodide ion, owing to the formation of the polyiodide complex ions. To a somewhat lesser extent iodine is generally more soluble in solutions of chlorides, bromides, and other salts than in pure water. Iodine dissolves more easily in many organic solvents.

Solvents for iodine fall into two classes referred to as either the violet or brown solvents of iodine. The brown solvents represented by Lewis base compounds such as ethyl alcohol give 1:1 complexes which produce a gradual

TABLE 2. PHYSICAL PROPERTIES

Atomic number	53
Atomic weight	126.9044

Solid Iodine

Color	Bluish-black
Melting point, °C	113.6
Density, g/cc, 20°C	4.93
60°C	4.886
Crystal structure	Orthorhombic
4 I_2 molecules/unit cell	
a = 4.7761 Å, b = 7.2501 Å, c = 9.7711 Å at 18°C	
Coefficient of cubical expansion, per °C, 0–113.6°C	2.81×10^{-4}
Specific heat, cal/g/°C, 25–113.6°C	$0.05058 + 4.688 \times 10^{-5}t$
Entropy, cal/g-mole/°C, 25°C	27.90
Heat of fusion, cal/g, 113.6°C	14.85
Heat of sublimation, cal/g, 113.6°C	56.94
Vapor pressure, mm Hg, 25°C	0.31
113.6°C	90.5
0–113.6°C, log P_{mm} = $-(3410.71/T) - 0.3523$ Log T $- 1.301 \times 10^{-3}T + 12.1891$	
Thermal conductivity, cal/sec/cm²/°C/cm, 24.4°C	1.006×10^{-3}
Electrical resistivity, ohm-cm, 25°C	5.85×10^{6}
110°C	8.33×10^{5}
Dielectric constant, 23°C	10.3
n_D	3.34
Thermal neutron absorption cross section, barns, I^{127}	7.0 ± 0.6
I^{129}	32 ± 5

Liquid Iodine

Color	Bluish-black
Boiling point, °C	185
Critical temperature, °C	553
Critical pressure, atm	116
Density, g/cc, 120°C	3.960
180°C	3.736
Viscosity, centipoises, 116°C	2.268
185°C	1.414
Specific heat, cal/g/°C, 113.6–184°C	0.0756
Heat of vaporization, cal/g, 185°C	39.28
Vapor pressure, 113.6–186°C log P_{mm} = $-(2300.24/T) + 7.900$	
Electrical resistivity, ohm-cm, 140°C	1.1×10^{5}
Dielectric constant, 118°C	11.08

Gaseous Iodine

Color	Violet (As $\sim$ 520 mμ)
Density, g/l, 185°C, 1 atm	6.75
Entropy, cal/mole/°K, 25°C	62.25
Specific heat, C_p, cal/g/°C, 25–1200°C	0.0350

shift of the visible absorption peaks to lower wave lengths. A violet solvent such as carbon tetrachloride, on the other hand, shows very little complexing and subsequent shift in its spectrum from that of iodine vapor.

Only one stable isotope, I^{127}, is found in nature. However, several isotopes of masses 123–135 have been prepared, one of which, I^{131}, with a half-life of eight days, finds utility as a tracer. These radioisotopes are produced by bombardment of I^{127} or tellurium with high-velocity particles and in slow neutron fission of U^{235}.

Chemical Properties of Iodine

Iodine, like the other members of the halogen family, is chemically very active in its elemental state but is usually less violent in its

TABLE 3. SOLUBILITIES OF IODINE IN VARIOUS SOLVENTS AT 25°C

Solvent	Solubility g/1000 g	Solvent	Solubility g/1000 g
Benzene	164.0	Ethylene chloride	57.6
Carbon disulfide	197.0	Glycerol	9.7
Carbon tetrachloride	19.2	n-Hexane	13.2
Chloroform	49.7	Isobutyl alcohol	97
Cyclohexane	27.9	Tetrachloroethylene	61†
Ethyl acetate	157.0	Toluene	182.5
Ethyl alcohol	271.7	Trichloroethylene	79†
Ethyl ether	337.3	p-Xylene	198.3
Ethylene bromide	115.1	Water	0.34

† Grams per 1000 ml of solution.

action. In addition to being the largest of the common halogens, it has a much lower electronegativity (2.5) than the others. The change in electronegativity between bromine and iodine is much greater than between chlorine and bromine. This accounts for the relatively high degree of instability and reactivity of iodide compounds compared to corresponding bromide and chloride compounds.

The electron configuration of the iodine atom is $[Kr] 4d^{10} 5s^2 5p^5$ and its ground state is $^2P^0_{3/2}$. Its principal valence numbers are -1, $+1$, $+3$, $+5$ and $+7$ and some examples of compounds having these oxidation states are KI, IBr, ICl_3, IF_5 and $Na_5 IO_6$.

Iodine forms compounds with all the other elements except the noble gases, sulfur and selenium. However, it does not react directly with carbon, nitrogen or oxygen except at high temperatures using a platinum catalyst. With the exception of copper and silver, most metals which form volatile iodides react rapidly with iodine vapor, especially when finely divided and strongly heated. Magnesium metal, which forms a nonvolatile iodide, has been heated up to 600°C in iodine vapor without any significant reaction taking place.

Iodine does not form compounds with CO, NO, or SO_2 corresponding to the carbonyl, nitrosyl or sulfuryl chlorides.

In general, iodine reacts with organic compounds in much the same manner as the other halogens; but, owing to the weakness of the carbon-iodine bond, the energy released is small and many reactions are readily reversible. This in part is due to the heat of reaction

($\triangle H$) for the displacement step with the iodine atom being endothermic by as much as 30.5 kcal for methane and 6.0 kcal for toluene. Also, the equilibria for the iodination reaction is unfavorable to such an extent that hydrogen iodide can be used to reduce an alkyl iodide to the hydrocarbon plus molecular iodine.

$$CH_3I + HI \longrightarrow CH_4 + I_2$$

However iodination, can, in some cases, be made to go to completion by preventing the formation of free hydrogen iodide. Three methods for accomplishing this are (1) oxidation of the HI by addition of a strong oxidizing agent such as nitric acid or a peroxide,

$$6C_6H_6 + 3I_2 + 2HNO_3 \longrightarrow$$
$$6C_6H_5I + 4H_2O + 2NO;$$

(2) neutralization of HI by addition of a base,

$$C_6H_5OH + I_2 + NaOH \longrightarrow$$
$$p\text{–}IC_6H_4OH + NaI + H_2O; \text{ and}$$

(3) removal of HI by formation of mercuric iodine or an iodomercurate complex,

$$2C_6H_5NHCOCH_3 + 2I_2 +$$
$$(CH_3COO)_2Hg \longrightarrow$$
$$2p\text{–}IC_6H_4NHCOCH_3 + HgI_2 +$$
$$2CH_3COOH.$$

The use of an oxidizing agent to prevent the formation of HI has the advantage that all the iodine is available for substitution.

Iodine also adds to unsaturated compounds

such as propylene to form the corresponding diiodo derivative.

$$CH_3CH = CH_2 + I_2 \longrightarrow$$
$$CH_3CHICH_2I$$

This addition to olefins is usually incomplete due to the reversibility of the reaction. Ethylene iodide, for example, can be decomposed into ethylene and iodine by introducing a small amount of free iodine and heating to 45°C.

Reactions in Aqueous Solution. The chemistry of iodine in dilute aqueous solution has considerable practical significance in determining its effectiveness as a disinfectant. To completely describe the reaction of iodine with water, five different factors and four different substances must be considered.

A. Hydrolysis of I_2.

$$I_2 + H_2O \longrightarrow HIO + H^+ + I^-$$

The equilibrium constant for this reaction is only about 3×10^{-13} at 25°C showing that iodine is not hydrolyzed to anywhere near the extent of the other halogens. The effect of pH on the reaction for total iodine concentrations of 0.5 ppm indicates that whereas at pH 5 about 99% is present as elemental I_2 and only 1% as HIO, at pH 7 the two forms are present in almost equal concentrations, and at pH 8 only 12% is present as elemental I_2 and 88% as HIO.

B. Formation of Hypoiodite.

$$HIO \rightleftharpoons H^+ + IO^-$$

The dissociation constant for hypoiodous acid is only 4.5×10^{-13} indicating its acidity is comparable in weakness to that of water. The pH has very little effect on the formation of hypoiodite ion. For example, at pH 9 the ratio of HIO to IO^- is still 2200 to 1. This is not the case with hypochlorous or hypobromous acid where the less active hypohalite anion prevails at higher pH values.

C. Formation of Tri-Iodide Ion.

Another factor is the possibility of the formation of bacteriocidally ineffective and subsequently less reactive tri-iodide ion, I_3^-. With an equilibrium constant of 1.4×10^{-3}, there is no measurable amount of tri-iodide ion at very low concentrations of iodine. However, at higher concentrations and with additional iodide present, there can be appreciable tri-iodide formation.

D. Formation of Iodate Ion.

$$3HIO + 2OH^- \longrightarrow HIO_3 + 2H_2O + 2I^-$$

The fourth factor is the conversion of HIO to iodate ion at higher pH values. High pH has considerable effect on the reactivity of iodine since the resulting iodate ion has been shown to possess no disinfection activity. An aqueous solution containing iodate, iodide, and free iodine or tri-iodide ion, has a pH of about 7; thus, a mixture of iodide and iodate can be used to determine the free-acid content of a solution by titrating liberated iodine. This method is frequently used in ammonia determinations.

Iodine is a mild oxidizing agent in acid solution and it readily oxidizes sulfite to sulfate, thiosulfate to tetrathionate, and stannous to stannic salts. The equilibrium potential of the iodine-iodide ion couple is -0.535 volts at 25°C. Ferric and cupric salts and compounds of vanadium, chromium, and manganese in their highest valence states will oxidize iodide ion in acid solution, with the liberation of free iodine. Also, solutions of such oxidizing agents as chlorine, bromine, nitrous acid, and hot nitric acid will liberate iodine from iodides. Iodine itself can be oxidized to iodate in acid solution by concentrated nitric acid and, in more dilute solutions by permanganate, bromates, chlorates, and even chlorine and bromine.

$$I_2 + 5Cl_2 + 6H_2O \longrightarrow 2HIO_3 + 10HCl$$

However, in strong hydrochloric acid this reaction is prevented by the formation of iodine monochloride which is stabilized as the ICl_2^- ion. In alkaline solutions iodine can be oxidized to iodate by sodium hypochlorite, while chlorine passed into a solution of iodine and alkali oxidizes all the way to periodate.

Inorganic Iodine Compounds

The iodides are by far the most important class of iodine compounds. Many metallic iodides are made safely by direct union of the elements because of the relatively small evolution of heat. Iodides of sulfur, selenium, cobalt (III), and those corresponding to the highest chlorides of antimony, arsenic, copper, gold, iron, lead, molybdenum, phosphorus, rhenium, thallium, tungsten, and vanadium are unknown. However, complexes of some of these iodides are known where a solvating group such as NH_3 or H_2O helps stabilize the compound. An example is $Cu(NH_3)_4I_2$.

At higher temperatures, even the more stable iodides show appreciable dissociation. The nickel salt loses iodine at temperatures below its melting point. The more volatile covalent iodides, notably those of aluminum and titanium, actually burn in air. At high temperatures where their vapor pressures are appreciable, these compounds can form explosive mixtures. Dry nitrogen triiodide, NI_3, formed by treating iodine with excess ammonia will explode at ordinary temperatures under the slightest shock. The phosphorus iodides, P_2I_4 and PI_3, are highly dissociated at their boiling points while those of the noble metals, except silver and mercury, decompose at relatively low temperatures.

Iodine forms five interesting compounds with other halogens, namely, IF_5, IF_7, ICl_3, ICl and IBr. All of these interhalogen compounds are readily formed by direct reaction of the two elemental halogens. Their stabilities and the number of atoms of the other halogen which combine with iodine increase in the order bromine, chlorine, fluorine.

The iodine halides such as ICl and IBr exhibit definite polar characteristics in the liquid state. They have appreciable electrical conductivities of their own and dissolve metallic halides to form conducting solutions. They are also powerful halogenating agents, but they differ in their action from the free halogens. Combination with iodine reduces the activity of the more reactive halogen so that the reaction is usually less vigorous. However, reactions frequently start more readily because of reduced energies of activation and higher polarity of these compounds.

Polyhalide compounds are formed between iodine or the iodine halides and other halide salts. These substances are represented by such formulas as CsI_3, $KIBr_2$, $KIBrCl$, $(CH_3)_4NICl_2$ and $RbICl_4$. The more stable polyhalides can be recrystallized from solvents usually producing highly colored orthorhombic crystals ranging from the black polyiodides through the orange and red

bromoiodates to the canary yellow chloroiodates. Polyhalides dissociate to give the free halogen leaving behind the most electronegative halogen in the form of the halide. Disproportionation of a mixed polyhalide into two different compounds is known to occur in some cases.

$$3KIBr_2 \longrightarrow KI_3 + 2KBr_3$$

Iodine does not react directly with oxygen, but three oxides, IO_2, I_4O_9 and I_2O_5, have been prepared by indirect methods, while derivatives of three others, I_2O, I_2O_3 and I_2O_7, are known. Iodine monoxide, I_2O, is the anhydride of hypoiodous acid. The sesquioxide, I_2O_3, exhibits pronounced basic properties and a number of its salts have been prepared. Iodine pentoxide, a powerful oxidizing agent, is a commercial product.

Iodates of most of the metals and a number of electropositive radicals are known. Iodic acid exists in two forms, the normal, HIO_3, and the pyro, HI_3O_8, both white crystalline solids. Iodates can be prepared in a number of ways: (a) oxidation of an alkaline iodide solution with chlorine; (b) reaction of iodine with a caustic alkali solution whereby 1/6 is converted to iodate, e.g., $6NaOH + 3I_2 \longrightarrow NaIO_3 + 5NaI + 3H_2O$; (c) oxidation of iodine by concentrated nitric acid, followed by neutralization of the iodic acid by an appropriate oxide or hydroxide; and (d) electrolytic oxidation of a neutral iodide solution in a nondiaphragm cell with a platinum anode and an iron cathode. Solid metallic iodates are stable but should be kept out of contact with organic substances. They are strong oxidizing agents in acid aqueous solutions.

Organic Iodine Compounds

The outstanding characteristics of the iodo compounds are their lower heats of formation, relative instabilities, and greater reactivities compared to the other halogen compounds. As in the case of the inorganic iodides, their specific gravities and indices of refraction are higher than the corresponding chloro and bromo derivatives. Their melting and boiling points are also higher, indicating that iodine's size is a greater factor than the decrease in polarity of the C-I bond.

The preparation of aliphatic iodo compounds is usually carried out using alcohols and a mixture of iodine and red phosphorus. Hydriodic acid is also used but less frequently. In preparing the monoiodo compounds, the degree of success and the stability of the product is a function of the position of the iodine. Compounds containing an iodine atom attached to a primary carbon are the most stable. Secondary compounds are less stable and tertiary least of all.

Other methods for preparing aliphatic iodine compounds are (1) addition of iodine halides or iodine itself to olefins, (2) replacement reactions between an alkyl bromide or chloride and an alkali iodide salt and (3) reaction of triphenyl phosphite with methyl iodide and an alcohol.

The preparation of aromatic iodine compounds is usually done by treating iodine and the aromatic system with oxidizing agents as previously described. Organic iodine compounds are used in relatively small quantities in industry.

The high reactivity of iodo compounds is one of their most important characteristics. According to one estimate, the alkyl iodides are, as a general rule, about 50 to 100 times more reactive than the corresponding chlorides, with the bromides occupying an intermediate position.

A number of positive iodine compounds have been synthesized in which iodide exists in a positive oxidation state. The most important of these are the iodoso compounds, RIO, the iodoxy compounds, RIO_2, and the iodonium salts, R_2IX. Iodobenzene reacts with chlorine to form iodobenzene dichloride, $C_6H_5ICl_2$, which like the foregoing reactions is peculiar to iodine and not the other halogens.

Commerical Uses of Iodine

One of the oldest and largest uses for iodine is in the disinfectant area. An almost universally known product is "Tincture of Iodine" for household disinfectant use. However, this form of iodine has been largely replaced by the "Iodophors" such as iodine complexed with polyvinyl pyrrolidine. Complexes of this type are said to have longer life, give less odor, no bleaching action and minimal irritation to the skin or eyes. In addition, iodine and its salts are finding utility in swimming-pool disinfection, purification of drinking water

and in detergent-sanitizers (formulations containing 2% iodine complexed with nonionic surfactants). A relatively new and promising antimicrobial use for iodine is in metal cutting fluids.

Certain iodides (e.g., titanium tetraiodide) have found use in the catalyst system for producing stereospecific polymers, such as polybutadiene rubber. Also, the dehydrogenation of butane and butylene to butadiene has been shown to be catalyzed by iodine. Iodine can be used as a catalyst in sulfuric acid oxidations. It is a well known fact that hydrogen iodide cannot be prepared by heating a metallic iodide with concentrated sulfuric acid. Instead, the reaction produces free iodine, sulfur dioxide and sometimes hydrogen sulfide. The most probable explanation is that hydrogen iodide is first formed and then reduces the sulfuric acid, being itself oxidized to iodine. Therefore, a dilute solution of iodine in concentrated sulfuric acid when treated with a substance which will convert the iodine to an iodide will undergo a reaction between the iodide and sulfuric acid to liberate SO_2 and other reduction products of the acid and regenerate the iodine for another cycle. The process becomes, in effect, an oxidation by sulfuric acid which usually is not considered a particularly active oxidizing agent.

A number of miscellaneous uses exist for iodine and some of its compounds. Among the most important of these uses are food supplements, x-ray contrast media using certain organic polyiodide derivatives, radioactive tracers, photographic processing chemicals, including cloud seeding using silver iodide. The U.S. Bureau of Mines mentions its use in metallurgy, particularly in the production of titanium, silicon, zirconium, and hafnium in high purity.

A new and interesting use for iodine is in metal cutting fluids. When added as a complex with a phenolic compound such as bisphenol A at about 0.6%, iodine is reported to impart spectacular friction reducing properties to cutting oils. This technique is reported to make it possible to machine exotic metals and alloys such as titanium, stainless steels and zirconium.

Although the relatively high cost of iodine compared with bromine (5x) and chlorine

(10–30x) limits its use in many areas, there are many compensating factors in some of its unique properties.

Physiological Aspects*

Courtois' discovery of iodine in seaweed ash in 1811 or 1812 apparently constitutes the first reference to iodine as a plant substance. Much work has been done since that time on the content, distribution, and function of this halogen in the plant kingdom. In studies of the quantities of iodine or iodide in plants or plant products, because the amount present is exceedingly small, their detection requires highly sensitive chemical methods and skillful manipulation by the analyst. The analytical methods developed in the last quarter of a century may be considered much more accurate and reliable than those in use prior to that time.

The amount present in land plants varies from 10–100 μg. per 100 grams of dry matter. The seaweeds richest in iodide contain 10,000 times more iodine, in easily detectable form, than the land species highest in iodine, but no plant species so far has been found completely devoid of iodine. Neither has anyone succeeded in creating an environment for the growth of plants entirely deprived of every trace of iodine which at the same time provided all other nutrients in adequate amounts. Therefore, the question of the indispensability of iodine for any phase of plant growth, development, or metabolism remains unanswered.

The many instances in which traces of added iodine or iodide cause plant growth stimulation suggest that iodine is a trace element producing its effect in the most minute concentrations. The increased nitrogen assimilation frequently noted following application of iodine as iodides to plants may be linked to the promoting effect of iodine on nitrofying soil bacteria, rather than to any direct effect of the element.

It is thought that Chatin (1813–1901) was the first to point out a relation of iodine deficiency in man's environment to goiter. Further great impetus to studies of the iodine content of plant and animal foods arose from the discovery in 1895 that iodine is a normal constituent of the thyroid gland.

Overwhelming evidence collected by numerous investigators all over the world during that last half century has proved that the major cause of goiter is iodine deficiency in soil, food, and water. In endemic goiter areas which have existed in many parts of the world the addition of one part of NaI or KI to 100,000 parts of NaCl used as table salt appears quite satisfactory in the prevention of the disease.

From studies of the cause and prevention of goiter there has developed extensive knowledge concerning iodine and iodides and the prominent and essential role this element plays in the thyroid gland of animals and man. Three specialized functions performed by the thyroid are (1) the collection of iodine from the plasma (2) the transformation of iodine into organically bound iodine, and (3) the storage and release of the thyroid hormone. The unique property of the thyroid gland to concentrate iodide from the blood plasma constitutes the first step in the organic binding of iodine by the thyroid gland. This concentrating mechanism may increase the concentration of iodide in the gland several hundred times over that occurring in the plasma. Low dietary iodide intake increases the iodide concentration ratio between the thyroid and the blood serum. Conversely, increasing dietary iodide during low intake depresses the concentration ratio. The antithyroid drug thiocyanate also prevents iodide concentration by the thyroid and causes collected iodide to be discharged from the gland. Antithyroid drugs of the thiocarbamide type, however, produce their effects not by inhibiting the concentration of iodides by the gland but by preventing their organic fixation. Drugs of these two types have aided investigators to differentiate between various stages of iodide collection and fixation in the thyroid.

The oxidation of iodide to iodine constitutes the second step in the organic binding process, but since no free iodine has been unequivocally detected in the thyroid gland it is presumed that as rapidly as free iodine is formed substitution on the tyrosine molecule takes place. The oxidation of iodide *in vitro* in thyroid gland homogenates has been observed to occur in two ways: (1) Cell free preparations of thyroid tissue either in the presence or absence of cupric ions (or some other oxidizing ions) forms free iodine which is then combined with free tyrosine to form mono-iodotyrosine in which process the enzyme, tyrosine iodinase, was identified; and (2) iodination of tyrosine within the protein molecule where the presence of the mono-iodotyrosine formed could be demonstrated only after hydrolysis. The mechanism of tyrosine iodination occurring in the thyroid gland is only partially understood and requires further exploration.

Thyroid hormone released from the thyroid gland enters the circulation and is carried to the peripheral tissues where it controls tissue metabolism primarily through regulation of a large and various number of enzyme activities. It has long been accepted that thyroxine acts on fundamental chemical reactions normally taking place in the cell by increasing the rate at which the reactions are carried out, although recent work suggests that triiodothyronine rather than thyrosine may be the active biocatalyst and that a part, or the whole effect, ascribed to thyroxine may be due to its conversion to triiodothyronine. No clear choice exists, however, between (1) direct participation of thyroid hormone as a sort of co-enzyme (2) or indirect release of metabolically active substances.

*HAROLD P. MORRIS

References

1. Ephraim, F., "Inorganic Chemistry," 3rd Ed. by P. C. Thorne and A. M. Ward, London, Gurney and Jackson, 1939.
2. Gmelin, Leopold, "Handbuch der Anorganischen Chemie," 8th Ed., Weinheim, Verlag Chemie, 1931.
3. Mellor, J. W., "Comprehensive Treatise on Inorganic and Theoretical Chemistry," Vol. VII, p. 89, New York, Longmans, Green & Co., 1927.
4. U.S. Bureau of Mines, "Minerals Yearbook," 1965–66.
5. Rolsten, R. F., "Iodide Metals and Metal Iodides," New York, John Wiley Inc., 1961.
6. Kirk, R. E., and Othmer, D. F., "Encyclopedia of Chemical Technology," 2nd Ed., Vol. II, pp. 847–870, New York, Interscience, 1966
7. Chang, S. L., "The Use of Active Iodine as a Water Disinfectant," J. Am. Pharm. Assoc. XLVIII, 417 (1958).
8. Kleinberg, J., and Davidson, A. W., Chem. Rev., 42, 601–610 (1948).
9. "Iodine, Its Properties and Technical Applications," Chilean Iodine Educational Bureau, Inc., New York, 1951.
10. Banks, D. F., "Organic Iodine Compounds," Chem. Rev., 66, 243–266 (1966).

J. F. MILLS

IRIDIUM

Iridium is a member of the platinum group of metals with which it is invariably found associated in nature. Some general information about this group of six elements and their relationship to neighboring elements in the Periodic Table appear under the entry for **Platinum Metals** (q.v.). Of all chemical elements iridium has the greatest density, and of all metallic elements it has the greatest resistance to corrosion. It is also remarkable for its great mechanical strength at high temperatures, and for the very high value of its elastic modulus (second only to osmium among all metals). The chemistry of iridium is characterized by the great nobility of the element itself toward chemical attack, and by the considerable range of oxidation states (and colors associated with these) of the element in its compounds.

Discovery and History

Iridium was discovered and named by a British scientist, Smithson Tennant. He was a man of independent means and wide-ranging scientific interests. About 1800 he began an extended association with W. H. Wollaston in London for the purpose of improving the technology of the fabrication of platinum, and also to investigate thoroughly the native platinum which at that time came almost entirely from the Spanish colonies in South and Central America. This metal had for some time been known to dissolve almost completely in aqua regia, but a small black residue always remained and was for a time thought to be graphite. In the summer of 1803 Tennant began a study of this material which ultimately resulted in the identification of both osmium and iridium.

Almost simultaneously in France, N. L. Vauquelin and A. F. de Fourcroy in Paris were working on the black residue left after three successive extractions of native platinum with aqua regia. They found that after fusion with potash part of the residue could be dissolved in water and part in aqua regia. The properties of these solutions were described in a paper read in October 1803, and these prompted the authors to propose the existence of a new metal in the black residue. Similar observations were also reported at the same time by H. V. Collet-Descotils.

There can be no question but that Tennant's work owed much to the French investigators but he displayed greater insight than the latter in identifying two distinct elements in the extracts from the black residue which he too obtained by the alternate action of alkali and acid. Tennant chose the name iridium, from the Greek *iris*, rainbow, "from the striking variety of colours which it gives while dissolving in marine acid." Tennant found, as the French workers had reported, that the aqua regia extract from the black residue, after fusion with alkali, was brown-colored (due to chloroiridate); that this turned green (due to chloroiridite) on the addition of iron or ferrous sulfate; and that when ammonium chloroplatinate was precipitated in the presence of the brown solution the precipitate was dark red (due to $(NH_4)_2IrCl_6$) instead of yellow.

Occurrence

The occurrence of the platinum metals has been described in some detail under the entries for platinum (q.v.) and palladium (q.v.) and will only be outlined briefly here. The six metals invariably occur together, platinum and palladium predominating. The major sources are the nickel-copper ores of Canada the pyroxinite deposits of the Transvaal, South Africa, and the extensive deposits of northern Siberia and the Kola Penninsula, U.S.S.R. These are all primary deposits where the platinum metal alloys are disseminated in an igneous mass at quite low concentrations. Secondary placer deposits, which have resulted from the weathering of certain primary deposits, are found in the Ural Mountains region of Russia, in Colombia, and in Alaska. These alluvial deposits were the exclusive sources of platinum metals in the Nineteenth

Century, but they account for only a tiny percentage of the new platinum metals being produced today.

The alloy found in these alluvial deposits is generally known as native platinum, and as a rule contains 75 to 85% platinum, with quite small amounts of the other platinum metals and gold, the remainder being made up of iron and copper. A small percentage (usually less than 1%) stubbornly resists chemical attack; this residue is rich in osmium and iridium, and is usually designated as *osmiridium* or *iridosmine*. Naturally occurring iridosmines, possessed of great hardness and resistance to chemical attack have been found in the Urals, in South Africa, in Tasmania, and elsewhere.

Iridium is less abundant than rhodium in most sources, and thus appreciably less abundant than either platinum or palladium. Its estimated abundance in the earth's crust is 0.001 g/ton.

Derivation

The isolation of pure iridium from the ores in which it occurs at such low concentrations is a lengthy and complicated operation. The precious metals accumulate in the anode sludges during the electrolytic refining of nickel and copper derived from these ores. The residue from another method of purifying nickel as the volatile carbonyl also contains precious metals. The bulk of the platinum metals from the South African deposits is secured by gravity concentration of the ground raw ore. The various concentrates are further treated to remove base metals, for instance by smelting with appropriate fluxes, or by treatment with acid. A precious metal residue is finally obtained; the first operation on this is digestion with aqua regia to bring gold, platinum, and palladium into solution.

Iridium is found in the residue not dissolved by aqua regia, along with rhodium, osmium, and ruthenium. The sequence of treatments by which pure iridium is obtained from this insoluble fraction varies somewhat among the major refiners, and is undoubtedly influenced by the composition prevailing in the material to be separated. One major refiner has recently published an account of current practice,[5] from which the following is a summary.

The entire residue is smelted with lead carbonate and fluxes to produce a slag and a lead alloy containing 20% precious metals. This is parted with dilute nitric acid, lead and silver going into solution. The insoluble fraction is fused with sodium bisulfate, which converts rhodium to a water-soluble sulfate but leaves the other metals scarcely attacked. After extraction of the rhodium sulfate the insoluble metals are heated with sodium peroxide in shallow iron trays at 500°C. The effect of this is to convert ruthenium and osmium into ruthenate and osmate, which can be dissolved in water and thereby separated from iridium, which is converted by the fusion of iridium dioxide.

To obtain pure iridium metal, this dioxide is dissolved in aqua regia, and from the resulting chloride solution ammonium chloro-iridate is precipitated by the addition of ammonium chloride and nitric acid. For further purification these crystals are dissolved in dilute ammonium sulfide solution in which iridium remains dissolved while impurities are precipitated. The latter are removed by filtration, and a second precipitation of $(NH_4)_2IrCl_6$ made as before. Ignition of this, and reduction by hydrogen, yields iridium powder of high purity.

Melting and Fabrication

Iridium is produced in the refinery in the form of a powder. To produce compact metal the powder may be consolidated into briquets, sintered at about 1500°C, and then forged, rolled, or swaged. The sintering is preferably performed in a vacuum, though it may be done in air. Alternatively, the powder may

TABLE 1.   PHYSICAL PROPERTIES OF IRIDIUM

Property	Units	Value
Symbol		Ir
Atomic number		77
Atomic weight	Cf C–12	192.2
Stable isotopes (with % relative abundance)		191 (38.5) 193 (61.5)
Density, 20°C	g/cc	22.65
Crystal lattice		Face-centered cubic
Lattice constant, a, 20°C	Å	3.8394
Allotropic forms		None known
Melting point	°C	2443
	°K	2716
Boiling point (estimated)	°K	4662
Thermal conductivity, 0–100°C	watts/cm/°C	1.48
Linear coefficient of thermal expansion, 20–100°C	per °C	6.8×10^{-6}
Specific heat, 0°C	cal/g/°C	0.0307
Heat capacity, C_p, 25°C	cal/mole/°C	6.00
Entropy, S, 25°C	cal/mole/°C	8.48
Latent heat of fusion	kcal/mole	6.3
Latent heat of evaporation, 25°C	kcal/mole	160.0
Electrical resistivity, 0°C	μohm-cm	4.71
Temperature coefficient of resistance, 0–100°C	per °C	0.00427
Thermal neutron absorption cross section	barns	440
Hardness (annealed)	Vickers units	200–240
Tensile strength (annealed)	tons/in²	80
Young's modulus (annealed)	tons/in²	3.75×10^4
Magnetic susceptibility, χ	cm³/g	0.133×10^{-6}
Work function	ev	5.40
Thermionic function, A	amp/cm²/°K	170

be partially consolidated by vacuum sintering, and then melted in an inert atmosphere. The melting may be done in an argon arc furnace on a water-cooled copper hearth, or with a high-frequency induction furnace in a crucible of zirconia. Melting in an inert atmosphere such as argon eliminates the absorption of oxygen by the liquid metal and results in castings freer of gas cavities.

The metal requires considerable care for successful forging or rolling. The temperature for such working must be in the range 1200 to 1500°C. Drawing of this material to wire or rolling it to strip in the temperature range 600 to 750°C results in a metal having a fibrous structure, high hardness, and good tensile strength and ductility.

Physical Properties

Physical properties for iridium are assembled in Table 1. Insofar as possible they apply to the metal in the purest available state.

The density of iridium exceeds that of any other element. This results from a combination of very heavy atoms and very small atomic size. The following sequence of elements within the third transition series all have crystals with close-packed structures, and their atomic volumes will be fairly indicative of the volumes of the respective atoms.

Element	Atomic Weight	Density, 20°C	Atomic Volume	Atomic Diameter †
Rhenium	186.2	21.02 g/cc	8.86 cc/mole	2.75 kX units
Osmium	190.2	22.61	8.41	2.70
Iridium	192.2	22.65	8.48	2.709
Platinum	195.09	21.45	9.10	2.77
Gold	197.0	19.30	10.21	2.878

† Goldschmidt's atomic diameter for coordination number 12.

The data show that osmium has the minimum atomic volume but not quite the maximum density. Many older books, however, state on the basis of contemporary evidence that osmium is the most dense element.

Iridium, and to a lesser degree rhodium, show a remarkable degree of work hardening. The hardness of the former, for instance, is more than doubled when annealed metal is subjected to a 20% reduction in cross section by cold-rolling. This behavior is not typical for face-centered cubic metals, and seems to be exhibited more by polycrystalline material than by very pure single crystals. For both iridium and rhodium the extraordinary work hardening is attributed to the segregation of unknown impurities at grain boundaries.

The tensile strength of iridium at high temperatures falls off as might be expected, but still remains higher than that of tantalum, molybdenum, or niobium (columbium) above 1000°C. Only tungsten shows a higher tensile strength in the temperature range 1000 to 2000°C. But all these refractory metals except iridium are subject to oxidation or carburiza-tion at high temperature, with consequent decrease in mechanical strength. Iridium shows a comparatively abrupt increase in ductility above 1100°C, though even at higher temperatures its ductility compared to that of most face-centered cubic metals is not very great.

There is one commercially important artificially radioactive isotope, Ir-192. This emits gamma rays of average energy 0.40 MeV, and has a half-life of 72 days. Because of its high specific activity this isotope has become an important source in industrial radiography for the examination of ferrous welds.

Iridium has been widely studied as an alloying element; the following comments summarize some of the characteristics of its important binary alloys. Complete miscibility with palladium and with platinum has been reported at high temperatures. However, in both these cases patient annealing has disclosed the existence of wide miscibility gaps at lower temperatures (with palladium below about 1500°C, and with platinum below about 980°C). A complete range of solid solutions has also been found with rhodium, and with iron, cobalt, and nickel. There is only slight mutual dissolving of iridium with either gold or silver. More extensive solubility is found with osmium and ruthenium, and with the transition metals of Groups VI and VII. Some general remarks about alloying characteristics of the platinum metals are given under the entry for palladium (q.v.).

Chemical Properties

The most striking characteristic of iridium is its resistance to chemical attack. Neither the common mineral acids nor aqua regia react with the metal even at high temperatures. Fused sodium or potassium hydroxide will attack iridium slightly. As an anodic material in aqueous solutions iridium shows excellent resistance to corrosion, but under the action of alternating current some attack has been reported by aqueous hydrochloric acid, potassium cyanide, or ammonium carbonate.

In air or oxygen at 600°C iridium undergoes superficial oxidation, appearing as a tarnish on the massive metal. The oxide formed is IrO_2. The dissociation pressure of this reaches one atmosphere at 1120°C. At higher temperatures the metal loses weight in oxygen because of formation of a volatile trioxide. Since the partial vapor pressure of the latter in one atmosphere pressure of oxygen is believed to be about 10^{-3} atm at 1200°C, it is not surprising that appreciable losses occur.

Iridium undergoes the least reaction with the halogens of all the platinum metals. At 250-300°C the metal reacts with fluorine, the principal product being IrF_6 with a small amount of IrF_4. Reaction with chlorine at 600°C yields $IrCl_3$. Iridium may be converted to water-soluble sodium chloroiridate by heating it on a bed of sodium chloride in a stream of chloride at 600°C. The metal may also be brought into solution by heating with a mixture of 20 volumes of hydrochloric acid and 1 volume of nitric acid or the equivalent of sodium chlorate, perchloric acid, or chlorine in a sealed tube.

Iridium suffers little or no attack from a wide variety of molten metals in the absence of oxygen. These, arranged by position in the Periodic Table, include

Li						
Na						
K	Ca		Ga			
Ag		Cd	In	Sn	Sb	Te
Au		Hg		Pb	Bi	

It also displays remarkable resistance to attack by a number of high-melting salts and oxides, including alkaline earth tungstates, rutile, and barium titanate.

The ground state of the gaseous atom, as deduced from spectroscopic evidence is $5d^9$. The absence of any $6s$ electrons is comparable to the absence of $5s$ electrons in palladium; these are the only two elements in the Periodic Table with such a deficiency. The first stage ionization potential is not precisely known, but is given as 9 volts. The standard electrode potential, $E°$, is not directly measurable for any couple involving the metal, but Latimer has estimated $E°$ for $3e + Ir^{+3}(aq) \rightarrow Ir(s)$ to be 1.15 volts.

Chemical Compounds

By comparison with rhodium, the element with which it shows closest kinship, iridium shows a greater variety in oxidation state in its compounds. The commonest valencies are 3 and 4, and of these the former is more common. Examples of compounds in which iridium exhibits other oxidation states are mentioned below. Unlike rhodium, the element fails to show evidence of an aqueous cation, but this behavior is quite typical of the platinum group of metals.

The commonest oxide is IrO_2, a black solid with the rutile structure. It is formed by direct union of the elements at about 1000°C, but decomposes above 1120°. When quadri-positive iridium salts, e.g., $IrCl_6^{2-}$, are treated with alkali an intensely blue-colored hydrous oxide is precipitated. This may be dried under nitrogen at 350°C to give the dioxide in a reasonably pure state. If alkali is added to a terpositive iridium salt, e.g., $IrCl_6^{3-}$, in an oxygen-free atmosphere, a hydrous trioxide is precipitated. This is a green or blue-black gelatinous solid, soluble in excess alkali, and prone to take up atmospheric oxygen to form the dioxide. Dehydration of this material fails to yield pure Ir_2O_3. The trioxide, IrO_3, is formed by fusion of the metal with alkaline oxidants such as sodium peroxide; it has not, however, been well characterized.

Iridium hexafluoride, IrF_6, is a yellow solid (m.p. 44°C) that fumes strongly in air and reacts vigorously with water. The tetrafluoride is also a yellow solid (m.p. 106°C) and very reactive. A black solid IrF_3 can be prepared with difficulty.

The trichloride may be prepared by direct union of the elements. It is colored olive-green, brown, or black according to particle size; it is insoluble in water. Dark-green, water-soluble hydrated iridium trichloride is also known, formed by reaction of hydrochloric acid on the dioxide. A tetrachloride of poor stability has been formed by the action of chlorine or aqua regia on $(NH_4)_2IrCl_6$.

A variety of sulfides, selenides, and tellurides have been identified as intermediate phases in the two-component systems with iridium. These include Ir_2S_3, IrS_2, Ir_3S_8, $IrS_3(?)$, Ir_2Se_3, $IrSe_2$, $IrSe_3$, $IrTe_2$, and $IrTe_3$. These are all dark solids, quite resistant to acids.

Iridium forms many complexes, and in these the element exhibits, in addition to the common oxidation states $+3$ and $+4$, examples of $+1$, $+2$, and $+5$ valency, and also the oxidation state zero in carbonyls. The commonest complexes are the chloroiridates, $IrCl_6^{2-}$, very dark red in color; and the chloroiridites, $IrCl_6^{3-}$, which are olive-green. The chloroiridates of many large cations and organic nitrogen bases are sparingly soluble in water. The hexachloro complexes and most of the anionic complexes are quite stable, and undergo substitution of one ligand for another only very slowly. Cationic complexes are not common and not particularly stable (another difference from rhodium). Chloroiridate is fairly easily reduced to chloroiridite, the $E°$ for the reaction $e + IrCl_6^{2-}(aq) \rightarrow IrCl_6^{3-}(aq)$ being 1.017 volts.

Importance and Uses

The world's annual production of new iridium is only a few thousand ounces, and to this supply will be added the metal recovered from scrap, used platinum equipment, and so on. The current (1967) price of iridium is $190.00 per troy ounce.

The following data outline the industrial demand for the metal. These show the percentages of the 9,652 troy ounces of iridium sold to the principal consuming industries in the United States during 1964: jewelry and decorative 45.1%, chemical 27.9%, electrical 23.7%, dental and medical 2.0%, petroleum 0.8%, miscellaneous 0.5%.

Iridium is used principally as an alloying element in platinum. Its effect is to increase greatly the tensile strength and hardness of the platinum, [6] but of equal importance it greatly increases its resistance to corrosion. The amounts of iridium to be added to platinum will depend on the mechanical or chemical properties desired, bearing in mind that the improvements in these are achieved at the cost of a decrease in workability of the alloys.

Owing to their resistance to chemical attack, platinum-iridium alloys containing up to 30% of the latter element have found applications such as the following: in vessels for handling corrosive chemicals and for electrodes subject to anodic oxidation; in electrical contacts exposed to corrosive environments; in jewelry, hypodermic needles, radium applicators and other medical accessories; in primary standards of weight and length.

In applications for the hardening of platinum, iridium is not as successful at high temperatures. This is because of the considerable weight losses sustained by iridium when heated above 1000°C in an atmosphere containing oxygen (see above). Hence, rhodium is preferred in such cases for this purpose.

Some iridium is applied to the hardening of palladium for jewelry and for electrical contacts.

The pure metal finds a limited number of applications. Some small crucibles for high-temperature reactions, for instance involving molten metals, have been fashioned. The metal has been used to make extrusion dies for high-melting glasses, or for crucibles in which to melt materials for laser crystals. Because of its resistance to attack by lead, the metal had been used for spark-plug electrodes in aircraft engines.

Thermocouples for use at very high temperatures have been developed in which one limb is pure iridium, and the other is an alloy of iridium with 40 or 50% rhodium. These show excellent performance in oxidizing or corrosive atmospheres.

References

1. Platinum Metals Review. A quarterly survey of research on the platinum metals and of developments in their application in industry. Johnson, Matthey and Co. Ltd., Hatton Garden, London, E.C.1, England, 1957–date.
2. Hampel, C. A., Editor, "Rare Metals Handbook," 2nd Edition, pp. 304–335, New York, Reinhold Publishing Corp., 1961.
3. "Iridium—the metal, its alloys, chemical compounds and catalytic properties," International Nickel Co. Inc., 67 Wall St., New York, 1965.
4. Cotton, F. A., and Wilkinson, G., "Advanced Inorganic Chemistry," pp. 832–845, New York, Interscience Publishers, 1962.
5. Clements, F. S., *Industrial Chemist* (*London*), **38**, 345–354 (1962).
6. Darling, A. S., *Platinum Metals Review*, **4**, 18 (1960).

W. A. E. McBryde

IRON

Iron, symbol Fe from the Latin *ferrum*, has an atomic number of 26 and an atomic weight of 55.847. The element is located in Group VIII of the Periodic Table as the first member of the triad: iron, cobalt and nickel.

Iron has four stable isotopes: 54 (5.90%), 56 (91.52%), 57 (2.245%), and 58 (0.33%). Its electronic configuration is $1s^2$, $2s^2$, $2p^6$, $3s^2$, $3p^6$, $3d^6$, $4s^2$. While iron can exist in the $+4$ and $+6$ oxidation states, they are rare and the common valences for it are $+2$ (ferrous) and $+3$ (ferric).

Iron is the most important metal known and used by man. The annual production of steel in the United States alone is about 130,000,000 tons (127 million in 1967 and 134 million in 1966). This quantity exceeds the total production manyfold of all the other metals combined. Next to oxygen, iron is the element used in greatest amount in elemental form by man. This is due to its widespread prevalence, the ease with which its ores are reduced to the metal, and its many desirable structural properties. In addition, iron is found in all mammalian cells and is absolutely vital to the life processes of animals.

History

Iron has been known since prehistoric times. The writings of most of the earliest civilizations refer to it, and there is evidence that it was known in the ancient world over 8000 years ago. However, prior to the period of 1000–2000 B.C. iron was a rare metal, evidently derived chiefly from meteorites. The association of iron with the heavens was common among most early peoples, including those in Pre-Columbian America, indicating that meteorites were the source of iron in ancient times. From about 1000–2000 B.C. onward iron derived from ore became an increasingly used metal and its smelting and fabrication were practiced all over the civilized world by processes functionally similar to those used now.

Occurrence

Iron is the fourth most prevalent element in the earth's crust, after oxygen, silicon and aluminum, and comprises about 5% of the earth's crust. It is a constituent of several hundred minerals, but fortunately, huge deposits of easily reduced iron oxide occur in many countries and these are the sources of most of the iron produced by man. The principal iron minerals are hematite, Fe_2O_3; magnetite, Fe_3O_4; limonite, $Fe_2O_3 \cdot xH_2O$, hydrated iron oxide; and the carbonate, siderite, $FeCO_3$. Minor use is made of iron pyrites, FeS_2, and of ilmenite, $FeTiO_3$, or $FeO \cdot TiO_2$.

By far the most important iron ore producing district in the world is the Mesabi range which stretches 100 miles across northern Minnesota. More than 1.5 billion tons of high-grade (over 50% Fe) ore have been produced from the Mesabi and probably much less than one-half billion tons remain at this time. However, untold billions of tons of low-grade ore remain from which a high-grade product can be made. Much of this material is in the form of taconite, a very hard rock consisting of fine black crystals of magnetite intermingled with crystals of silica and containing 25–30% iron. It is now being upgraded to about 65% iron in huge plants located on the north shore of Lake Superior.

In 1967 taconite operating capacity was 45 million tons/year of high-grade oxide as compared with total domestic iron ore shipments of about 90 million tons in 1966. Current iron ore consumption in the United States is about 140 million long tons annually, imports of ore meeting the demand.

The second largest domestic source of iron ore, after the Mesabi and other Lake Superior ranges, is the Birmingham, Alabama area where limestone and coking coal are also available.

Other iron ore deposits occur in most of the highly industrialized nations. Among them are those of the Lorraine area on the Franco-German border, Great Britain, Austria, Sweden, Germany and Russia. Future sources of iron ore, as yet largely untapped, are located in Brazil, Chile, Cuba, Venezuela and Canada.

The iron-bearing minerals of the Mesabi range, as well as many other iron ore deposits in the world, are undoubtedly of bacterial origin. Iron bacteria absorbed ferrous carbonate from sea water and oxidized it to secure their energy with the formation of ferric oxide, water and CO_2. The Fe_2O_3 was deposited on the ocean floor where it gradually built up into the deposits now hundreds of feet thick in places. Land uplifts raised the deposits to their present locations. Geologically younger deposits, called bog iron, which were the source of iron ore in Colonial times along the Atlantic coast, are probably still being formed in many locations by the precipitation of limonite from water containing dissolved iron mixing with organic materials in swampy areas.

Derivation

Only a minute portion of the iron produced is in the form of what might be called a pure metal, i.e., over 99.9% iron. The vast majority of the iron made and used is in the form of steel, an alloy of iron containing small amounts of carbon (usually less than 1%) that has properties much more attractive than those of pure iron. Actually, steel is a general term for hundreds of iron alloys containing, in addition to carbon, one or more additional elements, e.g., sulfur, silicon, manganese, chromium, nickel, vanadium, tungsten, molybdenum, columbium and titanium. The properties of a given steel are affected not only by the kinds and amounts of elements other than iron in it, but by the form of the iron and of the iron-carbon compounds in it as affected by heat treatment given the steel.

The first step in the extraction of iron from its ores is almost always the reduction of the iron oxide to pig iron in a blast furnace with carbon in the presence of limestone, whereby the noniron ore components, chiefly silica, are converted to a slag and the iron to a molten metal. A modern blast furnace is a vertical stack or tower 100–200 feet tall and 25 feet diameter lined with refractory bricks. Alternate charges of ore, coke and limestone are made at the furnace top and air is blown into the bottom of the furnace. The daily production of 1500 tons of pig iron in a typical blast furnace consumes about 3000 tons of iron ore, 1350 tons of coke, 600 tons of limestone and 4500 tons of air. As the solids descend in the furnace and the gases rise, several reactions occur which yield molten iron and slag that trickle to the bottom of the furnace from which they are tapped at intervals from the furnace hearth:

$$C + O \longrightarrow CO$$
$$3C + Fe_2O_3 \longrightarrow 2Fe + 3CO$$
$$CO + 3Fe_2O_3 \longrightarrow 2Fe_3O_4 + CO_2$$
$$CO + Fe_3O_4 \longrightarrow 3FeO + CO_2$$
$$CO + FeO \longrightarrow Fe + CO_2$$
$$CaCO_3 \longrightarrow CaO + CO_2$$
$$CaO + SiO_2 \longrightarrow CaSiO_3$$
$$CaO + FeS \longrightarrow CaS + FeO$$
$$CaO + FeS + C \longrightarrow CaS + Fe + CO$$

The average analysis of pig iron is about 1% Si, 0.03% S, 0.27% P, 2.4% Mn, 4.6% C (the solubility limit of carbon in iron), balance iron. It is a source of cast iron used in making a variety of products where the low tensile strength of cast iron is not objectionable.

Most of the pig iron is converted into steel, which requires the carefully controlled removal of sulfur, phosphorus and silicon; the elimination of most of the carbon but the maintenance of a definite carbon content; and the introduction of desired amounts of purifying and alloying elements. Steel is made from pig iron and scrap steel in open hearth furnaces, in Bessemer converters (formerly widely used but now accounting for only about 1% of steel production), in basic oxygen furnaces, and in electric furnaces. The open hearth process accounted for the greatest quantity of steel until just recently, but it is expected that by 1970 half of the total steel production will be by the basic oxygen furnace (BOF) process. Whereas the typical open hearth furnace produces 50 tons of steel in an 8-hour period, the BOF process requires less than an hour, chiefly because high-purity oxygen rather than air is used to oxidize the carbon in the charge.

High-Purity Iron. Pure iron, 99.9 + %, is a rare commodity for several reasons: the high chemical activity of iron which makes it difficult both to prepare and to maintain when made, the lack of attractive physical properties as compared with those of steel, and the high cost of pure iron. A small amount of quite pure, but not the 99.9 + % quality, is made for catalyst use and for incorporation in special magnets.

Among the methods used to prepare pure iron are: (1) thermal decomposition at about 250°C of iron carbonyl, $Fe(CO)_5$, a volatile compound made by the reaction at 180–200°C of carbon monoxide under pressure on iron powder; (2) hydrogen reduction of high-purity ferric oxide, or ferric oxalate, or ferric formate; and (3) electrolytic deposition from solutions of a ferrous salt. Electrolytic iron powder is made commercially in only one United States plant, based on the use of a mixed ferrous and ammonium sulfate solution, anodes of Armco iron, cathodes of Type 430 stainless steel, current density of 25 amp/sq ft and temperature of 120–140°F. The solid iron from the cathode is brittle and can be ground to powder.

Physical Properties

Most of the physical and mechanical properties of iron are altered by virtually all impurities, especially carbon, and many reported values of such properties are contradictory or in error because the iron tested was impure. An excellent compilation of physical properties is that of Moore and Shives of the National Bureau of Standards, published in the "Metals Handbook" of the American Society for Metals. Many of the data selected by them are listed in Table 1, where the physical properties of iron are summarized.

High-purity iron resembles platinum in appearance and can be highly polished. It is attracted by a magnet, but unlike steel, rapidly loses its magnetism. When heated to the Curie point, 768°C, ferromagnetic iron becomes paramagnetic. No crystal structure change occurs at this point. However, iron has three allotropic forms: (1) alpha iron below 910°C is body-centered cubic; (2) gamma iron from 910 to 1390°C is face-centered cubic; and (3) above 1390°C delta iron is body-centered cubic.

Iron is the most tenacious of all the ductile metals at ordinary temperatures with the exception of cobalt and nickel, but it becomes brittle at liquid air temperatures. Iron softens at red heat, where it is easily forged, drawn, etc., and it can be welded easily at a white heat. However, most high-purity irons are very ductile at room temperature and can easily be reduced or formed by any standard method.

Chemical Properties

Iron is a very reactive element and as indicated by its electrode potential of −0.4402 volts for $Fe = Fe^{++} + 2e$, it is a strong reducing agent. Thus, it will displace hydrogen from water, slowly at room temperature and rapidly at temperatures above about 500°C. The reaction with water is associated with the atmospheric rusting of iron by oxygen, the most familiar chemical property of iron. Both oxygen and water or moisture are needed for rusting which is definitely an electrochemical reaction that can be prevented by application of a proper potential to the iron structure.

Solutions containing ions of many metals, such as gold, platinum, silver, mercury, bismuth, tin, nickel and copper, are reduced by solid iron to the corresponding metal and the ferrous ion. For example, the reaction with copper salts is: $Cu^{++} + Fe \longrightarrow Fe^{++} + Cu$.

Iron combines with most nonmetals directly and at moderate temperatures to form binary compounds; included are oxygen, carbon, sulfur, arsenic, phosphorus, all the halides, and silicon. Iron reacts only to a limited degree with nitrogen at elevated temperature. However, exposure to ammonia at 400–700°C results in the formation of Fe_2N; this reaction is used commercially to form nitrided surfaces on steel which are hard and abrasion resistant.

TABLE 1. PHYSICAL PROPERTIES OF 99.9+% IRON

Atomic number	26
Atomic weight	55.847
Isotopes, natural, and abundance	54 (5.90%)
	56 (91.52%)
	57 (2.245%)
	58 (0.33%)
Electron configuration	$1s^2, 2s^2, 2p^6, 3s^2, 3p^6, 3d^6, 4s^2$
Density, 20°C, g/cc	7.8733
liquid, 1564°C, g/cc	7.00
Atomic volume, 25°C, cc/g-atom	7.094
Specific volume, 25°C, cc/g	0.12701
Melting point, °C	1536.5 ± 1
Boiling point, °C	3000
Curie point, °C	768
Transformation points, °C	
alpha (bcc) to gamma (fcc)	910
gamma to delta (bcc)	1390
Specific heat, C_p, cal/g-atom/°C, at 25°C	5.98
at melting point	9.60
Latent heat of fusion, cal/g	65.5
Latent heat of vaporization, cal/g	1598
Heat of combustion (Fe to Fe_2O_3), cal/g	1582
Thermal conductivity, 0°C, cal/cm/sec/°C	0.2
Linear coefficient of thermal expansion,	
micro-in./in./°C	
alpha (20–100°C)	12.3
gamma (916–1388°C)	23.04
delta (1388–1502°C)	23.6
Electrical resistivity, 20°C, microhm-cm	9.71
liquid, at melting point	139
Temperature coefficient of electrical resistivity, % increase/°C	0.651
Electrode potential, Fe $= Fe^{++} + 2e$, 25°C. volts	-0.4402
Hall effect coefficient, 13°C, volt-cm/amp/gauss	2.45×10^{-13}
Magnetic properties*, 25°C	
Permeability	88,400
Magnetic induction, gauss	
saturation	21,580
residual	11,830
Coercive force, H_c, oersteds	0.045
Hysteresis, ergs/cc/cycle	150
*for iron of 99.99% purity, resistivity 9.71 microhm-cm	
Velocity of sound, 20°C, meters/sec	5130
Viscosity, 1743°C, centipoise	4.45
Surface tension, 1550°C, dynes/cm	1835 to 1865
Vapor pressure, 1600°C, atm	8.0×10^{-5}
Modulus of elasticity, psi	28.5×10^6
Shear or torsion modulus, psi	11.6×10^6
Poisson's ratio	0.29
Tensile strength, psi	30,000
Hardness, Brinell	60
Thermal neutron absorption cross-section, barns	2.62

The most common valence states of iron are the +2 (ferrous) and the +3 (ferric), but it is possible to attain the +4 state in perferrite, $FeO_3^=$, and the +6 state in ferrate, $FeO_4^=$. The latter valences are both obtained by the action of strong oxidizing agents on Fe_2O_3

in concentrated alkaline media. Only a limited number of compounds of iron in the +4 or +6 state are known and the most important oxidation states by far are the ferrous and ferric, +2 and +3.

Iron dissolves in nonoxidizing acids, such as sulfuric and hydrochloric, with the liberation of hydrogen and the formation of ferrous ion. Since iron reduces ferric ion to ferrous ion, only ferrous ion is formed unless an oxidizing agent is present in excess.

It dissolves in cold dilute nitric acid with the formation of ferrous and ammonium nitrates and no liberation of gas. When hot acid is used or with stronger nitric acid, ferric nitrate is formed and nitrogen oxides are evolved.

The passivating effect of concentrated nitric acid on iron, whereby the iron will not subsequently react with acids or precipitate other metals from solution, was observed over a century ago by Faraday and others. The same effect is produced by anodic passivation or by other oxidizing ions, such as nitrate, chromate and chlorate, which result in the formation of an oxide film on the iron. This passivating film can be destroyed by scratching or hammering the surface, or by the action of reducing agents.

Principal Compounds

Iron forms two extensive series of compounds, the ferrous and the ferric, derived largely from the corresponding oxides, FeO and Fe_2O_3, in which iron has a valence of +2 and +3, respectively. A third oxide, magnetite, Fe_3O_4, is a mixed oxide, ferrous ferrite, $FeO \cdot Fe_2O_3$ or $Fe(II)Fe(III)_2O_4$.

Solutions of ferrous salts are difficult to maintain unless they are quite acidic, since the Fe^{++} ion is easily oxidized to the +3 state by oxygen in the air. Hydrated solid salts, like ferrous chloride, $FeCl_2 \cdot 4H_2O$, and ferrous sulfate, $FeSO_4 \cdot 7H_2O$, are more stable and more resistant to atmospheric oxidation.

$FeSO_4$, one of the most important iron salts, is produced chiefly as a by-product of the pickling of steel with sulfuric acid to remove the oxide scale from the surface. Ferrous sulfate is also made by the oxidation of moist pyrites in air: $2FeS_2 + 7O_2 + 2H_2O$ $\longrightarrow 2FeSO_4 + 2H_2SO_4$. It is used as a mordant in dyeing, as a disinfectant, as a reducing agent, in water purification and in the manufacture of ink and Prussian blue, ferric ferrocyanide, $Fe_4[Fe(CN)_6]_3$.

Ferrous chloride is made by the reaction of hydrochloric acid on iron or iron oxide. Since HCl is being used increasingly for pickling of steel, more and more $FeCl_2$ is being obtained as a by-product. Several processes, such as treatment of the pickle liquor with lime, have been devised for its disposal and for the recovery of magnetite from it.

When a base is added to a solution of a ferrous salt, such as $FeSO_4$, white ferrous hydroxide, $Fe(OH)_2$, is precipitated. When exposed to air the $Fe(OH)_2$ turns brown owing to the oxidation to hydrated ferric oxide, $Fe_2O_3 \cdot xH_2O$. The latter is sometimes call ferric hydroxide, but pure $Fe(OH)_3$ probably has never been prepared. Hydrated iron oxide is the basis, after dehydration, of a whole series of iron oxide pigments ranging in color from yellow (ochre) to red (Venetian red). Rouge is the red form and is used for polishing glass and plastics as well as for its cosmetic value.

Writing ink is prepared by adding ferrous sulfate to an extract of nutgalls which contains tannic and gallic acids. The ferrous salts that form are colorless, but they are rapidly oxidized by air to the intense black color of ferric gallate and tannate. To such an ink a colored dye is added to give the desired initial color before the ferrous to ferric change occurs.

Both ferrous and ferric iron form stable complexes with cyanides in which each iron atom is associated with six cyano groups as $Fe(CN)_6^{-4}$ and $Fe(CN)_6^{-3}$, the ferrocyanide and ferricyanide ions, respectively. These ions take part in some very complicated reactions to form useful compounds. Prussian blue, ferriferrocyanide, is a deep blue precipitate formed by mixing a solution of a ferric salt with a solution of potassium ferrocyanide, the reaction being:

$$3K_4Fe(CN)_6 + 2Fe_2(SO_4)_3$$
$$\longrightarrow Fe_4[Fe(CN)_6]_3 + 6K_2SO_4.$$

Prussian blue is the pigment of laundry bluing

309

whose color covers the yellow stain on white goods to make them appear white.

Among the most interesting iron compounds are the carbonyls. Ferropentacarbonyl, $Fe(CO)_5$, is formed by the action of carbon monoxide on finely divided iron; it is a pale yellow liquid which freezes at $-21°C$, boils at $102°C$, and decomposes to Fe and CO when heated above about $200°C$. The iron so formed is very pure. The pentacarbonyl is photochemically decomposed at ordinary temperatures to form the nonacarbonyl: $2Fe(CO)_5 \longrightarrow Fe_2(CO)_9 + CO$. The latter is a yellow crystalline solid that decomposes at $100°C$ to form $Fe(CO)_5$ and a greenish-black carbonyl whose formula is $Fe_3(CO)_{12}$.

Mention has been made earlier of iron bacteria. Use has been made of their ability to oxidize ferrous ion to ferric in a cyclic operation to recover copper from low-grade sources. The naturally occurring species *Thiobacillus ferrooxidans* has been adapted to withstand high concentrations of zinc, copper and other metals and to tolerate H_2SO_4 at a pH of 1.5–2.5. The bacteria are used to oxidize ferrous sulfate to ferric sulfate, which in turn oxidizes copper from mine waste dumps while being reduced back to the ferrous state. In the presence of the bacteria the reactions involved are:

$$2FeSO_4 + H_2SO_4 + \tfrac{1}{2}O_2 \longrightarrow Fe_2(SO_4)_3 + H_2O.$$
$$Fe_2(SO_4)_3 + Cu \longrightarrow CuSO_4 + 2FeSO_4.$$

The process is based on work of Zimmerley, Wilson and Brater.

Ferric thiocyanate, $Fe(SCN)_3$, is a compound whose bright red color makes it one of the most sensitive reagents for the detection of ferric ion which can be observed in concentrations as low as $10^{-5}M$.

Iron compounds are available as by-products of several industrial operations in quantities much greater than the amounts consumed by the rather limited number of applications for iron compounds. In many instances they represent waste disposal problems. Examples are the acidic pickle liquors of the steel industry which contain $FeSO_4$ or $FeCl_2$, and the "red mud" from the Bayer alumina process which contains hydrated ferric oxide from the bauxite raw material.

Applications of Iron

All but a minute fraction of the iron extracted from ores is used in the metallic form to make the multiplicity of devices and structures that characterize our modern civilization. In its applications iron is the major component of several types of alloys, the most prominent being those that contain carbon alone (up to 1.7%), the *carbon steels*. The properties of these steels can be varied not only by the amount of carbon present, but also by the heat treatment given the steel. Carbon has such potent effects that it is specified to hundredths of a per cent.

The next largest tonnage of iron alloys is found in the low alloy steels containing, in addition to carbon, varying amounts and combinations of alloying elements (up to 5%). These, too, are heat treated to attain desired structure and properties. A four-digit numerical system is used to identify these steels.

Other important types of steel are tool steels, stainless steels, heat-resistant steels and maraging steels, a new group which is heat treatable to unusually high strength levels. All of these types of steels contain 10 to 20% or more of alloying elements, chiefly chromium and nickel.

Iron alloys not classified as steels include cast iron, wrought iron, silicon iron (e.g., "Duriron"), nickel iron, and malleable iron, each of which has a variety of important applications in modern life.

Biochemical and Biological Aspects*

Although considered to be a "trace" element, iron occupies a unique place in the metabolic processes of the animal body. It is a vital constituent of every mammalian cell. The role of iron in the body is closely associated with hemoglobin and the transport of oxygen from the lungs to the tissue cells. It is also concerned with cellular oxidation mechanisms which are catalyzed by iron containing enzymes.

It has been variously estimated that the total iron in the blood and tissues of a 70 kilo man is about 5 grams. All of it is bound to proteins in one form or another. These may be divided into two groups: (a) The iron porphyrin or heme proteins which include hemoglobin, myoglobin (muscle hemoglobin), and the heme enzymes—the cytochromes, catalases, and peroxidases. Blood hemoglobin, about 900 grams, contains 3 grams of iron and represents, therefore, from 60 to 70% of the total body iron; myoglobin from 3 to 5% and, the heme enzymes about 0.2% of the body iron. (b) Non-heme compounds, including siderophilin (transferrin), ferritin, and hemosiderin. In this group of proteins a significant quantity of iron, about 0.6 gram or about 15% of the total body iron, is contained in ferritin.

The iron porphyrin, or heme, proteins function together to bring about oxidation of cell metabolites with oxygen. This vital process is accomplished in a series of steps. The first involves the transport of molecular oxygen by hemoglobin contained in the red cells. Chemically speaking, hemoglobin is a conjugated protein, with a prosthetic group, heme, united to the protein globin. In the heme portion of the molecule an atom of ferrous iron, with a coordination valence of six,

HEME

occurs at the center of each 4 tetrapyrrole rings. Four of the valences bind the pyrrole nitrogens in the plane of the ring, while a fifth linkage above or below and perpendicular to the plane, is attached to globin through the nitrogen of the imidazole group of histidine. This configuration permits the reversible combination with molecular oxygen, depending on the partial pressure, at the sixth coordination valence of the iron. In this manner the iron of

hemoglobin facilitates the uptake of oxygen in the lungs where the partial pressure is high, and its release in the tissues where the partial pressure of oxygen is low.

Since the iron of functioning hemoglobin remains in the reduced form, the combination with oxygen is spoken of as "oxygenation," rather than oxidation. (Unfortunately the affinity of hemoglobin for carbon monoxide exceeds that of oxygen by a factor of about 210.) In the tissues oxygen diffuses out of the red cells into the interstitial spaces and into the tissue cells. If the tissue is muscle, the oxygen may be combined temporarily with myoglobin, another iron-prophyrin-protein similar to hemoglobin with a greater affinity for oxygen. In a sense, myoglobin functions as a storage compound holding a reserve of oxygen in those muscles, e.g., heart muscle, which are required for emergency or for sustained work. The actual "burning" or oxidation of food fragments which takes place in the mitochondria of the cells is a complicated process catalyzed by the iron porphyrin enzymes: the cytochromes, cytochrome oxidase, catalase, and peroxidase. In these transformations a food fragment or metabolite, such as succinic acid from the citric acid cycle, is dehydrogenated (hence oxidized) with the loss of 2 hydrogen atoms and 2 electrons. The electrons are passed down through a series of cytochromes, b, c, a, in which the iron is alternately oxidized and reduced, and finally to cytochrome oxidase which activates oxygen to take up two electrons and hydrogen to form water. The net reaction is the removal of hydrogen from the metabolite and its combination with oxygen to form water. From the standpoint of energy involved in the reaction, the formation of 1 mole of water liberates 68,000 calories of heat. In this connection, it should be recalled that the opposite transformation takes place in plants. In the leaves, chlorophyll, a magnesium-porphyrin-protein, catalyzes the cleavage of water into hydrogen and oxygen.

Among the non-heme iron compounds of the body, ferritin, hemosiderin, and siderophilin (or transferrin) have been recognized as chemical entities. The first two are considered to be essentially iron storage proteins; the latter functions in the transport of iron in the blood.

In man, and in most other species investigated, the liver and spleen are the main storage organs for iron in the form of ferritin. Ferritin is also present in lesser amounts in the bone marrow, kidneys, and intestine. The protein devoid of iron is known as apoferritin, a colorless compound with a molecular weight of 460,000. Apoferritin is capable of combining with variable amounts of iron up to 23 % of its dry weight, to form the brownish pigmented protein, ferritin. Both ferritin and apoferritin have been crystallized with cadmium salt. Since ferritin is not a definite chemical compound, it is assumed that the iron is present in the form of ferric hydroxide micelles or clusters, with an average composition, $[(FeOOH)_8 \cdot FeOPO_3H_2]$.

The transport of iron in the blood stream is accomplished by siderophilin, a serum globulin having a molecular weight of about 88,000 and capable of combining with a maximum of 2 ferric atoms per molecule. In normal individuals the siderophilin, or iron-binding protein, is about one-third saturated, which represents about 4 milligrams of iron. This permits varying amounts of dietary iron to be transported from the active absorbing areas in the intestine to the liver and spleen, and also from these storage depots to the specialized tissues for the synthesis of hemoglobin and the cellular cytochromes. The iron contained in the hemoglobin of the red cell is not transport iron in the sense that it can be made available for the synthesis of other iron compounds. This occurs only when the red cell ceases to function in the transport of oxygen and the hemoglobin is degraded.

The nutritional requirements for iron are exceedingly small and vary somewhat with age and sex. Fortunately, nature has provided the newborn infant with an adequate reserve of this vital element which is normally sufficient to tide him over a dietary period restricted to milk which is low in iron. The human adult male absorbs less than 5 mg of iron per day. This is a liberal estimate if one compares it with the cumulative daily loss of 1 mg or less, in the urine, stool, and from the skin surfaces. Woman absorb slightly more to replace loss through the menses or during gestation for foetal requirements. In growing children the demand for iron is geared to increased blood formation, but absorption perhaps does not exceed 10 to 15 mg per day. Iron absorption takes place primarily in the duodenal region just below the pyloric sphincter. It is generally agreed that dietary iron must be reduced to the ferrous state before it can be absorbed. Numerous observations have established the fact that the iron of different foods is not equally "available," and may be only a fraction of that determined by ash analysis. Hemoglobin-iron present in meat products is probably not available. Much of the iron in food is in the ferric form, as ferric hydroxide or as iron loosely bound in organic molecules. These compounds are acted on by gastric HCl so that at least a part of the iron becomes ionized. Ferric ions in contact with reducing agents in the food, such as ascorbic acid, cysteine, and other sulfhydryl compounds, are converted to the divalent state. Ferrous iron is combined with apoferritin, present in the mucosal cells, to form ferritin, which in turn passes the iron on the blood stream to be transported as siderophilin. Thus, iron absorption is regulated by the ferritin mechanism of the mucosal cells to avoid both iron excess and iron deficiency.

Iron is frequently spoken of as a "one way" substance. Once it is incorporated into the body, whether by oral administration or by parenteral injection, there is no efficient mechanism for its excretion. Iron from outworn red cells is used over and over again as though it were a precious metal in the economy of the individual.

Among the foods rich in iron, meats—especially liver, fish, and egg yolk deserve prominent mention. Good vegetable sources are found in dried peas and beans, also in leafy green vegetables. Flour, fresh fruit, and milk are relatively poor in iron.

Since the availability of ingested iron is related to its solubility and its reduced state, ferrous salts (ferrous sulfate, ferrous gluconate) have proved to be effective in the treatment of anemia due to iron deficiency. It has been shown that ascorbic acid taken along with therapeutic iron increases the amount of iron absorbed. Iron replacement may also be accomplished by the transfusion of whole blood or by the use of a variety of organic-iron compounds which are available for parenteral administration. Perhaps the most widely used of the latter is saccharated oxide of iron. The therapeutic use of iron is a problem which should be left to the judgment of the physician.

*C. A. JOHNSON

References

1. Moore, G. A., and Shives, T. R., "Metals Handbook," 8th Edition, pp. 1206–1212, Metals Park, Ohio, American Society for Metals, 1961.
2. Bain, E. C., and Paxton, H. W., "Alloying Elements in Steel," 2nd Edition, Metals Park, Ohio, American Society for Metals, 1966.
3. Sharp, J. D., "Elements of Steel-Making Practice," Long Island City, N. Y., Pergamon Press, 1966.
4. Zimmerley, S. R., Wilson, D. G., and Brater, J. D., U.S. Patent 2,829,964, April 8, 1958 (to Kennecott Copper Co.).

CLIFFORD A. HAMPEL

ISOTOPES. I. PRE-WORLD WAR I STATUS

Definition

The term isotope (from the Greek meaning "same place") was introduced in the scientific literature by Soddy in 1913, a year notable for so many advances in atomic science.[1] Soddy postulated that isotopes occupied the same place in the periodic system of classification and therefore were atoms of the same element. In this classification the elements were listed according to increasing atomic weights and the numbered position of an element is known as its atomic number. We now know that all atoms of an element have in their nuclei protons in number equal to the atomic number. Likewise, the atoms being electrically neutral, they also contain electrons in number equal to the number of protons in the nucleus. However, the atomic nuclei may contain neutrons (which have almost the same mass as protons but a net electrical charge of zero) in differing numbers and so the net weight or atomic weight (strictly, atomic mass) of the atoms of an element may differ. Atoms of the same atomic number (i.e., the same element) but with differing atomic masses are isotopes.

Soddy's proposition of isotopy inferred nothing about the structure of nuclei. He was however, well aware that certain groups of radioactive species (then called elements) such as radiothorium and thorium, when mixed together, could not be separated by any known chemical procedure even after many attempts to do so. His proposal was to place together in one position in the Periodic Table such seemingly inseparable species, even though their radioactive properties and even their atomic weights were different. This was a bold step towards overcoming many difficulties which then existed, one of them being that nearly forty species with different radioactive properties were known, but only twelve positions between lead and uranium were available to accommodate them in the Periodic Table. Further applications of the concept of isotopy were to play an important role in the development of the atomic theory. These will be more readily evident after mention of some of the developments that occurred before 1913. Of particular importance were the measurement and interpretation of atomic weights.

Early Atomic Theory and Atomic Weights

The modern era in chemical science is usually considered to have begun with the proposal of the atomic theory of chemical action by John Dalton. This theory postulated the existence of minute indivisible particles or atoms, each of equal weight for the same element, atoms of different elements, however, having different weights. In his "New System of Chemical Philosophy" published in 1808, he discussed in detail his ideas concerning the atom as the unit of chemical structure. Many of Dalton's contemporaries had entertained ideas about atoms, but the theory as enunciated by him was not only specific, but provided an interpretation of many chemical facts; of even greater consequence, it acted as a guide to further experimentation and investigation.

Dalton is regarded as the founder of the atomic theory principally because he made it quantitative and introduced a feeling of reality by showing how the weights of different atoms, relative to one another, could be determined. Earlier investigators seem to have paid no attention to relative weights of particles, nor had they given much real thought to them in explaining the nature of chemical compounds. In a paper presented to the Literary and Philosophical Society of Manchester, England, in October, 1803, Dalton stated, "An inquiry into the relative weights of ultimate particles [atoms] of bodies is a subject, so far as I know, entirely new. I have lately been prosecuting this inquiry with remarkable success." Thus John Dalton initiated a continuing tradition of chemical atomism, although most of his weights were subsequently proved to be erroneous.

One of the factors responsible for the unreliability of Dalton's experimental work was his choice of hydrogen as the basis of comparison for atomic weights. This was a poor selection, not only because relatively few elements form compounds with hydrogen, but also because small errors in weighing led to large discrepancies, as a result of the lightness of hydrogen. Although few atomic weights were then known, and those only approximately, William Prout in 1816 postulated that all atomic weights were integral, i.e., whole numbers without fractions. All atomic weights, he reasoned, might be multiples of that of hydrogen. A major consequence of his hypothesis was the stimulus it gave to accurate determinations of atomic weights, although when fractional atomic weights such as those for chlorine (35.457) and copper (63.54) were obtained, doubt arose concerning the validity of the hypothesis.

Since most elements combine with oxygen, Berzelius used it as a standard, assigning to it an arbitrary combining weight of 100. Later on, while it was still believed that oxygen "as it occurs in air" consisted of a single isotope and that an atom of oxygen was about sixteen times as heavy as hydrogen, it was agreed to take the atomic weight of oxygen to be exactly 16. This was an entirely satisfactory standard until it was later discovered that oxygen is not simple but consists of atoms of three different atomic masses (i.e., there are three isotopes). This important discovery will be considered in more detail later on.

With improvements in the techniques and methods of analytical chemistry during the first half of the Nineteenth Century, there became available increasingly better values of the combining or equivalent weights of many elements. J. J. Berzelius in Sweden and J. S. Stas in Belgium were the major contributors. However, before these equivalent weights could be converted into atomic weights, there still existed the problem of finding for each element the integer by which the equivalent weight was to be multiplied. In this respect some help was obtained from the law of isomorphism, which states that substances which form crystals of similar shape have similar chemical properties and can usually be represented by analogous formulas, for example, Ag_2S and Cu_2S. Also helpful was the law of the constant heat capacity of atoms discovered in the same year, 1819. According to this law, the product of the atomic weight and the specific heat has approximately the same value for most elements. Since the specific heat can be readily measured, a rough atomic weight can be estimated. A more accurate value can then be obtained from the combining weights.

Advogadro's Hypothesis

No clear differentiation was made between atoms and molecules in the early years of the Nineteenth Century, and this resulted in considerable confusion. As a consequence, Avogadro's hypothesis, propounded in 1811, was not accepted by the early advocates of the atomic theory, although the hypothesis is a correct correlation of the atomic theory with the characteristics of ideal gases. However, some 47 years later Cannizzaro's logical development of the consequences of a proper distinction between atoms and molecules resulted in the opening of a new era in the determination of atomic weights. Avogadro's hypothesis states that equal volumes of different gases under the same condition of temperature and pressure contain the same number of molecules. This hypothesis introduced into the Daltonian concept of atoms the view that the atom was the smallest particle which could enter into chemical combination, while the molecule was the smallest particle of matter which was capable of independent existence.

As previously noted, the determination of atomic weights involves the determination of the combining weight of the element (M) with some reference substance such as oxygen (O), and also involves a knowledge of the number of atoms of M which are combined in a compound with the reference element (O). It is in the solution of the second step of this problem that Avogadro's hypothesis performed a most useful function following Cannizzaro's demonstration of its utility in this connection. Until this demonstration was made, no general agreement as to atomic weights was possible. Different observers used different values for the same elements depending on the experimenter's notion as to the atomic ratios prevailing in the compound analyzed.

It readily follows from Avogadro's law that by the comparison of densities it is possible to determine the weight of one molecular species with reference to that of another. For practical purposes it was desirable to choose a uniform basis of reference for expressing molecular weights. Cannizzaro's proposal to use the same standard as was employed for atomic weights was adopted. On that basis the molecular weight was recorded as the weight of a given molecule relative to the weight of the oxygen atom taken as 16.0000. Since the oxygen molecule consists of two atoms, the molecular weight of oxygen was taken as 32.0000. Defined in this way, the molecular weight is equal to the sum of the atomic weights of its constituent elements, due allowance being made for the number of atoms of each present in the molecule. Thus the proper application of Avogadro's law helped to remove one of the outstanding difficulties which had faced the chemists of the early 1800's.

Following the publication in 1858 by Cannizzaro of his "Sketch of a Course of Chemical Philosophy," in which he explained and clarified Avogadro's law, a number of reliable atomic weights became available. By the latter part of the Nineteenth Century, methods were developed for determining molecular weights without resort to gas densities, so that nonvolatile compounds could be used in atomic weight studies. Furthermore, greatly improved procedures based on the use of chlorides and bromides were employed for obtaining accurate combining weights. As a consequence, atomic weights were eventually determined for all the naturally occurring elements and, for the most part, to a considerable degree of accuracy. As we shall later see,

following the discovery of isotopes and as a consequence of the high developments of mass spectrometry, very high precision measurements have been made of atomic weights in recent years.

Periodic Classification of the Elements

Although several prior attempts had been made to correlate atomic weights with the properties of the elements, they met with only limited success until Mendeléev in 1869 published his periodic classification of the elements. Independently, Lothar Meyer also showed that certain properties of the elements were a periodic function of their atomic weights. The success of Mendeléev's arrangement of the elements lay in his emphasis on the repetition of physical and chemical properties at definite intervals. "When I arranged the elements," he wrote, "according to the magnitude of their atomic weights, beginning with the smallest, it became evident that there exists a kind of periodicity in their properties. I designate by the name periodic law the mutual relations between the properties of the elements and their atomic weights; these relations are applicable to all the elements and have the nature of a periodic function." The periodicity of chemical properties was emphasized by Mendeléev by placing chemically similar elements in the same group, even though this meant leaving gaps in the table. He boldly proposed that these gaps corresponded to elements then undiscovered, and that the chief properties of these elements could be predicted by a consideration of the properties of known elements surrounding the gaps. The discovery of these elements—gallium in 1875, scandium in 1879 and germanium in 1886—brilliantly confirmed his predictions, and it is in this connection that the periodic law achieved its most striking success. The fundamental principles of the law have remained unchanged and a close connection was later established between the positions of the elements in the periodic arrangement and the internal structure of the atoms.

The atomic weight basis of the Mendeléev table did, however, reveal certain difficulties such as the anomalies presented by the three pairs of elements, argon and potassium, cobalt and nickel, and tellurium and iodine, which had to be placed in the reverse order of their atomic weights. We shall later see that these atomic weight inversions were caused by the relative abundance of the stable isotopes of these elements. Such anomalies no longer appear in the modern Periodic Table for the elements are all arranged in the order of increasing atomic numbers (i.e., the number of protons in the nucleus) instead of increasing atomic weights. This change followed from the later recognition that the atomic number of an element is a more fundamental characteristic than the atomic weight.

Displacement Laws and Isotopes

We now return to 1913, a year in which we find substantial evidence that the basic nature of the atomic number was being recognized. As previously noted, two important perplexing facts were then forced on the attention of most of the principal investigators in the field of radioactivity. First, the number of radioelements was much larger than the number of places available in the periodic chart or any reasonable extension of the periodic system as it was then known. Naturally, there was keen competition among the scientists to be the first to provide a satisfactory correlation between radioactive transformations and the associated changes in the periodic chart. As knowledge of the properties of the elements formed in the successive steps of radioactive decay became more complete, it became evident that the loss of alpha particles and beta particles by a radioactive element corresponded to a definite shift of the group in the periodic classification of the elements produced in the process of decay. Secondly, a number of the radioelements showed a truly remarkable chemical similarity to each other or to one of the previously known inactive elements. For example, it had been found impossible to separate uranium I from uranium II, radio lead from ordinary lead, etc.

Both of these perplexities were removed in 1913 by the introduction of the displacement laws and the term isotope. These concepts were set forth by Soddy and independently by Fajans, although many persons, notably Fleck and Russell, shared in these important generalizations. The displacement laws as

formulated by Soddy are as follows: (1) the product resulting from an alpha emission is shifted two places in the periodic chart in the direction of diminishing mass from the place of the original substance; (2) the product resulting from a beta emission is shifted one place in the direction of the heavier elements from that of the original substance.

The term "isotope" was suggested by Soddy for a group of two or more substances of different atomic mass occupying the same place (i.e., same atomic number) in the Periodic Table and being in consequence chemically nonseparable and identical. Thus, under this concept radio lead and ordinary lead are not elements with remarkable chemical similarity but are merely different forms (isotopes) of the same element. Another example is thorium which has six species of different atomic weights and therefore has six isotopes.

The displacement laws and the isotope concept assisted enormously in the placement of the radioactive products in three series and in making understandable the chemical behavior of the elements. Furthermore, since the emission from the atomic nucleus of an alpha particle (helium nucleus containing two protons), carrying two positive charges, is accompanied by a decrease of two units in the atomic number, while the emission of a beta particle, with a single negative charge (electron) increases the atomic number by one unit, it had occurred to Soddy that there was a relationship between the atomic number and the positive nuclear charge. But before he had clearly formulated his thinking, van den Breck set forth the idea that the charge on the nucleus must be equal to the atomic number. Since the atomic number is the ordinal position of an element in the periodic system, successive places in the system represent unit differences of nuclear charge. The group displacement laws are in complete harmony with this view.

Atomic Number

The careful measurement of atomic weights and the application and understanding of them had occupied and challenged chemists for over a century, but interest in them was to become subordinate to the new concepts which had just been introduced into the development of the atomic theory. This change of view was clearly set forth by Soddy in his report to the British Association of Science in late 1913, when he stated that he was of the opinion that isotopy might apply quite generally over the whole Periodic Table, and therefore for any element the atomic mass was not a real constant, but a mean value of much less fundamental interest than had hitherto been supposed.

The new idea that the atomic number (q.v.) is related to the nuclear charge and therefore constitutes a real basis for distinguishing one element from another, along with the idea that isotopy might apply generally to the elements, were concepts of the utmost importance, and they posed a real challenge to scientists to produce experimental evidence in support of them. The situation was all the more intriguing because radioactivity, which had hitherto guided the research, was unable to produce any evidence either in support of or in opposition to these ideas. It was clearly apparent that research along other lines would be required.

Fortunately, results which would produce some startling confirmations of the new proposals were not long in coming. By 1913 the Bohr-Rutherford model of the atom had replaced Thomson's earlier model which Rutherford on the basis of experiments involving alpha particles had shown to be wrong. The Bohr-Rutherford model of the atom had not been immediately accepted even though Bohr, who was then at Rutherford's laboratory at Manchester, had succeeded in deriving the formula for the Balmer lines of hydrogen using this model. Bohr adopted the idea that the nuclear charge is equal to the atomic number, and used it in his theoretical work on the constitution and spectra of elements. According to the model, electrons move in orbits about the nucleus, which is composed of protons, and as one passes from one element to the next higher element, the number of protons increases by one so that the charge on the nucleus and hence the atomic number increases by one. The number of electrons also increases by one in the same manner. Thus certain properties of elements should arrange themselves in a pattern according to the atomic number. It appears that the idea of atomic number was fully accepted in the Manchester laboratory even though there was no direct experimental evidence for it.

Moseley's Discovery

In June 1913, Bohr discussed with Moseley, who was also at Manchester, the question of the proper sequence for the arrangement of the elements according to their atomic number and learned that Moseley had already planned to try to settle this problem by the systematic measurements of the x-ray spectra of the elements. Moseley thought that if the electrons were moving in orbits according to the Bohr theory, the x-ray spectrum of a heavy element should exhibit a line structure similar to that of the hydrogen spectrum. Moreover, the x-ray spectrum would change in a regular fashion according to the charge on the nucleus from one element to the next, if the Bohr-Rutherford model of the atom was correct.

This is precisely what Moseley found from his investigations. Such was his skill and tenacity as an experimentalist that the paper describing the first results of his research was published in December 1913. The photograph of the x-ray lines from copper, nickel and cobalt shown in the paper clearly displayed the step-by-step change in the frequencies of these lines as one progresses up the scale of nuclear charge. Moseley stated this relationship in a simple empirical formula which may be expressed as follows: The frequency of a particular line in the x-ray spectrum of an atom is equal to a universal constant multiplied by the square of the charge on the nucleus minus one. This is equivalent to the relation developed by Bohr for the frequencies of the lines in the hydrogen spectrum.

The real significance of these results is the discovery that the change in frequency depends not on the change in mass, but rather on the change in the charge on the nucleus, i.e., the atomic number. This discovery clearly has important bearing on van Breck's idea of atomic number, since the fact that the elements could be arranged in a step-by-step sequence, changing by one unit at a time, carried the implication that where the numerical sequence is uninterrupted, no undiscovered element could be present. Not only was the idea of atomic number fully supported by Moseley's research, but it also pointed out

317

that no other elements could exist except where the sequence was interrupted, since the number of protons increases by one from a given element to the next higher element, and therefore the charge on the nucleus, and hence the atomic number, also increases by one.

Moseley's discovery was of inestimable value in correctly determining the atomic number of many of the natural radioactive species. This information in conjunction with a consideration of the group displacement laws and the new term isotope led to the successful placing of all the natural radioactive species, some forty in number, between the atomic numbers 81 to 92, in what are known as the three natural radioactive series. These are designated as the uranium, thorium and actinium series.

Isotopy of Lead

As early as 1905, Boltwood had noted the presence of lead in uranium minerals and he thought that this metal might be the end product of the uranium series. As the result of a study of the ratio of lead to uranium in a large number of minerals, he concluded in 1907 that "the assumption would appear to be justified that lead is the final product of uranium." This view was generally adopted and the realization in 1913 that radium-G (lead-206), the end product of the uranium series, was isotopic with ordinary lead provided added proof. At the same time it was also realized that actinium D (lead-207) and thorium D (lead-208), the nonradioactive end products of the actinium and thorium series, respectively, were also isotopic with lead.

A consideration of the implications of the group displacement laws led Soddy to realize that although the end products of the uranium and thorium series were both isotopic with ordinary lead, the atomic masses should be 206 and 208, respectively, as compared to 207.2 for ordinary lead. This was indeed revolutionary since up to this time elements had been regarded as having integral atomic weights. If the group displacement laws and the concept of isotopes had any real basis in fact, it was inevitable that the isotopes of an element would have different atomic masses. Experimental proof that lead derived from uranium had a different atomic mass from lead derived from thorium, while both differ from that of lead obtained from nonradioactive sources, would provide convincing support for the theory of radioactive decay and the existence of stable isotopes.

The mineral thorite was chosen by Soddy and Hyman as a source of thorium, since it consists mainly of thorium and less than 2% of uranium, and it seemed reasonable that the less than 0.5% lead present was produced entirely by radioactive decay of thorium. They obtained from the thorite about 1 gram of purified lead chloride and then determined its atomic mass by making comparison measurements with lead chloride from a nonradioactive source. By May of 1914 they were able to report that, as had been expected, the atomic weight of the thorium-derived lead was about one unit of mass higher than that of ordinary lead.

At about the same time, M. E. Lembert of Germany, working with T. W. Richards in his laboratory at Harvard, made determination of the atomic mass of lead obtained from several uranium minerals and in every case found the atomic mass to be lower than that of ordinary lead. The same conclusion was also reached independently by Maurice Curie in France and by O. Hönigschmid and S. Horovitz in Austria. Although the atomic masses were not down to 206, the expected value, probably because the lead was of mixed origin, the low values were nevertheless significant.

By early 1915 Soddy concluded that his predictions of different atomic masses for lead from different sources had been essentially confirmed, even though the data available at that time were of a somewhat preliminary nature. He felt that further work on carefully selected minerals was warranted and that the early results would be confirmed. Subsequent measurements made with the greatest of care have fully confirmed the earlier results and provide the strongest possible support not only for the group displacement law, but also for the whole theory of radioactive disintegration. Thus the theory received its most triumphant justification in the research of the chemists who had the most reason to doubt its general application—the specialists in the determination of atomic masses.

Another significant consequence of the results just described is the remarkable fact that an ordinary nonradioactive element such as lead can exist in isotopic form. This discovery indicated the possibility that other nonradioactive elements might also occur in isotopic form. However, it would be necessary to resort to a careful study of such properties as could be conceived as being affected, to a greater or lesser extent, by means of the mass of the atom. Concurrent developments in a field apparently unrelated to isotopes were destined to amply confirm this possibility, and we now turn our attention to Sir J. J. Thomson's investigations of positive rays.

Positive Ray Analysis—
The Parabola Method

Cathode rays in the discharge of electricity through gases at low pressure were discovered by Goldstein in 1886. A detailed investigation of their properties was undertaken by J. J. Thomson, who designated them as positive rays, since they were shown to carry a positive charge. The rays are the residue from ionization processes produced by the ionization of gases at low pressures in an electric field of the order of 15-50 kV.

Thomson developed what is known as the "parabola" method for the purpose of investigating the charge and mass of such rays. In this method, the rays are generated by means of an electric discharge, and are accelerated towards the cathode, where they are allowed to pass through a very narrow tube. The narrow beam of rays thus produced is then subjected to deflection by electric and magnetic fields so arranged that the two deflections are at right angle to each other. This produces a curved beam which impinges on a screen of fluorescent material or a photographic plate, in the form of a parabola.

If both the electric and magnetic fields are constant and, if instead of one particle one considers a beam of positive particles with variable velocity, v, but with constant (m/e) (i.e., all particles have the same ratio of mass, m, to charge, e), then all particles will fall on a parabolic curve. The continuity of the curve implies that particles having all possible velocities between certain limits are present in the positive rays. Particles with a different value of (m/e) will fall on a different parabolic curve.

A mathematical analysis shows that the masses of two or more particles can be compared directly by merely measuring two lengths, their ratio being entirely independent of the dimensions of the apparatus and the experimental conditions. This is the fundamental principal of the method. A photographic record is obtained on which can be identified at least one parabola as being associated with atoms or molecules of known mass, for example, hydrogen or oxygen. All the other parabolas can be measured and compared with this one and their masses deduced.

Neon Studies

The first application of the principle of positive-ray analysis was made by Thomson in 1912.[2] The sharpness of the parabolas, obtained by using a photographic plate as a receiving screen for the rays, established experimentally for the first time the fundamental assumption of the Daltonian atomic theory, namely, that the atoms have discrete masses—or at least discrete values of (m/e), and are not spread over a continuous range. Many gases were analyzed and the positive-ray photographs obtained exhibited a number of interesting features, but the aspects to be considered here will be restricted to those having a direct bearing on the subject of isotopes. No results were obtained in 1912 which could not be accounted for until a sample of the lighter constituents of air was examined in November. In describing what was observed, we can do no better than quote Thomson's own words from his address to the Royal Society on January 17, 1913.

"I now turn to the photograph of the lighter constituents; here we find the lines of helium, of neon (very strong), of argon and in addition there is a line corresponding to atomic mass 22, which cannot be identified with the line due to any known gas. I thought at first that this line, since its atomic mass is one half that of CO_2, must be due to a carbonic acid molecule with a double charge of electricity (so that m/e would be 22) and on some plates a faint line at mass 44 could be detected. On passing the gas slowly through tubes immersed in liquid air (which would remove the CO_2) the line at mass 44 completely disappeared, while the brightness of the one at mass 22 was not affected. The origin of this line presents many points of interest; there are no known gaseous compounds of any of the recognized elements which have this molecular weight ... The fact that this line is bright in the sample when the neon line is extraordinarily bright and invisible when the neon is comparatively feeble, suggests that it may possibly be a compound of neon and hydrogen, NeH_2, though no direct evidence of the combination of these inert gases has hitherto been found ... From the relative intensities [estimated visually] of the 22 line and the neon line we may conclude that the quantity of the gas giving the 22 line is only a small fraction of the quantity of neon." Thomson also felt there was a possibility that what had been called neon is not a single gas, but is a mixture of two gases, one of which has atomic mass of about 20 and the other about 22.

Other samples of gas containing neon all gave similar results. One sample of extremely pure neon yielded the two separate parabolas with the same relative intensity as the other samples. This last result proved that the most careful purification had not appreciably altered the intensity ratio between the lines. From a study of the characteristics of the line at mass 22, Thomson concluded that it could not be attributed to any compound, and that therefore it represented a hitherto unknown constituent of neon. There was no room for such an element in the Periodic Table. The only other alternative was a novel and revolutionary one, namely that neon could exist in two forms. This concept that an element might consist of atoms of different atomic masses had just been promulgated by Soddy and the facts could be supported by the supposition that neon was a mixture of two isotopes of masses 20 and 22 in such proportions as to yield an atomic mass of 20.20. These considerations led Aston, who was at that time an assistant to Thomson, to undertake a searching investigation on the constitution of the gas by two distinct lines of attack, first, attempts at separation, secondly, examination by positive-ray analysis.

After an unsuccessful attempt at separation by fractional distillation, Aston employed diffusion through pipe clay. After months of arduous work he obtained two fractions with atomic masses, calculated from densities, of 20.15 and 20.28, respectively. The difference in these atomic masses is small, but nevertheless it is significant. Since the former value is less, while the latter is greater than the atomic mass of ordinary neon, the difference showed that a partial separation of the two constituents of neon had been achieved. There was sufficient alteration in the proportion between the two gas samples to produce noticeable changes in the relative brightness of the two parabolas for masses 20 and 22. This gave some ground for belief that neon might consist of two isotopic forms with masses 20 and 22, respectively, and it might be said that several lines of reasoning pointed to the conclusion that neon is a mixture of isotopes; but none of them could be said to carry absolute conviction. Before an answer could be supplied to this intriguing question, this highly productive era of atomic science suddenly came to a five-year halt, as all such research yielded in 1914 to the exigencies of World War I.

References

See reference list at the end of the following article on "Isotopes. II. Post-World War I Developments."

RUSSELL BALDOCK

ISOTOPES. II. POST-WORLD WAR I DEVELOPMENTS

Aston's Mass Spectrograph

By the time research work was resumed by Aston and others in 1919 the existence of isotopes among the products of radioactivity had been put beyond all reasonable doubt by the work on the atomic mass of lead, and was accepted generally. This fact automatically increased both the value of the evidence of the complex nature of neon and the urgency of its definite confirmation. Aston realized that separation could only be partial at best, and that the most satisfactory proof would be afforded by the measurements of atomic masses by the method of positive rays. These would have to be so accurate as to prove beyond dispute that the atomic mass lay between the real atomic masses of the constituents, but corresponded with neither of them. The parabola method was not capable of this accuracy so Aston began to systematically examine all possible alternative methods, particularly those in which the fine circular tube used to collimate the rays could be replaced by a pair of parallel slits.

Slits can be satisfactorily used if the electric and magnetic deflections are both in the same plane and both are at right angles to the slits. While investigating the most favorable orientation of the slits, fields and photographic plates, Aston hit upon an arrangement such that all particles having the same ratio (m/e) are brought to focus in a straight line rather than a parabola. The rays, after arriving at the cathode face, pass through two sets of very narrow parallel slits in line and the collimated beam of ions then passes between two parallel plates where the electric field spreads the ribbon into an electric spectrum. A group of these rays which pass through a slit in a metal plate then enters the magnetic field between the parallel poles of a magnet. With the proper disposition of the components, ions of the same (m/e) are refocussed along a short straight line even though they may have different initial energies. This is known as velocity focussing. The design is also of such a nature that the image plane is flat so that on a single photographic plate the focus is good enough over a range of values of (m/e) large enough for the accurate comparison of many masses. The complete instrument is a close analogue of the ordinary optical spectrograph and gives a "spectrum," each line of which corresponds to atoms or molecules of a particular mass. The instrument is called a "mass spectrograph" and the "spectrum" it produces is called a "mass spectrogram." A schematic diagram of Aston's mass spectrograph is shown in Fig. 1.

When neon was introduced into the mass spectrograph four lines were recorded at mass numbers 10, 11, 20 and 22.[3] The first pair of lines are due to doubly charged neon 20 and 22 and were much weaker in intensity than the latter two. All four lines were well placed for direct comparison with lines taken as standards and a series of consistent measurements showed that to within about one part in a thousand, the atomic masses of the isotopes comprising neon are 20 and 22, respectively. If the amount of the isotope 22 were 10% of the amount of the isotope of mass 20 (actually they exist in neon in the ratio of 8.82 to 90.92) this would bring the mean atomic mass to the accepted value of 20.20, and the relative intensity of the lines estimated visually agreed with this proportion. There was no evidence of a line at the fractional mass position 20.2 and so the isotopic nature of neon was considered settled beyond all doubt even though the third isotope of neon, mass 21 and in abundance of 0.25%, was not discovered until 1928.

The investigations of neon by Thomson and the subsequent verification by Aston were the first direct observations of the isotopic constitution of a stable element and verified the prediction made by Soddy that elements with atomic masses differing markedly from integral values would be found to consist of isotopes.

The familiar element chlorine, whose atomic mass was known with considerable accuracy to be 35.457, was naturally the next to be analyzed and the explanation of the fractional atomic mass was obvious from the first photograph taken. Both positively and negatively charged rays showed that chlorine consists of two isotopes of masses 35 and 37 in the approximate ratio of three to one. There was no evidence of a line at fractional mass position 35.457. The atomic mass of chlorine calculated from the estimated relative intensities of the lines at masses 35 and 37 was in excellent agreement with the chemically determined value.

Whole Number Rule

Within a few weeks following his analysis of chlorine, Aston demonstrated the isotopic composition of mercury and by the end of 1920 he had examined nineteen elements in his mass spectrograph. He found that nine of them consisted of two or more isotopes

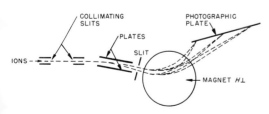

FIG. 1. Aston's mass spectrograph.

with masses which were close to integers. Furthermore, he concluded that elements like carbon, nitrogen, oxygen, fluorine and phosphorus which have atomic masses close to whole numbers do not consist of isotopes as do neon, chlorine, argon and other elements. The isotopes which were later discovered in carbon, nitrogen and oxygen occur in such small abundance that they do not sensibly shift the atomic mass of the elements from whole numbers. To date, no isotopes have been found in fluorine and phosphorus.

His observations led Aston to formulate the whole number rule which is essentially a modified form of Prout's hypothesis. According to this rule, all atomic masses are very close to integers, and the fractional atomic masses determined chemically result from the presence of two or more isotopes each of which has an approximately integral atomic mass.

In 1913 when Soddy introduced the concept of isotopes, he said, "Although matter is even more complex than chemical analysis has been able to reveal . . . the problem of atomic composition may be more simple than has been supposed from the lack of simple numerical relations between the atomic weights." In this conjecture he was of course correct, since as long as there existed the possibility of fractional atomic weights, there could be no simple theory of nuclear structure. The discovery of the whole number rule removed, in the words of Aston, "the only serious objection to the unitary theory of matter." The fact that all nuclear masses are approximately integral is in complete accord with the view that atomic nuclei are built up of neutrons and protons which have masses very close to unity on the atomic scale. Since the isotopes of a given element differ from one another by the number of neutrons in the nuclei, the isotopic masses should differ by small integers which they do.

Dempster's Mass Spectrometer

In 1918, even before Aston had built his first mass spectrograph, A. J. Dempster, at the University of Chicago, designed and built an instrument to determine the relative proportions or abundances of particles in a sample.[4] Electrical means rather than a photographic plate are used to measure the ions which are

generated and the instrument is known as a mass spectrometer. In his initial use of the mass spectrometer, Dempster produced ions either by employing electrons to bombard salts of the element under investigation, or the metal itself was vaporized by heating it electrically and the vapor was ionized by electron impact. The positive particles produced in this way have very low velocities (in contrast to the positive rays in Thomson's and Aston's instruments), and after they are accelerated by passage through an electric field of a few hundred volts, they may be regarded as emerging from the field with essentially uniform kinetic energy. After acceleration a thin beam of ions is separated out by a slit and the beam is bent in a semicircle by a magnetic field. The rays then pass through a second slit and fall on an electrode connected to an electrometer or similar device for measuring the ion current. A particular advantage of Dempster's method is that it gives "direction focussing" since ions having different initial directions, within limits, are brought to focus on the same line after traversing an arc of 180° in a magnetic field and in this way the intensity of the spectrum is increased. A schematic diagram of Dempster's mass spectrometer is shown in Fig. 2.

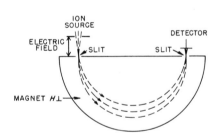

FIG. 2. Dempster's mass spectrometer.

With such an instrument Dempster first measured the relative abundance of the potassium isotopes, and by 1920 he had discovered most of the isotopes of magnesium, calcium, and zinc as well as confirming, as Aston had reported, that lithium has two isotopes. He also found that these elements, like many of the nonmetals studied by Aston, consisted of isotopes with atomic masses that are close to whole numbers.

The discovery of the isotopic composition

of other elements came rapidly and the importance of these discoveries was quickly recognized. In 1922, Aston was awarded the Nobel prize in chemistry "for his discovery, by means of the mass spectrograph, of isotopes in a large number of nonradioactive elements, and for his enunciation of the whole number rule." In his Nobel Lecture given December 12, 1922, he reported that of the thirty-four elements already investigated, nineteen were found to have altogether over sixty isotopes.

Optical Spectroscopy and Isotopes

The field of optical spectroscopy was also fruitful for the discovery of isotopes. Among the contributions from this field are the discovery of eleven isotopes and the confirmation of one isotope whose existence had been left doubtful by the mass spectrograph. The discoveries of five of these isotopes which are in the light elements are so interrelated as to warrant special consideration.

In band spectra the influence of nuclear mass is substantial, since it affects both the moment of inertia and the vibrational frequency of the molecule, which are predominant factors in the structure of spectral bands and band systems. There should, therefore, be a considerable difference between the band spectra of two "isotopic molecules," i.e., molecules in which an atom of one kind is combined in turn with two isotopes of another atom such as HCl^{35} and HCl^{37}. The difference of moment of inertia of two isotopic molecules arises almost entirely from a difference of the effective masses of the two molecules. The power of the band-spectrum method was demonstrated in 1924 by Mulliken's confirmation of silicon-30, an isotope which the mass spectrograph had previously left as doubtful.[5] The initial doubt was due to the presence of hydrides. Other band-spectrum investigations resulted in the discovery of four isotopes all in 1929.[6]

A discovery which had far reaching effects in physical science was the observation of Giauque and Johnston that the spectra of atmospheric air taken by Dieke and Babcock showed that the atoms of oxygen "as it occurs in air" consist not only of mass 16 but also contains atoms of masses 17 and 18. The complexity of oxygen raised doubts with

respect to the element carbon and these doubts were soon dispelled by the discovery of the carbon isotope of mass 13 by Birge and King. These discoveries were quickly followed by the discovery of Naudé of the nitrogen isotope of mass 15. That most of these isotopes escaped detection in the mass spectrograph is readily understood because of the presence of minute traces of hydrides. Thus O^{18}, O^{17}, N^{15} and C^{13} have the same mass number as, and would be coincident with, OH_2, OH, NH and CH. Such species, if present, create no real difficulty in the band spectra since their band systems are quite distinct from those in which the isotope effects are observed.

The correlation of mass ratios of hydrogen to oxygen obtained by mass spectrographic and ordinary chemical methods revealed a discrepancy, when an account was taken of the isotopes of masses 17 and 18 in oxygen. Birge and Menzel showed that the discrepancy between the chemical atomic weight of hydrogen and Aston's value by the mass spectrograph could be accounted for by the assumption of a hydrogen isotope of mass 2 present to the extent of 1 part in 4500 parts of hydrogen of mass 1. In 1932 the existence of this isotope was successfully demonstrated by Urey, Brickwedde and Murphy, employing the isotope effect in atomic spectra.[7]

Among the other isotopes discovered in the field of optical spectroscopy, indium-113 was discovered by Wehrli employing band spectra.[8] Studies involving the fine structure in line spectra led to the discovery of the remaining five isotopes as follows: thallium-203 and thallium-205 by Schuler and Keyston, lead-204 by Schuler and Jones, and iridium-191 and iridium-193 by Venkatasachar and Sibaiya.[8]

Packing Fraction—Binding Energy

Aston with his first mass spectrograph was able to demonstrate that the mass of a helium atom is somewhat less than the sum of the masses of four hydrogen atoms. It was quickly appreciated that this was direct experimental proof of Einstein's hypothesis that mass and energy are equivalent, and the difference represented the binding energy of the particles which made up the helium nucleus. By the late 1920's, Aston had studied many other elements and shown that the exact masses of the nuclides (nuclear species of any element) deviated from whole numbers if some particular nuclide such as O^{16} was chosen as a standard and arbitrarily assigned an integral mass. He constructed his famous packing fraction curve, as he called it, which plotted the fractional deviation of masses from whole numbers. As observed by Mattauch,[9] ". . . Aston, in his well-known Bakerian lecture,[10] published his famous packing fraction curve which at once aroused great interest everywhere. Aston, being an experimentalist, plotted a magnitude which he observed directly. By naming it the 'packing fraction,' and still more from the text of his paper, it is clear that he realized perfectly well that he had measured a new and important property of the atomic nucleus, namely, the total energy with which its constituents, the nucleons, are bound together." This curve depicts in a general way the changes of energy to be expected from transmutations of nuclei, not only by the aggregation of light atoms to form heavier ones, but also the prodigious release of energy to be expected from the fission of uranium by neutron bombardment, a phenomenon entirely undreamed of when the curve was first drawn.

Precision Isotopic Measurements

By the middle 1930's, it was appreciated that it is necessary to have double-focussing of ions to measure masses precisely with a mass spectrograph; that is, that ions of a given mass leaving the ion source, diverging in direction and having a spread in velocities should all converge at a common point or line. A number of new approaches led to instruments with greatly improved resolution and they were extensively used for precision mass measurements; in all these instruments the ion intensities were recorded on a photographic plate. More recently, considerable attention has been given to measuring precise masses by electrical means instead of employing a photographic plate.[11] This method has turned out to be a revolution in the mass-measuring field, with the result that the mass spectrographs and their photographic plates have become obsolete for precision mass measurements and are superseded by mass spectrometers using electronic means for matching peaks. All precision measurements today are made with some variation of this scheme. As one example of present-day precision, the mass of the hydrogen atom, H^1, compared with that of carbon-12 atom is believed to be known to 3 parts in one hundred million and many other masses are known to the same order of precision.[12]

It was not until the late 1930's, when high-vacuum and electronic techniques became an essential part of the physics laboratory work, that the single-focussing (directional focussing) magnetic mass spectrometer was developed to the point where it became an extremely useful tool. During World War II there was considerable progress in the development of mass spectrometers for isotopic analyses, mainly to meet the demand for the precision measurement of the abundance of the isotopes of uranium. Generally speaking, what had previously been a highly individualistic and often temperamental research instrument gradually became converted to a standard and more stable machine that could be operated on a routine basis. The past twenty years have seen an enormous advance in the instrumentation of mass spectrometers. Higher resolving power, increased sensitivity of ion detection and improved stability of electronic power supplies are among the dominant characteristics. The atomic energy era with its need for precise data, the availability of a wide variety of enriched isotopes for research, as well as the continued scientific interest in improved values of the physical and chemical constants have all contributed to a considerably increased emphasis on the determination of the isotopic abundance of the elements with a high precision.

Unified Mass Scale—C¹²

One of the changes which has come about as a consequence of the improved knowledge of atomic masses and isotopic abundances is the adoption of a new and unified mass scale. Until 1929, when Giauque and Johnson discovered the existence of the two rare isotopes of oxygen with masses 17 and 18, all oxygen atoms were thought to have the same mass and were arbitrarily chosen to be the standard by which all atomic masses were measured. Retaining natural oxygen with its mixture of three isotopes as a standard the chemists continued to use 1/16 the weight of this mixture as unit atomic mass. In the determination of atomic masses by means of the mass spectrograph, Aston chose a mass scale based on the mass of the single most abundant oxygen atom as exactly 16, and 1/16 of this as the unit of mass. The use of this scale was adopted for all mass measurements made by means of mass spectrographs or other physical means.

As isotope mass determinations became more and more accurate and the mass differences became more important, the slight differences between the two oxygen scales became an increasing problem. In 1960 the International Union of Pure and Applied Physics met in Ottawa and adopted the atomic mass scale based upon the carbon-12 isotope as having a mass of exactly 12. The same scale was adopted by the International Union of Pure and Applied Chemistry at their Montreal meeting in 1961. The standard unit of atomic mass is now accepted to be 1/12 of the mass of the carbon-12 isotope.[13] It is therefore imperative that the reference mass scale be cited when quoting atomic mass values. A complete tabulation of the masses of all isotopes based on the carbon-12 isotope can be found elsewhere.[14]

It is quite likely that no further chemical determination of atomic masses will be made and one will rely on mass spectrometry for further improvement. The adopted values of the atomic masses of forty-seven elements are now based entirely or in part on physical measurements. All the atomic masses are well known and the remaining uncertainty is in isotopic composition. These measurements must not only be made as precisely as possible but they must be referred to standards to eliminate instrumental errors.

Extent of Isotopy

The discovery of tantalum-180 by White, Collins and Rourke[15] in 1954 is the last discovery of a naturally occurring isotope reported in the literature and brings the total of naturally occurring species to 287. The discovery of this isotope prompted subsequent systematic searches for the existence of previously unobserved naturally occurring isotopes of low abundance, but none have been found. Mass spectrometers built with high sensitivity of ion detection have allowed "upper limits" to be placed on a large number of isotopes.[16,17] A list of the isotopes and their abundance as they occur in nature may be found elsewhere.[18]

The occurrence and degree of isotopy among the 83 most abundant elements found in nature is quite widespread. On the one hand, 21 elements possess no isotopes; each of these consists of one kind of atom only. The remaining 62 elements possess isotopes ranging in number from two to ten. Altogether 287 different isotopic species are found in widely different amounts in nature. For example, the relative amounts of O^{16} and Xe^{124} are of the order of 10^{17} to 1.

Regularities found in the tables of isotopes reveal certain facts concerning nuclear forces and several of the most elementary will be cited. The 287 species may be divided as follows: 168 even-even (even number of protons and even number of neutrons), 57 even-odd, 53 odd-even and 9 odd-odd. These numbers display the pairing tendency of the nuclear constituents and show that there is no significant difference in stability between odd-proton and odd-neutron configurations. The existence of a relatively large number of isotopes provides evidence for a particularly stable proton configuration. On this basis, for example, tin with ten isotopes of 50 protons each, suggests high stability for the 50-proton configuration. Such proton numbers in regions of high stability are known as "magic" numbers. Some other magic numbers are 20, 40, 82, and 126.

Radioactive Decay Chains

The naturally occurring element with atomic number greater than 83 (bismuth) are all radioactive. It was early suspected and ultimately became clear that all the nuclides in this region of the periodic chart may be arranged in three chains of successive decay, and the species comprising one chain is known as a radioactive series. Each of the series is headed by a long-lived isotope and terminates in a stable end product, an isotope of lead.

The chain which is known as the uranium series starts with uranium-238 as the parent substance and after fourteen major transformations (eight of them by alpha-particle emission and six by beta-particle emission) terminates in lead-206. Since the atomic mass changes by four units in alpha decay and with practically no change in beta decay, the various masses found in members of this family differ by multiples of four. A general formula then for the approximate masses is based on the mass of the parent isotope and the mass change due to alpha decay. This series is often designated as the $4n+2$ series where n is an integer. Radium-226 (ordinary radium) which is contained in this series is found in nature only in the presence of uranium-238. The actinium or $4n+3$ series has uranium-235 (actino-uranium) as the parent and after eleven major transformations decays to lead-207 as the stable end product. The thorium or $4n$ series starts with thorium-232 as the parent, and after ten major transformations, decays to lead-208.

As early as 1923 it was speculated that there should be a fourth series of the $4n+1$ type. Although careful searches have been made, no radioactive chain of this type, nor any of its individual members, has been found in nature. However, one of the interesting results of the research program connected with the Plutonium Project is that some of the experimental work carried out over a period of six or seven years led to the observation of all the members of the $4n+1$ series and to a complete elucidation of the decay scheme. Although the series includes several preneptunium members, the long-lived isotope Np^{237}, an isotope of a transuranium element, is usually considered the parent of the series.

This radioactive family bearing the name neptunium series is analogous in extent and complexity to the three natural radioactive series, but differs from them in several interesting respects. Unlike each of the other three series, there is no emanation, a radioactive gas, in this series since there is no representative of the element of atomic number 86; also unlike these series, there are representatives of the elements astatine (atomic number 85) and francium (atomic number 87). The series ends with the stable isotope bismuth-209 instead of with an isotope of lead. Finally, there is present in the series

the important isotope uranium-233, which undergoes fission with neutrons and is a possible nuclear fuel. Its importance lies in the fact that since uranium-233 can be formed by the absorption of neutrons by thorium, nonfissionable thorium may be used as a fuel source. Since the subject of radioactive series is covered in great detail in several standard works, the reader is referred to them for further information.[19]

As more sensitive means of detection of radioactivity have become available, more natural radioactive species other than those contained in the uranium, actinium and thorium series have been found. Among the presently known species are: potassium-40, vanadium-50, rubidium-87, indium-115, tellurium-123, lanthanum-138, cerium-142, neodymium-144, samarium-147, gadolinium-152, lutecium-176, hafnium-174, rhenium-187, and platinum-190. Carbon-14 with a half-life of 5600 years is a special case of "continuously induced activity" which is found in nature.

In 1919 in the course of a study of the effect of alpha particles on gases, Rutherford observed that the interaction of alpha particles with nitrogen atoms or molecules resulted in the ejection of highly energetic particles similar to those which had been previously obtained with hydrogen. He surmised that the highly energetic atoms arising from the collision of alpha particles with nitrogen were not nitrogen atoms but charged atoms of hydrogen. Further work proved that Rutherford was correct and that he had achieved the first controlled artificial disintegration of an atomic nucleus.

Artificial Radioactivity

In early 1934, I. Curie and F. Joliot announced that boron and aluminum could be made radioactive by bombardment with alpha particles. Of very great importance in this discovery of artificially produced radioactivity was the fact that the boron and aluminum continued to emit positrons after the removal of the alpha source and that the induced radioactivity in each case decayed with a characteristic half-life. This new phenomenon of induced radioactivity was quickly understood in terms of the production of new unstable nuclei.

At about the same time that artificial

radioactivity was discovered, several laboratories had developed and were using machines for the acceleration of the ions of hydrogen and helium to energies which were sufficient to produce nuclear transformations. With the discovery of the neutron in 1932 and the isolation of deuterium in 1933, there became available two additional particles which were especially useful for the production of induced activities. The growth in this field has been so rapid that the number of known artificially produced species had reached 1450 by the end of 1966.[20] For every element, there is now known at least one radioactive species, with the number ranging up as high as thirty-five in the element indium.

By the end of 1963, eleven new elements heavier than uranium as well as the elements technetium (atomic number 43) and promethium (atomic number 61), which do not occur naturally on the earth, had been produced by artificial transmutations. In 1964, scientists at Dubna (U.S.S.R.) announced that they had made the isotope 104^{260} with a half-life of 0.3 second. It was projected that the element should form a relatively volatile tetrachloride. In support of this supposition, results from new U.S.S.R. experiments reported in 1966 indicated that the chloride of the element is more volatile than those of the actinides, which are trichlorides.[21]

Variation in Abundance of Isotopes

For many years following the discovery of isotopes it was believed that the relative abundance of the stable isotopes of any element as found in nature was constant. As late as 1942, Aston wrote ". . . the determination of the abundance of the constituents of the same element by mass spectrum analysis is virtually free from the uncertainty of sampling . . . it is very nearly impossible to obtain a mixture of isotopes which is not a fair sample of a complex element." It is now known that there are a number of elements for which the stable isotopes of a given element do not occur together in constant proportions. Oxygen is an interesting case. Epstein[22] reported in 1959 that the O^{18}/O^{16} ratios in nature may vary by as much as 10% between the extremes of glacier ice found near the poles and that in atmospheric carbon dioxide. Various workers have shown that

the O^{18} content in fresh water may be as much as 3% less than in atmospheric oxygen and 2.3% less in sea water. Variations in the O^{18}/O^{16} ratio have also been found in many minerals.

Water from various sources shows a slight variation in the H^2/H^1 ratio. Heavy water has a slightly lower vapor pressure than ordinary water and is therefore concentrated by evaporation. Helium from gas wells probably has its origin in radioactive sources (alpha disintegrations) and contains a much smaller proportion of the rare isotope He^3 than does atmospheric helium. A slight enrichment in C^{13} is found in limestone and variations are found in many other natural sources. Variations have also been reported in the ratios of B^{11}/B^{10}, Si^{30}/Si^{28} and S^{34}/S^{32} [13].

We have previously noted the variation in the abundances in the lead isotopes from ores containing uranium and thorium. However, in 1938 Nier reported that he had found considerable variation in the isotopic abundances of common lead (lead from minerals that were free from uranium and thorium).[23] While this observation of the variation of abundances in such heavy isotopes may be surprising, it is perhaps even more so that at least two groups have reported a variation of 0.1% in the U^{235} content of certain ores.[24]

Crouch has recently found variations in the isotopic composition of naturally occurring molybdenum.[25] He measured the isotopic composition of ten samples of molybdenum which were extracted from ores that came from widely separated places and found that there was considerable variation in the isotopic abundances. He discussed his observation in terms of the proposition that the component isotopes of natural molybdenum were formed by various processes which produce heavy atoms and he proposed that the variations in isotopic abundance reflect the genetics of synthesis. He further observed that if it is true that these variations in natural abundance do reflect primal genetics it would be expected that similar effects would be found in other elements, seventeen of which he listed.

From the previously cited examples, it is evident that variations in the natural abundance of isotopes may stem from a variety of causes. In any case each element must be considered separately, for often it is possible in a variety of ways to alter, at least to a measurable extent, the isotopic composition. Great care needs to be exercised in the prepartion of samples for isotopic analyses lest the chemical procedures employed introduce unwanted and even unsuspected changes in the isotopic distribution.

The discovery of deuterium, the heavy isotope of hydrogen, in 1931 marked an important advance in understanding the chemical behaviour of isotopes in general. Up until that time increased concentrations of particular isotopes had been achieved for the isotopes of such elements as neon, potassium, zinc and mercury. The results were not outstanding and their chief purpose was to provide confirming evidence for the existence of isotopes. The striking success achieved in the concentration of deuterium, in spite of its small abundancy in ordinary hydrogen (average of 0.0145%), coupled with the many useful scientific applications found for it, resulted in a revival of interest in the over-all problem of the separation of isotopes. This interest was also greatly stimulated by the need for obtaining uranium enriched in the fissionable 235 isotope for the atomic energy program. There has since developed a well founded school of isotope separation; indeed it is possible to enrich the isotopes of any element.

Isotope Production

Over the past quarter century the know-how of enriching or producing isotopes by a wide variety of methods and means has grown at an astronomical rate. A very brief review will suffice to indicate the magnitude of the effort involved. We shall, therefore, restrict ourselves to consideration of only three programs, all of which had their origin in the war-time atomic energy program and have since been developed into a source of supply of isotopes as well as new and exciting fields of research.

The success of the Manhattan Project, the atomic energy program of World War II, both in obtaining uranium enriched in the 235 isotope and the production of the trans-uranium element plutonium, an artificially formed element of atomic number greater than

uranium, was brought about, under the stimulus of war-time demand, in an incredibly short time. The completeness of the historical records of this project leaves no need for further treatment here. There immediately followed a wide diversification of these two specific objectives. One of the enrichment processes, the electromagnetic, was developed and expanded to include the isotopes of a variety of elements; likewise, the production of artificially formed species in nuclear reactors encompassed an ever-increasing variety of nuclides.

The principle of the electromagnetic process as employed to enrich isotopes is the same as that of mass spectrometry. The configuration of the production equipment, the calutron, is essentially that of the Dempster mass spectrometer which has been previously described. Each unit operates in its own vacuum system, and it is customary to operate a number of units simultaneously but independently in a common magnetic field. Ions generated in an electric arc in the ion source traverse a path of 180° and impinge on receivers which are properly placed so that each one collects an isotope of the particular element. Within a span of only ten years the calutron was successfully adapted to enriching all the isotopes of the stable elements except the gases, for which other methods of concentration of isotopes are more suitable; the single nuclide elements are, of course, not considered. Continuous improvements in both the equipment and techniques of operation have produced a consistent upgrading in the degree of enrichment of the product isotopes and a very active program of development and production is now required to meet the demands of the scientific community.

We now consider only the most elemental aspects of the production of isotopes in a nuclear reactor. When fissionable isotopes such as uranium-235 are bombarded with neutrons of the appropriate energy, they undergo a splitting or fission into two components known as direct fission fragments which fall in the range of mass numbers from 72 to 158 and cover 34 elements. These fragments, when formed, have too large a proportion of neutrons for stability of the nucleus and in consequence exhibit negative beta-decay. Each fragment thereby initiates a radioactive series involving the successive emission of a beta particle. Although longer and shorter series occur, fission series on the average consists of three stages. Since there are more than 80 primary fission fragments, and with the assumption of an average of three stages per fragment, there could be produced perhaps 250 nuclides. The primary fission fragments together with the secondary species constitutes a group which is commonly called fission products. Although it is evident that the fission process yields mixtures of very great complexity, yet with great effort more than 60 chains comprising over 200 species have been established. It is readily seen that the fission products constitute a vast stockpile of nuclides. For many years a considerable effort has been expended in isolating a large number of species from this store of nuclides for a wide range of research as well as practical applications.

The third program of production of isotopes on a large scale, as measured by research requirements, is concerned with the production of the transuranium elements—the artificially formed elements heavier than uranium. In the Fall of 1966 there was put in full operation at the Oak Ridge National Laboratory a unique combination of three new facilities which make possible a new expansion of research, by chemists and physicists from all over the world, in the transuranium elements which are now known to encompass nearly 100 isotopes.

Briefly, the cycle of operation is as follows. Plutonium-242 which has been produced in the reactors at the Savannah River Plant in Aiken, South Carolina, is processed in the Transuranium Processing Plant and is then irradiated in the High Flux Isotope Reactor. This reactor was built primarily to produce experimental quantities of the known elements of atomic number greater than plutonium and, hopefully, to produce new elements. After an appropriate number of production cycles, it should be possible to recover, each year, gram quantities of californium, hundreds of milligrams of berkelium, tens of milligrams of einsteinium and about a microgram of fermium. Prior to the successful operation of this transuranic program, these elements have been available only in microgram quantities.

The Transuranium Research Laboratory provides for on-site research on these materials which will also be available to various research laboratories in the United States, and to interested research universities throughout the world.

The isotope californium-252 is an interesting example of these man-made materials. It is an alpha emitter with the comparatively long half-life of 2.65 years and a specific heat of 38 watts per gram. It could serve as a heat source for thermoelectric generators which furnish small packets of power for long periods of time. Of more importance to research, in transuranium elements, is the fact that californium-252 is the isotope of highest atomic mass which can be produced in gram quantities, sufficient to serve as a basic starting isotope for the production of a new element.

The term isotope, with its inference regarding the complexity of elements, when first proposed, was a bold and daring proposition. Today, barely more than a half century later, what was once a radical and oft suspect concept, has now become a commonplace. In the ever-continuing search for an understanding of the properties and behaviour of matter, isotopes are often a vital component of fundamental research. In practical applications there has been no bound; extensive applications are to be found in medicine, biology, agriculture, industry, and a wide variety of other fields.

References

1. Soddy, F., *Nature*, **92**, 399 (1913).
2. Aston, F. W., "Mass Spectra and Isotopes," Second Edition, p. 5, London, Edward Arnold & Co., 1942.
3. Aston, F. W., Vol. II Nobel Lectures, Chemistry, 1922–1941, p. 12, New York, Elsevier Publishing Co., 1966.
4. Dempster, A. J., *Phys. Rev.*, **11**, 316 (1918).
5 Mullikan, R. S., *Nature*, **113**, 489 (1924).
6. Jevons, W., "Report on Band-Spectra of Diatomic Molecules," p. 223, Cambridge, The University Press, 1932.
7. Urey, H. C., Brickwedde, F. G., and Murphy, G. M., *Phys. Rev.*, **39**, 164 (1932); **39**, 864 (1932); **40**, 1 (1932).
8. Bainbridge, K. J., and Nier, A. O., "Relative Isotopic Abundances of the Elements," Prelim. Report No. 9, Nuclear Science Series, National Research Council, Washington, D.C., 1951.

9. Mattauch, J. H., "Advances in Mass Spectrometry," Mead, W. L., Editor, Vol. III, p. 1, The Institute of Petroleum, 61 New Cavendish Street, London W.1, 1966.
10. Aston, F. W., *Proc. Roy. Soc.* (A), **115**, 487 (1927).
11. Nier, A. O. C., *American Scientist*, **54**, 375 (1966).
12. Benson, J. L., and Johnson, W. H., Jr., *Phys. Rev.*, **141**, 1112 (1966).
13. Cameron, A. E., and Wickers, Edward, *J. Am. Chem. Soc.*, **84**, 4175 (1962).
14. Mattauch, J. H., Thiele, W., and Wapstra, A. H., "1964 Atomic Mass Table," *Nuclear Physics*, **67**, 1 (1965).
15. White, F. A., Collins, T. L., Jr., and Rourke, F. M., *Phys. Rev.*, **97**, 566 (1955).
16. White, F. A., Collins, T. L., and Rourke, F. M., *Phys. Rev.*, **101**, 1786 (1956).
17. Leipziger, F. D., *Applied Spectroscopy*, **17**, 158 (1963).
18. "Handbook of Chemistry and Physics," page B-4, 46th Edition, Cleveland, The Chemical Rubber Co., 1965–66; "Chart of the Nuclides," Educational Relations, General Electric Co., Schenectady, N.Y., 1966.
19. Friedlander, Gerhart, Kennedy, Joseph W., and Miller, Julian, "Nuclear and Radiochemistry," New York, John Wiley and Sons, 1964; Seaborg, G. T., "The Transuranium Elements," New Haven, Yale University Press, 1958; Seaborg, G. T., *Chem. Eng. News*, **26**, 1902 (1948).
20. Private communication, Nuclear Data Project, Oak Ridge National Laboratory, Oak Ridge, Tennessee, December 20, 1966.
21. *Chem. Eng. News*, **44**, 43 (June 6, 1966).
22. Epstein, S., "Researches in Geochemistry," Abelson, P. H., Editor, p. 217, New York, John Wiley and Sons, Inc., 1959.
23. Nier, A. O. C., *J. Am. Chem. Soc.*, **60**, 1571 (1938).
24. Senftle, F. E., Steiff, L., Cuttilta, F., and Kuroda, P. K., *Geochem. et Cosmochim. Acta*, **11**, 189 (1957); Smith, L. A., Oak Ridge Gaseous Diffusion Plant, K-1462 (1961), available from Office of Technical Services, U.S. Dept. of Commerce, Washington, D.C.
25. Crouch, E. A. C., "Proceedings Thirteenth Annual Conference on Mass Spectrometry and Allied Topics," St. Louis, Mo., page 165 1965.
26. Glasstone, Samuel, "Sourcebook on Atomic Energy," New York, D. Van Nostrand Co., 1950.
27. Taylor, Hugh S., and Glasstone, Samuel, "Treatise on Physical Chemistry," Vol. I, "Atomistics and Thermodynamics," New York, D. Van Nostrand Co., 1942.
28. Fajans, Kasimir, "Radioelements and Isotopes," New York, McGraw-Hill Book Co., 1931.
29. Koch, J., Editor, "Electromagnetic Isotope Separations and Applications of Electromagnetically Enriched Isotopes," Amsterdam, North Holland Publishing Co., 1958.
30. Ihde, Aaron J., "The Development of Modern Chemistry," New York, Harper & Row, 1964.
31. Partington, J. R., "General and Inorganic Chemistry," 4th Edition, London, Macmillan & Co., 1966.
32. Boorse, Henry A., and Motz, Lloyd, Editors, "The World of Atoms," Vol. I, New York, Basic Books, Inc., 1966.

Russell Baldock

KRYPTON

The element krypton has the atomic number 36 and an atomic weight of 83.80 on the Carbon-12 scale. As a member of the Group 0 of the Periodic Table of elements it is at room temperature a colorless, odorless, and because of its chemical inertness, a completely nontoxic gas. (See also **Noble Gases**.) Krypton is found in nature mainly as one of the constituent gases of the atmosphere where it is present in a concentration of 0.000108% by volume of dry air. It is also found in small concentrations in certain natural gases, and gases emanating from hot springs and volcanoes. Next to its sister element xenon, krypton is the second rarest among the stable elements in the earth's crust (including the atmosphere and the oceans). Its abundance has been calculated as 1.9×10^{-8} weight-%.

The element was discovered in 1898 by Sir William Ramsay and M. W. Travers in the residual liquid left after evaporating liquid air to near dryness. The name "krypton" chosen by the discoverers is Greek and has the meaning "the hidden one."

The analytical detection and determination of krypton relies entirely on physical methods because of the chemical inertness of the element. Usually the krypton analyses are based on emission spectrometry or mass spectrometry. More recently gas chromatography has been added as an analytical tool for the determination of this element.

Production

The source for the commercial production of krypton is the liquid oxygen obtained from the large-scale liquefaction and rectification of air. (See **Oxygen**.) Because of their comparatively high boiling points, the two rare gases krypton and xenon are collected with the liquid oxygen fraction during the distillation of air. In order to recover the rare gases the liquid oxgyen is first subjected to a further rectification process in a separate column. A product is withdrawn from the column which contains about 1% rare gases, the rest being oxygen. Further enrichment by distillation is difficult because organic material tends to accumulate in the liquid oxygen causing an explosion hazard. However, there are processes in use mainly in Europe during which the enrichment of the rare gases by distillation and rectification is driven to very much higher levels. The liquid containing 1% rare gases is evaporated and passed through a chamber in which all organic matter is oxidized. Following this the rare gases are recovered by adsorption on silica gel at low temperatures. The final separation of krypton and xenon is achieved by selective adsorption and desorption on active charcoal.

Krypton is commercially available in Pyrex glass bulbs at about 1 atmosphere pressure, or in steel tanks at higher pressures. Its current (1966) price is $19.00 for 1 liter of STP gas.

Isotopes of Krypton

Naturally occurring krypton is a mixture of the six stable isotopes of this element with mass numbers 78, 80, 82, 83, 84, and 86, respectively. In addition to the stable isotopes 15 radioactive nuclides of krypton have been described which have been produced by suitable nuclear reactions. Table 1 gives a complete account of the known isotopes of krypton and lists their atomic masses, natural abundances, nuclear spin, and for radioactive isotopes their half-lives, methods of production, modes of disintegration, and energies. Among the nuclear reactions during which krypton isotopes are produced is the fission of such nuclides as U^{233}, U^{235} (with thermal neutrons), and U^{238} and Th^{232} (with fast neutrons). Because of the creation of krypton isotopes by fission of heavy nuclei,

TABLE 1. ISOTOPES OF KRYPTON

Isotope	Atomic Mass $C^{12}=12$	Natural Abundance, %	Nuclear Spin	Half-life	Method of Production	Type of Decay	Energy, MeV	γ-Transition Energy, MeV
Kr^{76}		0		~10 hr				0.028
								0.093
								0.267
								0.316
								0.400
Kr^{77}	76.92449	0		1.2 hr		EC† (20%)		
						β^+ (80%)		
						β^+	1.86 (61%)	0.87
						β^+	1.67 (32%)	
						β^+	0.085 (7%)	
Kr^{78}	77.92037	0.354		stable				
Kr^{79m}§				55 sec		IT‡		0.127
Kr^{79}	78.92009	0	1/2	34 hr		EC† (95%)		
						β^+ (5%)		
						β^+	0.598 (91%)	0.835
						β^+	0.33 (9%)	
Kr^{80}	79.91639	2.27		stable				
Kr^{81m}§			1/2	13 sec		IT‡		0.190
Kr^{81}	80.91661	0	7/2	2.1 × 10⁵ yr	Rb^{81}(n,p)	EC†		0.012
Kr^{82}	81.91348	11.56	0	stable				
Kr^{83m}§			1/2	114 mo	Br^{83}(p,n)	IT‡		0.046
					Rb^{83}(n,p)			
Kr^{83}	82.91413	11.55	9/2	stable				
Kr^{84}	83.91150	56.90	0	stable				
Kr^{85m}§		0	1/2	4.4 hr	Br^{85}(p,n)	β^- (77%)		
						IT‡ (23%)		0.305
						β^-	0.842	
						β^-	0.672	
Kr^{85}	84.91243	0	9/2	10 yr			0.15	0.513
Kr^{86}	85.91062	17.37	0	stable				
Kr^{87}	86.91337	0		—	Br^{87}(p,n)	β^-	3.80 (70%)	2.57
				78 mo		β^-	3.30 (5%)	
				—		β^-	1.3 (25%)	
Kr^{88}	87.91420	0	0		Br^{88}(p,n)	β^-	2.8 (20%)	2.40
				2.8 hr		β^-	0.9 (12%)	
						β^-	0.52 (68%)	
Kr^{89}	88.91651	0		3.2 mo		β^-	4	
Kr^{90}				33 sec		β^-	3.2	
Kr^{91}				9.9 sec		β^-	~3.6	
Kr^{92}				3.0 sec		β^-		
Kr^{93}				2.0 sec		β^-		
Kr^{94}				1.4 sec		β^-		
Kr^{95}				short		β^-		
Kr^{97}				~1 sec		β^-		

† EC = electron capture
‡ IC = internal transition
§ metastable nuclide

small amounts of isotopes previously not present in the atmosphere have been introduced through the explosion of atomic bombs.

Separation of the stable isotopes is best achieved by thermal diffusion. This is carried out in long vertical tubes along the axis of which a heated wire is strung. Thermal diffusion causes the lighter isotopes to accumulate near the warm wire, where they are carried to the upper part of the column by a convection current. In this arrangement the simple separative effect of thermal diffusion is multiplied by the superimposed convection current. The separation effected by this method is quite substantial and notably the isotope of mass number 86 has been obtained in an essentially pure state ($>99.5\%$ Kr^{86}).

Atomic Structure, Ionization Potentials, and Spectra

In the ground state krypton has the following electronic configuration: $1s^2, 2s^2p^6, 3s^2p^6d^{10}, 4s^2p^6$. Like the other rare gases it has a "closed shell" which causes its first ionization potential to be high in comparison to that of its neighbors in the Periodic Table and is responsible for the chemical inertness of this element. Only recently have attempts been successful to prepare chemical compounds of krypton.

The ionization potentials for first, second, third and fourth ionization are 13.999 v, 26.4 v, 36.8 v, and 68 v, respectively. The last value here is an estimate of lesser reliability than the preceeding data.

Ever since the discovery of the elements the light emitted by electrically excited krypton has played an important role for the analysis and the uses of this rare gas. The lowest lying electronic level above the ground state has the energy of 9.915 electron volts. Consequently, if an electrical discharge is passed through krypton at low pressure, the "first" spectrum, i.e., the spectrum of the neutral atom, is obtained for electron energies above 9.9 electron volts. The color of the discharge under these conditions can be described as greenish. As soon as the exciting electrons have energies exceeding 28 electron volts the "second" spectrum of krypton appears, produced by electronic transitions of the singly charged positive ion. Whereas the ground state of the neutral atom is a singlet state ($^1S_0$), the ground state of the positive ion is a doublet state ($^2P_{1/2}$, $^2P_{3/2}$). Consequently the second spectrum consists of a much larger number of lines than the first. The appearance of the discharge under these conditions is distinctly blue. Since the spectrum of krypton, as that of other rare gases, is easy to obtain and since the wavelengths are highly reproducible, its lines have been chosen for a class "A" secondary standard to be used in the calibration of spectral apparatus.

The sharpness of spectral lines increases, of course, if they are generated by an individual isotope of krypton instead of the natural mixture. Especially if the isotope is one with an even mass number so that hyperfine splitting is absent, the lines can be of extreme sharpness. One such line of the krypton isotope of mass number 86 has recently been chosen for the fundamental standard of length, replacing the standard meter bar in Paris. In 1960 it was internationally agreed that the fundamental standard of length should be the orange-red line in the spectrum of Kr^{86} corresponding to the transition $5p[0\frac{1}{2}]_1 - 6d[0\frac{1}{2}]_1$. The unit of length in the international system, the meter, is now defined by the following relationship:

1 meter = 1,650,763.73 wave lengths (in vacuo) of the orange-red line of Kr^{86}.

Physical Properties

Solid krypton is a white crystalline substance and has a melting point of 116.0°K. It has a face-centered cubic structure which is common to all the rare gases. At 88°K the length of one edge of the unit cell is 5.69×10^{-8} cm. The density calculated from the dimensions of the unit cell is 3.021 g/cc. Assuming a spherical shape of the atoms the radius of a krypton atom in the lattice has the value 2.01×10^{-8} cm. Experimentally obtained densities for solid krypton are given in Table 2 together with data on the expansivity, $1/V$ (dV/dT). The compressibility of this substance decreases from 5.6×10^{-11} cm^3/dyne at zero pressure to 3.5×10^{-11} cm^3/dyne at 1000 atmospheres and 1.7×10^{-11} cm^3/dyne at 4000 atmospheres. The vapor pressure of solid krypton between 87.2 and 115.6°K can be calculated from the equation:

$$(1) \qquad \log_{10}P_{mm\ Hg} = -\frac{579.6}{T} + 7.7447$$

TABLE 2. DENSITY AND EXPANSIVITY OF SOLID KRYPTON

T, °K	Density, g/cc	Expansivity, $\frac{1}{V}\left(\frac{\delta V}{\delta T}\right)$ /deg
0	(3.09)	0
20	3.078	4.8×10^{-4}
40	3.040	7.7×10^{-4}
60	2.988	9.7×10^{-4}
80	2.926	11.0×10^{-4}
90	2.893	11.2×10^{-4}
116.0	2.826	

A list of smoothed values between 75°K and the melting point is given in Table 3.

The variation of the melting point temperature with pressure can be expressed by the equation:

$$(2) \qquad T = T_o + 0.03220\ P - 0.00000623\ P^2,$$

where T_o is the temperature of the melting point at 1 atmosphere pressure, and P is the pressure in atmospheres. Eq. 2 is valid for pressures up to 200 atmospheres.

TABLE 3. THE VAPOR PRESSURE OF SOLID KRYPTON

T, °K	P, mm Hg†
75	1.01
80	3.11
85	8.34
90	20.05
95	43.94
100	89.2
105	169.4
110	302
115	507

† Millimeters mercury at 0°C and standard gravity (980.665 cm/sec²)

The best value for the temperature of the triple point of krypton seems to be 116.0 ± 0.05°K. The melting point under one atmosphere pressure should be about 0.01 degree higher than the triple point, but in view of the uncertainty of the latter value this difference can in general be neglected.

The molecular volumes of the solid and the liquid at the triple point are 29.65 cc/mole

and 34.13 cc/mole, respectively. The enthalpy of fusion is 1636 J/mole. The molal heat capacity under the saturation vapor pressure for solid as well as for liquid krypton is tabulated in Table 4.

The liquid range for krypton extends over about 93 degrees between the triple and the critical points. The critical data for this element are the following:
critical temperature, 209.39°K; critical pressure, 54.182 atmospheres; and critical density, 0.909 g/cc.

The vapor pressure of liquid krypton can be calculated from the following equation which is valid over the entire liquid range:

$$(3) \quad \log_{10} P_{atm} = -\frac{710.0193}{T} - 7.156931$$
$$\log_{10} T + 0.01039974\ T + 19.55820$$

According to this equation the normal boiling point occurs at 119.75 ± 0.01°K. At this temperature the enthalpy of vaporization has the value 9029 J/mole. The entropy of vaporization at the boiling point (Trouton's constant) is 75.4 J/deg/mole.

TABLE 4. MOLAL HEAT CAPACITY OF KRYPTON

T, °K	C_{sat}, J/deg/mole
Solid	
10	5.65
15	11.63
20	15.48
30	20.84
50	25.10
70	27.53
90	30.04
110	34.10
113	35.06
Liquid	
117 ⎱ average	44.77
123 ⎰	

Over most of the liquid range of krypton experimental values for the densities of the liquid and the vapor phases in equilibrium with each other are available. These data are listed in Table 5.

Gaseous krypton is monatomic as is evident from the ratio of the specific heats at constant pressure and at constant volume. This ratio has the value 1.689. The density of the gas at 273.15°K and 1 atmosphere pressure is 3.745 g/l.

Although the interaction between the atoms in the gas phase is limited to van der Waals forces only, the deviations of gaseous krypton from ideal behavior are appreciable. However, a host of accurate data as far as the equation of state is concerned are available. For detailed tabulations the reader is referred to Ref. 1. At low pressure van der Waals' equation can be used with the following constants: $a = 2.318$ atm (liter)^2 and $b = 0.03978$ liter/mole. Up to ten atmospheres and for temperatures ranging from 273 to 573°K the following equation of Beattie-Bridgeman type can be applied:

$$(4) \quad P = \frac{RT}{V^2} \left(1 - \frac{c}{VT^3}\right) (V + B)$$
$$- \frac{A_0}{V^2} \left(1 - \frac{a}{V}\right)$$

The constants in Eq. 4 have the following numerical values:
$R = 0.08206$ liter-atm/mole; $A_0 = 2.4230$ atm (liter)^2; $a = 0.02865$ liter; $B = 0.05261$ liter; and $c = 14.89 \times 10^4$ liter deg^3.

TABLE 5. DENSITIES OF LIQUID AND GASEOUS KRYPTON IN EQUILIBRIUM

(Extrapolated values are enclosed in parentheses)

T, °K	Density, g/cc Liquid	Density, g/cc Vapor
116	(2.441)	(0.0064)
118	(2.426)	(0.0075)
120	(2.412)	(0.0087)
122	(2.397)	(0.0099)
124	(2.382)	(0.0113)
130	2.334	0.0170
140	2.252	0.0305
160	2.072	0.077
180	1.842	0.175
200	1.504	0.373
208	1.193	0.647

A useful quantity in the discussion of gaseous behavior is the second virial coefficient. It may be used for calculations with a simple equation of state of the form

$$(5) \quad PV = RT + BP$$

if demands on accuracy of the results are not too high. For krypton, the second virial coefficient increases from -62.8 cc/mole at 273.15°K, to -29.0 at 373.15°K and to -10.9 at 473.15°K. It becomes zero in the neighborhood of 575°K (Boyle temperature).

The second virial coefficient has also been used to determine the constants occurring in the Lennard-Jones expression for the interatomic potential energy. It was found that the potential energy in ergs of two krypton atoms can be described by the following equation:

$$E = 920 \left[\left(\frac{3.68 \times 10^{-8}}{r}\right)^{12} - \left(\frac{3.68 \times 10^{-8}}{r}\right)^{6} \right]$$

The thermodynamic functions of gaseous krypton can be calculated without difficulty from statistical mechanics. For the temperature range from 10 to 1000°K the entropy, S^0, and the increment of the Gibbs free energy function, $-(G^0 - H^0)/T$, are listed in Table 6. The tabulated values refer to the gas in the standard state, i.e., the perfect gas at 1 atmosphere pressure. They contain only the translational contributions towards the thermodynamic functions because rotational and other internal degrees of freedom are absent for a monatomic gas. The lowest lying electronic level has the frequency 79,972.5 cm^{-1} and is therefore not excited at ordinary temperatures. Contributions to the entropy

TABLE 6. ENTROPY AND GIBBS FREE ENERGY OF GASEOUS KRYPTON IN THE STANDARD STATE†

T, °K	S^0 J/deg/mole	$-(G^0-H^0)/T$, J/deg/mole
10	93.40	72.619
20	107.81	87.026
30	116.24	95.454
40	122.22	101.434
50	126.86	106.072
100	141.27	120.480
200	155.67	134.887
298.15	163.97	143.187
400	170.08	149.295
600	178.51	157.723
800	184.49	163.703
1000	189.13	168.341

† Perfect gas at 1 atmosphere pressure.

arising from the mixing of the isotopes have been omitted from the calculation.

Of considerable practical and theoretical importance are the transport properties of the gas phase. Experimental data of the viscosity at 1 atmosphere pressure are given in Table 7. In the range of intermediate pressures the viscosity is independent of the pressure. This is also largely true for the thermal conductivity, which at 250°K is 0.0000803 J/cm/deg/sec at 1 atm, 0.0000879 at 2 atm and 0.0000912 at 10 atm. The values at 1 atm are 0.0001138 at 373.2°K and 0.0001661 at 600°K.

From viscosity data it is possible to calculate the atomic diameter of the atoms. In the case of krypton a value of 3.6 Å is obtained. This is about 10% smaller than the size of the atom in the crystal lattice. For the process of diffusion in the gas no single coefficient can be given as in the case of viscosity and thermal conductivity. The diffusion of two gases into each other depends on both gases. However, a special case can be distinguished: that of the diffusion of the gas into itself. For krypton the coefficient of self-diffusion at 1 atmosphere pressure assumes the values 0.0795 cm²/sec at 273°K and 0.140 at 373°K. According to the kinetic theory of gases the following relationship exists between the coefficient of self-diffusion, D, and the coefficient of viscosity:

$$(6) \qquad D = K \frac{\eta}{\rho}$$

where η is the viscosity and ρ the density of the gas. The proportionality constant, K, depends on the power, s, occurring in the expression for the potential energy of repulsion between the atoms of the gas, $\epsilon_{rep} = \frac{A}{r^s}$.

TABLE 7. VISCOSITY OF GASEOUS KRYTPON

T, °K	Viscosity, poise
273.15	0.0002327
288.35	0.0002436
293.15	0.0002480
372.55	0.0003062

For krypton, K has the value 1.28 corresponding to a repulsive potential varying with the inverse 22nd power of the distance.

Chemical Properties

Until recently the group of the rare gas elements was believed to be completely incapable of the formation of chemical compounds. The atomic theory seemed to support the chemists' experience because the closed shell structure characteristic for the rare gases required very high energies for the excitation of the electrons. Only few chemical reactions could be expected to liberate enough energy to break up a closed shell. However, a few loose addition compounds of the rare gases have been known for a long time. They are mostly of the clathrate type. The rare gas atoms in these compounds are contained in a cagelike structure of the host lattice. Interaction between the rare gas atoms and the surrounding molecules takes place by van der Waals type forces exclusively. Yet, owing to the rather well-defined structure of the clathrates which in turn leads to a well-defined stoichiometry they may justifiably be regarded as labile chemical compounds.

Krypton clathrates have been prepared with hydroquinone and phenol. In order to obtain the hydroquinone clathrate the organic compound is either heated in aqueous solution or melted and exposed to krypton at pressures ranging from 20 to 60 atmospheres. The phenol clathrate could be prepared by treating phenol crystals at room temperature as well as molten phenol with krypton. The dissociation pressure of the phenol clathrate is 20 atmospheres at 25°C and rises rapidly to 55 atmospheres at 40°C. In general no complete saturation of the organic compound with krypton is achieved. In the case of the hydroquinone clathrate the crystals richest in krypton have the composition $(C_6H_4(OH)_2)_3$ ·0.74 Kr, thus showing that only about $\frac{3}{4}$ of the available cavities in the lattice were occupied by rare gas atoms. Krypton has a surprisingly high solubility in water, as do many other chemically inert gases. Table 8 lists the solubility in terms of cc STP gas per gram of water at one atmosphere pressure. The high solubility has, of course, a direct relationship to the ease with which krypton hydrate can be formed. This hydrate has been known to exist since 1923. It forms if water is cooled under pressurized krypton. According to the ideal formula there should be one atom of Kr for every 5.75 molecules of water. The krypton hydrate has a decomposition pressure of 1 atmosphere at $-27.8°C$ and 14.5 atmospheres at $0°C$. The enthalpy of formation per mole hydrate is 58160 J/mole.

Mass-spectrometric evidence has been obtained for the existence of a number of diatomic species containing krypton. Thus, Kr_2^+ has been found to have an appearance potential of 13.23 v. Similarly, the molecule ions $ArKr^+$ and KrH^+ have been identified and investigated. Optical spectra provide additional evidence for the formation of either $KrXe$ or $KrXe^+$.

The first simple binary compound of krypton whose identity has been well established and which has been prepared in gram quantities is krypton difluoride. It can be made according to several methods: by

TABLE 8. SOLUBILITY OF KRYPTON IN WATER

T, °C	Dissolved gas at 1 atmosphere in cc STP per g of H_2O
0	0.1069
10	0.0783
20	0.0605
30	0.0492
40	0.0417
50	0.0372
60	0.0345

electron irradiation of a mixture of solid krypton and fluorine, by ultraviolet irradiation of krypton and fluorine dispersed in a matrix of argon at liquid helium temperature, and most efficiently by passing an electrical discharge through a mixture of the gaseous elements at low pressure while cooling the reaction vessels in liquid oxygen. Krypton difluoride forms colorless crystals which sublime easily. The vapor pressure at ice point temperature is estimated to be 30 mm Hg. It has not been possible to keep this compound at room temperature without decomposition. At $-78°C$, however, it can be stored for extended times.

The formation of a higher fluoride of krypton as well as the salt of an oxyacid of krypton has also been reported. The existence of these latter compounds, however, is still doubtful because corroborative experimental evidence is lacking.

Uses

Because of the rarity of the element it has found only limited applications. Its main commercial use occurs in the lighting industry. Together with argon it serves as a low-pressure filling gas for fluorescent lights because it improves the brightness and the efficiency of the tubes. It is further used in certain flash tubes for high-speed photography since it is capable of emitting very bright flashes in extremely short times. To a limited extent it serves as a filling gas for incandescent bulbs instead of or together with nitrogen in order to suppress the evaporation of the tungsten filaments and lengthen the lifetime of the bulbs. Attempts have been made to apply krypton in medicine, for instance, as an x-ray absorber and as an anaesthetic, but its high price has prevented its application other than on a limited experimental scale.

As mentioned before, a use has been found recently for the isotopic species Kr^{86}. The orange-red line in the emission spectrum of this isotope has been chosen to represent the fundamental standard of length.

Recently Kr_{85} has found an application in chemical analysis. By imbedding it in a variety of solids, so-called "Kryptonates" can be formed. The activity of these Kryptonates is sensitive to chemical reactions at the surface and thus permits the estimation of the concentrations of the reactants.

References

1. Cook, Gerhard A., Ed., "Argon, Helium and the Rare Gases," New York, Interscience Publishers, Inc., 1961, 2 volumes.
2. Claassen, Howard H., "The Noble Gases," "Topics in Modern Chemistry," Boston, D. C. Heath and Company, 1966.
3. Schreiner, F., Malm, J. G., and Hindman, J. C., "The Preparation and Nuclear Magnetic Resonance of Krypton Difluoride," *J. Am. Chem. Soc.*, **87**, 25 (1965).
4. Claassen, Howard H., Goodman, Gordon L., Malm, John G., and Schreiner, Felix, "Infrared and Raman Spectra of Krypton Difluoride," *J. Chem. Phys.*, **42**, 1229 (1965).

FELIX SCHREINER

L

LANTHANIDE ELEMENTS

The *lanthanide* elements (*lanthanides* or *lanthanoids*) are those elements of atomic numbers 57 through 71 that lie between barium and hafnium and often appear together in the scandium family of the third periodic group. The fact that yttrium (atomic number 39) is a lanthanide element in all its characteristics except those that are completely dependent upon electronic configuration permits its operationally useful classification and consideration as an additional member of the lanthanide series. The classic designation as *rare earth* elements, as based upon the original recovery of the elements as oxides (earths) from relatively rare minerals, was an unfortunate one because of its connotations of scarcity and lack of availability. Crustal abundance data (Table 1), indicate clearly that the lanthanide elements are at least as abundant as some of the commoner elements and that over-all supplies are potentially unlimited.

The origins of lanthanide chemistry are traceable to the parallel isolation of the similar earths *yttria* (from gadolinite by Gadolin in 1794) and *ceria* (from cerite independently by Klaproth and by Berzelius and Hisinger in 1803). As a consequence of extensive and highly painstaking effort continuing to 1907, simplification of these two complex mixtures yielded compounds of yttrium and all the lanthanide elements except promethium (atomic number 61). Promethium was identified as a product of the neutron-induced fission of uranium-235 by Marinsky, Glendenin, and Coryell in the

TABLE 1.   ABUNDANCES OF SELECTED ELEMENTS IN THE IGNEOUS ROCKS OF THE CRUST OF THE EARTH

Symbol	Atomic Number	Abundance, g/metric ton	Symbol	Atomic Number	Abundance, g/metric ton
Y	39	28.1	Be	4	6
La	57	18.3	B	5	3 –
Ce	58	46.1	N	7	46.3
Pr	59	5.53	Co	27	23
Nd	60	23.9	Cu	29	70
Pm	61	ca.0	Ga	31	15
Sm	62	6.47	Ge	32	7
Eu	63	1.06	As	33	5
Gd	64	6.36	Br	35	1.62
Tb	65	0.91	Mo	42	2.5–15
Dy	66	4.47	Ag	47	0.1
Ho	67	1.15	Cd	48	0.15
Er	68	2.47	Sn	50	40
Tm	69	0.20	Sb	51	1
Yb	70	2.66	I	53	0.1
Lu	71	0.75	Pb	82	16

1940's. As products of natural fission processes, promethium nuclides are indeed present in nature, but their over-all abundances are too small to permit their isolation by chemical means.

Atomic Structure and its Consequences

The marked over-all chemical similarity suggested by the difficulties encountered in simplifying the original yttria and ceria has its origin in the electronic configurations of the atoms and ions of the individual elements. The ground-state electronic configurations of the scandium, yttrium, and lanthanum atoms amount to noble-gas cores plus the arrangement $(n\text{-}1)d^1ns^2$ ($n = 4$ for Sc, 5 for Y, 6 for La). For atoms of elements following scandium and yttrium in atomic number, electrons are added to the $(n\text{-}1)d$ orbitals. For atoms of elements following lanthanum in atomic number; however, the energy of the $4f$ orbitals is below that of the $5d$. Electrons are added, therefore, to the $4f$ orbitals, and this process continues until each of the seven $4f$ orbitals is doubly occupied before filling of the $5d$ orbitals continues. Atoms of the fourteen elements so described may be expected to differ electronically from the lanthanum atom only in the number of $4f$ electrons present (Table 2). These differences are, however, slightly greater in that there is an observable tendency for the $4f$ orbitals to be occupied more rapidly and at the expense of the $5d$ orbitals (Table 2). This tendency reflects the enhanced energetic stabilization associated with complete single ($4f^7$) or complete double ($4f^{14}$) occupancy. The listed configurations may be revised slightly as interpretations of emission spectral data are refined. Whether the ground state of a particular atom is $4f^x\ 5d^1\ 6s^2$ or $4^{x+1}\ 6s^2$ is probably of much less chemical than physical importance. Except insofar as electrons may be lost from $4f$ orbitals in producing various oxidation states, electrons in these orbitals are sufficiently well shielded by intervening electron shells as to be largely unavailable for chemical interaction. This situation distinguishes the lanthanide elements from the d-type transition elements, in the atoms and ions of which the d electrons are in the valency shell and participate in bonding.

TABLE 2. GROUND-STATE ELECTRONIC CONFIGURATIONS OF ATOMS

Symbol	Atomic Number	Electronic Configuration	
		Idealized	Observed
Sc	21		$3d^1\ 4s^2$
Y	39		$4d^1\ 5s^2$
La	57		$5d^1\ 6s^2$
Ce	58	$4f^1\ 5d^1\ 6s^2$	$4f^1\ 5d^1\ 6s^2$
Pr	59	$4f^2\ 5d^1\ 6s^2$	$4f^3\ \ \ \ 6s^2$
Nd	60	$4f^3\ 5d^1\ 6s^2$	$4f^4\ \ \ \ 6s^2$
Pm	61	$4f^4\ 5d^1\ 6s^2$	$4f^5\ \ \ \ 6s^2$
Sm	62	$4f^5\ 5d^1\ 6s^2$	$4f^6\ \ \ \ 6s^2$
Eu	63	$4f^6\ 5d^1\ 6s^2$	$4f^7\ \ \ \ 6s^2$
Gd	64	$4f^7\ 5d^1\ 6s^2$	$4f^7\ 5d^1\ 6s^2$
Tb	65	$4f^8\ 5d^1\ 6s^2$	$4f^9\ \ \ \ 6s^2$ (or $4f^8\ 5d^1\ 6s^2$)
Dy	66	$4f^9\ 5d^1\ 6s^2$	$4f^{10}\ \ \ \ 6s^2$
Ho	67	$4f^{10}\ 5d^1\ 6s^2$	$4f^{11}\ \ \ \ 6s^2$
Er	68	$4f^{11}\ 5d^1\ 6s^2$	$4f^{12}\ \ \ \ 6s^2$
Tm	69	$4f^{12}\ 5d^1\ 6s^2$	$4f^{13}\ \ \ \ 6s^2$
Yb	70	$4f^{13}\ 5d^1\ 6s^2$	$4f^{14}\ \ \ \ 6s^2$
Lu	71	$4f^{14}\ 5d^1\ 6s^2$	$4f^{14}\ 5d^1\ 6s^2$

Ground-state electronic configurations of the f-type are not unique to the lanthanide species. Actinide species that resemble those of the lanthanide elements closely have similar $5f$ configurations. That the lanthanum atom has no $4f$ electrons does not in any way preclude the inclusion of this element in the lanthanide series since in a practical way the properties of lanthanum and its compounds vary but little from those of the other lanthanide elements.

Indirect Consequences

Two indirect consequences relate to the marked similarities among compounds that puzzled early investigators and to the slight differences among given compounds of the various elements that permitted separations to be made.

Oxidation States. In the majority of their compounds, all the lanthanide elements are in a uniform $+3$ state of oxidation. Solids containing *tetrapositive* ions are known for a few elements (Table 3), but only tetrapositive cerium can be distinguished in aqueous solution. In the *dipositive* state, only the ions Sm^{2+}, Eu^{2+}, and Yb^{2+} are known in aqueous solution. A few solid compounds

339

of other dipositive ions have been prepared (Table 3). In addition, dipositive ions of most of the lanthanide elements have been stabilized by isolation in crystals of calcium fluoride, but destruction of these crystals results in oxidation.

TABLE 3. DISTINGUISHING ELECTRONIC CONFIGURATIONS FOR OBSERVED OXIDATION STATES

Symbol	Configuration		
	+2	+3	+4
La		$4f^0$ (La^{3+})	
Ce	$4f^2$ (CeCl$_2$)	$4f^1$ (Ce^{3+})	$4f^0$(Ce^{4+})
Pr		$4f^2$ (Pr^{3+})	$4f^1$(PrO$_2$,PrF$_4$, Na$_2$PrF$_6$)
Nd	$4f^4$ (NdI$_2$)	$4f^3$ (Nd^{3+})	$4f^2$(Cs$_3$NdF$_7$)
Pm		$4f^4$ (Pm^{3+})	
Sm	$4f^6$ (Sm^{2+})	$4f^5$ (Sm^{3+})	
Eu	$4f^7$ (Eu^{2+})	$4f^6$ (Eu^{3+})	
Gd		$4f^7$ (Gd^{3+})	
Tb		$4f^8$ (Tb^{3+})	$4f^7$(TbO$_2$,TbF$_4$)
Dy		$4f^9$ (Dy^{3+})	$4f^8$(Cs$_3$DyF$_7$)
Ho		$4f^{10}$(Ho^{3+})	
Er		$4f^{11}$(Er^{3+})	
Tm	$4f^{13}$(TmI$_2$)	$4f^{12}$(Tm^{3+})	
Yb	$4f^{14}$(Yb^{2+})	$4f^{13}$(Yb^{3+})	
Lu		$4f^{14}$(Lu^{3+})	

Direct correlation between the observed oxidation state and the ground-state electronic configuration of the parent atom is the exception rather than the rule. The ubiquitous tripositive state apparently owes its existence to a fortuitous balance between *ionization* and either *hydration* (for solutions) or *lattice* (for solids) energies. Calculation suggests that in aqueous solution all tetrapositive species except possibly Ce^{4+} and all dipositive species except Eu^{2+} must revert to the tripositive.

Standard oxidation-potential data (Table 4) indicate that in acidic aqueous solution each of the lanthanide elements is a powerful reducing agent and yields its tripositive ion readily and vigorously. Data for the Ln(II)-Ln(III) and Ln(III)-Ln(IV) couples support the suggestion in Table 3 that empty, half-filled, and completely filled $4f$ shells represent conditions of stability. Thus $4f^\circ$ cerium(IV)

TABLE 4. STANDARD OXIDATION-POTENTIAL DATA FOR ACIDIC SOLUTIONS

Symbol	E°_{298}†, volts	Symbol	E°_{298}†, volts
	Couples Ln(O)–Ln(III)		
	Ln(s) $\rightleftarrows$ Ln^{3+}(aq) + 3e$^-$		
Y	+2.37	Gd	+2.40
La	2.52	Tb	2.39
Ce	2.48	Dy	2.35
Pr	2.47	Ho	2.32
Nd	2.44	Er	2.30
Pm	2.42	Tm	2.28
Sm	2.41	Yb	2.27
Eu	2.41	Lu	2.25
	Couples Ln(II)–Ln(III)		
	Ln^{2+}(aq) $\rightleftarrows$ Ln^{3+}(aq) + e$^-$		
Sm	+1.55	Yb	+1.15
Eu	0.43		
	Couples Ln(III)–Ln(IV)		
	Ln^{3+}(aq) $\rightleftarrows$ Ln^{4+}(aq) + e$^-$		
Ce	−1.74	Pr	−2.86

†Estimated in many cases

is much less readily reduced to the tripositive state than the $4f^1$ praseodymium(IV). Furthermore, $4f^7$ europium(II) and $4f^{14}$ ytterbium(II) are weaker reducing agents than samarium(II).

Size Relationships. In the series La-Lu and La^{3+}-Lu^{3+}, a general decrease in atomic or crystal radius with increasing atomic number results because addition of electrons to the shielded $4f$ orbitals cannot compensate for the contractive effect produced by increasing nuclear charge (Table 5). A similar, but more limited, trend characterizes the nontripositive ions. This general size decrease is known as the *Lanthanide Contraction.* Among the metals, the dramatic discontinuities characteristic of europium and ytterbium are believed to reflect the tendency of these elements to be dipositive in the metallic state as opposed to the tendency of the others to be largely tripositive. Among the tripositive ions themselves, there is a slight but discernible discontinuity at gadolinium.

Both the atoms and their derived cations are comparatively large. The strengths of the elemental lanthanides as reducing agents and the pronounced ionic character of their

TABLE 5. SIZE RELATIONSHIPS

Symbol	Atomic Number	Atomic Radius,† Å	Crystal or Ionic Radius, Å		
			Ln^{2+}	Ln^{3+}	Ln^{4+}
Sc	21	1.641		0.68	
Y	39	1.801		0.88	
La	57	1.877		1.061	
Ce	58	1.82		1.034	0.92
Pr	59	1.828		1.013	0.90
Nd	60	1.821		0.995	
Pm	61	—		(0.979)	
Sm	62	1.802	1.11	0.964	
Eu	63	2.042	1.09	0.950	
Gd	64	1.802		0.938	
Tb	65	1.782		0.923	0.84
Dy	66	1.773		0.908	
Ho	67	1.766		0.894	
Er	68	1.757		0.881	
Tm	69	1.746	0.94	0.869	
Yb	70	1.940	0.93	0.858	
Lu	71	1.734		0.848	

† For structures in which each atom has 12 other atoms as nearest neighbors.

compounds either as solids or in solution are consequences of large size. The dipositive ions resemble the heavier dipositive alkaline earths in size, and their compounds are thus often isomorphous or of comparable solubility. The magnitude of the lathanide contraction is such that the radius of the Y^{3+} ion is reached in the Ho^{3+}-Er^{3+} region. This resulting similarity in size couples with equality in cationic charge to account for the inevitable natural occurrence of yttrium with the heavier lanthanide elements; for the difficulties encountered in separating yttrium from these elements; and for the marked similarities in crystal structure, solubility, and chemical properties noted between yttrium compounds and those of the heavier lanthanide elements. Indeed, the behavior of the more abundant yttrium is so characteristic of the heavier lanthanide elements that the latter are often referred to as the yttrium earths.

The lanthanide contraction is responsible both for the small variations in basicity within a given oxidation state that permit separations by fractional means and for the parallel decrease in ease of oxidation of the metals with increasing atomic number. Certain of the effects of the lanthanide contraction continue beyond the lanthanide series. Thus, hafnium resembles zirconium much more closely than zirconium resembles titanium. Similarly, very close analogies exist between the chemistries of niobium and tantalum, molybdenum and tungsten, and technetium and rhenium.

Direct Consequences

The $4f$ electrons are directly responsible for the magnetic properties and the radiant energy absorption and emission characteristics of the lanthanide cations, in particular when these electrons are unpaired in spin. For this reason, the preferential single occupancy of each $4f$ orbital before pairing can occur is of particular importance (Hund's Rule).

Magnetic Characteristics. The ions Y^{3+}, La^{3+}, Lu^{3+}, Ce^{4+}, and Yb^{2+}, all of which contain no unpaired electrons, are diamagnetic. All the other cations derived from these elements are paramagnetic. Permanent magnetic moments, both theoretical and observed for specific magnetically dilute compounds, are given in Table 6. Agreement between theoretical and observed values is excellent. That two maxima are observed (at Nd^{3+} and Dy^{3+}-Ho^{3+}, but not at Gd^{3+} with 7 unpaired electrons) indicates that the moment is not dependent solely on the number of unpaired electron spins. Both spin and orbital motions of these unpaired electrons make significant contributions to the permanent moment. The relative magnitudes of separation between the multiplets (J states) and kT (k = Boltzmann constant; T = Kelvin temperature) are important for all the ions except Gd^{3+}, for which the kT contribution is negligible. For the ions Sm^{3+} and Eu^{3+}, the kT contributions are roughly equal to the energy separation contributions; for the other tripositive ions, they are much smaller.

The numerical magnitudes of the permanent moments of these ions are large. Contrary to what is observed with d-transition metal ions, the permanent moment of a given cation is largely unaffected by the nature of the anion present or the presence of complexing groups, providing the temperature and degree of

341

TABLE 6. PERMANENT MAGNETIC MOMENTS OF TRIPOSITIVE CATIONS

Ion	Unpaired Electrons	Theoretical (Van Vleck)	μ_B in Bohr Magnetons Observed $(Ln_2(SO_4)_3 \cdot 8H_2O)$	Observed $(Ln(C_5H_5)_3)$
La^{3+}	0	0	†	0
Ce^{3+}	1	2.56	—	2.46
Pr^{3+}	2	3.62	3.47	3.61
Nd^{3+}	3	3.68	3.52	3.63
Pm^{3+}	4	2.83	—	—
Sm^{3+}	5	1.55–1.65	1.58	1.54
Eu^{3+}	6	3.40–3.51	3.54	—
Gd^{3+}	7	7.94	7.9	7.98
Tb^{3+}	6	9.7	9.6	—
Dy^{3+}	5	10.6	10.3	10.0
Ho^{3+}	4	10.6	10.4	—
Er^{3+}	3	9.6	9.4	9.45
Tm^{3+}	2	7.6	7.0	—
Yb^{3+}	1	4.5	4.3	4.00
Lu^{3+}	0	0	—	—
Y^{3+}	0	0	0	—

†Does not give a salt of this composition.

magnetic dilution remain unaltered. Interactions of such groups with the 4f electrons are thus minimal. The measured permanent moment does not indicate the number of unpaired electrons present, the absolute nature of bonding, the degree of coordination, or the geometry of the species in question. It does suggest electronic configuration, and it is of importance in designing various electronic devices.

Color and Light Absorption. The striking colors that are characteristic of crystalline salts derived from a number of the tripositive ions persist in aqueous and nonaqueous solutions and are largely unaffected by alteration of the anion present or the addition

TABLE 7. COLOR SEQUENCE FOR TRIPOSITIVE CATIONS

Ion	Unpaired Electrons	Color	Unpaired Electrons	Ion
La^{3+}	0	Colorless	0	Lu^{3+}
Ce^{3+}	1	Colorless	1	Yb^{3+}
Pr^{3+}	2	Green	2	Tm^{3+}
Nd^{3+}	3	Reddish	3	Er^{3+}
Pm^{3+}	4	Pink; Yellow	4	Ho^{3+}
Sm^{3+}	5	Yellow	5	Dy^{3+}
Eu^{3+}	6	Colorless (?)	6	Tb^{3+}
Gd^{3+}	7	Colorless	7	Gd^{3+}

of complexing ligands. The interesting repetition of color in the series La^{3+}-Gd^{3+} and Gd^{3+}-Lu^{3+} (Table 7) suggests direct dependence upon the number of unpaired electrons. However, isoelectronic nontripositive ions do not have the same color (e.g., colorless Gd^{3+} vs. straw-yellow Eu^{2+}; colorless Lu^{3+} vs. green Yb^{2+}), and the ions Ce^{3+}, Eu^{3+}, Gd^{3+}, Tb^{3+}(?), and Yb^{3+}, all of which contain unpaired electrons, are colorless.

All of the tripositive ions except Y^{3+}, La^{3+}, and Lu^{3+} absorb radiant energy somewhere in the wave length range 2000-10000 Å. (Table 8). The absorption bands of the ions Ce^{3+} (ultraviolet) and Yb^{3+} (infrared) are broad; all the other spectra contain very sharply defined bands (Fig. 1). These line-like bands are further sharpened for the crystalline solids. Neither change from solution to solid, variation of the anion present, nor the introduction of complexing groups alters the general nature of the sharp-line spectrum of a given cation. However, many of these spectra contain hypersensitive bands the intensities and splittings of which are markedly enhanced by either the addition of strongly complexing ligands or conversion of the species to the gaseous state. The broad-band spectra of the ions Ce^{3+}, Yb^{3+}, and Yb^{2+} are substantially altered by environmental changes. These broad bands result from configurational

TABLE 8. PRINCIPAL ABSORPTION BANDS

Ion	Wavelength, Å	Ion	Wavelength, Å
La^{3+}	None	Tb^{3+}	3694, 3780, 4875
Ce^{3+}	2105, 2220, 2380, 2520	Dy^{3+}	3504, 3650, 9100
Pr^{3+}	4445, 4690, 4822, 5885	Ho^{3+}	2870, 3611, 4508, 5370, 6404
Nd^{3+}	3540, 5218, 5745, 7395,	Er^{3+}	3642, 3792, 4870, 5228, 6525
	7420, 7975, 8030, 8680	Tm^{3+}	3600, 6825, 7800
Pm^{3+}	5485, 5680, 7025, 7355	Yb^{3+}	9750
Sm^{3+}	3625, 3745, 4020	Lu^{3+}	None
Eu^{3+}	3755, 3941		
Gd^{3+}	2729, 2733, 2754, 2756	Y^{3+}	None

changes (e.g., $4f^x 4f \rightleftarrows ^{x-1}5d^1$). The sharp bands result from electronic transitions within the $4f$ arrangement that are allowed by the effects of the crystal fields imposed by surrounding anions or ligands. The absorption spectra of the ions Sm^{2+} and Eu^{2+} contain inner transition bands superimposed on more intense and broader configurational change bands.

The sharp absorption bands of individual lanthanide cations are used in the construction of selective filters and wavelength reference standards and in the spectrophotometric analysis of complex mixtures.

Fluorescence spectra are characteristic of a number of the lanthanide ions. The develop-

ment of europium-activated phosphors for television tubes and fluorescent lights represents a significant practical application of this phenomenon. A specific energy transfer pattern, based upon the absorption of radiant energy by the aromatic structure of an appropriate ligand in a europium(III) chelate [e.g., tetrakis(benzoylacetonato) europate(III)] to raise the system to a higher singlet state, followed by successive radiationless transitions to a lower triplet state, an excited europium ion state, and an ultimate drop to the ground state of the europium ion, produces, in the last step, highly coherent radiation and thus laser behavior. Certain of the dipositive ions trapped in a crystal matrix also act as

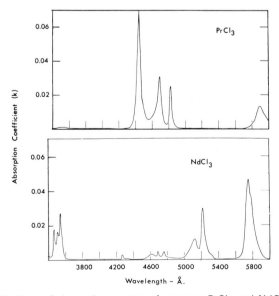

FIG. 1. Portions of absorption spectra of aqueous PrCl₃ and NdCl₃ solutions.

lasers, as do some of the other tripositive species in certain environments (e.g., Nd_2O_3 in $SeOCl_2$).

The Oxidation States—
Their Properties

The Zero State

Yttrium, scandium and the elemental lanthanides are all metals. Some of the more important physical constants are given in Table 9. Substantial ranges exist for density, melting point, and boiling point. Several of the thermal neutron absorption cross sections are remarkably large. Samarium, europium, and gadolinium are more effective in neutron absorption than the more commonly used boron or cadmium. Europium is of particular interest as a consequence of the fact that its isotopes may undergo successive, high cross-section (n,γ) reactions. The metals are quite generally soft, malleable, and ductile. When freshly cut, they have a silvery luster. In electrical conductivity, they cover the same range as cesium and mercury. Except for yttrium, which is only mildly so, the metals are paramagnetic. Gadolinium metal is ferromagnetic up to 16°C.

The metals are thermodynamically comparable to magnesium as reducing agents in acidic aqueous solution (Table 4). Under alkaline conditions, they are somewhat stronger reducing agents. Reactions with some typical reagents are listed in Table 10. Europium and ytterbium metals, like the alkali and heavier alkaline-earth metals, dissolve in liquid ammonia to give dark blue, strongly reducing solutions containing ammonated electrons.

The metals are obtained by the electrolytic reduction of the molten, anhydrous halides or by the metallothermic reduction of the anhydrous fluorides (with Ca), the anhydrous chlorides (with Mg, Li, or Na), or the oxides (with La).

The + 2 State

Only dipositive europium, ytterbium, and samarium have been investigated in detail. These cations are all strong reducing agents in acidic aqueous solutions as shown in Table 4, with reducing strength decreasing

TABLE 9. NUMERICAL CONSTANTS FOR THE ELEMENTS

Symbol	Atomic Weight ($C^{12}=$ 12.0000)	Density†, g/cc	Ionization Energy‡, ev/g-atom	Melting Point, °C	Boiling Point, °C	Cross-Section for Thermal Neutron Capture, § barns/atom
Y	88.905	4.478	6.6	1509	2927	1.31
La	138.91	6.166	5.61	920	3454	8.9
Ce	140.12	6.773	5.65	798	3257	0.73
Pr	140.907	6.769	5.76	935	3017	11.6
Nd	144.24	7.004	6.31	1016	3127	46
Pm	(147)	—	—	1080	—	—
Sm	150.35	7.536	5.6	1072	1900	5600
Eu	151.96	5.245	5.67	826	1439	4300
Gd	157.25	7.886	6.16	1312	3000	46,000
Tb	158.924	8.253	6.74	1356	2480	46
Dy	162.50	8.559	6.82	1407	2335	1100
Ho	164.930	8.78	—	1470	2720	64
Er	167.26	9.045	—	1522	2510	166
Tm	168.934	9.318	—	1545	1727	118
Yb	173.04	6.972	6.25	816	1193	37
Lu	174.97	9.842	5.0	1675	3315	108

† For stable modification at room temperature—all hexagonal close-packed except Sm(rhombohedral), Eu(body-centered cubic), Yb(face-centered cubic).
‡ For one electron.
§ For neutrons of velocity 2200 m/sec. Natural isotopic mixtures.

TABLE 10. TYPICAL CHEMICAL REACTIONS OF THE ELEMENTAL LANTHANIDES

Reagent(s)	Product(s)	Conditions
X_2 $(=F_2, Cl_2, Br_2, I_2)$	LnX_3	Slow at room temperature; burn above 200°C.
O_2	Ln_2O_3	Slow at room temperature; burn above 150–180°C.
S	Ln_2S_3	At boiling point of sulfur.
N_2	LnN	Above 1000°C.
C	LnC_2, Ln_2C_3 (also LnC, Ln_2C, Ln_3C, Ln_4C)	At high temperature.
B	LnB_4, LnB_6	At high temperature.
H_2	LnH_2, LnH_3	Rapid above 300°C.
H^+ (dil. HCl, H_2SO_4, $HClO_4$, $HC_2H_3O_2$, etc.)	$Ln^{3+} + H_2$	Rapidly at room temperature.
H_2O	Ln_2O_3 or $Ln(OH)_3 + H_2$	Slow at room temperature, more rapid at higher temperature.
$H_2O + O_2$	Ln_2O_3 or $Ln(OH)_3$	Rapid with Eu; slower with others.
Metal oxides	Metal	At high temperatures. Except CaO, MgO, Ln_2O_3 in general.

as $Sm^{2+} \gg Yb^{2+} \gg Eu^{2+}$. Both Sm^{2+} and Yb^{2+} ions are readily and rapidly oxidized to tripositive species by hydronium ion. The Eu^{2+} ion is slowly oxidized under these conditions. However, all three ions are oxidized rapidly by elemental oxygen in acidic solution. Water-insoluble compounds (e.g., sulfates, carbonates, or fluorides) are resistant to oxidation. Several solid halides of the composition LnX_2 are metallic conductors and are best formulated as $Ln^{3+}(e^-)(X^-)_2$. The tendency to form complex species is quite generally small and comparable to that of Sr^{2+} or Ba^{2+}.

The dipositive species are obtained by thermal reduction of anhydrous halides or chalocogenides with metals or hydrogen, by electrolytic reduction in solution (e.g., Eu^{2+}, Yb^{2+}), by chemical reduction in solution (e.g., Eu^{2+} with Zn in aqueous solution, Sm^{2+} with Mg in ethanolic solution), by thermal decomposition of the anhydrous triiodides, or by controlled oxidation of the free metals or their amalgams.

The + 3 State

The tripositive ions form crystalline salts with most of the known anionic species. Where the anions can be decomposed thermally (for example, OH^-, CO_3^{2-}, $C_2O_4^{2-}$), these salts, when heated, yield basic derivatives and ultimately oxides. Hydrated salts undergo thermal hydrolysis at elevated temperatures regardless of the nature of the anion. Anhydrous compounds containing thermally stable anions (e.g., O^{2-}, F^-, Cl^-, Br^-) melt without decomposition, but only at relatively high temperatures. Crystal structure data indicate that the solids are ionic. Aqueous solutions of the soluble salts are highly ionic. Hydrolysis in such solutions is extensive only when a strongly basic anion (e.g., CN^-, N_3^-, NO_2^-) is present. Similarities in crystal radii permit many cases of isomorphism among both simple and double salts. Water-soluble salts contain anions such as Cl^-, Br^-, I^-, ClO_4^-, NO_3^-, BrO_3^-, and $C_2H_3O_2^-$; water-insoluble salts contain anions such as F^-, OH^-, O^{2-}, CO_3^{2-}, $C_2O_4^{2-}$, and PO_4^{3-}. The sulfates vary widely in solubility. A division into cerium $(La^{3+}-Sm^{3+})$ and yttrium $(Y^{3+}, Eu^{3+}-Lu^{3+})$ groups is based upon similarities and differences in solubility behavior.

Basicity and ionic character vary with cationic radius (and thus with atomic number), the yttrium species lying close to the holmium species, as might logically be expected. Highly stable complexes form only with the strongly chelating ligands. The thermodynamic stabilities of complex species, as measured by their formation constants or the free energy changes during their formation, invariably increase from La^{3+} to Eu^{3+} or

345

Gd^{3+}; but for cations heavier than Gd^{3+}, stability may continue to increase, remain nearly constant, or pass through a maximum. Yttrium complexes have their expected stabilities if they contain ligands that give the first type of behavior; otherwise the yttrium complexes have reduced stabilities (often about those of the corresponding Nd^{3+} complexes). These variations in stability reflect combinations of factors, among which are differences in the degree of penetration by the ligand of the primary hydration sphere of the tripositive ion, and changes in the coordination number of the ions Ln^{3+} somewhere toward the center of the lanthanide series. Differences in the stabilities of specific complex species are fundamental to the success of separations procedures such as ion exchange and solvent extraction.

Bonding in these complex species is largely ionic in character. The coordination number is 6 only in isolated cases. More commonly, it is 7, 8, 9, or 10. Complexation has little effect upon properties that depend directly on the $4f$ electrons.

The tripositive state results from direct oxidation of the metals by most reagents. It is characteristic of these elements in their minerals.

The + 4 State

Only cerium(IV) has both a solid-state and a solution chemistry. The Ce(III)-Ce(IV) potential as shown in Table 4 is markedly affected by hydrolysis of the tetrapositive ion and by its reactions with complexing groups. Oxidation of cerium(III) in acidic medium is effected only by strong oxidants such as $S_2O_8^{2-}$ or O_3. Reduction of cerium(IV) in acidic medium is effected by many reductants (e.g., Fe^{2+}, Sn^{2+}, I^-, H_2O_2). This reversible one-electron change makes cerium(IV) a very useful analytical oxidizing agent. Under alkaline conditions, oxidation is quite readily effected (e.g., by OCl^-, H_2O_2, O_2). The commonest cerium(IV) compounds are the orange-red, soluble double nitrate, $Ce(NO_3)_4 \cdot 2NH_4NO_3$, and the white to cream-colored, insoluble oxide, CeO_2. The latter compound is widely used in glass polishing compositions.

The other tetrapositive species are stabilized only in crystals. Reduction occurs when the lattices are destroyed by dissolution. The oxide systems are characterized by the presence of numerous nonstoichiometric phases (e.g., Pr_6O_{11}, Tb_4O_7). Complexation by fluoride in the solid state effects stabilization.

Species containing the tetrapositive ions are obtained by thermal oxidation with elemental oxygen or fluorine. Cerium(IV) species can be obtained in solution by chemical or electrolytic oxidation.

Occurrence, Recovery, Separation, Purification

Occurrence

Yttrium, scandium and the lanthanide elements are commonly highly disseminated in crustal formations, and natural concentrations into economically workable deposits are limited in number. Although natural processes have produced essentially cerium-group and yttrium-group minerals, any mineral containing one of the elements also contains all the others (except promethium) in greater or lesser quantity. Thorium, in particular, and tantalum, niobium, and titanium, to a lesser degree, are found in association with the lanthanide elements.

The more common minerals are described in Table 11. Of these, monazite and bastnasite are technically the most important.

Gross Recovery

The procedure for chemically cracking the mineral depends and is based on the composition of the latter. Monazite is decomposed by digestion with either concentrated sulfuric acid (Scheme 1) or concentrated sodium hydroxide (Scheme 2). Thorium can then be removed by selective precipitation as fluoride or complex phosphate from strongly acidic medium, by selective precipitation as the dioxide, by selective extraction with reagents such as tri-*n*-butyl phosphate or high-molecular weight amines, or by selective anion exchange from nitrate or sulfate medium. Bastnasite is converted by concentrated sulfuric acid to soluble sulfates, with the loss of carbon dioxide and hydrogen fluoride.

Cerium is often removed at this stage by a procedure based upon the reduced basicity of the tetrapositive state. Useful procedures

TABLE 11.   IMPORTANT MINERALS

Name	Composition†		Location of Significant Deposits
	Idealized	Generalized	
1. Cerium-Group Minerals			
Monazite	$(Ce)PO_4$	49–74% Ce earths 1–4% Y earths 5–9% ThO_2 1–2% SiO_2 tr. U	Travancore, India; Brazil; Union of South Africa; Florida, North and South Carolina, Idaho
Bastnasite	$(Ce)FCO_3$	65–70% Ce earths 1% Y earths	California, New Mexico; Sweden
Cerite	$(Ce)_3M^{II}H_3Si_3O_{13}$ $(M^{II} = Ca, Fe)$	51–72% Ce earths tr. − 7.6% Y earths tr. Th, U, Zr	Sweden; Caucausus
2. Yttrium-Group Minerals			
Euxenite‡	$(Y)(Nb,Ta)TiO_6 \cdot xH_2O$	13–35% Y earths 2–8% Ce earths 20–23% TiO_2 25–35% $(Nb,Ta)_2O_5$	Australia; Idaho
Xenotime	$(Y)PO_4$	54–65% Y earths ca. 0.1% Ce earths up to 3% ThO_2 up to 3.5% U_3O_8 2–3% ZrO_2	Norway; Brazil
Gadolinite	$(Y)_2M_3^{II}Si_2O_{10}$ $(M^{II} = Fe,Be)$	35–48% Y earths 2–17% Ce earths up to 11.6% BeO tr. Th	Sweden; Norway; Texas, Colorado

† The symbols (Ce) and (Y) represent the cerium and yttrium-group lanthanides, respectively.
‡ Termed euxenite if $(Nb, Ta)_2O_5:TiO_2 = 1:4$ or more; polycrase if $1:3$ or less.

SCHEME 1

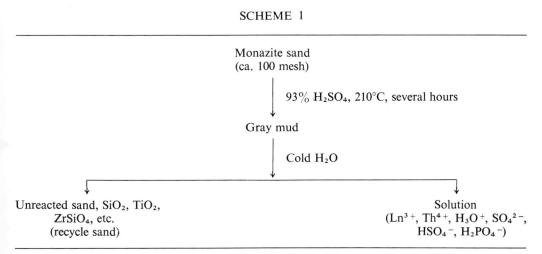

Monazite sand
(ca. 100 mesh)

↓ 93% H_2SO_4, 210°C, several hours

Gray mud

↓ Cold H_2O

Unreacted sand, SiO_2, TiO_2,
    $ZrSiO_4$, etc.
    (recycle sand)

Solution
$(Ln^{3+}, Th^{4+}, H_3O^+, SO_4^{2-},$
$HSO_4^-, H_2PO_4^-)$

SCHEME 2

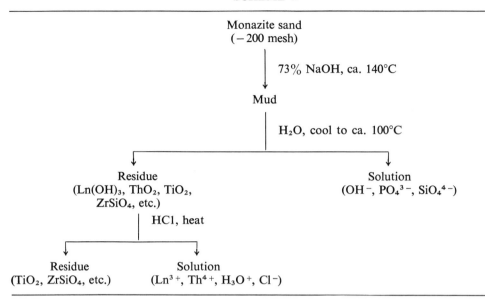

Monazite sand
(− 200 mesh)

73% NaOH, ca. 140°C

Mud

H₂O, cool to ca. 100°C

Residue
(Ln(OH)₃, ThO₂, TiO₂,
ZrSiO₄, etc.)

Solution
(OH⁻, PO₄³⁻, SiO₄⁴⁻)

HCl, heat

Residue
(TiO₂, ZrSiO₄, etc.)

Solution
(Ln³⁺, Th⁴⁺, H₃O⁺, Cl⁻)

involve oxidation to CeO_2 followed by selective dissolution of the more basic Ln_2O_3 compounds in acid, selective hydrolysis of Ce^{4+}-Ln^{3+} mixtures, selective oxidation under buffered conditions, selective crystallization of the double ammonium nitrate from nitric acid solutions, and selective solvent extraction, especially from nitric acid solutions with tri-*n*-butyl phosphate. In the last case, separation from thorium is effected by reducing the extracted cerium(IV), which then allows the cerium to return to the aqueous phase.

Separation of Yttrium and the Lanthanides

Separations may be effected by one or another or some combination of general procedures involving

1. Fractional crystallization of isomorphous salts
2. Basicity differences
   a. Fractional precipitation
   b. Fractional thermal decomposition of salts
   c. Ion exchange
   d. Solvent extraction
3. Selective oxidation or reduction
4. Physical differences

All procedures, except those involving oxidation or reduction, are fractional in character.

Since in most instances the single-stage separation factor differs only slightly from unity, many-fold repetitions of the single operation are required for effective separation.

Classically, separations were accomplished by fractional crystallization. Of the almost innumerable systems investigated, some of the most effective are the double ammonium nitrates, $Ln(NO_3)_3 \cdot 2NH_4NO_3 \cdot 4H_2O$, for the removal of lanthanum and the separation of praseodymium from neodymium; the double manganese nitrates, $2Ln(NO_3)_3 \cdot 3Mn(NO_3)_2 \cdot 24H_2O$, for the separation of members of the cerium group but not the yttrium group; and the bromates, $Ln(BrO_3)_3 \cdot 9H_2O$, and ethyl sulfates, $Ln(C_2H_5SO_4)_3 \cdot 9H_2O$, for the separation of members of the yttrium group. Fractional crystallization is seldom used at the moment, except for the separation of lanthanum.

Of the basicity procedures, both ion exchange and solvent extraction lend themselves to effective large-scale separations because of the ease with which they can be automated and of their operation as multistage processes. Ion exchange, based upon the sorption of the mixed ions on a cation exchanger followed by elution with complexing agents such as buffered citrate, ethylenediamine-N,N,N',N'-tetraacetate, or

N-hydroxyethylethylenediamine-N,N',N'-triacetate, is largely responsible for the production of the separated ions in commercial and reasonably priced quantities. Such a procedure enhances the selectivity of the exchanger by superimposing differences in thermodynamic stabilities of chelates of the various cations. The most stable complex species are eluted first. These are followed by the species in the order of decreasing stabilities. Solvent extraction, based in particular upon complexing extractants such as di(2-ethylhexyl)phosphoric acid and certain high-molecular weight carboxylic acids, has been particularly effective for the removal of yttrium.

The removal of cerium reflects its selective oxidation. Selective reduction to the Eu^{2+} ion with zinc in acidic solution, followed by precipitation of the divalent ion as sulfate or of the tripositive ions as hydroxides, is extremely effective for the separation of this element.

Methods dependent upon differences in physical properties have not proved to be highly successful. The discovery of some volatile, thermally stable 1,3-diketonates may permit effective separations by selective vaporization and condensation.

Purification

The tripositive cations are effectively separated from most cationic impurities, except the actinides, by precipitation as oxalates at low pH. Ultimate purification is by ion exchange or solvent extraction. Europium may be purified by repeated reduction-oxidation processes.

Applications

Broadly, compounds of these metals are most widely used in ceramics, in cored carbons for arc lights, as catalysts, in magnetic and electronic devices, in phosphor compositions, and as neutron absorbers. Specific applications are indicated in entries about the individual elements.

References

1. Eyring, L., Ed., "Progress in the Science and Technology of the Rare Earths," New York, Macmillan Company, Vol. 1, 1964; Vol. 2, 1966.
2. Kleber, E. V., and Love, B., "The Technology of Scandium, Yttrium, and the Rare Earth Metals," New York, Macmillan Company, 1963.
3. Moeller, T., "The Chemistry of the Lanthanides," New York, Reinhold Publishing Corporation, 1963.
4. Moeller, T., Martin, D. F., Thompson, L. C., Ferrús, R., Feistel, G. R., and Randall, W. J., "The Coordination Chemistry of Yttrium and the Rare Earth Metal Ions," *Chem. Rev.*, **65**, 1 (1965).
5. Spedding, F. H., and Daane, A. H., Eds., "The Rare Earths," New York, John Wiley and Sons, 1961.
6. Topp, N. E., "The Chemistry of the Rare-Earth Elements," New York, Elsevier Publishing Company, 1965.
7. Wybourne, B. G., "Spectroscopic Properties of the Rare Earths," New York, John Wiley and Sons, 1965.
8. Yost, D. M., Russell, H., Jr., and Garner, C. S., "The Rare-Earth Elements and Their Compounds," New York, John Wiley and Sons, 1947.

THERALD MOELLER

LANTHANUM

Discovery and History

Lanthanum (atomic no. 57), from which the name lanthanide or lanthanon series of elements is derived, is not a so-called "true" rare earth. The rare earths are inner transition elements and characterized by electrons successively filling the incomplete 4f orbital. Lanthanum with an outer electronic configuration $5d^1 6s^2$ has a vacant 4f orbital. The "true" rare earths occur in the Periodic Table between elements 58 and 71 inclusively. Geochemically lanthanum is found in nature closely associated with all the other rare earth elements. This fact of similarity contributed to one of the most puzzling, yet fascinating eras in chemical history.

In 1839, C. G. Mosander partially decomposed cerium nitrate by heating; he then treated the resulting salt with dilute nitric acid. From the extracted solution a new rare earth was isolated, which he named lanthana (meaning hidden) while retaining the name ceria for the original acid insoluble oxide. The lanthanum experimental work continued for the next three years with the results remaining unpublished. In 1841, Mosander again used dilute nitric acid to treat lanthana and extracted a rose-colored oxide which he named didymia (twin brother of lanthana).

In the 110 years following its discovery elemental lanthanum found little usage. Scientists were mainly concerned with separation and purification, determining properties, analysis, and spectra. Although knowledge of the rare earths has greatly increased within the past twenty years, lanthanum metal has still only limited applications.

Prevalence and Sources

Frequently the lanthanide series is divided into two groups. Elements with atomic numbers 57 to 63 are called the cerium group or light rare earths, while elements 64 through 71 are referred to as the yttrium group or heavy rare earths. Rare earths found in a given mineral will usually fit into one of the two groups. Lanthanum is classified as a cerium group element.

The free rare earth metals are never mined, since these elements occur in complex inorganic compounds. Lanthanum is fairly abundant in the earth's crust, to the extent of 0.0018% or 17.8 grams per metric ton. This represents a natural abundance greater than that of more familiar metallic elements: molybdenum, mercury, silver, cadmium, and bismuth. There are four lanthanum bearing minerals of consequence, monazite, bastnasite allanite, and cerite. The first two of these are of primary interest with regard to the economical production of lanthanum.

Monazite is a rare earth-thorium phosphate formed in monoclinic crystals found scattered in acid granites and pegmatites. The weathering of rocks and resulting placers causes the heavy monazite to concentrate in stream and beach sands. Major monazite deposits are located in India, Idaho, Brazil, Florida, North and South Carolina, Union of South Africa, and Australia. The United States ores are not rich enough to be processed for the rare earths alone. Domestic monazite production is associated with other marketable materials, e.g., ilmenite, rutile, zircon, garnet, and gold. The lanthanum content of monazite varies, but is typically 15 to 25%.

Bastnasite is a rare earth fluocarbonate with a lanthanum content from 8 to 38%. A principal deposit was discovered in 1949, at Mountain Pass, California. Lincoln County, New Mexico deposits of the mineral are also of commercial value. Industrial processing of bastnasite is simplified because of the high carbonate content and a minimum of fluoride.

Allanite is a rare earth-calcium-iron-aluminum silicate. It is rather common and found widely distributed throughout the western United States. There is no large scale processing of this mineral. Cerite is a silicate ore containing calcium and iron with 50 to 70% cerium group earths. It occurs primarily in Sweden, but is lacking in abundance and not considered a commercial source of rare earths.

Extraction

The lanthanum-containing monazite and bastnasite can be chemically cracked by heating with concentrated sulfuric acid. The reaction mixture is treated with excess water and the lanthanum sulfate dissolves. Thorium carried with the rare earths from monazite is removed from solution by precipitation as the pyrophosphate. Lanthanum is recovered from thorium-free solutions by precipitation as the oxalate or as sodium lanthanum double sulfate.

Crushed and ground bastnasite is concentrated by a flotation process. Physical separation followed by leaching of the gangue with dilute hydrochloric acid and calcining results in a 90% rare earth oxide. The concentrates are treated with mineral acids and lanthanum is recovered as oxalate or fluoride.

Separation

The procedures used for lanthanum separations are described as either classical or modern. Under the classical heading, the most important method is fractional crystallization. Prior to World War II this was the most commonly used technique. In the process a portion of a mixture is precipitated by changing the concentration of the salt. This means of separation is tedious and does not furnish a purified end-product.

From a cerium-free earth mixture lanthanum is easily separated as the double ammonium nitrate. The concentration of this salt rapidly builds up in the most insoluble fractions. Lanthanum salts commercially produced in this manner are 95 to 99% pure. The soluble ends from the fractionation contain neodymium as the principal rare earth and serve as a starting material for its separation.

Under modern methods, the most important technique for lanthanum separation is ion exchange. Highly purified materials can be produced by hydrogen ion exchange sorbing lanthanum ions on suitable resin beds. Selective removal of these ions is accomplished in successive steps by passing a complexing agent over the bed. In 1947, there was simultaneous publication of the rare earth ion exchange method by F. H. Spedding and associates at the Ames Laboratory, and by G. E. Boyd and his co-workers at Oak Ridge National Laboratory.

The industrially favored procedures employ acid chelate elutions with either nitrilotriacetate or ethylenediaminetetracetate on a cupric-state resin retaining bed. The purity of lanthanum oxide, as a final product after ion exchange, has reached 99.999%.

The technique of liquid-liquid extraction is considered a modern method although studies conducted with rare earths date back to 1937. Most lanthanide tripositive ion pairs are quickly removed from aqueous nitrate medium by one of several organic liquids, e.g., tri-n-butyl phosphate. Operationally the technique is well understood, but it is not competitive with ion exchange as a general method of separation except in the case of yttrium. The major employment is in the purification of cerium, thorium and lanthanum. Lanthanum (III) is not extracted as easily as other tripositive rare earths and can be isolated from them.

Derivation

Lanthanum metal is derived by two basic methods, metallothermic reduction and electrolysis of fused salt mixtures. The former scheme is employed commercially for the production of high-purity metal. Purified lanthanum oxide is the starting material. Anhydrous halides are prepared at 300–400°C, as represented in the reactions:

$$La_2O_3 + 6NH_4F \cdot HF \rightarrow 2LaF_3 + 6NH_4F \uparrow + 3H_2O \uparrow \text{ and } La_2O_3 + 6NH_4Cl \rightarrow 2LaCl_3 + 6NH_3 \uparrow + 3H_2O \uparrow.$$

These compounds can be reduced under vacuum or inert gas with alkali or alkaline earth metals at temperatures between 1000 and 1500°C, as shown by the reactions:

$$2LaF_3 + 3Ca \rightarrow 2La + 3CaF_2 \text{ and }$$
$$LaCl_3 + 3Li \rightarrow La + 3LiCl.$$

The first successful reductions of this type were carried out in steel bombs packed with a lime or dolomite lining using an iodine "booster" reaction. This caused excessive contamination of the rare earth metals by the refractory oxides. Today producers employ refractory metal crucibles (tantalum or tungsten) placed inside sealed stainless steel bombs or under argon gas in a vacuum system. Typical purity obtained for lanthanum prepared by this means is 99.9%.

In the electrowinning of lanthanum it is essential that the trichloride be previously dried to a nearly anhydrous product. This is accomplished by heating in an oxgyen-free atmosphere. Commercial electrolysis cells are made with an iron, carbon, or refractory lining capable of containing the molten bath. The cell charge consists of lanthanum trichloride with additions of NaCl, KCl, or $CaCl_2$, which is fused by heating with external burners. The electrolysis using carbon or tungsten anodes is conducted at 800 to 900°C with oxygen excluded. The molten metal product collects on the bottom of the cell. Lanthanum metal reportedly has been produced in 99.8% purity employing electrolytic techniques.

Fabrication

The success or failure realized in forming lanthanum metal is largely dependent on the tramp-element impurities. Proper fabrication of lanthanum requires that the residual gas content of the metal be minimal. The major offender is oxygen, normally found in the form of oxide or oxyhalide.

The metal can be melted by induction heating in a vacuum using tantalum, or preferably tungsten crucibles. Copper chill molds are used to produce ingots, rods, bars, and plates. Lanthanum of good purity is easily cut with a hacksaw, free-machined with a lathe tool or milling cutter, and rolled into sheets at room temperature. Fig. 1 displays some examples of fabricated lanthanum.

FIG. 1. Lanthanum sheet, rod, plate and ingot.

Caution must be exercised when handling lanthanum since it can be pyrophoric when in the finely divided form of chips or dust. A good grade of mineral oil serves to protect exposed metal surfaces during machining. Copious flow of coolant is advised in deep drilling and boring operations. High-flash point oil is a satisfactory medium in which to store the metal, however, a leak-tight container filled with argon gas is recommended.

Physical Properties

Lanthanum is soft and malleable; these characteristics depend on the degree of purity and previous treatment. Increased melting point and hardness with an accompanying decrease in ductility is attributed to the pres-

ence of impurity elements. Lanthanum experiences two allotropic transformations, from hexagonal to face-centered cubic at 310°C and to body-centered cubic at 868°C. It is the only rare earth found to be superconductive; this phenomenon occurs below 6°K. At room temperature the resistivity is quite high. An increase of about 10% occurs just above the second transition temperature. The metal should be diamagnetic since it has no unpaired electrons, however, it shows weak paramagnetism which is nearly temperature independent. Vapor pressure measurements made in the liquid region (1665–2182°K) follow the equation: $\log P_{mm} = 8.918 \pm 0.042 - (21980 \pm 40)/T$. Some important physical properties are listed in Table 1.

TABLE 1. SELECTED PROPERTIES OF ELEMENTAL LANTHANUM

Chemical symbol			La
Atomic number			57
Atomic weight			138.91
Natural abundance, %			0.0018
Crystal habit	α – hex	β – fcc	γ – bcc
Lattice constants, Å	a = 3.772 c = 12.144	a = 5.305	a = 4.26
Transformation temp., °C		$(\alpha - \beta)$ 310 $\pm$ 5 $(\beta - \gamma)$861 $\pm$ 5	
Atomic volume, cc/mole			22.35
Metallic valence			+ 3
Metallic radius, CN = 12 Å			1.877
Density, g/cc			6.166
Electronegativity			1.17
Electronic configuration			$6s^2 5d^1$
Oxidation state			III
Oxidation potential, 25°C, volts			2.522
Ionic radius, Å			1.061

TABLE 1—*continued*

Melting point, °C	920 ± 1
Boiling point, °C	3454
Temp. @ which vapor press. = 1 torr, °C	2192
Temp. @ which vapor press. = 10^{-3} torr, °C	1571
Heat capacity, C_p @ 0°C, cal/mole- °C	6.27
Entropy, S_o @ 300°K, cal/mole-deg	13.64
$(F_T^o-H_o^o)/T$, @ 300°K, cal/mole-deg	8.37
$(H_T^o-H_o^o)/T$, @ 300°K, cal/mole-deg	5.27
$\triangle$H transformation, kcal/mole, $\alpha-\beta$	0.095
$\triangle$H fusion, kcal/mole	2.75
$\triangle$H vaporization, kcal/mole	100.8
$\triangle$H sublimation, @ 25°C, kcal/mole	103.0
Thermal conductivity, @ 28°C, cal/cm²/cm/sec/°C	0.033
Ionization potential, eV	5.61
Electrical resistivity @ 25°C, ohm-cm × 10^6	56.8
Temp. coeff. of resistivity, 0° to 25°C, °C^{-1} × 10^3	2.18
Hall coeff. @ 25°C, volt-cm/amp-oer × 10^{12}	−0.8
Atomic susceptibility @ 25°C, 10^6 emu/mole	101
Effective mag. moment, +3 ion, Bohr mag.	0.49
Ferromagnetic Curie temp., °K	none
Paramagnetic Curie temp., °K	—
Neel point θ, °K	none
Hardness, as-cast, BHN	37
Ultimate tensile strength, as-cast, psi × 10^{-3}	19.2
Tensile yield strength, psi × 10^{-3}	18.2
Tensile elongation, %	7.9
Ultimate compressive strength, as-cast, psi × 10^{-3}	31.2
Compressibility, @ 25°C, cm²/kgm × 10^6	4.13
Young's modulus, dynes/cm² × 10^{-11}	3.84
Shear modulus, dynes/cm² × 10^{-11}	1.49
Poisson's ratio	0.288
Izod impact, as-cast, ft-lbs, @ 25°C	4.5
Coeff. of expansion, @ 400°C, 10^6	7.9
Air corrosion rate, @ 35°C mg/dm²/day	80
Air corrosion rate, @ 400°C mg/dm²/day	3200
Thermal neutron cross section, barns	8.9
Target isotope and % abundance	La^{139}, 99.91
Activation cross section, barns	8.2
Induced isotope	La^{140}
Half-life	40.2hr
MeV of principal radiations	β^- 1.34, others to 2.15; γ 0.09 to 1.60

Chemical Properties

Selected properties of elemental lanthanum are summarized in Table 1. Lanthanum has the largest atomic (and ionic) size of any of the trivalent elements in the series. It has one stable oxidation state of +3, formed with an electrode potential of 2.522 volts in aqueous solution. Lanthanum tripositive ion is colorless, with no absorption bands in the visible, ultraviolet or near infrared regions. It is the strongest reducing agent in the series and behaves as the most basic cation. Principal lanthanum isotopes are: La^{138} and La^{139}. Freshly cut metal has a silver luster, but tarnishes quickly.

The metal corrodes in the atmosphere at room temperature, particularly in moist air, to form a hydrated oxide with a large volume increase and sloughing away. Cold water will slowly attack lanthanum, hot water reacts faster. Reportedly surface passivation can be accomplished by immersion in a 2–5% solution of nitric acid in ethanol. Dilute

353

mineral acids readily dissolve lanthanum, but it reacts slowly in concentrated sulfuric. With hydrogen, interstitual hydrides are formed showing continuous miscibility from LaH_2 to LaH_3. Lanthanum will react by direct union with elemental carbon, silicon, phosphorus, sulfur, arsenic, nitrogen, boron, selenium, and tellurium. It burns vigorously in halogen vapors when heated above 200°C. Molten lanthanum reduces magnesia, lime, beryllia, alumina, silica, zirconia, and thoria at elevated temperatures.

Principal Compounds

Hundreds of lanthanum compounds have been prepared in efforts to find better means of separation and commercial applications. Lanthanum metal is strongly basic and will form compounds with most anions and anionic radicals. Organometallic compounds (e.g., ethylsulfate) form as well as the common inorganic and organic types.

Lanthanum sequioxide is an extremely important compound. It can be formed by direct combustion of the metal, or by ignition of the oxalate, hydroxide, carbonate, nitrate, and sulfate. The white oxide is almost as basic as calcium oxide, and will absorb both carbon dioxide and water vapor from the air. The latter causes complete hydration at ambient temperature. The oxide will dissolve in strong mineral acids and in the weak acids, acetic and formic. The anhydrous oxide is denser than lanthanum metal and has a larger coefficient of thermal expansion.

Lanthana added to glasses for lenses increases the index of refraction while reducing dispersion. Lanthanum oxide has been used in combination with other rare earths in glass polishes and in cores for carbon-arc electrodes. The compound melts at 2300°C, thus it is attractive for high-temperature refractory applications. The oxide serves as an effective activated host matrix in fluorescent type phosphors. The short-lived radiosotope La^{140} is a high intensity gamma ray source. Due to its low thermal neutron cross section, lanthana is an ideal diluent for thoria, urania and plutonia fuels.

Lanthanum halides, particularly the chloride and fluoride, have been extensively studied from the point of view of thermodynamics and preparation. Two methods of preparation have already been described in the section covering metal derivation. The water-soluble chloride can be formed by dissolving the oxide, hydroxide or carbonate in hydrochloric acid. The resulting salt is the heptahydrate which cannot be dehydrated by heating in air. The anhydrous form of the trichloride is very hygroscopic; when properly activated it displays luminescent character. Solutions of lighter rare earth chlorides, including lanthanum, have been used in a petroleum cracking catalyst. Lanthanum fluoride is sparingly soluble and can be readily precipitated from chloride or nitrate solutions with hydrofluoric acid. The fluoride, mixed with other rare earths, is used in cores of carbon arc-light electrodes. The bromides and iodides are of little industrial importance.

Lanthanum nitrate hexahydrate may be prepared by nitric acid dissolution of the oxide, hydroxide or carbonate. Historically the nitrates have played an important part in the isolation of lanthanum, especially as the ammonium double nitrate salt (see section on separation).

Chemistry of the sulfate is important since processing of monazite and bastnasite involves sulfuric acid. Lanthanum sulfate with nine waters of hydration can be dehydrated in the air at 400 to 450°C. The salt displays a retrograde solubility in water, hence it is less soluble in hot water.

Lanthanum hydroxide may be precipitated by addition of sodium, potassium or ammonium hydroxide to solutions containing La^{+3} ions. This is the least soluble compound and is useful in separation, purification, and reclamation procedures.

Precipitation of lanthanum carbonate trihydrate is accomplished by adding any alkali carbonate to a neutral salt solution. This compound provides a convenient form for storage and industrial use.

Lanthanum oxalate nonahydrate precipitates from slightly acid solutions on the addition of oxalate ions. This reaction is significant because lanthanum can be extracted from dilute solutions and purified free of other elements. The compound is useful because it is readily filterable, serves as an intermediate in metathetical reactions, and can be ignited directly to the oxide.

Applications

Approximately one-fourth of the total production of rare earths is utilized in the form of metals and alloys. Pure lanthanum metal has limited use and its consumption has been restricted almost entirely to research work. The metal does not have sufficient mechanical strength nor favorable properties to make it attractive for construction purposes. In alloys, particularly misch metal, it has numerous metallurgical applications. The effects of lanthanum on other elements have been extensively studied in binary systems. Investigations have shown that small additions of lanthanum to existing alloys often enhance their properties.

Misch metal and lanthanum act as scavengers for sulfur, oxygen, hydrogen, etc. in ferrous alloys with the result being cleaner metal. It was discovered that some rare earths when added in small amounts (0.05 to 0.1%) produced a nodular graphite structure in cast iron. The mechanical properties of this material are superior to those of ordinary malleable and cast iron.

In steel, including stainless, many investigators have reported vivid improvements in properties; others find no improvement and in some instances impairment. Rare earth inoculations of about 1% have produced steels with enhanced hot workability, impact strength, fluidity, weldability, and ductility. Lanthanum has increased notch sensitivity in molybdenum armor steels, but has also caused desirable grain refinement in stainless steels. The addition of cerium and lanthanum to Cr-Ni-Mo stainless eliminated hot shortness. There is no agreement as to which additive or method of addition is the best. Little comparative work has been done with individual rare earths, but most studies that are reported include lanthanum. An iron-25% chromium-1.5% lanthanum alloy exhibits good oxidation resistance and scale retention near 1000°C.

Misch metal and didymium additions to magnesium alloys produce improved creep resistance at elevated temperatures. Lanthanum is a less effective additive because of its low solubility in magnesium.

Lanthanum improves the strength, ductility and rupture resistance of aluminum. In the aluminum-10% magnesium alloy lanthanum affects the fluidity and surface tension characteristics.

Although the results of rare earth additives on titanium are not complete, indications are that they have little value except as impurity scavengers. Small additions of lanthanum (up to 1%) to titanium do not change the hardness nor tensile strength.

In many nickel-chromium alloys, 0.2 to 2% rare earths metal enhance high-temperature (1200°C) oxidation resistance. Inconel and nichrome remain uneffected by the additions. No oxidation improvement has been observed with cobalt-based alloys. Arc-melted vanadium, tantalum and niobium showed improvement in ductility and workability with rare earth additions. Lanthanum (0.2 to 5.0% additions) decreases the hardness and brittle transition temperature of cast molybdenum.

The effects of individual rare earths on chromium and chromium alloys have been studied in detail. One to four per cent lanthanum in iodide chromium alloys causes a slightly decreased hardness. A significant reduction of the oxidation rate and nitrogen absorption has been recorded during tests conducted above 1250°C.

Biochemistry and Toxicity

It has been discovered that in animals (rats, mice, rabbits) the effects of rare earth salt injections are pronounced. Injections of lanthanum solutions have produced hyperglycemia, decreased blood pressure, spleen degeneration, and fatty liver. The latter effect is more consistent in females and is characterized by increased neutral fat esters, reaching a maximum 48 hours after injection. Very small amounts of lanthanum are absorbed via the oral route. Intramuscular injections of radiolanthanum resulted in greater than 75% retention at the injection site. Of the remainder, 50% deposited in the liver and 25% in the skeleton. Liver bile slowly eliminated the lanthanum. After eight months, the skeleton retained two-thirds of the initial amount.

Lanthanum nitrate will cause a loss of muscle contractility in dogs, cats, and rabbits. Lanthanum compounds can cause eye irritation to the conjunctiva and opacification of a denuded cornea after a latent period of several hours or days. No damage or irritation to intact skin is observed, but there is injury to abraded skin resulting in epilation and scar tissue. Human exposure to lanthanum vapors can cause sensitivity to heat, itching, and a keener sense of taste and smell. Rare earth chlorides (e.g., $LaCl_3$) are known to act as anticoagulants, although they must be cautiously applied. Lanthanum complexes will distribute more completely in the body than will free ions. Organic salts of lanthanum have been observed to alter fungus spores and the influenza virus.

Lanthanum salts are considered to have a low-to-moderate acute toxicity rating. Mixed rare earths appear to be worse than the individual elements and intravenous doses can be lethal to animals. The most striking effects produced are both skin and lung granulomas with local injection or inhalation. The acute fatty liver produced, although serious, is self-limiting and reversible without therapy.

References

1. Gschneidner, K. A., Jr., "Rare Earth Alloys," New York, D. Van Norstrand Co. Inc., 1961.
2. Gschneidner, K. A., Jr., "Rare Earths—The Fraternal Fifteen," Oak Ridge, Tenn., U.S. Atomic Energy Comm., 1964.
3. Haley, T. J., *J. Pharm. Sci.*, **54**, 663 (1965).
4. Hampel, C. A., Ed., "Rare Metals Handbook," 2nd. Ed., Chapt. 19, New York, Reinhold Publishing Corp., 1962.
5. Kleber, E. V., and Love, B., "The Technology of Scandium, Yttrium and the Rare Earths," New York, Pergamon Press, 1963.
6. McMasters, O. D., and Gschneidner, K. A., Jr., *Nuclear Metallurgy Series*, **X**, 93 (1964).
7. "Minerals Yearbook," Vol. 1, (1964), 893, Washington, D.C., Bureau of Mines, 1965.
8. Moeller, T., "The Chemistry of the Lanthanides," New York, Reinhold Publishing Corp., 1963.
9. Spedding, F. H., and Daane, A. H., Eds., "The Rare Earths," New York, John Wiley and Sons, Inc., 1961.
10. Weeks, M. E., "Discovery of the Elements," 3rd Ed., 695, New York, *J. Chem. Educ.*, 1956.

JOHN L. MORIARTY, JR.

LAWRENCIUM†

In 1961 a group of scientists working at the Lawrence Radiation Laboratory, University of California,[1] announced the discovery of element 103 and suggested the name lawrencium in honor of E. O. Lawrence. This group reported preparing 103^{257} by irradiating a mixture of californium (element 98) isotopes with boron ions using their Heavy Ion Linear Accelerator. The possible nuclear reactions yielding 103^{257} are as follows:

$$Cf^{250,251,252} + B^{11} \rightarrow 103^{257} + 4 \text{ to } 6 \text{ neutrons}$$
or
$$Cf^{250,251,252} + B^{10} \rightarrow 103^{257} + 3 \text{ to } 5 \text{ neutrons}$$

The recoils from the boron bombardments were examined directly with solid state detectors and an 8.6 MeV alpha activity with a half-life of about 8 seconds was observed and assigned to 103^{257}. The half-life was too short to permit any chemical identification of the recoil atoms. Furthermore the double recoil technique used in preparing and identifying isotopes of nobelium (element 102) (q.v.) could not be employed because the properties of Md^{253}, the alpha decay product of 103^{257}, are still unknown and could not be used as a means of assigning the 8.6 MeV alpha emitter to element 103. The association of the 8.6 MeV alpha activity with 103^{257} was based primarily on the nuclear reactions used to produce this emitter and the variation of its yield (excitation function) with the energy of the projectile boron ions.

The excitation functions were very broad and could not be used to determine the particular nuclear reactions which produced 103^{257}. Of course this is not surprising since the target contained many isotopes of californium and the beam had both B^{10} and B^{11} ions so that several possible reactions could lead to 103^{257}. However, the California group felt that the shape of the excitation curves were consistent with their assignment of the 8.6 MeV alpha activity to 103^{257}. They also felt that they effectively eliminated the possibility that mendelevium (element 101) isotopes were responsible for the 8.6 MeV alpha activity because they were unable

†Based on work performed under the auspices of the U.S. Atomic Energy Commission.

to produce this activity in bombardments of Am^{243} with C^{12} ions.

In 1965, a group of scientists from the Dubna Laboratory in the U.S.S.R.[2] reported the synthesis of 103^{256} using the nuclear reaction

$$Am^{243} + O^{18} \rightarrow 103^{256} + 5n$$

The identification of 103^{256} could be accomplished by an adaptation of the double recoil technique, since one of the products of the decay of 103^{256} could be identified. 103^{256} can decay by either the emission of an alpha particle or by capture of an orbital electron, followed by further decay to Fm^{252}, a known isotope:

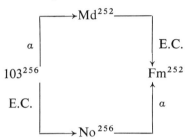

The Fm^{252} was identified by its nuclear radiations and by its elution characteristics from an ion exchange column. By varying the bombardment and recoil collection times a half-life of about 45 seconds was assigned to 103^{256}. Additional confirmation of the assignment was obtained from a study of the yield of Fm^{252} with O^{18} projectile energy. The excitation curve was reported to have a shape characteristic of an O^{18} projectile going into the Am^{243} nucleus and 5 neutrons evaporating from the resulting compound nucleus. Md^{252} was also prepared in a separate experiment by the reaction:

$$Am^{243} + O^{18} \rightarrow Md^{252} + He^4 + 5n$$

and was found to decay by electron capture with an 8-minute half-life. The longer half-life and the lower yield of recoils from the electron capture decay process makes it unlikely that Md^{252}, formed directly as a recoil product in the 103 experiments, was the source of the Fm^{252} recoils used to characterize the 103^{256}. The Soviet group reported a formation cross section for 103^{256} of 6×10^{-32} cm^2.

So far only the isotopes of lawrencium

reported to date are the two nuclides discussed above. A tabulation of their radioactive decay characterization and some methods of production is given on page 757 in the article on **Transuranium Elements.** Undoubtedly others will be made as research in this field continues. Both isotopes have too short a half-life to study chemically. Lawrencium should be the last member of the actinide series of elements. It has been shown experimentally to exhibit a stable $3+$ valence state in solution. In the event that longer lived isotopes are prepared, the same ion exchange techniques used in the case of elements 95-101 could be applied for the identification of the atomic number.

In a 1967 publication Flerov and associates at the Dubna Laboratory reported the inability to detect an alpha emitter with $E\alpha = 8.6$ MeV and a half-life of 8 sec which was assigned by the Berkeley group to 103^{257}. The latter assignment has now been changed for the 103 isotope to mass 258 or 259.

References

1. Ghiorso, A., Sikkeland, T., Larsh, A. E., and Latimer, R. M., "New Element, Lawrencium, Atomic Number 103," *Phys. Rev. Letters*, **6**, 473 (1961).
2. Donets, E. D., Shchegolev, V. A., and Ermakov, V. A., "A Synthesis of an isotope of Element 103 (Lawrencium) with Mass Number 256," Joint Institute for Nuclear Research, Dubna, U.S.S.R., P-2116, 1965.
3. Flerov, G. N., Korotkin, Yu. S., Mikheev, V. L., Miller, M. B., Polikanov, S. M., and Shchegolev, V. A., "Study of Alpha-Decay of 103^{256} and 103^{257}," Joint Institute for Nuclear Research, Dubna, U.S.S.R., E7-3257, 1967.

PAUL R. FIELDS

LEAD

Lead, symbol Pb from the Latin name *plumbum*, atomic number 82, atomic weight 207.19, is located in Group IVA of the Periodic Table. It is one of the most permanent of the metals.

Discovery and History

Lead was probably one of the first metals to be produced by man and is known to have been used prior to 3500 B.C. from discoveries made in Egypt. The oldest piece of lead in existence can be found in the British Museum and antedates 3800 B.C.

The manner in which prehistoric people extracted lead from its ores is largely unknown, but it can be supposed that primitive furnaces, consisting of small pits dug in the ground and enclosed by stones to form a shaft, were constructed and lead recovered from its oxide or sulfide ores by heating with wood or charcoal. Such furnaces dating back to 4000 B.C. have been discovered in Sinai, in which copper ores were smelted and similar installations of unknown date were used for lead-silver smelting at Bawdin, Burma and at Laurium, Greece.

Lead metal was also produced and used by the Chinese prior to 3000 B.C. and the Phoenicians worked deposits in Spain about 2000 B.C. In the Fifth Century B.C., the mines of Laurium were extensively exploited and in the Third Century B.C., the Romans operated the lead mines of Spain in the Rio Tinto district, which are still in operation today.

During the period 700 A.D. to 1000 A.D., the German lead-silver mines of the Rhine and the Hartz Mountains were opened and in 1200 A.D., further mines in Saxony, Silesia and Bohemia came into operation and were described in some detail by Georgius Agricola in "De Re Metallica" in 1556.

Lead smelting operations flourished in Great Britain in the Seventeenth Century, especially in Wales and in Derbyshire, England and from there spread to the colonies, as ore discoveries were made.

The United States is at present, the leading producer of lead in the world. During colonial times, some small mines were opened in the East, but the first significant discovery of lead ores was made in 1700 in the Mississippi Valley and worked on a relatively large scale in the early 1700's. The large Western deposits of Utah, Montana, Nevada, Colorado, New Mexico, Arizona and Idaho were all opened in the second half of the Nineteenth Century and about the same period, significant discoveries were made and smelting operations commenced in Canada, Africa, Australia, and Latin America.

Prevalence

Lead is not a particularly high constituent in the earth's crust and rates below such common metals as aluminum, iron, magnesium, titanium, manganese, nickel, vanadium, copper, uranium, tungsten, and zinc, but above other metals such as cobalt, molybdenum, arsenic, tin, antimony, cadmium, mercury, silver and gold.

As in the case with all metals, however, geological processes result in the concentration of metals in ore deposits, and it is from these deposits that the metals are extracted and recovered. The major known lead ore deposits at present being exploited, are as follows:

North America. The Tri-State deposits of Missouri, Arkansas and Oklahoma; Coeur d'Alenes, Idaho; Bingham, Tintic and Park City, Utah; Leadville, Colorado; Kimberley, British Columbia, Canada; and Santa Eulalia, San Francisco, Fresnillo and Sierra Mojada, Mexico.

South America. Cerro de Pasco, Peru; Altiplano, Bolivia; and Northern Argentina.

Australia. Broken Hill, New South Wales; and Mt. Isa, Queensland.

Africa. Broken Hill, Zambia; Tsumeb, South West Africa; and Morocco and Tunisia, North Africa.

Europe. Hartz and Silesia, Germany; Rio Tinto, Spain; Ronnskar, Sweden; Serbia, Yugoslavia; and Sardinia, Italy.

Regardless of the fact that lead is not overprevalent in the earth's crust (estimated at $2 \times 10^{-5}\%$), it is interesting to note that the metal can be produced relatively cheaply, because of the ease that it can be won from its ores.

Isotopes

Natural lead is composed of four isotopes: Pb^{208} (51.55%), Pb^{206} (26.26%), Pb^{207} (20.82%) and Pb^{204} (1.37%). Lead isotopes are the end products of each of the three series of naturally occurring radioactive elements, i.e., for the uranium series, Pb^{206}; for the thorium series, Pb^{208}; and for the actinium series, Pb^{207}. The determination of the atomic weight of lead from different radioactive sources contributed greatly to the development of knowledge about isotopes and of present atomic theory. (See **Isotopes**.)

Sources

Metallic lead has been known to occur in nature, but it is exceedingly rare. The principal ores of lead are the sulfide, galena (86.6% Pb); the sulfate, anglesite (68.3% Pb) and the carbonate, cerussite (77.5% Pb). Some other minor minerals are shown below:

Sulfide	— Galena, PbS
Sulfate	— Anglesite, $PbSO_4$
Carbonate	— Cerussite, $PbCO_3$
Oxide	— Minium, Pb_3O_4
Chlorocarbonate	— Phosgenite, $PbCO_3.PbCl_2$
Sulfatocarbonate	— Leadhillite, $PbSO_4.2PbCO_3.Pb(OH)_2$
Basic sulfates	— Plumbojarosite, $PbFe_6(OH)_{12}(SO_4)_4$
	— Linarite, $(Pb.Cu)SO_4$, $(Pb.Cu)(OH)_2$
Chlorophosphate	— Pyromorphite, $(PbCl)Pb_4(PO_4)_3$
Chloroarsenate	— Mimetite, $(PbCl)Pb_4(AsO_4)_3$
Chlororanadate	— Vanadinite, $(PbCl)Pb_4(VO_4)_3$
Chromate	— Crocoisite, $PbCrO_4$
Molybdate	— Wulfenite, $PbMoO_4$
Sulfantimonite	— Jamesonite, $2PbS.Sb_2S_3$
Sulfide of silver, lead and antimony	— Freieslebenite, $5(Pb,Ag_2)S.2Sb_2S_3$
Sulfotelluride of lead and gold	— Nagyagite, variable composition
Sulfide of copper, lead and antimony	— Bournanite, $3(Pb,Cu_2)S.Sb_2S_3$

Under conditions of ordinary atmospheric corrosion, the life of lead may be measured in centuries and even in sea water it has a serviceable life of generations. Thus, much of today's lead production may come from scrap, treated alone in secondary lead smelters and refineries, or treated together with new ores in primary lead smelters. In the United States alone, some 500,000 short tons of lead are produced annually from scrap, about the same as the amount of virgin lead produced. Additional lead is imported to meet consumption demands.

Derivation

As noted above, the chief ore of lead is galena, PbS, and is found in nature associated with other metal sulfides such as those of iron, zinc, silver, copper, bismuth, arsenic, antimony and tin.

The metallurgy and recovery of the metal is complex, not because the reduction of galena is difficult, but due to the separation of the other metals which are commonly associated with the lead sulfide. Some of these associated metals are valuable and it is, of course, economically desirable to separate them from the lead. Others must be removed because they would have adverse effects on the physical and chemical properties of the metal.

In modern practice, a considerable part of the associated metals are removed from the lead ore, together with gangue consituents, by a series of selective flotation processes, resulting in a relatively pure galena concentrate which may analyze up to 80% of Pb. In general, however, lead concentrates produced throughout the world will average 50% Pb and contain such impurities as iron, silica, zinc, arsenic and sulfur and valuable metals such as copper, tin, antimony, silver, gold and bismuth, according to the origin of the ore.

The most widely used method of treating the lead concentrate is by smelting in blast furnaces, after prior roasting for sulfur removal. In recent years, some smelting is carried out in electric furnaces, or in short rotary furnaces, especially if the concentrate is high grade. Various hydrometallurgical processes, among them the salt roast-brine leach method and chloride volatilization processes, have been investigated, especially in the field of oxidized or semioxidized complex ores, containing copper, bismuth and silver. However, it appears that the use of the blast furnace for treating lead ores and concentrates, will remain on the scene as the most important processing method for many years to come.

In smelting any type of lead ore or concentrate in the blast furnace, the sulfur must be largely removed prior to introduction in the furnace, to oxidize the lead, prevent the formation of undue quantities of matte and control the formation of sulfide crusts inside the furnace shaft. In addition, the impurities must be combined in a slag, fusible at 1100–1200°C.

The sulfur is eliminated in modern plants almost universally by sintering the lead ore or concentrate plus slag-forming reagents on continuous travelling-grate sinter machines. The sinter process serves a two-fold purpose, namely, to remove most of the sulfur present in the feed to form lead oxide, and to produce a material with suitable physical characteristics for smelting in the blast furnace.

The principal reactions involved in sintering are as follows:

$$2PbS + 3O_2 \rightarrow 2PbO + 2SO_2$$
$$2PbO + SiO_2 \rightarrow Pb_2SiO_4$$
$$PbS + 2PbO \rightarrow 3Pb + SO_2$$

Sinter is normally screened for the separation of fines on removal from the machines and then charged as coarse hard lumps together with lump coke to the blast furnace.

The blast furnace consists essentially of a rectangular refractory brick and water-jacketed shaft, mounted above a crucible and fitted with tuyeres along the lower sides, for the introduction of blast air. Suitable tapping arrangements are made at the crucible for the removal of molten lead and slag from the furnace. The modern tendency is to standardize on continuous removal of lead and slag in one operation.

The air introduced under blast through the tuyeres causes the coke in the charge to burn and thus provide heat for smelting, as well as for the formation of CO gas to reduce the lead oxide to metallic lead. The gangue material, consisting of silica, iron oxide and lime, combines with the zinc oxide and alumina, if present, to form slag, while the reduced lead acts as a collector for such valuable metals as copper, silver, gold, bismuth and antimony, as well as some arsenic. These metals are dissolved in the lead bullion which is withdrawn from the furnace at 900–1000°C. Some sulfur, usually less than 2%, is always left in the sinter and will combine with copper and arsenic during smelting, to form matte and speiss, respectively.

Normally, molten lead is tapped from the furnace crucible continuously, at a point below the slag line, and slag, matte and speiss which float on top of the lead inside the furnace, are tapped intermittently at a higher point into a refractory-lined settler car, where separation of the three products can be effected due to the difference in density of these materials. If continuous tapping of all materials is practiced, similar separations are made in the settler.

The principal reactions which take place in the blast furnace are as follows:

$$2PbO + C \rightarrow 2Pb + CO_2$$
$$PbO + CO \rightarrow Pb + CO_2$$

$$Pb_2SiO_4 + CaO + FeO \rightarrow$$
$$2PbO + CaO.FeO, SiO_2 \text{ (slag)}$$
$$CO_2 + C \rightarrow CO$$

The products of the blast furnace are therefore lead bullion, matte, speiss, slag, dust and gas.

The matte and speiss are generally sent for treatment to a copper smelter, for recovery of the contained values. The slag may be dumped as waste, but if it contains sufficient zinc, may be treated to recover zinc.

The dust and gas are passed through suitable gas cleaning plants, such as electrostatic separators or baghouses, and the dust recovered for retreatment.

The lead bullion, as mentioned above, may contain many other metals which are all removed in subsequent refining steps, effected either by pyrometallurgical methods, or by electrolysis.

The first step in refining of lead bullion is the removal of copper, which is achieved simply by cooling the bullion as it comes from the blast furnace to about 350°C, or close to its freezing point, at which temperature the copper compounds become insoluble and separate out as a dross, leaving a copper-lead eutectic containing only traces of copper. Elemental sulfur is often added to aid copper separation as the sulfide. The dross is treated for the recovery of its copper and lead content.

The resultant lead may contain as low as 0.002% Cu, but still contains the other metals listed above. It can be further refined directly by electrolysis by the Betts process, or by a continuing series of pyrometallurgical methods. In *electrolytic refining*, the electrolyte is a solution of lead fluosilicate; the anode is cast from the impure lead and the cathode consists of a thin sheet of pure lead. An electric current is caused to flow into the anode, through the solution and out at the cathode, where lead is deposited.

The impurities ordinarily associated with lead bullion all have lower solution potentials than lead and remain undissolved during electrolysis at the anode, forming a slime, which remains attached to the anode. The slime is removed after the electrorefining cycle is complete and treated for the recovery of its values.

In *pyrometallurgical refining*, the lead bullion after copper removal is next treated for the elimination of arsenic, antimony and tin. This may be achieved by two methods, known as "softening" and the "Harris" process.

In the softening process, molten lead bullion at about 750°C is blown with air by means of pipe lances and the metals alloyed with the lead are converted to their oxides together with some lead and slagged off. The operation is performed continuously. The resultant "softened" bullion will normally contain only 0.02% Sb and 0.0003% As.

In the Harris process, liquid lead bullion at a temperature just above its melting point is pumped through molten sodium hydrate. Arsenic, antimony and tin are thereby removed completely from the lead and may be recovered separately from the caustic mixture by leaching, etc. Both the above methods are used in actual practice for softening lead.

Continuing with pyrometallurgical refining, the next step is to remove silver and gold from the bullion, if present. Again, two processes, known as the Pattinson process and the Parkes process, are used.

The Pattinson process for desilverizing lead bullion has to a large extent been replaced in modern lead refineries by the Parkes process, but is still in operation in some plants. This method is based on the fact that when molten lead containing silver is cooled to its freezing point, crystals of lead containing less than 0.0015% Ag separate. The crystals are removed and more molten lead added to the vessel and the procedure repeated. Finally the molten bath contains up to 1.5% Ag and is cupelled to recover the silver, while the crystals are remelted for sale as refined lead.

In the Parkes process for removing silver and gold from lead bullion, molten zinc is used to extract the silver and gold from the lead bullion. The zinc alloy of silver and gold rises to the top of the lead bullion as a crust, which also contains considerable lead, and is distilled in retorts to produce zinc metal for reuse in the process and an enriched bullion for cupellation and recovery of the silver and gold. This process may be conducted continuously.

The bullion after desilverizing by the Parkes process normally contains only traces of gold and silver, but is saturated with zinc which is removed either by vacuum distillation or by treatment with gaseous chlorine. In the latter method zinc chloride is formed and recovered.

The last remaining metal to be separated from the lead bullion is bismuth, which remains unremoved by the foregoing refining processes, except when lead is refined electrolytically. Bismuth is removed by the Kroll-Betterton process which involves the use of calcium and magnesium. When introduced into the lead bullion they form the compounds Ca_3Bi_2 and Mg_3Bi_2 which are removed as a dross that is then treated for the production of refined bismuth.

Physical Properties

The important physical properties of lead are listed in Table 1.

The physical properties of lead are not conducive to a widespread use of the metal for structural purposes, due to its low tensile strength and the tendency for the metal to flow under very low loads. It is generally conceded that it is unwise to subject lead to a continuous load of more than 200 psi. However, the tendency for lead to flow even at room temperature makes it particularly easy to fabricate and very light mills are required for rolling lead sheet from large castings.

The ductility of the metal is shown by the ease with which it may be extruded under pressure through small die openings, exhibiting a high degree of fluid flow.

Since lead is very soft, the fatigue strength is naturally low. In construction, however, the metal is usually supported by other stiffer materials and its fatigue strength is seldom a limiting factor. When a higher fatigue strength is required, it is obtained by the use of alloying additions.

TABLE 1. PHYSICAL PROPERTIES OF LEAD

Symbol	Pb
Atomic number	82
Atomic weight	207.19
Isotope, natural lead	208 (51.55%), 206 (26.26%), 207 (20.82%), 204 (1.37%)
Density, 20°C	11.34 g/cc
400°C	10.51 g/cc
Melting point	327°C (621°F)
Boiling point	1737°C (3159°F)
Latent heat of fusion	5.89 cal/g
Latent heat of vaporization	204.6 cal/g
Mean specific heat, 15°C to m.p.	0.032 cal/g/°C
400–500°C	0.037 cal/g/°C
Vapor pressure, 987°C	1 mm
1167°C	10 mm
1417°C	100 mm
1508°C	200 mm
1611°C	400 mm
Thermal conductivity, 18°C	0.083 cal/cm²/sec/cm/°C
330°C	0.039 ,, ,, ,, ,, ,,
700°C	0.036 ,, ,, ,, ,, ,,
Viscosity, 441°C	2.116 centipoise
551°C	1.700 ,,
703°C	1.349 ,,
844°C	1.185 ,,
Surface tension, 350°C	442 dyne/cm
450°C	438 ,, ,,
Thermal expansion coefficient	29.1 × 10⁻⁶/°C
Electrical resistivity, 20°C	20.65 microhm-cm
327°C (l)	94.6 ,,
Electrochemical equivalent	3.865 g/amp-hr
Thermal neutron absorption cross section	0.17 barns
Crystal pattern	face-centered cubic
Brinell hardness number	4.2
Tensile strength	2000 psi
Elongation, % in 2 in.	64
Young's modulus in tension	2,560,000 psi
Color	bluish gray
Streak	gray
Fracture, cold	hackly
hot	columnar
Average pouring temperature	382°C (720°F)

Another property of lead which permits many unique operations at room temperature, is its ready weldability under very moderate pressures. Advantage is taken of this in many extrusion processes, most notable of which is the widely used method of extruding lead sheathing around an insulated copper cable.

The low melting point of lead permits ready utilization of the metal by extremely simple and inexpensive handling techniques, particularly as a principal component in the majority of the low-temperature fusible alloys.

Considering the low melting point, the boiling point of the metal is surprisingly high. This fact permits certain unique uses for lead, particularly as a collector for gold and silver in assaying at elevated temperatures and as a liquid heating bath in drawing, or tempering steel.

Lead is by far the densest common metal

and this has brought the metal into almost universal use for weighing and ballast purposes. It is also a favored metal for shielding x-ray equipment, because of its ability to absorb gamma rays and is widely used for this purpose.

Chemical Properties

Lead is divalent and tetravalent with an atomic weight of 207.19. Lead is amphoteric; in addition to forming plumbous and plumbic salts, it forms plumbites and plumbates in which the valence of lead is $+2$ and $+4$, respectively.

It tarnishes rapidly in moist atmosphere, although its surface undergoes no change in perfectly dry air, or in water which is free from air. When melted in contact with air, the metal oxidizes and at dull red heat is converted into lead oxide, PbO. If the heating is continued at 430°C, the PbO gradually changes to the red oxide, Pb_3O_4, which dissociates at 550°C to PbO and oxygen. Other oxides of lead are the sesquioxide, Pb_2O_3, and peroxide, PbO_2, which also decompose at 630°C to PbO and oxygen.

Lead combines directly with chlorine, fluorine and sulfur.

The best solvent for lead is nitric acid, the very dilute acid acting more rapidly than the strong. Dilute hydrochloric and sulfuric acid have little effect on lead, as coatings of $PbCl_2$ and $PbSO_4$ protect the surface from further action. The metal is only slightly attacked by strong concentrations of these acids up to 200°C, a fact which gives the metal wide use for tank and chamber linings in chemical plants, such as for the manufacture of sulfuric acid. Above 200°C, the action becomes stronger and at 260°C, lead is completely dissolved.

Acetic, citric, tartaric and other organic acids, act slowly on lead in the presence of moist air. It is also attacked by sulfur dioxide between 550 and 850°C and by hydrofluoric acid. The dissolution in hydrofluoric acid is quickly checked by the formation of PbF_2; hence the acid can be stored in lead vessels.

Principal Compounds

Lead oxide, PbO, is the oxide of greatest industrial importance and is produced in two forms—massicot and litharge. Massicot is an amorphous yellow powder produced by heating lead on flat hearths at a full red heat, continually removing the film of suboxide and oxidizing it to the yellow oxide at a low temperature avoiding fusion. Litharge is obtained on a commercial scale by cupelling refining lead and collecting the oxide as a skimming or fume.

Litharge is a strong base and quickly corrodes furnace linings forming the silicate with silica refractories and the chromate with chrome-based refractories. It is extensively used in industry in the glazing of ceramic ware and in the manufacture of certain types of glass.

Minium or red lead, Pb_3O_4, is prepared by heating a mixture of PbO_2 and PbO at about 250°C. A bright red powder is formed, which is used as a pigment in corrosion protecting paints, especially as a first coat applied to structural steel.

The lead peroxide, PbO_2, is a powerful oxidizing agent, detonating with phosphorus. It is used in the manufacture of matches and in lead-acid storage batteries. In batteries, the compound is repeatedly destroyed and reformed during the operations of discharging and recharging.

The lead oxides PbO and PbO_2 dissolve readily in dilute acids to form plumbous salts. Plumbates are also formed by reaction with concentrated alkali hydroxides and by fusion with alkali earths. Concentrated hydrochloric acid reacts with the dioxide to form lead chloride, $PbCl_2$. At low temperature, however, the tetrachloride, $PbCl_4$, is formed.

Lead sulfide, as previously explained, occurs in nature as the important lead ore, galena; in this form it is a heavy, cubically crystalline, silver-gray to black substance, with a metallic luster. The same compound may be prepared by precipitation with hydrogen sulfide from an acidic solution of a lead compound, or by direct combination of lead and sulfur at elevated temperatures. When prepared by these methods, the sulfide formed is black.

Lead sulfate likewise occurs in nature as the mineral anglesite and is formed during roasting of lead sulfide with air and by precipitating lead salts in solution with sulfuric acid.

When lead sulfide is roasted in an air blast, basic lead sulfate, $PbO.PbSO_4$, is formed, which is used as a white paint pigment under the name of "sublimed white lead." A much more important white paint pigment is the basic carbonate, $Pb(OH)_2.2PbOCO_3$, known as "white lead." It is prepared by a number of different processes, all of which involve the action of air, carbon dioxide and acetic acid. The lead is oxidized to basic lead acetate, which reacts with carbon dioxide and water to give the basic carbonate.

Another important lead pigment is lead chromate, $PbCrO_4$, which is marketed under the name of "chrome yellow." Lead chromate is only very slightly soluble in water, but dissolves readily in solutions of strong acids and alkalis.

The most important soluble lead salt is the nitrate, $Pb(NO_3)_2$, which may be obtained by the dissolution of metallic lead in nitric acid. Another soluble lead salt is the acetate, which crystallizes as $Pb(C_2H_3O_2)_2.3H_2O$. This substance is only very slightly dissociated in aqueous solutions; as a result of this fact, many slightly soluble lead salts dissolve readily in solutions containing the acetate ion, with the formation either of the undissociated lead acetate, or in the presence of an excess of the acetate ion, of such complexes as $Pb(C_2H_3O_2)_3$, or $Pb(C_2H_3O_2)_4$. Lead acetate, because of its extensive dissolving power for other lead compounds, is used in analytical work and both the soluble nitrate as well as the acetate are employed in gold cyanidation plants to precipitate soluble sulfides from solution and to decompose thioarsenite.

Among the more familiar lead salts of low solubility, in addition to the sulfate, chromate, sulfide and carbonate, are the halides. The halides may be precipitated from solutions containing lead ions by means of the corresponding hydrogen halide. The solubility of the lead halides decreases in the order $PbCl_2$, $PbBr_2$, PbI_2, PbF_2, the fluoride and iodide having nearly the same solubility.

The fluosilicate, $PbSiF_6$, is formed by the action of hydrofluosilicic acid on lead oxide. A solution containing about 8% $PbSiF_6$ and 11% free H_2SiF_6 is used as electrolyte in the electrolytic refining of lead bullion, according to the Betts process previously described.

Lead tetraethyl, $Pb(C_2H_5)_4$, is of considerable importance in industry, because of its use as an antiknock material in gasoline. It is prepared by the action of ethyl chloride, C_2H_5Cl, on a lead-sodium alloy at 40–60°C in an autoclave, according to the reaction:

$$4PbNa + 4C_2H_5Cl \rightarrow Pb(C_2H_5)_4 + 3Pb + 4NaCl.$$

Applications

Lead is one of the major metals in use in industry and is outflanked by only a few other metals such as iron, copper, zinc, and aluminium. World consumption is some 3 million tons annually, of which the United States' usage is about 1.25 million tons and that in the United Kingdom about 480,000 tons.

In the United States the distribution of applications (by %) is roughly that given in Table 2. For comparison similar figures are listed for usage in the United Kingdom.

TABLE 2. USES OF LEAD
(by %)

	United States	United Kingdom
Batteries (as metal)	18.8	10
Batteries (as oxide)	17.7	10
Tetraethyl lead	18.5	8.5
Other oxides, compounds	8	6
Cable covering	5	31
Lead ammunition, shot	5	1.4
Sheet and pipe	3.6	16
Solder	6	3.6
Other alloys (e.g., type metal)	6	5.5
Miscellaneous†	11.4	8.0

† In the United States—weights, ballast, foil, white lead.

In this country the most important use of lead is in lead storage batteries (36.5%) with tetraethyl lead the second largest application (18.5%). Also of interest, metallic lead, including alloys, accounts for some 55% of the total used and lead in compounds for about 45% of the consumption. By contrast, in the United Kingdom over 2/3 of the lead consumed is in the form of metal and alloys. Much of the difference between the two nation's use of metallic lead is due to

TABLE 3. LEAD SPECIFICATIONS BY TYPE

	Corroding Lead	Chemical Lead	Acid-Copper Lead	Common Desilvered Lead
Silver, max. %	.0015	.02	.002	.002
Silver, min. %	——	.002	——	——
Copper, max. %	.0015	.08	.08	.0025
Copper, min. %	——	.04	.04	——
Silver+copper, max. %	.0025	——	——	——
Arsenic+antimony+tin, max. %	.002	.002	.002	.005
Zinc, max. %	.001	.001	.001	.002
Iron, max. %	.002	.002	.002	.002
Bismuth, max. %	.05	.005	.025	.150
Lead (by difference), min. %	99.94	99.90	99.90	99.85

increased application in this country of plastics for lead in cable coverings and for piping and equipment linings for chemical plants.

The use of lead oxides and other compounds has been previously dealt with. Lead metal finds many uses in industry as can be seen in Table 2, and certain standard specifications have been set up by the American Society for Testing Materials under the code number ASTM-B29-55, to cover refined lead in pig form, made from ore or other material by processes of reduction and refining.

The chemical composition of the four types of lead covered are as given in Table 3.

Corroding lead is a designation which has been used for many years to describe high-purity refined lead. Chemical lead describes unsilverized lead produced from Southern Missouri ores. Acid-copper lead is made by adding copper to fully refined lead and common desilverized lead is used to describe fully refined desilverized lead.

Lead forms alloys with most of the non-ferrous metals and is the base of a large number of important industrial alloys. The principal lead-base alloys are: type metal, bearing or babbitt metal, shot, solder, casting metals, leaded brasses and fusible alloys.

From 0.1% to 0.2% arsenic is added to lead used for making shot, to increase the hardness and sphericity of the product. Antimony imparts the quality of hardness required for some types of ammunition and the property of expansion on solidification essential in type metals and casting alloys in general. The addition of antimony hardens the lead so that it resists mechanical injuries

and abrasion, to a greater extent than pure lead. The addition of small amounts of tin, especially to the lead-antimonial alloys, greatly improves the ease with which the alloys are cast. Bearing metals comprise the alloys of lead and antimony, or further alloyed with copper, tin, and zinc.

It has been found that as little as 0.02% calcium added to pure lead produces an age-hardening alloy, which over a period of weeks gradually strengthens until its tensile strength has doubled, or even tripled. The fatigue strength of the hardened alloy may be three to five times that of pure lead. Calcium-lead alloy has been used in the manufacture of certain types of telephone cable sheathing and is also employed in the manufacture of storage batteries used for stand-by purposes.

The physical properties of lead-antimony or lead-tin alloys used for cable sheathing have been improved by the addition of cadmium. These alloys are capable of precipitation hardening, where the hardening is easier to control than in the plain antimonial lead alloys.

Tellurium when added to lead or its alloys, even in amounts as small as 0.06%, produces an alloy which can be cold worked from an initial tensile strength of about 3,000 psi to as high as 5,000 psi and retain this cold worked strength for many years. Thus, tellurium-lead pipes can be frozen a greater number of times without bursting, owing to the tendency of the work-hardening to afford increased resistance to stress, etc. Tellurium-lead is also often used in tank linings to give less "creep" tendency.

365

Solder is a common alloy of lead and tin with a varying melting point according to the proportion of these and other constituents sometimes added for special purposes.

The addition of bismuth, cadmium or mercury to lead lowers the melting point below the boiling point of water and such alloys have many commercial uses, especially in the case of automatic fire sprinkler systems, etc.

Type metal used in the printing industry has a wide range of composition according to its use and will vary between 58 and 80% lead; 2 to 35% tin and 5 to 30% antimony and may contain nickel, copper and bismuth.

The addition of lead to brass produces an alloy which is soft and machines easily. It is sometimes added to steel and aluminum to also improve machinibility.

The most extensive single application of lead in casting alloys is in the manufacture of battery grids from an alloy containing 6% antimony and 94% lead.

Biological, Biochemical and Toxicological Characteristics

The compounds of lead are poisonous to animal and human life, practically in proportion to their solubility. The effect on plant life does not appear to be too serious, as witnessed by the previous use of lead arsenate as an insecticide for crop spraying. Plants will however, absorb lead and thereby cause poisoning of animal and man, if consumed. Thus, the use of lead compounds as insecticides has been practically eliminated in recent years, as well as the use of lead pigments in paints where human contact may be prevalent. The former have been replaced to a great extent by organic substances and the latter, by other harmless pigments.

Lead metal itself and the sulfide, are incapable of absorption as such into the system and are almost innocuous, while the soluble salts, chloride, nitrate, acetate, etc., are active irritant poisons. The oxide, sulfate and carbonate are less active, but continued exposure to fume or dust in the atmosphere is dangerous and will result in lead absorption, leading to plumbism or lead intoxication.

This condition is entirely curable and can be prevented by adequate ventilation of working places, the use of respirators, protective clothing and personal cleanliness. By reason of such measures and careful medical inspection, modern lead industries offer no greater hazards to the worker than do most other industrial fields.

By far the most important source of plumbism is inhalation of lead fume or dust, caused by melting or machining operations, when lead or its compounds are absorbed in the blood. The most common form of intoxication is that which affects the gastrointestinal tract and it is characterized by abdominal discomfort, culminating in severe pain or cramps. Associated with the pain, is a severe obstinate constipation, preceded sometimes by diarrhea, loss of appetite, nausea and vomiting. Workers frequently complain of a metallic or sweet taste in the mouth, general weakness, joint pains, dizziness and headache. Physical signs such as pallor, malnutrition and the so-called "lead-line" on the gums, can be clearly noted.

Most of these common cases of gastrointestinal plumbism require nothing more than withdrawal from exposure. Frequently the disturbance is so mild that the affected person may continue work if assigned to a job free from exposure to lead, which will become eliminated from the systems by natural means, after which the worker may be returned to his normal job. Severe cases require hospitalization for medical treatment.

Statistics show that there has been a progressive decline in the incidence of serious plumbism in all areas for more than fifty years, indicating that the more hazardous types of occupational lead exposure have been brought under control. This tremendous decrease has taken place despite the fact that the use of lead in industry has considerably increased in recent years.

Industry and government throughout the world are now turning their attention to relatively dilute pollution of the atmosphere and waterways, in an attempt to even further decrease the hazard to animal and man.

References

1. Liddell, Donald M., "Handbook of Nonferrous Metallurgy," 2nd Ed., New York, McGraw-Hill Book Co., Inc., 1945.
2. Hofman, H. O., "Metallurgy of Lead," New York, McGraw-Hill Book Co., Inc., 1918.

3. Read, H. A., "Rutley's Elements of Mineralogy," 23rd Ed., London, Thomas Murby and Co., 1944.
4. Mathewson, C. H., Editor, "Modern Uses of Nonferrous Metals," 2nd Ed., New York, American Institute of Mining and Metallurgical Engineers, 1953.
5. Newton, Joseph, "An Introduction to Metallurgy," 2nd Ed., New York, John Wiley and Sons, Inc., 1957.
6. "Year Book of the American Bureau of Metal Statistics–1965," New York, 1966.
7. Sisler, Harry H., Vander Werf, Calvin A., and Davidson, Arthur W., "General Chemistry—A Systematic Approach," 2nd Ed., New York, The Macmillan Co., 1965.
8. Johnstone, Rutherford T., M.D., "Clinical Inorganic Lead Intoxication," paper presented at the Symposium on Lead held at the Kettering Laboratory in the Department of Preventive Medicine and Industrial Hygiene, University of Cincinnati, 1963.
9. Hamlin, Lloyd E., M.D., "Medical and Hygiene Aspects of Plant Lead Control," and Wilentz, William C., M.D., "A Medical View of the Lead Problem," papers presented at the Hygiene Conference held in New York, 1948.
10. Hanley, J. W., "Lead Electrorefining and Electroplating," in "Encyclopedia of Electrochemistry," C. A. Hampel, Editor, pp. 764–771, New York, Reinhold Publishing Corp., 1964.
11. Rudling, Bengt, "Lead, Electrothermic Smelting," *ibid.*, pp. 771–774.

L. HARRIS

LITHIUM

Lithium, atomic number 3, atomic weight 6.939, is the lightest of the metallic elements and the first member of the alkali metals, Group IA of the Periodic Table. Its two isotopes, Li^6 and Li^7, have a natural abundance of 7.39% and 92.61%, respectively. The name lithium is derived from the Greek *lithos* (stone).

The element was discovered in 1817 by Arfvedsen in the mineral, petalite, a lithium aluminum silicate, but the metal was first isolated in 1855 by Bunsen and Matthiessen.

Occurrence

Lithium is found widely distributed in the earth's crust, calculated to be approximately 0.004%. By way of comparison, the amount of lead is 0.002% and that of tin, 0.0006%. The major lithium minerals of commercial interest are:

(1) Spodumene (spar): $Li_2O \cdot Al_2O_3 \cdot SiO_2$ (approx. 8% Li_2O)
(2) Lepidolite (mica): $R_3Al(SiO_2)_3$ (+F) (approx. 3–5% Li_2O)
(3) Amblygonite: $LiAlFPO_4$ (approx. 8–10% Li_2O)
(4) Petalite: $Li_2O \cdot Al_2O_3 \cdot SiO_2$ (approx. 2–4% Li_2O)
(5) Desert lake brines: Li_2NaPO_4 (approx. 22% Li_2O) (0.03% Li_2O in brine)
(6) Eucryptite: $Li_2O \cdot Al_2O_3 \cdot SiO_2$ (approx. 8% Li_2O)

Lithium minerals are usually found in pegmatite dikes whose depths vary from 200 to 500 feet; in some cases up to 1000 feet. The average content of these dikes is 1–1.5% Li_2O (12–15% spodumene).

For economical recovery low-grade ores must be beneficiated, generally by froth flotation, to 5–6% Li_2O. On limited quantity production, hand picking or "cobbing" usually suffices. Dependent on the amount of "slimes" produced, froth flotation should yield 75–95% of the lithium mined. Much of the mining can be open pit rather than underground operation.

Sources of lithium minerals (in order of importance) are: (1) North America (United States and Canada); (2) Africa (Congo), (Rhodesia); (3) South America (Brazil and Argentine); (4) Australia; and (5) Europe (Czechoslovakia, Spain, Russia, Finland).

Extraction of Lithium from Ores

Classically, sulfuric acid has been the prime reagent for chemically treating many ores, and the complex silicates are no exception. Digestion of spodumene concentrates with sulfuric acid at elevated temperature has been established for a long time. Preferably α-spodumene is heated to almost the fusion point to convert it to β-spodumene, rendering the lithium more readily soluble. The Ellestad-Leute process extracts the lithium as lithium sulfate by treating the β-spodumene with sulfuric acid. The lithium sulfate is then converted to lithium carbonate by reaction with sodium carbonate: $Li_2SO_4 + Na_2CO_3 \rightarrow Li_2CO_3 + Na_2SO_4$. Hader, Nielsen and Herre describe the process in detail, and also the methods of producing other lithium products from lithium carbonate.

By ultrafine grinding with autoclave treatment under moderate heat and pressure required by steam formation, very high recovery of lithium can be obtained by use of the Robinson process, U.S. Patent 2,983,576. This method also utilizes the "slimes" from froth flotation as well as the major concentrates.

Digestion with calcium hydroxide is used for lithium recovery as hydroxide. This has been applied to lepidolite as well as spodumene. Recoveries are lower than realized by the sulfuric acid method. Lithium hydroxide has limited solubility (approx. 10 g/100 g solution).

Ralston of the U.S. Bureau of Mines has shown the potential value of substituting spodumene for aluminum silicate in cement manufacture. This method is feasible only if commercial portland cement is produced simultaneously with large quantities of lithium compounds produced by volatilization from the cement kiln.

Digestion with sodium carbonate causes an exchange whereby lithium is liberated from the silicate complex.

High-intensity arc application can be used to break down the complex silicate, producing a finely-divided silica and material from which lithium and aluminum can be leached, preferably as sulfates.

Consumption and Prices

The demand for lithium products calculated as lithium carbonate in the United States rose from less than 400,000 pounds per year prior to World War I to a peak after World War II of over 25,000,000 pounds per year; it is currently about 10,000,000 pounds per year.

Lithium metal sells for $7.50/lb. Lithium salts and other compounds are much less in price on the basis of the contained lithium: lithium carbonate, 42–45¢/lb; lithium chloride, 82–85¢/lb; lithium fluoride, $1.56–1.61/lb; lithium hydrate monohydrate, 53–60¢/lb; lithium nitrate, $1.25–1.55/lb; lithium stearate, 50–55¢/lb; and lithium sulfate, $1.20–1.30/lb. The prices vary with the quantity ordered.

Production of Lithium Metal

Various methods have been proposed or tried to reduce lithium compounds to metal, but any results obtained have not compared favorably in purity of metal or cost of recovery with the classical method of electrolysis of the fused lithium chloride.

Lithium is produced by the electrolysis of fused lithium chloride in a lithium chloride-potassium chloride bath at 400 to 450C° held in a cell designed somewhat like the Dow magnesium cell or the Downs cell for sodium production so that the intermixing of the lithium metal and the chloride gas is prevented. The LiCl-KCl mixture is approximately the eutectic mixture (about 45 per cent LiCl) whose melting point is 352°C; the melting point of LiCl is 606°C. Compared with the use of fused LiCl alone, this mixture improves operational efficiency, decreases corrosion problems, minimizes deterioration of the graphite anodes, and permits continuous operation.

The raw material is lithium chloride of high purity, particularly with respect to water and sodium content, although water can be removed to a degree from the bath by a pre-electrolysis at low amperage. Since lithium chloride is very hygroscopic, the handling of it to deter water pick-up is a problem.

The physical properties of lithium and the LiCl-KCl eutectic mixture influence cell design. Lithium melts at 179°C and at 400°C has a density of 0.49 g/cc, a viscosity of 0.402 centipoises, a vapor pressure much less than 1 mm Hg, and a surface tension of about 400 dynes/cm. The eutectic mixture has a density of 1.65 g/cc at 450°C and a viscosity of 5 centipoises at 500°C. Lithium chloride has a decomposition potential of 3.684 v at 450°C calculated from thermodynamic data, and the formal electrode potential for Li^{+1} in eutectic LiCl-KCl at 450°C is -3.41 v measured against a Pt, Pt^{+2} reference electrode.

One type of cell used commercially is constructed of a covered steel pot suspended in a firebrick heating chamber, much like the magnesium cells. Gas or oil is used to heat the cell. Top entering graphite anodes dip into the fused salt bath, and the steel cathodes are so positioned that the lithium rising from them to the surface of the bath is prevented from approaching the chlorine gas rising from the anodes. Separate collecting means are used for withdrawal of the lithium and the chlorine. The molten lithium is carefully protected from contact with air, and is withdrawn from a collecting vessel and cast into moulds.

Another type of cell described by Motock is designed much like the Downs sodium cell. It is a covered, brick-lined cylindrical pot 26 in. diameter and 30 in. deep with a single bottom entering graphite anode 6 to 8 in. diameter centered vertically in the pot. A steel cylindrical cathode 9 to 12 in. inside diameter and 8 to 12 in. high surrounds part of the anode, and between them is a cylindrical diaphragm of perforated, 24-gage, 316 stainless steel sheet, which keeps the chlorine rising along the anode from mixing with the lithium rising along the inside of the cathode. A vertical hoodlike nickel chlorine collector is positioned over the top of the anode, and a steel collector placed over the cathode is used to hold and guide the molten lithium to a vertical takeoff line continuously into a stainless steel holding tank. Auxiliary electric heating elements in the bath maintain the temperature. While designed to operate at 1000 amperes, the cell can be operated up to 3500 amperes with no abnormal behavior.

The lithium cells hold only a few hundred pounds of bath, and the production rate from cells using 900 to 1000 amperes is in the range of 8 to 10 lb of lithium per day per cell.

Some typical operating data for commercial cells are given in Table 1.

TABLE 1. LITHIUM CELLS—OPERATING DATA

(from Landolt and Sittig)

Current, amp	850–900
Temperature, °C	400–420
Voltage	8–9
Anode c.d., amp/in.^{2}	9.0
Cathode c.d., amp/in.^{2}	13.0
Current efficiency, %	85–90
Unit energy, kwh/lb	18.2
Chemical consumption, LiCl/lb Li	7.3
Chemical efficiency, %	83.7
Cell capacity, lb/24 hrs	220
Chlorine production, lbs/lb Li	5

Lithium metal thus produced will contain certain impurities, principally sodium to the extent of 0.4 to 0.7% Na. Practically all of the sodium present in the lithium chloride is deposited with and remains in the lithium metal produced. By subjecting molten lithium to an elevated temperature under vacuum (less than 100μ), the sodium is vaporized, leaving the lithium nearly sodium-free (less than 0.001 to 0.005% Na).

Typical analyses of lithium metal produced in cells are given in Table 2.

TABLE 2. LITHIUM METAL PRODUCED BY ELECTROLYSIS

(Maywood Chemical Co.)

Constituent	Regular Grade	Low Sodium
Na	0.710%	0.020%
Si	0.004	0.015
Al	0.002	0.03
	0.001	
Fe	0.001	0.06
Ca	0.001	0.06
Cu	0.001	—
Mg	0.0003	—
K	0.020	—
N_2	—	0.03
Cl	—	0.003
Heavy metals	—	0.09
O_2	Not reported	Not reported
Li	99.260	99.750

Lithium Corporation of America and Foote Mineral Company also produce a substantial quantity of lithium metal.

Physical Properties

Lithium is a silvery white metal whose hardness is 0.6 on the Mohs scale. The lightest of the nongaseous elements, 0.534 g/cc, it has the highest melting point and boiling point and the largest liquid range among the alkali metals. The high specific heat, high thermal conductivity and low viscosity of lithium also make it an attractive metal for many purposes, such as heat transfer applications. Its heat of fusion and heat of vaporization are very high, exceeded among the metals only by those of beryllium.

Lithium is a soft metal that can be cut with a knife, although it is harder than the other alkali metals, and it can be extruded, drawn and rolled with considerable ease.

TABLE 3. PHYSICAL PROPERTIES OF LITHIUM

Atomic number	3	Thermal conductivity,	
Atomic weight	6.939	cal/sec/cm/cm²/°C	
Atomic radius, Å	1.56	0°C	0.17
Isotope abundance, %		216°C	0.109
Li⁶	7.39	539°C	0.073
Li⁷	92.61	Viscosity, centipoise	
Melting point, °C	179	183.4°C	0.5918
Boiling point, °C	1317	193.2°C	0.5749
Density, g/cc,		200°C	0.562
20°C	0.534	208.1°C	0.5541
200°C	0.507	250.8°C	0.4917
400°C	0.490	285.5°C	0.4548
600°C	0.474	400°C	0.402
800°C	0.457	600°C	0.317
1000°C	0.441	Ionization potential, volts	5.363
Heat of fusion, cal/g, 170°C	103.2	Electron work function, eV	2.49
Heat of vaporization,		Electrical resistivity, microhm-cm,	
cal/g, 1317°C	4680	0°C	8.55
Vapor pressure, mm Hg		100°C	12.7
745°C	1	230°C	45.25
890°C	10	Surface tension,	
1077°C	91	dynes/cm, 200–500°C	app. 400
1084°C	100	Volume change in fusion,	
1156°C	200	% solid volume	1.5
1236°C	400	Coefficient of linear thermal	
Heat capacity, cal/g/°C		expansion @ 20°C, per °C	56×10^{-6}
0°C	0.784	Thermal neutron absorption cross	
50°C	0.844	section, barns/atom	
100°C	0.900	Natural mixture	71 ± 1
186°C	1.01	Li⁶	945
300°C	1.02	Li⁷	0.033
800°C	0.99	Crystallography, Å	
Enthalphy, cal/g, 25°C	203 ± 0.7	α (BBC) 20°C a₀	3.502
Entropy, cal/mole, 0°C	6.70 ± 0.06	β (FCC) −196°C a₀	4.41

The physical properties of lithium are listed in Table 3.

Chemical Properties

Like the other alkali metals, lithium is a very reactive element. However, many of its chemical properties and those of its compounds are more like those of the alkaline earth metals than those of the alkali metals. It is the least reactive of the alkali metals.

Lithium can be melted and poured in dry air without losing its luster and it does not react with dry oxygen below 100°C. Near the melting point it may ignite in air and burn with an intense white flame to form chiefly Li_2O.

Unlike the other alkali metals which are inert to nitrogen, lithium reacts exothermically with nitrogen in the presence of moisture at ordinary temperature. Nitrogen reacts rapidly with molten lithium to form the black nitride, Li_3N, which melts at 275°C. The nitride can be remelted in a vacuum or in a nitrogen atmosphere. It reacts with water to form ammonia, as do the nitrides of the alkaline earth metals. In contrast, the nitrides of sodium and potassium are difficult to form and nitrides of rubidium and cesium are unknown. Complex nitrides of lithium and iron are readily formed. Lithium is soluble in liquid ammonia, slowly forming the amide, $LiNH_2$.

Lithium and hydrogen combine easily at elevated temperatures, forming a stable salt-like compound, LiH, whose melting point is 688°C. It can be fused and electrolyzed comparable to a halogen salt. The electrical conductivity is relatively good at 640°C. The vapor pressure of lithium hydride does not exceed 70 mm Hg. In electrolysis of lithium hydride hydrogen is set free at the anode.

One kilogram of lithium combines with approximately 1600 liters of hydrogen to form lithium hydride. By reaction with water: $2LiH + H_2O \rightarrow Li_2O + 2H_2$, one kilogram of lithium hydride produces nearly 2800 liters of hydrogen (nearly 45 cubic feet per pound of lithium hydride).

Lithium forms complex hydrides, such as lithium borohydride, $LiBH_4$, and lithium aluminum hydride, $LiAlH_4$, which are useful reducing agents and sources of hydrogen.

Lithium hydride is essential to the formation of certain high-energy compounds, diborane, $(BH_3)_2$ and the penta- and deca-boranes. These in turn may be alkylized to produce the final high-energy fuels.

Lithium amide, $LiNH_2$, is made by the action of ammonia on lithium hydride: $LiH + NH_3 \rightarrow LiNH_2 + H_2$. It is an intermediate in the manufacture of pharmaceuticals such as the antihistamines, because of its stability advantages over sodium amide.

Lithium reacts with water to liberate hydrogen and form LiOH, but the reaction is slow in cold water, perhaps due to the low solubility and adherence of lithium hydroxide on the metal surface.

Lithium combines directly and vigorously with the halogens and it reacts rather violently with inorganic acids, liberating hydrogen. At high temperature it reacts with carbon to form an acetylide which yields acetylene when treated with water. Molten lithium at high temperature reacts with all known molecular gases and with phosphorus, arsenic, antimony, silicon, sulfur and selenium.

Lithium is of increasing interest in the field of organic reactions. Several characteristics of the free metal and its compounds indicate that lithium is superior to sodium both in reaction versatility and selectivity. Of particular interest and value in organic chemistry are:

(1) Lithium alkyls and aryls produced from lithium metal.
(2) Lithium hydride produced from lithium metal.
(3) Lithium metal in place of magnesium in Grignard reactions.
(4) Lithium metal in condensation reactions.
(5) Lithium metal in acetylation reactions (vitamin A synthesis, rubber synthesis).
(6) Lithium amide, $LiNH_2$, produced from lithium metal in amination reactions.
(7) Lithium aluminum hydride, $LiAlH_4$, produced from lithium hydride. It is an ether-soluble hydride, and a powerful reducing agent at low temperature.
(8) Lithium alkyls in stereoscopic polymerization of isoprene to cis-polyisoprene.

Principal Compounds and Their Uses

Lithium forms compounds analogous in composition to those of sodium and potassium, but whose properties in many cases are similar to those of the corresponding alkaline earth elements. For example, LiOH, Li_2CO_3, Li_3PO_4 and LiF have relatively low solubility in water; LiCl is very hygroscopic and forms a hydrate like $CaCl_2$ but unlike NaCl; and the heats of formation of Li_2O, LiH, Li_2S and LiF are much higher than those of the sodium compounds, approaching those of the calcium compounds. In all of its compounds lithium is monovalent.

The low molecular weight of lithium compounds due to the low atomic weight of lithium makes them attractive when high weight ratios of the anion are desired, as in the case of the hydride, hydroxide and hypochlorite. Lithium hydroxide is thus of interest as a CO_2-absorber in submarines and space vehicles.

When a lithium salt is placed in a nonluminous flame an intense carmine color is observed; this makes possible the spectroscopic detection of minute traces of the element.

Two lithium oxides are known. Li_2O is a stable compound that reacts with water to form LiOH; with CO_2 to form Li_2CO_3; and with many refractory oxides and silicates to form ceramic systems whose freezing points are often depressed several hundred degrees by small amounts of Li_2O. Lithium carbonate, however, is usually the reagent used to prepare Li_2O-containing refractory systems. One lithium peroxide, Li_2O_2, is known and it is usually made by addition of H_2O_2 to lithium

371

hydroxide. This peroxide is much more stable than sodium peroxide.

Lithium hydroxide, LiOH, m.p. 445°C, is made by the action of water on lithium metal, by addition of Li_2O to water or by the reaction of $Ca(OH)_2$ with Li_2CO_3. It is much less soluble in water than are NaOH and KOH. In some alkaline storage batteries it is mixed with KOH as the electrolyte.

Lithium carbonate, Li_2CO_3, is probably the most common lithium compound and other lithium compounds can be prepared from it. This sparingly soluble compound is derived in quantity from the industrial process by which the lithium in spodumene is extracted. Lithium carbonate melts at 735°C and decomposes into Li_2O and CO_2 at approx. 1200°C. It is used in the preparation of ceramic glazes and special grades of glass.

The lithium halides can be made by the reaction on lithium carbonate or hydroxide of the corresponding hydrohalide acids as well as by the more expensive direct combination of lithium and the halogen. Lithium fluoride, LiF, m.p. 840°C, has the highest heat of formation of all the alkali metal halides and is one of the most stable compounds known. It is used in enamels and in welding and soldering fluxes. Lithium chloride, LiCl, m.p. 614°C, and lithium bromide, LiBr, m.p. 552°C, have unique thermodynamic properties, greatly depressing the vapor pressure over their solutions, making them of particular interest in air conditioning and as drying agents. Lithium chloride is quite soluble in alcohols, permitting it to be separated from other alkali chlorides which are not soluble in alcohols.

Lithium soaps, such as lithium stearate, are made by the saponification of fatty acids with LiOH and are used in many types of lubricating greases.

Electrochemistry of Lithium

The electrochemical behavior of lithium is quite remarkable. In aqueous solution the single potential of Li/Li^+ is -3.02 volts — ($H_2/H^+ = 0.00$ volts) as compared with sodium -2.71 volts, potassium -2.92, rubidium -2.92, and cesium -2.923. Lithium therefore appears more electronegative than the other alkali metals; however, this is not the case, as evidenced by the hydration of the alkali ions. The lithium ion combines with more H_2O molecules than, for example, cesium. The mobility of the small lithium ion is approximately half of that of the cesium ion.

The lithium ion in the fused state is less complex, particularly in molten halides. Lithium fluoride appears to have a higher conductivity than any other halogen salt.

Lithium Alloys

Lithium forms alloys with many other metallic elements and is the only one of its group to alloy or combine with silicon. The degree of knowledge about alloy systems of lithium is summarized in Table 4. Lithium forms many

TABLE 4. LITHIUM ALLOY SYSTEMS

Phase Diagrams Established	Some data on Systems	Probable Insolubility	No data available
Aluminum	Antimony	Chromium	Barium
Cadmium	Beryllium	Indium	Columbium
Calcium	Boron	Iron	Germanium
Copper	Cesium	Molybdenum	Hafnium
Indium	Gallium	Osmium	Manganese
Lead	Gold	Palladium	Strontium
Magnesium	Nickel	Platinum	Tantalium
Mercury	Rhenium	Rhodium	Thonium
Potassium	Rubidium	Ruthenium	Titanium
Silver	Selenium	Tungsten	Vanadium
Sodium	Silicon	Uranium	Zirconium
Thallium	Tellurium		
Tin			
Zinc			

intermetallic compounds with Mg, Al, Zn, Cd, Hg, Tl, Pb, Bi, Ag and Sn whose properties are described by Landolt and Sittig, who also present phase diagrams for several alloy systems. These intermetallic compounds are usually hard and brittle and often with high melting points. Lithium in amounts approaching trace quantities has a marked effect on the base metal so treated, lithium acting as a "hardener."

Magnesium alloys containing up to 8–12% Li (sodium free) were first produced during World War II. These alloys had tensile strengths approaching mild steel but poor temperature characteristics, losing strength rapidly above 150°C. The alloy crystal is a cubic-centered body as compared with the hexagonal structure of magnesium.

Aluminum alloys containing very small amounts of lithium, and with zinc substituted for copper, were first produced during World War I and known as "scleron" alloys.

Lead alloys were also produced during World War I, being used for heavy-duty bearings in place of "babbitts" and containing less than 0.05% lithium plus calcium. These alloys were known as B-Metal, and used in railroad bearings in Germany.

Forms of Lithium Metal

Lithium is available in several forms so devised and packaged as to prevent deterioration of the metal by reaction with air, etc. Cartridges containing definite weights of $\frac{1}{2}$ in. or larger rods of the metal encased in sealed thin sheaths of copper, aluminum or other suitable metal are used for making additions of lithium to molten metals for alloying or purification purposes. Lithium wire and ribbon is wound on a reel and shipped in an airtight container under dry kerosene. Molten lithium can be formed into shot by agitation under hot dry paraffin oil. Wire, ribbon and shot are used in organic syntheses.

Uses of Lithium Metal

While lithium is metallic, it is not a structural metal, owing to its limited thermal properties and its reactivity. Lithium is of interest because of its unique physical and chemical properties and as a chemical reagent.

In addition to its use in alloys and organic reactions mentioned previously, lithium is used as a degasifier and refining agent for molten metals. It combines with oxygen, sulfur, nitrogen and perhaps hydrogen in such metals and the lithium compounds resulting from its addition to molten metals have relatively low densities and low melting points. This is of importance in removing solid impurities from the metal.

Lithium metal is regularly used in the degasification of copper, particularly for high-conductivity castings, and of bronzes. The amounts applied are only a few hundredths of a per cent of lithium. It also acts as an agent for grain refinement in certain bronzes, and it greatly increases the fluidity of molten metal.

Over a period of years various efforts have been made to utilize the properties of lithium, as are those of magnesium, in the improvement of cast irons. It was found that the physical properties of cast iron are somewhat enhanced by adding minor amounts of lithium. In the development of nodular iron considerable evidence has been accumulated to show that additions of lithium to the iron facilitate the production of a nodular structure. The evidence further shows that smaller additions of lithium than of magnesium are required to obtain these properties.

Considerable work has been done over many years in treating molten steel with lithium and lithium alloys. By adding minor amounts of lithium to low-carbon steels some improvement in tensile strength without loss of elongation was evidenced, but to this date no method has been evolved satisfactorily to introduce lithium into steel. The difficulty arises from the fact that the molten steel temperature is appreciably above the boiling point of the lithium, which vaporizes violently.

Lithium in Atomic Energy Developments. Lithium metal, Li^7, was the first element fussioned to produce alpha particles (Rutherford *et al*) under the input of highly accelerated protons.

A significant nuclear reaction with lithium has been noted in the past few years for the production of tritium, H^3, through neutron irradiation:

$$_3Li^6 + O^{n1} \rightarrow {}_2He^4 + {}_1H^3$$

The isotope lithium-7 may also be used for control rods in fast reactions, in view of the fact that the absorption product, $_2$He, will not contaminate the pile. The lithium could be molten and would have to be encased in thin beryllium tubing. Nuclear power generation from light elements such as lithium may become an important possibility.

The isotopes lithium-6 and lithium-7 can be separated by electrochemical methods. Two techniques can be used: (1) electrolysis of lithium chloride solution in a mercury cathode cell in which the lithium amalgam formed at the cathode gradually becomes enriched in its lithium-6 content; and (2) electromigration in which molten lithium chloride in a U-tube is subjected to an electric current which results in the gradual enrichment of lithium-6 at the cathode, and a gradual enrichment of lithium-7 at the anode. Gallone describes the theory and practice of the electrochemical separation of lithium isotopes.

Molten Lithium. Molten lithium has certain advantages for heat exchanger application: high specific heat, large liquid range, low vapor pressure, low viscosity, low density.

Its disadvantages are its corrosive action on metal surfaces, and its content of isotope Li^6 which produces an adverse reaction with neutrons.

More detailed information is available in the "Liquid Metals Handbook," which also gives data on corrosion by liquid lithium and precautions about handling the metal.

Biological, Biochemical and Toxicological Aspects

Lithium is claimed to be somewhat more toxic than the other alkali metals, but its effects are minor and do not present an important health hazard. Lithium compounds resemble those of potassium in systemic and local action. Large doses of lithium compounds should be avoided, as they cause prostration and dizziness when ingested.

While lithium chloride has been recommended and used as a substitute for sodium chloride in "salt-free" diets, cases have been observed in which the ingestion of LiCl has resulted in dizziness, visual disturbance, tremors and mental confusion. The discontinuance of the use of lithium chloride has caused these symptoms to disappear, indicating that lithium is not a cumulative toxic agent. The use of LiCl in "salt-free" diets has

been largely discontinued since the adverse effects became apparent.

Lithium is not considered an essential element in plant growth, and there are no indications that it plays any part in animal biology. The adverse effects mentioned above probably arise in part from the disturbance caused by lithium in the sodium-potassium-calcium balance in living cells. Toxic levels have been observed in the citrus areas of Southern California where local well water was used in newly developed desert areas. The symptoms were noted on leaves containing more than 12 ppm of lithium on a dry basis.

References

Gallone, P., "Isotopes—Electrochemical Separation," in "Encyclopedia of Electrochemistry," C. A. Hampel, Editor, pp. 747–750, New York, Reinhold Publishing Corp., 1964.

Hader, R. N., Nielsen, R. L., and Herre, M. G., "Lithium and Its Compounds," in "Modern Chemical Processes," Vol. II, pp. 86–96 (American Chemical Society), New York, Reinhold Publishing Corp., 1951.

Landolt, P. E., and Sittig, M., "Lithium," chapter in "Rare Metals Handbook," C. A. Hampel, Editor, 2nd Ed., pp. 239–270, New York, Reinhold Publishing Corp., 1961.

Lyon, R. N., Editor, "Liquid Metals Handbook," NAVEXOS P-733 (Rev.), 2nd Ed., Washington, D.C., U. S. Atomic Energy Commission and Department of the Navy, June 1952.

Motock, G. T., *Electrochem. Tech.*, **1**, 122–127 (1963).

Robinson, G. P. (to Basic Atomics, Inc.) "Recovery of Lithium from Ore," U.S. Patent 2,983,576, May 9, 1961.

PERCY E. LANDOLT AND
CLIFFORD A. HAMPEL

LUTETIUM

Lutetium is a metallic element with atomic number 71 and atomic weight 174.97. It is the final member of the lanthanide rare earth series and the last naturally occurring rare earth of this series to be discovered. In the condensed Periodic Table, elements with atomic numbers 58 through 71 all possess properties which seem to place them in the same space as that occupied by element 57, lanthanum. (See **Lanthanide Elements.**) This anomaly was one of the important clues which helped scientists arrive at our present understanding concerning the structure of the atoms. As the charge on the nucleus increases with atomic number, the charge is balanced by an extra electron being added to the electron cloud which surrounds the nucleus. According to the Bohr-Stoner scheme for understanding the elements of the Periodic Table, the electron cloud about the nucleus is built up of shells of electrons with total quantum number $n = 1, 2, 3, 4 \cdots$. Shells with lowest n fill first. Each of the shells is subdivided into subshells with quantum number l, related to the angular momentum of the electrons. For any n, the subshell $l = 0$ fills first. In spectroscopic nomenclature the letters s, p, d, f, correspond to l values 0, 1, 2, 3. High n-value subshells with low l values, may be more stable than n-1 subshells with high l values. The l quantum numbers of any n shell can take only values from 0 to n-1 and the Pauli exclusion principle states that any subshell is filled when it contains $2(2l + 1)$ eleetrons. The $5s^2\ 5p^6$ subshells have lower energy than the $4f^x$ subshell; however, the radial distribution of the former lie well outside that of the $4f$ subshell, so the $4f$ electrons are well shielded from neighboring atoms and do not take any substantial part in the valency forces of the rare earth atoms or ions.

At element 58, cerium, the $4f$ subshell starts filling and, since $l = 3$, there are 14 elements which belong to the true rare earth series. With lutetium, element 71, the $4f$ subshell is filled so the electronic structure for the trivalent ion of this element when it is present in solid compounds or in solution is $1s^2, 2s^2, 2p^6, 3s^2, 3p^6, 3d^{10}, 4s^2, 4p^6, 4d^{10}, 4f^{14}, 5s^2, 5p^6$. Lutetium has three valence electrons which occur in the $5d, 6s^2$ subshells in the gaseous hot metal vapor, but when the valency forces are active, the valency electrons spend most of their time on the adjacent negative ions in compounds or solutions, or in the conduction electron bands of molten or solid metal.

At the present time, instead of trying to crowd these 14 elements into a space in the third column, sixth row, of the chart along with lanthanum, most authorities prefer to make a second sixth row which they place at the bottom of the chart. Similarly, where the

$5f$ shells start filling in to give the actinide rare earth series, elements starting with number 90 are also listed as a second seventh row below the lanthanide rare earths.

As the charge on the nucleus increases with atomic number, all the completed shells are pulled in closer to the nucleus so the radii of the rare earth ions or atoms get slightly smaller across the series. Lutetium, with its completed $4f$ subshell, has the smallest radius of the rare earth atoms or ions. This effect is known as the lanthanide contraction.

The soluble rare earth salts ionize into trivalent rare earth ions in aqueous solutions. The high charge on these ions exert strong electric fields on the water dipoles. Therefore, each ion is surrounded by a sheaf of oriented water molecules which are held very strongly and, as a result, stabilize the ionic form of the rare earth atoms. Reactions in aqueous solutions usually involve these encased trivalent ions and this makes the properties of the rare earths in such media very much alike. Reactions and properties vary only slightly from one rare earth to the next. Since their ions are very nearly the same size, precipitates from aqueous solution tend to form mixed crystals or solid solutions of one rare earth compound in another. Reactions carried out in such media only give a very slight enrichment of one rare earth over its nearest neighbor and reactions have to be carried out a great many times before a reasonable purity of a given rare earth compound can be obtained. It was not unusual before 1940 to perform 20 to 40 thousand fractionations in order to obtain in pure form a few grams of the heavy rare earth salts.

Isotopes

The two naturally occurring isotopes of lutetium are $Lu^{175}(97.41\%)$ which is stable and $Lu^{176}(2.59\%)$ which is radioactive with a half-life of 2.2×10^{10} years. This radioactive isotope can be used to determine the age of meteorites relative to the age of the earth. In addition to the naturally occurring isotopes, four radioactive isotopes have been prepared and studied.

History

The earliest members of the rare earth series to be discovered were yttria in 1794 and ceria in 1804. These elements were isolated in the form of their oxides and it was soon realized these oxides were complex in that they contained considerable amounts of other unknown elements closely resembling them. During the 19th century, modern high-temperature techniques and equipment had not yet been developed nor had the theories which explain the building up of the Periodic Table been conceived. Therefore, during this period, most of the work on the rare earths was carried out in aqueous solutions by laborious fractionation processes. No one had any idea how many rare earths there should be and the spectra by which they were identified were not well understood. As a result, during the century, the discoveries of a great many new rare earth elements were announced. Invariably these new elemental compounds would be resolved into further components and frequently, due to the uncertainty in correlating the spectra with specific elements, many of them could not be confirmed. Nevertheless, by 1912, at least 13 of the rare earth series had been fairly well established.

Lutecium (now called lutetium) was first isolated in the form of a fairly pure oxide in 1907 by G. Urbain, who separated the so-called elemental compound, ytterbia of J. Marignac, into two oxide fractions which he named lutecia and neoytterbia. The latter is now called ytterbia. About the same time, A. von Welsbach also performed the same separation and named the new elements cassiopeium and aldebaranium. Until a few years ago, lutecium was referred to in German literature as cassiopeium. Also, during this same period, C. James of New Hampshire isolated lutecia, but he was the last of the three to make his findings public. The name lutecium was derived from Lutetia, the ancient Latin name of Urbain's native city, Paris. The spelling of the element was changed from lutecium to lutetium on the recommendation of the 15th Conference of the International Union of Chemistry in September, 1949. Shortly thereafter, most countries adopted this name and spelling for element 71.

Lutetium is one of the rarest of the naturally occurring rare earths, although it is estimated to be present in the earth's crust in the ratio of eight parts in ten million. It is, therefore, more abundant than Hg, I, Cd, or the noble metals; however, it has been found only in very low concentrations in the earth's crust and then always mixed with much greater quantities of other rare earths. The main reason it remained hidden so long was probably its low concentration, the great difficulty in separating it from the other rare earths, and the fact that it does not have any absorption bands in its spectra either in the visible or near ultraviolet. Even in Marignac's ytterbia, it was present in low concentrations. The metallic element was not prepared until many years later.

During the late 1940's and early 1950's, separation methods were developed at the Ames Laboratory of the Atomic Energy Commission which carried out fractionation processes automatically. These methods utilized the synthetic ion exchange resins and took advantage of the tendency of the rare earth ions to form chelate complexes. The chelates are organic molecules which also encase the rare earth ion, thereby replacing some of the water dipoles and lead to higher enrichment factors between adjacent rare earth ions for each chemical operation. The Laboratory tested these methods on a pilot plant scale to produce hundreds of pounds of the pure rare earth compounds of 99.99% purity with regards to adjacent rare earths. At the same time, the Laboratory developed methods for producing the highly pure metals. These processes were made available to industry and a number of companies are now selling rare earth compounds or metal up to ton quantities if requested. Since lutetium is one of the least abundant of the rare earths and the demand for it is not yet large, it is the most expensive of the rare earth series. Current quotations for small amounts of the oxide are now in the neighborhood of $10.00 per gram, but it could be considerably less than this if a large market for lutetium developed.

Occurrence

While lutetium is widely distributed throughout the earth's crust in extremely minute concentrations, it also exists in low concentrations in many rare earth minerals such as xenotime, gadolinite, samarskite, fergusonite and euxenite. In most of these it constitutes from 0.05 to 1.0%. Much of the present-day lutetium oxide is obtained commercially from monazite where the concentration of lutetium varies around 0.003%. Monazite is worked extensively by industry as a source of cerium, mischmetal and thorium, so lutetium, as well as the other heavy rare earths, can be recovered as a by-product of the large scale operations. Major deposits of monazite are found in India, Brazil, Africa, Australia and in the states of Idaho, Florida and the Carolinas in North America.

Lutetium Metal Preparation

The preparation of the metal in massive quantities is usually accomplished by the reduction of anhydrous $LuCl_3$ or LuF_3 by an alkali or alkaline earth metal. Since metallic lutetium resembles closely metallic erbium and holmium, except that it melts at a slightly higher temperature and is essentially non-

magnetic, the details of producing, purifying and fabricating it are almost identical with those described under **Holmium**.

Physical Properties

Lutetium is soft and ductile with a bright metallic luster. Due to its high cost, it has not been used much industrially as yet, although it is of considerable interest to basic research scientists for the same reasons as described under **Erbium**. Average properties (January, 1967) of lutetium metal are listed in Table 1.

Magnetic and Electrical Properties

Although most other rare earths have unpaired $4f$ electrons and are, therefore, strongly paramagnetic and order at low temperatures, lutetium does not become strongly magnetic. Lutetium does, however, exhibit a slight paramagnetism due to its conduction electrons. A plot of the electrical resistivity versus temperature of lutetium is well behaved without the anomalies of other rare earth metals noted at low temperatures. Lutetium has a lower room-temperature resistivity than the other rare earths, but it is still quite high (59 microhm-cm) compared with copper (1.67 microhm-cm). Its alloying behavior is similar to that of erbium or holmium.

Chemical Properties

The valency of lutetium in aqueous media or in the crystalline solid state is $+3$ and in the metal there are three electrons in the conduction bands. The tripositive ion has a radius of about 0.848Å, gives colorless solutions and forms white salts. Since the $4f$ subshell is complete, lutetium does not exhibit sharp absorption bands in the photographic region of the spectra. Lutetium forms a water-insoluble fluoride, hydroxide, carbonate, oxalate and phosphate. The chloride, bromide, iodide, nitrate, sulfate and acetate are soluble and crystallize to form hydrated salts. The physical properties of the sesquioxide and anhydrous halides of lutetium are given in Table 2. The oxides and anhydrous halides can be prepared in the same manner as described under **Holmium**.

TABLE 1. PHYSICAL PROPERTIES OF LUTETIUM METAL

Melting point	$1675°C \pm 10°C$
Vapor pressure, 1675°C	0.013 mm
Boiling point	3315°C
$\triangle H°_{298}$ sublimation, kcal/mole	102.16
Density	9.84 g/cc
Crystal structure	Hexagonal close-packed
Lattice constants	$a = 3.505$
	$c = 5.553$
Atomic volume	17.79 cc/mole
Metallic radius, Coordination #12	1.735Å
Cp, 25°C	6.37 cal/mole/ deg
Coefficient of thermal expansion	$12.5 \times 10^{-6}/°C$ (400°C)
Grüneisen constant, γ	1.15
Compressibility	2.3×10^{-6} cm²/kg
Hardness, Vickers Diamond Pyramid	77 kg/mm²
Electrical resistivity, 4°K	5 microhm-cm
77°K	16 microhm-cm
298°K	59 microhm-cm
Coefficient of resistivity, 298°K	0.19
Thermal neutron cross section, barns	108

TABLE 2. SOME PROPERTIES OF ANHYDROUS LUTETIUM HALIDES AND THE OXIDE

Properties	Lu_2O_3	LuF_3	$LuCl_3$	$LuBr_3$	LuI_3
Melting point, °C	$\sim(2490)$	1182	890	960	1045
Boiling point, °C		(1430)†	1480	(1410)	(1210)
$\triangle H_F$, kcal/mole	(−453)	(−392)		(−200)	−133.2
		(1)			
Structure		Orthorhombic	Monoclinic		Hexagonal
		a = 6.181			a = 7.395
Lattice constants, Å	10.391	b = 6.731			c = 20.71
		c = 4.446			
Density, g/cc	9.43	8.44			3.38
$\triangle H$ fusion, kcal/mole		8		10	11
$\triangle H$ vaporization, kcal/mole	(215)	60		42	38

(1) Hexagonal above 940°C.
† Figures in parentheses are estimates (R. E. Thoma, 1965, ORNL 3804)

Toxicity

The toxicity of various lutetium salts has been studied. When inhaled, taken orally, or injected into the blood stream in massive amounts, lutetium salts can cause serious damage. However, the conclusion of the investigators is to classify the rare earths as having a low toxicity rating. Since their effect in low concentrations on humans over long periods of time has not been determined, these materials should be handled with reasonable care.

References

1. Mellor, J. W., "Treatise on Inorganic and Theoretical Chemistry," Vol. 5, pp. 480–709, New York, Longmans, Green and Company, 1946. (Early work.)
2. Weeks, Mary Elvira, "Discovery of the Elements," Easton, Pensylvania, Mack Printing Company, 1945.
3. Yost, Don N., Russell, H., and Garner, C. S., "The Rare-Earth Elements and Their Compounds," New York, John Wiley & Sons, Inc., 1947.
4. Spedding, F. H., and Daane, A. H., Editors, "The Rare Earths," New York and London, John Wiley & Sons Inc., 1961.
5. Gschneidner, Karl A., Jr., "Rare Earth Alloys," Princeton, N.J., D. Van Nostrand Company, Inc., 1961.
6. Eyring, LeRoy, Editor, "Progress in the Science and Technology of the Rare Earths," Vol. 1, New York, Pergamon Press, 1964.
7. Trombe, F., Loriers, J., Gaume-Mahn, Mme. F., and La Blanchetais, Mlle. Henry, "Elements des Terres Rares (Ou Lanthanides) Scandium, Yttrium," Vol. I, Vol. II, Paris, Masson et Cie, 1960.
8. Topp, N. E., "Chemistry of the Rare-Earth Elements," New York, Elsevier Publishing Company, 1965.
9. Moeller, Therald, "The Chemistry of the Lanthanides," New York, Reinhold Publishing Company, 1963.
10. "Rare Earths", *Chem. Eng. News*, May 10, 1965 (special report on uses).
11. Haley, T. J., "Pharmacology and Toxicology of the Rare Earth Elements," *J. Pharm. Sci.*, **54**, 5 (1965).

F. H. SPEDDING AND B. J. BEAUDRY

M

MAGNESIUM

Magnesium, symbol Mg, atomic number 12, atomic weight 24.312, is located in Group IIA of the Periodic Table below beryllium and above calcium, strontium, barium and radium. The metal is silvery white in color and its crystalline structure is close-packed hexagonal. Natural magnesium is comprised of three isotopes: Mg^{24} (78.8%), Mg^{25} (10.1%) and Mg^{26} (11.1%). Because of its low density, 1.74 g/cc (0.0628 lb/cu in.), plus the fact that appreciable mechanical property improvement results in alloying with other metals, magnesium has often been referred to as the world's lightest structural metal.

History

Sir Humphry Davy is generally credited with the discovery of magnesium in the year 1808. He did not actually isolate the magnesium in metallic form but did announce that he had determined magnesia was the oxide of a new metal. Davy produced magnesium by chemical and electrochemical methods. His chemical process consisted of passing potassium vapors over magnesia heated to red heat and then using mercury to extract the magnesium. His electrochemical method consisted of electrolyzing magnesium sulfate using metallic mercury as the cathode. Both methods yielded magnesium as an amalgam and not as the pure metal.

It was 20 years later in 1828 that the French scientist, A. Bussy, obtained magnesium in metallic form by fusing magnesium chloride with metallic potassium and became the first to actually isolate the metal. In 1833 Michael Faraday, who was a protege of Davy, electrolyzed magnesium chloride and obtained metallic magnesium. Faraday thus laid the foundation for today's most widely used method of producing primary magnesium. Robert Bunsen in 1852 developed an electrolytic cell very similar in principle to those currently used for the production of magnesium.

An early, and perhaps the first, commercial production of magnesium took place in France when Deville, Caron, and Sonstadt employed a modification of the process developed by Bussy. They substituted sodium for potassium to reduce magnesium chloride, followed by distillation in a hydrogen atmosphere to produce pure magnesium metal. Their process was used commercially in France, England, and was introduced into the United States in the early 1860's. The manufacturer in this country was the American Magnesium Company of Boston which continued to produce magnesium largely for use in photography until 1889. Commercial production of magnesium commenced in Germany about 1886 using a modification of the Bunsen electrolytic cell. The electrolytic process was soon recognized as being superior to the reduction of anhydrous magnesium chloride by metallic sodium and the consequent lower price put the American Magnesium Company out of business. Germany remained the sole source for magnesium used in the United States until 1915 when the British blockade of Germany at the beginning of World War I shut off this source. Three magnesium producers started in the United States in the year 1915, which marks the birth of the magnesium industry in this country.

Occurrence

Magnesium is very abundant in nature but is always found in combined form as a compound. Elemental magnesium constitutes

2.5% of the earth's crust, making it the eighth most abundant chemical element and the sixth most abundant metallic element. It is the third most plentiful structural metal, being exceeded only by aluminum and iron. The fact that magnesium occurs in sea water —comprising 0.13%—makes the metal readily obtainable from a plentiful source. Each cubic mile of seawater contains six million tons of magnesium. Since it has been estimated that there are approximately 331 million cubic miles of seawater on the face of the earth, it is obvious that the world need never fear a shortage of this metal.

In addition to its presence in sea water magnesium occurs in such abundant minerals as magnesite, $MgCO_3$; dolomite, $CaCO_3 \cdot MgCO_3$; and many common silicates, among them asbestos, $H_4Mg_3Si_2O_9$; talc, $Mg_3(Si_4O_{10})(OH)_2$; and olivine, $(Mg,Fe)_2 SiO_4$. It also occurs as brucite $Mg(OH)_2$; carnallite, $KCl \cdot MgCl_2 \cdot 6H_2O$; and kieserite, $MgSO_4 \cdot H_2O$. Many natural underground brines contain magnesium, mainly in the form of magnesium chloride.

Derivation

There are two basic processes in use throughout the world today for the production of magnesium. One method is the electrolysis of molten magnesium chloride and the other is a thermal reduction of magnesium oxide using ferrosilicon. The electrolytic process accounts for well over half of the world's production of magnesium. The Dow Chemical Company at Freeport, Texas, received worldwide recognition in 1941 when it began operation of a process for producing magnesium from seawater. In this method, which is shown in the diagrammatic flow sheet of Fig. 1, sea water is treated with lime produced by roasting oyster shells dredged from the bottom of the Gulf of Mexico. The calcium in the lime releases magnesium from its chloride yielding magnesium hydroxide and calcium chloride according to the equation:

$$MgCl_2 + Ca(OH)_2 \rightarrow Mg(OH)_2 + CaCl_2$$

The insoluble magnesium hydroxide is filtered off and the filtrate, which contains calcium chloride in solution, is returned to the sea. The magnesium hydroxide is then treated with hydrochloric acid produced from natural gas, which is also readily available along the coast of Texas, and chlorine. The resulting magnesium chloride solution is evaporated to the hexahydrate, $MgCl_2 \cdot 6H_2O$. This compound is then further dehydrated in the

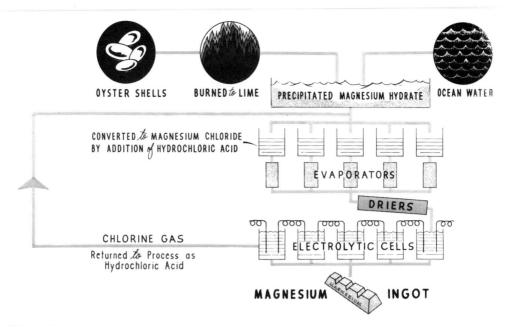

FIG. 1. Flow sheet of seawater process for the production of magnesium by the electrolytic method (*Courtesy The Dow Chemical Co.*).

dryers to a water content of 1.5 H_2O. In this partially dried state, the magnesium chloride is now ready for electrolysis. The electrolytic cells are equipped with graphite electrodes which serve as anodes, and a steel pot functions as the cathode and contains the molten $MgCl_2$. During electrolysis, molten magnesium and chlorine gas are produced. The magnesium rises to the top of the magnesium chloride cell bath where it is trapped by inverted troughs which lead it to metal storage wells from which it is removed to be cast into ingots or pigs. The chlorine gas is burned with natural gas and steam to produce hydrochloric acid which is returned to the process.

The ferrosilicon process is frequently referred to as the Pidgeon process since the method in current use in the United States and Canada was perfected in 1941 by L. M. Pidgeon who at the time was Director of Research for Dominion Magnesium Limited of Haley, Ontario. The process, which is illustrated in Fig. 2, begins with crushed ferrosilicon which is mixed with powdered, calcined dolomite. The mixture is briquetted and placed in steel retorts under vacuum somewhat below 0.2 mm of mercury. The

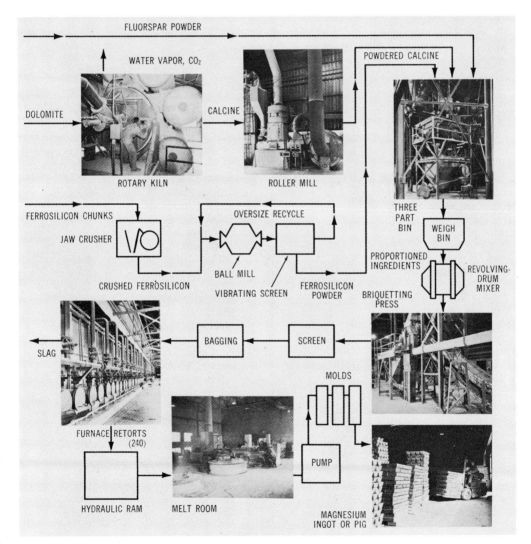

FIG. 2. Illustrated flow sheet shows how magnesium is recovered from dolomite by the ferrosilicon process *(Courtesy of Calumet & Hecla, Inc., Alamet Div.).*

batch is then heated to a temperature somewhat in excess of 1200°F and held for several hours. The silicon reacts with the magnesium oxide in the dolomite according to the equation:

$$2MgO \cdot CaO + Si(Fe) \rightarrow$$
$$2Mg + (CaO)_2 \cdot SiO_2(Fe)$$

In practice there is a secondary reaction between the CaO and SiO_2 as follows:

$$2CaO + SiO_2 \rightarrow Ca_2SiO_4$$

The iron does not at any time enter into the reaction but like the calcium orthosilicate, remains as a residue. The magnesium, re- duced from its oxide, comes off as a vapor which condenses into crystals at the cool end of the iron retort. These magnesium crystals are then melted and cast into ingots.

Primary magnesium production in the United States was 79,000 tons in 1966. Information from the Mineral Resources Division, Canadian Department of Mines and Technical Surveys discloses that production of magnesium in the United States, Norway and the USSR is by electrolytic reduction. The remaining countries use the ferrosilicon reduction method. A small proportion of the production in the United States is also by the ferrosilicon process.

TABLE 1.   PHYSICAL PROPERTIES OF MAGNESIUM

Symbol	Mg	Thermal expansion coefficient, cm/cm/°C	
Atomic number	12		
Atomic weight	24.312	20–100°C	0.0000261
Atomic volume, cc/g-atom	14.0	20–200°C	0.0000271
Crystal structure	close-packed hexagonal	20–300°C	0.0000280
		20–400°C	0.0000290
Lattice parameters		20–500°C	0.0000299
$a_0 = 3.203$ Å, $c_0 = 5.199$ Å, axial ratio, $c/a = 1.624$		Thermal conductivity, cal/cm/sq cm/sec/°C, 20°C	0.37
Electron arrangement in free atoms	2,8,2	Thermal diffusivity, sq cm/sec, 20°C	0.87
Density, g/cc,		Electrical resistivity, microhm-cm,	
20°C	1.74	20°C	4.46
650°C (solid)	1.64	300°C	9.5
650°C (liquid)	1.57	600°C	17.0
700°C	1.54	650°C (liquid)	28.0
Volume contraction, 650°C		900°C	28.0
liquid to 650°C solid, %	4.2	Temperature coefficient,	
Linear contraction, 650°C		microhm-cm/°C, 20°C	0.017
solid to 70°C solid, %	1.8	Electrical conductivity, 20°C	
Melting point, °C	650	mass % annealed copper	
Boiling point, °C	1110 ± 10	(standard)	198.0
Critical temperature		volume % annealed copper	
(calculated), °C	1867	(standard)	38.6
Flame temperature		Surface tension, dyne/cm,	
(theoretical), °C	4850	681°C	563
Latent heat of fusion, cal/g	88	894°C	502
Latent heat of vaporization,		Vapor pressure, mm Hg,	
cal/g	1260	702°C	10
Latent heat of sublimation,		909°C	100
cal/g	1460	967°C	200
Heat of combustion, cal/g	5980	1034°C	400
Specific heat, cal/g/°C,		1110°C	760
20°C	0.245	Modulus of elasticity, lb/sq in.	6.5×10^6
300°C	0.275	Modulus of rigidity, lb/sq in.	2.42×10^6
650°C (solid)	0.325	Poisson's ratio	0.35
650°C (liquid)	0.316		

TABLE 1—*continued*

Thermodynamic Data				
Magnesium reference state: Solid from 298 to 923°K				
Liquid from 923 to 1390°K				
Ideal monatomic gas from 1390 to 3000°K				

T, Temperature, °K	C_P°, Heat capacity, cal/deg/gfw	$H_T^\circ - H_{298}^\circ$, Heat content, cal/gfw	S_T°, Entropy, cal/deg/gfw	$-(F^\circ - H_{298}^\circ)/T$, Free energy function, cal/deg/gfw
298	5.96	0	7.81	7.81
300	5.97	10	7.85	7.82
400	6.24	620	9.60	8.05
500	6.48	1256	11.02	8.51
600	6.76	1920	12.23	9.03
700	7.08	2610	13.29	9.57
800	7.42	3330	14.26	10.10
900	7.81	4095	15.15	10.60
1000	7.88	7010	18.29	11.28
1100	8.14	7810	19.06	11.96
1200	8.40	8640	19.78	12.58
1300	8.66	9490	20.46	13.16
1400	4.97	41074	43.19	13.86

$\triangle H_m(923°K) = 2{,}140$ cal/gfw
$\triangle H_v(1390°K) = 30{,}750$ cal/gfw

Heat of reaction (2900°K, 1 atm)

	Btu/lb metal	Btu/lb O_2
Magnesium	8,180	12,430

Nuclear		
Isotope concentrations in natural magnesium	%	Mass
Mg^{24}	78.8	23.9924
Mg^{25}	10.1	24.9938
Mg^{26}	11.1	25.9898
$Mg^{Natural}$	100.0	24.312

Thermal neutron absorption cross section, barns, 0.069

Physical Properties

Magnesium is the lightest of the metals that can be used for structural purposes. Its density of 1.74 g/cc is 65% that of aluminum (2.7) and 22% that of iron (7.87). The thermal and electrical conductivities of magnesium are close to those of aluminum and the melting points are almost identical, 650 and 660°, respectively. Values of physical properties are given in Table 1.

Chemical Properties

Magnesium possesses good resistance to many dry and liquid chemicals and substances used in everyday living. Generally speaking, the chemical behavior of magnesium can be considered opposite that of aluminum which is attacked by alkalies but is resistant to many acids. Magnesium on the other hand is resistant to attack by most alkaline substances but reacts with most acids. In the case of magnesium, however, there are notable exceptions. For example, magnesium displays excellent stability in the presence of chromic and hydrofluoric acids.

Although magnesium burns rapidly in air when heated, especially when in powder or ribbon form, it is not attacked by the air at ordinary temperatures. Likewise, while it will react with steam at elevated temperatures, it is very unreactive with water, partly due to formation of a thin protective film on the surface.

When heated, magnesium is a powerful

reducing agent and is used to produce many metals from their compounds, chiefly the halides, by the reaction: $Mg + MX_n \rightarrow M + (n-2)MgX_2$, where X is a halide, M such metals as Ti, Zr, and Hf, and n is a whole number. Magnesium unites directly with many other elements, such as chlorine, iodine, bromine, fluorine, boron, silicon, sulfur, nitrogen, phosphorus and other non-metallic elements, the rate of the reaction depending on the temperature.

Magnesium is resistant to dilute alkali solutions and even to 50% NaOH at temperatures as high as 140°F. The rate of attack increases rapidly at higher temperatures.

The reaction between magnesium and salt solutions is varied. There is little or no attack by alkali metal and alkaline earth metal chromates, fluorides and nitrates; but solutions of chlorides, bromides, iodides, and sulfates of these metals usually corrode magnesium. Because of magnesium's high position in the electromotive series of metals (the electrode potential is -2.363 volts), practically all heavy metal salt solutions are likely to cause corrosion. The magnesium displaces heavy metals from the solution, usually leaving a loose deposit of the metal on the magnesium surface which provides areas for galvanic corrosion in the presence of moisture.

Magnesium can be used in contact with many organic compounds including hydrocarbons, ketones, esters, ethers, glycols, phenols, amines, aldehydes, oils of various types, and most alcohols. Methyl alcohol is one exception, however, since it does react chemically with magnesium.

Magnesium reacts with a great variety of organic halides in ethereal solution to form the well-known Grignard reagents, whose general formula is RMgX, where R signifies a carbon-linked organic radical, and X a halogen other than fluorine.

Magnesium Compounds

Magnesium forms only divalent compounds of a variety equal to those of sodium and calcium. Its compounds are very stable with high heats of formation. For this reason magnesium oxide with a melting point of about 2800°C is widely prepared and used as a refractory for electric and other furnaces operating at very high temperatures.

Magnesium oxide is made by calcining the carbonate or the hydroxide in large tonnage operations. Two forms are produced, one is a light fluffy material prepared by a relatively low-temperature dehydration of the hydroxide, and the other a dense material made by high-temperature furnacing of the oxide after it has been formed from the carbonate or hydroxide. The latter is the principal refractory type used for lining steel and other types of furnaces. Much of the magnesia is now made from sea water via the hydroxide by the process described previously.

Magnesium carbonate, also called magnesite, is mined as a natural mineral or is made by the carbonation with CO_2 of MgO or $Mg(OH)_2$. It is used as a refractory and as an insulating material. A basic carbonate, such as $MgCO_3 \cdot Mg(OH)_2 \cdot 3H_2O$ or $3MgCO_3 \cdot Mg(OH)_2 \cdot 3H_2O$, made by precipitation from a magnesium salt solution, is used widely as pipe insulation after being formed into the desired shapes.

Magnesium chloride, found in nature in sea water and salt springs and in deposits of chloride salts, is very soluble and highly deliquescent. When heated the hydrate, $MgCl_2 \cdot 6H_2O$, hydrolyzes to form MgO and HCl; thus, the anhydrous salt is difficult to make other than by heating the hydrate under an atmosphere of HCl or by the high-temperature reaction: $MgO + C + Cl_2 \rightarrow MgCl_2 + CO$. It is also obtained as the by-product of the reduction of metal chlorides with magnesium, e.g., $TiCl_4 + 2Mg \rightarrow Ti + 2MgCl_2$. In addition to being the source of metallic magnesium, magnesium chloride is used as a flocculating agent, catalyst, and as a dressing for cotton and woolen goods. Basic magnesium chloride, an indefinite compound formed when $MgCl_2$ plus MgO or $Mg(OH)_2$ plus water are mixed together, is used as a cement under the name Sorel cement or oxychloride cement.

Magnesium sulfate, $MgSO_4$, occurs naturally in salt deposits and in mineral waters. The hydrate, $MgSO_4 \cdot 7H_2O$, is known as Epsom salts. In addition to being used medically as a purgative, it is used industrially in paints and soaps, in tanning and dyeing, and as a filler in cotton fabrics. It is added to fertilizers in those areas where there is a magnesium deficiency in the soil.

Alloys

Most magnesium is consumed in the form of alloys in which the magnesium content usually is 90% or more.

Magnesium alloys comprise several alloy systems. In most cases the quantity of alloying ingredients is relatively small. Such elements, however, greatly improve strength of primary magnesium at room temperature, and in the case of certain selected alloying elements, good properties are obtained at moderately elevated temperatures as well. Alloys of magnesium can be further strengthened by precipitation hardening and cold working. Because of the hexagonal crystal structure of magnesium, twining can occur readily in wrought products under compressive loading and therefore control and retention of fine-grain structure becomes an important factor. The typical magnesium alloy systems in use today are listed in Table 2 along with the nominal chemical compositions, the forms in which the alloys are commonly supplied, and an indication of the outstanding characteristics of the alloys.

The basic systems include the Mg-Al-Zn series of alloys which have been established for a long time and are still considered the work horses of the industry. This group of alloys is supplied in all common forms. The Mg-rare earth-Zn-Zr and the Mg-Th-Zr and Mg-Th-Mn alloy systems are used where property retention at elevated temperatures is important. Such alloys have found extensive use in aircraft, missiles, and space vehicles. For superior strength in the form of castings, a Mg-Ag-didymium-Zr alloy has been found desirable. For above average strengths in extrusions and forgings, a Mg-Zn-Zr alloy has been developed.

Mechanical strength, which is the criterion used to select alloys and tempers for structural applications, is shown in Table 3.

Fabrication

The fabrication of magnesium alloys into useful shapes is accomplished by substantially the same methods used on other metals and includes casting, rolling, extruding and forging. Sheet, plate and extrusions are then further fabricated in the usual manner by forming, joining and machining operations.

Sand and Permanent Mold Casting. The earliest method of fabrication used for magnesium alloys was sand casting. This still remains a very common method of fabricating

TABLE 2. COMPOSITION, FORMS AND CHARACTERISTICS OF TYPICAL MAGNESIUM ALLOYS

Alloy	Chemical Composition	Forms Available	Characteristics
AZ31B	3%Al, 1%Zn	Sheet and plate, extrusions, forgings	Moderate strength; good formability, dent resistance, and good weldability.
AZ91B	9%Al, 0.6%Zn	Die castings	Good strength, ductility, and castability.
AZ91C	8.7%Al, 0.7%Zn	Sand and permanent-mold castings	Good castability; strength, pressure tightness and weldability.
EZ33A	3% rare earths, 2.7%Zn, 0.7%Zr	Sand and permanent-mold castings	Good tensile and creep strengths; good weldability; excellent pressure tightness & damping capacity.
HK31A	2%Th, 0.7%Zr	Sand and permanent-mold castings, sheet and plate	Good short-time elevated-temperature properties; good formability; excellent weldability.
HM21A	2%Th, 0.6%Mn	Sheets and plate, forgings	Exceptionally stable at elevated temperatures; better creep strength than HK31A; good formability; excellent weldability.
QE22A	2.5%Ag, 2%Didymium, 0.7%Zr	Sand and permanent-mold castings, forgings	Superior tensile-yield strength plus excellent creep resistance and fatigue strength up to approx. 500F.
ZK60A	5.7%Zn, 0.5%Zr	Extrusions, forgings	High strength; good toughness; limited arc weldability; good spot weldability.

TABLE 3. MECHANICAL PROPERTIES OF MAGNESIUM ALLOYS†

Alloy	Temper‡	Forms Available	Tensile Strength, 10³ psi		Tensile Yield Strength, 10³ psi		Elongation in 2 in, %		Compressive Yield Strength, 10³psi		Typical Shear Strength, 10³ psi	Typical Bearing Strength, 10³ psi		Hardness, Brinell
			Typ	Min	Typ	Min	Typ	Min	Typ	Min		Ult	Yield	
AZ91C	–T4	Sand and	40	34	12	11	14	7	12	—	17	60	44	53
AZ91C	–T6	permanent-	40	34	19	16	5	3	19	—	20	75	52	66
EZ33A	–T5	mold cas-	23	20	15	14	3	2	15	—	22	57	40	50
HK31A	–T6	tings	32	27	15	13	8	4	15	—	22	61	40	55
QE22A	–T6		40	35	30	25	4	2	30	—	—	—	—	78
AZ91B	–F	Die castings	33	—	22	—	3	—	22	—	20	—	—	67
AZ31B	–F	Extruded bars, rods, shapes	38	35	29	22	15	7	14	12	19	56	33	49
ZK60A	–T5		53	45	44	36	11	4	36	30	26	79	59	82
AZ31B	–F	Extruded tube	36	32	24	16	16	8	12	10	—	—	—	46
ZK60A	–T5		50	46	40	38	11	4	30	26	—	—	—	82
AZ31B	–H24	Sheet and plate	42	39	32	29	15	6	26	24	29	77	47	73
AZ31B	–0		37	32	22	18	21	12	16	12	26	66	37	56
HK31A	–H24		38	34	30	26	9	4	23	20	26	67	41	57
HM21A	–T8		35	33	23	18	11	6	19	15	19	63	37	56
AZ31B	–F	Forgings	38	—	28	—	9	—	12	—	19	70	36	55
HM21A	–T5		34	—	22	—	9	—	16	—	18	36	23	50
QE22A	–T6		43	—	34	—	7	—	26	—	—	—	—	—
ZK60A	–T6		47	43	39	32	11	4	25	—	—	—	—	—

† Properties determined at room temperature.
‡ Temper: –F, as fabricated; –H24, strain hardened, then partially annealed; –O, fully annealed; –T4, solution heat treated; –T5, artificially aged; –T6, solution heat treated, then artificially aged; –T8, solution heat treated, cold worked, then artificially aged.

the metal. Green sand molds are used along with sand addition agents to prevent excessive reaction with oxygen of the air and moisture in the sand.

Permanent mold casting also is used as a means of producing magnesium parts.

Die Casting. Die casting is used extensively to produce magnesium parts. The low heat content per unit volume of the metal and its lack of tendency to solder to the die make high casting speeds possible. The cold chamber process is employed almost exclusively on magnesium. In its simplest form die casting consists of melting the alloy in a separate melting pot from which the metal can be hand ladled into the shot well of the die casting machine. A plunger drives the metal into the chamber of the die at pressures of 4000 psi or higher to produce the die casting.

Extrusion. The extrusion process usually begins with an ingot made by the direct chill (DC) casting process. The DC process yields a continuous ingot which can be automatically sawed to the desired length. The extrusion process produces bars, rods, structural shapes, tubes, as well as special solid and hollow shapes to a user's own design. Ingots are machined (scalped) to remove the casting skin and preheated to 600–850°F depending on the alloy. In the next step the ingot is placed in the container of the extrusion press and a hydraulically actuated ram pushes the ingot through a die.

Rolling. The rolling of magnesium into sheet and plate, like the extrusion process, usually begins with a cast ingot designed for the purpose. Rolling of magnesium alloy sheet requires several separate operations. The "break-down" rolling is first. The slab is heated to 800–900°F and reduced in thickness by repeated passes through the rolls of a hot mill. Following break-down, the sheet, after reheating, can be semifinished on the same mill to as thin as 0.051″. From here the sheet is transferred to a finishing mill and rolled to the desired thickness and temper.

Forging. Magnesium forgings usually are made by the press forging process in closed dies. The size of magnesium forgings seems to be limited only by the size of available equipment.

Forming. Forming operations on magnesium sheet or extrusions can be done by practically all of the methods practiced by the experienced metal worker. Relatively mild deformation of magnesium such as bending around generous radii can be done at room temperature. The formability at elevated temperatures (400–600°F) is so greatly improved, however, that most magnesium forming is done hot. This improved formability at elevated temperature is a function of magnesium's hexagonal crystalline structure. When the metal is heated, additional slip planes become available and lower forming pressures are required to produce plastic deformation. In addition to press drawing, magnesium alloys are formed by bending, stretch forming, spinning, impact extrusion, drop hammer forming and other common methods.

Joining. The joining methods in common use on magnesium include arc welding, electric resistance welding, brazing, riveting, bolting and adhesive bonding.

Machining. Magnesium is considered the easiest of all structural metals to machine. On many occasions the excellent machinability of magnesium alloys has been the reason for their use in applications where a large number of machining operations are required. Magnesium alloys can be machined at high speeds, feeds and depths of cut. The low cutting pressures and high thermal conductivity of the metal provide long tool life, dimensional accuracy of the part, and a fine surface finish.

Finishing. Magnesium parts are finished by processes involving cleaning, chemical treatment, anodizing and electroplating or painting.

Electroplating of magnesium has been done successfully in several commercial applications. The process requires a preliminary dip to provide a so-called zinc immersion coating. This is followed by a copper strike after which parts may be electroplated in standard plating baths. Any metal which can be electrodeposited can be applied successfully to magnesium alloys.

Painting may be done for the purpose of applying a decorative finish or as a means of protection against corrosive influences. Porcelain enamels which can be applied at relatively low temperatures have been developed for magnesium alloys. Such enamels are available in attractive colors, provide excellent adhesion and resist chemical attack and abrasion.

Uses

The uses for magnesium and magnesium alloys are divided into nonstructural and structural. The nonstructural uses pertain largely to primary magnesium. A list of the various nonstructural uses for the primary metal is given in Table 4. Alloying with aluminum accounts for the greatest usage of magnesium. In fact, it actually exceeds total structural usage. The nonstructural uses for magnesium in alloyed form include batteries, anodes for cathodic protection of underground structures and photoengraving.

Structural uses of magnesium are numerous and quite varied. Table 5 lists most of the types of applications where magnesium alloys in their various fabricated forms are being used or have been used successfully. At one time, aircraft with its need for light weight was the greatest user of magnesium alloys. In recent years aerospace applications still utilize considerable magnesium, but with the phasing out of piloted aircraft by the military, the tonnage consumption has dropped. Electronic systems find the properties and characteristics of magnesium highly desirable. In addition to strength and lightness, such features as damping capacity, thermal properties, electrical properties and the ability of magnesium to be readily fabricated are important.

Materials handling equipment presents a sizable market for magnesium.

Magnesium alloys, particularly in the form of die castings, are finding increasing use in

TABLE 4. NONSTRUCTURAL USES OF MAGNESIUM

Uses	Remarks
CHEMICAL	
General	Purification of argon and hydrogen gases; production of boron, lithium and calcium hydroxide; as a deoxidizer; for neutralizing lubricating oils; and deoxygenating and declorinating boiler water.
Grignard process	Production of organic and organo-metallic compounds difficult to synthesize efficiently by other methods.
Explosives and pyrotechnics	In powder form for blasting compositions, signal flares, incendiary devices, underwater flares, explosive sensitizer, and match head ingredient.
ELECTROCHEMICAL	
Batteries	Small, lightweight batteries with high current output. Used in dry cell and reserve wet cell batteries.
Cathodic protection	Provides effective corrosion protection of domestic water heaters, underground pipe lines, ship hulls and ballast tanks, tower footings and other underground and underwater structures.
METALLURGICAL	
Alloying	Aluminum– for improvement in strength and corrosion resistance. lead – for greater strength, hardness and creep resistance. nickel – improves heat treated strength and hardness of nickel-copper alloys. zinc – improves dimensional stability and reduces susceptibility to stress corrosion.
Ductile iron	Removes sulfur and spheroidizes graphite resulting in improved strength and ductility.
Scavenger uses	Debismuthizing lead, deoxidizing copper and brass, desulfurizing iron and nickel.
Thermal reduction	Reducing agent in the production of beryllium, hafnium, titanium, uranium, zirconium, and many other metals.

TABLE 5. STRUCTURAL USES OF MAGNESIUM ALLOYS

Aircraft, missiles and space vehicles	Ladders
Automobile parts	Lawnmower housings
Bakery and garment rack trucks	Levels
Binocular and Camera bodies	Luggage
Business machines	Masonry tools
Carrying cases	Memory discs and tape reels
Chain saws	Military vehicles
Containers	Portable shelter frames
Conveyors	Portable tools
Dock boards	Racing car wheels, engine and chassis parts
Electronic systems	Reciprocating parts of machinery
Engines, 2- and 4-cycle	Sporting goods
Furniture	Tooling jigs and fixtures
Hand trucks	Toys

passenger automobiles. An outstanding example is the German VW which uses as much as 60 lbs of magnesium die castings per car.

Moving parts of machinery and manually handled tools and equipment represent usage where magnesium's lightness is the prime reason for its choice. Numerous consumer products utilize magnesium to reduce weight.

Over the years magnesium has displayed healthy growth in both nonstructural and structural applications. The growth of magnesium in existing applications, the anticipation of new uses and the increased consumption that will result from the development of new alloys and advances in technology point strongly toward a bright future for magnesium as one of our common metals.

Biological, Biochemical and Toxicological Aspects

Magnesium is a key element in both plant and animal life. The photosynthetic activity of most plants is based on the absorption of energy from light induced by the presence of chlorophyll pigments in the plants. The chlorophylls (there are at least three types) are magnesium-centered porphyrins containing as most distinctive substituents a hydrophilic 5-member carbocyclic ring and a lipophilic phytol tail. In the conversion of radient energy into chemical form, the chlorophyll pigmented plants combine water and carbon dioxide to form carbohydrates and oxygen. It is this regeneration of oxygen from CO_2 formed by the respiration of animal life that makes life on earth possible. Therefore, photosynthesis by plants containing chlorophyll is the most important of all biological processes.

In animal systems magnesium has a significant role in enzyme-catalyzed reactions involving the phosphate groups that are associated with the transfer of energy and the stimulation of muscular action. A close association exists in the balance in the body among magnesium, calcium and phosphorus. While it is almost impossible to lower the dietary supply of magnesium to the body, since most foods contain adequate amounts, a deficiency can arise because of protracted diarrhea or vomiting. The two chief evidences

of magnesium deficiency are hyperirritability and soft tissue calcification. The former takes the form of tremors, twitching, disorientation and convulsions that can terminate in death. The symptoms can be relieved by administration (injection or ingestion) of magnesium salts and can be prevented by providing extra magnesium in the diet.

The daily adult requirement of magnesium is about 300 mg/day, but this is affected by the type of carbohydrate in the diet and the dietary concentrations of calcium, phosphorus, potassium and protein. Excess magnesium is easily eliminated with body wastes, but, as is well known, magnesium compounds such as the sulfate (Epsom salts) and hydroxide (milk of magnesia) are laxatives and purgatives and can have distressing effects when ingested in excess.

References

1. Beck, A., "The Technology of Magnesium and its Alloys," translation of "Magnesium und seine Legierungen," 2nd Ed., 512 pp., (London), F. A. Hughes & Co. Limited, 1941.
2. Gross, W. H., "The Story of Magnesium," 1st Ed., 258 pp., Metals Park Ohio, American Society for Metals, 1949.
3. Roberts, C. S., "Magnesium and Its Alloys," 230 pp., New York, John Wiley & Son, 1960.
4. Comstock, H., "Magnesium and Magnesium Compounds," a Materials Survey. 128 pp., Washington, D.C., U.S. Dept. of the Interior, Bureau of Mines, 1963.
5. "Magnesium—Metal on the Move," *Precision Metal Molding*, **23**, No. 7, 35–61 (July 1965).
6. Hanawalt, J. D., and Gross, W. H., "Magnesium," *Machine Design*, **37**, No. 21, 81–88 (Sept. 9, 1965).
7. Church, F. L., "Magnesium: Starting to Make Out in Mass Markets," *Modern Metals*, **22**, No. 6, 57–81 (July 1966).
8. Emley, E. G., "Principles of Magnesium Technology," 1013 pp, London, Pergamon Press, Ltd., 1966.

WILLIAM H. GROSS

MANGANESE

Manganese, a hard brittle metal melting at 1245°C, was first recognized as an element by the Swedish chemist Scheele in 1774 while

TABLE 1. ORES OF MANGANESE

Mineral	Color	Hardness	Manganese content when pure, %	Chemical form	Density, g/cc
Pyrolusite	Soft gray to black; metallic luster	6–6.5	63.2	MnO_2	4.8
Psilomelane	Black, dull, semimetallic luster	5–6	45–60	$BaMn^2Mn_8^4O_{16}(OH)_4$	3.7–4.7
Manganite	Dark gray to black	4	62.4	$Mn_2O_3H_2O$ or $MnO(OH)$	4.2–4.4
Braunite	Brown	6–6.5	62	$3Mn_2O_3 \cdot MnSiO_3$	4.8
Hausmannite	Brown to black; veins in igneous rock	5.5	72	Mn_3O_4	4.8
Rhodochrosite ⎱ Dialogite ⎰	Pink, red, gray, brown; vitreous luster	3–4	48	$MnCO_3$	3.0
Rhodonite	Red, pink, brown	6–6.5	42	$MnSiO_3$	3.63

working with pyrolusite, the MnO_2 ore, and was isolated by his associate, Gahn, in the same year. Frequently found in conjunction with iron ores, the metal was named for the magnetic properties exhibited by pyrolusite from the Latin *magnes,* or magnet; the German equivalent is *Mangan* and the French, *manganése.*

The addition of manganese as spiegeleisen in the Bessemer steelmaking process initiated in 1856 by Robert Mushet made that process a practical success. In 1888 Robert Hadfield discovered the high-Mn (14%) steels which bear his name. The use of manganese is essential in steel manufacture for the control of sulfur content, and today this application accounts for the major portion of the manganese consumed in all forms in this country. Somewhat less than 14 pounds of manganese, chiefly in the form of ferromanganese, is used for each ton of steel produced.

The element, symbol Mn, atomic number 25, atomic weight 54.938, is located in Group VIIA of the Periodic Table between chromium and iron horizontally. Until rhenium, atomic number 75, and technetium, atomic number 43, were discovered in 1924 and 1937, respectively, manganese was the only known element in Group VIIA.

While manganese had been known and commonly used in alloy and compound form for a long time, the pure metal did not become an industrial metal until the late 1930's with the development of the electrolytic process for its recovery. Relatively impure metal, made by aluminothermic or silicothermic reduction of the oxides, had been available, but only with the advent of the very pure electrolytic product has precise and extensive work on the potentialities of manganese been possible. For example, much of the work on alloy systems must be and is being reviewed.

Occurrence

Manganese is widely distributed in the combined state, ranking twelfth in abundance among the elements in the earth's crust. It is commonly found in association with iron ores in concentrations too low in most cases, however, to make its commercial recovery attractive. The ores of manganese are listed in Table 1.

The United States is a "have not" nation insofar as deposits of high-grade manganese are concerned, as pointed out in the Paley Report of 1952. The known manganese deposits in this country are estimated to total 3,500 million long tons (2240 lb) of ore with 75 million tons of contained manganese. More than 98% of this ore is in 12 large low-grade deposits, of which the most important are at Chamberlain, South Dakota; Cuyuna, Minnesota; Aroostook County, Maine; and Artillery Peak, Arizona. Details of these deposits are given in Table 2.

Over 90% of the country's consumption of manganese ore is imported and most of the domestic ore is derived from the Butte, Montana district as the carbonate mineral, rhodochrosite. In recent years imports of manganese

TABLE 2. MANGANESE ORE DEPOSITS IN UNITED STATES (Long Tons)

	Tonnage (millions of ore)	Tonnage (millions, manganese)	Manganese, %
Estimated total	3,500	75	3–48
Artillery Peak, Arizona	200	8	3–4
	20	1	5
	2–3	0.3	10
	0.5	0.6	15
Chamberlain, South Dakota	2,000	50	3–15
	78	10	15
Aroostoock County, Maine			6–9
Phillipsburg and Butte, Montana	0.2	0.1	48

ore have amounted to about 2.5 million short tons per year. Brazil provided the major portion of imports, followed in order by Gabon, India, Ghana and Union of South Africa. In early 1967 the Congo (Kinshasa) has become the leading source of imported manganese ore. Ghana and Gabon supply most of the battery- and chemical-grade ore containing more than 47% Mn.

Of strategic interest, most of the manganese required for the steel industry could be obtained from the basic open hearth slag containing 10 to 15% Mn. This concentration is equal to or better than much of the low-grade ore available in this country, and it is located at the steel mills. The lack of domestic sources of this vital raw material has impelled the development of feasible methods of utilizing our low-grade deposits and open hearth slag for the production of suitable manganese oxides. This program has been conducted by the U.S. Bureau of Mines, the American Iron and Steel Institute, and private companies. At the present time imports offer a much cheaper source of manganese than do domestic deposits that would have to be upgraded to match foreign ores in quality.

Derivation

Manganese metal can be made by several reactions or processes:

1. *Reduction of oxides with carbon.* Frequently conducted in an electric furnace, this process results in impure metal containing carbon and carbides, as well as many of the constituents originally present in the oxide used.

2. *Reduction of oxides with other metals.* Until the advent of the electrolytic process the best grade of manganese metal, seldom exceeding 95 to 98% Mn, was made by the high-temperature reduction of manganese oxides with aluminum or ferrosilicon.

3. *Reduction of anhydrous halogen salts with metals.* Sodium and magnesium can be used to convert halides to metal, but no commercial practice of the technique appears to be used.

4. *Reduction of solutions of manganese salts with metals.* Sodium amalgam and magnesium have been tried for this purpose, but they form some hydroxide as well as metal and the method is not too satisfactory even for laboratory preparation of manganese.

5. *Electrolysis of sulfate solutions of manganese.* This is the basis of the only commercial source of pure manganese and is used in this and other countries.

The American development is based on a process using the electrolysis of manganous sulfate and was extensively investigated in laboratory and pilot plant operations in the 1930's by Shelton and co-workers at the U.S. Bureau of Mines. After further development and engineering studies the process was brought to full-scale operation in 1939 by the Electro Manganese Corporation plant in Knoxville, now owned by Foote Mineral Co. During the period of 1942–1946 the Bureau of Mines operated an experimental plant at Boulder City, Nevada that produced about 1.5 million pounds of electrolytic manganese. While differing in many details, both operations used a diaphragm cell whose anolyte contained manganous sulfate, ammonium sulfate, and sulfuric acid to give a pH of about 1, and whose catholyte was maintained at a pH of 7.2 to 7.6 in the presence of added sulfur dioxide. Similar systems are currently used in electrolytic manganese plants.

The fact that manganese is considerably more electropositive than zinc makes the commercially attractive deposition of it from aqueous solutions a real achievement. Further, manganese cannot be deposited from an acid solution due to re-solution of the metal at acid pH's, and the oxide source of manganous

391

sulfate cannot be dissolved by a basic solution. Two-compartment cells are required to meet these conditions. The acid anolyte is drawn from the cell to leach manganous sulfate from the divalent oxide raw materials. The latter are prepared by the roasting of ores. In one plant (Union Carbide Corp.) a manganese silicate slag is leached to provide the $MnSO_4$ feed solution. After careful purification to remove such impurities as iron, arsenic, antimony, tin, lead, nickel, cobalt, molybdenum, silica, aluminum, calcium and magnesium, the leach solution is returned to the cells as the catholyte. Optimum conditions for the electrowinning of manganese are given in Table 3.

A manganese plant cell room is shown in Fig. 1.

The anode of the cell is a lead-1% silver alloy, and the cathode is either a stainless steel or a "Hastelloy" alloy. Manganese cathode deposits are removed as chips from the cathode by flexing and hammering after the deposit has reached a thickness of about $\frac{1}{8}$ inch. The chips of 99.9% manganese are shown in Fig. 2.

Process details, including flowsheets, are given by Bacon, Jacobs *et al.*, Mantell, Carosella and Fowler, and Sully.

TABLE 3. ELECTROLYTIC MANGANESE CELL OPERATING DATA

1. Purified feed solution	
Mn as $MnSO_4$, gpl	30–40
$(NH_4)_2SO_4$, gpl	125–150
SO_2, gpl	0.10
Glue, gpl	0.008–0.016
2. Anolyte composition	
Mn as $MnSO_4$, gpl	10–20
H_2SO_4, gpl	25–40
$(NH_4)_2SO_4$, gpl	125–150
3. Current density, amp/sq ft	40–60
4. Catholyte pH	6–7.2
5. Anode composition	Pb-1% Ag
6. Cathode composition	"Hastelloy," Type 316 stainless steel, or Ti
7. Cell voltage, volts	5.1
8. Diaphragm	18 oz. canvas
9. Power used per lb Mn, kwh	3.6–4.0
10. Current efficiency, %	60–65

The rise in production of electrolytic manganese has been great since the industry began. In 1941 some 600 tons were made, in 1952 over 3,500 tons, and in 1966 the market amounted to 27,500 tons. In 1967 the production capacity rose to over 40,000 tons/year.

FIG. 1. Cell room in Marietta, Ohio electrolytic manganese plant. *(Courtesy Union Carbide Metals Co.).*

FIG. 2. Chips of manganese removed from the cathode sheets of the electrolytic process. The smooth side was against the cathode; the rough side faced the solution. These chips are about 1½ by 2 in. in size.

The price of pure manganese metal is 28.5¢/lb.

Electrolytic manganese of at least 99.9% Mn is produced by Foote Mineral Company, Union Carbide Corporation and American Potash and Chemical Corporation.

Ferroalloys

More than 90% of the manganese consumed is used in the form of ferroalloys by the metal industries, chiefly for steel manufacture. These are made by smelting operations in high-temperature furnaces, starting with suitable ores. The predominant type, ferromanganese (78–82% Mn, 12–16% Fe, 6–8% C, 1% Si), is made in blast furnaces and to a lesser extent in electric furnaces by the reduction with carbon of high-grade ores containing 48% or more Mn. Low carbon grades of ferromanganese containing 0.07–0.75% C require the reduction of ores with ferrosilicon, a more expensive process that results in a price premium for this grade. Other types include spiegeleisen (15–30% Mn, 6.5% C, 1–3% Si, balance Fe) and silicomanganese (65–70% Mn, 17–20% Si, 1.5% C, balance Fe).

In recent years a material that might be called a ferromanganese, but containing only 1 to 2% iron, has been made on a commercial scale by the fused salt electrolysis of purified MnO in a bath of fluorides; this product is also very low in carbon (0.01%). A grade containing 6 to 15% iron can be prepared by the same process when the MnO is derived directly from ores and slags.

Physical Properties

Manganese exists in four allotropic modifications, the alpha being the one stable at room temperatures. Alpha and beta manganese are hard brittle metals that will scratch glass. The pure metal cannot be fabricated. Gamma manganese, which changes to alpha at ordinary temperatures, is reported to be flexible and soft and can be bent and easily cut. Data on the allotropism and transition temperatures of manganese are summarized in Table 4.

The physical properties of manganese are summarized in Table 5, and its vapor pressure temperature relationship is shown in Fig. 3.

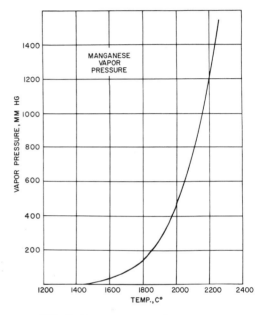

FIG. 3. Vapor pressure of manganese.

Natural manganese is comprised of 100% of Mn^{55}. Artificial isotopes of Mn^{51}, Mn^{52}, Mn^{54} and Mn^{56}, of which Mn^{54} has the longest half-life, 310 days, have been prepared.

Chemical Properties

Although somewhat similar to iron in general chemical reactivity, manganese can exist in its compounds in the valence states of 2, 3, 4, 6 and 7, the most stable salts being those of the divalent form and the most stable oxide the dioxide, MnO_2. The lower oxides, MnO and Mn_2O_3, are basic; the higher oxides, acidic. The most stable compounds other than MnO_2 are those of valence 2, 6 and 7, exemplified, respectively, by the manganous salts, such as $MnCl_2$, $MnSO_4$; and $Mn(NO_3)_2$ the manganates, such as K_2MnO_4; and the permanganates, such as $KMnO_4$. Divalent

TABLE 4. ALLOTROPISM OF MANGANESE

Density	Form	Stability range	Crystal structure
7.44	Alpha	Below 700°C (1292°F)	Body-centered cubic, 58 atoms to unit cell, a = 8.894Å
7.29	Beta	700–1079°C (1292–1974°F)	Body-centered cubic, 20 atoms to unit cell, a = 6.300Å
7.21	Gamma	1079–1143°C (1974–2089°F)	Face-centered tetragonal, 4 atoms to unit cell, a = 3.767Å c/a = 0.934
	Delta	1143°C–MP (2089°F)	Body centered a = 3.075
6.54	Liquid	Above 1244° ± 3°C (2271 ± 5°F)	

Transition Points

From	To	Temperature	Condition
Alpha	Beta	700° ± 3°C (1292 ± 5°F)	Heating
Beta	Alpha	700–665°C (1292–1229°F)	Cooling
Beta	Gamma	1079° ± 3°C (1974 ± 5°F)	Heating and cooling
Gamma	Delta	1140° ± 3°C (2084 ± 5°F)	Heating and cooling
Delta	Liquid	1244° ± 3°C (2271 ± 5°F)	Heating and cooling

TABLE 5. PHYSICAL PROPERTIES OF MANGANESE

Atomic number		25		
Atomic weight		54.938		
Stable isotope		55		
Density, Solid		Alpha	Beta	Gamma
g/cc at 20°C		7.44	7.29	7.18
lb/cu in. at 68°F		0.268	0.263	0.259
Liquid, g/cc		6.54		
lb/cu in.		0.236		
Atomic volume, cc/g-atom		7.4		
Melting point		1244 ± 3°C (2271 ± 5°F)		
Boiling point, 760 mm		2097°C (3806°F)		
Specific heat, cal/g/°C at 25°C (Btu/lb/°F at 77°F)	Alpha	Beta	Gamma	Delta
	0.114	0.154	0.148	0.191
Latent heat of fusion, cal/g		63.7		
Btu/lb		114.7		
Latent heat of vaporization, cal/g (at BP)		997.6		
Btu/lb		1,760		

TABLE 5—*continued*

	Alpha	Gamma
Linear coefficient of thermal expansion,		
Per °C (0–100°C)	22×10^{-6}	14×10^{-6}
Per °F (32–212°F)	12.2×10^{-6}	7.8×10^{-6}
Electrical resistivity at 20°C (68°F),		
Alpha, microhm-cm		185
Beta, microhm-cm		44
Gamma, microhm-cm		60
Magnetic susceptibility, 18°C (64°F), cgs units		9.9
Hardness,		
Mohs scale		5.0
Rockwell C scale		
Alpha manganese		71
Gamma manganese		23

Vapor pressure, mm Hg

°C	°F	
1244	2271	0.9
1327	2420	2.4
1527	2780	18.3
1727	3140	89
1927	3500	315
2027	3680	541
2127	3860	880
2227	4040	1,380

Heat of transformation, cal/g-atom	
Alpha to beta, 727°C (1341°F)	535
Beta to gamma, 1100°C (2012°F)	545
Gamma to delta, 1138°C (2080°F)	430

Heat capacity equations, cal/g-atom

Manganese (alpha), $Cp = 5.70 + 3.38 \times 10^{-3}T - 0.375 \times 10^{5}T^{-2}$ (298–1000°K)
Manganese (beta), $Cp = 8.33 + 0.66 \times 10^{-3}T$ (1000–1374°K)
Manganese (gamma), $Cp = 10.7$ (1374–1410°K)
Manganese (delta), $Cp = 11.30$ (1410–1450°K)
Manganese, liquid, $Cp = 11.0$

Standard electrode potential, $Mn = Mn^{++} + 2e$ (referred to hydrogen electrode)	+1.1 volts
Thermal neutron absorption cross-section, barns	13.2

manganese is a reducing agent, tetravalent manganese is a good oxidizing agent, and heptavalent manganese is one of the most powerful oxidizing agents. The trivalent and hexavalent forms undergo auto-oxidation and reduction in acid solutions:

$$2Mn^{+3} + 2H_2O \rightarrow MnO_2 + Mn^{+2} + 4H^+$$

$$3MnO_4^{-2} + 4H^+ \rightarrow MnO_2 + 2MnO_4^- + 2H_2O$$

These factors make manganese compounds useful for a variety of industrial applications and for analytical procedures.

Manganese metal oxidizes superficially in air and rusts in moist air. It burns in air or oxygen at elevated temperatures like iron; decomposes water slowly in the cold and rapidly on heating, forming manganous hydroxide, $Mn(OH)_2$, with hydrogen evolution; and dissolves readily in dilute mineral acids with hydrogen evolution and the formation of the corresponding divalent salts.

Fluorine, chlorine, and bromine react with manganese when heated. When heated with nitrogen, various nitrides are formed; when heated with ammonia, it also forms the nitride. Manganese reacts with sulfur to form sulfides.

Fused manganese dissolves carbon, as does iron, ultimately forming a carbide. It reacts with carbon monoxide at temperatures above 330°C (626°F) and with carbon dioxide when strongly heated.

Hydrides of manganese have not been detected, but solid and liquid manganese dissolves appreciable quantities of hydrogen; electrolytic manganese normally contains 150 parts of hydrogen per million.

A dehydrogenated, furnace-treated metal is a commercial product, as are nitrogen-bearing manganese metals employed to introduce manganese and nitrogen into special-quality corrosion resistant alloys and valve steels.

Boiling concentrated solutions of potassium or sodium hydroxide have little action on manganese.

The reported chemical reactivity may be affected by impurities.

Principal Compounds and Uses

As might be expected for an element of five different valence states, a wide variety of manganese compounds is known. However, less than a dozen are made and used in more than minor quantities: the two oxides, manganous oxide, MnO and manganese dioxide, MnO_2; manganous sulfate, $MnSO_4$, and manganous chloride, $MnCl_2$; potassium permanganate, $KMnO_4$; and a few organic compounds, such as manganese naphthenate, oleate, linoleate, etc., used chiefly as dryers in paint and varnish.

Manganous oxide is more easily dissolved by acids than are the higher oxides present in ores and most ores destined for preparation of chemicals are first furnaced in a reducing atmosphere to reduce the oxides present to MnO. While most of the MnO is used as an intermediate to produce other manganese compounds, it is also currently being produced and used as a source of manganese in fertilizers. MnO can be made in pure form by thermal decomposition of $MnCO_3$ or by reduction of MnO_2 with hydrogen. When MnO is treated with mineral acids the corresponding manganous salts are formed, e.g., $MnSO_4$ from which electrolytic manganese is made.

Manganese dioxide, MnO_2, is the manganese compound made and used in the greatest tonnage. A special grade of natural MnO_2 is used in the manufacture of the LeClanché and other primary batteries at the rate of about 40,000 tons/year. Most of this MnO_2 comes from mines in Africa and Mexico. This battery grade is the gamma form of MnO_2 which is characterized by a less well-defined crystal structure than the pyrolusite form which is not suitable for batteries.

Synthetic MnO_2 is produced by chemical processes, but most of it is derived by an electrolytic process which is used to produce about 7,000 tons/year of the material in this country and over 30,000 tons/year in Japan. Manganese sulfate, obtained by the leaching with sulfuric acid of an ore whose manganese has been reduced to the acid-soluble divalent state, is purified and fed to a cell where MnO_2 is plated on the anode. The reaction involved is: $MnSO_4 + 2H_2O \rightarrow MnO_2 + H_2SO_4 + H_2$. Process details are given by Clapper. The electrolytic MnO_2 is of the gamma form and is eminently suitable for dry cell manufacture.

Manganese dioxide is used as the oxidizing agent in a number of chemical processes, for example, to prepare hydroquinone from aniline. Such processes usually yield $MnSO_4$ as a by-product. Pure MnO_2 can be made by the reaction of a permanganate on a manganous salt, as by:

$$2KMnO_4 + 3MnSO_4 + 2H_2O \rightarrow 5MnO_2\downarrow + K_2SO_4 + 2H_2SO_4.$$

Manganous sulfate, $MnSO_4$, is a soluble, pale pink salt which forms several hydrates, the most common being $MnSO_4 \cdot 4H_2O$. It is prepared by the action of H_2SO_4 on MnO or by the action of SO_2 on MnO_2, but most of it is obtained as a by-product of processes using MnO_2 or $KMnO_4$ as oxidizing agents. Manganous sulfate is a good reducing agent and the MnO_2 which generally is formed by its use can easily be reconverted to $MnSO_4$ by the reaction with SO_2: $MnO_2 + SO_2 \rightarrow MnSO_4$. It is used in the manufacture of paint and varnish driers; in the formulation of fertilizers to provide the small amount of manganese needed as a trace element; in the production of electrolytic manganese and manganese dioxide; in textile dyeing; and in ceramics.

Manganous chloride, $MnCl_2$, is a soluble, rose-colored salt usually obtained as the hydrate, $MnCl_2 \cdot 4H_2O$. It is formed by the action of HCl on manganous oxide or on MnO_2—the latter yields chlorine as a byproduct and was the basis of the Weldon process of a century ago to manufacture chlorine from HCl. Manganous chloride is added to molten magnesium to introduce the manganese present in most magnesium alloys. Other applications of $MnCl_2$ are similar to those of $MnSO_4$.

Potassium permanganate, $KMnO_4$, is a dark purple compound that is a powerful oxidizing agent. It is produced by a multistep process wherein manganese dioxide or pyrolusite is fused with KOH in the presence of air or an oxidizing agent to form potassium manganate, K_2MnO_4, which is then converted to $KMnO_4$ by treatment with chlorine or carbon dioxide, or by anodic oxidation in an electrolytic cell. The reactions involved are:

(1) $2MnO_2 + 4KOH + O_2 \rightarrow$
$$2K_2MnO_4 + 2H_2O$$

(2) $3K_2MnO_4 + 2H_2O \rightarrow$
$$2KMnO_4 + 4KOH + MnO_2\downarrow$$

This is an auto-oxidation reaction induced by carbon dioxide or other reagents that remove hydroxyl ions.

(3) $K_2MnO_4 + H_2O \rightarrow$
$$KMnO_4 + KOH + \tfrac{1}{2}H_2$$

This is the reaction occurring during electrolysis, and yields only $KMnO_4$ and KOH; the latter can be recycled to produce more K_2MnO_4.

When the purple $KMnO_4$ solution is concentrated by evaporation and cooled, slender opaque crystals of $KMnO_4$ are formed. The reason that $KMnO_4$ and not $NaMnO_4$ is produced commercially is that $KMnO_4$ is much less soluble than $NaMnO_4$, making it possible to separate it in a high state of purity and much more efficiently.

Potassium permanganate is a disinfectant, deodorant and oxidizing agent. These properties make it useful for water purification, bleaching, air purification, descaling of steel, and preparing organic chemicals such as saccharine.

Applications for Manganese

Outside of its use as a desirable source for the preparation of high-purity manganese chemicals, chiefly salts, for pharmaceutical, food, analytical, catalytic, and scientific work,

electrolytic manganese is consumed entirely as a purifying and scavanging agent and as an alloying element in ferrous and nonferrous alloys, particularly stainless steels.

Manganese is vital for sulfur control in steelmaking and is the most commonly and widely used deoxidizer of molten steel. The greater part of it ends up in the slag of the steelmaking process. Ferromanganese, the form in which about 90% of all manganese is consumed, is the standard additive agent for these purposes in the steel industry. However, pure manganese is used in many instances, especially where preparation of special steels is involved and low carbon and phosphorus contents must be maintained. It can be added to basic open hearth steel, to both acid and basic electric furnace steel, and to crucible steel for purifying purposes.

The hard brittle nature of the alpha form of electrolytic manganese, which is the stable one at room temperature, has prevented the fabrication of the pure metal alone for any purpose. It can be transformed to a ductile alloy by the addition of 2% copper and 1% nickel.

Manganese is present in several ferrous alloys of the chromium-nickel type. In some, most of the nickel is replaced by manganese to form alloys whose usefulness approaches that of the 17–7 stainless steels but whose corrosion resistance is somewhat less. Examples are the 16 to 17% chromium-14% manganese-1% nickel steels. In others only a portion of the nickel is replaced by manganese and these have been assigned AISI numbers: Type 201 has a composition of 16 to 18% chromium-5.5 to 7.5% manganese-3.5 to 5.5% nickel, and Type 202 contains 17 to 19% chromium-7.5 to 10% manganese-4 to 6% nickel. Their strength and formability properties are such that they can be substituted for Types 301 and 302, respectively, but their corrosion resistance is less.

Practically all commercial alloys of aluminum and magnesium contain manganese. Corrosion resistance and mechanical properties, such as hardness, are improved by its presence. The amounts used are seldom above 1.2% for magnesium and 1.5% for aluminum. For use in aluminum alloys, electrolytic manganese competes with pure manganese oxides or carbonate or the low-iron ferromanganese described in the section on "Ferroalloys." For use in magnesium it competes with pure manganous chloride that is added to the melting pots.

The instrument alloy, manganin, comprised of 11 to 12% manganese-3 to 4% nickel-balance copper, is prepared with electrolytic manganese, as are the high-resistance nickel-chromium alloys containing about 2% manganese. An extremely high ability to damp vibrations is possessed by binary copper-manganese alloys. Manganese has been used as a substitute for nickel in the nickel silvers, and in alloys of copper, zinc and nickel. It is also added to bronzes and brasses.

Many data on the properties and applications on the alloy systems Cu-Mn, Mn-Ni, Cu-Mn-Ni, and Cu-Zn-Mn are given by Dean, and Sully has collected data on many other alloy systems.

Biological, Biochemical, and Toxicological Aspects

Manganese is generally considered one of the five essential trace elements, along with boron, zinc, copper and molybdenum, for the vast majority of higher plants. At least one reason for their necessity is that they form essential constituents of certain enzymes. A number of enzymes concerned with the oxidation of carbohydrates in respiration are activated by manganese and for one of them, oxalosuccinic decarboxylase, it may be essential.

In plants a shortage of manganese first becomes evident in the form of an intervenal chlorosis (lack of chlorophyll) which results in the appearance of yellow or gray streaks between the veins of leaves or in a mottling. Some of the conditions have been given names: gray-streak or gray stripe in oats, rye, barley or wheat; the Pahala blight of sugar cane; speckled yellow of sugar beets; and marsh-spot in peas.

The soil of at least 25 states, in particular, Florida, Michigan, Ohio and Indiana, is deficient in manganese. For this reason manganese is frequently added to fertilizers used in these areas, usually in the form of $MnSO_4$, but more recently as a soil-acid soluble MnO. For some crops, chiefly citrus, $MnSO_4$ solution is sprayed on the leaves. About 10,000 tons/year of manganese compounds containing 54% MnO equivalent are used in mixed fertilizers and another 5,000 tons/year are directly applied to the soil or sprayed on leaves.

Manganese is widely distributed throughout the animal kingdom and may possibly be generally essential for the utilization of vitamin B_1. Deficiency of it in chickens results in deformity of the leg bones ("slipped tendon" or "broken leg"). Small concentrations of manganese compounds are added to many animal and chicken feed formulations to overcome deficiency of this element.

Many of the iron-depositing bacteria form deposits of manganese oxides as well as iron oxides. This bacterial activity may account for the occurrence of manganese in the iron ores of the Lake Superior and other regions, and for many of the high-grade manganese ore deposits. The manganese nodules found in recent years on ocean floors are possibly of biochemical origin.

Manganese glycerophosphate and manganese hypophosphite are added to some vitamin-mineral formulations to provide small amounts of manganese as a nutritional supplement. Potassium permanganate is used in medicine as a disinfectant.

Manganous compounds are not in general regarded as poisonous due to the manganous ion alone, as compared to the toxicity of other metal ions such as mercury, cadmium, thallium, lead, etc. The strong oxidizing properties of manganates and permanganates can cause skin irritation. Chronic manganese poisoning is a disease which results from the inhalation of fumes or dusts of manganese and usually develops after one to three years of exposure to heavy concentrations of dusts or fumes. The central nervous system is the chief site of damage. Sax describes the symptoms and results. However, companies which have produced manganese compounds for long periods of time have experienced few cases of toxicity as a result of exposure to manganese compounds. In the battery industry adequate precautions are taken in the handling of ores and oxides of manganese, particularly in milling operations, to provide ventilation and masks for workers, and few cases of damage to health have occurred over a period of several decades.

References

1. Anon. "The Paley Report-Manganese," *J. Metals*, **4**, 1141–1142 (1952); also, "Materials Survey-Manganese," National Security Resources Board, U.S. Department of Commerce, National Production Authority, Washington, D.C., U.S. Government Printing Office, 1952.
2. Bacon, F. E., "Manganese Electrowinning," in "Encyclopedia of Electrochemistry," C. A. Hampel, Editor, pp. 792–796, New York, Reinhold Publishing Corp., 1964.
3. Carosella, M. C., and Fowler, R. M., "A New Commercial Process for Electrowinning Manganese," *J. Electrochem. Soc.*, **104**, 352–356 (1957); for flowsheet, see *Chem. Eng.*, **64**, No. 10, 136–139 (May 19, 1958).
4. Clapper, T. W., "Manganese Dioxide, Electrolytic," in "Encyclopedia of Electrochemistry," C. A. Hampel, Editor, pp. 789–792, New York, Reinhold Publishing Corp., 1964.
5. Dean, R. S., "Electrolytic Manganese and Its Alloys," New York, The Roland Press, 1952.
6. Hampel, C. A., "Rare Metals Handbook," 1st Edition, pp. 255–270, New York, Reinhold Publishing Corp., 1954.
7. Jacobs, J. H., Hunter, J. W., Yarroll, W. H., Churchward, P. E., and Knickerbocker, R. G., "First Two Years Operation of the Bureau of Mines Electrolytic Manganese Pilot Plant," *Trans. AIME*, 159, 408–28 (1944).
8. Jacobs, J. H., Hunter, J. W., Yarrol, W. H., Churchward, P. E., Knickerbocker, R. G., Lewis, R. W., Heller, H. A., and Linck, J. H., *U.S. Bur. Mines Bull.*, **463** (1946).
9. Mantell, C. L., "Manganese," in "Rare Metals Handbook," C. A. Hampel, Editor, 2nd Edition, pp. 271–282, New York, Reinhold Publishing Corp., 1961.
10. Sax, N. Irving, "Dangerous Properties of Industrial Materials," 2nd Edition, p. 955, New York, Reinhold Publishing Corp., 1963.
11. Sully, A. H., "Manganese," New York, Academic Press, Inc., 1955.

Clifford A. Hampel

MENDELEVIUM (element 101)

Mendelevium is the ninth of the man-made transuranium elements, and the twelfth member of the actinide series. Its electron configuration is predicted to be $5f^{13}\ 7s^2$ outside the radon core.

Discovery of Mendelevium

Element 101 was first synthesized in 1955 at the University of California Radiation Laboratory, Berkeley, by A. Ghiorso, B. G. Harvey, G. R. Choppin, S. G. Thompson, and G. T. Seaborg. Einsteinium (element 99), which had become available in small amounts from irradiations of plutonium in the Materials Testing Reactor, was bombarded with 41 MeV helium ions from the Berkeley 60-inch cyclotron. The isotope produced was assigned the mass number 256, and the nuclear reaction involved in its formation may be written:

$$_{99}Es^{253} + {}_2He^4 \rightarrow 101^{256} + {}_0n^1$$

These experiments are noteworthy for the extremely small amount of target material (about 10^9 atoms of Es^{253}), the use of a new bombardment technique and the minute yield of product (17 atoms in all, or an average of about one atom detected per experiment).

The bombardment technique (which has since proved useful in many studies of short-lived nuclides) used the recoil energy of the newly-formed product atoms to separate them from the very thin layer of target material. The product atoms were collected in thin gold foils placed close to the target foil. The gold "catcher" foils could be dissolved, and the gold removed chemically in a few minutes, leaving the target foil intact for repeated bombardments.

The final separation of the actinide elements was by cation exchange, using ammonium alpha-hydroxy-isobutyrate as the eluting agent, an improvement on the citrate eluting agent used in earlier work. No alpha activity was detected in the fraction corresponding to element 101. However, spontaneous fission events were observed infrequently but consistently in both the element 100 (fermium) and the element 101 fractions. By combining the results of many experiments, it was concluded that the spontaneous fissions in both fractions decayed with a half-life of about 3 hours, and were probably due to the same nuclide. It was suggested that this 3-hour activity was due to Fm^{256}, produced in the element 101 fraction by electron-capture decay of 101^{256}, after chemical separation, and in the fermium fraction by decay of 101^{256}

before separation. This hypothesis was supported by the observation in neutron-irradiated samples of a fermium isotope decaying by spontaneous fission with a 3-hour half-life, which could only be ascribed to Fm^{256}.

On this rather indirect evidence, the investigators claimed the discovery of element 101, and suggested the name mendelevium, symbol Mv, in honor of Dmitri Mendeleev, who originally predicted the existence and properties of undiscovered elements by means of the Periodic Table. The symbol was subsequently changed to Md. Later experiments, using much larger quantities of einsteinium as the target material, confirmed the original results, and indicated a half-life of about 1.5 hours for Md^{256}. In this work, a second fermium daughter of mendelevium was detected, with the decay properties of Fm^{255}, and it was suggested that this was formed from Md^{255} with a half-life of about 30 minutes.

In neither of these investigations were the radiations of a mendelevium isotope detected directly. However, in 1964 and 1965, Ghiorso and co-workers at Berkeley produced mixtures of fermium and mendelevium isotopes by bombarding californium-252 with boron-11, carbon-12, and carbon-13 ions accelerated in the Heavy Ion Linear Accelerator. The nuclear reactions involved were "stripping" reactions, in which some protons and neutrons are transferred from the projectile to the target nucleus, but the whole heavy ion is not captured. Studies of the chemically separated mendelevium fractions confirmed the earlier observations on Md^{255} and Md^{256}, and showed for the first time the emission of alpha particles from these isotopes. In addition, alpha particles decaying with a half-life of about 3 hours were ascribed to the isotope Md^{257}. Mendelevium isotopes have also been produced by heavy ion reactions in the U.S.S.R. Table 1 summarizes the properties of the five known isotopes. Announcement of the discovery of Md^{258} with a half-life of two months was made in September 1967.

Chemical Properties of Mendelevium

The chemical properties of mendelevium appear to be consistent with its position as the 12th member of the actinide series, analogous to thulium in the lanthanide rare earths. The only chemical experiments reported are the ion exchange separations involved in its production, and some limited solvent extraction experiments in the U.S.S.R. This situation existed through 1966.

However, in late 1967 Hulet and co-workers at the Lawrence Radiation Laboratory, Livermore, California, reported their studies on the chemical properties of mendelevium. Mendelevium is the first actinide element found to give a divalent ion stable in solution. Reduction from the 3+ oxidation state is accomplished with Zn dust, zinc amalgam, Cr^{2+}, Eu^{2+}, and V^{2+}; additionally, measurements of the equilibrium with V^{2+} provides an estimate of +0.2 volt for the couple: $Md^{2+} = Md^{3+} + e$. The chemical behavior of Md^{3+} is similar to that of the other trivalent actinides and lanthanides. Oxidation from the trivalent to higher valence states with sodium bismuthate was not detected.

At the present time, mendelevium isotopes can only be made in very low yields by charged particle bombardments. With increasing supplies of very heavy elements as target materials, it may perhaps be possible to make as many as a million atoms. To make mendelevium by multiple neutron capture in a reactor or thermonuclear explosion would require the production of mass 259, since it can be predicted that Fm^{259} will beta-decay to Md^{259}. This has not yet been achieved by

TABLE 1. ISOTOPES OF MENDELEVIUM

Mass No.	Half-life	Modes of Decay	Preparation
252	8m	EC	$U^{238}(F^{19},5n)$
255	30 min.	EC, α	$Es^{253}+\alpha$
256	1.5 h	EC, α	$Cf^{252} + HI$
257	3 h	EC, (SF?),α	$Cf^{252} + HI$
258	60d	α	$Es^{255}(d,n)$

EC = orbital electron capture, α = alpha decay, or helium ion as bombarding particle, SF = spontaneous fission, and HI = heavy ion (B^{11}, C^{12}, C^{13}).

See also the tabulation on page 755 in the article on **Transuranium Elements.**

either method, and at the present time, the prospects appear doubtful (see **Fermium**).

References

1. Hyde, E. K., Perlman, I., and Seaborg, G. T., "Nuclear Properties of the Heavy Elements," Vol. II—"Detailed Radioactivity Properties," New York, Prentice-Hall, 1964.
2. Seaborg, G. T.,"The Transuranium Elements," New Haven, Yale University Press, 1958.
3. Hulet, E. K., Lougheed, R. W., Brady, J. D., Stone, R. E., and Coops, M.S., "Mendelevium: Divalency and Other Chemical Properties," *Science*, **158**, 486-488 (October 27, 1967).

JOHN MILSTED

MERCURY

Prevalence

Very little mercury exists in the native state; practically all is obtained from the pyrolysis of red mercuric sulfide (cinnabar) and in lesser amount from the black sulfide (metacinnabar), a harder, lighter mineral. An additional, commercially significant ore is livingstonite, $HgSb_4S_7$. Other native minerals of mercury are tiemannite, $HgSe$; coloradite, $HgTe$; and calomel, $HgCl$. Some oxychlorides and gold amalgam are occasionally found too.

The major deposits are of primary magmatic origin, with most in belts of late Tertiary and Quaternary volcanic and tectonic activity. These were formed at relatively low temperature and near-surface conditions. Ores below the 1500-ft level have been seldom worked.

Mercuric sulfide is soluble in acid and alkaline solutions; attack by these liquids upon limestones and silica-containing rocks leads to replacement in part with the metal sulfide. A second mechanism found commonly is the filling of voids in shattered rock with stringers of cinnabar. Mineralization is prevalent in viens, breccia zones, and other permeable zones generally near to major faults. Oreshoots intrude into trap structures where chemically resistant formations block further ore channeling. Gangue minerals associated with the ore include opal, chalcedony, quartz, calcite, dolomite, pyrite, marcasite, fluorite, stibnite and sulfur.

The element is widely distributed, but in trace amount. The earth's crust is estimated as containing $1-30 \times 10^{-6}$ weight %; among plant life one-tenth to one-hundredth this concentration appears. In foodstuffs including milk, bread, fish, olive oil and vinegar similar levels are found. Human fingernails and head hair contain approximately 1×10^{-4} and 2×10^{-4} weight %, respectively. The concentration of mercury in sea water is 0.00003 mg/liter; in a cubic mile 0.1 ton and in all the oceans, 46×10^6 tons.

Sources, Derivations

Production of the element from native-mined ores takes place in more than two dozen countries around the globe. The world's largest supplier is the Almaden mine in Ciudad Réal Province, Spain; estimates of its entire output to-date are about seven million flasks. In 1964, the peak performance was 78,262 flasks (76 lb net weight); for 1966 less metal, perhaps 72,000 flasks, will flow from it into world markets which consume approximately one-quarter million flasks per year. Official estimates of Spanish reserves, of which the Almaden provides 85-95%, are 5.44 million metric tons or 157.66 million flasks. Italy is second in tonnage output capability with more than 57,000 flasks in 1965, the Monte Amiata mine being its major source and the Siele next.

Another large mine, the Idria near Trieste in Yugoslavia, began operations in the fifteenth century and has delivered about one-third the total output of the Almaden. Additional producers include the United States, Mexico, the Union of Soviet Socialist Republics, China, Japan, Turkey, Canada, Phillipine Islands, Iran, Peru and Chile. Mining figures reported for 1965 list the U.S.S.R. at 40,000 flasks, China 26,000, compared to 18,700 (9,695 in the first half, 1966) for the United States.

Records maintained by the U.S. Bureau of Mines covering the period, 1850–1961, disclose California as the major domestic producer with 2,772,180 flasks and Texas second with less than one-fifteenth this output.

The estimated existing United States resources are 1.5 million flasks. A thirty-year supply is in sight at present consumption rates of 60,000 flasks per year and selling price of $500 per flask. Newly mined ore in the United States is of greatly inferior quality compared to that of Spain and Italy. In the last decade it averaged 7.5–9.2 lb mercury per ton. The richest ores, found in the Almaden mine, contain at least 6% by weight of mercury and even beyond 20%. The next grade, such as in the Monte-Amiata of Italy, runs from 0.6–3% mercury content and Mexican mine assays range from 0.3–0.8%.

Metal recovery from sulfide ores, the source of practically all world production, is essentially a roasting process in the presence of air. Mercury vapor is readily condensed and the by-product gases vented to the atmosphere,

$$HgS + O_2 \rightarrow Hg + SO_2.$$

The theoretical conversion temperature is 350°C, but the rate is impractical, and roasting is done at 600 to 700°C.

Several types of furnaces are in use, batch retort and muffle units for small capacities and continuous roasters in which the ore moves vertically as in the Hereshoff furnace or horizontally in rotary tubes. A flowsheet (Fig. 1) illustrating the refining methods of the New Idria Mining and Chemical Company plant in Idria, California typifies the efficiencies possible with low-grade ore feed. Mine-run ore is broken down to two-inch size and fed to four direct oil-fired rotary furnaces, each having a capacity of 100 tons per twenty-four hours. Oil consumption ranges from 5 to 7 gallons per ton of ore processed.

Furnace gases pass to dust collectors and then a bank of air-cooled condensers strips two-thirds of its mercury content; the remainder is trapped in a series of wood boxes from which the waste gases, sulfur dioxide, sulfurous acid and sulfuric acid are finally vented to the atmosphere. The overall recovery is 95% from ore having an average mercury content of 10 lb per ton. From the dust collectors and condensers the mixture of mercury with small amounts of cinnabar and soot is thickened using water to separate the lighter wastes. The concentrate is reacted with lime in the hoeing tables to reduce cinnabar chemically,

$$4HgS + 4CaO \rightarrow 4Hg + 3CaS + CaSO_4.$$

Mercury separated at this stage moves through cleaning tanks in which 1% aqueous HNO_3 solution wash removes any zinc or other metals. The mixed solids, separated at the hoeing tables, are fed to indirect-fired retorts where the mercury contained is freed by distillation and sent to the cleaning tanks.

Physical Properties

As the only metal which exists in the liquid state to temperatures below 0°C and as the one with highest vapor pressures, mercury differs sharply in physical properties from all other metals. Its unique physical and chemical

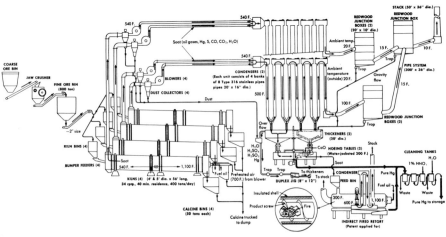

FIG. 1. Process flowsheet: Mercury extraction from low-grade ore (New Idria Mining and Chemical Company, Inc., California).
[Excerpted with permission from *Chem. Eng.*, **67**, No. 4, 121 (1960).]

TABLE 1. PHYSICAL PROPERTIES OF MERCURY

Accommodation coefficient, a	1.00 at -30 to $60°C$
Angle of contact	$128°$ at $18°C$
Atomic distance	3.005 Å
Atomic number	80
Atomic volume	14.81 cc/g-atom
Atomic weight	200.59
Boiling point	$356.9°C$
Boiling point rise with pressure	$0.0746°C/mm$
Compressibility	4×10^{-6} cc at $20°C$ from 99 to 493 atm
Condensation, temperature of	-130 to $-140°C$ on glass *in vacuo* (Seddig and Haase, 1949)
Conductivity	0.022 cal/sec/cc/$°C$ (variation with temperature—Hulm, 1950)
Critical density	3.56 g/cc (Lewis, 1953)
Critical pressure	732 atm
Critical temperature	$1677°C$
Crystal system	rhombohedral
Density	13.546 g/cc at $20°C$
	14.43 g/cc at m.p.
	13.959 g/cc at $0°C$ (Batuecas and Fernandez Alonso, 1948)
Diffusion of vapor	0.1124 cm²/sec
Diffusion of metals in mercury, D, cm²/sec $\times 10^5$	
Lithium	0.9
Sodium	0.9
Potassium	0.7
Rubidium	0.5
Cesium	0.6
Calcium	0.6
Strontium	0.5
Barium	0.6
Copper	1.06 (Cooper and Furman, 1952)
Silver	1.1
Gold	0.7
Zinc	1.57 (Stromberg, 1952)
Cadmium	2.07 (Stromberg, 1952)
Mercury	0.007
Thallium	1.03 (Cooper and Furman, 1952)
Tin	1.68 (Cooper and Furman, 1952)
Lead	1.16 (Cooper and Furman, 1952)
Bismuth	0.99 (Cooper and Furman, 1952)
Electrochemical equivalent	1.0394 mg/coulomb (univalent)
	2.0788 mg/coulomb (divalent)
Electrode potentials, normal	
$Hg^{++} + 2e = Hg$	0.85 v
$Hg_2^{++} + 2e = 2Hg$	0.79 v
$2Hg^{++} + 2e = Hg_2^{++}$	0.92 v
Emf, thermal, rel. to Pt—cold junction, $0°C$; hot, $100°C$	-0.60 mv (American Inst. Physics, 1941)
Enthalpy	6.942 abs joules/g at $50°C$ (Douglas et al, 1951)
Entropy	
S_1	18.19 cal/deg/mole at $25°C$ (Busey and Giauque, 1953)
S_s	76.2 cal/deg/mole at $25°C$
Expansion coefficient of liquid	182×10^{-6} cc at $20°C$

TABLE 1—*continued*

Freezing point	− 38.87°C (Chino, 1949)
Heat capacity	0.0334 cal/g at 20°C (Busey and Giauque, 1953)
Heat of fusion	2.7 cal/g
Hydrogen overvoltage	1.06 v (Post and Hiskey, 1950)
Ionization potentials	10.43 v 1st electron
	18.75 2nd
	34.3 3rd
	(72) 4th
	(82) 5th

Isotopes of mercury

Mass No.	Half-life	
189	20 min	Au^{197} (p, 9n)
191	55 min	Au^{197} (p, 7n)
192	5.7 hr	Au^{197} (p, 6n)
193	10 hr	Au^{197} (p, 5n)
194	0.40 sec	Au^{197} (p, 4n), Hg(p,)
195	40 hr	Au^{197} (p, 3n), Au(d, 4n)
196	0.16%	
197	65 hr [24 hr]	Au^{197} (d, 2n) [Au^{197} (p, n)]
198	10.02% [2.3×10^{-11} sec]	[Hg^{198} (γ, γ)i
199	16.92% [42 min]	[Hg(n, n)]
200	23.10%	[Hg^{199} (n, γ)]
201	13.22%	
202	29.72% [2.4×10^{-11} sec]	[Hg^{202} (γ, γ)]
203	43.5 days	
204	6.84%	
205	5.5 min	

(National Bureau of Standards, 1950–1952; Atomic Energy Commission, 1952–1955)

Magnetic moment Hg^{199}	+ 0.4993 nuclear magnetons (Proctor and Yu, 1949)
Magnetic susceptibility	− 0.15×10^{-6} cgs (18°C)
Potential, contact Hg/Sb	− 0.26 v
Hg/Zn	+ 0.17 v
Pressure, internal	13.05 atm
Reflectivity	71.2% at 550 mμ
Refractive index	1.6 to 1.9 at 20°C
Resistance, pressure effect on	cf. Bridgman, 1952
temperature coeff. of	0.9×10^{-3} at 20°C
Resistivity	95.8×10^{-6} ohm/cm at 20°C
Solubility of mercury in water	20–30γ/liter (Pariaud and Archinard, 1952)
Specific heat	0.033 cal/g/°C
Surface tension	480 dynes/cm at 0°C
affected by adsorbed gases	(Foryst, 1951)
temperature coefficient	− 0.19 d/cm/°C (Pugachevich, 1947)
Vapor pressure	
100°C	0.2729 mm Hg
200°C	17.287 mm Hg
300°C	246.8 mm Hg
350°C	672.7 mm Hg
Vaporization, heat of	14.67 cal/g-atom at 25°C
Viscosity (liq.)	0.0155 poise at 20°C

Reprinted from Gordon and Wickers, Ref. 1, by permission of The New York Academy of Sciences.

properties which set it apart from even the other two members of Group IIB of the Periodic Table, zinc and cadmium, are attributable to its having only two valence electrons of 6s configuration which are considered relatively inert. A listing of some important physical data is found in Table 1.

Both the solid and liquid forms have a rhombohedric structure, each atom being surrounded by six others. In the liquid the interatomic distance is 3.005 Å, approximately twice the covalent bond length of 1.48 Å. The solid's interatomic distance is slightly shorter, 3.000 Å. All physical states of the element are diamagnetic:

	Magnetic susceptibility, cgs $\times 10^6$
solid, $-78°C$	-0.137
liquid, $18-20°C$	-0.162
vapor, $18-20°C$	-0.39

The vapor is colorless and entirely monatomic; at the critical temperature association to Hg_2 molecules is complete. Mercury is the only element other than the rare gases which forms monatomic vapor to such a degree at ambient temperatures. W. T. Hicks [*J. Chem. Phys.*, **38**, 1873, (1963)] calculated fugacity-to-pressure ratios treating the vapor as entirely monatomic but an imperfect gas. At the lower range, from 298.15 to 450°K the ratio was unity. The density of mercury vapor compared to air is close to the theoretical value, 6.93, corresponding to monoatomic species.

At ambient temperatures purified mercury in still air (47.5 g spread over a surface of 10.5 cm^2) vaporizes at an hourly rate of 0.007 mg/cm^2. The vapor pressure drops appreciably with lower temperatures, 8.5×10^{-4}mm at 15°C compared with 19.7×10^{-4} mm at 25°C, and one precaution used in the mercury-processing industry for minimizing toxic exposure hazard is to maintain indoor working areas somewhat cool.

The vapor index of refraction varies from 1.000924 at 6000 Å to 1.001238 at 3000 Å. Its thermal conductivity is 1.844×10^{-5}cal/cm^2/sec/°C/cm at 203°C and 2.035×10^{-5} at 607°C.

Some of the most effective mercury vapor absorbants are activated manganese dioxide which takes up 41.8 g Hg/100 g without any globules of the metal microscopically visible; cobaltous oxide and Hopcalite, a solid activated mixture of copper and manganese oxide. Activated carbon at 20°C absorbs a maximum of 0.6 g Hg/g carbon from air saturated with the element.

The compressibility of liquid mercury is approximately one-tenth that of water and is comparable to the solid metal. It is 50% higher than lead but much lower than the alkali metals. In hardness the solid approximates lead, Mohs scale 1.5.

Surface tension values vary considerably dependent upon whether the liquid is in contact with air, dry air, or in vacuum, and with its degree of purity. In carbon dioxide and water-free air at 0°C the surface tension is 480 dynes/cm whereas exposed to the atmosphere it falls to 472–477 dynes/cm. Measurements in vacuum at 20°C upon freshly formed surfaces using dynamic methods yield 475.5 ± 2 dynes/cm. Trace amounts of alkali metals lower the surface tension, whereas alkaline earth metals increase it and heavy metals have little influence.

The specific surface energy at 0°C has been reported as ranging from 513.4 to 545.4 ergs/cm^2, according to different investigators.

Interfacial tension between solid and liquid mercury surfaces is low, 7.7 dynes/cm; between water saturated with air and liquid mercury, $\gamma_{12} = 385.1$ at 18°C. Very little change in interfacial tension occurs when the water is saturated with neutral salts, but the presence of alkali or alkaline salts causes a marked increase and aqueous acids a marked decrease. Interaction of mercury with organic liquids, determined as the difference, between the interfacial tension and the interfacial tension calculated as though there were only dispersion force interactions, is maximal with highly polarizable organic liquids such as methyl iodide, ethyl mercaptan and nitroethane (50 ergs/cm^2). Aliphatic carboxylic acids are less reactive, (33 ergs/cm^2), while organic bases including aniline, diisoamylamine and diethylether show negligible binding. With the exception of *n*-butanol and *sec*-octanol most aliphatic alcohols are nonreactive. Electron donor-type compounds and dipoles do not interact, but electron acceptors and highly polarizable organic molecules do.

405

Parachor determinations based on measuring the surface tension of either elemental mercury or in its chemically combined form, diphenylmercury, are in approximate agreement,

$$[P] = M\gamma^{1/4}/D_{\text{liq.}} - D_{\text{vap}}.$$

$M = $ mol. wt.
$\gamma = $ surface tension

= 69.0–69.4 (free Hg)
= 68.7 (diphenylmercury)

Viscosity of the elemental liquid decreases with rising temperature and from capillary tube determination between 0 and 299°C, in dynes/sec/cm^2, is expressed as:

$$\eta_t = \eta_{0\circ}(1 + at + \beta t^2 + \gamma t^3)$$

where $\eta_{0\circ} = 0.016969$; $a = -0.0038926$; $\beta = +0.0000123$; $\gamma = -0.0000000144$.

Many metals have poor solubility in liquid mercury, but the element readily forms liquid metallic solutions or amalgams. Solubility data for metals in mercury (g/100g mixture) at 18–20°C are:

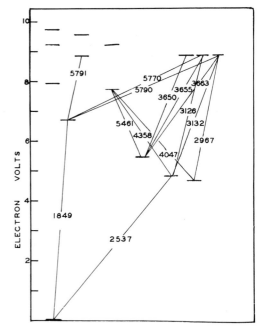

FIG. 2. Simplified energy-level diagram for mercury from Ref. 1, E. F. Lowry, p. 417. (Permission of The New York Academy of Sciences).

Most Soluble	Soluble	Least Soluble
In 56.5	Sn 0.62	Al 3×10^{-3}
Ti 42.8	Ba 0.33	Cu 2×10^{-3}
Cd 4.92	Ca 0.30	V $< 5 \times 10^{-5}$
Cs 4.34	Mg 0.24	Mo $< 2 \times 10^{-5}$
Zn 2.15	Au 0.13	Ti,W $< 1 \times 10^{-5}$
Pb 1.3	Ag 0.042	Fe 1.5×10^{-6}
Bi 1.4	Li 0.09	Ni $< 2 \times 10^{-6}$
K 0.8	Pt 0.02	Co $< 1 \times 10^{-6}$
Na 0.68		Cr 4×10^{-7}

Energy Level, electron volts	Frequency, Å	Application
4.86	2537	fluorescent and germicidal lamps
5.43	3650	black light for fluorescent signs inspection devices
	5460	standard of length for interferometry
6.7	1849	ozone-producing devices
8.8	3126, 3132	sun, photochemical lamps
	4047 4358 5461	visible light

Mercury is poorly soluble in organic solvents: at 20°C 2.0 mg/liter in benzene and 7.0 mg/liter in dioxane. It dissolves in liquid white phosphorus, forming a perfectly clear solution; the concentration reached is 0.285 mg Hg/g P$_4$ at 25°C, or 3.7×10^{-5} Hcc g/cc P$_4$.

Mercury absorbs energies and upon return to lower and ground states emits radiation at frequencies of significance for practical applications. The energy levels and resultant emissions, noted in angstroms, are diagrammed in Fig. 2.

The metastable levels at 4.7 and 5.4 electron volts, because of a relatively long lifetime, approximating one millisecond, are important in cumulative ionization; this effect is put to use in mercury pool rectifiers and thyratrons. In the gaseous state there are two ionization potentials, 10.38 and 18.67 volts; even the first is higher than any cation-forming element except hydrogen (13.53 volts).

The electrochemical properties are extensively reviewed in Gmelin, Part A, Number 2 (1962), (Ref. 4).

Purification

The metal is freed from impurities by using a combination of physical and chemical properties systematized in Table 2. The U.S. National Bureau of Standards utilizes a practical and efficient technique: dirt is removed by filtration through fritted glass, and base metals with a 12–16 hr air-agitated nitric acid wash (1 part conc. HNO_3 + 9 parts H_2O) followed with distilled water washing and drying. Repetition of these steps further lowers impurity levels. The metal is then distilled under reduced pressure in the presence of air, filtered through perforated filter paper, distilled under high vacuum in all-glass equipment and finally stored in acid-cleaned soft-glass bottles.

A recent report indicates that a counter-current wash of mercury with a mercuric nitrate-nitric acid solution, both fed continuously in a glass column packed with stainless steel Raschig rings, yields metal in a single pass with one-tenth the oxide content of redistilled mercury. Nuclear fission-contaminated mercury in the same treatment is purified from an initial dose rate of 5,000 milliroentgens/hr to one milliroentgen/hr.

Chemical Properties

In liquid or vapor state the metal is non-reactive with molecular hydrogen but readily forms a hydride when its vapor is mixed with atomic hydrogen and exposed to radiation from a mercury arc. Electric discharge also causes mercury to combine when mixed with neon, argon, krypton or xenon. The resultant addition products, held together by van der Waals forces, correspond to HgNe, HgA, HgKr and HgXe.

TABLE 2. REMOVAL OF METALS FROM MERCURY BY DIFFERENT METHODS IN DESCENDING ORDER OF EASE OF REMOVAL

Order of absorption of oxygen by amalgams (a)	Metals removed by KOH (b)	Order of removal by HNO_3 (b)	Order in vacuum distillation (b)	Order in arc distillation (b)	Order in $1 N$ H_2SO_4 (c)	Order in acid $KMnO_4$ (d)	Order in potential series (e)
Na	Sn	Mg	Au	Mg	Zn	Zn	Na
Mg	Zn	Al	Pt	Al	Cd	Cd	Mg
Zn	Pb	Cr	Ag	Ni	Tl	Mn	Al
Cd		Mn	Cu	Cu	Cu	Tl	Mn
Pb		Cd	Sn	Sn	Fe	Sn	Zn
Sn		Ni	Pb	Pt	Co	Pb	Cr
Tl		Sn	Zn	Ag	Ni	Bi	Fe
		Pb	Cd	Au		Cu	Cd
		Cu				Cr	Tl
						Fe	Co
						Mo	Ni
						Co	Sn
						Hg	Pb
						Ni	H
						W	Cu
							Hg
							Ag
							Pt
							Au

(a) Christiansen, 1897
(b) Cowsik, 1934
(c) Coriou, Hure, and Meunier, 1953
(d) Russell, 1929
(e) Latimer, 1940

Reprinted from Gordon and Wickers, Ref. 1, by permission of The New York Academy of Sciences

Other chemical activities are:

Nonreactive to

Dry oxygen	Dry sulfur dioxide and trioxide
Nitrogen	Carbon dioxide, lower oxides of nitrogen
Phosphorus	Hydrogen sulfide
Hydrogen fluoride	Neutral chromate solution

Highly reactive with

Ozone	Hot aq. nitric or conc. sulfuric acid
Halogens	Phosphorus trichloride or bromide
Nitrogen dioxide	Ferric chloride, perchlorate
Hydrogen bromide, iodide	Sulfur monochloride, thionyl chloride
Hydrogen peroxide	Hydrogen chloride + traces of water

Oxygen slowly attacks the metal in the presence of traces of water; metallic impurities increase the rate. In air or oxygen red mercuric oxide forms; but at the elevated temperatures employed, the compound dissociates completely at 440°C to the elements. The bonding weakness of the two $6s$ valence electrons is apparent. Oxidation of the element forms either mercurous, Hg_2^{2+}, or mercuric, Hg^{2+}, valence states.

Ammonia gas containing traces of water causes one of the most hazardous reactions with liquid mercury. At one atmosphere pressure it forms a highly unstable, explosive reddish-brown compound, $(Hg_2N)O(NH_3)_x$, $x = 1$ or less. The oxygen is derived from the water. At ammonia pressures above one atmosphere a stable ammoniacate results, $(Hg_2N)O(NH_3)_x$, $x = 1$ to 8.

Hydrogen peroxide is catalytically decomposed by the metal, and in acetic acid can convert it to mercuric acetate. Other oxidants including alkaline permanganate, sodium persulfate, acid chromate, and vanadic salts form mercuric compounds.

Industrially, inorganic salts are produced by direct reaction of the metal with chlorine to yield mercurous and mercuric chlorides; with hot aqueous nitric acid to form the nitrates; and with fuming sulfuric acid, the sulfates. Excess reagent completes the oxidation to mercuric salts.

A variety of compounds results by reacting the element with metals. For example, the alkali metals interact exothermically and in the presence of air producing flame. Exclusion of air, using a solvent overlay such as toluene for shielding, prevents ignition. With sodium a series of products has been synthesized:

Compound	$NaHg_4$	$NaHg_2$	$NaHg_8$
Heat of formation, Q, kcal/mole	36	39.7	324.4

Compound	$NaHg$	Na_3Hg_2	Na_3Hg
Heat of formation, Q, kcal/mole	47.1	154.5	165.9 —

A sampling of some additional intermetallic compounds includes:

Hg_2K, Hg_2NaK, Hg_3Sb_2, $HgBi_2$, Hg_5Sr_2, Hg_5Ca, Hg_4Cs, and $Hg_{11}Rb$.

In chemical combinations mercury is also unique compared with other metals. It forms covalent bonding and stable linkages with a shared quartet of valence electrons. The halide salts are practically nonionized, whereas the organomercurials such as the covalent-bound alkyl-and arylmercury compounds are not affected by air or water.

The various hydrolyses of mercury ions have been determined,

$$Hg_2^{2+} + H_2O \leftrightarrows$$
$$Hg_2OH^+ + H^+ \quad pK_A = 5.0$$
$$Hg^{2+} + H_2O \leftrightarrows$$
$$HgOH^+ + H^+ \quad pK_A = 3.7$$
$$Hg^{2+} + 2H_2O \leftrightarrows$$
$$Hg(OH)_2 + 2H^+ \quad pK_A = 2.60$$

but none of its hydroxides have ever been isolated.

Mercurous compounds contain primarily the diatomic mercurous ion, $^+Hg\text{-}Hg^+$, in which one electron is removed from each atom and the remaining two valency electrons are shared by the two atoms. Practically all the mercurous salts, other than those of the strong monobasic oxy-acids, are highly insoluble compared with the corresponding mercuric compounds. In general, mercurous salts form no complexes and differ from mercuric ion in not being able to form stable covalent linkages with carbon or nitrogen. They convert fairly readily to mercury and mercuric compounds.

Mercuric salts compare with no element but hydrogen in dependence on anions for their degree of ionization. The least ionized are the halides, cyanide and thiocyanate. Sodium chloride is capable of converting mercuric sulfate to the chloride; this accounts for the so-called sodium chloride "poisoning" of mercuric-type catalysts in organic chemical processes such as sulfonation of aromatic compounds.

Neutron bombardment of the metal yields radioactive isotopes of gold, and alpha particle reaction produces platinum. Mercury isotopes can be synthesized by neutron bombardment of the element or its compounds. When gold is subjected to neutron interaction mercury forms,

$$Au^{197} + neutron \rightarrow Hg^{198} + beta\ particle$$

Quantitative determination of mercury in air can be made by measuring its light absorption at 2537 Å with an ultraviolet filter photometer (commercial mercury vapor meter).

In a sensitive radiochemical method contaminated air first passes through an aqueous solution of mercuric acetate and potassium chloride, the acetate salt labeled with Hg^{203}. The scrubbed air contains the same concentration of mercury as it did initially, but because of isotope exchange the metal is now labelled with the same specific activity as the solution. After quantitative absorption from air by Hopcalite, gamma scintillation counting measures the radioactive mercury. At concentrations up to 0.2 microgram/l in air the standard deviation is 0.004 microgram Hg/l and in the range, 0.2–1.2 microgram/l, 0.075 microgram Hg/l.

One of the newest and most sensitive techniques for determining mercury in all types of materials is neutron activation anaylsis. For a 0.5 g sample containing mercury in any form, irradiation for two to three days in a thermal flux of 10^{12} neutrons/sq cm/second provides a sensitivity limit of 5×10^{-4} ppm of mercury. After chemical treatment and mercury separation by distillation, the metal is deposited electrolytically on gold foil and gamma-spectrometry is used to measure the Hg^{197} activity (68-KeV x-quanta and 77-KeV gamma-quanta of 65-hour Hg^{197}).

Uses, Principal Compounds

The major consumption of mercury is for use in electrical equipment and control apparatus where its stability, fluidity, high specific gravity and electrical conductivity are unmatched. Additional applications are typified in Table 3, a summary of United States consumption in 1965, in 1966 and in the first three quarters of 1967. Total 1967 consumption in the United States was probably less than 70,000 flasks.

Mercury represents a substantial part of plant costs for electrolytic manufacture of chemicals. Chlorine-alkali production capacity of 100 tons/day requires at start-up from 75,000 up to 220,000 lb to serve as cathodes in the electrolysis cells. The latest advance to minimize such inventory is the use of rotating or centrifugal cathodes, whereby the mercury is maintained as a continuous thin film over a broad surface area.

In atomic energy-type power plant applications the liquid metal can be used to remove heat from nuclear fuel elements and control nuclear fission by neutron absorption simultaneously. It can also shield molten sodium from water and steam, and transfer heat in a novel three-concentric pipe arrangement.

Commercially, mercurous compounds have limited application. Mercurous chloride (calomel) as one of the oldest of drugs is still used for topical antisepsis. It is an effective antifoulant for marine paints, and in admixture with mercuric chloride (corrosive sublimate) eradicates several turf fungal diseases. In scientific usage it is best recognized as the calomel reference electrode mainstay.

Mercuric salts are readily converted in alkaline solution to yellow and red mercuric oxide, which are indistinguishable chemically; the yellow form is of smaller particle size, approximately two microns and the red, 10 microns or larger.

The major requirement for red mercuric oxide is the mercury battery, developed in World War II as a compact, stable power source. The yellow oxide is most widely used in the manufacture of mercury compounds, its finer size increasing chemical reactivity. A

409

TABLE 3.   MERCURY CONSUMED IN THE UNITED STATES (FLASKS, 76 lb.)

Use	Total 1965	Total 1966	Jan.-Sept. 1967
Agriculture (includes fungicides and bactericides for industrial purposes)	3,116	2,374	3,069
Amalgamation	495	485	320
Catalysts	924	1,932	2,077
Dental preparations	1,619	1,350	803
Electrical apparatus	14,764	13,643	9,271
Electrolytic preparation of chlorine and caustic soda	8,753	11,541	10,987
General laboratory use:			
Commercial	2,827	1,569	837
Government	—	—	—
Industrial and control instruments	4.628	4,280	2,067
Paint:			
Antifouling	255	140	}4,424
Mildew proofing	7,534	7,762	
Paper and pulp manufacture	619	612	334
Pharmaceuticals	3,261	3,668	1,479
Redistilled †	12,257	7,045	5,203
Other	15,402	15,632	5,829
Total	76,454	‡72,038	‡48,500

† Redistilled mercury is also consumed for many of the same uses as virgin mercury but a breakdown is not available quarterly.
‡ The items do not add to the total which has been increased to cover approximate total consumption.

From Mineral Industry Surveys, U.S. Department of the Interior, Bureau of Mines, Washington, D.C. *Mercury* (1966, 1967)

relatively small quantity is employed as an antifoulant for marine paints and in pharmaceutical formulations for topical disinfection. Mercuric chloride absorbed on activated carbon catalyzes the addition of hydrogen chloride to acetylene forming vinyl chloride. The chloride effectively prevents fungal attack upon seeds, plants bulbs and cuttings, and is used to amalgamate aluminum, zinc and other metals.

Organomercury compounds are of importance commercially as industrial antimicrobial agents.

Phenylmercury salts, including the acetate, borate, dodecenylsuccinate, nitrate, oleate and propionate are in tonnage usage as bactericides and fungicides for preserving aqueous systems against microbial spoilage; to prolong the useful service life of paint films; and in the protection of textiles, plastics, wood and other substrates against fungal deterioration. In agriculture they are effective for the eradication of fungal diseases such as apple scab, pineapple disease of sugar cane and rice blast. Alkylmercury salts are in worldwide demand for the control of seed- and soil-borne fungal diseases of barley, cotton, flax, oats, rye, sorghum and wheat. Among these salts are methylmercury acetate, dicyandiamide, hydroxide, 2,3-dihydroxypropylmercaptide, 8-hydroxyquinolinate, iodide and nitrile; ethymercury compounds, especially the chloride, are among the earliest effective seed protectants of an organometallic nature. The onetime important mercurial diuretics, sodium mercaptomerin and meralluride, have been replaced by nonmetallics. Several topical disinfectants, thimerosal and merbromin, are still in popular use.

Biological-Toxicological Nature

The main route of mercury absorption is via the respiratory tract. For an eight-hour daily exposure to air containing 0.1 mg Hg/m^3 (the maximum allowable under present health standards) and a mercury absorption efficiency of 25%, two to four micrograms Hg/kg body weight will be taken in. Normally, this quantity is excretable in 24 hours, mainly in urine and in minor amount from feces, tears, saliva, sweat and bile.

Passage through skin is a second, significant means of uptake. The earliest writings on mercury poisoning describe topical mercurial unctions for syphilis as the causative toxicant. Mercurialism was one of the first recognized occupational diseases; miners were put on a six-hour work day and shifted to the outdoors periodically as a preventive measure.

The gastrointestinal tract serves only occasionally as a mercury sorption pathway. However, mercury is found in most tissues of adults and this source is thought to be dietary intake; approximately 20 micrograms are present in the average daily food consumed. Present regulations of the U.S. Food and Drug Administration allow as a residue in foodstuffs 0.00 part per million Hg addition to the background level.

Apparently the relatively high lipid solubility of the element assists in its widespread distribution to tissues, including migration through the brain "barrier membrane." It resembles the lipoidal dialkyl and mono-alkylmercurials in this respect. The metal is oxidized after transport *in vivo* and binds to proteins, through linkage with sulfhydryl groups and possibly amino and hydroxyl substituents as well. For periods as long as six months following such exposure mercury has been found in urine at levels of 0.03 to 0.07 mg/liter.

Actually, the question remains as to how much mercury can be absorbed without harmful effects. In studies reported by Dr. L. Goldwater and associates (Ref. 5) workmen who were exposed for significant time periods to phenylmercury compounds in air at concentrations equivalent to 0.1 mg/m^3 of Hg showed no harmful effects. In other medical literature accounts the ingestion of 500 g Hg (elemental) caused no poisoning; two g of metallic mercury taken intravenously in a suicide attempt produced subacute poisoning which cleared after 3 days.

The toxic signs of mercury illness are readily recognized. Vapor inhalation chronic toxicity is marked by sore throat, listlessness, tremors, abdominal discomfort and other signs, along with urinary mercury excretion ranging from 300 to 1200 micrograms/24 hr. Loss of kidney function leads to death. Other chronic disease

indications are nervousness, irritability and personality changes termed erethism. High air concentrations damage lung tissue. Acute poisoning is accompanied by severe gastro-intestinal symptoms.

Preventative measures are necessary for the safe handling of mercury and its compounds. All materials should be kept segregated under good ventilation, both in the immediate working area and generally. Atmospheric concentrations of the metal must be monitored and good "housekeeping" is essential. Personnel exposed to the hazards should employ protective equipment such as impermeable gloves and eye protection; in work areas containing dust or vapor inhalation possibilities, respirators equipped with specially prepared absorbants must be worn (see Ref. 1, L. J. Goldwater, p. 501).

Interestingly, certain plant species including roses and sunflower are extremely sensitive to mercury vapor in a confined atmosphere.

Metal chelating agents are of value in helping to remove or inactivate mercurials. N-acetylpenicillamine, 2,3-dimercaptopropanol (BAL) and ethylene diaminetetraacetic acid have been employed clinically as complexants to speed the excretion of mercury and heavy metals.

References

1. *Annals of The New York Academy of Sciences,* O. v. St. Whitelock, Editor-in-Chief, "Mercury and its Compounds," **65** (5), 357 (1957).
2. Battigelli, M. C., "Mercury Toxicity from Industrial Exposure," *J. Occupational Medicine,* **2** (7, 8), 337, 394 (1960).
3. Bidstrup, P. L., "Toxicity of Mercury and its Compounds," New York, Elsevier Publishing Co., 1964.
4. Meyer, R. J., "Gmelin's Handbuch der Anorganische Chemie," 8th Edition, "Quecksilber, History, Occurrence, Preparation, Physical Properties," Part A, No. 1, Weinheim/Bergstrasse, Germany, Verlag Chemie, GMBH, (1960); *ibid,* "Electrochemistry, Chemical Properties, Alloys," Part A, No. 2 (1962); *ibid,* "Compounds of Mercury," Part B, No. 1 (1964).
5. Ladd, A. C., Goldwater, L. J., and Jacobs, M. B., "Absorption and Excretion of Mercury in Man," *Archives of Environmental Health,* **9,** 43 (1964).

6. Pascal, P., "*Nouveau Traite De Chimie Minerale*," Vol. 5, Paris, France, Masson et Cie, 1962.
7. Sidgwick, N. V., "The Chemical Elements and Their Compounds," Vol. 1, p. 285, London, England, Oxford University Press, 1950.
8. Smithells, C. J., "Metals Reference Book," Vol. 1 and 2, No. 3, Washington, D.C., Butterworth & Co., Inc., 1962.
9. Spiegl, C. J., "The Industrial Hygiene and Toxicology of Mercury," UR-469, The University of Rochester Atomic Energy Project, Rochester, New York, The University of Rochester, 1957.
10. United States Department of the Interior, Bureau of Mines, Information Circular 8252, "Mercury Potential of the United States," (1965); *ibid*, Information Circular 7941, "Mercury, A Materials Survey," (1959).

NATHANIEL GRIER

MOLYBDENUM

Molybdenum, symbol Mo, atomic number 42, atomic weight 95.94, is in Group VIB of the Periodic Table and is thus related to chromium and tungsten. The neutral Mo atom contains, in addition to the completed shell of krypton with 36 electrons, another 5 electrons in the N shell and one in the O shell, in which the arrangement of electrons is $4s^2, 4p^6, 4d^5, 5s^1$. Some characteristic properties of molybdenum, e.g., paramagnetism, the tendency of ions to form complex compounds, and the color of compounds, have been attributed to the fact that the N shell is incomplete. There are seven natural stable isotopes with mass numbers (in order of decreasing abundance) 98, 96, 95, 92, 100, 97, and 94; several artificial radioactive isotopes (91, 93, 101, 102, and 105) are known.

Historical Perspective

Molybdos is the term first applied by the Greeks and Romans to describe minerals that were soft and lead-like in appearance. The word *molybdenum* itself was first introduced around 1816.

Molybdenite was first identified by the Swedish chemist, Karl Wilhelm Scheele, in 1778 when he demonstrated that treatment with nitric acid produced a "peculiar white earth" with acidic properties. He assigned the name molybdic acid to this substance. He further observed that sulfurous fumes were given off when the mineral was heated and concluded that molybdenite was a sulfide of molybdenum. In 1782 P. J. Hjelm isolated the metal itself by reducing the oxide with carbon.

For the next hundred years little was done with the metal except to use it in certain chemicals and dyes. Then, in 1893, two German chemists, Sternberg and Deutsch, obtained a 96% pure metal by reducing molybdate of lime with carbon and then removing the lime with hydrochloric acid. The impure metal reportedly was used in experiments to substitute molybdenum for tungsten in tool steels. In 1894 an attempt was made to produce molybdenum in an electric furnace but the carbon content—9%—made it unsatisfactory for use.

The first recorded use of molybdenum as an alloying element in steel occurred in 1894 when Schneider & Co. produced molybdenum bearing armor plate at its Creusot Works. A short time later the French chemist, Henri Moissan, succeeded in obtaining 99.98% pure metal by reduction in an electric furnace. Moissan devoted a considerable amount of study to the metal's physical and chemical properties. He established the atomic weight, electrical conductivity and many of its other now known qualities. As a result of Moisson's work, the metal achieved commercial importance for the first time.

Production of molybdenum ore was sporadic until 1900; since then there has been commercial production every year. Among the early producing areas were the Knaben Mine in Southern Norway, plus several mines in Australia and the United States. Production in the United States halted in 1905 and was not resumed until 1914. World War I provided the stimulus that brought the fabulous Climax, Colorado, deposit into production and despite many lean years between 1919 and 1933 the prominent position of molybdenum as an additive and as a pure metal was assured.

At the outbreak of World War I, world production totalled some 200,000 pounds. The combined pressure of an inadequate tungsten supply (for which molybdenum was used to a small extent as a substitute) and a widespread rumor that the Germans were using molybdenum in their armament steels (which proved later to be untrue) started an intensive search for molybdenum deposits. By 1918, 1.8 million pounds were being produced.

The close of World War I left large inventories of ferromolybdenum in the hands of United States consumers who had accumulated the stocks in anticipation of military orders for "Liberty" aircraft engines and "baby" tanks. These large stocks, along with stocks at the mines, were more than sufficient to meet the small peacetime demand. As a result, the United States molybdenum industry collapsed; production ceased completely in 1920.

Since 1925, when the first industrywide specification for chromium-molybdenum steels was approved by the Society of Automotive Engineers, a chain reaction of metallurgical research and development has carried forward with notable effects. In 1933 world molybdenum production was approximately 5 million pounds and in 1938, over 20 million pounds. In 1966, Free World production was nearly 130 million pounds, principally in the United States and Canada.

Occurrence

Molybdenum does not occur free in nature. The only important production at present is from deposits containing the mineral molybdenite, MoS_2; however, some powellite, calcium tungstomolybdate, $Ca(MoW)O_4$, is treated to recover molybdenum, and in the past, deposits containing wulfenite, lead molybdate, $PbMoO_4$, were worked.

Free World production of molybdenum is concentrated in the United States, Canada and Chile. The largest producer is the Climax mine at Climax, Colorado. The second most important producing area (from primary molybdenum mines) is British Columbia, Canada. The next largest source is the copper industry, which obtains molybdenite concentrate as a by-product from several mines in the United States and Chile. The largest producer in this group has been the copper mine at Bingham, Utah. Molybdenum is also recovered as a by-product of tungsten mining at Pine

Creek, California. United States reserves of commercial ore are estimated to contain more than 3 billion pounds of molybdenum.

Derivation

At the Climax mine the ore contains about 0.4% MoS_2 and must be concentrated by crushing, fine grinding and flotation to form a molybdenite concentrate containing 80 to 95% MoS_2. Virtually all molybdenite concentrate is roasted in Nichols-Herreshoff-type furnaces to form technical-grade molybdic oxide, MoO_3, also known as roasted concentrate, which in turn is the starting material for manufacturing almost all other molybdenum products. It contains most of the residual gangue present in the mine concentrate.

The technical-grade MoO_3, either alone or in the form of briquettes with pitch, is used to add molybdenum to iron and steel melts. It is also used to make ferromolybdenum containing 55–75% Mo both by the electric arc furnace or thermite process.

Purified molybdic oxide is made by volatilization of roasted concentrate, the MoO_3 content generally exceeding 99.5%. Roasted concentrate is fed as a thin layer onto a "doughnut"-type sand-hearth electric furnace with a hearth temperature of 2000–2200°F. Air drawn over the heated surface removes the volatile MoO_3 through ports leading to bag filters. Since only 60% of the charge is converted to molybdic oxide, the remainder is collected and reclaimed for other processing. Other methods of producing high-grade MoO_3 include chemical processing, sublimation and distillation of the roasted concentrate.

Molybdenum Metal Preparation

Molybdic oxide and ammonium molybdate $(NH_4)_2 MoO_4$, are the major starting materials for the production of molybdenum powder. They are reduced by hydrogen in tube furnaces similar to those used for tungsten reduction (q.v.) at a temperature of about 1000–1100°C. A high-purity molybdenum powder is produced which can be consolidated either by powder metallurgy techniques or by arc casting.

Molybdenum powder is compacted mechanically or hydrostatically into ingots or bars, which are sintered by resistance heating. The sintering is done in a vacuum or in a hydrogen atmosphere, with the maximum temperature about 4000°F. Large ingots do not lend themselves to resistance heating and must be sintered by radiation or induction heating; ingots weighing several hundred pounds are produced in this way. The primary processing of sintered ingots is done by hot rolling, swaging or forging.

Commercially, arc casting is the main means of obtaining cast molybdenum ingots. The arc casting process comprises vacuum or inert gas arc melting in a water-cooled copper mold. The melting takes place in an arc, which operates between a vertical consumable molybdenum electrode and a pool of liquid metal in the mold. The electrode, composed of molybdenum powder, a deoxidizing medium (usually carbon) and sometimes alloying additions, is compacted and sintered before melting in a continuous operation. Ingots weighing more than a ton can be made in this way. The arc-cast ingots are extruded to billets, which may then be rolled or forged to the desired size.

Special production methods, such as electron beam melting, skull melting, zone melting, slip casting, direct rolling and vapor deposition from the carbonyl or pentachloride, have been tried experimentally.

Physical Properties

Probably the most important physical property of molybdenum in its present commercial uses is its high melting point of 2610°C. Only tungsten and tantalum among the more readily available metals have higher melting points. Other important properties are its high elastic modulus-density ratio over a wide temperature range, its high thermal conductivity, which is several times as great as that of most high-temperature superalloys, and its electrical conductivity which is approximately one-third that of copper. Further, no allotropic transformations are known.

TABLE 1. PHYSICAL PROPERTIES OF MOLYBDENUM

Atomic Properties	
Atomic number	42
Isotopes	
Natural	92, 94, 95, 96, 97, 98, 100
Artificial	90, 91, 93, 99, 101, 102, 105
Atomic weight	95.94
Atomic radius, coordination number 8, Å	1.36
Ion radius, Å	
Trivalent	0.92
Hexavalent	0.62
Atomic volume, cc/g-atom	9.41
Lattice	
Type	Body-centered cubic
Constant at 25°C, Å	3.1469
Thermal-neutron data	
nuclei per cc	0.0640×10^{24}
cosine of scattering angle $(1-\mu_o)$	0.9931
average logarithmic energy decrement (ϵ)	0.0207
2200 m/sec cross sections, barns	
microscopic	
absorption (σ_a)	2.5
scattering (σ_s)	7
total (σ_t)	9.5
macroscopic, per cm	
absorption (Σ_a)	0.160
scattering (Σ_s)	0.448
total (Σ_t)	0.608

TABLE 1—*continued*

mean free path, cm	
absorption (λ_a)	6.25
scattering (λ_s)	2.23
total (λ_t)	1.64
resonance integral (Critoph), barns	13
diffusion length, cm	2.09
diffusion coefficient, cm	0.699
Fast neutron absorption cross section, barns	
10/250 KeV	9
1230	6
Ionization potential, eV	7.2
Apparent positive-ion work function, eV	8.6
Apparent electron work function, eV	4.2

Thermal Properties

Melting point, °C	2610
Heat of fusion (estimated), kcal/mole	6.7
Boiling point, °C	5560
Heat of vaporization, kcal/mole	117.4
Heat content from 298.16 to 1800°K in cal/mole	$H_T - H_{298.16} = 5.48T + 0.65 \times 10^{-3}\,T^2 - 1692$
Heat capacity from 298.16 to 1800°K in/cal/deg/mole	$C_p = 5.48 + 1.30 \times 10^{-3}T$
Entropy (crystals), $S^0_{298.16}$, cal/deg/mole	6.83
Vapor Pressure, atm	
1727°C	3.9×10^{-10}
2227	4.3×10^{-7}
2610	1.7×10^{-5}
2727	4.0×10^{-5}
3227	8.6×10^{-4}
3727	8.3×10^{-3}
4227	4.7×10^{-2}
4727	1.8×10^{-1}
5227	5.5×10^{-1}
5560	1.0
Rate of evaporation in g/sq cm/sec	$\log(\text{rate of evaporation}) = 17.11 - 38{,}600\,T - 1.76\log T$
Diffusivity, sq cm/sec	
200°C	0.43
540	0.40
870	0.38
Specific heat	see Fig. 1
Coefficient of linear expansion	see Fig. 2
Thermal conductivity	see Fig. 3

Electrical and Magnetic Properties

Electrical conductivity at 0°C, % IACS	34
Electrical resistivity	see Fig. 4
Hall constant, cc/amp/sec	
(work hardened)	$+17.75 \times 10^{-5}$
Franz-Wiedemann or Lorenz constant	2.72
Hydrogen overpotential, volts	
(1×10^{-2} amp/sq cm)	0.44
Electrochemical equivalent, mg/coulomb	
(hexavalent)	0.1658
Minimum arcing voltage	17

TABLE 1—*continued*

Minimum arcing amperage	
24-v line voltage	10
110	1.5
220	1.0
Magnetic susceptibility, χ, emu/g	
25°C	0.93×10^{-6}
1825	1.11

Optical and Emissivity Properties

Optical reflectivity, %	
5000 Å	46
100,000	93
Total optical emissivity	
1000°C	0.13
1500	0.19
2000	0.24
Total normal emissivity	see Fig. 5
Thermionic emission in high vacuum, ma/sq cm	
1600°C	about 0.7
2000	85
Spectral emissivity	
3900 Å	about 0.43
6700	0.40
Radiation for 5500 Å at 20°C	54% of black-body radiation
Total radiation, watts/sq cm	
527°C	about 0.2
1127	3.0
1727	19
2327	68

Other Properties

Density at 20°C, g/cc	10.22
lb/cu in.	0.369
Coefficient of friction	see Fig. 6
Coefficient of friction vs steel at Rc44	
Dry	
static	0.271
dynamic	0.370
Humid	
static	0.405
dynamic	0.465
Internal friction after 100 cycles of reversed bending stress equal to fatigue strength at 2×10^7 cycles, in. lb/cu in./cycle	
room temperature	0.1
900 °F	0.1
Compressibility at 293°C. sq cm/kg	3.6×10^{-7}
Velocity of sound at 2.25 Mc, cm/sec	
Longitudinal wave (V_L)	$6.37 \pm 0.02 \times 10^5$
Shear wave (V_s)	$3.41 \pm 0.06 \times 10^5$
"Thin rod" (V_o)	5.50×10^5
Surface tension at melting point, dynes/cm	2240
Dynamic modulus of rigidity	
Dynamic Young's modulus of elasticity	see Fig. 7
Dynamic Poisson's ratio	
Static modulus of elasticity	see Fig. 8
Ratio of modulus of elasticity to density	see Fig. 9

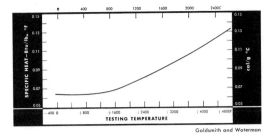

FIG. 1. Effect of temperature on specific heat of unalloyed molybdenum *(Courtesy of Goldsmith and Waterman).*

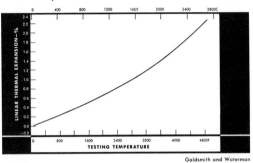

FIG. 2. Effect of temperature on linear thermal expansion of unalloyed molybdenum *(Courtesy of Goldsmith and Waterman).*

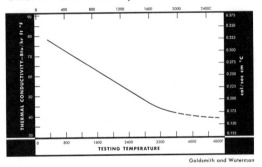

FIG. 3. Effect of temperature on thermal conductivity of unalloyed molybdenum *(Courtesy of Goldsmith and Waterman).*

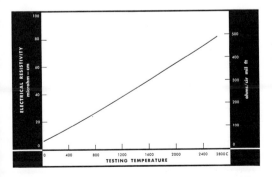

FIG. 4. Effect of temperature on electrical resistivity of unalloyed molybdenum *(Courtesy of Goldsmith and Waterman).*

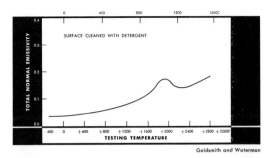

FIG. 5. Effect of temperature on total normal emissivity of unalloyed molybdenum *(Courtesy of Goldsmith and Waterman).*

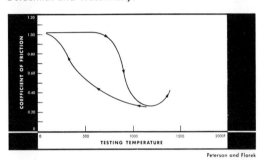

FIG. 6. Effect of temperature on the coefficient of friction of molybdenum vs molybdenum (load-1880 g; velocity-1.5 ft/min) *(Courtesy of Peterson and Florek).*

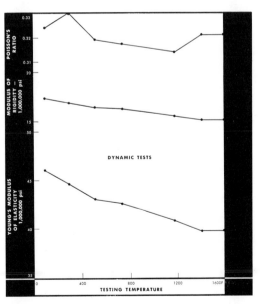

FIG. 7. Effect of temperature on Young's modulus of elasticity, modulus of rigidity and Poisson's ratio. (Tests conducted on $\frac{1}{2}$-in. rounds of unalloyed arc-cast molybdenum by the "Reflectroscope" method. Experimental error about $\pm$ 2% in modulus values and $\pm$ 4% in Poisson's ratio. In cold-worked sheet, modulus will vary with direction and amount of cold working).

417

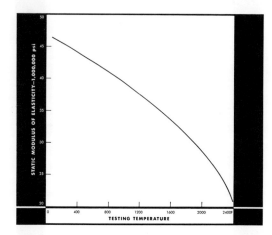

FIG. 8. Effect of temperature on the static modulus of elasticity of arc-cast molybdenum. (Values calculated from microformer-type strain-gage readings and represent averages of tests on molybdenum metal and three molybdenum-base alloys with alloying contents under 0.6%).

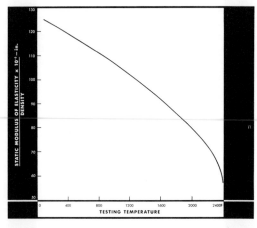

FIG. 9. Effect of temperature on the ratio of static modulus of elasticity to density of arc-cast molybdenum.

Chemical Properties

The position of molybdenum in the electromotive series depends on the surface condition. When passivated by treatment with concentrated chromic acid solution, $E_h = -0.66$ v, and when activated by cathodic treatment in caustic, $E_h = 0.74$ v. The potential in aqueous solutions depends on the pH. In one series of tests in buffered chloride solutions, the irreversible potential of molybdenum could be expressed by the following equation: $0.37 - 0.045$ (pH).

Molybdenum has particularly good resistance to corrosion by mineral acids provided oxidizing agents are not present. Table 2 presents data on corrosion rates in HCl, HF, H_3PO_4 and H_2SO_4. It is attacked by HNO_3 and aqua regia, molten oxidizing salts, such as KNO_3, and fused alkali.

TABLE 2. CORROSION RESISTANCE OF UNALLOYED MOLYBDENUM

%	Temperature, °F	Aerated	Corrosion rate,[a] mils per year
		Hydrochloric acid	
5	68	Yes (air)	0.40
		Yes (oxygen)	0.27
	160	No	1.1
		Yes (oxygen)	1.4
	Boiling	No	3.6
20	68	Yes (air)	0.10
	160	No	0.58
		Yes (oxygen)	1.4
	Boiling	No	0.90
37	68	Yes (air)	0.16
		Hydrofluoric acid	
25	68	No	0.13
		Yes (air)	0.22
	212	No	3.1
		Yes (air)	20.0
49	68	No	0.14
		Yes (air)	0.08
	212	No	2.3
		Yes (air)	16.0
		Phosphoric acid	
10	68	Yes (air)	0.27
	212	No	2.4
	Boiling	No	1.3
85	68	Yes (air)	0.20
	212	No	0.29
	Boiling	No	1.4
		Sulfuric acid	
10	160	Yes (nitrogen)	0.22
		Yes (air)	1.4
		Yes (oxygen)	nil to 9.1[b]
	Boiling	No	6.6
50	160	No	0.52
		Yes (air)	nil to 0.52[b]
	Boiling	No	2.5
95	160	No	0.12
		Yes (air)	nil to 0.21[b]
	Boiling	No	dissolved

[a] Average of five 48-hour periods.
[b] Range of five 48-hour periods.

Molybdenum shows good resistance to many liquid metals being considered for heat transfer media, such as Na, K, NaK, Li, Ga, Pb, Bi, Cu and Hg, even at elevated temperatures, but it is attacked more or less rapidly by molten Sn, Zn, Al and Fe.

At elevated temperatures molybdenum reacts with sulfur and with H_2S to form molybdenum disulfide, MoS_2. At moderate temperatures it reacts very slowly with iodine, while at higher temperatures the iodide is unstable. Molybdenum reacts with chlorine and with bromine above 250°C and with fluorine at room temperature. It does not appear to react with phosphorus, but at high temperatures it reacts with carbon and hydrocarbons to form carbides and with silicon to form silicides, chiefly $MoSi_2$, a highly refractory substance having good resistance to air oxidation up to about 1700°C.

Water vapor, SO_2, N_2O, NO and CO_2 have an oxidizing action on molybdenum at elevated temperatures.

Oxidation resistance. At temperatures over about 1000°F, unprotected molybdenum oxidizes so rapidly in air or oxidizing atmospheres that its confined use under these conditions is impractical. The stable oxide, MoO_3, melts at 795°C, but begins to sublime at 650–700°C. The rate of oxidation of solid molybdenum is not so extreme, however, as to cause combustion of the metal. There is no grain boundary weakening or internal oxidation; the molybdenum oxidizes evenly although there may be some preferential attack of corners or protruding sections. Uncoated molybdenum, therefore, is being used satisfactorily where very short lives are involved (as in some missile parts) or where the surrounding atmosphere is non-oxidizing.

Molybdenum's oxidation tendencies depend on the amount of oxygen and water vapor in the atmosphere. In vacuum, uncoated molybdenum has unlimited life at high temperatures. This is also true in the vacuum-like conditions of outer space. For example, the oxidation rate of molybdenum at altitudes approaching 200,000 feet may be as low as 1% of that at sea level.

Pure hydrogen, argon and helium are completely inert with molybdenum at all temperatures. Molybdenum is also relatively inert in carbon dioxide and nitrogen atmospheres up to about 2000°F. A thin carbide case may be formed in carbon monoxide at these high temperatures and a thin sulfide case in hydrogen sulfide. The type of stress in service will determine whether these cases will impair the usefulness of molybdenum parts. In some oxygen-deficient combustion gases, uncoated molybdenum appears feasible for temperatures up to 2500°F where a short life is acceptable.

Although much work has been done on coatings for molybdenum, no one coating—whether metallic or ceramic—has been found that provides long-term protection at temperatures in excess of 2500°F. Manufacturers of missile components have found that silicide coatings are effective for up to 10 hours protection at 2500°F.

Molybdenum Compounds

Molybdenum forms compounds in which it has the valence numbers 0, $+2$, $+3$, $+4$, $+5$, or $+6$. The chemistry of molybdenum compounds is complex because of the following factors: (a) molybdenum compounds readily disproportionate to yield mixtures of compounds in which molybdenum occurs in different valence states; (b) shifts between the several coordination numbers (4, 6 and 8) of molybdenum atoms result from only minor differences in controlling conditions; (c) molybdenum has a strong tendency to form complex compounds. With the exception of the halides and sulfides, almost no simple salts of molybdenum are known; (d) one of the most striking properties of the $+6$ valence state is the tendency to form isopoly and heteropoly acids.

Any system containing molybdenum, therefore, can only be extremely complex since two or more variables must each reach equilibrium independently to define a specific condition. These equilibria are independent of each other and are easily distributed individually. The product of an apparently simple reaction must thus consist of a mixture of compounds whose identities and proportions are determined by temperature, pressure, concentration, pH, redox potential, and proportions of the several original constituents and are changed by even minor variations of any of these.

In this work, it is not possible to exhaustively list the various compounds of molybdenum. Instead, the reader is referred to Killefer and Linz, and to Larson, who have published extensively on the subject.

Applications of Molybdenum

The consumption of molybdenum in the United States is primarily by the steel industry. In 1966, the steel industry accounted for 72%, alloy cast iron almost 9%, high-temperature alloys 6%, chemicals and miscellaneous approximately 9% and molybdenum metal somewhat over 4% of the total amount of molybdenum consumed. Experience indicates that this is generally the pattern of other nations as well.

Steel. The reasons for the extensive and growing use of molybdenum in steel and cast iron are straightforward. They involve a combination of factors including economy, availability, and equally important, metallurgy. Except for relatively short periods when demand exceeded supply, users of molybdenum have been assured of a supply of metal more abundant than either tungsten or vanadium and less subject to price fluctuations (especially relative to tungsten). A further consideration is the high recovery rate of molybdenum additions to the steel or iron; unlike boron, chromium, manganese, titanium and vanadium, the molybdenum addition is completely recovered in the ingot. Furthermore, substantially complete recovery is obtained from the molybdenum contained in scrap, a fact of considerable economic significance.

The form in which molybdenum is added to cast and wrought steels depends largely on the steel making process, on local conditions, and on the proportion of molybdenum to be added. Ferromolybdenum is adaptable to any steel making process but molybdic oxide additions are usually cheaper.

Molybdenum is at present used in nearly all kinds of steel: constructional steels (for better strength and ductility); stainless steels (for better corrosion resistance); elevated-temperature steels (for its remarkable contribution to creep strength); and tool steels (for better strength and hardness at elevated temperatures). The chief reason for molybdenum's extensive use in irons and steels is due to its significant contribution to the hardenability of the base material.

Chemicals. The application of molybdenum to colors was probably its earliest commercial use. Other applications today include reagents, ceramics (for manufacturing white pigments and to promote the adherence of vitreous enamels to iron and steel), and catalysts (especially in oxidation-reduction reactions). In the production of high-octane gasoline, molybdenum is one of the preferred catalytic agents because of its resistance to sulfur and other poisons.

Lubricants. Molybdenum disulfide was first used commercially as a solid lubricant in the early 1940's. With an operating temperature range of $-450°F$ to $+750°F$, molybdenum disulfide is often replacing both graphite and conventional hydrocarbon lubricants when extreme pressure and/or high vacuum environments are encountered. MoS_2 has a low coefficient of friction, resists extreme pressures, shears readily, and bonds to metals and plastics. Molybdenum disulfide is giving outstanding service by prolonging the life of parts where conventional lubricants have proved inadequate.

Selected Applications by Industry

Many applications (such as in the glass and missile industries) have depended strongly on the availability of large ingots. These ingots of molybdenum and molybdenum-base alloys (up to 3000 pounds) are produced in consumable electrode vacuum arc furnaces using a product of Climax Molybdenum Co. research, the PSM (press-sinter-melt) device for continuous electrode production from molybdenum powder.

Missiles and aircraft. Arc-cast molybdenum alloys have been applied as leading edges of control surfaces (as in the ASSET and Dyna-Soar space gliders) for rocket nozzles, and support vanes where high resistance to erosion is required at elevated temperatures. In jet engines, guide vanes, blades, combustion liners and after-burner parts have been fabricated of molybdenum.

Glass. Resistance to the action of molten glass, high-temperature strength and good electrical properties are the reasons for molybdenum use in resistance heating electrodes, stirring devices, pumps, and wear parts.

Nuclear. Most of the molybdenum going into nuclear energy today is in the form of conventional steels and alloys. Some of the most important nuclear power facilities in the United States, for example, have reactor vessels made of ASTM 302 Grade B alloy steel which contains, in %: C, 0.20–0.35; Mn, 1.15–1.50; Si, 0.15–0.30; Mo, 0.45–0.60.

Die-casting. Of considerable interest is the INCRA (International Copper Research Association) sponsored program to develop a better die material for die casting copper-base alloys than the commonly used chromium-tungsten-molybdenum hot-work steels. In a production mold made of TZM alloy, 26,000 parts have been run with no evidence of heat checking. A hot-work steel die is generally considered unuseable for a part of this type after 6,000 shots.

Biological Aspects

Acute toxicity and acute percutaneous toxicity tests on molybdenum disulfide have demonstrated that it falls in the "relatively harmless" class, the highest classification for describing the safety of a material. As a result the U.S. Food and Drug Administration raised no objection to the use of molybdenum disulfide lubricants for bakery oven chains. U.S. Public Health Bulletin No. 293 reports tests on several molybdenum compounds and concludes: "A careful study of the histopathological changes produced by long continued exposure of animals to the fumes or dust of molybdenum compounds and of animals fed these substances indicates that molybdenum compounds in general are of a low order of toxicity both from the point of view of observed chemical effects as well as from the histophathological point of view."

Molybdenum is an essential trace element for plant growth and is considered by some scientists to be essential for animal nutrition as well. Although minimum daily requirements for molybdenum have not been established, the element is contained in some of the mineral and vitamin supplements now on the market. A molybdenized iron sulfate has been prescribed in the United States for many years to combat anemia in pregnant women. Moreover, current investigations indicate that molybdenum in the diet contributes to healthy tooth enamel.

Apart from laboratory tests specifically designed to learn the possible effects of extremely high levels of molybdenum, the only deleterious effects of molybdenum that have been observed occur in cattle, sheep and other ruminant animals grazing on certain abnormal soils. A number of research organizations have demonstrated the interrelation of molybdenum and copper in the nutrition of these animals. Where molybdenum in the forage is low, sheep suffer chronic copper poisoning, which can be prevented by treating the soil with molybdenum. On the other hand, where molybdenum in the forage is high, cattle and sheep suffer from copper starvation. This can be corrected by feeding the animals supplemental copper, by treating the soil with copper salts, or by injections of copper glycinate suspensions. Both conditions have been found only in local areas with very limited soil types.

References

1. Archer, R. S., "Rare Metals Handbook," Hampel, C. A., Editor, 2nd Edition, pp. 283–303, New York, Reinhold Publishing Corp., 1961.
2. Archer, R. S., Briggs, J. Z., and Loeb, C. M., Jr., "Molybdenum Steels, Irons, Alloys," New York, Climax Molybdenum Co., 1948.
3. Harwood, J. J., "The Metal Molybdenum," Cleveland, Ohio, American Society for Metals, 1958.
4. Killefer, D. H., and Linz, A., "Molybdenum Compounds, Their Chemistry and Technology," New York, Interscience Publishers, 1952.
5. Jaffee, R. I., Editor, "Refractory Metals and Alloys III: Applied Aspects," Proceedings of an AIME Technical Conference, December 9–10, 1963; New York, Gordon and Breach Science Publishers, 1966.
6. Larson, M. L., "Organic Complexes of Molybdenum," Molybdenum Chemicals Bulletin Cbd–9, New York, Climax Molybdenum Co., 1950.
7. Manzone, M. G., and Briggs, J. Z., "The Less Common Alloys of Molybdenum," New York, Climax Molybdenum Co., 1960.

8. "Molybdenum Metal," New York, Climax Molybdenum Co., 1960.

9. Semchyshen, M., and Harwood, J. J., Editors, "Refractory Metals and Alloys," Proceedings of an AIME Technical Conference, May 25–26, 1960; New York, Interscience Publishers, 1961.

10. Semchyshen, M., and Perlmutter, I., "Refractory Metals and Alloys II," Proceedings of an AIME Technical Conference, April 12–13, 1962; New York, Interscience Publishers, 1963.

11. Goldsmith, A., and Waterman, T. E., "Thermophysical Properties of Solid Materials," *WADC TR 58–476*, 1959.

12. Peterson, M. B., and Florek, J. J., "Sliding Characteristics of Metals and High Temperature," *GE no. 58GL278*, October, 1958, quoted by F. Marks, "Lubrication Reference Manual for Missile and Space Vehicle Propulsion at Temperatures above 700°F," *WADC TR 58–638*, Vol. I, Part I, 1959.

A. J. HERZIG
J. Z. BRIGGS

N

NEODYMIUM

Discovery and History

Neodymium (atomic no. 60) is the fourth member of the lanthanide series and is a so-called "true" rare earth element. The rare earths are inner transition elements characterized by electrons successively filling the incomplete $4f$ subshell. Neodymium has an idealized outer electronic configuration $4f^3 5d^1 6s^2$, with a probable configuration $4f^4 6s^2$. All of the rare earths including neodymium are geochemically similar and occur in nature closely associated with one another. The separation and identification of these elements has proved to be an outstanding achievement in chemical history.

In June of 1885, Baron von Welsbach announced to the Vienna Academy of Sciences that he had succeeded in splitting didymia into two new rare earths; this was accomplished by repeated fractionation of ammonium didymium nitrate. He proposed the names praseodymia (green twin) and neodymia (new twin) for the new compounds. Although many chemists were skeptical his former professor Robert Bunsen immediately recognized that a splitting of didymium had been accomplished. Neither neodymia nor praseodymia have ever been decomposed into simpler oxides.

During the ensuing years, from the time of its discovery until the late 1940's, little use was made of elemental neodymium. Chemists were largely concerned with improving separation and purification, property determination, analysis, spectra, and reactivity of the element. Even with the rapid and extensive advances in rare earth technology during the past twenty years only limited applications have been devised for neodymium metal.

Prevalence and Sources

The lanthanide series is conveniently divided into two groups. Elements with atomic number 57 to 63 are classed as the cerium group or light rare earths and elements 64 through 71 are known as the yttrium group or heavy rare earths. During the formation of rocks nature distinguished to some extent between the two groups. Neodymium is associative with the cerium group elements.

Neodymium is quite abundant in the earth's crust, to the extent of 0.0024 per cent or 23.8 grams per metric ton. Neodymium is more plentiful than the common metallic elements: platinum, mercury, beryllium, lead, and cobalt. Free rare earth metals are never mined since they are found as cations in complex compounds.

Neodymium is found in significant quantities in four minerals, monazite, bastnasite, allanite, and cerite. The first two of these are primary sources of neodymium for industrial production.

Monazite is a rare earth-thorium phosphate with a monoclinic structure occurring in granites and pegmatized gneisses. After weathering, the heavy monazite concentrates as alluvial residues in stream beds and beach sands. The principle monazite deposits are located in India, Idaho, Brazil, Florida, North and South Carolina, Union of South Africa, and Australia. The United States ores are not sufficiently rich to be processed for the rare earths alone. Domestic monazite is produced with other marketable materials, usually zircon, rutile, ilmenite, garnet, and gold. Typical neodymium content in monazite ranges from 9 to 20%

Bastnasite is a rare earth fluocarbonate assaying from 2 to 15% neodymium. In 1949, a vast bastnasite deposit was located at Mountain Pass, California. Additional deposits of commercial importance are located in Lincoln County, New Mexico. Due to the favorable ratio of carbonate to fluoride, commercial processing of bastnasite is simplified.

The rare earth-calcium-iron-aluminum silicate ore is called allanite. It is common in occurrence and widely distributed in the western United States. No large scale processing of allanite is carried out. Cerite is a silicate ore containing calcium and iron with about 50 to 70% cerium group elements. This ore is found mainly in Sweden, but it is scarce and of only historical interest.

Extraction

Neodymium-containing monazite and bastnasite are cracked by heating with concentrated sulfuric acid. The resulting mixture is treated with an excess of water to dissolve the neodymium sulfate. Thorium obtained with the rare earths from monazite is removed by precipitation as the pyrophosphate. Neodymium is removed from thorium-free solutions by precipitation as the oxalate or as sodium neodymium double sulfate.

A flotation process is employed to concentrate bastnasite which has been crushed and ground to -100 mesh. After a physical separation and leaching of the gangue with dilute hydrochloric acid, calcining yields a 90% concentration of rare earth oxides. The concentrates are treated with mineral acids and neodymium is recovered as fluoride or oxalate.

Separation

Methods for neodymium separation can be discussed in terms of two broad categories, classical and modern. Under classical procedures, the most important one is fractional crystallization. Preceding World War II this was the technique generally employed. In the process part of a mixture is precipitated by altering the concentration of a salt solution. This type of separation is time consuming and does not yield a purified end-product.

Lanthanum is readily removed as the double ammonium nitrate from a cerium-free rare earth mixture. The remaining soluble fractions from this separation contain principally neodymium; continued fractionation recovers neodymium as the double magnesium nitrate at the insoluble ends. Commercial neodymium salts produced by this procedure are about 95% pure.

The most important modern method for purification of neodymium is ion exchange. High-purity materials are produced by hydrogen ion exchange sorbing neodymium ions on resin packed columns. Selective stripping of the ions is carried out in successive stages by flowing a complexing agent down the loaded column. The ion exchange method was recognized as an efficient means of rare earth separation in simultaneous publications which appeared in late 1947. F. H. Spedding and associates at the Ames Laboratory, and C. E. Boyd and co-workers at Oak Ridge National Laboratory pioneered in these studies.

Industrially, acid chelate elutions of either ethylenediaminetetracetate or nitrilotriacetate are used with a cupric-state retaining bed to resolve rare earth mixtures. Neodymium oxide with a purity of 99.999% is possible as a final product after ion exchange separation.

Another modern method, which dates from the mid 1930's is the liquid-liquid extraction technique. Emphasis has been placed on the tri-n-butyl phosphate-nitric acid system for separating the tripositive rare earth ions. The operational technique is well understood and it has proved to be successful on a large scale, but it is not economically competitive with the ion exchange method except for yttrium separation. Its major use has been in the isolation of cerium, thorium and lanthanum. Favorable distribution coefficients have been determined for neodymium and also samarium.

Derivation

The two principal means for deriving neodymium are metallothermic reduction and electrolysis of fused salts. The industrial production of high-purity metal employs the first method. The starting material is purified neodymium oxide. Anhydrous halides are prepared at 300 to 400°C as shown in the reactions:

$$Nd_2O_3 + 6NH_4F \cdot HF \rightarrow 2NdF_3 + 6NH_4F\uparrow + 3H_2O\uparrow \text{ and } Nd_2O_3 + 6NH_4Cl \rightarrow 2NdCl_3 + 6NH_3\uparrow + 3H_2O\uparrow.$$

The halides are reduced under vacuum or inert gas with alkali or alkaline earth metals at temperatures between 1000 and 1500°C, according to the reactions:

$2NdF_3 + Ca \rightarrow 2Nd + 3CaF_2$ and $NdCl_3 + 3Li \rightarrow Nd + 3LiCl$.

The first successful reductions of this kind were conducted in steel bombs packed with a lime or dolomite lining employing an iodine "booster" reaction. With this scheme the refractory oxides caused excessive contamination of the metal. Producers presently use refractory metal crucibles (tantalum or tungsten) placed inside sealed stainless steel bombs or under argon gas in a vacuum system. Neodymium prepared in this manner is 99.9% pure.

Commercial electrolytic cells are constructed of iron, carbon, or refractory linings suitable to contain the molten bath. Very little neodymium is electrowon, more significant is the alloy didymium. In the electrowinning of didymium (Nd 72%-Pr 27%) the mixed chloride is previously dried to a nearly anhydrous state away from atmospheric air. The electrolytic cell charge consists of the didymium chloride and NaCl, KCl, or $CaCl_2$, which is melted by externally heating. Graphite rods serve as anodes with the electrolysis run at temperatures between 800 to 900°C. The molten metal settles to the bottom of the cell and is periodically extracted. Didymium metal commercially prepared is often 98 to 99% pure.

Fabrication

The degree of success in forming neodymium metal is determined by the extent of tramp-element impurities. Fabrication of pure neodymium requires that the gas content of the metal be low. The major contaminate is oxygen, normally distributed in the form of oxide or oxyhalide.

The metal is melted by induction heating in a vacuum using tantalum or preferably tungsten crucibles. Copper chill molds are used in casting rods, bars, ingots, and plates. High-purity neodymium is readily cut with a hacksaw or free-machined with ordinary lathe tools and milling cutters.

Sheets can be warm rolled with intermittent annealing in an inert atmosphere. Examples of neodymium cast ingots and rolled sheet are shown in Fig. 1. In boring or deep drilling operations a copious flow of a nonreactive coolant is recommended. Neodymium does not tend to be pyrophoric in finely divided chips or powder, although care in handling should be exercised. A good grade of high-flash point mineral oil serves to protect exposed machined surfaces. This is a suitable

FIG. 1. Neodymium cast ingots and rolled sheet.

medium in which to store the metal; however, a leak-tight container filled with argon gas is recommended.

Physical Properties

Neodymium is soft and malleable; these qualities are dependent upon purity and previous treatment. An increased melting point and hardness with a decrease in ductility is caused by the presence of impurities. Neodymium undergoes an allotropic change from hexagonal to body-centered cubic at 862°C. Its electrical resistivity is quite high at room temperature and an additional increase of about 10% is observed on passing through the transition temperature. The metal is paramagnetic and obeys the Curie-Weiss law over a limited temperature interval. Vapor pressure data obtained in the liquid region (1528-1923°K) follow the equation: $\log P_{mm} = 8.102 \pm 0.034 - (16320 \pm 59)/T$.

Some important physical properties are shown in Table 1.

Chemical Properties

Selected properties of elemental neodymium are summarized in Table 1. Neodymium has a large atomic (and ionic) size compared with the trivalent heavy rare earths. There is only one stable oxidation state of $+3$, formed in aqueous solution with an electrode potential of 2.431 volts. Neodymium tripositive ion is reddish-violet in color with principal absorption spectra bands in the visible, ultraviolet and near infrared regions. It is a moderately strong reducing agent, the cation being more basic than Sm^{3+}, but less basic than Pr^{3+}. Principal neodymium isotopes are: Nd^{142}, Nd^{143}, Nd^{144}, Nd^{145}, Nd^{146}, Nd^{148}, and Nd^{150}. A freshly cut surface has a silver luster which will tarnish.

The metal slowly corrodes when exposed to

TABLE 1. SELECTED PROPERTIES OF ELEMENTAL NEODYMIUM

Chemical symbol		Nd
Atomic number		60
Atomic weight		144.24
Natural abundance, %		0.0024
Crystal habit	α-hex	β-bcc
Lattice constants, Å	$a = 3.659 \quad c = 11.799$	$a = 4.13$
Transformation temp., °C	$(\alpha\text{-}\beta)$	855 ± 9
Atomic volume, cc/mole		20.60
Metallic valence		$+3$
Metallic radius, CN $= 12$ Å		1.822
Density, g/cc		7.003
Electronegativity		1.19
Electronic configuration		$4f^3 6s^2 5d^1$
Oxidation state		III
Oxidation potential, 25°C (volts)		2.431
Ionic radius, Å		0.995
Melting point, °C		1016 ± 5
Boiling point, °C		3127
Temp. @ which vapor press. $= 1$ torr, °C		1741
Temp. @ which vapor press. $= 10^{-3}$ torr, °C		1197
Heat capacity, C_p @ 0°C, cal/mole-deg		6.51
Entropy, S_o @ 300°K, cal/mole-deg		17.54
$F\text{-}_o^T H_o^o)/T$, @ 300°K, cal/mole-deg		11.48
$(H_T^o\text{-}H_o^o)/T$, @ 300°K, cal/mole-deg		6.06
$\triangle H$ transformation, kcal/mole, $\alpha\text{-}\beta$		0.713
$\triangle H$ fusion, kcal/mole		1.71
$\triangle H$ vaporization, kcal/mole		74.7
$\triangle H$ sublimation, @ 25°C, kcal/mole		77.3 ± 1
Thermal conductivity, @ 28°C, cal/cm²/cm/sec/°C		0.031
Ionization potential, eV		6.31
Electrical resistivity @ 25°C, ohm-cm $\times 10^6$		64.3
Temp. coeff. of resistivity, 0° to 25°C, °C$^{-1} \times 10^3$		1.64

TABLE 1—*continued*

Hall coeff. @ 25°C, volt-cm/amp-oer × 10¹²	+ 0.97
Atomic susceptibility @ 25°C 10⁶ emu/mole	5650
Effective mag. moment, + 3 ion, Bohr mag.	3.3
Ferromagnetic Curie temp., °K	—
Paramagnetic Curie temp., °K	4.3
Neel point θ, °K	7.5
Hardness, as cast, BHN	35
Ultimate tensile strength, as cast, psi × 10⁻³	23.9
Tensile yield strength, psi × 10⁻³	22.9
Tensile elongation, %	10.6
Ultimate compressive strength, as-cast, psi × 10⁻³	35.5
Compressibility, @ 25°C, cm²/kgm × 10⁶	3.06
Young's modulus, dynes/cm² × 10⁻¹¹	3.79
Shear modulus, dynes/cm² × 10⁻¹¹	1.45
Poisson's ratio	0.306
Izod impact, as cast, ft-lbs, @ 25°C	8.28
Coeff. of expansion, @ 400°C, 10⁶	8.3
Air corrosion rate, @ 35°C, mg/dm²/day	2
Air corrosion rate, @ 400°C, mg/dm²/day	380
Thermal neutron cross section, barns	46
Target isotope and % abundance	Nd¹⁴⁶, 17.18
Activation cross section, barns	1.8
Induced isotope	Nd¹⁴⁷
Half-life	11.1 day
MeV of principal radiations	β^- 0.83, 0.38, 0.60; γ 0.53, 0.32 (others)

a dry atmosphere at room temperature, but at an accelerated rate in moist air. A hydrated oxide forms with an accompanying volume expansion resulting in sloughing away and exposure of fresh surfaces to additional attack. Neodymium will react slowly in cold water; hot water speeds the reaction. A surface passivation reportedly can be imparted by immersion in a 2-5% solution of nitric acid in ethanol. The metal dissolves readily in dilute mineral acids, but with difficulty in concentrated sulfuric acid. A phase field of interstitial hydrides forms from NdH_2 to NdH_3. Neodymium reacts by direct combination with elemental boron, carbon, silicon, phosphorus, sulfur, nitrogen, selenium, tellurium, and arsenic. Above 200°C the metal actively burns in halogen vapors. Liquid metal reduces lime, magnesia, alumina, silica, beryllia, thoria, and zirconia at elevated temperatures.

Principal Compounds

Several hundred neodymium compounds have been prepared in attempts to develop better methods of separation and commercial uses. Neodymium is moderately basic and will form compounds with most anions and anionic groups. In addition to the common inorganic and organic compounds, organometallics (e.g., ethylsulfate) form with neodymium.

Neodymium sequioxide is an important compound, particularly when employed in the mixture didymia. It may be formed by direct ignition of the metal, or by firing the oxalate, carbonate, nitrate, hydroxide, or sulfate. The light blue oxide will absorb both water vapor and carbon dioxide from the air. A completely hydrated oxide will result at room temperature. The oxide dissolves in strong mineral acids and in the weaker organic acids, formic and acetic. The anhydrous oxide is more dense than neodymium metal; and has a larger coefficient of thermal expansion.

Crude neodymia (about 65% pure) is used in counteracting the color of iron in glass. Purified neodymium oxide is employed to produce bright purple colored glasses. A number of neodymium activated host crystals (e.g., yttrium vanadate, calcium tungstate,

427

calcium silicate, or glass) are effective room-temperature lasers. An important microwave device is yttrium aluminum garnet doped with a small quantity of neodymium. Neodymium oxide supported on alumina serves as an active catalyst for the dehydrogenation of alcohol. The oxide melts at 2270°C, making it attractive for high-temperature refractory purposes. The compound has been used in combination with other light rare earths in glass polishes and in cores for carbon arc-light electrodes. Didymia strongly absorbs the sodium D line, making it useful in instrument filter lens, and welders and glass-blowers goggles.

Both the thermodynamics and preparative procedures of neodymium chloride and fluoride have been investigated. Two methods of preparation were described in the section on metal derivation. The water-soluble chloride may be formed by dissolving the hydroxide, oxide or carbonate in hydrochloric acid. Neodymium chloride hexahydrate will decompose to form the oxychloride when heated in the air. The anhydrous trichloride is very hygroscopic at room temperature. The compound has been a successful catalyst in the formation of condensed polyesters. Chloride solutions containing neodymium and other light rare earths are useful in industrial petroleum cracking. The fluoride forms as a gelatinous precipitate on the addition of hydrofluoric acid to chloride or nitrate solutions. Neodymium fluoride, mixed with other rare earth fluorides and oxides, is placed in cores of carbon-arc electrodes. The bromides and iodides have found little industrial application.

Neodymium nitrate hexahydrate is formed by nitric acid dissolution of the hydroxide, oxide or carbonate. Nitrates, specifically the double magnesium nitrate, have played an important role in the purification of neodymium.

The industrial process for opening monazite and bastnasite ores involves sulfates, therefore, their chemical behavior is important. Neodymium sulfate octahydrate may be dehydrated at 400 to 450°C in the atmosphere. There is an inverse solubility effect, thus the sulfate is less soluble in hot than in cold water.

Neodymium hydroxide can be removed from solutions containing Nd^{+3} ions by adding sodium, potassium or ammonium hydroxides. The hydroxide is a very insoluble compound and is used in purification, separation, and reclamation techniques.

The insoluble carbonate is easily removed from most salt solutions on addition of alkali carbonates. Significant quantities of this compound are prepared for convenient storage and industrial use.

Neodymium oxalate decahydrate is precipitated from acid solutions by the addition of oxalic acid or alkali oxalates. The reaction is important because it furnishes an excellent method for the recovery of neodymium free of other elements. The compound is easily filtered, serves as an intermediate in metathetical reactions and may be fired directly to the oxide.

Applications

About one-fourth of the rare earths produced are consumed in the form of metals and alloys. The use of pure neodymium in metallurgy is limited, the greatest demand being for research purposes. The metal does not possess adequate mechanical strength nor other characteristics to make it suitable for construction. In alloys, especially didymium, it does find metallurgical applications. The behavior of neodymium with other elements has been investigated in numerous binary systems. Research has shown that small quantities of neodymium or didymium added to alloys can improve their properties.

In cast iron and steel neodymium is added as either mischmetal or didymium. Few studies have been reported with the individual metal as the principal additive. Neodymium, along with other rare earths, acts as a "getter" for oxygen, sulfur, nitrogen, hydrogen, etc. The primary effect is a refining and cleansing in iron-base alloys. There is considerable disagreement among investigators as to the benefits derived by adding rare earths to steels. The complexity of the problem coupled with the expense in using individual rare earths has resulted in few applications, except in nodular cast iron.

Significantly higher strengths and creep resistance at all temperatures have been realized in magnesium alloys treated with didymium. A 75% neodymium inoculant has a substantial solubility in magnesium, thus promoting the improvements. Commercial alloys containing silver-didymium-zirconium exhibit exceptional properties in both cast and wrought magnesium.

The minor changes noticed by using didymium in aluminum and titanium alloys are attributed to its scavenging effects. Based on published data no differences are seen in the mechanical properties of such alloys.

Nickel and cobalt-based alloys have not been sufficiently examined with either neodymium or didymium as additives to draw reliable conclusions. Several workers indicate that the ductility and workability of arc-melted tantalum, vanadium and niobium are improved with rare earth additives. Neodymium (0.2 to 5.0%) in cast molybdenum reduces the hardness and lowers the brittle transition temperature.

Detailed studies have been conducted on the effects of rare earth elements on chromium and chromium alloy systems. Neodymium metal has been added to iodide chromium in 0.5 and 2% amounts and the alloy tested above 1250°C. The hardness values remained unaffected, but there was a substantial reduction in the rate of oxidation and nitrogen absorption.

Biochemistry and Toxicity

Investigators have found that in animals (mice, rats, rabbits) rare earth injections have pronounced effects. Injections of neodymium salts induced fatty liver, decreased blood pressure, caused hyperglycemia, and degeneration of the spleen. The fatty liver, which is more consistent in females, reached a maximum in 48 hours after injection and is characterized by an increase in neutral fat esters. It was noticed that neodymium phosphate is stored in rabbit liver and spleen. Only small quantities of stable neodymium are absorbed when introduced orally. Experiments with intramuscular injections of radio-neodymium have been conducted. Over 75% of the inoculant remained at the injection site. About 50% of the remainder absorbed in the liver and 25% was found in the skeleton. Elimination from the liver via the bile occurred slowly. The skeleton retained two-thirds of the initial concentration after eight months.

Neodymium nitrate causes decreased muscle tonus and loss of contractility in dogs, cats and rabbits. Neodymium salts cause intense irritation to the eye conjunctiva requiring one to three weeks for healing. On denuded cornea opacification is produced after a latent period of several hours or days. No damage or irritation occurs on intact skin. Extensive injury to abraded skin is noted, causing epilation and scar formation. In humans, neodymium vapors may cause sensitivity to heat, itching and a sharper sense of taste and smell. Rare earth chlorides (e.g., $NdCl_3$) are known to act as anticoagulants. They serve to decrease prothrombin and heparin, but have produced undesirable side effects. Neodymium nicotinate is a more active, less toxic anticoagulant. Experiments with the neodymium salt of sulfoisonicotinic acid proved it to be a suitable anticoagulant. Exercise of caution in the clinical use of these compounds is recommended. Antibacterial effects have been observed with didymic acid application to cultures.

Neodymium salts are rated as having a low-to-moderate acute toxicity. Mixtures of rare earths appear to be worse than the individual elements and intravenous inoculations can be lethal to animals. The dominant effects caused are both lung and skin granulomas with local inhalation or injection. The acute fatty liver is serious, but self-limiting and reversible without treatment.

References

1. Gschneidner, K. A., Jr., "Rare Earth Alloys," New York, D. Van Nostrand Co. Inc., 1961.
2. Gschneidner, K. A., Jr., "Rare Earths—The Fraternal Fifteen," Oak Ridge, Tenn., U.S. Atomic Energy Comm., 1964.
3. Haley, T. J., *J. Pharm. Sci.*, **54**, 663 (1965).
4. Hampel, C. A., Ed., "Rare Metals Handbook," 2nd Ed., Chapt. 19, New York, Reinhold Publishing Corp., 1962.
5. Kleber, E. V., and Love, B., "The Technology of Scandium, Yttrium and the Rare Earths," New York, Pergamon Press, 1963.
6. McMasters, O. D., and Gschneidner, K. A., Jr., *Nuclear Metallurgy Series*, X, 93 (1964).
7. "Minerals Yearbook," Vol. 1, (1964), 893, Washington, D.C., Bureau of Mines, 1965.
8. Moeller, T., "The Chemistry of the Lanthanides," New York, Reinhold Publishing Corp., 1963.
9. Spedding, F. H., and Daane, A. H., Eds., "The Rare Earths," New York, John Wiley and Sons, Inc., 1961.

10. Weeks, M. E., "Discovery of the Elements," 3rd Ed., 695, New York, J. Chem. Educ., 1956.

JOHN L. MORIARTY, JR.

NEON

Neon (Ne) is a member of the helium group of gases which also contains helium (He), argon (Ar), krypton (Kr), xenon (Xe), and radon (Rn). The helium group has also been referred to as the rare gases, noble gases, inert gases, and Group 0 elements referring to their place in the Periodic Table. (See article on **Noble Gases**.)

Neon (Greek *neos*, new) was discovered by Ramsay in 1898 as the volatile fraction from argon condensed at liquid air temperatures. The argon was obtained as a residue from atmospheric nitrogen after reaction of the nitrogen with hot magnesium.

Neon (along with the other helium group gases) is distributed throughout the universe. At very high temperatures in stars thermonuclear reactions between carbon and oxygen and helium can yield neon. Some stars become nova or supernova, a state where the energy release becomes so large as to cause the star to explode. Large quantities of gas are ejected into space and this at least partially accounts for the existence of neon in interstellar gas clouds.

Probably neon was part of the material which condensed to form the earth. Neon originally was trapped or occluded in the minerals of the earth's crust, but later escaped to the atmosphere as weathering of the crust occurred. A small amount of neon has been brought to earth by meteors and an even smaller amount has been formed by cosmic radiation. The largest part of the neon now found on earth probably has been present since the origin of the earth.

Derivation

The atmosphere is the commercial source of neon. Neon is recovered in plants operated for the separation of oxygen and nitrogen from the air. In a typical air separation plant, air is liquefied yielding a mixture consisting of nitrogen, oxygen, and small quantities of argon, krypton, and xenon. Neon and helium, which are also components of air, have boiling points below that of liquid air. Being noncondensable at liquid air temperatures, they collect as gases and must be removed from the condenser so as not to reduce the thermal efficiency of the condenser. This gas stream which is withdrawn has a neon-helium content varying from less than 1% to 12%. The composition of the gas varies with the rate of withdrawal and the condenser construction. The main constituent of this purge stream is nitrogen. Most of the nitrogen is removed by passing the gas mixture at 5-6 atm thru a small condenser maintained at liquid nitrogen temperatures. This causes a large fraction of the nitrogen to separate as liquid yielding a residual gas product containing about 46% neon, 19% helium, 20% hydrogen, and 33% nitrogen. Even in large air separation plants, the quantity of crude neon recovered is small compared to the quantity of oxygen separated. (See article on **Oxygen** for details.)

There are several processes for purifying the crude neon. The hydrogen can be removed by chemical oxidation followed by a drying step and the nitrogen removed by condensation from the pressurized gas at liquid nitrogen temperatures followed by adsorption on charcoal at liquid nitrogen temperatures. The product, sold as technical grade neon, contains about 75% neon and 25% helium. In another process pure neon and pure helium are separated from the crude neon in a single condensation-differential adsorption step. Usually, the separation of neon from helium is done by differential adsorption of the technical grade neon on cold charcoal.

The direct separation of neon from helium can be done by the condensation of neon at liquid neon temperatures. This is particularly useful when liquid neon is the desired product.

Small quantities of neon are shipped in low-pressure glass bulbs. Larger quantities are shipped in small, high-pressure gas cylinders. The total United States annual production of neon (all grades) in 1964 is estimated to be 3,200,000 liters (STP). A typical high purity product contains 99.99% neon.

Physical Properties

Table 1 shows the physical properties of neon as well as its abundance in the earth's atmosphere, earth's crust, and the universe. Neon is a colorless, odorless, and tasteless gas at ambient temperatures.

TABLE 1. PHYSICAL PROPERTIES OF NEON

Abundance in universe, number of atoms per 10,000 atoms of silicon	8.6×10^4
Abundance in earths crust, number of atoms per 10,000 atoms of silicon	2.68×10^{-4}
Abundance in earths crust, parts per million by weight	5×10^{-3}
Abundance in dry air, parts per million by volume	18.18
Stable isotopic abundance	$Ne^{20} = 90.92\%$
	$Ne^{21} = 0.257\%$
	$Ne^{22} = 8.82\%$
Atomic number	10
Atomic weight, $C^{12} = 12$	20.183
Critical point	
Temperature	44.40°K
Pressure	26.19 atm
Density	0.483 g/ml
Normal boiling point	27.09°K
Triple point	
Temperature	24.54°K
Pressure	0.4273 atm
Density	
Gas, 1 atm, 273.15°K	0.90002 g/l
Gas, normal boiling point	9.552 g/l
Liquid, normal boiling point	1.206 g/ml
Liquid, triple point	1.247 g/ml
Solid, triple point	1.444 g/ml
Volume of gas (1 atm, 273.15°K) equivalent to unit volume of liquid at normal boiling point	1340
Heat of vaporization at boiling point	429 cal/g-mole
Heat of fusion at triple point	80.1 cal/g-mole
Heat capacity at constant pressure, gas, 1 atm, 25°C	4.969 cal/g-mole/°K
liquid, normal boiling point	8.9 cal/g-mole/°K
Sonic velocity, gas, 1 atm, 0°C	433 meters/sec
Thermal conductivity	
gas, 1 atm, 0°C	110.1 cal/cm/sec/°K
liquid, normal boiling point	310 cal/cm/sec/°K
Viscosity	
Gas, 1 atm, 25°C	317.3 μ poise
liquid, normal boiling point	1.24 m poise

TABLE 1—continued

Dielectric constant	
Gas, 1 arm, 0°C	1.000134
1st ionization potential	21.563 eV
Minimum excitation potential	16.618 eV

Table 2 lists the unstable isotopes of neon.

TABLE 2. UNSTABLE NEON ISOTOPES

Isotope	Disintegration Mode	Half-life
Ne^{18}	$B + (3.2 \text{ MeV})$	1.6 sec
Ne^{19}	$B + (2.2 \text{ MeV})$	18 sec
Ne^{23}	$B - (4.39 \text{ MeV}, 67\%)^a$	
	$B - (3.95 \text{ MeV}, 32\%)^b$	40 sec
	$B - (2.4 \text{ MeV}, 1\%)$	
	$B - (1.98 \text{ MeV}, 92\%)^c$	3.4 months
	$B - (1.10 \text{ MeV}, 8\%)^d$	

a γ-transition at 1.65 MeV
b γ-transition at 0.436 MeV
c γ-transition at 0.878 MeV
d γ-transition at 0.472 MeV

Chemical Properties

Although neon does not form true chemical compounds, the following ions are known from optical and mass spectrometric studies: $(HeNe)^+$, Ne_2^+, $(NeAr)^+$, NeH^+. These ions are formed in electric discharge tubes. Although observed spectroscopically, they have only a transitory existence. Some typical reactions forming these ions are

$$Ne + He^* \rightarrow (HeNe)^+ + electron$$
$$Ne^* + Ar \rightarrow (NeAr)^+ + electron$$

where the * indicates an excited state of the atom.

Neon forms an unstable hydrate having a dissociation pressure of 160 atm at 0°C.

Uses and Applications

The liquid range of neon is 24.54 to 44.50°K. Liquid neon is beginning to find use as a cryogenic fluid in spite of being quite expensive. In some applications it is used as a replacement for liquid hydrogen because it is nonflammable and has a higher heat of vaporization per unit volume of the liquid. It has been proposed that gaseous neon be used in an intermediate stage of a hydrogen liquefier.

One of the most commonly encountered uses of neon is in "neon" signs, a name synonymous with any colored, tubular lighting display or advertisement. The neon sign is a high-voltage discharge tube containing gas at low pressure. These tubes do not always contain pure neon. The tube may contain pure neon or neon mixed with argon and/or helium. Mercury vapor may be used and sometimes the tube contains no neon at all. The color of the illumination depends on the gas mixture as well as the color of the glass used. In a colorless glass tube pure neon gives a red color. An orange color is obtained by placing neon in a yellow glass tube. Blue light is obtained with neon-argon or neon-argon-helium mixtures in colorless glass. These same mixtures give green light in yellow glass tubes. Phosphor coatings may be used.

Neon is used in some fluorescent light tubes where its purpose is to start and maintain an electric discharge. However, the illumination does not come from the discharge but from a phosphor coating inside the tube. The phosphor is excited by ultraviolet radiation from the discharge. Neon may be used with argon and krypton. Mercury vapor is usually present. Other illumination sources using neon are pilot lamps for electronic equipment (which may also contain argon), stroboscopic lights for timing fast moving machinery (which may also contain argon, krypton, or xenon), and sodium vapor lamps for street lighting. The sodium vapor lamp contains sodium and sometimes argon.

Numerous voltage regulating tubes and switching devices as well as special types of cathode tubes are filled with neon. Krypton and xenon may be used with neon in these applications. Neon mixed with argon is used in starter switches for fluorescent light tubes and in lightning arrestors.

Geiger-Muller tubes, used for the detection and counting of nuclear particles, frequently are filled with mixtures of neon and bromine or neon and chlorine. Also, ionization chambers, proportional counters, neutron fission counters, scintillation counters, and cosmic ray counters may use neon, argon, helium or mixtures of these gases with hydrocarbons, halogens, and carbon dioxide. Special grades of neon are employed in spark chambers to detect nuclear particles. The particle leaves an ionized path between electrically charged plates causing electric breakdown or a spark which is recorded photographically.

The laser is an increasingly useful tool and one of the more important gas lasers utilizes a mixture of helium and neon.

Neon has been suggested for use in decompression chambers to accelerate the removal of gases dissolved in the body fluids at higher pressures without itself dissolving appreciably during the pressure reduction steps.

Neon also serves as an inert gas shield in zircaloy welding for UO_2 fuel element fabrication.

References

1. Cook, G. A., Ed., "Argon, Helium and the Rare Gases," Vol. 1 and 2, New York, Interscience Publishers, 1961.
2. Hemstreet, R. A., and Kirk, B. S., "Helium Group Gases," in "Encyclopedia of Chemical Technology," Eds., Kirk and Othmer, 2nd Ed., New York, John Wiley and Sons, 1965.

R. A. HEMSTREET

NEPTUNIUM

Neptunium, atomic number 93, was the first of the transuranium elements to be discovered. The first isotope to be identified was $_{93}Np^{239}$, produced in cyclotron experiments by E. M. McMillan and P. H. Abelson at the University of California at Berkeley in 1940. Their observations were interpreted on the basis of the nuclear reactions

$$_{92}U^{238} (n, \gamma) \,_{92}U^{239} \xrightarrow[t_{1/2} = 23 \text{ min}]{\beta} \,_{93}Np^{239}$$

Using this β-emitting isotope, $t_{1/2} = 2.35$ d, McMillan and Abelson were able to show that the element possessed at least two oxidation states and differed in chemical properties from any other elements in the Periodic Table. Although it was suspected that decay of $_{93}Np^{239}$ should lead to the formation of an isotope of an element of higher atomic number, confirmation came only after the discovery of plutonium in 1940 by Seaborg, McMillan, Kennedy and Wahl. That decay of the $_{93}Np^{239}$ isotope leads to the formation of the important fissile isotope of plutonium, $_{94}Pu^{239}$, was established in 1941 by Kennedy, Seaborg, Segre and Wahl.

The principal neptunium isotope of chemical interest is the long-lived α-emitter, $_{93}Np^{237}$, $t_{1/2} = 2.20 \times 10^6$ y, discovered by Wahl and Seaborg in 1942. Weighable amounts of the $_{93}Np^{237}$ isotope were first isolated by L. B. Magnusson and T. J. La-Chapelle at the wartime Metallurgical Laboratory of the University of Chicago in 1944. The name of the element derives from that of Neptune, the first planet beyond Uranus in the solar system.

Source

Although both $_{93}Np^{239}$ and $_{93}Np^{237}$ are formed in uranium ores by neutron capture, the concentrations are exceedingly low and chemical recovery not practical. Kilogram quantities of the isotope $_{93}Np^{237}$, are produced as a by-product of the large-scale synthesis of plutonium in nuclear reactors. $_{93}Np^{237}$ is formed from $_{92}U^{238}$ by the nuclear reactions

$$_{92}U^{238}(n, 2n)_{92}U^{237} \xrightarrow[t_{1/2} = 6.8d]{\beta} {}_{93}Np^{237}$$

and in U^{235}-enriched power reactors by the process

$$_{92}U^{235} (n, \gamma) {}_{92}U^{236} (n, \gamma) {}_{92}U^{237}$$
$$\xrightarrow[t_{1/2} = 6.8d]{\beta} {}_{93}Np^{237}$$

In the usual processes for the recovery of uranium and plutonium from the nuclear fuel, neptunium is left in the wastes along with the fission products. Because neptunium has a multiplicity of oxidation states, each with its characteristic chemical properties, a variety of chemical procedures can be devised for the recovery and purification of the neptunium from these wastes. These include solvent extraction, ion exchange, precipitation and volatility processes. In some of the plutonium chemical recovery

plants, modifications have been introduced in the processes which allow the routine separation of neptunium as a by-product.

The known isotopes of neptunium, with their half-lives, modes of disentegration and some methods of formation are given on page 743 in the article on **Transuranium Elements.**

Neptunium Metal

The methods for the preparation of neptunium in the metallic state are very similar to those used for uranium. Commonly, neptunium metal is prepared by reduction of a fluoride with an alkaline earth metal at high temperature. The early microscale preparations of neptunium metal were carried out by reduction of neptunium trifluoride with barium vapor. After initiation of the reaction at 1200°C, rapid cooling of the reaction vessel was required to prevent loss of the low melting neptunium metal by diffusion into the crucible. Multigram preparations have been made by heating neptunium tetrafluoride intimately mixed with a 30% excess of metallic calcium in an argon atmosphere. Initiation of the reaction occurs at 740°C.

Neptunium metal is silvery in appearance. It is not obviously affected by short term exposure to air. The metal exhibits three crystalline forms between 20°C and the melting point. Crystallographic data for the different phases are given in Table 1. While

TABLE 1. CRYSTAL STRUCTURE DATA FOR NEPTUNIUM METAL

Phase	Symmetry Class	Lattice Parameters, Å			Density, g/cc
		a_o	b_o	c_o	
α-Np	orhthorombic	4.723	4.887	6.663	20.45
β-Np	tetragonal	4.897		3.388	19.36
γ-Np	cubic	3.52			18.00

the crystallographic properties of the α and β phases are well established there are some questions with respect to the γ phase. It has been suggested that diffraction lines due to NpO may obscure the lines of γ-neptunium, making it difficult to establish the structure of this phase with certainty. The best available evidence favors the assignment of a body-centered cubic structure to this phase.

Our knowledge of the physical properties of neptunium metal is by no means complete. In Table 2 are collected values for a number

TABLE 2. PHYSICAL AND THERMAL PROPERTIES OF NEPTUNIUM

Property	Value
Melting point	$640° \pm 1°C$
Boiling point	$3902°C$ (extrapolated)
Vapor pressure,1700–1950°K	$\log P(atm) = -(20610 \pm 1280/T + (5.10 \pm 0.70))$
Density, 20°C	20.25 g/cc
Transformation temperatures	
$\alpha \longrightarrow \beta$	$280 \pm 5°C$
$\beta \longrightarrow \gamma$	$577 \pm 1°C$
Latent heat of transformation	
$\alpha \longrightarrow \beta$	2.0 ± 0.2 kcal/mole
Heat of vaporization	$\triangle H_{1800°K} = 94.3 \pm 5.9$ kcal/mole
Entropy of vaporization	$S_{\triangle 1800°K} = 23.3 \pm 3.2$ cal/mole/°C
Heat capacity, 25°C	7.0 cal/°C/mole

of measured physical and thermal properties. The normal boiling point was obtained by extrapolation, using an estimated heat capacity change, $\Delta c_p = -2.6$ cal/mole/deg. The specific heat for the α-neptunium phase was determined calorimetrically. The values of the heat capacity at constant pressure, C_p, increase from 0.031_4 cal/g at 60°C to 0.040_2 cal/g at 207°C. The atomic heat capacity of neptunium calculated from these C_p values increases from 7.0 cal/°C/mole at 25°C to 9.5 cal/°C/mole at 207°C, thus, as in the case of uranium and plutonium, rising rapidly above the Dulong-Petit value of 6.0 cal/°C/mole. This has been attributed to a high electronic specific heat. Extrapolation of the experimentally determined entropy of vaporization to the boiling point gives $\triangle S°_{3902°C} = 21.1$ cal/mole/deg., in agreement with the value predicted by the Pictet-Trouton rule, $\triangle S°$ (normal boiling point) $= 22 \pm 2$ cal/mole/deg. The heats of vaporization of the actinides decrease as the atomic number increases.

The value of $\triangle H_{vap}$ for neptunium lies on a smooth curve through the points for Th, U, Pu and Am.

Electrical resistivity data for neptunium metal are summarized in Table 3. Above

TABLE 3. ELECTRICAL RESISTIVITY OF NEPTUNIUM

Phase	Resistivity, ohm-cm $\times 10^6$	Temp. Coeff, cm/ohm/°C $\times 10^5$
α	116-121	$43 \rightarrow 2$
β	105-110	$32 \rightarrow 0$
γ	110	-6

60°K, the temperature coefficient of the resistivity decreases monotonically with temperatures up to the temperature of the α-β transformation at 550°K. The high values obtained for the resistivity indicate that the metallic properties of neptunium are closer to the semimetals than the true metals. This is also true for other metals in the actinide series.

The thermal emf of a neptunium-platinum thermocouple has been measured between 20°C and 620°C. Changes in slope of the emf-temperature curve are noted at the phase-transition temperatures, i.e, there are discontinuities in thermoelectric power. The absolute thermoelectric power, $d\theta/dT$, has a low negative value in all three phases. The order of magnitude is -2 to -4 microvolts per degree Kelvin.

Neptunium Intermetallic Compounds and Alloys

Complete solid solubility between γ-neptunium and γ-uranium has been reported at elevated temperatures. An extensive solubility of uranium in the α and β phases of neptunium with considerable lowering of the α-β transition temperature has also been reported. A single crystal of α-Np-Pu alloy (43.9 at. % Pu), monoclinic in structure, with an axis length of 19.37 Å has been prepared. It would be expected that the alloying behavior of neptunium metal would be very similar to that of uranium, where the unique nature of the crystal structures for the different phases limits the extent of solid solution formation with many metals.

Several intermetallic compounds of neptunium have been prepared but little is known of their properties beyond the crystal structure data (Table 4). The Np-Al compounds are all isostructural with the corresponding U-Al compounds.

TABLE 4. NEPTUNIUM INTERMETALLIC COMPOUNDS

Compound	Symmetry	Lattice Parameters, Å		
		a_o	b_o	c_o
NpAl$_2$	cubic	7.785		
NpAl$_3$	cubic	4.262		
NpAl$_4$	orthorhombic	4.42	6.26	13.71
NpBe$_{13}$	cubic	10.266		

Chemical Properties

Reactivity. Like uranium and plutonium, neptunium is a reactive metal. It dissolves readily in hydrochloric acid, forming a black residue unless an oxidizing agent or a small amount of fluosilicate is present. The heat of solution corresponding to the dissolution of the metal to give the Np^{+3} ion in molar acid has been measured, $-\triangle H_s = 125.6$ kcal/mole. Neptunium metal is also classed as a highly electropositive metal in the sense that it is a strong reducing agent as indicated by the positive value for its oxidation potential.

The potential of the Np°-Np^{+3} couple in molar perchloric acid is

$$Np^\circ \rightarrow Np^{+3} + 3e \quad E^\circ = 1.83 \text{ volts}$$

making neptunium metal a somewhat stronger reducing agent than aluminum.

Valence States. Both in solution and in the solid state, neptunium, like its neighbors in the Periodic Table, uranium and plutonium, exhibits a variety of valence states. In solution the known oxidation states are $+3$, $+4$, $+5$ and $+6$. Solid compounds corresponding to all of these valence states have been prepared.

Componnds of Neptunium

Despite the fact that neptunium is now available in gram quantities, the bulk of our information about the anhydrous compounds of this element is derived from preparations made on the microscale. Because of the scale of preparation, x-ray crystallography was the primary tool used in the characterization of new compounds and the crystal structure parameters constitute the bulk of the physical data available for these compounds. The crystal structure data for the most important neptunium compounds are summarized in Table 5. The chemical procedures used in the preparation of the various neptunium compounds are generally based on those

TABLE 5. CRYSTAL STRUCTURE DATA FOR NEPTUNIUM COMPOUNDS

Compound	Color	Symmetry	Lattice Parameters, Å			Density, g/cc
			a_o	b_o	c_o	
NpO$_2$	apple green	cubic	5.425			11.11
Np$_2$O$_5$	dark brown	monoclinic	4.183	6.584	4.086	
Np$_3$O$_8$	brown	orthorhombic	6.584	4.086	4.183	
Np$_2$S$_3$	black	orthorhombic	10.3	10.6	3.05	8.9
NpOS	black	tetragonal	3.817		6.641	9.71
NpSi$_2$	metallic	tetragonal	3.96		13.67	9.03
NpN	black	cubic	4.887			14.19
NpF$_3$	purple	hexagonal	4.108		7.275	9.12
NpF$_4$	green	monoclinic	12.67	10.62	8.31	6.0
NpF$_6$	brown	orthorhombic	9.91	8.97	5.21	5.00
NpO$_2$F$_2$	pink	hexagonal	4.170		15.77	6.40
NpCl$_3$	white	hexagonal	7.405		4.27	5.56
NpCl$_4$	red-brown	tetragonal	8.25		7.46	4.92
α-NpBr$_3$	green	hexagonal	7.97		4.302	6.61
β-NpBr$_3$	green	orthorhombic	12.65	4.11	9.15	6.62
NpI$_3$	brown	orthorhombic	14.00	4.29	9.93	6.82

used for the preparation of the analogous compounds of uranium. Information on the preparation and chemical properties of the more important classes of compounds are summarized in the following paragraphs.

Heating neptunium metal in hydrogen at 50°C and one atmosphere pressure leads to the disintegration of the metal and the formation of a hydride having an analytical composition, $NpH_{3.6-3.8}$.

When neptunium compounds such as the hydroxide, peroxide, nitrate, oxalate, etc., of any oxidation state of neptunium are heated in air at 700-800°C, the product is neptunium dioxide, NpO_2. Although this compound is soluble in concentrated acids, the rate of dissolution is slow. Oxides richer in oxygen cannot be prepared by the procedure of heating the dioxide in oxygen as for uranium. An oxide analogous to U_3O_8 can be made by heating of ammonium dineptunate, $(NH_4)_2$ $Np_2O_7 \cdot H_2O$ or neptunium (V) hydroxide in air at temperatures between 275 and 425°C. This oxide dissolves readily in dilute acids yielding a mixture of Np(V) and Np(VI) ions. An intermediate oxide, $NpO_{2.5}$, has been prepared by a novel procedure. One process involves the addition of neptunium metal to molten lithium perchlorate. On bubbling ozone through the melt, a dark precipitate separates. The dried material yields pure Np(V) on dissolution in dilute acid. The same compound has been obtained by layering a solution of Np(V) in concentrated perchloric acid on top of the molten lithium perchlorate. After evaporation of the perchloric acid, passage of ozone through the melt yields the neptunium(V) oxide. Conventional procedures fail to yield the trioxide of neptunium, NpO_3 presumably because of the thermal instability of this compound relative to the analogous uranium compound. In an attempt to prepare this compound, ozone was bubbled through a solution of Np(V) in a lithium nitrate-potassium nitrate eutectic at 150°C. The dark brown compound formed was separated from the salt by washing with water. The formation of a higher oxide was indicated by the fact that dissolution of the dried material in dilute acid yielded a solution of Np(VI). From an x-ray examination it was deduced that the compound was $NpO_3 \cdot 2H_2O$, structurally similar to the uranium trioxide dihydrate. An anhydrous trioxide has not yet been prepared. The sulfide, Np_2S_3, is obtained by heating the dioxide with a hydrogen sulfide-carbon disulfide mixture at 100°C for 12 hours. The oxysulfide, NpOS, is formed as an intermediate in the reaction.

Two carbides are known, NpC and Np_2C_3. These have been obtained as a mixture by reacting metallic neptunium with graphite at 1200°C. A silicide, $NpSi_2$, has been prepared by heating the trifluoride with silicon at 1500°C. This is a hard metallic appearing material which reacts vigorously with $6M$ hydrochloric acid.

A nitride, NpN, has been prepared by reacting neptunium hydride with ammonia at 800°C. It appears to be inert to water but reacts slowly with hydrochloric or nitric acid. The phosphide, Np_3P_4, prepared by direct combination of neptunium metal with red phosphorus in a sealed tube at 750°C, does not react with water. With 6 molar hydrochloric it reacts vigorously to give phosphine.

A number of halides are known. The trifluoride, NpF_3, is prepared by heating neptunium dioxide with hydrogen and hydrogen fluoride at 500°C. Under the same conditions, replacement of the hydrogen by oxygen, leads to the formation of the tetrafluoride, NpF_4. The hexafluoride, NpF6, is prepared by heating NpF_4 in a fluorine atmosphere at 600-700°C. To prevent thermal decomposition, the product must be cooled rapidly. The hexafluoride is a moderately stable, volatile compound with physical properties intermediate between those of the uranium and plutonium compounds. Two chlorides are known, $NpCl_4$, obtained by reacting the oxalate or dioxide with carbon tetrachloride vapor at 560°C, and $NpCl_3$, formed by reduction of the tetrachloride with either hydrogen (450°C) or ammonia (350-400°C). Neptunium tetrachloride sublimes at the preparation temperature and the trichloride can be sublimed at 750-800°C. Attempts to prepare higher chlorides have been unsuccessful. The stability of the higher halides decreases with increasing atomic number of the halide. Two bromides can be prepared, reaction of neptunium dioxide with aluminum bromide in a sealed vessel at 350-400°C leading to the formation of the tetrabromide $NpBr_4$, and with excess aluminum, to the formation of the tribromide $NpBr_3$. Neptunium tri-iodide, NpI_3, is prepared in a similar fashion using aluminum iodide.

In addition to the compounds prepared by solid state reactions, a number of compounds have been prepared by precipitation from aqueous solution. These include a number of insoluble compounds of neptunium(IV), and insoluble oxalate of neptunium(V), and the neptunium analogue of the uranium(VI) compound, sodium neptunyl acetate.

References

1. Katz, J. J., and Seaborg, G. T., "The Chemistry of the Actinide Elements," London, Methuen and Co., 1957.
2. Seaborg, G. T., "Man-Made Transuranium Elements," New York, Prentice-Hall, Inc., 1963.
3. "Proceedings of the 2nd International Conference on the Peaceful Uses of Atomic Energy," Vol. 28, Geneva, United Nations, 1958.
4. Eick, H. A., *J. Chem. Phys.*, **41**, 1475 (1964).
5. Lee, J. A., Evans, J. P., Hale, R. O. A., and King, E., *J. Phys. Chem. Solids*, **71**, 278 (1959).
6. Cohen, D., and Walter, A. J., *J. Chem. Soc.*, 2696 (1964).
7. Meaden, G. T., *Proc. Roy. Soc.* (London), **A276**, 553 (1963).

J. C. HINDMAN

NICKEL

Nickel, Ni, atomic number 28, atomic weight 58.71, is a ductile face-centered-cubic metal, essentially "white" in color. It occurs in the Periodic Table in the first triad of Group VIII after iron and cobalt and just before copper (Group 1B).

Isolated first by Cronstedt in 1751, relatively pure metal was prepared in 1804 by Richter who also gave a quite accurate description of its properties. Fleitmann discovered in 1870 that a small addition of magnesium would render nickel malleable.

It is estimated that the earth's crust contains an average of about 0.01% nickel. Nickel ranks twenty-fourth in the order of abundance of the elements in the earth's crust. The total amount of nickel is greater than that of copper, zinc and lead combined. However, there are relatively few known nickel deposits that are important enough to be economically worked.

Sources

Nickel is not found as native metal. There are a considerable number of nickel minerals classified as sulfides, arsenides, oxides, or antimonides. Some of the minerals of commercial importance or of historical interest are shown in Table 1. Nickel is also found in a number of less common secondary silicate minerals and is known to substitute for magnesium in certain primary minerals such as olivine, hypersthene, hornblende and biotite.

The principal classes of nickel ores are the sulfide and oxide (silicate) types, with Canada, U.S.S.R., New Caledonia, Cuba and United States, the leading nickel producing countries.

In the sulfide ores, nickel occurs mainly as the mineral pentlandite. Iron and copper are also present along with amounts of cobalt and the precious metals, including the platinum group and gold and silver. These sulfide ores will contain about 0.4 to 3% nickel, 0.2 to 3% copper, 10 to 35% iron, 5 to 25% sulfur, with the balance consisting of refractory oxides. Such sulfide deposits are found in Canada, South Africa, U.S.S.R., Finland and Minnesota.

One of the world's largest nickel deposits was discovered in the district of Sudbury, Ontario, Canada in 1883 and by 1910 the Sudbury district sulfide ores had become the world's principal source of supply.

The oxide ores, called laterites, are the result of chemical action by weathering of nickel-containing rocks high in magnesium and iron. In the silicate type of oxide ore, nickel is contained in the lattice of hydrated magnesium iron minerals such as garnierite. The limonitic type of oxide ore consists mainly of hydrated iron oxide (goethite) in which nickel is dispersed. Although the oxide ores constitute the largest nickel reserves and are widely distributed, nickel production from them at present constitutes only about a third of the total.

TABLE 1. NICKEL MINERALS

	Formula	Crystal System
Sulfides		
Pentlandite	$(Ni,Fe)_9S_8$	Isometric
Millerite	NiS	Hexagonal
Polydymite	Ni_3S_4	Isometric
Siegenite	$(Co,Ni)_3S_4$	Isometric
Silicate and Oxide		
Garnierite	$(Ni,Mg)_6Si_4O_{10}(OH)_8$	Amorphous
Nickeliferous Limonite	$(Fe,Ni)O(OH) \cdot nH_2O$	—
Arsenides		
Niccolite	$NiAs$	Hexagonal
Gersdorffite	$NiAsS$	Isometric
Chloanthite	$(NiAs_{2-2.5})$	Isometric
Annabergite	$Ni_3As_2O_8 \cdot 8H_2O$	Monoclinic
Antimonide		
Breithauptite	$NiSb$	Hexagonal

Processing and Refining of Nickel Ores

The *sulfide* ores, concentrated by usual mechanical methods of crushing, grinding, flotation, magnetic separation, etc., are subsequently roasted to form a matte. The sulfide matte is further roasted to an oxide which is subsequently reduced in a pyrometallurgical operation and cast into nickel anodes which are then electrically refined to produce high-purity cathode nickel. Alternately, the sulfide matte is melted and cast directly into anodes which are electrolytically processed to provide nickel of similarly high purity. In another refining process, nickel from sulfide ores is extracted utilizing the carbonyl process discovered in 1899 by Langer and Mond. In this refining process, nickel and carbon monoxide are reacted under certain conditions to form a volatile nickel carbonyl which, when heated, decomposes to form nickel and carbon monoxide. The nickel is deposited upon nickel nuclei or seeds in a "fluidizer." The product is a very high-purity nickel in which cobalt is essentially absent.

The *oxide* ores (which are high in iron) are treated somewhat differently since the usual mechanical methods of separation employed in the sulfide ores are not readily applicable and the entire ore must be treated by pyro-, hydro- or vapometallurgical procedures.

Hydrometallurgical refining of nickel usually involves the chemical leaching of the various ores. Metallic nickel is then precipitated from the aqueous nickel salt solutions by hydrogen reduction at appropriate pressures and temperatures.

Some of the oxide ores are processed by a pyrometallurgical method involving melting, reduction and refining, the end product in this case being a ferronickel rondelle with about 25 or 48% nickel. The reduction is accomplished with ferrosilicon or with coke, depending upon the variation of the process used.

Physical Properties of Nickel

Nickel is fabricated readily using normal hot and cold working methods. The wrought metal is highly malleable, moderately strong, tough, ductile and highly resistant to corrosion in many media. It has good strength and ductility that persist to subzero temperatures. Nickel is ferromagnetic and exhibits negative magnetostriction.

Some important physical constants of pure nickel are given in Table 2. The atomic weights and the natural abundance of the stable isotopes of nickel are 58 (67.7%), 60 (26.2%), 62 (3.66%), 61 (1.25%) and 64 (1.16%).

Chemical Properties

In its chemical reactions nickel is similar to iron and cobalt, as well as to copper. However, it is less reactive than iron, as indicated by the

TABLE 2. PHYSICAL PROPERTIES OF NICKEL

Atomic number	28
Atomic weight	
(representing composite of stable isotopes)	58.71
(International value)	58.69
Stable isotopes	58,60,61,62,64
Radioactive isotopes	54,56,57,59,63,65,66
Crystal structure	fcc
Lattice constant, 24.8°C, Å	3.5168
Specific gravity, 20°C	8.908
Liquid nickel density, g/cc	7.9
Surface tension 1550°C, dynes/cm	1924
m.p., dynes/cm	1756
Melting point, °C	1453
Boiling point (by extrapolation of v.p. data), °C	2730
Vapor pressure, mm Hg, 1000°C	1.2×10^{-6}
m.p.	9.4×10^{-3}
2000°C	213
Thermal expansion coefficient	
at 0–100°C, per °C	0.0000133
Thermal conductivity, cal/cm/°C/sec	
(99.94% purity) 100°C	0.198
300°C	0.152
500°C	0.148
Specific heat, 200°C, cal/g	0.1225
Latent heat of fusion, cal/g	73.8
Latent heat of vaporization, cal/g	1487
Electrical resistivity, 20°C, microhm-cm	6.844
Temp. coeff. of electrical resistivity	
(0–100°C) per °C	0.0068
Magnetic transformation temp, °C	357
Modulus of elasticity, psi	
tension	30,000,000
torsion	11,000,000
Poisson's ratio	0.31
Emissivity (total)	
<25°C	0.045
<1000°C	0.19
Reflectivity, 0.30 micron (ultraviolet), %	41.3
0.55 micron (yellow green), %	64
3.0 micron (infrared), %	87
Work function, eV	5.0
Thermal neutron cross section (for neutron velocity of 2200 m/sec)	
absorption, barns	4.5
scattering cross section (avg), barns	17.5

electrode potential of -0.250 volts for the reaction $Ni = Ni^{++} + 2e^-$, much different from the -0.4402 volts for the reaction $Fe = Fe^{++} + 2e^-$.

Nickel is subject to attack by sulfur and sulfur gases at temperatures above about 350°C and at temperatures above about 650°C a molten eutectic of nickel and nickel sulfide forms which rapidly disintegrates the metal. When heated it also reacts directly with boron, silicon, nitrogen and phosphorus to form binary compounds. No compound seems to be formed with carbon except the quite unstable Ni_3C, but molten nickel dissolves 6.25% carbon.

No dry gases attack nickel at or near atmospheric temperatures, but, when wet, such gases as nitric oxides, chlorine and other halogens, SO_2, and NH_3 are appreciably corrosive. On the other hand, nickel is one of the most useful metals for handling HCl, Cl_2, HF, F_2, and Br_2 (when dry and in the absence of air) at temperatures of a few hundred degrees.

Probably the most impressive of nickel's chemical properties is its practically complete resistance to alkalis, particularly concentrated NaOH and fused caustics. This lack of reactivity exists at temperatures of several hundred degrees. The inertness is due to a thin black film of nickel oxide that forms on the surface of nickel exposed to alkalis. Widespread industrial use of nickel for the production and handling of caustic soda (NaOH) over long years of service has proved its value in this field. Nickel oxide, NiO, is formed by the direct reaction of nickel and oxygen above 400°C.

Nickel reacts with oxidizing acids, such as nitric acid, and also with hot sulfurous acid solutions, but it resists air-free sulfuric acid under 80% concentration.

Corrosion

Commercially pure nickel and most of the high-nickel alloys, are used to a considerable extent for the fabrication of equipment in the chemical and process industries and in others where their corrosion resistance is an important consideration. Nickel does not discharge hydrogen readily from the common nonoxidizing acids. The presence of some oxidation agent, such as dissolved air, is necessary for corrosion to proceed at a significant rate. Reducing conditions usually retard the corrosion of nickel, while oxidizing conditions usually accelerate it. However, nickel has the ability to protect itself against certain forms of attack by development of a corrosion resisting, or passive, oxide film, and, consequently oxidizing conditions do not invariably accelerate corrosion.

Nickel Compounds

Nickel has a $3d^8 4s^2$ electronic configuration and forms compounds in which the nickel atom has oxidation states of -1, 0, $+1$, $+2$, $+3$, $+4$. By far the majority of nickel compounds are of the nickel (II) species. Powerful oxidants are required to generate the Ni(III) and Ni(IV) moieties. The only well established examples of stable crystalline derivatives of

Ni(III) and Ni(IV) are the complex fluoride anions, $(NiF_6)^{-3}$ and $(NiF_6)^{-4}$. Even these materials are not stable in water solution, yielding oxygen and Ni(II). In general, nickel (I) complexes are binuclear and diamagnetic, examples of which are $K_4[Ni_2(CN)_6]$ and $K_6[Ni_2(C_2H)_8]$. An example of nickel in the formal oxidation state of (-1) is the hydrocarbonyl, $H_2Ni_2(CO)_6$, in which material hydrogen has no acid function. A number of derivatives of Ni(R) are known, the most common of which is nickel carbonyl, $Ni(CO)_4$. Examples of other nickel (R) derivatives include $Ni(PF_3)_4$, $(\phi_3P)_2Ni(NO)_2$, $(\phi NC)_4Ni$ and the anion, $[Ni(CN)_4]^{-4}$; R = radical, ϕ = phenyl.

The majority of nickel compounds exist as one of three geometric configurations: square planar, tetrahedral (coordination number = 4) or octahedral (coordination number = 6), the latter being the most common. The octahedron is usually slightly distorted. Frequently nickel achieves a hexacoordinated configuration through association of less stable structures of solvation to satisfy requirements.

Zerovalent Nickel Compounds. Zerovalent nickel, Ni(0), compounds are colorless and are often somewhat unstable. They are produced by formation of semipolar bonds between electron-rich ligands, i.e., NO, CO, PF_3, $P\phi_3$, etc., and the unfilled orbitals of nickel.

Nickel Carbonyl. Probably the most important zerovalent nickel compound is nickel tetracarbonyl, $Ni(CO)_4$. It is made by the reaction of CO on finely divided nickel at 200°C and 100–400 atm. Nickel carbonyl, as it is normally called, is a colorless mobile liquid with a high vapor pressure: 320.6 mm of Hg at 20°C. Although nickel carbonyl is extremely toxic, it has found use industrially for making high-purity nickel powder and pellets, by its controlled decomposition at temperatures ranging from 60–120°C. This same property has been utilized to produce continuous nickel coatings on steel and other substrates.

Nickel (I) Compounds. Only a few nickel (I) compounds have been prepared. The best known are the cyanide complexes, especially $[Ni_2(CN)_6]^{-4}$, which is termed the hexacyano dinickelate anion.

Nickel (II) Compounds. By far the largest number of known nickel compounds have an oxidation number of $+2$. They are commonly called nickel (II) compounds and embrace not only the substitution products from simple organic and inorganic anions, but highly complex materials from reaction with cycloalkenes, alkynes, and other organic moieties having unbonded π orbitals.

Inorganic Nickel (II) Compounds.

Nickel bromide forms a brownish yellow dihydrate, $NiBr_2 \cdot 2H_2O$, that is stable at $80°C$. Recrystallization of this material from water yields the green hexahydrate. Anhydrous nickel bromide is made by the bromination of nickel powder or of nickel carbonyl.

Nickel carbonate, $NiCO_3$, is difficult to prepare and isolate, hence has not become a chemical of any importance. Nickel carbonate is found in nature, however, in the mineral zaratite, which is a basic nickel carbonate having the formula, $NiCO_3 \cdot 2Ni(OH)_2 \cdot 4H_2O$. Commercially produced basic nickel carbonates of somewhat indefinite structure are reduced with hydrogen to prepare finely divided nickel for catalytic applications.

Nickel chloride is deliquescent and hence usually is encountered as the hexahydrate which forms bright green monoclinic crystals. The hexahydrate is usually prepared by reaction of hydrochloric acid and nickel metal. Its major use is in nickel electroplating baths. Anhydrous nickel chloride can be prepared by the direct combination of the elements as well as by the reaction of nickel acetate and acetyl chloride using a nonaqueous solvent such as benzene.

Nickel fluoride, NiF_2, usually isolated in the form of green tetragonal crystals, is only slightly soluble in water (2.6 g/100 ml H_2O at $20°C$). It is normally produced by evaporation of a solution of nickel carbonate in aqueous hydrofluoric acid.

Nickel hydroxide, $Ni(OH)_2$, is a fine, voluminous, light green powder which is usually considered a definite compound rather than hydrated NiO. It is normally prepared by reaction of nickel salts with caustic, nickel sulfate and sodium hydroxide being the most commonly used reagents. $Ni(OH)_2$ is also prepared in high purity by electrolysis of nickel anodes.

Nickel iodide is formed by direct combination of Ni and I_2.

Nickel nitrate, usually as hexahydrate, $Ni(NO_3)_2 \cdot 6H_2O$, which forms emerald green monoclinic crystals, is extensively used for some impregnated nickel catalysts. This application of the nitrate is due to the low melting point of crystals, $55°C$, which then decompose to NiO at about $105°C$. Nickel nitrate is usually prepared by the direct action of nitric acid on nickel metal, but also can be prepared from nickel oxide.

Nickel oxide, NiO, is prepared by heating the metal above $400°C$ in the presence of oxygen. NiO is nonamphoteric, being insoluble in caustic solutions.

Nickel subsulfide, Ni_3S_2, is a well defined, yellow-brown metallic appearing material formed by heating nickel and sulfur, but also found in nature in certain minerals. Nickel subsulfide is the active constituent of the "sulfur active" nickel catalysts.

Nickel sulfamate, $Ni(SO_3NH_2)_2 \cdot 4H_2O$, prepared by reacting nickel carbonate with sodium sulfamate, is used in nickel electroplating baths.

Nickel sulfate is sold commercially in two crystalline forms of $NiSO_4 \cdot 6H_2O$, blue tetragonal crystals and green monoclinic crystals. Nickel sulfate is the cheapest and most widely used of all nickel salts, primarily in nickel plating baths and in catalyst preparation. The usual method of preparing $NiSO_4$ is by direct reaction between sulfuric acid and nickel metal.

Nickel sulfide, NiS, when it occurs naturally as needle-like or fibrous yellow-brown crystals of the orthorhombic type is called millerite. This mineral is extremely water-insoluble.

Organic Nickel (II) Compounds.

Nickel acetate is usually produced as the tetrahydrate by reacting nickel hydroxide or carbonate with dilute acetic acid. The anhydrous yellow-green nickel acetate powder decomposes upon heating at $250°C$ to yield metallic nickel, carbon, CO_2, water, hydrogen, and acetic acid. Nickel acetate is used as a catalyst and as a textile mordant.

Nickel formate occurs as the green crystalline dihydrate, $Ni(HCOO)_2 \cdot 2H_2O$. Preparation can be effected either by reaction of sodium formate and nickel sulfate or by dissolving nickel hydroxide or carbonate in formic acid solution. When the dihydrate is heated at 140° the anhydrous nickel formate is produced. Further heating at 200° to 250°C causes complete decomposition to finely divided, metallic nickel, which is catalytically active, water, and CO and CO_2. Thus one of the major applications of nickel formate is the production of nickel catalysts.

Nickel isodecylorthophosphate has become an important nickel compound in recent years due to its inclusion in motor fuel as an additive to reduce engine "rumble," corrosion, and carburetor icing.

Nickel naphthenate, oleate and stearate are mixtures of varying composition usually in the form of tacky, dark green solids. They are used in a similar manner as a jelling agent for hydrocarbons, as specialty metal drawing lubricant and to a very minor extent as a crankcase lubricant additive.

One might expect the nickel naphthenate and other nickel soaps to be used as paint driers as are the corresponding cobalt salts. Such is not the case however, and the nickel salts are completely ineffective in this application.

Nickel (II) Complexes

The fact the nickel (II) ion has unfilled electron orbitals enables a large number of complexes to be formed. Only the better known complexes are listed, although the total number of nickel complexes is of course much larger. These complexes may contain inorganic, and/or organic groups in varying amounts. π complexes, where π orbitals of organic groups are shared with the nickel, are discussed separately.

Nickel acetylacetonate, either as a green crystalline material or amorphous powder, is probably the best known of the nickel β-dicarbonyl complexes.

Nickel azo yellow, a pigment, is a nickel (II) complex containing two molecules of 2,4-dihydroxy, 3-(p-chlorophenyl) azo quinoline.

Nickel bis (triphenyl phosphine) dichloride, a blue powder insoluble in water and most organic solvents, is illustrative of organo-phosphorus and halogen-containing nickel (II) complexes.

Nickel di-n-butyldithiocarbamate is an olive green powder that is sold commercially as an oxidation inhibitor for neoprene, GR-S and other synthetic rubbers.

Nickel dimethylglyoxime is one of the better known complexes due to the fact it is a bright-red, water-insoluble, flocculent precipitate and thus is utilized as the qualitative test for Ni^{+2} ion.

Nickel hexammine, $[Ni(NH_3)_3]^{+2}$, having an intense dark blue color is perhaps the best known inorganic nickel complex and has a very high degree of stability. It and other ammine complexes are utilized in the refining of nickel.

Nickel phthalocyanine, a deep blue, crystalline complex has found some applications as a pigment.

Nickel 2,2'-thiobis (p-tert. octyl phenolate) a light green powdery material and related sulfur complexes, such as the sulfoxide and sulfone derivatives, have recently found application as light stabilizers for polypropylene fibers.

Tetracyanonickelates (II) are bright yellow orange complexes formed by reacting nickel cyanide with alkaline or alkaline earth cyanides. The nickel is in the anion $[Ni(CN)_4]^{=}$. They possess a fair degree of stability and water solubility. Tetracyanonickelates can be reduced with alkali metals in anhydrous ammonia to give zerovalent nickel compounds of the type $M_4[Ni(CN)_4]$.

Organonickel π Complexes

Nickel in the oxidation number of two forms a number of π complexes with unsaturated organic compounds. π complexes are formed by the sharing of electrons present in unsaturated organic compounds.

Nickelocene in the form of deep green crystals is the best known of the nickel π complexes or "sandwich" complexes as they are often called. It is formed when nickel bromide complexed with the dimethyl ether of ethylene glycol is reacted with sodium cyclopentadienide. Nickelocene, nickel (II) bis (cyclopentadiene), $(\pi\text{-}C_5H_5)_2Ni$, has each ring bonded to the nickel with three pairs of π electrons.

A related group of π complexes are the π allyl compounds such as bis (π allyl nickel dibromide).

Applications

Nickel consumption. Approximately 825 million pounds of nickel were consumed in the Free World in 1967, of which an estimated 352 million pounds were consumed in the United States. The Free World consumption was distributed as follows:

Stainless steels	37%
Nickel plating	15%
High-nickel alloys	15%
Construction alloy steels	11%
Iron and steel castings	9%
Copper and brass products	4%
All others	9%

Under "all others" are such uses as salts, catalysts, ceramics, magnets, etc.

Alloys of Nickel. Nickel is readily alloyed with many other metals. It has long been a useful constituent in the low-alloy constructional steels to which it contributes strength and toughness as well as other useful characteristics. Such steels are included in SAE and AISI specifications and customarily contain chromium, molybdenum or chromium and molybdenum in addition to nickel. Higher nickel steels (9%) possess excellent strength and toughness at temperatures as low as −320°F and provide an economically priced metal for cryogenic applications. Within the past few years, an entirely new family of iron-base alloys called the maraging steels, containing up to about 20% nickel, together with other alloying additions, uniquely combines the familiar martensitic hardening reaction of steels with an age-hardening reaction. These materials are outstanding in that they exhibit good ductility and high toughness in conjunction with the very high strengths developed. Nickel in relatively small amounts is a useful addition to the cast irons, acting as a combined strengthener and graphitizer to improve mechanical properties and machinability. Austenitic cast irons with 14 to 35% nickel are used for applications calling for corrosion resistance or special physical properties.

Nickel-iron alloys containing from 30 to 80% nickel have found extensive use in magnetic applications and for controlled thermal expansion or elastic modulus characteristics.

Nickel is a most useful addition to copper, and the copper-nickels (often called cupro-nickels) which contain 10 to 30% nickel have found wide use because of resistance to corrosion, especially in marine environments. One of the oldest uses of the copper-nickels has been in the field of coinage where alloys containing up to about 25% nickel have been in use for several thousand years. The copper-nickel-zinc alloys, usually containing up to about 20% nickel, known earlier as German silver and in latter years as the nickel silvers, are commonly used as a base for quality silver-plated flatware, in architectural trim, and electrical contact springs. The strong, ductile nickel-copper alloys (e.g., 70/30 Ni-Cu alloy) have a long history of commercial use because of their ability to resist attack in many corrosive media.

Electrical resistance alloys, varying from a 45% nickel-copper alloy for heating elements operating at moderately elevated temperatures to the well-known 80% nickel-chromium alloys for high-temperature service, meet most varieties of industrial needs. Nickel-chromium alloys, such as the 80/14/6 Ni-Cr-Fe, are used in many applications calling for heat resistance or resistance to stress corrosion cracking in aqueous environments, etc. The evolution of the aircraft jet engine to its present high level of performance has been made possible to a considerable degree by the development of nickel-base superalloys. These alloys provide first-stage turbine blades strong enough to operate at temperatures as high as 1900°F. These nickel-chromium base superalloys owe their high-temperature strength primarily to an age hardening effect due to co-present aluminum and titanium in critical amounts, with the alloy matrix further strengthened by one or more of the elements Cb, Mo, W, Co, Ta.

The most widely used of all of the nickel-containing alloys are probably the stainless steels, iron-base alloys containing about 7 to 13% nickel and 17–25% chromium, which are widely used in applications where corrosion resistance, product purity, color, appearance, etc. are important, for example, in food and chemical processing equipment, architectural trim and structural components, household appliances and a large number of other uses.

Nickel Plating. Nickel is widely used as a coating for functional and decorative applications. It is plated electrolytically or by chemical reduction from aqueous solutions of its salts. Deposits with a variety of properties can be produced by altering the composition of the plating bath and the plating conditions. Nickel coatings, therefore, are characterized by their versatility.

Industrial nickel coatings are used to: (1) reclaim worn or corroded parts of machinery, (2) recover parts machined "undersize" that would otherwise be scrapped, and (3) provide a wear-resistant or corrosion-resistant surface.

Decorative nickel coatings are used where appearance is the prime requisite. Bright nickel coatings in many applications, however, perform a dual function of enhancing appearance and providing resistance to corrosion. They are usually subsequently plated with a very thin deposit of chromium. Decorative nickel coatings, therefore, are sometimes referred to as "chrome plate." Applications include jewelry, household appliances, furniture and automobile parts.

A specialized use of plating is known as electroforming, whereby an electrodeposit is produced on a mandrel that is subsequently removed from the deposited metal leaving an exact mirror-image replica. Nickel electroforms are used as phonograph record stampers, electrotype printing plates, molds and dies, and wave-guides.

Catalysis. Nickel, in both metallic and chemical form, is widely used for catalysis at a rate of about 2 million lb per year. One of the most widely used nickel catalysts is Raney nickel which is produced by first forming intermetallic compounds such as $NiAl_3$. The aluminum is dissolved away with caustic leaving a porous, highly active form of nickel metal. One important application of Raney nickel is as a catalyst for producing amines by the reaction of alcohols or ketones and ammonia. The precipitated type of catalyst is prepared by mixing a soluble nickel salt such as the chloride or sulfate with sodium or potassium hydroxide, carbonate or bicarbonate. The precipitated nickel carbonate or bicarbonate is reduced with hydrogen after it has been washed and dried.

Biological and Biochemical Aspects

Because of its location near iron and cobalt in the Periodic Table and the similarities of properties of the three elements, it might be expected that nickel would have important biological and biochemical activity as do iron and cobalt. However, the demonstration of the presence of nickel in plant and animal tissues has not been accompanied by any conclusive evidence of a physiological effect of nickel.

Nickel and its compounds do not appear to cause systemic poisoning, despite the considerable intake of nickel in most diets due to its presence in plant and animal foods. It is regarded as a relatively nontoxic element. Because of the wide use of nickel and nickel alloys in equipment and utensils used in food preparation many investigations have been made of the effects of nickel ingested from such sources. The conclusion is that nickel contamination of foods does not present an appreciable health hazard.

References

1. Cotton, F. Albert, and Wilkinson, G., "Advanced Inorganic Chemistry," New York, Interscience Publishing Co., 1962.
2. Emeleus, H. J., and Sharpe, A. G., Editors, "Advances in Inorganic Chemistry and Radio Chemistry," Chapter 4 by J. R. Miller, "Recent Advances in the Stereo-Chemistry of Nickel, Palladium and Platinum," New York, Academic Press Inc. 1962.
3. Stone, F. G. A., and West, Robert, Editors, "Advances in Organo-metallic Chemistry, Vol. 2, Chapter 1 by G. N. Schranzer, "Some Advances in the Organometallic Chemistry of Nickel," New York, Academic Press Inc., 1964.
4. Bailar, John C., Editor, "Chemistry of the Coordination Compounds," New York, Reinhold Publishing Corp., 1956.
5. Harewood, J. H., "Industrial Applications of the Organometallic Compounds," New York, Reinhold Publishing Corp., 1963.
6. *Ind. Eng. Chem.*, **44**, No. 5, 950–1027 (May 1962). Reprints of a symposium of seventeen papers presented on nickel metal, nickel chemicals and nickel catalysts.
7. "Nickel and Its Alloys," Nat. Bur. Standards Circ. No. 592, 1958 (revised 1967).
8. Howard-White, F. B., "Nickel, An Historical Review," New York, D. Van Nostrand & Co., 1963.

9. Boldt, J. R., Jr., "The Winning of Nickel," P. Queneau, Tech. Editor, New York, D. Van Nostrand & Co., 1967.

J. B. ADAMEC AND
D. B. SPRINGER

NIOBIUM

History

Niobium and tantalum are closely associated in nature and the similarity of their chemical properties caused much difficulty in establishing their individual identity. In 1801, Charles Hatchett, an English chemist, analyzed a heavy, black ore sample sent to the British Museum in 1753 from Connecticut. He discovered that it contained a new element which he named columbium in honor of the country of its origin, Columbia, the synonym for America. In 1844, Rose, another chemist, announced the discovery of what he considered to be a new element which he called niobium after Niobe, the mythological Goddess of Tears, and the daughter of Tantalus. There followed considerable controversy about the identity of the elements known as columbium, niobium, and tantalum. Finally, it was established that there were only two elements, tantalum and another, which was called columbium by some and niobium by others. After more than 100 years of controversy, the name niobium was adopted as the international name at the Fifteenth International Union of Chemistry Congress at Amsterdam in 1949. However, even today both names are commonly used.

Niobium metal was first prepared by Blomstrand in 1866, who reduced niobium chloride with hydrogen. At a later date, Moissan prepared niobium by reducing the oxide with carbon in an electric furnace. Even later, Goldschmidt reduced the oxide with aluminum powder. About 1905, interest arose in both niobium and tantalum as possible materials for the manufacture of filaments for incandescent lamps to replace the carbon filaments then in use. Tantalum was finally chosen for this purpose. Also at that time, Von Bolten prepared niobium metal in a relatively pure state by sodium reduction of the fluoniobate and evaluated some of its more important properties. The first samples of niobium rod and sheet were prepared by Balke who used powder-metallurgy techniques. Samples of the metal were first exhibited before the American Chemical Society in 1929.

Sources

The ore minerals of niobium are mostly multiple oxides of niobium and tantalum together with rare earth elements. In any given occurrence, either metal may predominate. However, niobium far outranks its sister element in abundance in the earth's crust.

Until 1950, niobium was derived almost exclusively from the mineral niobite in occurrence with pegmatitic rocks or their derived weathered products. Since then unexpectedly large resources of niobium have been discovered in carbonatites (carbonate-silicate rocks), mostly as a constituent of the mineral pyrochlore.

A broad, world-wide distribution of niobium is indicated. Despite proven world reserves of over nine million tons of Nb_2O_5 in ores, however, large resources of economic importance are concentrated in a very few countries. In terms of Nb_2O_5 content, the world's presently known niobium resources are distributed as follows: South America, 70%; Africa, 15%; North America, 14%; and Europe, 1%.

Free-World production of niobium concentrates was 7,600 tons in 1966. Canada supplied over 30% of these concentrates, Africa (principally Nigeria), 37%, and Brazil 29%. Lacking important resources of niobium, the United States imported most of its needs for niobium concentrates and in 1966, 4,800 tons were shipped to this country.

Canada is one of the major United States sources. In 1966, 864 tons of Canadian pyrochlore concentrate (mined near Montreal), containing approximately 55% niobium pentoxide and costing about $1.10 per pound, were imported. Brazil also supplied another 2,400 tons of pyrochlore concentrate. The United States also imported 1,536 tons of niobate in 1966, mostly from Nigeria. This concentrate contains about 56% niobium and tantalum pentoxides and costs about $0.85 a pound.

Separation of Niobium from Tantalum

The association of niobium with tantalum in nature, together with the great chemical similarity of these two elements, has been the major fact in preventing the rapid development of efficient processes for their commercial production. Therefore, an important step in any full-scale extractive process for niobium is the separation of niobium and tantalum compounds from each other. Ores destined for use in ferroalloy production normally are converted into niobium-rich ferroniobium/tantalum by carbon reduction in an electric furnace, without separation.

Fractional Crystallization. Based on an 1866 discovery that the limited solubility of potassium fluotantalate, K_2TaF_7, could be utilized to separate it from the more soluble potassium oxyfluoniobate, $K_2NbOF_5 \cdot H_2O$, by fractional crystallization, a relatively effective but rather tedious process was developed and used successfuly for many years on a commercial basis. At present, this fractional crystallization of complex fluorides is used only to a limited extent, the current trend being toward the application of methods based on solvent-extraction (liquid-liquid extraction).

Solvent Extraction. In the past few years, newer niobium separation techniques based on solvent extraction have been receiving considerable attention. A solvent-extraction process used by an industrial niobium producer is outlined below to illustrate the principles involved.

The process involves grinding the niobate-tantalite ore in a ball mill to less than 100-mesh particle size (or smaller) and feeding this ore to a leach tank, together with appropriate amounts of anhydrous hydrogen fluoride and deionized water. The resulting slurry is digested for 10 hours at 80°C (176°F) which causes dissolution of the niobium and tantalum oxides. Most of the impurities remain in the undissolved gangue. Dissolved impurities are removed in subsequent stages of processing. The gangue is filtered, the filter cake repulped and refiltered once, and the residue discarded. The niobium-tantalum liquor is fed to a holding tank, and the pH adjusted for proper acidity. The treated liquor then goes to the extraction cascade where mixing and settling operations are carried out in tandem. In the cascade, methyl isobutyl ketone is added in the tantalum extraction section. The niobium-bearing aqueous phase from this section is acidified, and pure methyl isobutyl ketone is then added to this product in the niobium extraction section. Finally, the niobium-bearing extract is treated with deionized water and led to a precipitation tank where ammonia is added to cause precipitation of niobium as the oxyfluoride. The precipitate is filtered, dried, and calcined to remove fluorine, yielding high-purity niobium oxide.

Other Methods. Efficient separations of niobium and tantalum can be done by ion exchange techniques which may permit more effective removal of impurities than solvent extraction. However, this method is more applicable to producing small quantities of high-purity niobium and tantalum.

Sharp separations of niobium from tantalum can be made by chromatographic methods, provided only that the amount of tantalum present is less than the amount of niobium.

Niobium can be separated from tantalum by treating pentoxide mixtures with aluminum halides (chloride, bromide, and iodide) under conditions of elevated temperature and reduced pressure. Fractional sublimation is used to isolate the halides formed. Aluminum iodide appears to be the most favorable agent in this application.

Niobium Metal Purification

Many methods have been used for the preparation of niobium metal. However, only carbide or carbon reduction of the oxide and sodium reduction of the pentachloride or other halide compounds have been found suitable for commercial application.

Carbide-Oxide and Carbon-Oxide Reduction. In the commercial carbide-oxide reduction process for the production of niobium metal, a pressed bar of niobium carbide/niobium oxide mixture is resistively heated in vacuum at a temperature in the range 1600 to 1800°C (2912 to 3272°F). For the premium grade of metal, reprocessing of the product yielded by this initial reduction is necessary. This is accomplished by analyzing the initial product, adding an approximately stoichiometric amount of carbide or oxide, as required, and resintering. In this way, metal of fairly high purity can be produced. However, metal lower in both carbon and oxygen is desirable for some important applications, and additional refining operations are necessary.

In the reduction of niobium oxide with carbon, the processing temperature is on the order of 2000°C (3632°F) in a vacuum of 1 micron or less.

Sodium Reduction of the Chloride. No detailed information concerning the industrial sodium-reduction processes used in preparing niobium metal has been published. By analogy with similar processes for titanium and zirconium production, however, one feasible process would cause molten niobium pentachloride to contact a pool of molten sodium floating on fused sodium chloride in an appropriate reaction vessel. The niobium pentachloride would be reduced to niobium metal powder or granules which would sink to the bottom of the reaction vessel; sodium chloride would be the by-product formed. Periodically, the accumulated metal would be removed, crushed, and leached to remove the salt, and the metal would be consolidated by appropriate means.

Alternatively, niobium pentachloride vapor could be made to contact the molten sodium, or both constituents could be vaporized and reacted.

Consolidation and Purification

The products of the various reduction processes for niobium may be in the form of fine powder, small granules, or roundels. These must be consolidated into ingot form to permit further fabrication into useful shapes. In general, additional purification is required, since the unwanted nonmetallic impurity content, principally carbon, nitrogen, and oxygen, is often quite high.

Methods useful for the consolidation and purification of niobium include consumable electrode arc melting, electron-beam or high-frequency induction melting, sintering, and iodide or zone refining. Refinement in these processes is dependent upon reactions, such as carbon-oxygen, volatility of the various impurities, and the actual conditions of time-temperature-pressure during the consolidation operation.

Physical Properties

A summary of some of the most important physical properties of niobium are given in Table 1.

TABLE 1. PHYSICAL PROPERTIES OF NIOBIUM

Property	Value
Atomic and Nuclear Properties	
Atomic number	41
Atomic weight	92.906
Atomic diameter, kX	2.94
Atomic volume, cc/g-atom	10.83
Density, g/cc	8.57
Isotopes, atomic wts (half-lives)	89 (1.9 hrs), 90 (15 hrs), 91 (62 days), 92 (13 hrs, 10 days), 93 (natural), 94 (2.7×10^4 yrs), 95 (35 days), 96, 97 (74 min), 98 (30 min), 99 (25 min)
X-Ray absorption energies, level (KeV)	$K(18.9_{86})$, $L_I(2.7_{00})$, $L_{II}(2.4_{67})$, $L_{III}(2.3_{72})$, $M_I(0.4_{71})$, $M_{II}(0.381)$, $M_{III}(0.365)$, $M_{IV}(0.2_{09})$, $M_V(0.2_{06})$, $N_I(0.0_{58})$, N_{II}-N_{III}avg(0.0_{34})
X-Ray emission spectra, line (wavelength, Å)	$K_{\alpha2}(0.7504_0)$, $K_{\alpha1}(0.7461_5)$, $K_{\beta1}(0.6657_2)$, $K_{absorption\ edge}(0.652_9)$
Electron configuration	$4d^45s^1$
Thermalneutron absorption cross section (for a neutron velocity of 2200 m/sec), barns/atom	1.15 ± 0.05

TABLE 1—*continued*

Crystallographic Properties

Structure	bcc
Coordination number	8
Lattice constant, Å	3.294
Goldschmidt radius (Coordination No. 12), Å	1.47
Schonflies space group	O_h^9-Im3m; a = 3.16, A = 2

Thermal Properties

Melting point, °C (°F)	2468 ± 10 (4474 ± 18)
Boiling point, °C (°F)	4927 (8901)
Heat of combustion, cal/g	2379
Heat of melting (est.), cal/g-atom	6400
Heat of vaporization, at b.p., kcal/g-atom	166.5
Heat of sublimation, kcal/g-atom	
at -273°C (-459°F)	171.800 ± 0.490
at 15°C (59°F)	172.530
Specific heat, cal/g/°C	
at 0°C (32°F)	0.06430
at 300°C (572°F)	0.06683
at 700°C (1292°F)	0.07086
at 900°C (1652°F)	0.07316
at 1300°C (2372°F)	0.07852
at 1600°C (2912°F)	0.08267
Heat capacity, solid, cal/°C/g-atom	
at 15°C (59°F)	5.95
at 227°C (441°F)	6.14
at 727°C (1341°F)	6.62
at 1277°C (2241°F)	7.10
at 1727°C (3141°F)	7.58
at 2227°C (4041°F)	8.06
at m.p.	8.25
Heat content, at m.p., kcal/g-atom	17.05
Entropy, cal/°C/g-atom	
at 15°C (59°F)	8.73
at m.p.	23.51
Enthalpy, at 15°C (59°F), cal/g-atom	1264
Free energy function, cal/°C/g-atom	
at 15°C (59°F)	8.73
at m.p.	17.20

Vapor pressure, atm for 2304–2596°C (3688–4213°F):

$$\log P_{atm} = -\left(\frac{40,169}{T}\right) + 8.872, \text{ (T in °K)}$$

at 2304°C (3688°F)	2.63×10^{-8}
at 2596°C (4213°F)	2.44×10^{-7}
Thermal conductivity, cal/cm²/cm/sec/°C	
at 0°C (32°F)	0.125
at 200°C (392°F)	0.135
at 400°C (752°F)	0.145
at 600°C (1112°F)	0.156
Coefficient of linear thermal expansion, 10^{-6} cm/cm/°C	
at 20°C (68°F)	7.1
0–400°C (32–752°F)	7.39
0–600°C (32–1112°F)	7.56
0–800°C (32–1472°F)	7.72
0–1000°C (32–1832°F)	7.88

TABLE 1—*continued*

Electrical and Magnetic Properties

Volume conductivity, at 18°C (64°F), % IACS	13.2
Electrical resistivity, microhm-cm	
at 0°C (32°F)	15.22
at 100°C (212°F)	19.18
at 200°C (392°F)	23.13
at 400°C (752°F)	31.04
at 600°C (1112°F)	38.96
Temperature coefficient of electrical resistivity, $10^{-3}/°C$	
at 18°C (64°F)	3.95
0–600°F (32–1112°C)	3.96
Superconductivity transition temp., °K	8.3
Electrochemical equivalent (with valency of 5), mg/coulomb	0.1926
Standard electrode potential (European sign convention), Nb/Nb^{+5}, volt	− 0.96
Magnetic susceptibility [average values for − 194°C to 305°C (− 317 to 581°F)], 10^{-6} cgs	
gram	2.225
atomic	207
Hall coefficient [independent of temperature from − 273 to 627°C (− 459 to 1161°F)], m^3/amp-sec	9×10^{-11}

Optical Properties

Emittance	
Total hemispherical [760–1260°C (1400–2300°F)],	
sandblasted	0.30–0.45
oxidized	0.70–0.75
Normal spectral (1–15 μ)	
at 249°C (480°F)	0.05–0.35
at 749°C (1380°F)	0.40.0.85
Total radiation, watts/cm^2	
at 1880°C (3416°F)	22
at 1980°C (3596°F)	
Radiation capacity [at 1730°C (3146°F), $\lambda = 0.650\mu$], %	37
Refractive index	1.80

Thermionic and Electronic Properties

Ionization potential, volts	6.77
Electronic emission, amp/cm^2K^2	37, 57
Work function, eV	4.01
Secondary emission (primary energy at δ_{max} 400v), volt	1.18
Positive ion emission, eV	5.52

Mechanical Properties

Unalloyed niobium is soft, ductile, and very malleable at room temperature, and it maintains excellent ductility at cryogenic temperatures. Niobium is readily fabricated by conventional methods, and can be welded using tungsten inert gas or electron-beam welding processes which exclude contaminating air from the hot metal zone. The mechanical properties of niobium are very greatly dependent on the purity, particularly the interstitial content, as well as the test conditions and fabrication history. Selected mechanical property data for good commercial purity niobium are given in Table 2 and Figs. 1 and 2.

TABLE 2. MECHANICAL PROPERTIES OF NIOBIUM

Property	Value
Modulus of elasticity, 10^6 psi	
at 25°C (77°F)	15.1
at 870°C (1598°F)	13.6
Modulus of rigidity, at 25°C (77°F), 10^6 psi	5.44
Poisson's ratio at 25°C (77°F)	0.38
Tensile properties, at 25°C (77°F)	
Tensile strength, 1000 psi	
wrought	85
annealed	40
Yield strength, 0.2% offset, 1000 psi	
annealed	30
Elongation, %	
wrought	5
annealed	30
Hardness, at 25°C (77°F), VHN	
annealed	54
cold-worked 20%	91
„ „ 40%	112
„ „ 60%	130
„ „ 80%	145
„ „ 90%	154
Impact strength, ft-lb	
at 38°C (100°F)	> 90
at −73°C (−100°F)	> 90

TABLE 2—continued

at −157°C (−250°F)	70
at −196°C (−320°F)	15
Ductile to brittle transition temperature, °C (°F)	−196 (−320)
Fatigue life, cycles to failure	
at 45,000 psi	10^5
at 30,000 psi	10^6
at 27,000 psi	10^7

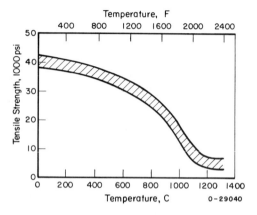

FIG. 1. Effect of temperature on the tensile strength of annealed niobium. *(Courtesy Frank F. Schmidt, Research Metallurgist, Nonferrous Metallurgy Division, Battelle Memorial Institute).*

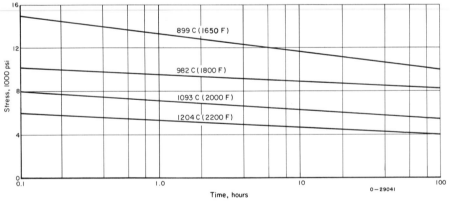

FIG. 2. Stress-rupture curves for annealed niobium. *(Courtesy Frank F. Schmidt, Research Metallurgist, Nonferrous Metallurgy Division, Battelle Memorial Institute).*

Chemical Properties

Chemical Corrosion. Niobium is characterized by the acidic properties of its most stable oxide, niobium pentoxide, and the volatility and nonpolar properties of its halides. In lower valence states, it exhibits basic properties. Generally niobium does not corrode in noncombining solutions over a wide range of pH values due to the formation of protective oxide films. However, the active-metal nature of niobium is illustrated by its rapid dissolution in hydrofluoric acid and in aqueous alkali solutions in which a protective oxide does not form.

The corrosive attack of niobium by various

selected media at room and elevated temperatures is detailed in Ref. 7. The general corrosion resistance of niobium is inferior to that of tantalum. Niobium is attacked slowly by most of the reagents to which tantalum is inert, and rapidly by others. In no instance is it unaffected by aqueous materials which corrode tantalum. For example, niobium is less satisfactory than tantalum for use in aqua regia, in hydrochloric acid, or in sulfuric acid. Although it is not attacked by nitric acid at temperatures up to 100°C (212°F), a mixture of nitric and hydrofluoric acids consumes the metal rapidly. Hot concentrated hydrochloric, sulfuric, and phosphoric acids attack the metal although hot concentrated nitric does not. Niobium is unaffected at room temperature by sulfuric, hydrochloric, nitric, phosphoric, tartaric, lactic, acetic, or perchloric acids, or by aqua regia, 5% phenol, ammonium hydroxide, 30% hydrogen peroxide, or 10% ferric chloride. Acids which attack the metal slowly release sufficient hydrogen to embrittle it. For example, although the corrosion rate of niobium in 10% oxalic acid at 21°C (70°F) is < 1 mpy, it will become brittle in about 3 months. Precautions should be taken to prevent the metal from becoming the cathode in a galvanic couple in electrolytes, since the discharged hydrogen can cause embrittlement.

Niobium is much less resistant than tantalum to alkaline solutions. Although the corrosion rates of niobium vary considerably in hydroxide solutions, depending upon concentration and temperature, severe loss in ductility caused by hydride formation is associated with both low and high corrosion rates.

Niobium has become well established as a material of construction in many types of nuclear reactors because of the metal's ability to withstand attack by high-temperature water, by liquid metals (bismuth, sodium, sodium-potassium alloy), and by other media, often at quite elevated temperatures. Niobium is not corroded or embrittled by sodium or sodium-potassium at 800°C (1472°F) and above, provided that the liquid metals contain less than 40 ppm oxygen. In addition, niobium exhibits a high resistance to mass transfer and corrosion in liquid lead over a thermal gradient of 800 to 300°C (1472 to 572°F).

The impurities oxygen, nitrogen, hydrogen, and carbon have such a potent effect on both the physical and mechanical properties of niobium that a discussion of the reaction of these elements with niobium is required.

Oxygen and Air. Niobium's lack of oxidation resistance is by far its most serious shortcoming. This handicap must be successfully overcome before niobium can be used in the many high-temperature applications for which it is most suitable.

At low temperatures and oxygen pressures, the niobium-oxygen reaction proceeds at a very low linear rate and no scale is formed. At slightly higher temperatures and pressures, an adherent scale forms and the reaction proceeds parabolically. A visible tarnish film appears at about 400°C (752°F). At 400 to 500°C (752 to 932°F), microscopic blisters of porous Nb_2O_5 erupt on the surface of the adherent tarnish film, and the reaction kinetics change from parabolic to linear. Metallic oxide phases are no longer found at the metal-oxide interface since the protective properties of the scale no longer exist. Above 700°C (1292°F), the rate of oxidation increases rapidly with temperature. The scale formed consists of porous Nb_2O_5 overlaying a thin adherent layer of oriented Nb_2O_5 with traces of other suboxides. The pentoxide has been observed to sinter at 900°C (1652°F) and above. In one atmosphere of oxygen, the niobium-oxygen reaction becomes catastrophic at 1400°C (2552°F).

The niobium-air reaction generally is similar to the niobium-oxygen reaction except that lower rates are observed in air. Moist air increases the oxidation rate at 400 and 600°C (752 and 1112°F), but has no effect at 800°C (1472°F) and higher. Contamination of niobium metal during oxidation in both air and oxygen is appreciable due to the high solubility and diffusion rate of oxygen in niobium. The depth of contamination and accompanying embrittlement may easily exceed the amount of metal consumed by oxidation.

Nitrogen. At all temperatures, the niobium-nitrogen reaction is much slower than the niobium-oxygen reaction. Adherent nitride films are formed at temperatures up to 1600°C (2912°F). Contamination hardening of niobium during reaction with nitrogen occurs in a similar manner as with oxygen. However, the solubility and diffusion rate of nitrogen are much less than for oxygen, resulting in a shallower case of hardened metal with nitrogen.

Hydrogen. Niobium will absorb hydrogen between about 100 and 900°C (212 and 1652°F) from hydrogen-containing atmospheres. The absorption of hydrogen results in the formation of a single-phase solid solution throughout most of the niobium-hydrogen system. A two-phase region is present at relatively low temperatures and pressures with the critical point located at 140°C (284°F), 0.01 mm of Hg pressure, and 0.3H/Nb ratio. Although sizable quantities of hydrogen can be absorbed by niobium, which causes a lower tolerance for deformation and ultimately leads to severe embrittlement, the hydrogen is evolved in vacuum at about 250°C (482°F) and above.

Carbon. Carbon reacts directly with niobium to form the monocarbide, which is stable to 2500°C (4532°F) in nitrogen but decarburizes slightly when heated in air. Niobium monocarbide can be formed by reaction of the metal or oxide with free carbon or by reaction with a hydrocarbon. Coatings of NbC up to 0.5 mm thick can be formed on graphite by vapor decomposition of $NbCl_3$. Fig. 3 indicates the condition of temperature and pressure under which the carbide can be formed. Such coatings are of interest in nuclear engineering applications. Although excessive carbon in niobium can cause severe loss in ductility, controlled amounts of carbon and reactive metal additions, such as zirconium, are important in achieving an optimum combination of strength and ductility in many niobium-base alloys.

Reaction with the Halogens. The halides of niobium are formed by direct combination with the halogens. They also can be formed by treatment of the oxide with carbon and halogens, or of the carbide with halogens. Niobium trifluoride, with high chemical stability, can be prepared by treatment of niobium hydride with a mixture of hydrofluoric acid-hydrogen mixture at 570°C (1058°F). The bromides are formed by methods similar to those used for chlorides. The reaction of the metal with iodine is slow. More rapid formation of the iodide takes place when the bromide is reacted with anhydrous hydrogen iodide.

Being nonpolar, the halides of niobium have comparatively low melting and boiling points.

Borides, Silicides, and Intermetallic Compounds. Niobium-boron compounds, of which only the monoboride is sufficiently stable to melt without decomposing, are attacked in air at temperatures between 1100 to 1200°C (2102 to 2192°F). The high electrical resistivity, high reflectivity, and low volatility of niobium borides, however, render them useful in such applications as internal resistance and induction heating, as well as for radiation shields. These compounds retain their hardness relatively well at elevated temperatures and hence have good high-temperature abrasion resistance.

The silicides, Nb_4Si, Nb_5Si_3, and $NbSi_2$, are prepared by sintering or arc-furnace melting. They are neither very hard nor oxidation resistant.

A listing and discussion of the many intermetallic compounds of niobium is beyond the scope of this chapter. However, some of the intermetallic compounds, such as Nb_3Sn, have outstanding superconducting characteristics.

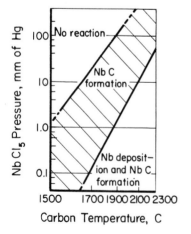

FIG. 3. Conditions for formation of NbC coatings on graphite by vapor deposition. *(Courtesy Frank F. Schmidt, Research Metallurgist, Nonferrous Metallurgy Division, Battelle Memorial Institute).*

Uses

As in previous years, ferroniobium producers purchased over 95% of the niobium concentrates sold in the United States. Use of ferroniobium in the United States has been continuously increasing to the present level of about 1,400 tons (as measured by contained niobium). About 24% of the total ferroalloy consumption goes into stainless steels to stabilize carbides for improved weldability and resistance to intergranular corrosion, 21% to high-temperature alloys for improved elevated temperature strength, 12% to carbon steels for control of grain size, and most of the remaining to other types of alloy steels.

Serious interest in niobium as a metal first developed in 1955 when it was considered for use as a matrix material as well as a cladding material in fuel elements in atomic reactors. When this reactor design was abandoned the process industry, heavily committed as it was to producing the metal, began to seek alternative uses.

The refractory nature, ductility and workability, relatively high strength and moderate density of niobium served to guide the investigators in seeking new applications. However, niobium failed to make much progress in refractory uses because the metal oxidizes quite rapidly causing embrittlement. A great deal of research and development has gone into the physical metallurgy of niobium to overcome this shortcoming.

Since then the research has taken three directions. One has been to alloy the metal with active oxide-forming elements. Another has been to alloy niobium with metals that form a spinel coating on the surface which retards oxidation. The third has been to coat the metal to avoid oxidation at the high operating temperatures envisioned. So far these efforts have met with only moderate success.

A number of promising alloys have been developed. Among them is Nb_3Sn, a superconductive material. Although the entire realm of superconductivity research depends heavily upon this alloy, this is a relatively small potential market.

Good high-temperature strength over short exposure times in rocket engines and reentry vehicles exposed to oxidation environments have been achieved with several other niobium alloys. One of these is the so-called 85 metal, containing tantalum, tungsten, and zirconium.

Another is the SU-16 alloy containing tungsten, molybdenum and hafnium. The latter has been suggested for use in aircraft turbine blades and some structural parts of vehicle power plants, but, as yet, has not gained acceptance.

Perhaps the most encouraging development for niobium in commercial use occurred between 1960 and 1962. At this time interest was revived for its use in a spacecraft atomic reactor program. Unlike the earlier experience the technical progress was most encouraging. By 1962 niobium consumption had risen to 250,000 pounds but then the entire program was phased out and the demand for the metal went with it.

For the past few years about 100,000 pounds per year of niobium have been used by airframe manufacturers as shapes in a few advanced systems such as the Gemini program (now phased out) and in general R & D usage. In 1966 this general usage nearly tripled in response to a substantial price reduction in the metal.

For the future the largest applications foreseen for niobium are in liquid-cooled and other thrust chambers and as tubing. These hopes are based upon current plans in United States military and space programs, and are accordingly speculative. Nevertheless, producers of niobium are quite optimistic about the future of the metal and its alloys over the next decade.

References

1. Bartlett, E. S., and Houck, J. A., "Physical and Mechanical Properties of Columbium and Columbium-Base Alloys," DMIC Report 125 (PB 151082), Cameron Station, Alexandria, Virginia, Defense Documentation Center, February 22, 1960.
2. "Columbium and Tantalum," U.S. Bureau of Mines "Minerals Yearbook," published annually.
3. Sisco, F. T., and Epremian, E., Editors, "Columbium and Tantalum," New York, John Wiley and Sons, Inc., 1963.
4. "Columbium and Tantalum, A Materials Survey," U.S. Bureau of Mines Information Circular 8120, 1962.
5. Miller, G. L., "Tantalum and Niobium," New York, Academic Press, Inc., Publishers, 1959.

6. Schmidt, F. F., and Ogden, H. R., "The Engineering Properties of Columbium and Columbium Alloys," DMIC Report 188 (AD 426255), Cameron Station, Alexandria, Virginia, Defense Documentation Center, September 6, 1963.
7. Sherwood, E. M., "Columbium," in "Rare Metals Handbook," Hampel, C. A., Editor, 2nd Edition, pp. 149–177, New York, Reinhold Publishing Corp., 1961.
8. Gonser, B. W., and Sherwood, E. M., Editors, "Technology of Columbium (Niobium)," New York, John Wiley and Sons, Inc., 1958.

FRANK F. SCHMIDT

NITROGEN

A Swedish druggist, Carl Scheele, and a Scotch botanist, Daniel Rutherford, discovered nitrogen independently in 1772. Lavoisier was the first to recognize nitrogen as an element and in 1790 J. A. C. Chaptal introduced the name "nitrogen" to indicate that the element is a constituent of nitre—potassium nitrate.

Nitrogen is found in the air and in combinations as niter or saltpeter (potassium nitrate), chile saltpeter (sodium nitrate), ammonia, and ammonium salts in the atmosphere, in rain, soil and guano, and as complex organic compounds (proteins). In living organisms the average nitrogen concentration is 16% and the natural abundance is 0.3 parts per 1000.

The nitrogen concentration in the atmosphere is 78.03%. A typical composition of air is given in Table 1 and air thus serves as

TABLE 1. TYPICAL COMPOSITION OF AIR AT GROUND LEVEL

Component	Freezing Point, °K	Boiling Point, °K	Concentration
Nitrogen	63.14	77.36	78.03%
Oxygen	54.8	90.19	20.99%
Argon	83.9	87.3	0.93%
Carbon dioxide	—		300 ppm
Neon		27.2	18 ppm
Helium		4.2	5 ppm
Krypton		119.8	1.1 ppm
Xenon		165	0.1 ppm

the primary source of commercial nitrogen. The liquefaction of air involves the Joule-Thomson effect. This is followed by fractional distillation to separate the liquid air into its components. (See article on **Oxygen** for details.) As a matter of fact nitrogen was first liquefied in 1883 by Wrobliski and Olzewski.

Nitrogen can also be produced by burning carbon or a hydrocarbon with air and removing the carbon dioxide and water from the gaseous products by appropriate techniques.

There are several other methods that can be used to produce nitrogen. Ammonium nitrite in hot aqueous solutions gives nitrogen:

$$NH_4^+ + NO_2^- \rightarrow N_2 + 2H_2O.$$

The thermal decomposition of ammonium dichromate yields nitrogen:

$$(NH_4)_2Cr_2O_7 \rightarrow N_2 + Cr_2O_3 + 4H_2O.$$

The reaction of ammonia and bromine water gives N_2:

$$8NH_3 + 3Br_2 \rightarrow N_2 + 6NH_4^+ + 6Br^-.$$

The high temperature reaction of ammonia and cupric oxide gives nitrogen:

$$2NH_3 + 3CuO \rightarrow N_2 + 3H_2O + 3Cu.$$

The careful thermal decomposition of metal azides give N_2, e.g., $2NaN_3 \rightarrow 2Na + 3N_2$.

Molecular sieves can also be used for separating oxygen and nitrogen.

Commercially, gaseous nitrogen is available in cylinders (120 atm) and as liquid in cryogenic storage devices. In 1965, 71.7 billion standard cubic feet of gaseous nitrogen were produced and by 1970, the consumption should be in the range of 175-265 billion standard cubic feet.

Physical Properties

Gaseous nitrogen is odorless, colorless, nonflammable, nontoxic and nonexplosive. The liquid is a clear waterlike liquid. The general physical properties are given in Table 2.

Solid. There are two crystalline forms of molecular nitrogen; the α-form is a low-temperature form that is a cubic crystal; the β-form is a high-temperature hexagonal crystal. The transition from α to β occurs at 35.62°K with a heat of transition of 54.7 cal/mole.

TABLE 2. GENERAL PROPERTIES OF N₂

Atomic number	7
Atomic weight	14.0067
Melting point, °K	63.14
Normal boiling point, °K	77.36
Critical temperature, °K	126.1
Critical pressure, atm	33.50
Critical density, g/cc	0.311
Triple point temperature, °K	63.166
Triple point pressure, atm	0.1237
Heat of vaporization, cal/mole	1335
Heat of fusion, cal/mole	172
Density of solid at 20.6°K, g/cc	1.0265
Density of solid 63°K, g/cc	0.8792
Dielectric constant at 77.4°K	1.4335
Velocity of sound at 77°K, m/sec	880
Thermal conductivity of gas at STP, cal/cm/sec/°K	0.571×10^{-4}
Thermal conductivity of liquid at 77.4°K, cal/cm/sec/°K	3.34×10^{-4}

Liquid. There is considerable interest in liquid nitrogen and some of the cryogenic properties are given in Tables 3, 4 and 5. More detailed information can be found in the references listed below.

TABLE 3. DENSITY AND VISCOSITY OF SATURATED LIQUID NITROGEN

Temperature, °K	Density, g/cc	Temperature, °K	Viscosity, cp
64.73	0.8622	63.9	0.292
77.31	0.8084	64.3	0.290
78.00	0.8043	64.8	0.284
90.58	0.7433	69.1	0.231
99.36	0.6922	69.25	0.228
111.89	0.6071	71.46	0.209
119.44	0.5332	76.1	0.165
125.01	0.4314	77.33	0.158
		111.7	0.074

Gas. Molecular nitrogen is diamagnetic and has a specific susceptibility of 0.430×10^{-6} cgs units at 20°C. Density of saturated vapor is given in Table 6. Other gas property data may be found in the references. N_2 is soluble to some degree in liquids, e.g., N_2 dissolves in water at 0°C to 0.0231 volume of N_2/volume of water at one atm. Nitrogen solubilities in

TABLE 4. VAPOR PRESSURE OF SOLID AND LIQUID N₂

Temperature, °K	Vapor Pressure, atm	Temperature, °K	Vapor Pressure, atm
52	0.0075	85	2.25
58	0.0387	90	3.548
60	0.0621	100	7.70
63.14	0.1268	110	14.52
66	0.2028	120	24.81
70	0.3785	125	31.94
76	0.847	126.1 ± .01	33.50
77.36 ± .02	1.0000		

TABLE 5. HEAT CAPACITY OF LIQUID NITROGEN

Temperature, °K	Heat Capacity, Cp, cal/g/°K
65	0.481
70	0.484
75	0.490
85	0.500
95	0.518
105	0.561
115	0.650

TABLE 6. DENSITY OF SATURATED NITROGEN VAPOR

Temperature, °K	Density, g/cc
70	0.0019
75	0.0035
77.35	0.0047
80	0.0062
100	0.032
110	0.062
120	0.119

various organic liquids have been measured as well as adsorption on activated carbon, silica gel, and molecular sieves.

Thermodynamic Data

A temperature-entropy diagram has been established for pure N_2 as well as for mixtures with oxygen and methane.

Phase Equilibria. As already mentioned N_2 and O_2 form a homogeneous liquid mixture.

455

In addition studies have been made of other liquid nitrogen systems, e.g., nitrogen-helium, nitrogen-argon, nitrogen-CO_2, nitrogen-methane, nitrogen-ethane.

Nitrogen Isotopes. Ordinary nitrogen consists of two stable isotopes; N^{14} with an atomic weight of 14.00308 and N^{15} with an atomic weight of 15.00011 in the relative ratio of 99635 to 36.5. Some of the characteristics of these two nuclei are given in Table 7.

TABLE 7. PROPERTIES OF THE STABLE NITROGEN ISOTOPES

	N^{14}	N^{15}
Atomic weight	14.00308	15.00011
Spin moment	1.0	1/2
Magnetic dipole moment, magnetions	+0.40357	−0.28304
Electric quadripole moment,	+0.02	0
Nuclear magnetic resonance, frequency in 100,000 megacycles	3.076	4.315

Nitrogen-15 can be separated from nitrogen-14 by thermal diffusion, chemical exchange or both. Simple fractional distillation of NO can be used to concentrate N^{15}.

There are four radioactive nuclei that are very short-lived and their characteristics are given in Table 8.

TABLE 8. RADIOACTIVE ISOTOPES OF NITROGEN

Half-life, secs		Particles Emitted
N^{12}	0.0125	Positron and alpha
N^{13}	603	Positron
N^{16}	7.35	Beta, electron and γ-ray
N^{17}	4.14	Beta, electron and neutron

Chemical Reactions

Nitrogen is not a reactive element due to the large heat of dissociation of the molecule into the atoms. The molecular structure of nitrogen can be explained by the Lewis octet theory

$$:N:::N:$$

There are ten valence electrons—six are bonding electrons and the other four form two lone pairs. The molecular orbital theory can also be used to explain the molecular structure.

The oxidation state of nitrogen can be -3 to $+5$.

Ammonia. High pressures and/or temperatures are required in order to make chemicals from nitrogen directly. The most important use for elemental nitrogen is the manufacture of ammonia.

In the production of ammonia by the Haber Process, nitrogen and hydrogen are reacted at high temperature and pressure in the presence of a catalyst. A pressure of 1000 atm and a temperature of 500°C are considered typical conditions. Selected properties of ammonia are given in Table 9.

TABLE 9. PROPERTIES OF AMMONIA

Triple point, °K	195.46
Triple point pressure, mm	45.58
Boiling point, °K	239.78
Critical pressure, atm	112.3
Critical temperature, °K	405.6
Heat of vaporization at boiling point, kcal/mole	5.581
Density of liquid at 240.2°K, g/cc	0.6814
Viscosity of liquid at 239.7°K, cp	0.254
Dielectric constant at 240.2°K	~23

The production of ammonia in 1966 is estimated at 11,000,000 short tons and the predicted production in 1968 is 18,000,000 short tons. Ammonia serves as a starting material in making fertilizers, nitric acid, and organic compounds, such as aniline, explosives, synthetic fibers and resins.

Liquid ammonia is an excellent solvent and an excellent ionizing media. Table 10

TABLE 10. SOLUBILITY IN AMMONIA

Salt/Metal	Temperature, °K	Solubility, g/100g NH_3
NH_4Cl	298	102.5
NH_4NO_3	298	390.0
KI	298	182.0
KNH_2	298	3.6
Lithium	273.2	1.63
Sodium	273.2	1.00
Potassium	273.2	1.24

TABLE 11. OXIDES OF NITROGEN

Formula	Name	M.p., °K	B.p., °K	Discoverer
N_2O	Nitrous oxide	182.32	184.70	J. Priestley, 1712
NO	Nitric oxide	109.53	121.41	VanHelmont, 1620
N_2O_3	Dinitrogen trioxide	162.18	275.18	J. R. Glauber, 1648
N_2O_4	Dinitrogen tetroxide	261.98	294.33	
NO_2	Nitrogen dioxide	$2NO_2(g) \leftrightharpoons N_2O_4(g)$		
N_2O_5	Dinitrogen pentoxide	sublime 305.58		Deville, 1849
N_3O_4	Trinitrogen tetroxide			R. L. Hasche, 1925
NO_3		Unstable intermediate		

shows some typical solubilities. Ammonia forms ammoniates in much the same manner as water forms hydrates.

Nitric Acid. Another important nitrogen containing compound is nitric acid. Nitric acid is made by oxidizing ammonia to NO_2 followed by absorption in water. Pure nitric acid (100%) is produced by distilling a mixture of aqueous nitric acid and fuming sulfuric acid.

Nitric acid is an excellent oxidizing agent and forms nitrates. It is used in the production of ammonium nitrate, other nitrates, nitro compounds, explosives, lacquers, synthetic fabrics and dyes.

The production of nitric acid in 1966 was estimated to be 5 million short tons.

Calcium Cyanamide. Calcium cyanamide, $CaCN_2$, can be produced by reacting nitrogen with calcium carbide at high temperature. This cyanamide finds use as a fertilizer and as an intermediate in forming nitrogen-containing chemicals such as guanidine. Calcium cyanamide can also be used as a herbicide and defoliant.

Sodium Cyanide. Sodium cyanide can be formed by reacting nitrogen with a mixture of red-hot charcoal and sodium.

Hydrogen Cyanide. A mixture of methane (hydrocarbons) and nitrogen when passed through an electric arc is converted to acetylene and hydrogen cyanide.

Nitrogen Oxides. Joseph Priestley in 1780 found that an electric spark passed through a mixture of nitrogen and oxygen gave nitric oxide, NO. Ionizing radiation and shock tube techniques can also be used to produce nitrogen oxides.

The nitrogen oxides are an excellent example of the law of multiple proportions and the $+1$ to $+5$ oxidation states of nitrogen. Table 11 presents data on these eight oxides.

Metal Nitrides. Metals under the appropriate conditions of temperature form nitrides. Lithium and calcium form nitrides at 218°K and 293°K, respectively.

Other Nitrogen Compounds. The chemistry of nitrogen-containing compounds is broad and covers the general fields of organic and inorganic compounds. In addition to the nitrogen oxygen compounds already mentioned, nitrogen forms compounds with the halogens, hydrogen, sulfur, phosphorus, and boron and various combinations of these such as oxyhalogens. Compounds containing the carbon-nitrogen bond are also common. The three main classes of these compounds are (1) ammonia derivatives, e.g., amines and amides (2) cyanogen derivatives, e.g., nitriles and (3) oxy derivatives, e.g., nitroso and nitro compounds.

Uses of Nitrogen

Gas. Gaseous nitrogen has been used successfully in the chemical, food, electrical and metal industries as an inerting gas.

In the chemical industry, the use has been associated with the following:

a. to dilute a reacting gas
b. to increase the yield of a product
c. to serve as a carrier gas (heat and chemicals)
d. to eliminate or reduce a hazard potential, e.g., fire or explosion
e. to serve as a scavenger gas
f. to prevent oxidation, decomposition, or hydrolysis of a reactant or product

In the food industry the uses have in general been associated with the prevention of spoilage—oxidation, mold growth and insect infestation.

In the electrical industry, nitrogen has been used to prevent oxidation and chemical reaction. Nitrogen has been used for pressurizing cable jackets, lasers, and shielding motors.

In the metals industry, nitrogen, in excess, has been used to prevent metal oxidation, carburization and decarburization, e.g., in welding, soldering and brazing.

Nitrogen has also been used as a non-reactive gas to make foamed or expanded rubber, plastics or elastomers. Nitrogen has been used in wind tunnels, for agitating liquid baths, balloon inflation, propellant gas for aerosol cans, for fluidizing gas, for pressurizing liquid propellants for reaction jets.

Liquid nitrogen uses are associated with availability, inertness and low temperature. The food processing and transportation industries are using liquid nitrogen for refrigeration systems, and for freeze drying. Linde's "Polarstream," Chemtron's "Cold Wall," Airco's "Cold Flow" and Air Product's "Cryo Guard" are all in-transit refrigeration systems. Rapid food freezing using liquid nitrogen is claimed to preserve original texture and natural flavor. There is recent evidence to support the use of liquid nitrogen in the field of cryobiology in the preservation of blood, bone marrow, tissues, germ strains and semen. Cryosurgery has also been used with some success.

The electronics industry has used liquid nitrogen for the cooling of electronic components. Shrink fitting, strain relief and particle size reduction are other areas in which liquid nitrogen has been tried successfully.

Biological and Biochemical Aspects

The biochemistry of nitrogen compounds involves the complex subject of protein chemistry. Proteins are characterized by the fact that they yield 20-25 different α-amino acids on hydrolysis. In the class of materials there are naturally occurring proteins (albumin, globulin, glutelins, alcohol soluble, albuminoids, histones and protamines), conjugated proteins, combinations of protein with other substances (nucleoproteins, glycoproteins, phosphoproteins, chromoproteins, lipoproteins), and derived proteins, formed from hydrolysis of the protein molecule (proteans, metaproteins, coagulated proteins, proteoses, peptones, and peptides). Some enzymes also contain nitrogen.

"Nitrogen fixation" is the name given to any process in which free nitrogen is caused to combine with other elements to form nitrogen compounds. This fixation can be done chemically and also by certain bacteria, e.g., *azotobacter chroococcum* and *clostridium pasteurianum*. A cooperative action between bacteria and certain plants, e.g., peas, beans and clover also fixes nitrogen.

The nitrogen cycle involves the fact that animals derive the nitrogen for their tissue from animal and vegetable proteins (as food). Plants synthesize their proteins from inorganic compounds in the soil and to some extent from free nitrogen in the atmosphere with the help of certain soil bacteria.

Bends. When animals are exposed to high-pressure air, some of the nitrogen dissolves in the blood and other body fluids. If the pressure is suddenly released the dissolved nitrogen forms bubbles and is set free within the body. This sudden release can cause partial paralysis, fainting, pains in the muscles and joints and eventually death. Slow decompression prevents the above symptoms.

References

1. Jolly, W. L., "Inorganic Chemistry of Nitrogen," New York, W. A. Benjamin, Inc., 1964.
2. Hilsenrath, J., *et al*, Washington, D.C., National Bureau of Standards Circ. 564, 1955.
3. Vance, R. W., and Duke, W. M., "Applied Cryogenic Engineering," New York, John Wiley and Sons, 1962.
4. *Chemical & Engineering News*, "Facts and Figures for the Chemical Process Industries," **44**, No. 36 (September 5, 1966).
5. Johnson, V. J., "A Compendium of Properties of Materials at Low Temperature (Phase I)," Part I, "Properties of Fluids," NBS Cryogenic Laboratory, Boulder, Colorado, 1960.
6. Clark, G., and Hawley, G. G., "Encyclopedia of Chemistry," Second Edition, New York, Reinhold Publishing Co., 1966.
7. Franklin, E. C., "Nitrogen System of Compounds," ACS Monograph No. 68, New York, Reinhold Publishing Co., 1935.

8. *Chemical Week*, "Gases—Jetting to Sales Records," p. 51, September 3, 1966.
9. Sittig, M., "Nitrogen in Industry," Princeton, New Jersey, Van Nostrand, 1964.
10. Mellor, J. W., "Comprehensive Treatise on Inorganic and Theoretical Chemistry," Vol. 8, Suppl. 1, "Nitrogen" (Part I), New York, John Wiley and Sons, 1964.

CHARLES K. HERSH

NOBELIUM

The discovery of nobelium, element 102, is still an unresolved question. Its present status resulted from the fact that three separate groups have reported the discovery of this element. The first group, consisting of scientists from Argonne National Laboratory, U.S.A., Harwell Atomic Energy Research Establishment, England, and the Nobel Institute of Physics, Sweden, reported the isolation of element 102 in 1957. In these experiments a $Cm^{244, 246, 248}$ target was irradiated with C^{13} ions generated in the 225 cm Nobel Institute heavy-ion cyclotron. The atoms produced in these irradiations were separated from the target atoms by a recoil technique developed earlier by Ghiorso, and co-workers at the Lawrence Radiation Laboratory. The same technique was employed by all groups working on element 102. The recoil procedure involves irradiating a thin target with heavy ions and then catching the recoil atoms on a foil. See Fig 1. The advan-

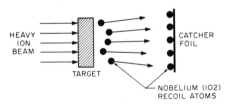

FIG. 1. Direct recoil technique.

tages of this method are (1) immediate separation of the short-lived recoil atoms from the intense radioactivity of the target, (2) the ability to do repeated irradiations with the same target, (3) the confinement of the radioactive target in a sealed system and (4) the adaptation of the technique to identify the original recoil atoms by collecting recoils

from the alpha decay of the initial product atoms.

The Argonne-Harwell-Nobel Institute group reported producing an 8.5 ± 0.1 MeV alpha emitter with a half-life of approximately 10 min which eluted in the 102 position from an ion exchange column using an organic complex agent as an elutrient. They suggested that this activity might be due to an odd isotope of element 102 in the mass range 251–255, and recommended the name Nobelium.

Approximately a year later another group of scientists working at the Lawrence Radiation Laboratory, University of California, using the newly constructed Heavy Ion Linear Accelerator (HILAC), attempted to repeat the work reported by the first group, but were unable to duplicate the results of the earlier experiments. They employed C^{12} (and some C^{13}) bombardments of a mixed $Cm^{244, 246, 248}$ target, and reported a different isotope, 102^{254}, which they claimed had a half-life of 3 seconds and an alpha energy of 8.3 MeV. Since this isotope had too short a half-life to identify chemically, they used a double recoil technique to identify the new element. In this method (see Fig. 2) the iso-

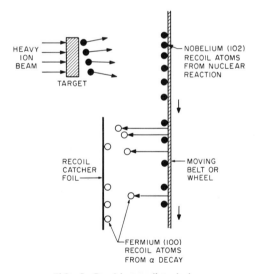

FIG. 2. Double recoil technique.

tope produced in the initial nuclear reaction recoiled out of the target and was caught on a moving belt and then the product of its alpha decay, an isotope of fermium, was in turn caught on another foil where the fermium was characterized. In several experiments the fermium decay product was identified chemically and from its alpha particle energy and half-life was identified as Fm^{250}, thus indicating the parent to be 102^{254}.

This group also claimed to have produced another isotope, 102^{255}, which they prepared by irradiating Cf^{252} with boron ions. The assignment of this isotope was based on its nuclear properties, becay by emission of an 8.2 MeV alpha particle and a 15-second half-life, and by using other types of bombardments which would also yield this same product or where absence of this product indicated further confirmation of the assignment.

The third group of scientists working in 1957 at the Dubna Institute in the U.S.S.R. also reported the production of isotopes of element 102. Their early attempts involved irradiating Pu^{239} and Pu^{241} with O^{16} ions generated in their heavy-ion cyclotron, and then exposing the recoil atoms to a nuclear emulsion to determine the alpha-particle energies emitted by these atoms. The recoil atoms were found to emit a fairly broad range of alpha particles, 8.8 ± 0.5 MeV, and later work showed that some of the observed alpha particles were due to products from lead impurities in the plutonium target. Since there was no attempt to establish the identity of the recoils from the alpha decay and since it was not possible to do any chemical identification, there was no unique determination of element 102 in these experiments. By varying the recoil collection and exposure times, a half-life of greater than 2 and less than 40 sec was set for the $8.8 \pm .5$ MeV alpha activity.

In 1963 the Dubna group reported the production of No^{256} by irradiating U^{238} with Ne^{22} ions using the recoil technique. This isotope was found to have a half-life of 8 seconds, and its mass assignment was confirmed by identifying the Fm^{252} resulting from the alpha decay of No^{256}.

Very recently, in 1965, the Dubna group conducted a more sophisticated series of experiments in which they produced and studied the properties of No^{254}, the same isotope produced by the California group in 1958. However, the results of the Russian experiments are in disagreement with the California experiments. The Russians irradiated U^{238} with Ne^{22}, also Am^{243} with N^{15}, and the No^{254} produced in these experiments decayed with an alpha energy of 8.1 MeV and a half-life of 20 to 50 seconds. The mass of the isotopes was confirmed by identifying the Fm^{250} recoils resulting from the alpha decay of No^{254}. In addition the Dubna group found a smaller production of No^{524} than was observed by the California group.

In 1967 Ghiorso, Sikkeland and Nurmia reported that the Russian work on 102^{254} was essentially correct and now believe that their data on No^{254} best fits the properties of No^{252}. They also showed that the carbon ion bombardments have a higher production rate for nobelium than the reactions used by the Soviet group.

Other methods of producing nobelium have been tried without success. High-energy helium ion bombardments of fermium holds some hope of producing larger amounts of nobelium, but useful amounts of fermium will not be available for another year or so. Possibly, production in thermonuclear tests will provide the neutron rich isotopes of this element.

The known isotopes of nobelium, with their radioactive decay characteristics and methods of production, are given on page 756 in the article on **Transuranium Elements.**

Scientists at the Lawrence Radiation Laboratory (Berkeley), using the 3.6 min No^{255} as a tracer, have been able to determine some of the chemical properties of nobelium. They demonstrated that nobelium has a trivalent and divalent state and that the latter is probably the more stable in solution. They also showed that the divalent state elutes from a Dowex 50 ion exchange column, using as an eluent the complexing agent, α-hydroxy-isobutyric acid, after the trivalent actinides and before the alkaline earths. Hence, nobelium does not appear to follow the elution characteristics of the lighter trivalent actinides. The position of elution from this type of column was used to identify the atomic number of elements 95 through 101.

Research in this field is still quite active and the question of the discovery of element 102 will probably be resolved by further experiments.

References

1. Fields, P. R., Friedman, A. M., Milsted, J., Atterling, H., Forsling, W., Holm, L. W., and Aström, B., "Production of the New Element 102," *Phys. Rev.* **107**, 1460, (1957).
2. Flerov, G. N., Polikanov, S. M., *et al.*, "Experiments on the Production of the 102d Element," *Doklady Akad. Nauk. S.S.R.*, **120**, 73, (1958).
3. Ghiorso, A., Sikkeland, T., Walton, J. R., and Seaborg, G. T., "Attempts to Confirm the existence of the 10-Minute Isotope of 102," *Phys. Rev. Letters*, **1**, 17 (1958).
4. Ghiorso, A., Sikkeland, T., Walton, J. R., and Seaborg, G. T., "Element No, 102," *Phys. Rev. Letters*, **1**, 18 (1958).
5. Fields, P. R., Friedman, A, M., Milsted, J., Atterling, H., Forsling, W., Holm, L. W., and Aström, B., "On the Production of Element 102," *Arkiv Fysik*, **15**, 225 (1959).
6. Flerov, G. N., Polikanov, S. M., Karamyan, A. S., Pasyuk, A. S., Parfanovich, D. M., Taratin, N. I., Karanaukhov, V. A., Druin, V. A., Volkov, V. V., Semchinova, A. M., Oganesyan, Yu. C., Khalizev, V. I., Khlebrikov, G. I., Myasoedov, B. E., and Gavrilov, K, A., "Experiments on the production of the 102nd Element," *Zhur. Eksptl. i Teoret. Fiz.*, **38**, 82 (1960).
7. Ghiorso, A., Sikkeland, T., Larsh, A. E., and Latimer, R. M., "New Element, Lawrencium, Atomic Number 103," *Phys. Rev. Letters*, **6**, 473 (1961).
8. Donets, E. D., Shchegolev, V. A., and Ermakov, V. A., "Synthesis of Element 102 Isotope with Mass Number 256," Joint Institute for Nuclear Research, Dubna, U.S.S.R., P-1383, (1963).
9. Driun, V. A., Shobelev, N. K., Fefilov, B. V., and Flerov, G. N., "On Spontaneous Fission of Element 102 with Mass Number 256," Joint. Inst. for Nuclear Research, Dubna, U.S.S.R., P-1580, (1964).
10. Zager, B. A., Miller, M. B., Mikheev, V. L., Polikanov, S. M., Sukhov, A. M., Flerov, G. N., and Chelnokov, L. P., On Properties of No^{254} Isotope," Joint Inst. for Nuclear Research, Dubna, U.S.S.R., P-2470, (1965).
11. Donets, E. D., Shchegolev, V. A., and Ermakov, V. A., "On Properties of a No^{254} Isotope," Joint Inst. for Nuclear Research, Dubna, U.S.S.R., P-2471, (1965).
12. Ghiorso, A., Sikkeland, T., and Nurmia, M. J., "Isotopes of Element 102 with Mass 251 to 258," *Phys. Rev. Letters*, **18**, 401 (1967).

PAUL R. FIELDS

NOBLE GASES †

When Mendeleeff first published his guess at the most reasonable systematic arrangement of the elements, one family in the Periodic Table we know today was strikingly unrepresented, Group 0, made up of the noble gases. (See **Argon, Helium, Krypton, Neon, Radon and Xenon**).

Chemists exhibited great interest in these elements after their existence was demonstrated, in spite of their very limited chemical behavior. Perhaps it is more realistic to recognize that their principal interest revolved around their inert character, for studies dealing with the noble gases as inert chemical entities have played a significant role in the development of modern concepts of chemical bond formation.

History

As early as 1785, Henry Cavendish observed that the most extensive electric sparking, which converts most of the air ultimately to nitric acid, was unable to chemically combine the last trace. Interestingly enough, he formulated his report of this observation as setting an upper limit to the amount of a new nonreactive constituent of the atmosphere. For a hundred years chemists ignored the possibility of any such constituent in spite of repeated and presumably detailed analyses of air samples drawn from all over the world.

In 1882, Rayleigh became interested in the relative density of gases with particular emphasis on the deviation from integral ratios of atomic weights. He developed sound techniques and made a number of careful measurements on the density ratios for hydrogen, nitrogen, and oxygen. In 1890, following the suggestion of Professor Ramsey, he observed and reported a difference between the density of nitrogen from ammonia and atmospheric nitrogen. Pursuing the problem with growing interest and insight, first independently and finally in the closest collaboration, Rayleigh and Ramsey were able to announce in August, 1894, that there was indeed a constituent of the atmosphere

† Based on work performed under the auspices of the U.S. Atomic Energy Commission.

that not only was a new element but that obviously belonged to a whole new family in the Periodic Table. The noble gases are now so familiar that it is hard to appreciate the reluctance with which many chemists accepted the concept of this new group of elements. Rayleigh and Ramsey established the absence of chemical reaction under reasonably severe conditions with a wide variety of reagents, although because of the experimental difficulties the reaction with fluorine was not investigated until many years later. The postulated absence of chemical reaction met with less resistance than their assignment to this new substance of the particular atomic weight and position in the Periodic Table they chose. Soon after isolating significant amounts of argon, (from Greek for lazy) as they named their new discovery, they measured the velocity of sound in this gas and calculated the ratio of specific heats ($\gamma = c_p/c_v$) by well established techniques. The relationship between the ratio of the specific heat at constant pressure to specific heat at constant volume and the number of atoms in a molecule was accepted by physicists, but its rather firm foundation was not recognized by many chemists. (For monatomic gases $\gamma = 1.67$, for diatomic gases $\gamma = 1.40$ and with increasing molecular size γ decreases towards 1). The measured value was very close to 1.66 and established to their satisfaction that argon was a monatomic gas whose atomic weight and absence of chemical properties could best be explained by slipping it between chlorine and potassium in the Periodic Table, even though their observed weight of 40 was above the 39 found for potassium.

Samples of the new gas were investigated by spectroscopists who unequivocally demonstrated the differences between argon and nitrogen. These observations foreshadowed both the obvious use of spectroscopy for analyzing each of the members of the family to be discovered and to some extent one of their most striking industrial uses, in colorful electric discharge tubes. Next year, in 1895, Ramsey demonstrated that the gas isolated from clevite (a uranium ore) had a spectrum containing lines which had been previously found in the solar spectrum and attributed to an unknown substance then called helium.

He rapidly established helium as the lightest member of the noble gas family.

In the next few years, Ramsey and his co-workers isolated the remaining stable elements in the group, neon, krypton and xenon. Very soon afterwards radon, a radioactive noble gas, was noted by Dorn and studied by Ramsey as well as by the Curie's and other scientists working with radioactive elements. (A variety of names have been offered for this heaviest elemental gas: actinon, thoron, and radon depending on the radioactive series where it originates and niton and emanon for the element. At present radon is used).

All of the gases are found in the atmosphere (Table 1). The earth is not massive enough to

TABLE 1. THE CONCENTRATION OF NOBLE GASES IN THE ATMOSPHERE

Gas	Concentration by Volume, ppm
He	5.24
Ne	18.18
Ar	9,340.
Kr	1.14
Xe	0.086
Rn	6×10^{-14}

retain helium as a permanent atmospheric constituent and the helium found on earth is essentially the equilibrium amount formed by emission of alpha particles from radioactive elements.

The short-lived isotopes of radon are also in equilibrium with their radioactive parents and daughters while the slow decay of radioactive potassium (K^{40}) steadily increases the argon content.

The growing nuclear energy industry is adding fission-product krypton and xenon to the world supply at a small but at least for the latter, a detectable rate.

Helium is found as an important constituent in natural gas wells, and radon is a decay product of each of the natural radioactive series, while the others are recovered from the atmosphere in commercial quantities as a by-product of liquid air plants. Although helium is not a particularly abundant element

TABLE 2. PHYSICAL PROPERTIES OF GROUP VIII ELEMENTS

Property		He³	He	Ne	Ar	Kr	Xe	Rn
Atomic weight	$C^{12} =$ 12.0000	3.01603	4.0026	20.183	39.948	83.80	131.30	(222)
Gas density 0°C & 1 atm	g/l		0.17847	0.89994	1.78403	3.7493	5.8971	9.73
Triple point	°K			24.55	83.78	115.95	161.3	202
Pressure at triple point	torr			324	516	548	612	~500
Heat of fusion at triple point	cal/mole	43.0†	44.5†	80.1	281	390.7	548.5	
Solid density at triple point	g/cc			1.444	1.623	2.826	3.540	
Boiling point	°K	3.19	4.215	27.07	87.27	119.8	165.05	211
Heat of vaporization at boiling point	cal/mole	6.09	19.4	414	1557.5	2158	3020	
Liquid density at boiling point	g/cc	0.0589	.1249	1.207	1.3798	2.413	3.06	
Critical temperature	°K	3.33	5.3	44.5	150.9	209.4	289.71	378
Critical pressure	atm	1.15	2.26	26.9	48.3	54.3	57.64	62
Critical density	g/cc	0.04131	0.0693	0.484	0.536	0.908	1.100	
Solubility in water at 0°C	cc(STP)/1000g		9.78	14.0	52.4	99.1	203.2	510
Dielectric constant, 25°C & 1 atm			1.0000639	1.0001229	1.0005085	1.000768	1.001238	

Value given is at 25°K.

on earth, it is second only to hydrogen among all the elements in cosmic abundance.

The noble gases have played a most important role in the development of theories of chemical bonding. As concepts of electronic structure were developed by physicists for the atom, the idea of closed shells of electrons was introduced. Such shells corresponded to the structure of the appropriate inert gas at the end of each period in the accepted arrangement of elements. This concept permitted the systematic description of much chemical behavior. Indeed the idea that a filled shell was associated with inert chemical properties was so convenient pedagogically that the lack of chemical reactivity was overemphasized. The discovery that the heavy noble gases could form true chemical compounds with at least fluorine surprised many scientists when this observation was reported in 1962, although such behavior had been clearly anticipated by students of chemical bond theory (Pauling and others) 30 years earlier.

Physical Properties

Some of the physical properties of the inert gases are summarized in Table 2. Values for these elements have rather greater interest than their intrinsic values as properties of these individual elements. Representing as they do, monatomic elements with closed shells, the physical properties of the noble gases represent values unaffected by those forces associated with valence electrons and potential for chemical bond formation. As such they form not only a base line from which to calculate the perturbation due to

these latter forces but also a test of many suggested calculations from first principles.

A good deal of effort has gone into comparing the equation of state of these elements with various explanations for deviation from the perfect gas laws. Van der Waal's constants are given in Table 3 calculated by some

TABLE 3. VAN DE WAALS CONSTANTS FOR THE NOBLE GASES

| Gas | a, l^2/mole^2-atm | | b, l/mole | |
	Critical†	Gas‡	Critical†	Gas‡
He³	0.0274		0.0297	
He	0.0353	0.03412	0.0240	0.02370
Ne	0.210	0.2107	0.0175	0.01709
Ar	1.339	1.345	0.0329	0.0322
Kr	2.294	2.318	0.0406	0.0398
Xe	4.136	4.194	0.0530	0.0511
Rn	6.55		0.0644	

† Calculated from critical constants in Table 2.
$$a = 27R^2Tc^2/64 \ Pc$$
$$b = R \ Tc/8 \ Pc$$
$$R = 0.08206 \ l \ atm/mole$$
‡ Taken from a recent compilation based on virial coefficient measurements.

generalized relationships from the critical data shown in Table 2 while the more elaborate constants used in the Beattie and Bridgman equation are given in Table 4.

Estimates of atomic size and attractive and repulsive force operating between atoms invariably start with the inert gas properties. The parameters governing the growth of crystals and the arrangement of molecules in a liquid may be approximated from theories which are first tested against the observed properties of the Group VIII elements.

TABLE 4. CONSTANTS OF THE BEATTIE-BRIDGMAN EQUATION FOR SOME NOBLE GASES

Gas	A_0, l^2atm/mole^2	a, l/mole	B_0, l/mole	c × 10^{-4}, l-deg^3/mole
He	0.0216	0.05984	0.01400	0.0040
Ne	0.2125	0.02196	0.02060	0.101
Ar	1.2907	0.02328	0.03931	5.99
Kr	2.4230	0.02865	0.05261	14.89
Xe	4.6715	0.03311	0.07503	30.02

Simplified form of the Beattie-Bridgman Equation of State as applied to these gases:
$$PV = RT + [(RT \ B_0 - A_0 - Rc/T^2)/V]$$
$$+ [(A_0 \ a - R \ B_0 \ c/T^2)/V^2]$$
$$R = 0.08206 \ l \ atm/deg/mole$$

Perhaps the most interesting test of fundamental physical theory is offered by the behavior of helium. Helium at low temperature has unique properties which are completely inexplicable in terms of the familiar physics of the early Twentieth Century. Below the temperature 2.173°K (called the lambda point from resemblance to the Greek letter of the shape of the heat capacity curve at that point) liquid helium is transformed into a substance with a number of remarkable properties, particularly that of "superfluidity." Helium II, as this phase is called, is a liquid which as the temperature is decreased further contains an increasing fraction of a superfluid component with zero viscosity. This has been interpreted in terms of the quantum statistical laws (Bose-Einstein vs Fermi-Dirac statistics) governing energy distribution, which differ for aggregations of even or odd numbers of fundamental particles. He^4 atoms are even numbered and the properties of He^4 contrast strongly with the only suitable comparison liquid He^3. For all other atoms, the interatomic forces which produce ordered solids dominate at low temperature. For both He^3 and He^4 no triple point has been found and solid helium exists only under external pressure, but for He^3 the viscosity increases smoothly with decreasing temperatures and no evidence is found for superfluidity or such peculiar properties as the extremely good thermal conductivity found for He^4 at these low temperatures. Values have been reported for the latter more than 1000 times that found for copper.

Helium at low temperatures has been described as a macroscopic quantum liquid with properties that demonstrate the deviation from conventional physics on a larger than usual scale. Detailed explanations of these remarkable properties, starting perhaps with the work of Landau, are now available. Such explanations lend substantial credence to modern theories of physics in the important sense that they accurately describe and even predict observed behavior that defies "common sense" understanding.

The electrical properties of the noble gases have been studied in great detail, particularly in connection with their use in electrical discharge tubes.

The ionization energies for these elements

TABLE 5. FIRST AND SECOND IONIZATION POTENTIALS FOR THE NOBLE GASES

Gas	I, volts	II, volts
He	24.58	54.40
Ne	21.56	41.11
Ar	15.76	27.62
Kr	14.00	24.56
Xe	12.13	(21.21)
Rn	10.75	

are quite interesting (Table 5). If one remembers that one electron volt corresponds to 23.06 kcal/mole, it is clear that for the lower noble gases the energies associated with ionization are very high compared to those normally encountered in chemical bond formation.

If we accept the concept of filled shells, we are led to the conclusion that no chemical reaction is likely to involve electron transfer to one of the noble gas atoms. Since we can also expect a rough correlation with ionization potential for chemical reactions which involve these elements acting as electron donors, it is clear that at least for helium, neon, and argon, we are indeed dealing with elements which are not likely to participate in chemical reactions. The chemistry of the heavier noble gases will be discussed below.

We have noted how almost the first property of argon that was observed was the spectrum emitted in an electric discharge. For each of these gases, such spectra have been studied in detail, both theoretically and experimentally, and the energy levels available to electrons between the ground states and the ionization region are fully mapped.

Such information has been vital in the development of noble gas illumination sources. Light sources depending on the properties of the inert gases include not only the brightly colored advertising signs and the inert gas-filled lamps that furnish almost all the lighting found in home and factory, but also the powerful lasers which have aroused such widespread interest as a research tool in recent years.

Isolation

Helium (q.v.) is the most important and interesting of the noble gases, scientifically and to many important industrial users. Since it is relatively rare in the atmosphere, its large-scale industrial use depends on its availability in natural gas wells, particularly in the United States. The separation of helium from all other gases is readily effected since it remains as a gas to a temperature so low that all possible contaminants are frozen out. However, for a final separation from nitrogen and especially hydrogen, treatment with activated charcoal at low temperatures is even more convenient and is usually employed. Helium is less readily absorbed in charcoal than any other gas.

Helium is available commercially both as a gas under pressure in steel cylinders and as a liquid in well-insulated tanks at −452°F.

A modern processing plant for extracting helium from natural gas uses five major processing steps:

1) Preliminary treatment of natural gas, removing carbon dioxide and water vapor.

2) Liquefaction and removal of natural gas.

3) Crude helium separation and nitrogen rejection as liquid nitrogen.

4) Purification of the helium over activated charcoal.

5) Helium liquefaction.

Each of the other stable gases in the series is recovered directly from the atmosphere as a by-product of liquid oxygen production. (See Oxygen). A modern plant for air reduction employs large multistage distillation columns to yield a number of crude fractions which are discussed below in order of increasing boiling point. Carbon dioxide and water vapor are usually removed first to prevent the plugging of lines with solids.

The neon fraction includes helium, hydrogen and nitrogen as the principal impurities. Hydrogen is removed by reaction with copper oxide and subsequent drying and neon is separated from the nitrogen and helium either by fractional distillation or selective absorption in charcoal or most frequently by successive operations involving both techniques.

The large nitrogen fraction is collected next (b.p., −195.8°C). The argon fraction collects between the nitrogen and oxygen fraction and must be dealt with even if no argon recovery is justified. The crude argon fraction contains oxygen ($\sim 10\%$) as the principal impurity.

Combination with excess hydrogen followed by removal of the hydrogen on copper oxide and the water by intensive drying leaves nitrogen as the only significant impurity. For most industrial needs small amounts of nitrogen ($<1\%$) are not deleterious.

The bulk of the oxygen is removed for use as such, but a high boiling oxygen fraction containing most of the krypton and xenon is taken for isolation of these gases. While distillation separation of krypton and xenon from oxygen is simple in principle, the presence of hydrocarbon impurities in this fraction offers a potential explosion hazard if they are allowed to accumulate extensively in the liquid oxygen. Recovery techniques for krypton and xenon are rather small-scale chemical operations, depending usually for final purification on selective adsorption on charcoal but including a catalytic combustion step to remove hydrocarbons, a chemical absorption step to remove carbon dioxide and water vapor and often a silica gel absorption step to concentrate the krypton and xenon.

While impurities in the noble gases may be detected and determined by chemical means, analysis of the gases themselves depend on spectroscopic properties or more likely mass spectroscopic analysis.

Uses

As has been noted, the noble gases are important intellectual curiosities, but, of course, they play a more direct and specific role in commerce and industry. Both helium and argon are consumed in multimillion dollar amounts and the others have smaller though still significant industrial uses.

The first large-scale use of helium was for lighter-than-air craft where the lack of flammability provided a substantial advantage over hydrogen at only a slight decrease in efficiency. At one time it seemed possible that such lighter-than-air craft might become important commercial vehicles but the unfortunate experiences with some early models, particularly those using hydrogen, and the rapid development of airplanes eliminated them from serious consideration. The development of nuclear power has led to suggestions for nuclear powered helium-filled lighter-than-air vessels particularly for the transport of very large objects over land, but in 1967 the actual use of the lifting power of helium was restricted to nonrigid blimps used largely for advertising purposes and balloons used largely for upper atmosphere observations and research. These uses total only a small fraction of the helium consumed.

A major use of helium lies in the use of an inert gas to provide an inert atmosphere in welding and to a lesser extent in a variety of metallurgical operations in which an inert atmosphere is desired. In these operations argon is also used and in many cases, it is preferred.

Unique uses for helium involve its cryogenic behavior. Liquid helium is unrivaled as a low-temperature liquid and a wide variety of physical phenomena are exhibited and studied either solely or most effectively in a liquid helium or a liquid helium-cooled system. The development of superconducting magnets and the potential value of very powerful magnets with relatively low power demands promise to increase very substantial the already large demand for the cryogenic fluid.

As a diluent for oxygen, helium has many physiological advantages over nitrogen in an atmosphere supplied to divers or others working under artificial high-pressure atmospheres, and as a medical aid for patients with respiratory problems. The illness known to divers as the bends, resulting from the formation of bubbles of nitrogen in the blood in returning from a high pressure to normal pressures too rapidly, is greatly minimized when helium-oxygen mixtures are employed and the available depth and working times at depth have been substantially increased by the use of artificial inert gas-oxygen mixtures to replace compressed air supplies.

There are many small-volume, high-value uses of helium in science and medicine, commerce, and industry. These include the use of helium for detecting leaks in vacuum and pressure systems using a mass spectrometer detector, as a diluent for anesthetics in operating rooms, as a constituent of the filler gases used in advertising signs of the neon type and as a heat-exchange medium in nuclear reactors.

Among the noble gases other than helium, tonnage uses exist only for argon. The major use for argon, however, depends principally on its being by far the most available of the noble gases, and therefore the element of choice when an inert atmosphere must be provided. Argon-shielded welding procedures and argon atmospheres for metallurgical operations involving metals which react with moisture, air or any of the other constituents of the atmosphere, account for most of the volume in commercial use of the inert gases.

A widespread use of the helium-group gases may be found in their use in most modern types of electric light. Today, electricity is converted into light in lamps which can be divided into two broad classes: incandescent and gaseous discharge lamps. In incandescent lights the electricity is carried by a solid filament which is heated until significant amounts of energy are emitted in the required spectral region. Since this means a temperature of some thousands of degrees centigrade the filament must not be exposed to a reactive atmosphere. While early incandescent lamps often used vacuum to protect the filament, it was soon found that the over-all efficiency could be improved with an inert gas atmosphere. Nitrogen, argon and krypton have all been used with tungsten filaments, with krypton giving in general the highest light output per watt. The output per dollar on the other hand depends on the rather complex relationship between the cost of electricity and the cost of isolating particular noble gases, and at the moment a filling consisting mostly of argon with small amounts of nitrogen seems to be the preferred incandescent lamp-filling medium in the United States. The lamp is filled to yield about 1 atm pressure at operating temperatures. Where electricity is relatively expensive and efficiency or smaller bulb size more important, for example, in miners' lamps, the use of krypton-filled lamps may well be more economical in spite of the greater initial cost of the noble gas. Where efficiency may be traded off for longer life, krypton-filled lamps may become more economical for uses where the cost of replacement is a significant economic factor.

In gas discharge tubes electric current is carried by the gas itself. While the current is flowing the gas is of course ionized, but the process of light emission involves the movement of the bound electrons from states of higher energy to states of low energy. This results in emission of light at precise wavelengths so that there are characteristic colors associated with particular noble gas fillings and advantage has been taken of this to dazzle the visitor to most commercial areas all over the world.

The bright red color associated with simple colorless tubing filled with neon has fastened the name of this gas on the whole variety of electric discharge lighting with inert gas filling. Lights which are colored red depend on neon filling although the color may be slightly modified with colored glass tubing, while argon-filled lamps emit blue light which can be modified towards the green by the use of yellow-colored glass tubing. Often the argon is mixed with neon or neon and helium to maintain optimum electrical characteristics. Sometimes mercury vapor is included. For best results electric discharge lamps require reasonable strict control of pressure, purity and composition of the inert gas filling. For most light systems pressures of 6-12 torr are employed.

Mercury is the most important constituent of the widely used fluorescent light sources where the intense ultraviolet radiation associated with discharge in mercury vapor is converted to visible light by a fluorescent coating on the interior of the glass tube. Mercury is present as a liquid with a rather low vapor pressure when cold. The addition of an inert gas, either argon, or argon-krypton mixtures (at a pressure of a few torr) vastly improves the starting characteristics of the lamps and such fillings are normally used. Helium may replace mercury vapor as an initial UV light source, with lower efficiences at moderate temperatures. Above 40°C, the increased mercury vapor content of the gas absorbs enough light to reduce the net output and at relatively high operating temperature, helium-filled fluorescents may be more efficient.

There are many low-volume lighting sources which use special inert gas fillings. Xenon lamps, for example, offer intense sources with color characteristics of high-temperature black bodies and are widely used in photography while very low-power, neon-filled night lights are convenient in the home. And

inert gas-filled discharge tubes are used in a variety of electrical experiments.

One of the most promising developments in recent years has involved lasers, light sources in which large numbers of atoms emit light in synchronized fashion. Many important continuous wave lasers are noble gas-filled lamps providing an intense coherent, monochromatic light. A He-Ne source yields a widely used red beam, an argon-filled source, very powerful blue and green lines, and a krypton source provides intense red light and somewhat weaker yellow, green and blue radiation.

The radioactive gas radon has long been used in medicine as a chemically inert short-lived source for treatment of tumors. The availability of artificial radioactive sources has reduced the need for this rather expensive material.

Radioactive krypton and xenon isotopes have been used in biological research.

Chemistry

For many years the most striking property of the noble gases was the absence of chemical combination. A number of reports of compound formation were refuted by more careful work.

A number of molecular combinations particularly with water were well known. While these combinations have reproducible formulas, they have been shown to be a special type of compound called a clathrate (cage) which does not involve the formation of true chemical bonds.

Some organic compounds, such as hydroquinone, share with water, the property of crystallization in complex formations containing openings ("cages") in which foreign nonreactive atoms or molecules can be trapped. The number of such openings per molecule of crystallizing substance is fixed and therefore the upper limit to the inert gas content is determined by the geometry of the matrix and not by chemical combining power. The combined molecule exists in a fluid phase, and only weak van der Waal's forces such as those found between all molecules are involved, so that chemists distinguish rather carefully between such clathrates and true chemical compounds. Some typical clathrates are described in Table 6.

TABLE 6. SOME NOBLE GAS CLATHRATES WITH WATER, HYDROQUINONE AND PHENOL

Theoretical Formula	Noble Gas Wt. % Theoretical	Observed	Noble Gas Dissociation Pressure, atm. at 0°C
$8Ar \cdot 46H_2O$	27.8	~27	105.
$8Kr \cdot 46H_2O$	44.7	~44	14.5
$8Xe \cdot 46H_2O$	56.0	~53	1.5
$8Rn \cdot 46H_2O$	68.2		<1
$Ar \cdot 3C_6H_4(OH)_2$	10.8	8.8	Very low
$Kr \cdot 3C_6H_4(OH)_2$	20.3	15.8	,, ,,
$Xe \cdot 3C_6H_4(OH)_2$	28.5	26.0	,, ,,
$Ar \cdot 3C_6H_5OH$	12.4	9.4	33
$Kr \cdot 3C_6H_5OH$	22.9	18.0	6
$Xe \cdot 3C_6H_5OH$	31.8	31.8	1

In 1962, Neil Bartlett at the University of British Columbia observed and published the first valid account of a true chemical reaction involving a noble gas, the reaction between xenon and platinum hexafluoride. This work was followed first by the synthesis of xenon tetrafluoride at Argonne National Laboratory and rapidly by the synthesis of a variety of xenon compounds and the demonstration that krypton and radon compounds could also be formed. Some rather simple generalizations appear to govern the reactions of these gases. Chemical bond formation is possible only with the most electronegative elements, fluorine and oxygen, and only for the heavy noble gases. The most stable isotope of radon has a half-life less than four days and there has been little research on radon compounds. A krypton fluoride may be formed with much greater difficulty than its xenon homolog and no compound has yet been demonstrated for argon.

Xenon exhibits every even oxidation number from two to eight and stable compounds have been isolated for each of these. The compounds of xenon may be conveniently described in three categories: xenon fluorides and oxyfluorides, the xenon metal hexafluoride adducts and the xenon oxides, xenates and perxenates.

Xenon Fluorides and Oxyfluorides. The fluorides and oxyfluorides of xenon are probably the most studied and best understood group of noble gas compounds. Table 7 lists these xenon compounds as well as the simple oxides and a possible chloride with some brief comments on their stability and ease of preparation.

The two lower fluorides form sparkling, large, colorless crystals, such as those in Fig. 1 and Fig. 2, with vapor pressures in the range of a few torr at room temperature and melting points above 100°C. Xenon difluoride is a linear symmetrical molecule in the gas phase while xenon tetrafluoride has the square planar structure, as shown in Fig. 3 and Fig. 4. The solids are both molecular crystals in which the structure of the individual molecule is maintained. An equimolar mixture of these two compounds forms an interesting mixed crystal with the empirical formula XeF_3 but in which the crystal is made up of a regular array of equal numbers of xenon difluoride and tetrafluoride molecules.

Xenon hexafluoride is a white solid which melts to a yellow liquid at 49.5°C. and boils

TABLE 7. SIMPLE COMPOUNDS OF XENON

Oxidation No.	Formula	Comment
2	XeF_2	A S
2	XeO	C U
2	$XeCl_2$	C U
4	XeF_4	A S
4	$XeOF_2$	B U
4	XeO_2	D U
6	XeF_6	A S
6	$XeOF_4$	A S
6	XeO_2F_2	A U
6	XeO_3	A U
8	XeF_8	E S
8	XeO_4	A U

Comments cover the situation in July 1967.

A—Prepared as a reasonably pure material in substantial quantities (at least many milligrams).
B—Probably prepared, never adequately purified or characterized.
C—Not yet isolated in ponderable amounts. Identified by optical and mass spectrometry.
D—Only observed as a positive ion in a mass spectrometer with no evidence for long-lived independent existence.
E—Reported by one group, not adequately confirmed.
S—Thermodynamically stable.
U—Thermodynamically unstable.

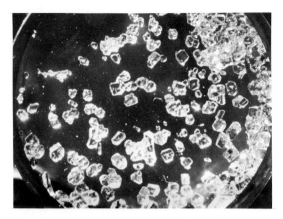

FIG. 1. Crystals of xenon tetrafluoride grown at room temperature on the window of a 22 mm diameter silica spectrophotometer cell. *(Courtesy Argonne National Laboratory)*.

FIG. 2. Crystals of xenon tetrafluoride. The diagonal of the slightly larger of the two rectangular adjacent crystals is about one millimeter. It is easy to grow large clear crystals of both xenon difluoride and xenon tetrafluoride much larger than these early specimens. *(Courtesy Argonne National Laboratory)*.

at 75.6°C. High volatility and a short liquid range are generally attributed to the highly symmetrical structure associated with hexafluorides. In this respect, since xenon hexafluoride is the least volatile of the known hexafluorides and has a longer liquid range than any other, the physical properties tend to support the suspected lack of symmetry predicted by a simple valence bond description

of the xenon fluorides. Alone among the stable xenon compounds and those hexafluorides for which data are available, xenon hexafluoride is extensively ionized in solution in anhydrous hydrogen fluoride.

Studies of the structure of solid xenon hexafluoride using both x-ray and neutron diffraction have revealed the existence of a number of phases none of which are

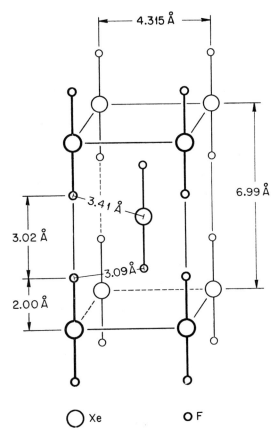

FIG. 3. The structure of xenon difluoride. *(Henri A. Levy and Paul A. Agron (Oak Ridge National Laboratory) in "Noble-Gas Compounds," p. 224).*

isomorphous with those found for other hexafluorides. It has proved most difficult to unravel the data, but there is evidence that the solid phases involve the association of xenon hexafluoride molecules into polymeric units which, of course, implies distortion of the primary octahedron. Calorimetric observations suggest similar polymer formation in the liquid with an appreciable heat of dissociation observed as the temperature is raised.

Lower symmetry is also suggested by the somewhat more complicated infrared absorption spectrum of the vapor, which, however, has been shown to be monomeric, and Raman spectra found for solid, liquid and solutions of xenon hexafluoride are complex as compared with the corresponding spectra predicted and observed for the well-established symmetrical compounds of this type. Electron diffraction studies of the vapor unequivocally eliminate an octahedrally symmetrical vapor molecule as a sole species. It must be pointed out, however, that calculations based on molecular orbital theory favor a symmetrical structure for the ground state of the molecule and the accumulated data are not good enough to rule out this hypothesis. If the ground state is in fact symmetrical, all of the experimental observations must be interpreted in terms of an equilibrium mixture of species

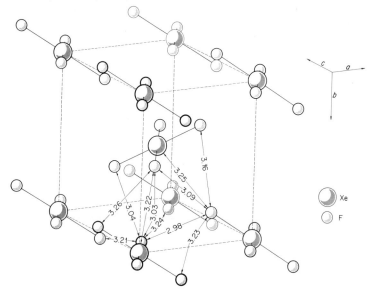

FIG. 4. The structure of xenon tetrafluoride. *(John H. Burns, Paul A. Agron, and Henri A. Levy (Oak Ridge National Laboratory) in "Noble-Gas Compounds," p. 219).*

and a less symmetrical, low-lying excited state must be occupied by a substantial fraction of the molecules at ordinary temperatures.

In general, one oxygen may be expected to replace two fluorines in combining with xenon. The resulting xenon-oxygen bonds are probably somewhat weaker than a single xenon-fluorine bond but the difference in thermodynamic stability between the xenon fluorides and the corresponding oxygen compounds is largely due to the difference in stability between the fluorine-fluorine bonds in the fluorine molecule and the much stronger oxygen-oxygen bonds in molecular oxygen. As a result, except for xenon monoxide which appears to be formed in trace amounts in an electrically excited xenon-oxygen mixture, the compounds containing oxygen can be made only by reacting the fluorides with oxygen-containing materials, particularly water.

The only thermodynamically stable oxygen containing xenon compound is $XeOF_4$, formed by the controlled partial hydrolysis of the hexafluoride. This is a colorless volatile liquid with an unusually long liquid range, melting at -46 and boiling at $101.5°C$. The dielectric constant is a substantial 25 at room temperature and while the electrical conductivity of the pure material is a modest 10^{-5}, the addition of the alkali metal fluorides yields high electrical conductivities. The molecule has a square pyramidal structure with the oxygen at the apex and the xenon in the plane of the four fluorines much as in the xenon tetrafluoride.

All the simple xenon fluorides may be made directly from the elements or by the exposure of xenon to a wide variety of fluorinating reagents and conditions. These include heating mixtures of xenon and fluorine or xenon and halogen fluorides, and with the use of the electric discharge even such mild fluorinating agents as carbon tetrafluoride or silicon tetrafluoride are effective. Mixtures of xenon and fluorine react even at room temperature at moderately elevated pressure while a photochemical reaction has been demonstrated for ordinary daylight in glass vessels. Ultraviolet light through silica or sapphire windows or even more energetic ionizing radiation are more effective, however, in activating the fluorine and effecting low-temperature synthesis.

At low pressures and particularly with an excess of xenon, the predominant product is xenon difluoride. As the pressure and fluorine excess are increased the tetrafluoride and eventually the hexafluoride predominate in the direct combination.

All of the xenon fluorides may serve as fluorinating agents, (for example, with hydrogen). The difluoride is the least reactive while the hexafluoride is a most effective fluorinating agent. Krypton difluoride is an even more potent fluorinating agent than xenon hexafluoride and the tetrafluoride of krypton is so reactive or unstable that its isolation has not been adequately demonstrated. Similarly, the existence of xenon octafluoride lacks adequate verification.

Complex Fluorides of Xenon. The first compound of xenon actually prepared was a complex with platinum hexafluoride whose formula and properties are not yet well established. $Xe(PtF_6)_2$ is a likely candidate for the most important species in the mixture actually found. Similar reactions have been noted between xenon and rhodium, ruthenium and plutonium hexafluorides, but not with tungsten, molybdenum, uranium and neptunium hexafluorides.

Complex compounds of xenon have also been prepared by combining the simpler xenon fluorides with other metallic fluorides. Among the more interesting and thoroughly studied complexes are those formed by xenon hexafluoride. These include compounds with fluoride ion donors such as alkali metal fluorides (e.g., $CsXeF_7$ and Cs_2XeF_8) and fluoride ion acceptors such as antimony pentafluoride (e.g., $XeF_6 \cdot 2SbF_5$). The list of established complex compounds is far from exhaustive, but already includes $XeF_2 \cdot 2SbF_5$ $(Xe(SbF_6)_2?)$ and some relatively less stable addition compounds of $XeOF_4$ and the alkali metal fluorides. The reversible association with the alkali metal fluorides has been used as a purification method for xenon hexafluoride. Similar methods have been used for purifying some other similar materials such as uranium hexafluoride.

Such nonvolatile complexes may well play a role in the utilization of noble gas compounds as well as contributing to our understanding of the nature of bond formation in complex inorganic compounds.

Xenon Oxides, Xenates and Perxenates. The hydrolysis reactions of the xenon fluorides lead to stable aqueous solutions of xenon compounds with interesting and potentially useful properties. Xenon difluoride dissolves in water without ionization and reacts rather slowly at room temperature to yield xenon, hydrogen fluoride and oxygen. No intermediate oxygen compound has been isolated although, like the higher fluorides, the difluoride shows a transient bright-yellow color when hydrolyzed in basic solution or when an aqueous solution is made basic.

Xenon tetrafluoride and hexafluoride react more rapidly with water to yield a variety of products which depend somewhat on the composition of the aqueous solution, but not on whether tetrafluoride or hexafluoride are involved. In neutral or mildly acid solution the predominant final product is usually XeO_3 which is appreciably soluble and appears to be neither ionized nor significantly complexed in solution. While the dry powder is a sensitive and powerful explosive, a solution of XeO_3 is reasonably stable, can be prepared free of other reagents, and is a good starting material for studying the aqueous chemistry of xenon.

In alkaline solution, xenon is found as the perxenate radical, however, most perxenates are relatively insoluble in water. The direct alkaline hydrolysis normally yields precipitates heavily contaminated with fluoride.

When an XeO_3 solution is made alkaline with sodium hydroxide the XeO_3 disproportionates slowly and about half the xenon is lost while the remainder precipitates as the perxenate. In the presence of ozone, all of the xenon is converted to the Xe(VIII) salt, $Na_4XeO_6 \cdot xH_2O$, where, depending on the final conditions, x ranges from 8 to 2.2 (or less on intensive drying).

When potassium hydroxide solutions are used, an intensely colored yellow complex precipitates containing xenon (VI) associated with the potassium perxenate, although with very concentrated alkali a reasonably pure white potassium perxenate can be prepared. All aqueous xenon solutions are good oxidizing media; for example, in dilute acid sodium perxenate quantitatively oxidizes manganese to permanganate, thus providing what is perhaps the best analytical procedure for small amounts of manganese in metal alloys.

Although in the hydrolysis of xenon fluorides an intense yellow color is often observed, the species responsible has not been clearly identified. The best guess probably relates this to a charge transfer complex involving both xenon (VI) and xenon (VIII) in the same molecular complex as suggested for the potassium compound. An unstable xenon compound of lower oxidation number has been postulated during the disproportionation of the xenon (VI) fluoride solution, but a polarographic reduction of an aqueous solution of XeO_3 shows a 6-electron transition with no evidence for a xenon species of lower oxidation number.

Uses of Noble Gas Compounds

The scarcity of xenon and even krypton tends to prevent their use in any industrial process consuming these materials. The fluorides may, however, play a role as highly specialized fluorinating agents where the noble gas is recovered and recirculated. The compounds may become valuable in systems where the gases are now used, but higher concentrations at lower gas pressure may be more effective, as in flash lamps or in medical applications involving radioactive isotopes. The water-stable perxenates and related compounds may have some specialized uses in analytical procedures where high price and relative scarcity would be less important. It is very likely, however, that the most important use of noble gas compounds will be reflected in the stimulation of informed speculation on the nature of chemical bond formation; much as the discovery of the inert gases themselves stimulated similar speculation some years ago.

References

1. Asimov, Isaac, "The Noble Gases," New York, Basic Books, 1966.
2. Bartlett, Neil, *Endeavour*, **23**, 3 (1964).
3. Claassen, Howard H., "The Noble Gases," Boston, D.C. Heath, 1966.
4. Cook, Gerhard A., Ed., "Argon, Helium and the Rare Gases," New York, Interscience, 1961.

5. Hyman, Herbert H., Ed., "Noble-Gas Compounds," Chicago, University of Chicago Press, 1963.
6. Hyman, Herbert H., "The Chemistry of Noble Gas Compounds," *Science*, **145**, 773–83 (1964).
7. Malm, J. G., Selig, Henry, Jortner, Joshun, and Rice, Stuart A., *Chem. Rev.*, **64**, 199 (1965).
8. Moody, G. J., and Thomas, J. D. R., "Noble Gas Chemistry," *Rev. Pure and Appl. Chem.*, **16**, 1 (1966).
9. Selig, Henry, Malm, John G., and Claassen, Howard H., *Scientific American*, **210**, 66 (1964).

HERBERT H. HYMAN

NUCLEAR FISSION

The term "fission" was first used by Meitner and Frisch (1939) to describe the process of the disintegration of a heavy nucleus into two lighter nuclei of roughly equal size. The conclusion that this unusual nuclear reaction occurs was the culmination of a truly dramatic episode, and set in motion an extremely intense and productive period of investigation. After the discovery of the neutron by Chadwick in 1932, Fermi undertook an extensive investigation of the nuclear reactions produced by the bombardment of various elements with this uncharged projectile. He observed (1936) that at least four different radioactive species resulted from the bombardment of uranium with slow neutrons. These new radioactivities emitted beta particles and were thought to be isotopes of unstable "transuranium elements" of atomic numbers 93, 94 and perhaps higher. There was, of course, intense interest in examining the properties of these new elements and many radiochemists participated in the studies. The results of these investigations, however, were extremely perplexing and the confusion persisted until Hahn and Strassmann (1939), following a clue supplied by Curie and Savitch (1938), proved definitely that the so-called "transuranic elements" were, in fact, radioisotopes of barium, lanthanum and other elements in the middle of the Periodic Table.

Armed with the unequivocal results of Hahn and Strassmann, Meitner and Frisch invoked the new liquid drop model of the nucleus (Bohr, 1936; Bohr and Kalckar, 1937) to give a qualitative theoretical interpretation of the fission process, and called attention to the large energy release which should accompany it. There was almost immediate confirmation of this reaction in dozens of laboratories throughout the world. These experiments confirmed the formation of extremely energetic heavy particles and extended the chemical identification of the products.

Most of the energy of fission is released in the form of kinetic energy of the fission fragments. The initial velocities of the separating particles are of the order of 10^9 cm/sec, and since this is greater than the orbital velocities of the outermost electrons, the latter are stripped from the fragments by interaction with the medium, leaving a positive charge of about 20 units. In passing through matter, the fission fragments cause intense initial ionization. As the fragment is slowed down, outer electrons are captured, decreasing the positive charge, and the ionization intensity decreases. The energy loss at low velocities is due mainly to elastic collisions with the nuclei of the medium. Ranges of from 2 to 3 cm of air are observed for the fission fragments. The ionization produced by fission fragments is many times greater than that due to the most energetic alpha particles, and hence they are readily observed in ionization chambers, photographic plates and semiconductor detectors. The recoil of the fragments is sufficient to eject them from the surface of the fissioning material and they can be collected on "catcher foils" or on a water surface in close proximity and identified by their radioactivity and chemical properties. These methods have all been used in confirming and studying the fission process.

The chemical evidence which was so vital in leading Hahn and Strassmann to the discovery of nuclear fission was obtained by the application of the "carrier" and "tracer" techniques. Since invisible amounts of the radioactive species were formed, their chemical identity had to be deduced from the manner in which they followed known "carrier" elements, present in macroscopic quantity, through various chemical operations. Known radioactive species were also added as "tracers" and their behavior compared with that of the unknown species to aid in the identification of the latter.

The impetus in research in nuclear science provided by the atomic bomb project in the United States (1941-1945) led to the identification of some 37 elements, from zinc to holmium, among the fission products of uranium, as well as to the production of the new, heavy elements beyond uranium. The ion-exchange technique was applied to the separation of the rare earths and led to the discovery of element 61 (promethium). Macroscopic quantities of technetium (which had been discovered in 1936 as a product of the deuteron bombardment of molybdenum) were produced in nuclear fission, and its chemical properties were established. The wide range of radioactivities produced in nuclear fission makes this reaction a rich source of tracers for chemical, biological, and industrial use.

Although the early experiments involved the fission of normal uranium with slow neutrons, it was rapidly established that the rare isotope, U^{235}, was responsible for this phenomenon. The more abundant isotope, U^{238}, could be made to undergo fission only by fast neutrons with energy greater than 1 MeV. The nuclei of other heavy elements, such as thorium and protactinium, were also shown to be fissionable with fast neutrons, and other particles, such as fast protons, deuterons and alphas, as well as γ-rays, proved to be effective in inducing the reaction. Bismuth, lead, thallium, mercury, gold, platinum, tantalum, and even medium-weight elements, such as copper, bromine, silver, tin and barium, have been made to undergo fission by excitation with high-energy projectiles (the order of 100 MeV or more). Some other nuclides which do not occur in nature but have been produced by transmutation reactions also undergo fission. Among these, U^{233} and Pu^{239} are fissionable with slow neutrons, while Np^{237} requires fast neutrons.

The very interesting and rare occurrence of spontaneous fission in uranium was first observed in 1940. In this reaction, the nucleus undergoes fission in its ground state, without excitation from external sources. Although the parial half-life for this process in uranium is about 10^{16} years, isotopes of the new "transplutonium elements" have been discovered in which spontaneous fission represents the principal mode of decay, with half-lives of the order of a few hours or less. This process probably sets a limit for nuclear stability.

The outstanding feature of nuclear fission is the tremendous energy release which accompanies it. A chemical reaction such as the explosion of TNT releases about 1.5×10^{11} ergs per gram; nuclear fission releases approximately 8×10^{17} ergs per gram. Fundamentally, the source of this energy lies in the fact that the total mass of the final products of fission is appreciably less than that of the reactants. This loss in mass appears as energy in an amount given by the famous Einstein relation, $E = mc^2$, one atomic mass unit being equivalent to 931 MeV. (1 MeV $= 1.6 \times 10^{-6}$ erg.)

The nature of the fission process may perhaps be best understood through a consideration of the structure and stability of nuclear matter. Nuclei are composed of neutrons and protons, the total number of them being equal to the mass number. The actual weight of the nucleus is always less than the sum of the weights of the free nucleons, the difference being the mass equivalent of the energy of formation of the nucleus from its constituents. This difference is known as the "mass defect" and is a measure of the total binding energy of the nucleus.

The neutrons and protons of which nuclei are composed are bound by a short-range attractive force which acts only between nearest neighbors. As long as the total number of protons is small, the long-range electrostatic repulsion between them will be insufficient to overcome the cohesive forces between all nucleons. As the number of nucleons increases, the fraction of them near the surface (and hence with fewer neighbors) decreases, and the average binding energy per nucleon increases. At about mass number 55, this trend reaches a maximum, and a further increase in the number of nucleons decreases the average binding energy per nucleon due to the repulsive coulomb force between protons. In fact, in order to maintain stability, the number of protons must be diluted with an excess of neutrons as the mass number increases. Since a decrease in binding energy per nucleon means a decrease in the mass defect or an increase in the average mass per bound nucleon, uranium (with a greater mass per nucleon than that for nuclei of elements of medium atomic weight) will be energetically unstable with respect to fission. Qualitatively, at least, the fission process is thus seen to be a consequence of the coulomb repulsion between protons.

Coulomb repulsion between protons causes heavy nuclei to have rather high neutron-to-proton ratios (of the order of 1.5) and when such a nucleus undergoes fission, the primary fragments formed will possess a similar ratio. For nuclei in the mass region of these products, however, such a ratio is higher than is consistent with stability. A ratio corresponding to stability is attained by the evaporation of neutrons from the highly excited primary fragments (within about 10^{-14} sec of the fission event), and by conversion of neutrons to protons through the beta decay process.

The average number of neutrons emitted per fission in U^{235} fission is 2.5, and hence a chain reaction becomes possible, the excess neutrons causing fission in other U^{235} nuclei which, in turn, contribute more neutrons. A vast energy source is thus made available for utilization in a controlled form (nuclear reactor or "pile") or in an explosion (atomic bomb).

A typical fission event in U^{235}, for example, may be described by the following equation:

$$_{92}U^{235} + _{0}n^{1} \rightarrow (_{92}U^{236})^{*} \rightarrow$$
$$_{38}Sr^{95} + _{54}Xe^{139} + 2_{0}n^{1} + \gamma + Q.$$

A slow neutron is absorbed by a U^{235} nucleus forming the excited compound nucleus, U^{236}, which then splits into two fission fragments, Sr^{95} and Xe^{139}, and two neutrons. The subscript at the left of the chemical symbol indicates the atomic number (nuclear charge) and the superscript to the right indicates the mass number. The fission fragments possess about 20 MeV of excitation energy which will be emitted in the decay process they undergo in reaching the stable members of their respective "decay chains," $_{42}Mo^{95}$ and $_{57}La^{139}$. In addition, about 5 MeV of gamma radiation, represented by γ, is released at the instant of fission. (Some

energetic alpha particles have also been observed in the fission act, but they are rather rare). Q represents the kinetic energies of the fission fragments and neutrons and is approximately 170 MeV. Thus, the total energy of a fission event is close to 200 MeV. Both nuclear charge and mass number must be conserved in the fission process. Other combinations of primary fragments and number of neutrons are possible, but they are not all formed with equal probability. For example, the formation of the complementary fragments of masses 95 and 139 is about 600 times as probable as the formation of two mass 117 fragments and almost 10^{6} times as probable as the formation of masses 72 and 162.

The probability distribution of masses in fission is an important feature of the process. The percentage of fissions that leads to a given mass is referred to as the "fission yield" of that mass. A fission yield curve is obtained by plotting the yields against mass number. Such curves have been obtained by radiochemical investigations for fission of many nuclides at low and high energy of excitation. Ionization chamber and velocity measurements indicate a spread in the kinetic energy of the fragments for a given mass split. This is associated mainly with a variation in the number of neutrons per fission. In general, fission induced by low-energy particles (generally referred to for convenience as "low-energy fission") is characterized by an asymmetric splitting into two main groups of mass numbers (the "light" and "heavy" groups) the most probable mass ratio of light to heavy product being about 2/3. As the mass number of the fissioning nucleus increases, the light group distribution shifts towards heavier masses while the heavy group remains relatively stationary. As the energy of excitation increases, the probability of symmetric fission increases, and at very high energies it becomes the most probable mode. The fission yield curves are not entirely smooth functions of mass, and regions of fine-structure have been observed. These are attributed to an enhanced probability for the formation of particularly stable nuclei having "closed shells" of 50 and 82 neutrons.

In addition to a distribution in mass, a

distribution in nuclear charge for a particular mass split also occurs. The present data on charge distribution in slow-neutron induced fission indicate that the most probable primary charge of complementary fragments is that for which both fragments are equally displaced from the most stable charge for their respective mass numbers. Each primary fragment undergoes, on the average, about three beta disintegrations before achieving stability, each beta disintegration increasing the nuclear charge by one, but leaving the mass number unchanged. Since the primary fragments are highly excited, the decay energy of the first few numbers of a decay chain may be quite large. For some nuclides near closed-shells this decay energy may exceed the binding energy of a neutron, and the latter may be emitted in preference to a beta particle. Since these neutrons follow beta-emitting precursors in the decay chain, they are referred to as "delayed neutrons," thus distinguishing them from the "prompt neutrons" which are coincident with the fission event. Although delayed neutrons account for less than one per cent of all fission neutrons, they are an extremely important factor in the control of nuclear reactors.

Many different techniques have been employed in an attempt to understand the very interesting and complicated phenomena associated with nuclear fission. Advances in instrumentation continue to open new avenues of approach, and the application of solid-state detectors, multiparameter pulse-height analyzers, computer data processing, etc. have given new impetus to the studies and yielded extensive new data. These studies concern such aspects of the reaction as the role of angular momentum (as evidenced, e.g., by the angular distribution of the fragments, the ratio of formation of isomeric states, and fissionability), the spectra and numbers of γ-rays, x-rays, and neutrons emitted in the process, the occurrence of ternary splitting, etc. The dependence of such data on the energy and type of particle inducing fission and the mass and charge of the fissioning species is of particular importance.

Although an extensive phenomenology of nuclear fission has been accumulated, no comprehensive theoretical treatment has yet emerged. The liquid-drop model has been considerably extended and improved, and other approaches such as a statistical treatment, and the "unified model" (which combines the liquid-drop "collective" properties with the single-particle or "shell" model) have been invoked to interpret fission phenomena. Each has had significant, though limited, success in accounting for particular aspects of the reaction. Perhaps the complexity of nuclear fission, along with some other nuclear reactions, will necessitate the adoption of several complementary theories for a complete description, in analogy with the wave-particle dualism of electromagnetic radiation.

References

1. Hyde, E. K., "The Nuclear Properties of the Heavy Elements III. Fission Phenomena," New York, Prentice-Hall, Inc., 1964.
2. Wilets, L., "Theories of Nuclear Fission," Oxford, Clarendon Press, 1964.
3. Perfilov, N. A., and Eismont, V. P., Eds., "The Physics of Nuclear Fission," (translated from Russian), Jerusalem, Israel Program for Scientific Translations, 1964.
4. International Atomic Energy Authority, "The Physics and Chemistry of Fission;" proceedings of a Symposium held in Salzburg, Austria, March 22–26, 1965, 2 vols., Vienna, IAEA, 1965.
5. Turner, L. A., *Revs. Mod. Phys.*, **12**, 1 (1940).
6. Glendenin, L. E., and Steinberg, E. P., *Ann. Revs. Nucl. Sci.*, **4**, 69 (1954).
7. Halpern, I., *Ann. Revs. Nucl. Sci.*, **9**, 245 (1959).
8. Fraser, J. S., and Milton, J. C. D., *Ann. Revs. Nucl. Sci.*, **16**, 379 (1966).

ELLIS P. STEINBERG

NUCLEAR FUSION*

Introduction

When nucleii of certain light elements fuse together, there is an excess binding energy which appears in the form of heat. This is the energy source of both the sun and the hydrogen bomb, and it is the object of fusion research to liberate the energy in a controlled manner on earth; because of the abundance

*From "Encyclopedia of Physics" edited by Robert M. Besançon, New York, Reinhold, 1965.

of light elements, such power is virtually unlimited.

In order to promote nuclear fusion, the reacting nucleii must have sufficient inertia to overcome their mutual coulomb repulsion. Thus nucleii with a high ratio of mass to charge, such as deuterium and tritium, heated to a high temperature are most suitable. The reaction of interest is

$$D + T = He^4 \ (3.5 \ \text{MeV}) + n \ (14.1 \ \text{MeV})$$

where the numbers in parenthesis are the energies of the reaction products. The cross section (σ) peaks at about 5×10^{-24} cm^2 and deuteron energy of 107 KeV, liberating a total energy of 17.6 MeV and giving an energy gain of 160. This is emphasized by noting that 8 gallons of sea-water contain 1 gram of deuterium, which yields a maximum of 8.10^{10} calories on fusion, equivalent to 2500 gallons of gasoline or 80 tons of TNT. Many methods have been proposed, but are as yet untested, for harnessing this energy. Among these are the generation of electric current by the interaction of the charged helium particles with a magnetic field, the dissipation of the neutron energy as heat in a water jacket, using the neutrons to release fission energy in uranium placed round the fusion reactor (making a combined fusion/fission reactor), and the generation of steam power by using the heat radiated from the hot gases.

Although the cross section peaks at a directed deuteron energy of 107 KeV, it is possible to use a much lower mean energy if the nucleii are thermalized. This is because there is an exceedingly sharp rise of cross section with energy and most of the fusion reactions are produced by nucleii with energies far in the tail of the Maxwellian distribution. For example, in a thermal mixture of deuterium and tritium most of the reactions are produced by deuterium of energy $1.3 \times 10^{-4} \ T^{2/3}$ KeV (where $T°$K is the temperature). Even so, the temperature required is extremely high, typically near $10^8 °$K.

Plasma in a Fusion Reactor

At such high temperature, atoms are ionized by collisions and the electrons are not bound to any particular nucleus; this state of matter is called a plasma. Since stars are in the plasma state, plasmas are by far the most common form of matter in the universe (though they are rare on earth) and the problems of controlled thermonuclear fusion are closer to astrophysical plasma physics than nuclear physics.

Because of the unbound electrons, plasmas are good electrical conductors and a magnetic field cannot easily diffuse through them (the "skin depth" in a hydrogen plasma after a time t is $3 \times 10^6 \ t^{1/2} T^{-3/4}$cm). While the diffusion proceeds there is a current induced in the plasma skin which interacts with the field to cause a pressure perpendicular to the field lines of $\sim B^2/8\pi$ atmospheres, where B is the field in kilogauss; effectively the plasma pressure is balanced by the field pressure which is supported by the magnet coils generating the field. Thus the magnetic field affords the means of insulating the plasma from the material walls against which it would rapidly cool.

Often, as the result of the method of forming the plasma or because of field diffusion, magnetic field becomes mixed with the plasma. The confining magnetic field pressure must then balance the sum of the plasma pressure and the pressure of the field in the plasma. In this connection, an important parameter of the plasma is β, the fraction of the confining field pressure that supports the plasma pressure, which varies from 0 to 1 as the field inside the plasma goes from the confining field to zero. For a particular plasma pressure, the lower the β, the more the confining field and the more the energy required to operate the magnet.

Operating Regime

The operating regime of a fusion reactor is determined by the variation of the reaction cross section with temperature, the economics of energy conversion into useful work, and material properties such as the strength of the magnet metal, vaporization of the wall of the containment vessel, etc. Energy balance in the reactor gives a minimum requirement for the product nt where t is the reaction time and n is the number of nucleii per cubic centimeter. If the total energy released in the reaction vessel (the nuclear energy plus the energy of the plasma particles plus energy radiated) is returned with an efficiency of 1/3 to maintain the plasma temperature and make up the radiation losses, then nt must be greater than 10^{14} and the minimum temperature is about 3×10^{7}°K. For this minimum condition, 1 per cent of the nucleii fuse together. Also, since the reaction rate depends on n^2, too high an n rapidly leads to wall vaporization and too low an n to a negligible rate. If we assume that a power density of 100 watts/cc can be handled continuously (equal to present fission reactor levels), n must be $\approx 10^{16}$ nucleii/cc (about a thousandth of an atmosphere); this is probably correct to within an order of magnitude, being on the low side for pulse operated, highly compressed plasmas that fill only a small fraction of the reaction vessel. The condition $nt > 10^{14}$ then demands that $t > 10$ msec, and for a $\beta = 1$ plasma a confining field of 34 kilogauss.

If the helium from the fusion reaction is trapped in the plasma, its energy can maintain the plasma temperature against losses by radiation. This avoids inefficiency of recycling the fusion energy to heat more plasma. The minimum temperature for this approach, called the "ideal ignition temperature," is 4.6×10^{7}°K. All the energy of the neutrons from the fusion reaction can then be applied to produce useful power.

Radiation

One of the many problems to be solved in devising a fusion reactor is that of radiation at these high temperatures. Fortunately, the plasma required is so diffuse that it does not act as a blackbody which would follow a fourth-power law of temperature for the radiant energy $(6 \times 10^{-13} \ T^4 \ \text{watts/cm}^2)$. Instead, the radiation mean free path is larger than the plasma dimensions and the dominant radiation process is caused by electrons deflected in the coulomb field of the nucleii. This is called bremsstrahlung and peaks in the soft x-ray region at a wavelength of around 1Å. The power radiated is $0.54 \times 10^{-30} Z^2 n_e n_i T^{1/2}$ watts/cc (Z = nuclear charge; n_e and n_i are electron and nuclear density) which is proportional to the square root of the temperature and, for reasonable sized reactors, is far less than blackbody radiation. However, even hydrogenic bremsstrahlung is considerable and an increase of two orders of magnitude could kill the concept of fusion reactors. Because of the $n_e Z^2$ factor, ionized impurities

could produce a serious radiation loss; for instance, only 1 per cent of ionized oxygen increases the radiation by 77 per cent. Impurities also absorb a disastrous quantity of energy during ionization, not only because of the ionization potential of the electrons but also in the excitation of the partially ionized atoms by free electrons with insufficient energy to produce complete ionization; this excitation energy is radiated a few nanoseconds after excitation. It is therefore very important to ionize impurities rapidly.

A further important mechanism of energy loss in the plasma is charge exchange produced between a neutral impurity molecule (liberated, for instance, at the wall of the vacuum vessel by the radiation) drifting into the plasma and donating an electron to a hot ion. The hot ion now becomes neutral, is no longer held by the magnetic field, and is lost from the plasma. Meanwhile the cold impurity ion absorbs plasma energy in being further ionized and heated, and the hot neutral particle bombards the wall to liberate further impurities.

Therefore because of both radiation and charge exchange every effort is made to produce a highly pure plasma, typically with an impurity level of less than 0.1 per cent. This is difficult considering the low operating density and the high temperatures involved.

Plasma Heating

For temperatures up to a few million degrees, the conductivity of the plasma is sufficiently small for ohmic heating to be effective. Above these temperatures, the conductivity $(8 \times 10^{-6} \ T^{3/2} \ \text{mhos/cm})$ becomes too large and other forms of heating must be used. Ohmic heating is often used as preheating so that when a magnetic field is later applied to the plasma surface it exerts a pressure rather than diffusing into the plasma.

A common method of heating is to compress the plasma with the magnetic field; the energy put into the plasma is then

$$\int_{v_1}^{v_2} p \ dv$$

where p is the magnetic field pressure and $v_1 - v_2$ is the volume change. The volume change is limited by the size of the magnet, so it is desirable to use a high value of p. In the

"Theta" and "Z" pinch experiments the gas is heated in a cylindrical tube first ohmically, then by a powerful magnetic pressure. The magnetic field is produced by current from a very low inductance, high voltage capacitor energy store. The compression is then so rapid that shock fronts develop in the plasma; subsequently isentropic compression is produced by raising the field still further. Temperatures of the order of $10^7°$K are commonly quoted, and even $10^8°$K has been claimed for late in the life of the plasma. A method of obtaining high plasma compressions without large volumes of magnetic fields is to transfer the plasma into successively smaller magnets as the compression increases. The transfer is achieved in an experiment called "Toy Top" by using a larger field at one end of the plasma than at the other.

Another method of heating the plasma by magnetic compression without large volume changes is magnetic pumping. The plasma is alternately compressed and decompressed at one point on its length, and the problem is to choose conditions in which the plasma does not cool on decompression (that is, an irreversible cycle is required). The heating depends on the pumping period compared to the ion/ion collision time and the transit time of an ion through the pumping region. If the pumping period is of the order of the transit time and much shorter than the collision time, the ions gain energy while the field is increasing and leave the region before decompression. The heating is then proportional to $T^{3/2}$ and becomes more effective at high temperatures. This system and ion cyclotron heating (another system depending on oscillating magnetic fields) are being tested on the "Stellarator" experiment to bring ohmically heated plasma up to thermonuclear temperatures.

A third important means of forming the plasma is to accelerate individual nucleii in an electrostatic field, then inject them into the confining magnetic field. This has the advantage that high particle energies (on the order of tens of keV) are relatively easy to produce, but the problem of injecting the nucleii is difficult because it is not possible in general to trap the nucleii in a static magnetic field under conservative conditions. The procedure is to change the particle orbit discontinuously either by a collision against

background plasma or by altering the charge-to-mass ratio. For collision with background plasma, a very long path length is required: in the "Sinelnikov" experiment this is achieved by carefully angling the injection down a long cylindrical field with regular ripples along its length and high "mirror" magnetic fields at the ends, so that the particles are reflected back and forth between the mirrors and the ripples cause the particles on their first return to avoid the injection gun. In the "D.C.X. Mirror" experiment, fast D_2^+ molecules are injected, and dissociated in an arc. In the "Phoenix Mirror" and "Alice Mirror" experiments, excited neutral atoms are injected which are ripped apart when they reach the magnetic field because, due to the difference in charge, the negative electrons and positive ions in the atom gyrate in opposite directions (this is called "Lorentz" trapping).

Confinement

One of the difficulties of confining a plasma with a magnetic field is to eliminate end loss down the plasma axis. One way is to increase the magnetic field at the plasma ends so that the field lines bend towards the axis. In a collision-dominated high-density plasma, a mode of operation of the "Theta" pinch, the system then acts like a gas trapped in a double ended rubber balloon. Due to the curvature at the ends there is a component of force parallel to the axis which reflects the particles; this is called a collision-dominated magnetic mirror. However, even a very small amount of field accidentally mixed in the plasma will prevent the ends from closing completely and allow particles to escape. It is estimated that a field in the plasma of only 1 per cent (equivalent to $\beta = 0.999$) will produce an unacceptable loss.

Another type of magnetic mirror is the collision-free mirror. This is used with a low-β plasma when the ions gyrate around the magnetic field lines and move along them because of axial components of velocity gained by collisions. When the particles reach the collision-free mirror region there is again a component of magnetic force parallel to the axis which, if the axial energy is not too great, will reflect the particle back to the main plasma volume. A certain fraction, depending on the coulomb collision cross section, of the particles gains axial energy sufficient to overcome the mirror and is lost. The collision cross section varies inversely as the square of the particle energy ($= 2.6 \times 10^{-18}/W^2$ cm^2 where W is the particle energy in keV) and is always greater than the fusion cross section, so the majority of nucleii make coulomb collisions before fusion collisions. Even so, it is possible that sufficient fusion collisions can occur for the reactor to be economical. One method of reducing the effect of end loss is to make the reactor very long so that the end area is a small fraction of the total plasma area.

A further method of avoiding end losses is to join the ends forming a plasma loop. This is, however, unstable since the confining field lines are more closely bunched on the inside of the loop compared to the outside, the pressure is higher on the inside and the plasma drifts outwards. To avoid this, the "Stellarator" experiment uses a figure-eight shaped plasma mixed with magnetic field. Then plasma moving along a field line tends to drift in opposite directions at opposite loops of the figure eight, so if the particle flow around the tube is more rapid than the drift in each loop, the total drift is zero.

Stability

The stability of the plasma/field system is an extremely important factor in the success of a fusion reactor and is the subject of many experiments. A prevalent form of instability is the "flute" or "interchange" in which the plasma develops deep ridges parallel to the field lines. The condition for these ridges to develop is that the field lines are curved with the centre of curvature inside the plasma so that the intensity of the field falls off from the plasma surface. This is a cause of instability in the "z-pinch" and in some regions of the mirror geometry. To prevent this instability, it has been suggested that the field be mixed in the plasma at a skew angle to the confining field. Then, for the instability to develop and the plasma and confining field to be interchanged, the internal skew field has to be stretched and turned, requiring energy; thus, under certain theoretical conditions the plasma should be stable. However experiments with z-pinches show such a system still to be unstable for reasons which are not clear.

It may be that finite plasma resistance is affecting the stability criteria.

One method of making the mirror system stable, used by Ioffe, is to add a hexapole field produced by a series of six bars placed parallel to the axis equally spaced around a circumference. Opposing currents flow in alternate bars producing a magnetic field which falls off with distance from the bars. Thus the system has a minimum of magnetic field at its center and increasing field both radially and towards its mirror ends, and plasma at the center experiences a curved field in all directions with the center of curvature always outside the plasma. This is now recognized to be a particular case of a general class of field geometries called minimum B configurations which are inherently stable against hydromagnetic flute instabilities. Preliminary experiments show a large increase in containment time when the Ioffe bars are in operation.

Another form of flute instability may grow when the plasma is accelerated, as in a rapid magnetic compression or by centrifugal forces if the plasma rotates. These are similar instabilities to the gravitational instabilities of a mercury/water layer, with mercury above, first investigated theoretically by Rayleigh. The origin of the rotation is not definitely understood, but it is known that again the Ioffe bars also suppress these instabilities.

A further and important class of instabilities, the "velocity space" instabilities, can arise for particular conditions of plasma β if the plasma is not thermalized so that the mean energy parallel to the field lines differs from the energy perpendicular to the lines. When the perpendicular energy is the greater, the plasma tends to form bunches, called "mirror instability", and when the parallel energy is the greater, the plasma wriggles like a fire hose—"fire-hose instability".

These examples of instability are given to illustrate the many types that can occur. It is obvious, however, that the lower the plasma β (so that the vacuum field is approached), especially with a minimum B configuration, the more stable is the plasma.

Conclusions

Only a few problems of fusion research have been mentioned and demonstrated by reference to some of the many experiments proceeding in the field. The main centers of research are Russia (35 per cent of total effort), the United States (25 per cent), Great Britain (10 per cent), and the rest are in Europe. The cost of the research in the United States is about 25×10^6 dollars/yr, in Great Britain, 10×10^6 dollars/yr, in Europe, 6.2×10^6 dollars/yr.

At present (1964), the theta pinch has the greatest nt of 10^{12} at densities of 10^{16} to 10^{17} and temperatures $\approx 10^{7}$°K. The major difficulties are particle loss from the ends, radiation and plasma rotation. Injected mirror experiments have the highest energy ($\sim$10 to 100 keV), but only low densities of $\sim 10^{10}$ have been attained because of instabilities. Great hopes are centered around the application of minimum B field configurations to the injection mirror experiments.

References

Glasstone, S., and Lovberg, R. H., "Controlled Thermonuclear Reactions" Princeton, N. J. D. Van Nostrand Co., 1960.

J. A. REYNOLDS

O

ORIGIN OF THE ELEMENTS

Historical Introduction

Theories of the origin of the elements are guided, in large measure, by our knowledge of their abundances. It is clear, therefore, that nucleogenesis is a young subject. The occurrence of natural radioactive elements was recognized early in this century. The presence of appreciable amounts of the radioactive parents implies that these elements were born at some point in time. A knowledge both of the abundances of the parent elements and their decay products and of the decay lifetimes allows us to determine the age of these elements. Estimates of the age range from five billion to fifteen billion years, depending on whether the parent nuclei are assumed to have been formed at a given time or, rather, to have been formed continuously.

Early studies of element abundances were limited, necessarily, to the earth. The development of spectroscopy in the 19th century provided a vast new area of investigation. The same spectral lines that were seen in laboratory studies could be found as absorption features in the solar spectrum. It was concluded that the elements of which the sun is composed are the same as those existing on the earth. Studies of the spectra of other stars led to similar conclusions. Although the presence of these elements was established, it was not possible to make accurate determinations of their relative abundances. It was therefore quite reasonable to assume that the composition of the galaxy is everywhere uniform.

Early Theories of the Origin of the Elements. A universe of uniform chemical composition strongly suggests a single event theory of the origin of the elements. This led physicists to search within the framework of cosmology for a set of physical conditions which would produce the present abundance distribution. Three different theories were developed, the details of which have been summarized in a review article by Alpher and Herman (1950). As certain aspects of those early theories have survived, it is instructive to consider their essential features.

Most of the early treatments of the problem of element formation were governed by considerations of equilibrium. It was assumed that at an early stage in the universe the matter was gathered together in a high-temperature, high-density state. Under these conditions nuclear reactions take place very rapidly. The relative abundances of the various nuclear species for a specified temperature and density can be determined from statistical mechanics, provided we know the energies and spins of the ground and excited states of the nuclei involved. A major difficulty with these theories arises from the fact that for a specified temperature and density the equilibrium abundances are sharply peaked in a narrow range of mass number. For example, for temperatures of a few billion degrees and densities of the order of 10^6 g/cc, the nuclear statistical equilibrium equations predict a peak in the iron region, which is consistent with the observed abundance distributions. However, under the same conditions the predicted abundances of the heavy elements fall many orders of magnitude below the observed values.

Many attempts were made to construct a massive "stellar "model possessing the correct distribution of density and temperature so that the total composition of the body would have the observed composition of the elements. These models encountered the further difficulty that it was not possible to cool such massive bodies rapidly enough to "freeze in" the abundances of the elements with the composition characteristic of the original high densities and temperatures. Current theories of nucleosynthesis attribute only the iron peak to an equilibrium process, as will be seen in our subsequent discussion.

Mayer and Teller (1949) proposed a polyneutron fission theory of nucleogenesis that assumed the universe in its early state to consist of large bodies composed of a cold nuclear fluid. The surfaces of these bodies would be unstable and polyneutron fragments of various sizes would be cast loose. Nuclear processes proceeding on these fragments—fission, beta decay and neutron evaporation—would result in the production of heavy elements. It was found that the relative isotopic compositions of the heavy elements could be rather well reproduced, subject to the right choice of the parameters of the theory. The major problem with this theory is the formation of the polyneutron bodies. It is not clear how such bodies can arise in any cosmology or be formed in any stellar interior.

Alpher, Bethe, and Gamow (1948) proposed another nonequilibrium theory of nucleogenesis. This model pictured the early stage of matter as a compressed neutron gas. The expansion of this neutron fluid following an initial explosion would result in the decay of some of the neutrons into protons and electrons, the relative numbers of protons and neutrons being fixed at an early stage by the equilibrium between direct and inverse beta (electron) reactions. Subsequent neutron captures would then build up all of the heavier elements, with some readjustment due to beta decay.

In a continuation of this work, Alpher observed that the abundance peaks in the heavy element region corresponded to regions in which the neutron capture probabilities were small. This correlation made apparent the need for a neutron capture process in the synthesis of the heavy elements. A rapid neutron capture process alone cannot, however, account for the detailed features of the relative abundances of heavy isotopes. Furthermore, there are no stable nuclei with mass numbers five and eight, suggesting that

the production of nuclei with mass numbers higher than helium $(A = 4)$ cannot proceed in this manner.

Evidence for Element Synthesis in Stars. These early theories assumed that the period of element formation was of brief duration, consistent with the belief held at that time that the observed element distribution was uniform throughout the galaxy. While the need for nuclear processes in stars had been established by the calculations of Bethe and Critchfield (1938) of the reaction rates for the proton-proton chain, it was not recognized that subsequent stages of nuclear burning in stellar interiors might contribute to the formation of the heavy elements observed in nature.

The recognition that nucleosynthesis was a continuing process in stellar interiors followed the discovery by Merrill (1952) of the presence of the element technetium in the atmospheres of red giant stars. As technetium has no stable isotopes (the longest-lived isotope has a half-life of less than two million years), its presence in abundances sufficient to be observed suggested that element synthesis had taken place quite recently in those stars.

This conclusion was confirmed by the discovery, in the mid-1950's, that there are general abundance differences between certain broad classes of stars, in the sense that the ratio of the abundances of the heavy elements to hydrogen was variable and this ratio could be correlated with the age of the star. It was found that the ratio of all elements with proton number $Z > 2$ to hydrogen was an increasing function of the time of formation of the star in the galaxy.

The presence in stars of anomalous abundances of elements which we believe are largely produced by a specific nuclear burning process provides somewhat more direct evidence for nucleosynthesis in stars. The presence of technetium in red giant stars, for example, strongly suggests that element synthesis by neutron capture has occurred recently in those stars. The high abundance of carbon in "Carbon stars" is believed to result from helium burning in the interior, assuming that mass has been carried to the surface by convection.

These observations suggest a simple model of galactic evolution. Assuming the primordial gas to be composed of hydrogen, with perhaps some small amount of helium, the first generation of stars will be formed with this composition. The evolution of these stars is characterized both by element synthesis during various stages of nuclear burning and by mass loss. In this manner, the heavy element content of the interstellar medium will be increased. Subsequent generations of stars will be formed from gas enriched in these heavy elements.

Mechanisms of Mass Loss. The enrichment of the interstellar medium in the products of the various nuclear burning stages of stellar evolution implies mass loss by these stars. There are three principal ways by which this mass loss is known to take place. The most spectacular mechanism is the supernova explosion. In such an explosion a major portion of the mass of the star may be ejected, leaving behind an imploded remnant which, if stable, might become a neutron star. The detailed features of these explosions are currently under investigation. The rate of supernova explosions in an average galaxy is estimated to be approximately one event every 50-300 years.

A second mechanism of mass loss is the nova explosion. These are much less spectacular events than are supernovas, only about one part in 1000 of the stellar mass being cast off. However, many of the nova explosions are found to be recurrent in which case, during the course of many explosions, a substantial fraction of the stellar mass may be returned to the interstellar medium.

There is also evidence that mass loss takes place continuously during many stages of evolution. It is felt that mass loss can take place during the final stages of contraction of the star from the interstellar medium. A significant amount of mass loss has been observed for stars in the red giant phase. This continous ejection of mass appears to be associated with intense magnetic fields on the stellar surfaces.

The Abundances of the Elements

We wish to consider in detail the role of nuclear reactions in stars in the synthesis of the elements. A great deal of insight into these modes of element synthesis can be gained from a study of the observed abundances.

Early estimates of the abundances of the elements were based to a great extent on chemical analyses of various constituents of the earth's crust. This is clearly a poor choice of such information, due both to the fact that the earth has lost most of its volatile constituents and to the fact that the remaining material has been subjected to extreme chemical differentiation. It was evident, nevertheless, that the general features of the observed distribution of element abundances cannot be correlated with their chemical properties.

The best sources of information regarding the abundances of nonvolatile elements are the meteorites. It is generally assumed that these bodies have not undergone the same degree of differentiation of their chemical constituents as has the earth. The degree of material differentiation is sufficient, however, to serve as a means of classification, viz: iron meteorites (siderites), stony-irons, and chondritic meteorites. Of these, the chondritic meteorites are thought to best represent the nonvolatile constituents of the solar system.

The classic compilation of element abundances by Suess and Urey (1956) has played a major role in recent analyses of the modes of element synthesis. They relied heavily on studies of abundances in chondritic meteorites for the nonvolatile constituents. The abundances of the volatile elements, notably H, He, C, N, O, and Ne, can best be determined from spectroscopic analyses of the light coming from stars and from gaseous nebulae. These analyses are complicated by the need both for accurate determinations of atomic oscillator strengths and for a detailed model for the stellar atmospheres. For both classes of elements, accurate relative isotopic abundances are available from mass spectroscopic data.

At the time that Suess and Urey made their abundance compilation, there were relatively few reliable determinations of abundances in chondritic meteorites. Some interpolation was required in order to construct a complete abundance pattern. Their primary criterion was that the abundances of nuclei of odd mass number should show a smooth variation with mass cumber. This procedure was helped by the fact that many elements have two stable isotopes with odd mass numbers, establishing the slope of the abundance curve in these regions.

A revised compilation of element abundances has been presented by Cameron (1963). This compilation is based almost entirely on abundances measured in chondritic meteorites and, where available, in carbonaceous chondritic meteorites. The carbonaceous chondrites are a class of chondritic meteorites which have been subjected to a minimum of chemical differentiation. As much as half of their mass may be composed of water of crystallization and various complex carbon compounds.

TABLE 1. COMPARISON OF ABUNDANCE COMPILATIONS (based on $Si = 10^6$ atoms.)

Element	Suess-Urey	Cameron	Element	Suess-Vrey	Cameron
1 H	4.00×10^{10}	3.2×10^{10}	44 Ru	1.49	1.58
2 He	3.08×10^9	2.6×10^9†	45 Rh	0.214	0.26
3 Li	100	38	46 Pd	0.675	1.00
4 Be	20	7	47 Ag	0.26	0.26
5 B	24	6	48 Cd	0.89	0.89
6 C	3.5×10^6	1.66×10^7	49 In	0.11	0.11
7 N	6.6×10^6	3.0×10^6	50 Sn	1.33	1.33
8 O	2.15×10^7	2.9×10^7	51 Sb	0.246	0.15
9 F	1600	$\sim 10^3$†	52 Te	4.67	3.00
10 Ne	8.6×10^6	2.9×10^6†	53 I	0.80	0.46
11 Na	4.38×10^4	4.18×10^4	54 Xe	4.0	3.15
12 Mg	9.12×10^5	1.046×10^6	55 Cs	0.456	0.25
13 Al	9.48×10^4	8.93×10^4	56 Ba	3.66	4.0
14 Si	1.00×10^6	1.00×10^6	57 La	2.00	0.38
15 P	1.00×10^4	9320	58 Ce	2.26	1.08
16 S	3.75×10^5	6.0×10^5	59 Pr	0.40	0.16
17 Cl	8850	1836	60 Nd	1.44	0.69
18 Ar	1.5×10^5	2.4×10^5	62 Sm	0.664	0.24
19 K	3160	2970	63 Eu	0.187	0.083
20 Ca	4.90×10^4	7.28×10^4	64 Gd	0.684	0.33
21 Sc	28	29	65 Tb	0.0956	0.054
22 Ti	2440	3140	66 Dy	0.556	0.33
23 V	220	590	67 Ho	0.118	0.076
24 Cr	7800	1.20×10^4	68 Er	0.316	0.21
25 Mn	6850	6320	69 Tm	0.0318	0.032
26 Fe	6.00×10^5	8.42×10^5	70 Yb	0.220	0.18
27 Co	1800	2290	71 Lu	0.050	0.031
28 Ni	2.74×10^4	4.44×10^4	72 Hf	0.438	0.16
29 Cu	212	39	73 Ta	0.065	0.021
30 Zn	486	202	74 W	0.49	0.11
31 Ga	11.4	9.05	75 Re	0.135	0.054
32 Ge	50.5	134	76 Os	1.00	0.73
33 As	4.0	4.4	77 Ir	0.821	0.500
34 Se	67.6	18.8	78 Pt	1.625	1.157
35 Br	13.4	3.95	79 Au	0.145	0.13
36 Kr	51.3	20	80 Hg	0.284	0.27
37 Rb	6.5	5.0	81 Tl	0.108	0.11
38 Sr	18.9	21	82 Pb	0.47	2.2
39 Y	8.9	3.6	83 Bi	0.144	0.14
40 Zr	54.5	23	90 Th	—	0.069
41 Nb	1.00	0.81	92 U	—	0.042
42 Mo	2.42	2.42			

† Revised abundances due to Cameron (1966, private communication).

They also contain semivolatile elements such as mercury which may be entirely missing in the ordinary chondrites. The abundances of the light volatile elements must still be determined from studies of the sun and stars. A comparison of the abundance compilation by Cameron with that by Suess and Urey is given in Table 1. The abundances arrived at by Cameron are plotted as a function of mass number in Fig. 1. Abundance data are amounts relative to 10^6 Si atoms.

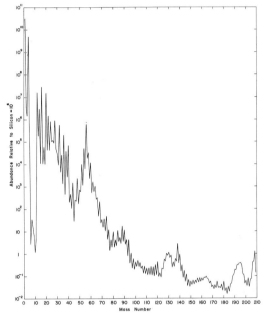

FIG. 1. The relative abundances of the elements according to Cameron (1963) are plotted as a function of mass number (the number of protons and neutrons in each nucleus).

The general features of these two compilations are the same. The most abundant element is hydrogen, followed closely by helium. The elements lithium, beryllium and boron are low in abundance but the products of helium burning, carbon and oxygen, are present in considerable amounts. The abundances in the mass region $24 \leq A \leq 32$ are roughly 10^{-2} to 10^{-1} of the abundances of C^{12} and O^{16}. The general decrease in the abundance level through mass number $A = 100$ is interrupted by a broad abundance peak centered on Fe^{56}. This iron peak is generally attributed to the equilibrium process. It should be noted that the abundance of Fe^{56}

relative to its neighbors determined from meteoritic data is approximately a factor of five greater than the solar abundance (Aller, 1961).

Relative to the general decrease in abundances through mass number $A = 100$, the abundance level in the heavy element region is rather constant. Superimposed on this trend are peaks corresponding to nuclides with neutron numbers of 50, 82 and 126 ($A \sim 88$, 138 and 208, respectively). These neutron numbers are known to represent closed nucleon shells, which are characterized by increased stability. We shall see how these peaks can be produced by neutron capture processes.

The Primordial Composition of the Galaxy

Current theories attribute the major role in the synthesis of the elements to nuclear reactions in stellar interiors. It is usually assumed that in its early stages the galaxy was composed of pure hydrogen. This assumption may, in fact, be incorrect.

The heavy element ($A > 4$) abundance of the proto-galaxy should be less than that observed for the oldest stars. Abundance studies of these stars reveal heavy-element deficiencies of at least a factor of 100 compared to younger stars like the sun, for which the fraction by mass of heavy elements $Z \sim 0.03$. It is reasonable to suppose that the primordial value of Z was $Z = 0$.

The primordial abundance of helium in the galaxy is currently a subject of considerable discussion. Its formation as the product of the first stage of nuclear burning in stellar interiors would seem to be consistent with its high abundance in nature ($Y \sim 0.35$ for the sun). On this basis, it has been usual to assume that the primordial helium abundance by mass, $Y = 0$. In conflict with this view, current theories of cosmology predict a primordial helium composition $Y \sim 0.25$, resulting from the buildup from neutrons and protons during the early stages of expansion of the universe from a primordial fireball.

Recent studies of stellar spectra have yielded evidence for a low helium abundance in the atmospheres of horizontal branch old halo B stars. This would seem to be strong evidence against the cosmological synthesis of

487

helium. It has been suggested, however, that the surface helium in these stars has diffused below the photosphere, and that they may indeed possess a normal helium abundance (in the sense of the cosmological predictions) in their interiors. Estimates of the diffusion velocities in these stars indicate that the helium diffuses downward one scale height in a time far less than the typical lifetime for the star on the horizontal branch. For main sequence B stars, the downward diffusion of helium will be opposed by meridional circulations induced by their rapid rotation— hence, studies of their spectra should reveal a normal helium abundance. If this explanation is correct, then there is no evidence against the cosmological interpretation of the helium abundance. Further research is clearly necessary on this subject.

Nucleosynthesis in Stars

Burbidge, Burbidge, Fowler and Hoyle (1957) first discussed in detail the various nuclear processes which play a role in the synthesis of elements in stellar interiors. According to their model, charged-particle reactions are mainly responsible for element production through iron, beyond which neutron capture becomes the predominant mechanism. Subsequent studies by these authors and by Cameron (1963) and others have modified various aspects of this model.

In general the history of a star is defined by a succession of stages of gravitational contraction and nuclear burning. During the contraction the interior of the star is heated by the release of gravitational potential energy. When the temperature is increased to the point at which the nuclear fuel present in the medium can begin to burn, the contraction is halted. Thermonuclear reactions then provide the source of energy generation necessary to maintain the stellar luminosity. With the exhaustion of this nuclear fuel, gravitational contraction resumes.

The Destruction of the Light Elements. During its initial contraction from the interstellar medium, the star is heated by the release of gravitational potential energy. When the temperature reaches 10^6°K any deuterium present in the medium is destroyed by thermonuclear reactions with itself and

with hydrogen. The main deuterium burning reactions are as follows:

$$D^2 \,(p, \gamma)\, He^3$$
$$D^2 \,(d, n)\, He^3$$
$$D^2 \,(d, p)\, He^3$$

After the exhaustion of the deuterium, the star will continue to contract and its central temperature will continue to increase. In rapid succession the elements lithium, beryllium and boron will be destroyed by thermonuclear reactions with hydrogen. These reactions are oulined in Table 2, and the temperatures at which they will proceed are indicated.

TABLE 2. LITHIUM, BERYLLIUM AND BORON THERMONUCLEAR REACTIONS

	Reaction	Temperature
Lithium Burning	$Li^6(p, \alpha)He^3$	$\sim 3 \times 10^6$ °K
	$Li^7(p, \alpha)He^4$	$\sim 4 \times 10^6$ °K
Beryllium Burning	$Be^9(p, d)Be^8$ }	
	$Be^8(2\alpha)$	
		$\sim 5 \times 10^6$ °K
	$Be^9(p, \alpha)Li^6$ }	
	$Li^6(p, \alpha)He^3$	
Boron Burning	$B^{10}(p, \alpha)Be^7$ }	
	$Be^7(e-, \nu)Li^7$	
	$Li^7(p, \alpha)He^4$ }	
		$\sim 8 \times 10^6$ °K
	$B^{11}(p, \alpha)Be^8$ }	
	$Be^8(2\alpha)$	

Hydrogen Burning. At slightly higher temperatures hydrogen thermonuclear reactions will be initiated. The contraction of the star is halted, and the star settles down to a long period of stability while the hydrogen in the interior is converted into helium. The major portion of the active lifetime of a star is spent in this hydrogen burning stage, defining the main sequence.

There are two basic sequences of reactions by which hydrogen can be converted into helium. Stars of mass $\lesssim 2$ M. (M. being the mass of the sun) burn hydrogen at temperatures $\lesssim 1.7 \times 10^7$ °K by the proton-proton chains. These reactions are summarized in Table 3. The interaction of two hydrogen nuclei (protons) accompanied by the emission of a positive electron, β^+, and a neutrino

TABLE 3. HYDROGEN BURNING REACTIONS: THE PROTON-PROTON CHAINS

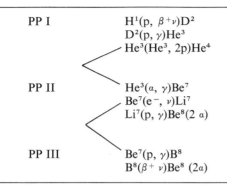

PP I	$H^1(p, \beta^+\nu)D^2$
	$D^2(p, \gamma)He^3$
	$He^3(He^3, 2p)He^4$
PP II	$He^3(\alpha, \gamma)Be^7$
	$Be^7(e^-, \nu)Li^7$
	$Li^7(p, \gamma)Be^8(2\,\alpha)$
PP III	$Be^7(p, \gamma)B^8$
	$B^8(\beta^+\,\nu)Be^8\,(2\alpha)$

TABLE 4. HYDROGEN BURNING REACTIONS: THE CNO CYCLE. (The arrows indicate a recycling of CNO nuclei.)

$$C^{12}(p, \gamma)\ N^{13}\ (\beta^+\nu)\ C^{13}$$
$$C^{13}(p, \gamma\ N^{14}$$
$$N^{14}(p, \gamma)\ O^{15}\ (\beta^+\nu)\ N^{15}$$
$$N^{15}(p, \alpha)\ C^{12}$$
$$N^{15}(p, \gamma)\ O^{16}$$
$$O^{16}(p, \gamma)\ F^{17}\ (\beta^+\nu)\ O^{17}$$
$$O^{17}(p, \alpha)\ N^{14}$$
$$O^{17}(p, \gamma)\ F^{18}\ (\beta^+\nu)\ O^{18}$$
$$O^{18}(p, \alpha)\ N^{15}$$
$$O^{18}(p, \gamma)\ F^{19}$$
$$F^{19}(p, \alpha)\ O^{16}$$

results in the production of a deuterium nucleus. The deuterium thus formed can capture a proton to form He^3. The interaction of two He^3 nuclei then results in the formation of He^4 with the release of two protons. The net result of this sequence is the fusion of four protons to one He^4 nucleus, with the release of 26.730 million electron volts (MeV) of energy, or 6.68 MeV per nucleon. In contrast, subsequent nuclear transformations by which the helium is converted to iron release only ~ 2.22 MeV per nucleon.

At somewhat higher temperatures the He^3 concentration becomes small, and an alternate reaction sequence is favored, as

$$He^3\ (\alpha, \gamma)\ Be^7$$

The destruction of Be^7 then proceeds either by

$$Be^7\ (e^-, \nu)Li^7\ (p, \alpha)He^4$$

or

$$Be^7\ (p, \gamma)B^8(\beta^+\nu)\ Be^8\ (2\alpha)$$

both of which result in the production of He^4.

For stars more massive than $\sim 2M.$, the initial contraction will continue until the central temperature exceeds$1.\ 7 \times 10^7$ °K. At these temperatures, hydrogen burning by the carbon-nitrogen-oxygen cycle provides more energy generation than do the proton-proton chains. In these reactions the carbon and nitrogen act as catalysts for the conversion of hydrogen to helium, as illustrated in Table 4. Further, for stars of several solar masses, which burn their central hydrogen at temperatures of $\sim 3 \times 10^7$ °K, the isotopes of oxygen and F^{19} will be largely transformed into CNO—cycle nuclei.

Calculations of the abundances of carbon, nitrogen and oxygen in equilibrium for the CNO cycle predict that N^{14} will be the most abundant nuclei. This is an important result with regard to our subsequent discussion of neutron capture, as N^{14} may provide an important source of neutrons for the synthesis of the heavy elements. These equilibrium calculations also predict that the ratio $C^{12}/C^{13} \sim 4$ over a wide range of temperatures. There is good observational confirmation that the ratio C^{12}/C^{13} reaches values close to four in carbon stars, suggesting that this material has been processed by the CNO cycle.

Helium Burning. The exhaustion of the hydrogen fuel in the core is followed by the contraction of the core, the temperature increasing until the helium in the core ignites. Helium burning proceeds at temperatures $\gtrsim 10^8$ °K by means of the triple-alpha reaction

$$3\alpha \rightarrow C^{12}$$

The carbon formed in this way can capture another alpha-particle to form O^{16}

$$C^{12}\ (\alpha, \gamma)\ O^{16}$$

The production of heavier nuclei is impeded by the slow rate of alpha-particle capture by O^{16}

Uncertainties associated with the rate of alpha capture by C^{12} make it difficult to determine with any accuracy the final abundances of the products of helium burning. The greater sensitivity of the rate of the triple-alpha reaction to the abundance of alpha particles, however, suggests that if helium burning goes to completion O^{16} should be the major product.

Heavy Ion Thermonuclear Reactions. Following helium burning, the core is composed predominantly of the nuclei C^{12} and O^{16}. The next nuclear burning stage must involve the interactions of these heavy ions with themselves.

The destruction of C^{12} will proceed at temperatures $\gtrsim 7 \times 10^8$ °K by the reaction $C^{12} + C^{12}$. The dominant reactions are

$$C^{12} + C^{12} \rightarrow Na^{23} + p$$
$$\rightarrow Ne^{20} + \alpha$$

where the products are in roughly equal amounts. There is also a weak branching to $Mg^{23} + n$, but the direct effects of this neutron emission are of minor importance at these temperatures.

At slightly higher temperatures ($T \sim 10^9$ °K) oxygen burning by $O^{16} + O^{16}$ is also possible. The dominant reactions in this case are

$$O^{16} + O^{16} \rightarrow P^{31} + p$$
$$\rightarrow Si^{28} + \alpha$$

where again the neutron branching is rather weak. Experimental data for these reactions are quite limited, but it is probable that the proton and alpha-particle yields are comparable.

The Equilibrium Process. The protons and alpha-particles released in the heavy ion reactions will be rapidly recaptured. The final products of this nuclear burning stage should then be the alpha nuclei Mg^{24}, Si^{28} and S^{32}. Core contraction at this stage results in a further increase in the temperature.

If the temperature in the core can rise above 3×10^9 °K, then a great variety of nuclear reactions can occur with very rapid rates. The products of the earlier burning stages, now present mainly in the form of the more stable Si^{28}, can be "photodisintegrated" at these temperatures. In this process, an energetic gamma ray excites the nucleus, resulting in particle emission as

$$Si^{28} \ (\gamma, \ \alpha) \ Mg^{24}$$

$$Si^{28} \ (\gamma, \ p) \ Al^{27}$$

The protons, neutrons and alpha particles released in this manner can then be captured on the remaining nuclei resulting in a buildup toward the iron region.

The rapidity of the various reaction rates under these conditions suggests that the relative abundances of the various nuclear species should come into equilibrium. These equilibrium abundances can be calculated from statistical mechanics, as was done in the earlier theories. Fig. 2 shows an equilibrium

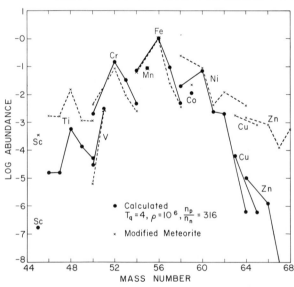

FIG. 2. An equilibrium calculation of the abundances in the iron region for a temperature of 3×10^9 °K and a density $= 10^6$ g/cc is compared to the observed abundances. Meteoritic abundances have been employed, except that the iron abundance has been reduced to agree with the solar value. The ratio of the numbers of free protons to free neutrons for this fit was $n_p/n_n = 316$.

fit to the iron peak region by Cameron (1963) for a temperature of 4×10^9 °K ($T_9 = 4$) and a density $\rho = 10^6$ g/cc. The meteoritic abundances have been modified by reducing the abundance of iron relative to its neighbors by a factor of ~ 5 to agree with the solar value. These results are in reasonably good agreement in the immediate vicinity of iron.

Supernova Explosions. The nuclear burning stages discussed in the previous paragraphs have been exoergic, that is, the net result of the various nuclear reactions has been the formation of heavier nuclei with the release of energy. This energy generation was sufficient to provide the stellar luminosity. However, Fe^{56}, the most abundant nucleus formed in the equilibrium process, has the largest binding energy per nucleon of any nucleus. Any further nuclear processing of this Fe^{56} will therefore result in a loss of energy by the star.

The only source of energy available is gravitational potential energy. As the core contracts, the temperature will increase. At temperatures above $\sim 6 \times 10^9$ °K, for a density of $\sim 10^6$ g/cc, the endoergic conversion of Fe^{56} to helium will proceed. This helium production must then be accompanied by a further contraction, or the collapse of the core.

There is another mechanism by which the collapse of the core might be initiated. At the high densities and temperatures existing in the core, electron capture by nuclei and free protons can proceed rapidly. The decrease in the electron number density will be accompanied by a decrease in the electron pressure which may be sufficient to trigger the collapse.

As the collapse proceeds, the density in the core can approach nuclear densities. Neutrinos released under these conditions can diffuse outward, depositing energy in the outer regions of the core. This deposition of energy can result in the formation of a shock wave in the region surrounding the core. If this shock is sufficiently energetic, the outer layers of the star can be blown off with high velocities in a supernova explosion. By this means, the interstellar medium may be enriched in the abundances of heavy elements. The characteristics of these shock waves are currently under investigation (Arnett, 1966).

The passage of the shock wave through the outer regions of the star will result in an increase in both the temperature and the density of the gas. It has been proposed that a large amount of element synthesis might take place under these conditions. Recent calculations carried out by the writer indicate that regions composed initially of C^{12}, O^{16} or Si^{28} can be processed rapidly to nuclei in the iron peak. Neutron capture processes may also be important under these conditions.

Deuterium, Lithium, Beryllium and Boron. We have seen that the elements deuterium, lithium, beryllium and boron are destroyed rapidly by interactions with protons during the initial contraction stage of a star. In general, these elements are known to be unstable at the temperatures characteristic of stellar interiors. There arises, therefore, the question as to how these elements might be synthesized.

Several mechanisms have been proposed for the production of these light elements. Fowler, Greenstein and Hoyle (1962) have suggested that lithium, beryllium and boron might be formed by high-energy spallation reactions during the early history of the solar system. Cameron has suggested that the passage of a supernova shock wave through a region of helium might result in the production of these elements. Further studies of this problem are required in order to decide whether either of these two mechanisms is correct or, rather, whether an entirely different mechanism is responsible for the production of the light elements.

Element Synthesis by Neutron Capture. The buildup of the abundances of nuclei heavier than iron takes place predominantly by neutron capture. In general these neutron capture processes can be divided into two distinct groups, defined by the relative stability of the product nuclei against electron (beta) emission. If the products have beta decay half-lives longer than the half-lives for destruction by neutron capture, they can be regarded as stable in the neutron capture sense. This corresponds to the process of neutron capture on a fast time scale (the r-process of Burbidge *et al*). If the half-life for beta decay is shorter than the half-life for neutron destruction, then this decay must be assumed to take place before the capture of a neutron. This is neutron capture on a slow time scale (the s-process).

A typical section of a nuclide chart is shown in Fig. 3; beta-stable nuclei are

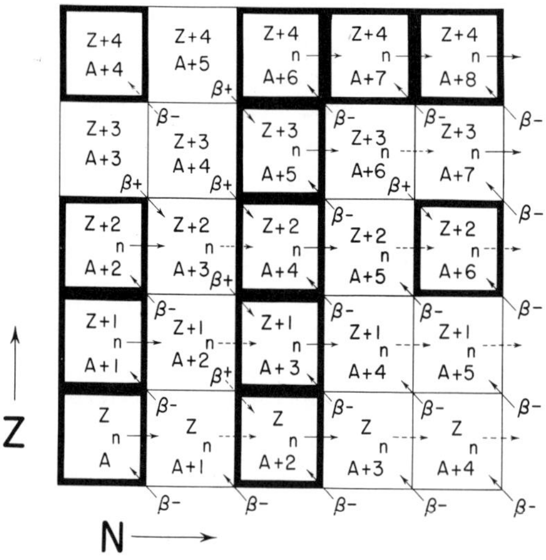

FIG. 3. A typical section of a nuclide chart in which the proton number, Z, is plotted vertically and the neutron number, N, horizontally.

indicated by heavy black borders. In this figure the proton number, Z, is plotted vertically and the neutron number, N, is plotted horizontally. The mass number, the total number of protons and neutrons, is then given by $A = Z + N$. Neutron capture proceeds horizontally, along lines of constant Z. Beta decay processes, the decay of a neutron to a proton, involve no change in mass number and therefore proceed along the diagonals as

$$(Z, A) \rightarrow (Z + 1, A) + \beta^- + \bar{\nu}$$

where $\bar{\nu}$ is an antineutrino and β^- is an electron.

If we begin with the nucleus in the lower left hand corner (Z, A) and capture a neutron, the product nucleus is beta-unstable. If the beta decay half-life is long compared to the mean time between captures, neutron capture will continue through the nuclei $(Z, A + 1)$ and $(Z, A + 2)$. If the neutron capture times are long, then the nucleus $(Z, A + 1)$ will beta decay to $(Z + 1, A + 1)$ which can then undergo neutron capture and subsequent beta decay to $(Z + 2, A + 2)$. This sequence

of neutron captures and beta decays corresponds to the process of neutron capture on a slow time scale. It is clear that the path for this process will proceed through regions of stability for the heavy elements (the "valley of beta stability").

From these considerations, it is clear that we can determine a unique capture path provided we have some knowledge of the neutron capture and beta-decay lifetimes. The beta-decay rates are not extremely sensitive to the physical conditions. On the other hand, the rate of neutron capture is proportional to the number of neutrons available per unit volume in the medium. It is necessary, therefore, to consider the nature of the neutron sources available for neutron capture.

Neutron capture on a slow time scale is believed to take place at various presupernova stages of evolution. In the early stages of helium burning, $T_8 \sim 1$, the $C^{13} (\alpha, n) O^{16}$ reaction provides a source of neutrons. At somewhat higher temperatures, a significant flux of neutrons can result the reaction $Ne^{22} (\alpha, n) Mg^{25}$. This Ne^{22} is thought to be formed by the following sequence of reactions

$$N^{14} (\alpha, \gamma) F^{18} (\beta^+ \nu) O^{18}$$

$$O^{18} (\alpha, \gamma) Ne^{22}$$

taking place during helium burning, where the N^{14} represents the product of hydrogen burning by the CNO cycle. Further neutron capture processing can take place during carbon burning, where the protons and alpha-particles released in the $C^{12} + C^{12}$ reaction can initiate the following sequence of reactions

$$C^{12} (p, \gamma) N^{13} (\beta^+ \nu) C^{13} (\alpha, n) O^{16}$$

This source of neutrons is less certain as, for temperatures greater than $7.5 + 10^8$ °K, the N^{13} will be destroyed by $N^{13} (\gamma, p) C^{12}$ before it can β^+ decay.

Neutron capture on a fast time scale is thought to take place in supernova explosions. It is felt that large fluxes of neutrons may be produced under these extreme conditions. Successive neutron captures proceeding rapidly compared to the typical beta decay lifetimes will result in the production of neutron-rich nuclei far from the valley of beta stability. Current studies of this problem by this writer indicate that the extent of element synthesis by neutron capture under these conditions is rather sensitive to the detailed characteristics of the supernova explosion.

The abundances in the heavy element region are displayed in Fig. 1. Superimposed on this abundance pattern are peaks at $A \sim 88$, 138 and 208 corresponding to nuclei with neutron numbers 50, 82 and 126. These peaks can be accounted for by neutron capture on a slow time scale. Neutron numbers 50, 82 and 126 correspond to stable, closed-shell nucleon configurations. The neutron capture probabilities for these nuclei are small. Nuclei in these regions, in the absence of a large neutron flux, will tend to beta decay before they can capture another neutron. Thus there is a tendency to accumulate nuclei at the closed shell positions.

In Fig. 1 we note the presence of somewhat broader and lower subsidary peaks occurring about ten mass units before the closed-shell peaks. These features are attributed to neutron capture on a fast time scale. This neutron capture process will generally form nuclei in neutron-rich regions far off the valley of beta stability. Following the exhaustion of the neutron flux, the capture products approach the valley of beta stability by a series of beta decays.

The peaks at mass number $A \sim 103$ and in the rare earth region, $A = 150-170$, are not explained by these mechanisms. Cameron (1963) has suggested that these peaks might result from fast neutron capture for a smaller value of the neutron flux. The mass peak at $A \sim 103$ has also been interpreted as resulting from the fission of the transuranic elements. There are also a number of heavy nuclei which cannot be formed by any of these neutron capture processes. These "by-passed" nuclei are thought to be produced by (p, γ) and (γ, n) reactions occurring, perhaps, in supernova explosions.

Summary

Detailed models of stellar evolution for stars of different masses have been carried through the helium burning phase. The thermonuclear reaction rates required for studies of these early stages are well known. Uncertainties

associated with the rate for the reaction C^{12} (α, γ) O^{16} and, more important, with the products of the $C^{12} + C^{12}$ and $O^{16} + O^{16}$ reactions render models of these later stages less reliable. The characteristics of supernova shock waves, and hence the extent to which element synthesis might take place under these conditions, are sensitive to the structure of the star in the presupernova stage. It is clear that further research is required in these areas. Also, the process responsible for the formation of the light elements is as yet unknown.

The general features of the theory of nucleosynthesis presented in this section have won wide acceptance. Energy generation by gravitational contraction alone is not sufficient to account for stellar lifetimes of billions of years, hence the need for nuclear processes is clear. There is also strong evidence that the synthesis of elements heavier than helium is currently taking place in stars. The many problems yet to be solved make this an active area of investigation.

References

1. Aller, L. H., "The Abundances of the Elements," New York, Interscience Publishers, Inc., 1961.
2. Alpher, R. A., Bethe, H. A., and Gamow, G., "The Origin of Chemical Elements," *Phys. Rev.*, **73**, 803 (1948).
3. Alpher, R. A., and Herman, R. C., "Theory of the Origin and Abundance Distribution of the Elements," *Rev. Mod. Phys.*, **22**, 153 (1950).
4. Arnett, W. D., "Gravitational Collapse and Weak Interactions," *Can. J. Phys.* (in press, 1966).
5. Bethe, H. A., and Critchfield, C. L., "The Formation of Deuterons by Proton Combination," *Phys. Rev.*, **54**, 248 (1938).
6. Burbidge, E. M., Burbidge, G. R., Fowler, W. A., and Hoyle, F., "Synthesis of the Elements in Stars," *Rev. Mod Phys.*, **29**, 547 (1957).
7. Cameron, A. G. W., "Nuclear Astrophysics," compilation of notes from lectures given at Yale University, 1963.
8. Fowler, W. A., Greenstein, J. L., and Hoyle, F., "Nucleosynthesis during the Early History of the Solar System," *Geophys. J. Roy. Astron. Soc.*, **6**, 148 (1962).
9. Mayer, M. G., and Teller, E., "On the Origin of Elements," *Phys. Rev.*, **76**, 1226 (1949).

493

10. Merrill, P. W., "Technetium in the Stars," *Science*, **115**, 484 (1952).
11. Reeves, H., "Stellar Energy Sources," Chap. 2 in "Stars and Stellar Systems," Vol. VIII, Aller and McLaughlin, Chicago, University of Chicago Press, 1965.
12. Suess, H. E., and Urey, H. C., "Abundances of the Elements," *Rev. Mod. Phys.*, **28**, 53 (1956).

JAMES W. TRURAN

OSMIUM

Osmium is the rarest, and economically the least important of the platinum group of metals. (See **Platinum Metals.**) The element itself is notable for its great density, high melting point, considerable hardness, and low ductility. Chemically, osmium shares with ruthenium the unusual feature of forming a volatile tetroxide, and of the two oxides OsO_4 is somewhat more easily produced. The element displays considerable variety in the oxidation states assumed in its compounds, and of these $+3$, $+4$, $+6$ and $+8$ are the most important. The properties of osmium bear a number of resemblances to those of rhenium.

Discovery and History

Osmium was discovered, and certain of its chemical properties first described, by the English amateur scientist Smithson Tennant. From 1800 onward he and W. H. Wollaston established a loose partnership in London intended initially to improve and standardize the production and fabrication of platinum. Working with a considerable quantity of native platinum from South America, they discovered four additional elements. Tennant applied himself to the portion of the native platinum that failed to dissolve in aqua regia, and which contemporary workers had dismissed as being graphite. He was able to render the black residue gradually soluble first by fusion with alkali and then by treatment with acid.

Simultaneous experiments by N. L. Vauquelin and A. F. de Fourcroy in Paris also were demonstrating the dissolution of this same residue by repeated alternating treatments with potash and aqua regia. These findings were announced in 1803. The French scientists believed their yellow alkaline extracts to consist of chromate, but suspected the brown acidic extracts to contain a new element. Tennant was able to profit by the experience of the French workers, and by June 1804 was able to announce that the yellow alkaline solution extracted from his platinum residues contained a new element—osmium. He also recognized the presence of a second new element, iridium, in the brown acidic extracts.

Tennant showed that the alkaline extract contained a volatile oxide which could be removed by distillation once the extract was acidified. The gaseous oxide was condensed to an oily liquid, and then to a semitransparent solid. He noted that the oxide possesses a "pungent and peculiar smell," and on this account assigned the name osmium to the newly discovered element, from the Greek *osmé*, a smell. It has been related that Tennant first proposed the name ptène for the element, derived from the Greek *ptenos*, winged, no doubt in recognition of the volatility of the oxide. But he was persuaded that this name would be awkward, and so altered it to the present term. There is an interesting parallel here with bromine, named from the Greek *bromos*, a stench, but initially given the name muride by its discoverer, Balard.

Occurrence

Osmium is always found associated with the other platinum metals, among which it is by a good margin the least abundant. The occurrence of the platinum metals has been described in some detail under the entries for platinum (q.v.) and palladium (q.v.), and will not be repeated here.

Osmiridium or iridosmine is a naturally occurring alloy in which the elements osmium and iridium predominate. The composition of iridosmine varies considerably according to its source, but three representative compositions are given below.

	South Africa	Tasmania	Urals
Iridium	29.6%	42.2%	55.2%
Osmium	32.7	45.6	27.2
Platinum	12.9	1.9	10.1
Ruthenium	14.3	7.9	5.9
Rhodium	1.0	0.2	1.5

These alloys are exceedingly hard and resistant to chemical attack. Granules of iridosmine are recovered in the course of concentrating gold on corduroy tables, for instance in South Africa. The name osmiridium is also frequently applied to the insoluble residue left after treatment of native platinum with aqua regia.

The abundance of osmium in the earth's crust has been estimated as 0.001 g/ton but in the view of the writer this figure ought to be lower if it is to relate to similar estimates for the other platinum metals.

Derivation

Concentrates containing platinum metals are obtained by working up the anodic sludges arising from the electrolytic refining of nickel and copper from both Canadian and South African ore bodies. In the case of the latter a considerable amount of rich gravity concentrate is also obtained. These are treated to eliminate base metals, and then the precious metals are brought into solution for a lengthy wet separation process. The initial dissolving is brought about by digestion with aqua regia, which leaves a residue containing the more refractory metals, iridium, rhodium, osmium, and ruthenium.

The treatment of this insoluble material varies somewhat among the major refiners, but at some stage it is subjected to an oxidizing alkaline fusion, e.g., with sodium peroxide. This converts ruthenium and osmium to water-soluble ruthenate and osmate. Solutions of the latter are then acidified and subjected to distillation of the volatile tetroxides of these elements. The separation of osmium from ruthenium at this stage is achieved by adding nitric acid prior to distillation. From the nitric acid solution OsO_4 is readily distilled, but ruthenium is retained in the pot in the form of nitric oxide complexes, to the formation of which this element is uniquely prone (q.v.).

The distilled OsO_4 is collected in a solution of sodium hydroxide usually containing alcohol. This absorbate is then digested with ammonium chloride to cause osmyltetrammine chloride, $OsO_2(NH_3)_4Cl_2$, to precipitate. Osmium metal is obtained by ignition of this compound in hydrogen.

The treatment of native platinum is essentially the same as the foregoing except that special procedures are sometimes required to bring iridosmine or other refractory alloys into soluble forms. One such treatment is to form an alloy with zinc, and then subsequently to dissolve the zinc away with hydrochloric acid. This produces a material that is finely divided, and which is then fused with sodium peroxide and hydroxide. Such treatment renders the osmium, most of the ruthenium, and a small part of the iridium water soluble. The aqueous solution is acidified with nitric acid, and osmium tetroxide distilled out in a stream of air. Another approach to the attack on iridosmine, which dates back to Wohler, amounts to high-temperature chlorination on a bed of salt. The metals are converted thereby to soluble sodium chloroosmate, sodium chloroiridate, etc.

Melting and Fabrication

Osmium is produced in the refinery in the form of a sponge or powder. There is not much published information on the technology of melting osmium, but one may assume that it is similar to that employed for iridium and for a number of comparably high-melting metals, such as rhenium or tantalum. This generally involves preliminary sintering of compressed blocks of the metal powder at high temperature and in either a vacuum or an oxygen-free atmosphere. The metal may then be melted in an argon arc furnace on a water-cooled copper hearth.

The cast metal is virtually unworkable. Even the annealed forms are enormously hard, and the hardness persists even at 1200°C. Small arc-melted beads crack under rolling or squeezing after 2 to 5% reduction in diameter.

Physical Properties

A selection of physical properties for osmium is given in Table 1. They relate, insofar as possible, to the metal in the purest available form. Because of the extremely high values of the melting point, and several of the mechanical properties, the values given below probably suffer from a lower degree of precision than the corresponding values for most other metals. Moreover, the hexagonal close-packed crystal structure of the metal introduces a degree of anisotropy in certain mechanical and

TABLE 1. PHYSICAL PROPERTIES OF OSMIUM

Property	Units	Value
Symbol		Os
Atomic number		76
Atomic weight	Cf C-12	190.2
Stable isotopes		184 (0.018), 186 (159),
(with % abundance)		187 (1.64), 188 (13.3),
		189 (16.1), 190 (26.4),
		192 (41.0).
Density, 20°C	g/cc	22.61
Crystal lattice		Hexagonal close-packed
Lattice constants, 20°C, a	Å	2.7341
c/a		1.5800
Allotropic forms		None known
Melting point	°C	3050
	°K	3323
Boiling point (estimated)	°K	4500
Thermal conductivity, 0–100°C	watts/cm/°C	0.87
Linear coefficient of thermal expansion,		
20–100°C	per °C	6.1×10^{-6}
Specific heat, 0°C	cal/g/°C	0.0309
Heat capacity, C_p, 25°C	cal/mole/°C	5.90
Entropy, S, 25°C	cal/mole/°C	7.8
Latent heat of fusion	kcal/mole	7.6
Latent heat of evaporation, 25°C	kcal/mole	162.0
Electrical resistivity, 0°C	μohm-cm	8.12
Temperature coefficient of resistance, 0–100°C	per °C	0.0042
Thermal neutron absorption cross section	barns	15
Hardness (annealed)	Vickers units	300–670
Young's modulus	tons/in²	4.0×10^4
Magnetic susceptibility, χ	cm³/g	0.052×10^{-6}
Work function	ev	4.7

thermal properties. These vary somewhat according to the orientation of their measurement with respect to the crystal faces.

A few of the foregoing properties call for some comment. For many years osmium was described as the substance of greatest density, but more recent measurements show that it ranks close behind iridium (q.v.) in this property, the difference in density amounting to about 2 parts per thousand. Osmium has the smallest atoms (minimum atomic volume) in the series of transition elements in the third long period of Mendeléev's Table.

Assignment of an atomic diameter on the basis of x-ray diffraction studies is beset with a complication. In the hexagonal close-packed structure, if the axial ratio c/a is 1.633, the distance between an atom in the basal plane (0010) and its six neighbors in that plane is a, and so is the distance to the three nearest neighbors in each of the layers above and below. When the axial ratio is not 1.633, all these atoms are not at the same distance. The dimensions in osmium are such that two interatomic distances are obtained from the structure analysis, 2.674 Å and 2.734 Å, the latter figure applying to the distance of approach in the basal plane. A mean atomic diameter for 12-coordination according to Goldschmidt is 2.70 Å.

The melting point of osmium has been measured in recent years by three groups of investigators,[4] and the results are given below to demonstrate the difficulty in securing precise high-temperature data of this sort. These are 3000 ± 10°C (1958), 3045 ± 30°C (1960), and 3010 ± 10°C (1961). On the other hand, the value quoted in the table above is published by the two principal suppliers of platinum metals in the western world.

As might be expected on the basis of similarity in atomic size and a common crystal structure, osmium and ruthenium are miscible in all proportions. With the other platinum metals solubility in the solid state is incomplete owing to difference in crystal structure. Osmium will dissolve in iridium to the extent of about 40 atomic-%, and to about 20 atomic-% in palladium. Osmium-rich solid solutions containing up to about 50 atomic-% of molybdenum and of tungsten have also been studied. Data on alloy systems are less readily available for osmium than for the other platinum metals.

Chemical Properties

Osmium differs considerably from the other platinum metals in its reaction with oxygen. The compact metal, when heated in air or oxygen to 200°C, forms the volatile tetroxide. Finely divided osmium undergoes slow oxidation even at room temperature, so that a certain amount of odor of the tetroxide is apparent as a consequence. At higher temperatures in oxygen or air the metal loses weight in a fashion parallel to the other platinum metals, and this property is attributed to the formation of a volatile trioxide in the temperature range 800 to 1500°C.

The metal is virtually unattacked by mineral acids and aqua regia up to the boiling points of these. Fused alkali, however, especially if an oxidizing agent is present, will bring the metal into a form that is water-soluble. Sodium peroxide, or sodium hydroxide with sodium chlorate are suitable materials for such fusions. Even fused potassium hydroxide, sodium nitrite, or sodium bisulfate will attack the finely divided metal. So also will hypochlorite solutions or neutral or acidic solutions of potassium chlorate. The alkaline fusion reaction generally produces an osmate (see next section).

Fluorine acting on osmium at 300°C yields OsF_4 and OsF_6, chiefly the latter. Chlorination of the metal at 650–700°C yields $OsCl_3$ and $OsCl_4$, and the higher the temperature the higher, in general, is the yield of tetrachloride. At elevated temperatures osmium will absorb considerable hydrogen.

The ground state of the gaseous atom, deduced from spectroscopic evidence, is $5d^6 6s^2$. The first-stage ionization potential is 8.7 volts. The only reliably known electrode potential applies to the conversion of the element to the $+8$ state; for $8e + HOsO_5^-$ $(aq) + 4H_2O \rightarrow Os(s) + 9OH^-$, $E° = 0.02$ volt.

Chemical Compounds

Compounds or complexes of osmium have been described in which the element exhibits each of the nine oxidation states from 0 to $+8$. The following information on osmium compounds indicates that the more frequently observed oxidation states are $+3$, $+4$, $+6$, and $+8$. As with the other platinum metals for the most part, osmium does not form a simple cationic species in aqueous solution.

The tetroxide, OsO_4, is a colorless molecular solid (m.p. 40°C, b.p. 101°C) with a characteristic pungent odor reminiscent of ozone. This compound is toxic, and exposure of the eyes or respiratory system to it must be avoided. This oxide is formed directly by heating the element in air above 200°C, but also by oxidation of many osmium compounds by nitric acid. It is soluble in water as molecular OsO_4, but is converted by alkali to the osmate ion, $HOsO_5^-$ or $OsO_4(OH)_2^{2-}$ which is yellow. It was undoubtedly this ion that was mistaken for chromate in the work leading to the discovery of the element.

A dioxide, OsO_2, can be prepared in hydrous form by the addition of alkali to $OsCl_6^{2-}$. An anhydrous form can also be formed, e.g., by heating the metal in a stream of OsO_4 vapor. It is a dark network solid with the rutile structure, and is fairly reactive chemically.

Osmium hexafluoride is a yellow-green solid (m.p. 32.1°C, b.p. 47°C), readily reduced by iodine or hydrolyzed by water. An octafluoride, OsF_8, was generally described in literature prior to 1958, when its existence was disproved. The pentafluoride is formed from OsF_6 by ultraviolet irradiation, or by the action of iodine dissolved in IF_5. It is a green solid (m.p. 70°C), melting to a blue liquid (b.p. 226°), and yielding a colorless vapor.

Three chlorides are known, of which the trichloride is best characterized. It is a brown solid, very soluble in water or alcohol. When heated in a vacuum at 500°C it disproportionates to a solid dichloride and a volatile tetrachloride.

There are a disulfide, a diselenide, and a

ditelluride, formed by a direct union of the elements above 600°C. They are all dark-colored solids with the crystal structure of pyrite, and they all are quite unreactive chemically.

Osmium and ruthenium form well-characterized oxy compounds that have no counterparts among the other platinum metals. The osmate (VIII) ion, formed when osmium tetroxide dissolves in alkali, has already been mentioned. Mild reduction of this, for example by alcohol, produces the osmate (VI) ion, pink in aqueous solution or blue in methanol. Both these osmate species are octahedral in structure and should be represented respectively as $OsO_4(OH)_2{}^{2-}$ and $OsO_2(OH)_4{}^{2-}$. Treatment of aqueous osmate (VIII) with concentrated aqueous ammonia leads to the formation of an osmiamate, OsO_3N^-; in this a nitrogen atom is bound to the metal atom by what appears to be a multiple bond. Structurally this ion is a distorted tetrahedron; similar species are found for rhenium and molybdenum.

A thorough review of osmium compounds has appeared recently[5]. Some general comments from this concerning the stabilization of oxidation states by various ligands in the osmium complexes may be of interest. Complexes in the more positive oxidation states ($+5$ to $+8$) all contain oxygen, fluoride or nitride ligands, all of which are small and good π-donors. The low oxidation states (0 to $+2$) are stabilized by good π-acceptor ligands such as CO, CN^-, NO^+, 2,2'-bipyridyl, phosphines, arsines, and stibines. Intermediate oxidation states ($+3$ and $+4$) involve ligands that are good σ donors, but poor π donors or acceptors, e.g., NH_3, Cl^-, Br^-, I^-, ethylenediamine. Osmium complexes are generally octahedral and the tetroxide is known to be tetrahedral.

In its compounds with oxygen and fluorine the element bears resemblances to rhenium. But in its complexes with the remaining halogens and with nitrogen compounds its relationship with ruthenium is more apparent, and this is also evident in a tendency to form polynuclear complexes with ligands linked through nitrogen or oxygen atoms.

Importance and Uses

The annual production of osmium is much less than that of any of the other platinum metals. Some indication of its importance as an industrial metal is given by the sales to consuming industries in the United States. In 1965 these amounted to 1,634 troy ounces, within a total sales of platinum metals amounting to 1,186,701 ounces—little more than a tenth of 1%. Of the osmium sold 90.4% went to the chemical industry, 4.6% to the petroleum industry, 0.6% in electrical uses, and the remaining 4.3% unclassified. The current (1967) price is $300–$450 per troy ounce.

The metal is used almost entirely to produce alloys of great hardness which are used in tips of fountain pen nibs, long-life phonograph needles, or instrument pivots. Such alloys contain about 60% osmium, some ruthenium, and the remainder other platinum metals. Although the element possesses catalytic powers like those of the other platinum metals, there is little evidence that they are superior to those of platinum or palladium, and the high cost of the metal discourages its application commercially.

Osmium tetroxide finds a number of laboratory applications. It is used as an oxidizing agent and as a catalyst for oxidations. In particular, it is very effective for hydroxylation of organic compounds at double bonds. It also finds limited application as a histological stain.

Toxicity of Osmium Tetroxide

This compound is highly poisonous, and may attack the eyes to produce temporary blindness. In contact with organic matter, including living tissue, the tetroxide is reduced to a black dioxide. It is presumably the latter that is responsible for the damage to the eyes and respiratory system. Fortunately the strong odor of the vapor is a deterrent to excessive dosages.

References

1. Platinum Metals Review. A quarterly survey of research on the platinum metals and of developments in their application in industry. Johnson, Matthey and Co. Ltd., Hatton Garden, London E.C.1, England, 1957.
2. Hampel, C. A., Editor, "Rare Metals Handbook," 2nd Edition, pp. 304–335, New York, Reinhold Publishing Corporation, 1961.

3. Cotton, F. A., and Wilkinson, G., "Advanced Inorganic Chemistry," pp. 832–845, New York, Interscience Publishers, 1962.
4. (a) Baird, J. D., *et al, Plansee Proc.*, 371–9, 1958.
   (b) Knapton, A. G., *et al, J. Less Common Metals*, **2**, 357–9 (1960).
   (c) Douglas, R. W., and Adkins, E. F., *Trans. Met. Soc. AIME*, **221**, 248–9 (1961).
5. Griffith, W. P., *Quart. Rev.*, **19**, 254–273 (1965).

W. A. E. McBryde

OXYGEN

Oxygen in chemically combined form is the most abundant element in the earth's crust and oceans. The uncombined oxygen that exists as a gas in the atmosphere and dissolved in terrestrial waters is vital to all animals and to most plants, as the supporter of the respiration-metabolism process, from which all living things derive their internal energy, and of combustion, from which most of our external energy is obtained. Oxygen removed from the air by respiration and combustion processes is restored by the natural process of photosynthesis, in which carbon dioxide and water, energized by light, react in the presence of the chlorophyll in green plants to form nutrients and liberate oxygen.

Oxygen, separated from air on a large scale by liquefaction and distillation processes, is of importance in the production, welding, and cutting of steel, as a raw material for chemical syntheses, in the propulsion of space rockets, and in other applications.

The element oxygen has atomic number 8. Its atomic weight is 15.9994 on the new carbon-12 = 12.0000 basis. In its ordinary form, oxygen is a colorless, tasteless, and odorless gas which has the formula O_2, i.e., two atoms per molecule. Oxygen is a reactive element and is found in combined form in a great many chemical compounds, of which the most abundant are water, H_2O, sand, SiO_2, and the silicates. Most of the solids, such as rocks and clays, in the earth's crust are essentially silicates.

The element oxygen exists not only in the form of O_2, but also as atomic oxygen, O, and as ozone, O_3. There are also various ionic (electrically charged) species.

Discovery and Early History

Early recognition of oxygen as a separate chemical element was made difficult by two aspects of chemical theory in the latter half of the eighteenth century, namely, the phlogiston theory, and the lack of a clear concept of what constitutes an element.

According to the phlogiston theory, all combustible materials consisted of two parts. One part was a substance called phlogiston, which was given off when the substance burned; the other was what was left after combustion. Coal, for example was considered to be mostly phlogiston, whereas a metal like copper had very little phlogiston. When the phlogiston theory was introduced, no quantitative combustion experiments had been performed and there was no conception of the role played by air in combustion; the theory was a simple explanation of what one appears to see when something burns.

Experiments on combustion date back at least to the time of Leonardo da Vinci (1452-1519), who observed that some air is consumed during combustion and respiration, but that it is not consumed completely. In the succeeding centuries, a number of other men studied the phenomenon of burning, but not until much later was it realized that air is a mixture and that one of the components of the mixture is a separate substance that supports combustion. This realization arose principally from the work of three men, Joseph Priestley (1733-1804), Carl Wilhelm Scheele (1742-1786), and Antoine-Laurent Lavoisier (1743-1794).

Although several experimenters had previously prepared oxygen-containing gas mixtures, the first persons to prepare oxygen, collect it, and show by experiment that it was not the same as air, were Priestley and Scheele. Apparently Scheele did his experiments first (about 1772), but the results were not published until 1777.

Priestley was trained in England as a clergyman and actually held several pastorates, but his chief interests were scientific. His most important chemical experiments were carried out while he was employed as a literary companion to Lord Shelburne. He reported his work in a book entitled "Experiments and Observations on Different Kinds of Air." On August 1, 1774, he heated mercuric oxide and collected over water the gas which was evolved. He called it "dephlogistigated air." He found that the new gas would support both combustion and respiration. He found that mice could live well in an atmosphere of oxygen, and he himself tried breathing the gas.

Scheele was a Swedish pharmacist. He obtained his oxygen, which he called "fire air," by heating such compounds as silver carbonate, mercuric carbonate, and mercuric oxide. The book in which he disclosed his results was called "Treatise on Air and Fire."

Lavoisier was the son of a wealthy French tradesman. He lived in Paris and was active in politics as well as in scientific work. He performed the first adequate quantitative experiments on oxidation, and he was the first to give the correct explanation of the combustion process. He used the results of his experiments, carried out in 1774 and succeeding years, to show that the phlogiston theory was false.

In one experiment Lavoisier heated tin and air together in a closed vessel and noted that there was no overall increase in weight. When he opened the vessel, air rushed in, indicating that part of the original air had been used up. Lavoisier showed that the increase in weight of the tin was equal to the decrease in weight of the air in which the tin was oxidized. He repeated and extended the work of Priestley. In 1777 he published his work on combustion under the title "Sur la combustion en general." Lavoisier showed that air is essentially a mixture of two gases, which he called "vital air" and "azote." Later he changed the name "vital air" to "oxygen," which means "acid former." "Azote" became nitrogen" in English. Lavoisier was the first to recognize oxygen as a chemical element.

Occurrence and Origin

Gaseous oxygen constitutes 20.95 volume % or 23.14 wt.% of the lower part (up to 50 or so miles above the earth's surface) of the earth's atmosphere. In spite of the fact that there are localized changes in the composition of the air caused by respiration, combustion, and various industrial processes, the continual turbulence in the air keeps the average concentration of oxygen extremely constant.

Gaseous oxygen is dissolved in ocean water and in most other natural waters. The respiration of fish and of most other marine animals depends upon this dissolved oxygen, and it also serves the purpose of gradually oxidizing waste matter in rivers and lakes.

In the chemically combined form, oxygen constitutes a large part of water, minerals, and clays. Water contains 88.81 wt.% oxygen. The total content of oxygen in the earth's crust, the oceans, and the atmosphere is approximately 50% by weight, equal to that of all other elements put together.

Outside the earth, oxygen is much less important. The sun and stars consist mostly of hydrogen and helium. About 0.87% of the weight of the sun is oxygen.

The atoms which make up the oxygen of the air are 99.759% O^{16}, 0.037% O^{17}, and 0.204% O^{18}, and the oxygen molecules in the air represent the various possible combinations of these three isotopes, e.g., $O^{16}O^{16}$ $O^{16}O^{17}$, $O^{16}O^{18}$. The isotopic composition of oxygen in water is not the same as that in air. In fact, air has a slightly greater proportion of the heaviest isotope, O^{18}, than does water; this is the opposite of what one would expect from normal isotope exchange processes, and probably had its origin millions of years ago when the isotopic ratios of the elements were different. Ocean water is slightly richer in O^{18} than fresh water (0.1995% vs. 0.1981%), but this is easy to understand, because the molecules of water which continually evaporate from the ocean are slightly richer in the lighter isotopes and fall as rain or snow to feed the bodies of fresh water.

The origin of the elements is not known with certainty. (See **Origin of the Elements**.) One hypothesis is that oxygen was (and is) formed in the stars at very high temperatures and pressures by such nuclear reactions as

$$\text{carbon-12} + \text{helium-4} \rightarrow \text{oxygen-16} \quad (1)$$

The carbon and helium nuclei were, in turn, formed from smaller nuclei. At first there seems to have been only hydrogen in the universe, and all the other elements were gradually produced from the hydrogen. In condensing to the solid mass with which we are familiar, the earth lost the lighter elements hydrogen and helium, by transfer into space.

The gravitational pull of the earth is not great enough to hold molecules of hydrogen and helium.

Commercial Production and Distribution

At the present time (1967) there is only one important commercial process for producing oxygen, namely, its separation by fractional distillation from liquefied air, which accounts for over 97% of the pure oxygen produced. When small quantities of both hydrogen and oxygen are required, the electrolysis of water is occasionally used, but the preparation of high-purity oxygen from air and high-purity hydrogen by nonelectrolytic methods are such well-developed and economical processes that electrolysis can no longer compete on a large scale.

At one time, before air liquefaction was developed, oxygen was made commercially by the Brin process. A bed of barium oxide was kept at a temperature of about 650°C. Air at a high pressure was admitted to oxidize the BaO to the peroxide, BaO_2. The air supply was then shut off and the pressure reduced. The hot BaO_2 gave off oxygen and returned to the BaO state. The Brin process did not produce high-purity oxygen. Moreover, it was expensive to keep the bed of barium oxide heated to the required temperature.

Modern Oxygen Plants. The separation of oxygen from air requires purification, compression, cooling, heat exchange and distillation stages. The two pioneers chiefly responsible for devising processes in this field are Carl von Linde (1842-1934), a German engineering professor, and Georges Claude (1870-1960), a French engineer, both of whom developed successful processes some 70 years ago. In this country Linde Air Products Co. produced the first commercial oxygen from liquid air in 1907.

For many years oxygen plants utilized a process in which the incoming air was compressed to pressures as high as 3000 psi and then cooled to liquefaction temperature by a combination of Joule-Thomson throttling and expansion through a reciprocating engine. It has, however, recently been found more economical to work at low pressures, and to depend entirely on producing the necessary low-temperature refrigeration by letting the gas do work in a rotating expansion turbine. A simplified flow diagram for a modern air-separation plant is shown in Fig. 1; practically all the new large oxygen-producing plants are designed to utilize this general process.

Air is compressed to about 75 psig in a rotary compressor, and is then cooled by heat exchange with ordinary water. Next the air is passed through the reversing part of the main heat exchanger. In the reversing part, the

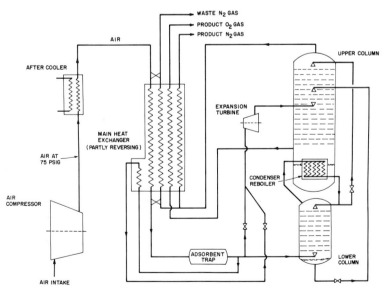

FIG. 1. Simplified flow diagram of modern air-separation plant *(Courtesy Union Carbide Corp.).*

passages are used alternatingly for incoming air and for waste nitrogen. The incoming air is here cooled enough so that practically all the carbon dioxide and water are condensed out as solids. When the valves are adjusted for gas flow in the opposite direction, a stream of waste nitrogen sublimes the solid carbon dioxide and water and carries them out of the plant to the atmosphere.

Acetylene and other impurities are removed by adsorption on silica gel or other adsorbent.

The air stream is then divided. Most of it passes directly to the lower column. The remainder is warmed slightly in (and contributes some additional refrigeration to) the main heat exchanger, and then flows to an expansion turbine. The purpose of rewarming the feed to the expansion turbine is to prevent the formation of significant amounts of liquid in the turbine; the presence of liquid interferes with the smooth and efficient operation of the turbine. The cold gas leaving the expansion turbine enters the upper column near its midpoint.

During operation, all parts of the plant are kept at a steady temperature state. The refrigeration produced in the expansion turbine is exactly sufficient to cover all heat influx into the plant through the main heat exchanger and through the insulation on all the equipment.

Liquid air from the bottom of the lower column, enriched in oxygen by distillation, is fed to the upper column near its midpoint.

Nitrogen from the top of the lower column is liquefied (at the lower-column pressure) in a heat exchanger installed in, but isolated from, the bottom of the upper column; this liquid serves as reflux for both the columns.

Gaseous nitrogen (containing most of the argon from the incoming air) passes from the top of the upper column through the main heat exchanger to cool the incoming air. High-purity oxygen gas from near the bottom of the upper column is also passed through the main heat exchanger (but not through the reversing portion) before being fed to the oxygen pipeline. If liquid oxygen is desired, the gaseous high-purity oxygen stream is liquefied in a separate process (not shown in the diagram) operating at a maximum pressure of about 300 psi.

If argon is to be produced as well as oxygen and nitrogen, part of the liquid in the upper column is redistilled in a separate column not shown in Fig. 1. Other noble gases, i.e., neon, krypton and xenon, are also produced by modification of the liquid air plant facilities.

Distribution. Before modern liquid-oxygen technology was well developed, oxygen was distributed only as a compressed gas in steel cylinders. Some oxygen is still handled in this way, but most of it is now distributed either as gas in pipelines, or in liquid form. In a steel cylinder of compressed gas the ratio of weight of gas (payload) to weight of steel is very low. The ratio becomes much higher in the smaller liquid-containing cylinders (Fig. 2), and still higher and more economical in large semitrailer tanks (Fig. 3) and railroad tank cars.

Distribution of oxygen in liquid form, which began in the United States in 1932, was made possible in large part by the development of highly efficient insulation for the tanks. In a modern large shipping tank the liquid oxygen remains at a temperature very near its normal boiling point, and the heat leak is so small

FIG. 2. A cylinder of pressurized gaseous oxygen standing beside a superinsulated cylinder filled with liquid oxygen *(Courtesy Union Carbide Corp.).*

502

that even in a week, little or no oxygen has to be vented to the atmosphere.

Fig. 2 shows a comparison of the old and the new types of oxygen cylinders. On the right is a compressed gas cylinder of the type in which gaseous oxygen has been distributed under a pressure of 2000 to 2200 psi for several decades. Containers of this type are still in use; but for applications in which many such cylinders per day are required, the new insulated liquid-containing vessel shown on the left, is used. When the valve is opened, liquid is withdrawn and vaporized in a coil located outside the insulation but inside the outer jacket of the cylinder. One liquid-oxygen cylinder, although it can be handled by only one man, holds the same quantity of oxygen as 17 of the compressed gas cylinders.

Fig. 3 is a photograph of a modern air-separation plant. The distilling columns are in the left background. The trucks and semitrailers in the foreground have insulated tanks in which liquid oxygen and other liquefied gases are shipped.

On-Site Plants. In recent years the demand for oxygen in the steel and chemical industries has become so large that in many cases it is no longer economical to make oxygen in one location, liquefy it, and then ship it to another location. As a result, a high proportion of all oxygen used in the United States is now made in plants built on or near the customer's property. These plants are largely automatic in operation. They produce oxygen gas, which is delivered to the customer in pipelines. The output of these plants varies from 10 to 2400 tons of oxygen per day.

Industrial Consumption. Industrial consumption of oxygen in the United States has been increasing rapidly. During 1965, 228 billion cu ft (measured at 70°F and 1 atm pressure) of oxygen gas were used. During 1966 the consumption approximated 250 billion cu ft, and by 1970 the consumption is expected to reach 400 billion cu ft.

High-Purity Oxygen. In the older plants it was much more costly to produce 99.5%-pure ("high-purity") oxygen than oxygen with lower purities, but now that the oxygen-making process has been developed to such a high state of efficiency, there is only a small

FIG. 3. Modern air-separation plant and liquid oxygen tank trucks and trailers *(Courtesy Union Carbide Corp.).*

cost differential between producing high-purity and low-purity oxygen. For this reason, and also because often at least a portion of the oxygen produced in a plant has to be at high purity, it is usually more economical to design the plant to yield the high-purity product only. Thus, most of the new oxygen plants in the United States produce oxygen that is at least 99.5% pure.

Physical Properties

Some of the physical properties of oxygen were given in the introduction to this article; some others are given in Table 1.

Liquid oxygen is pale blue. When an open vessel of liquid oxygen is set beside a vessel of liquid nitrogen, it is easy to distinguish the liquids, because the nitrogen is completely colorless.

For practical purposes, liquid oxygen may be considered to be a nonconductor of electricity. Oxygen is strongly paramagnetic. This property is fairly unique; nitric oxide, NO, is the only other diatomic molecule that is paramagnetic.

There are three different crystalline forms of solid oxygen, called alpha, beta, and gamma. Unfortunately, there is disagreement among scientists as to whether the high-temperature solid phase should be called alpha or gamma. In reading on this subject, therefore, it is necessary to note which phase is meant when the terms alpha and gamma are used. The temperature ranges for the equilibrium existence of each of these three solid phases at its own vapor pressure are:

Alpha or gamma	43.8 to 54.35°K
Beta	23.8 to 43.8°K
Gamma or alpha	0 to 23.8°K

At higher pressures, the transition temperatures are higher.

Atomic and Molecular Structure and Bonding

Oxygen Atoms. Each atom of oxygen has 8 protons in the nucleus. Outside the nucleus are 8 electrons with the configuration, in the most stable, least energetic form, $1s^2 2s^2 2p^4$. It is the six electrons in the second shell which are involved in the chemical reactions of the oxygen atoms.

In accordance with the octet rule, the oxygen atom in forming compounds tends to surround itself with eight electrons. In the water molecule, H_2O, for example, each

TABLE 1. PHYSICAL PROPERTIES OF OXYGEN, O_2

Atomic number	8
Atomic weight	15.9994
Boiling point, 1 atm	$-182.97°C$ ($=90.18°K$)
Melting point, 1 atm	$-218.79°C$ ($=54.363°K$)
Triple point, pressure $=0.0015$ atm	$-218.80°C$ ($=54.353°K$)
Upper transition temperature for solid beta phase	$-229.4°C$ ($=43.8°K$)
Lower transition temperature for solid beta phase	$-249.4°C$ ($=23.8°K$)
Critical temperature	$-118.4°C$ ($=154.8°K$)
Critical pressure	50.15 atm
Critical density	0.430 g/ml
Density of gas at 0°C and 760 mm pressure	1.429 gpl
Density of liquid at b.p.	1.142 g/ml
Density of solid average between 43.8 and 54.4°K	2.0 g/ml
Heat of vaporization of liquid at b.p.	50.94 cal/g
Heat of fusion at the triple point	3.3 cal/g
Solubility in water at 20°C, 1 atm	0.031 cc (STP) of gas/cc water
Heat capacity of gas, 25°C, 1 atm	7.02 cal/deg/mole
C_p/C_v for gas, 0°C, 1 atm (STP)	1.396
Viscosity of gas, 25°C, 1 atm	0.192 centipoise
Dielectric constant of gas, 0°C, 1 atm (STP)	1.0005233
Diffusion coefficient into air, 0°C, 1 atm (STP)	0.178 cm²/sec
Velocity of sound, 25°C, 1 atm	330 m/sec
Thermal neutron absorption cross section	<0.0002 barn

oxygen atom has its own six outer electrons and one each from the two hydrogen atoms. Two of the four $2p$ electrons in an oxygen atom have unpaired spins; these electrons form pairs with the electrons of the hydrogen atoms to give the strong (about 100 kcal/mole) O-H bonds which hold the water molecule together. In addition to this major bond with hydrogen, oxygen in water forms secondary bonds, called hydrogen bonds, with hydrogen atoms in other water molecules, thus:

$$O\text{—}H \cdots O \begin{matrix} H \\ \diagup \\ \diagdown \\ H \end{matrix}$$

Hydrogen bonding is thought to be caused by electrostatic attraction between the positively charged hydrogen nucleus (proton) and the highly electronegative oxygen atom. One result of hydrogen bonding is that all the water molecules in any body of water are held loosely together, so that in a sense, the ocean may be thought of as one giant molecule. Although the hydrogen bonds are rather weak, they are sufficiently strong so that the molecules in ordinary steam are polymers, e.g., $(H_2O)_2$ and $(H_2O)_3$. As the temperature is raised, the monomeric state (H_2O) is approached.

The usual method of preparing oxygen atoms is to subject molecular oxygen at a low pressure (~ 1 mm Hg) to an electric discharge. Atoms may also be produced by exposing gaseous oxygen to ultraviolet radiation at wavelengths less than 1930 Å. As soon as the oxygen atoms are produced, they tend to recombine again. Oxygen atoms are formed when gaseous oxygen is heated, but it takes a very high temperature to reach any great degree of dissociation; thus at 3000°C, the partial pressure of oxygen atoms at thermal equilibrium is only about 0.1 atm when the total pressure (atoms plus molecules) is one atmosphere. The energy required to dissociate molecular oxygen into its atoms is 117 kcal/g-mole of O_2.

Oxygen Molecules. Molecular oxygen is paramagnetic, i.e., attracted to a magnet, in the gaseous, liquid, and solid states. To explain this fact it is necessary to assume that each molecule of oxygen has at least one unpaired electron in the outer shell. This rules out the most obvious structure for the oxygen molecule (the dots stand for electrons):

$$:\overset{..}{\underset{}{O}}: \; :\overset{..}{\underset{}{O}}:$$

Modern theory indicates the presence of two unpaired electrons in each oxygen molecule. Two electronic structures have been proposed:

$$:\overset{..}{\underset{\cdot}{O}}:\overset{..}{\underset{\cdot}{O}}: \text{ and } :O::\!\cdot\!:\!: O:$$

Neither of these is entirely satisfactory. In the right-hand structure the unpaired electrons are parts of triple bonds.

In the liquid and solid states, oxygen molecules are weakly associated to form O_4. The bonding is so weak, however, that no O_4 molecules can be isolated as such.

Oxygen Ions. When gaseous oxygen is subjected to an electric discharge, a number of different ions, as well as oxygen atoms (and, if the pressure is not too low, ozone molecules) are produced. The most common ions are $O_2{}^-$, $O_2{}^+$, $O_2{}^{++}$, O^+, and O^{++}, but in a sufficiently strong discharge, more highly charged positive ions, such as $O_2{}^{6+}$, also appear.

One of the most interesting oxygen ions is the negative $O_2{}^-$. In an electric discharge, oxygen molecules readily and spontaneously pick up electrons in a reversible manner:

$$O_2 + \text{electron} \leftrightharpoons O_2{}^- \tag{2}$$

The gross electronic structure of the $O_2{}^-$ ion may be represented as $:\overset{..}{\underset{\cdot}{O}}:\overset{..}{\underset{\cdot}{O}}:$, but the detailed energy-level structure is not yet known in spite of a great deal of experimental work, because no way has been found of isolating the $O_2{}^-$ ions for study.

Chemical Properties

Oxygen can form compounds with all other elements except the lower molecular weight helium-group elements. (See **Noble Gases.**) It used to be thought that none of the helium-group elements were chemically reactive, but in 1961 Neil Bartlett, a Canadian chemist, prepared a stable compound, xenon trioxide, XeO_3. It forms colorless crystals which detonate with little or no stimulus.

Since oxygen and fluorine are both electronegative, it might be thought that they would not combine with each other, but in fact several oxygen fluorides are known. OF_2 is a poisonous gas which can be readily liquefied and does not decompose spontaneously except at high temperatures. O_2F_2, O_3F_2, and O_4F_2 are all unstable at room temperature but can be prepared and stored at low temperatures.

Reactions at or Near Room Temperature. The oxygen molecule itself is not generally reactive at room temperature, but it does react with certain strong inorganic reducing agents, such as ferrous sulfate in aqueous solution. Oxygen also reacts spontaneously with a number of organic compounds. This spontaneous action of oxygen at or below room temperature in the absence of catalysts is called "autoxidation."

Oxygen at room temperature can also react when there is a catalyst or other special situation that provides a path for the oxidation.

The most important reaction of oxygen that takes place in the neighborhood of room temperature is the metabolic process in which oxygen taken from the air oxidizes nutrients inside living cells with the help of enzymes. This process is the source of energy in all animals and in most plants.

Other examples are the rusting of metals and the decay of wood. In all these cases, the presence of water is required to bring about spontaneous oxidation. In the rotting of wood, bacteria also play an important role.

Ordinarily a flame or spark is required to start a reaction between hydrogen and oxygen, but a catalyst, such as platinum black, can start the reaction at room temperature or even below.

Reactions at Higher Temperatures. Most materials have to be heated before they will react with oxygen at an appreciable rate. Undiluted oxygen supports combustion at a much faster rate than does air. Thus a glowing splint relights in oxygen, iron wire burns vigorously, and in general most types of combustion go very fast.

Most free elements react with oxygen at higher temperatures to give the corresponding oxides. Many oxides can be made by some kind of indirect process as well as by direct reaction with oxygen. For example, calcium oxide can be made either by heating calcium carbonate or by burning metallic calcium in air.

Thermal Reaction With Hydrogen. One of the most investigated chemical reactions is that of oxygen with hydrogen. An example of the complexity of this reaction is as follows:

A mixture of 2 volumes of hydrogen with one volume of oxygen in a KCl-coated vessel 7.4 cm in diameter will explode if it is heated to 500°C, provided the pressure is at least 3000 mm Hg. If the pressure is between 50 and 3000 mm, no explosion takes place. Between 1.5 and 50 mm the mixture is explosive again. Below 1.5 mm the reaction is very slow. It is a triumph of modern reaction kinetics that the mechanism of this complicated reaction can be quite well explained quantitatively. The explanation is complicated, and we can here give only an example of how the explosive reaction is thought to take place. First, the thermal energy breaks bonds in a few hydrogen and oxygen molecules, giving some H and O atoms. These then carry on by a very fast "branching chain" reaction:

$$H + O_2 \rightarrow OH + O \qquad (3)$$

$$O + H_2 \rightarrow OH + H \qquad (4)$$

Note that each time a hydrogen atom or an oxygen atom reacts, *two* new reactive species are formed; that is how the rate of the reaction becomes so great that it ends in explosion. The hydroxyl radicals continue the reaction chain, though not by a branching mechanism:

$$OH + H_2 \rightarrow H_2O + H \qquad (5)$$

Hydrogen Peroxide. A mixture of about 96 to 98% hydrogen (by volume) and 4 to 2% oxygen, when passed through an electric discharge under suitable conditions, gives hydrogen peroxide, H_2O_2, but the conversion per pass through the reactor is too low to permit this reaction to be a commercially profitable one. Hydrogen peroxide is actually manufactured by indirect but more economical methods; one of these involves the autoxidation of a recycled organic intermediate. For example, 2-ethylanthrahydroquinone dissolved in an organic solvent is oxidized to H_2O_2 and 2-ethylanthraquinone. The latter is then reduced back to the hydroquinone, and cycle is repeated.

Classification of Inorganic Oxides. Since this chapter is primarily a description of the element oxygen rather than of its oxdies, only a little will be said about the latter, but it is interesting to note that, when oxides are dissolved in water:

Oxides of many metals form alkaline solutions.

Oxides of several nonmetals form acids.

Thus sodium oxide dissolves in water to give sodium hydroxide, a strong base, and phosphorus pentoxide dissolves in water to form phosphoric acid.

Two classes of oxides are interesting because they retain some of the original structure of the oxygen molecule. They are the peroxides and the superoxides. Hydrogen peroxide, H_2O_2, has already been mentioned. When metallic sodium is burned in oxygen, the main product is white or light yellow sodium peroxide, Na_2O_2. The peroxide ion in the crystal lattice probably has the structure $:\ddot{O}:\ddot{O}:$, in which each atom of oxygen has its octet of electrons and there are no unpaired electrons. On the other hand, when potassium reacts with oxygen the main product is an orange-yellow solid called potassium superoxide, KO_2. This product still has one unpaired electron for each two oxygen atoms; the structure of the superoxide ion in the crystal of KO_2 may therefore be represented as $:\ddot{O}:\ddot{O}\cdot$.

Silicates and Silica. Most chemically combined oxygen is in silicates. (See article on **Silicon**.) These have complex polymeric structures subject to many variations. In nature they exist mostly in rocks and clays. Crystalline silicates have a basic structure of silicon-oxygen tetrahedra

$$
\begin{array}{c}
\mid \\
O \\
\mid \\
Si \\
\diagup \quad \diagdown \\
-O \quad \mid \quad O- \\
O \\
\mid
\end{array}
$$

linked to metal-oxygen polyhedra by sharing of oxygen anions. The metal cations may,

for example, be sodium, calcium, aluminum, or iron. Looked at another way, all crystalline silicates are structures consisting of the relatively large oxygen anions in a three-dimensional crystal lattice, the interstices of which are occupied by metal cations.

Water-soluble silicates are of commercial importance as adhesives and detergents. Examples of such silicates are polymers having the basic composition Na_4SiO_4, Na_2SiO_3, and $Na_2Si_2O_5$. The higher the ratio of SiO_2 to Na_2O in the structure, the greater is the molecular weight of the dissolved polymer, and the smaller is the solubility in water. Acidification of a soluble silicate precipitates "silica gel," which is widely used as an adsorbent for water vapor and other vapors.

Silica occurs in nature as the mineral quartz. The most abundant form of quartz is sand. Silica is an inorganic crystalline three-dimensional polymer, $(SiO_2)_n$.

Reaction with Organic Compounds. There are thousands of organic compounds which contain oxygen, but most of these are prepared indirectly rather than by the direct action of oxygen. However, there are a number of commercially important reactions of gaseous oxygen with organic compounds. Some examples are:

$$
\underset{\text{ethylene}}{C_2H_4} + 1/2 O_2 \quad \underset{\text{catalyst}}{\rightarrow} \quad \underset{\text{ethylene oxide}}{C_2H_4O} \quad \text{(a)}
$$

$$
\underset{\text{acetaldehyde}}{CH_3CHO} + O_2 \quad \underset{\text{catalyst}}{\rightarrow} \quad \underset{\text{peracetic acid}}{CH_3\overset{\overset{\displaystyle O}{\|}}{C}OOH} \quad \text{(b)}
$$

$$
\underset{\text{cumene}}{C_6H_5\text{-}CH(CH_3)_2} + O_2 \rightarrow \underset{\text{cumene hydroperoxide}}{C_6H_5\text{-}\overset{\overset{\displaystyle OOH}{\mid}}{C}(CH_3)_2} \rightarrow
$$
$$
\underset{\text{phenol}}{C_6H_5OH} + \underset{\text{acetone}}{(CH_3)_2CO} \quad \text{(c)}
$$

$$
\underset{\text{methane}}{CH_4} + \underset{\text{ethane}}{C_2H_6} + \quad O_2 \rightarrow \underset{\text{acetylene}}{C_2H_2} +
$$
$$
CO + 3H_2 + H_2O \quad \text{(d)}
$$

(a) Ethylene oxide is employed, among other things, to make ethylene glycol, the principal antifreeze used in automobiles in the United States. (b) Peracetic acid is used to make a number of different epoxy

507

compounds with varied uses. (c) Cumene hydroperoxide is decomposed to phenol and acetone. This method of making phenol is becoming increasingly important because of the availability of cumene from petroleum and because there is a large market for both phenol and acetone. (d) This reaction is not actually stoichiometric as shown here, but typifies one of the important commercial chemical reactions of oxygen: the production of acetylene and a mixture of hydrogen and carbon monoxide by the direct oxidation of natural gas.

As illustrated above by the formation of cumene peroxide, a number of organic compounds readily form peroxides with oxygen. This may be a hazard in the laboratory. Thus, ethers slowly form peroxides when stored in the presence of air. Later, when these ethers are used in experiments, the peroxides may explode with great violence.

Principal Uses

A number of uses for oxygen have already been described.

The three largest classes of uses for oxygen are (1) in the iron and steel metalworking industries, (2) in the large-scale manufacture of certain chemicals, and (3) in rocket propulsion. Thousands of tons of oxygen are consumed per day in these areas. Besides the major uses, there are many minor ones which cannot all be mentioned in this article.

Iron and Steel. The oldest uses for oxygen were for the welding and cutting of steel (Fig. 4). Gas welding (as opposed to electric welding) is done with a torch in which acetylene is burned with oxygen to give a very hot flame. Cutting is done with a special torch in which the metal to be cut is first heated with one or more relatively small oxygen-acetylene flames, and then cut by a large stream of oxygen. Some of the oxygen reacts chemically with the iron, and the heat of the reactions melts some of the iron in the kerf. Oxygen cutting can be carried out at a fair speed even when slabs of steel two feet or more thick are to be cut.

A somewhat newer use for oxygen is the automatic scarfing of hot steel billets and slabs in steel mills. In this process, surface imperfections are removed by directing pre-heating flames and streams of oxygen gas

FIG. 4. Oxygen-cutting of steel plate (*Courtesy Union Carbide Corp.*).

against all four sides of hot billets or slabs as they move through the rolling process.

In some blast furnaces the input air is enriched with 3 to 5% oxygen. This reduces the consumption of coke and raises the temperature, thus increasing the rate at which iron can be produced. It is expected that the practice of adding oxygen to the blast furnace air will greatly increase in the future; newer blast furnaces are especially designed to operate on oxygen-enriched air.

Oxygen is now extensively used in making steel from molten iron, both in the older open hearth process and in a new process carried out in a "basic oxygen converter." In the open hearth, the refining process is speeded up because direct oxidation of carbon by oxygen is faster than oxidation by oxides of iron (e.g., Fe_2O_3). The new basic oxygen converter is especially designed for the production of steel directly by the action of oxygen. Use of air instead of oxygen is not practicable because it would produce a poor grade of steel in which nitrogen is dissolved. Steel production in the basic oxygen converter is growing rapidly; during 1966 more than two million tons per month of steel was made in the United States by this process.

Chemicals. A large use of oxygen is for the production of synthesis gas, a mixture of hydrogen and carbon monoxide employed to synthesize methanol. Synthesis gas may be made by the oxidation of natural gas:

$$CH_4 + \tfrac{1}{2}O_2 \rightarrow CO + 2H_2 \qquad (6)$$

(In practice, it is impossible to carry out the reaction exactly as written. Some carbon dioxide and water are always formed along with the carbon monoxide and hydrogen.)

Another way to make synthesis gas is to pass steam over hot coal or coke:

$$H_2O + C \rightarrow CO + H_2 \qquad (7)$$

This reaction is endothermic, and stops as soon as the bed of carbon cools off. The carbon may then be reheated by burning some of it in a stream of air. A better way is to mix enough oxygen with the steam to make the original process exothermic, and therefore continuous:

$$H_2O + O_2 + 3C \rightarrow 3CO + H_2 \qquad (8)$$

Closely related to the manufacture of synthesis gas is the manufacture of hydrogen for the production of ammonia and for other purposes. To make hydrogen, synthesis gas is treated with steam at a high temperature. The hydrogen is not affected, but the carbon monoxide is changed to the dioxide, while additional hydrogen is formed:

$$CO + H_2O \rightarrow CO_2 + H_2 \qquad (9)$$

The carbon dioxide is removed from the gas stream by one of several known methods, such as scrubbing with ethanolamine or some other suitable solvent.

Other chemical uses, a few of which have been mentioned elsewhere in this article, include the production of acetylene, acrolein, hydrogen peroxide by the organic inter-mediate process, chlorine by the oxidation of low-cost HCl, ethylene oxide, phthalic anhy-dride, and ozone.

Rocket Propulsion. Large rockets are usually propelled upward from the launch pad, i.e., "boosted," by the combustion of a mix-ture of a petroleum fraction similar to kerosene, called an "RP" (rocket propulsion) fuel. The liquid oxygen and the fuel are kept in separate tanks until the count-down is complete. At the moment of blast-off, streams of the liquids are mixed and ignited. The pipes, pumps, and valves have to be so large that the entire combustion process can take place within a few seconds.

Some of the largest rockets are designed to use liquid hydrogen instead of petroleum fuel in a second-stage firing, i.e., one that takes place after the rocket has already been lifted some miles above the earth's surface. Liquid hydrogen supplies more energy per pound during combustion than does RP fuel, but is much more expensive and bulky. Liquid hydrogen will probably never be used exten-sively for the first, or booster, stage, because the weight of fuel used to get the rocket off the ground is much less important than the weight that must be transported into space for use in an upper-stage firing.

Mining. One method of drilling holes through exceptionally hard ore preparatory to blasting, is to spall the ore with heat from a special oxygen-kerosene burner. This "jet piercing" process is extensively used in the mining of taconite, an iron ore.

Physiological Uses and Toxicology

The vital part played by oxygen in the respiration-metabolism process has already been mentioned. Probably the only living cells which do not need oxygen are those of certain anaerobic bacteria which derive energy by other metabolic processes.

In man, air is breathed into the lungs. The lungs have a great deal of membranous surface in which an exchange can take place between blood on one side and air on the other. Oxygen from the air diffuses through the membrane into the blood. There the hemoglobin picks up the oxygen and gives up carbon dioxide, which diffuses through the membrane into the lung cavity and is exhaled. The blood carries the oxygen-loaded hemo-globin to all the living cells in the body. An exchange process again takes place, with oxygen diffusing into the cell and carbon dioxide out into the blood. Inside the cell, nutrient compounds are oxidized by an extremely complicated enzymatic process which chemically resembles photosynthesis in reverse. This intracellular oxidation is the

509

source of man's body energy. The final products are carbon dioxide and water.

Oxygen in concentrations greater than that of air is used in connection with space travel, in the decompression of divers who have been at great depths, and in medical therapy.

The earlier American astronauts were generally supplied with pure oxygen for breathing. However, human lungs are adapted to breathing a mixture of oxygen and an inert gas diluent, and for longer trips into space it will probably be necessary to add helium or nitrogen to breathing oxygen in order to avoid lung damage.

Oxygen has been found helpful in the treatment of pneumonia, emphysema, some disorders of the heart, and a number of other diseases. Treatment may be carried out in a hospital room (Fig. 5) or even at home with the help of a tent or mask.

Hyperbaric Oxygen Chambers. In recent years (1960–1967) there has been a revival of interest in oxygen therapy in which patients are treated under pressure in steel "hyperbaric oxygen chambers," Some of these chambers are large enough so that not only the patients, but also physicians and nurses,

can be inside. In some cases, surgical operations are carried out at hyperbaric oxygen pressures.

The most important and successful therapautic uses for hyperbaric oxygen chambers are in the treatment of gas gangrene, carbon monoxide poisoning, and decompression sickness (the "bends"). Gas gangrene is caused by anaerobic bacteria; when sufficient oxygen reaches these bacteria, they are killed. If a patient suffering from carbon monoxide poisoning can be brought to a hyperbaric oxygen chamber in time, the carbon monoxide can be displaced from the hemoglobin by the high-pressure oxygen. In decompression sickness, bubbles of nitrogen or other inert gases are formed in the bodies of persons who are being decompressed after having been exposed to gas mixtures at high pressures for a period of time. Part of the treatment consists in supplying pressurized oxygen to the victim as soon as possible.

Hyperbaric oxygen is also valuable in treating some diseases involving conditions which impair respiration, and there are indications that it may help in tetanus therapy. Oxygen enhances the effects of radiation on

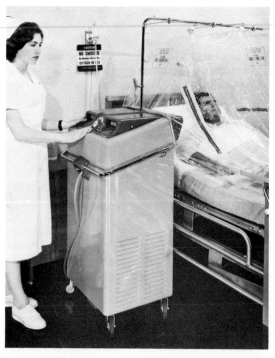

FIG. 5. Nurse administering oxygen to a patient under an oxygen tent (*Courtesy Union Carbide Corp.*).

cancer cells. Because of this, the effectiveness of cancer radiation therapy can be increased by carrying it out under hyperbaric oxygen conditions.

Precautions. Oxygen therapy must be carried out carefully, as the risk of fire is increased in an oxygen-enriched atmosphere. There is also a toxicity problem; large overdoses can bring about convulsions and other difficulties. These difficulties may be avoided by exercising appropriate precautions.

Ozone

Each molecule of ozone, O_3, has three atoms arranged in the form of a hinge having an angle of about 117°. There is no chemical bond between the first and third atoms, hence the ozone molecule should not be thought of as a triangle. Ozone occurs in low concentrations in the earth's atmosphere. It is produced at an altitude of about 25 miles in a two step-reaction. First, oxygen molecules are dissociated into atoms by photons of ultraviolet light (wavelength $<$1930 Å), and then the atoms react with the molecules of oxygen to give ozone:

$$O + O_2 + M \rightarrow O_3 + M^* \qquad (10)$$

In this reaction M is any molecule capable of carrying off the excess energy of the reaction, and M* is the excited molecule. Ozone in city smog is also produced by a photochemical reaction, but this reaction is somewhat more complicated than the one that takes place in the upper atmosphere. The concentration of ozone in air near the earth's surface is variable, usually ranging from 0.01 to 0.02 ppm, but in smog it can get as high as several parts per million.

Ozone is a very toxic gas with a characteristic, pungent odor. The U.S. Health Service lists 0.1 ppm as the maximum concentration that should be breathed by anyone for periods of an hour or more. Most people can detect by odor the presence of ozone at a concentration of 0.1 ppm when they first walk into a contaminated room, but after a few minutes the olfactory sense is dulled and the ozone is no longer noticed unless the concentration is so high as to be irritating.

Ozone can be prepared at the anode by the electrolysis of chilled sulfuric or perchloric acids when the current density is considerably higher than that at which oxygen is the main product, but the most economical way of manufacturing ozone is by passing air or oxygen, preferably at a pressure between one and two atm abs, through a silent electric discharge produced by applying a high a-c voltage (5000 to 25,000 volts) to a pair of parallel electrodes separated by a glass dielectric. Any frequency between 50 and 10,000 cycles per second may be used, but the optimum is in the neighborhood of 500. The use of oxygen instead of air produces about twice the quantity of ozone for the same consumption of electrical power.

Undiluted ozone gas is blue. The blue color can readily be seen even at concentrations as low as 4% by sighting down a four-foot tube filled with the gas. Liquid ozone is blue-black, and solid ozone is violet-black. A few of the physical properties of ozone are given in Table 2.

In aqueous solution at room temperature, ozone is a powerful oxidizing agent; only fluorine has a higher oxidation potential. Dry ozone attacks both saturated and unsaturated organic compounds. Its characteristic reaction with unsaturated organic compounds is rapid and useful in organic syntheses; the reaction usually takes place at or below room

TABLE 2. PHYSICAL PROPERTIES OF OZONE, O_3

Boiling point	$-111.9°C$ ($=161.3°K$)
Melting point	$-192.5°C$ ($=80.7°K$)
Critical temperature	$-12.1°C$ ($=261.1°K$)
Critical pressure	54.6 atm abs
Density of liquid ozone at $-183.0°C$ (boiling point of liquid oxygen)	1.57 g/ml
Density of solid ozone at $-195.8°C$ (boiling point of liquid nitrogen)	1.728 g/ml

temperature. With saturated hydrocarbons, higher temperatures are usually required for ozone reaction.

Ozone is an excellent sterilizing and deodorizing agent for water. When air containing 1% ozone is bubbled through water, the ozone reacts with phenolic wastes and other types of compounds that make water taste bad. Ozone is also a good bleaching agent for wet paper pulp or cloth; bleaching does not take place in the dry state.

The largest use for ozone is in carrying out reactions with unsaturated organic compounds. Ozone readily attacks most kinds of double bonds. The largest ozone plant in the United States (and probably in the world) is in Cincinnati, Ohio, where thousands of pounds of ozone per day are used by Emery Industries to convert oleic acid to azelaic and pelargonic acids by the over-all reaction:

$$CH_3(CH_2)_7CH = CH(CH_2)_7COOH + 4/3O_3 \rightarrow CH_3(CH_2)_7COOH + HOOC(CH_2)_7COOH \qquad (11)$$

Most drug manufacturers in the United States use ozone in one or more of their commercial organic syntheses.

Ozone can be separated from oxygen, nitrogen, and argon by either selective adsorption on cooled silica gel or by fractional condensation to the liquid, but great care must be used in handling concentrated ozone because it is highly explosive in both the liquid and gaseous states.

On account of its instability, ozone is usually made on location as needed. It is, however, possible to transport dilute, refrigerated ozone in either the gaseous or dissolved state; this is done to some extent in Europe and in the United States. It would also be possible to transport ozone in the adsorbed state on refrigerated silica gel.

Acknowledgments

The help of the following members of the research staff of Linde Division of Union Carbide Corporation is gratefully acknowledged: Dr. L. C. Matsch drew up the flow diagram and supplied information on the operation of a modern oxygen plant; Miss Edith Flanigen helped with the section on silicates; and Dr. R. W. Hamilton assisted with the section on physiological uses and toxicology. All illustrations were supplied through the courtesy of the Linde Division of Union Carbide Corporation.

References

1. Ardon, Michael, "Oxygen," New York, Benjamin, 1965.
2. Bailey, P. S., "The Reactions of Ozone with Organic Compounds," *Chem. Rev.,* **58**, 925 (1958).
3. Benenati, R. F. "Oxygen," p. 718, and V. A. Mann and T. C. Manley, "Ozone," p. 735, in Kirk-Othmer "Encyclopedia of Chemical Technology," Vol. 9, New York, Interscience /Wiley, 1952.
4. Cook, Gerhard, Ed., "Argon, Helium, and the Rare Gases," in two volumes, New York, Interscience/Wiley, 1961.
5. Cotton, F. A., and G. Wilkinson, "Oxygen," pp. 270–285 in "Advanced Inorganic Chemistry," New York, Interscience/Wiley, 1962.
6. Gmelins "Handbuch der Anorganischen Chemie," 8th Edition, System No. 3, "Oxygen" (including Ozone), six volumes issued over the years 1943–1964, Weinheim, Verlag Chemie, Germany.
7. Lewis, B., and von Elbe, G., "Combustion, Flames, and Explosions of Gases," Second Edition, New York, Academic Press, 1961.
8. Shaner, R. L., and L. C. Matsch, "Advances in Large-Scale Oxygen Production," pp. 3–44 in "Advances in Petroleum Chemistry and Refining,"Volume 9, New York, Interscience /Wiley, 1964.
9. Streng, A. G., "Tables of Ozone Properties," *J. Chem. Eng. Data,* **6**, 431 (1961).
10. Weeks, M. E., and H. M. Leicester, "Discovery of the Elements," 6th Edition, p. 209, Easton, Pennsylvania, *Journal of Chemical Education,* 1956.

GERHARD A. COOK
AND CAROL M. LAUER

P

PALLADIUM

Palladium is a member of the platinum group of metals and is distinguished among these by being the least noble or most reactive chemically. (See **Platinum Metals**.) In resistance to tarnish and corrosion, as well as in cost, it lies between silver and gold. It is soft and ductile, and like the other platinum metals retains a lustrous appearance in massive form. (See also **Platinum, Rhodium, Iridium, Ruthenium, Osmium**.)

Discovery and History

In 1800 there began in London a fifteen-year collaboration between W. H. Wollaston and Smithson Tennant that was to result in great improvements in the refining and fabrication of platinum, and also in the discovery of four additional chemical elements in the native platinum that was being imported from South America. Between 1800 and 1803 these men treated 7000 ounces of native platinum with aqua regia as a first step in the purification of platinum. Wollaston undertook a study of the solution remaining after platinum had been largely removed as ammonium chloroplatinate, and in this discovered palladium (1803) and rhodium (1804). Palladium was isolated as a yellow precipitate when mercurous cyanide was added to the precious metal solutions. The precipitate was washed and ignited to yield a white metal. Wollaston named the element palladium after the recently discovered asteroid Pallas.

Wollaston chose a most extraordinary device for the introduction of the new metal by offering it for sale in London through an anonymous leaflet. A young Irish chemist Richard Chevenix, who acquired the first lot became obsessed with the idea that it was an amalgam of platinum, and sought to expose what he believed to be a fraud by a publication which appeared in 1803 in the *Philosophical Transactions* of the Royal Society. For nearly two years following the introduction of the metal in this unusual way Wollaston withheld his identity as the person responsible for its discovery. One is left to speculate on Wollaston's motives in this procedure, but it has been surmised that he was seeking to establish priority in the discovery of palladium while at the same time endeavoring to protect his commercial interest in the wholesale production of malleable platinum.

Occurrence

Palladium is found almost always associated with platinum, and to some extent with the other platinum metals. The most abundant deposits occur in the Soviet Union, especially in the Noril'sk region of northern Siberia and in the Kola peninsula, and to some extent in the Ural Mountains region. Next in importance are the deposits in the Sudbury district in northern Ontario, Canada, followed by those in the Bushveld Igneous Complex northwest of Johannesburg in the Transvaal, South Africa. Minor deposits occur in other parts of the world, but of these reference will be made only to those of economic significance in Colombia, South America, and in Alaska.

Each of these occurrences has its own distinctive geological and mineralogical environment. Not too much information is available concerning the Russian deposits. The platinum metals evidently occur in strongly basic igneous rock formations such as peridotite or gabbro in the Noril'sk region, and probably associated with sulfide minerals. In the Kola peninsula the precious metals are found with iron, nickel, and copper sulfides (cupriferous pentlandites). A considerable amount of platinum metals in Russia occurs as native platinum in placer form, especially in the Ural district. This is also the form in which these metals occur in Colombia and Alaska. In the Canadian deposits the platinum metals are associated with copper and nickel sulfide minerals in an igneous rock mass that is predominantly norite, but they amount to only about 0.5 ppm in the ore body. In South Africa the metals mainly occur in a pyroxene rock mass to the extent of from 4 to 10 ppm, and always associated with chromite and sulfides of iron, copper, and nickel.

From the proportions of the metals offered for sale it has been inferred that the Russian deposits in the far north are appreciably richer in palladium than in platinum. In fact, it has been estimated that this country now provides about 80% of the world's annual supply of palladium. In the Canadian ore bodies palladium is roughly equivalent in abundance to platinum, but in the South African sources it amounts on the average to less than one-third of the platinum content. Goldschmidt estimated that the abundance of palladium in the whole of the earth's crust was 0.005 gram per ton (about the same as gold) but more recent estimates place the abundance at double the earlier figure.

Derivation

Because of the association of palladium with platinum in nature its extraction from ore bodies is identical with that for platinum (q.v.) The concentrates obtained from these ores, or native platinum or precious-metal residues, are dissolved as far as possible by aqua regia. The solution is heated to expel residual nitric acid, and then treated to precipitate gold. Platinum is then largely removed by precipitation as ammonium chloroplatinate.

Palladium is precipitated from the filtrate resulting from these operations by the addition of ammonia in excess followed by hydrochloric acid; this produces palladous diammine chloride, $Pd(NH_3)_2Cl_2$. This compound is generally purified by dissolution in excess ammonia and reprecipitation with hydrochloric acid. After suitable purification this compound is ignited to yield a sponge of palladium metal.

Melting and Fabrication

Although the melting point of palladium is somewhat lower than that of platinum, it is still high enough to require special facilities for melting the metal. A brief account of the history of melting platinum is given under the entry for that metal (q.v.), and the fusion of palladium has evolved in the same way. Today the metal is melted in high-frequency induction furnaces.

Palladium is produced in the refinery in the form on a sponge. This may be converted to compact metal either by melting and casting into ingots, or by the technique of powder metallurgy followed by forging and rolling. These operations are aided by the fact that palladium softens a good deal below its melting point.

Physical Properties

A selection of physical properties of palladium is listed below. They refer wherever possible to the purest form of the metal that is available. Certain properties, such as electrical resistance or hardness, are appreciably altered by the presence of even traces of other elements including the other platinum metals. The metal is also prone to take up gases, especially hydrogen and oxygen, and contamination by these and the effect of such foreign atoms on properties may be overlooked.

Certain of the above properties may vary slightly according to the previous history of the specimen. For instance the hardness of commercial palladium has been more than doubled as a result of cold rolling to a reduction in thickness of 50%. The tensile strength and limit of proportionality are similarly increased by cold work.

The addition of such elements as copper or nickel, gold, iridium, rhodium, or ruthenium brings about changes in the physical properties of palladium and produces alloys that often have certain practical advantages over the pure metal. In general the alloying agents tend to increase the resistivity, hardness, and tensile strength of palladium.

The platinum metals have been widely studied from the point of view of their alloying characteristics with each other and with other metals. Within the block of

TABLE 1. PHYSICAL PROPERTIES

Property	Units	Value
Symbol		Pd
Atomic number		46
Atomic weight	Cf C-12	106.4
Stable isotopes		102 (0.8), 104 (9.3),
(with % relative abundance)		105 (22.6), 106 (27.2),
		108 (26.8), 110 (13.5).
Density, 20°C	g/cc	12.02
Crystal lattice		Face-centered cubic
Lattice constant, a	Å	3.8907
Allotropic forms		None known
Melting point	°C	1552
	°K	1825
Boiling point (estimated)	°K	3020
Thermal conductivity	watts/cm/°C	0.76
Linear coefficient of thermal expansion,		
20–100°C	per °C	11.1×10^{-6}
Specific heat, 0°C	per °C	0.0584
Heat capacity, C_p, 25°C	cal/mole/°C	6.21
Entropy, S, 25°C	cal/mole/°C	9.06
Latent heat of fusion	kcal/mole	4.2
Latent heat of evaporation	kcal/mole	84.3
Electrical resistivity, 0°C	μ ohm-cm	9.93
Temperature coefficient of resistance, 0–100°C	per °C	0.00377
Thermal neutron cross section	barns	8
Hardness, annealed	Vickers units	40–42
Tensile strength, annealed	tons/in²	12.5
Proportional limit, annealed	tons/in²	2
Young's Modulus, annealed	tons/in²	8.5×10^3
Magnetic susceptibility, χ	cm³/g	5.231×10^{-6}
Work function	ev	4.99
Thermionic function, A	amp/cm²/°K²	60

TABLE 2. ATOMIC RADII AND CRYSTAL TYPE OF GROUP VIII AND IB ELEMENTS

Periodic Group	VIIIA	VIIIB	VIIIC	IB
	Iron	Cobalt	Nickel	Copper
Atomic radius, Å	1.27	1.25	1.245	1.275
Crystal type	α BCC	FCC	FCC	FCC
	γ FCC			
	Ruthenium	Rhodium	Palladium	Silver
Atomic radius, Å	1.335	1.34	1.375	1.442
Crystal type	HCP	FCC	FCC	FCC
	Osmium	Iridium	Platinum	Gold
Atomic radius, Å	1.35	1.354	1.385	1.439
Crystal type	HCP	FCC	FCC	FCC

BCC = body-centered cubic; FCC = face-centered cubic; HCP = hexagonal closest packed elements comprising Groups VIII and IB of the Periodic Table palladium forms solid solutions in all proportions with all but ruthenium and osmium. Ruthenium exhibits a moderate solubility in palladium.

Extensive or complete solubility of one metal in another is favored by (1) similarity in crystal structures of the two metals, (2) similarity in atomic radii, (3) similarity in valency type. On the basis of these criteria extensive miscibility would be expected among the four face-centered cubic platinum metals. But limits of solubility, imposed by differences in crystal type, would be expected in the case of alloys of these four metals with ruthenium or osmium. The complete miscibility of iron with palladium is evidently associated with a stabilization of the γ modification of iron by small amounts of palladium. (The same effect is found with platinum). Alloys containing as little as 5% of the precious metal solidify as face-centered crystals.

Hume-Rothery[2] has recently discussed the formation of alloys by the platinum metals in terms of the numbers of electrons available for bond formation in the solid state. Many lines of evidence support the notion that among the elements of the second and third transition series bonding forces and numbers of valency electrons in the metals are maximized in the region of Groups V to VIIIA. The cohesion among the atoms of these elements, manifested in properties such as hardness and melting point, is attributed to a considerable contribution by d electrons to the bonding. In passing from Group VIIIA to VIIIC the number of bonding electrons is believed to decrease, with consequent weakening in the metallic cohesion, lowering of the melting point, and so on. Some of the differences in alloying character between palladium and platinum support the view that palladium has the lower number of valency electrons and lower proportion of d function in its bonding. This view is supported on chemical grounds by the preference for bivalency among palladium compounds and for quadrivalency in platinum compounds.

One qualification is required to what has been said about the formation of alloys by palladium. Although continous series of solid solutions are formed with rhodium and iridium at high temperatures, at lower temperatures extensive immiscibility gaps have been found, with iridium below 1500°C and with rhodium below 850°C. The study of these systems is plagued by slowness in the attainment of equilibrium, and the limits of these immiscibility gaps cannot be said to have been fixed with certainty yet.

Chemical Properties

Palladium is the least noble of the platinum metals, and it differs from platinum in its limited ability to exist as simple aqueous cations. The compact metal is attacked by hot concentrated nitric acid and by boiling sulfuric acid, and the spongy metal may be completely dissolved by these acids. Aqua regia will readily dissolve palladium with formation of chloropalladic acid, H_2PdCl_6, but on evaporation of this solution the metal is recovered as palladous chloride.

Palladium is corroded by moist chlorine or bromine at room temperature. At 500°C it reacts with fluorine to form PdF_3 and with chlorine to form $PdCl_2$. The metal dissolves if made an anode for electrolysis in chloride solutions. There is also appreciable corrosion of the metal by molten oxides, hydroxides, peroxides, cyanides, or nitrates of the alkali metals.

The metal is superficially oxidized when heated in air above 350°C, but above 870°C the oxide decomposes to the metal and oxygen. There is a small gain in weight when the metal is heated in air or oxygen in the temperature range 900-1000°C, but whereas this was at one time attributed to an uptake of gaseous oxygen, it is now believed to be due to the oxidation of traces of impurities in the commercial metal. At still higher temperatures there is a loss in weight which is accounted for by the vapor pressure of palladium (being higher than those of the other platinum metals).

Palladium exhibits remarkable behavior toward hydrogen. The metal can absorb as much as 800 to 900 times its own volume of the gas over a range of temperatures. The uptake of hydrogen corresponds roughly to the stoichiometric proportions Pd_2H and a great many investigations have been carried out to establish whether such a compound does actually exist. On the basis of absorption isotherms, and more recently of x-ray and neutron diffraction studies, it is now believed that two solution phases are present rather than a pure substance. In one of these (α-phase) at room temperature there is only a slight increase in the crystal lattice constant, whereas in the other (β-phase) the lattice constant is expanded by nearly 4%. With increasing temperatures the phases become more similar, until at about 300°C a critical point is reached above which only one phase is discerned. The β-phase consists of hydrogen atoms located randomly in the octahedral sites between the palladium atoms, but only up to a maximum of about 70% of the sites at room temperature. With the absorption of hydrogen there is a decrease in both electrical conductivity and magnetic susceptibility, and from this and other evidence there is assumed to be actual chemical bonding involved in these phases. Deuterium resembles hydrogen in its action on palladium, but its absorption by the metal is less. Both gases are able to diffuse through hot palladium sheets.

The ground state of the gaseous atom has been deduced, from spectroscopic evidence and the absence of magnetic moment, to be $4d^{10}$. It is rather unexpected to have no $5s$ electron. The first-stage ionization potential is 8.33 volts. The standard electrode potential, $E°$ (for $2e + Pd^{++}$ (aq) = Pd (s)) is 0.987 volt.

Chemical Compounds

Palladium in its compounds is predominantly bivalent, though quadrivalent and a few tervalent compounds are known. As with all the platinum metals there is a strong tendency to the formation of complexes. Those of bivalent palladium are square planar in structure with four as the coordination number of the metal.

Palladous oxide, PdO, is formed as a black powder when palladium sponge is heated in oxygen. An alternative preparation, recommended for the preparation of palladium catalyst, is to fuse palladous chloride with potassium nitrate at 600°C and then to leach out the water-soluble residue. The oxide is insoluble in water or boiling acids (including aqua regia). It can readily be reduced by hydrogen to form an active hydrogenation catalyst. A yellow hydrous oxide is produced by the addition of alkali to aqueous palladous salts. When heated to 100°C this loses water

and turns black, but does not become completely anhydrous even when heated to 500 to 600°C. The dissociation pressure of the oxide becomes 1 atm at 875°C.

Palladous chloride, $PdCl_2$, may be formed by direct union of the elements at 500°C. It is a red deliquescent solid. From its aqueous solution, or from a solution of palladium in aqua regia, crystals of $PdCl_2.2H_2O$ are obtained. The existence of the corresponding acid, H_2PdCl_4, is doubtful though salts derived from it, like K_2PdCl_4, are obtained by adding sufficient of the appropriate metal chloride to palladous chloride and evaporating to dryness. The corresponding bromide and iodide are dark-colored solids, insoluble in water but soluble in excess of the halide ion as complex ions, $PtX_4{}^{2-}$.

Fluorine reacts with metallic palladium or palladous chloride to form PdF_3, a black solid. It is a very reactive oxidizing agent. Reduction of this yields PdF_2, generally contaminated with palladium. Pure PdF_2, prepared by reduction of PdF_3 by SeF_4, is a pale violet crystalline solid, completely hydrolyzed by water.

Palladium forms a number of different compounds with sulfur (and also with selenium and tellurium). For instance, the following sulfides have been deduced from the phase diagram and, in part, characterized by x-ray measurements: Pd_4S, $Pd_{14}S_5$, $Pd_{11}S_5$, PdS, PdS_2. These are dark, comparatively inert chemically, and show some semimetallic characteristics.

Palladous nitrate, $Pd(NO_3)_2$, may be formed by dissolving finely divided palladium in warm nitric acid. The salt may be crystallized from this solution, but may be contaminated with basic salts and is very hygroscopic. The solution is prone to hydrolyze, especially if heated.

The extensive coordination chemistry of palladium is characterized by the comparatively great stability of its complexes, though they are less stable than those of platinum. In the majority of the complexes palladium is bivalent; these are uniformly diamagnetic and square planar. The ligands in them are linked most commonly through nitrogen, halogen (other than fluorine), carbon, or heavy donor atoms like phosphorus or arsenic. Representative complexes include:

$Pd(NH_3)_2Cl_2$, of importance in refining palladium; Pd (dimethylglyoxime)$_2$, important in analysis; $[Pd(CO)Cl_2]_2$, the dark color of which is the basis of a common method of detecting carbon monoxide with $PdCl_2$. This last complex is binuclear

$$\begin{array}{ccccc} OC & & Cl & & Cl \\ & \diagdown \diagup & & \diagdown \diagup & \\ & Pd & & Pd & \\ & \diagup \diagdown & & \diagup \diagdown & \\ Cl & & Cl & & CO \end{array}$$

Quadrivalent palladium complexes are mainly restricted to hexahalides, e.g., K_2PdCl_6, and ammine halides, e.g., $Pd(NH_3)_2Cl_4$.

Importance and Uses

The world production of new palladium in 1965 has been estimated as nearly 50 tons. Each year a considerable amount of secondary production from the refining of scrap, spent catalyst, outmoded jewelry, etc. contributes to the available supply. The price of palladium is currently $39 per troy ounce.

The following figures show the distribution of sales of palladium to the principal consuming industries in the United States for the year 1965: electrical 60.2%, chemical 21.8%, dental and medical 7.0%, petroleum 5.2%, jewelry and decorative 2.5%, miscellaneous 3.2%. (Total sales 717,085 troy oz.)

The chief use of the metal is for contacts in electrical relays and other automatic switch gear in the telecommunications field. For this purpose palladium is used in an alloy, for instance with 40% copper or 40% silver. The freedom from tarnish or corrosion, which assures long dependable service, is achieved at reasonable cost. The 40% silver alloy is also used for resistance windings because it possesses an unusually low temperature coefficient of resistance.

In the petroleum industry palladium has joined platinum as a catalyst for the reforming of cracked petroleum fractions. By this process the octane rating of gasoline is considerably upgraded, and furthermore a substantial amount of aromatic hydrocarbons is formed and can be separated for uses other than fuel. The chemical and pharmaceutical industries are the second largest consumers of palladium. Most of their use is for catalyst in hydrogenation and dehydrogenation reactions. The catalyst is added to the reaction vessel in the form of powdered palladium oxide which is reduced *in situ* to the metal, or in the form of finely divided metal on an inert supporting material such as pumice or silica gel. The special advantage of palladium (or platinum) as a catalyst in organic synthesis is that many hydrogenations can be carried out at comparatively low temperatures and pressures of hydrogen.

Some palladium is used as an alloying element in complex wrought and cast dental alloys. It is also used in jewelry, and for this purpose the metal is usually hardened with 4 to 5% of ruthenium, and sometimes with rhodium. "White gold" is an alloy of gold decolorized by the addition of palladium.

An innovation in the use of palladium is as an additive to increase the passivity of stainless steel or titanium. As little as 0.1% of palladium in titanium renders the latter resistant to boiling solutions of sulfuric or of hydrochloric acid, for example.

The unusual dissolving of hydrogen in palladium has some practical applications. The solubility of hydrogen in the metal falls rapidly as the temperature is increased while the rate of diffusion increases. Advantage is taken of this to admit hydrogen into vacuum apparatus in the laboratory. Palladium thimbles are sealed into the apparatus to act as hydrogen valves. When these are heated in the presence of gases containing hydrogen, even by a burner flame, hydrogen, but no other gas, diffuses through the metal. The same principle is used to purify hydrogen gas.

References

1. "Platinum Metals Review." A quarterly survey of research on the platinum metals and of developments in their application in industry. Johnson, Matthey and Co. Ltd., Hatton Garden, London, E.C.1, England, 1957.
2. Hume-Rothery, W., *Ibid*, **10**, 94, (1966).
3. White, A. M., and Friedman, H. B., *J. Chem. Ed.*, **9**, 236 (1932).
4. McBryde, W. A. E., "Platinum Metals," pp. 304–335 in "Rare Metals Handbook," 2nd Edition, C. A. Hampel, Editor, New York, Reinhold Publishing Corporation, 1961.
5. Cotton, F. A., and Wilkinson, G., "Advanced Inorganic Chemistry," pp. 845–860, New York, Interscience Publishers, 1962.

6. "Mineral Facts and Problems, 1965," Washington, U.S. Dept. of the Interior, Bureau of Mines, 1965.

W. A. E. McBryde

PERIODIC LAW AND PERIODIC TABLE

When the chemical elements are compared in order of increasing atomic number, many of their physical and chemical properties are observed to vary periodically rather than randomly or with steady progression. The similar relationship between atomic weight and properties was recognized empirically a century ago by de Chancourtois in France, Newlands in England, Lothar Meyer in Germany, and Mendeleev in Russia. Since the work of Moseley, atomic number has been recognized to be more fundamental than atomic weight. The relationship between atomic number and properties is now understood to be the logical and inevitable consequence of a periodicity of atomic structure. The familiar statement of the Periodic Law is this: "The properties of the chemical elements vary periodically with their atomic number." A more informative statement of this same law is *the atomic structures of the chemical elements vary periodically with atomic number; all physical and chemical properties that depend on atomic structure therefore tend also to vary periodically with atomic number.*

According to the modern concept, the atom consists of a positively charged nucleus imbedded in a cloud of electrons. The wave mechanical theory of atomic structure postulates that these electrons are distributed in "principal quantum shells" representing successively higher energy levels (1, 2, 3, 4. . . .). Within these shells, the electrons occupy regions of space called orbitals, each of two electron capacity, which are of different types designated as *s*, *p*, *d*, and *f*, having different energies increasing in that order. As the nuclear charge is increased one by one, each successive electron goes into the most stable orbital available to it. The periodicity of atomic structure arises from the recurrent filling of new outermost principal quantum levels, but it is complicated by the fact that although the principal quantum levels represent very roughly the general order of magnitude of the electron energy, the less stable orbitals of one level may be of higher energy than the most stable orbital of the next higher level. The result of this overlapping is that the outermost shell of an isolated atom can never contain more than 8 electrons. In the building up of successively higher atomic numbers, electrons always find more stable positions, once the *s* and three *p* orbitals in a given principal quantum level are filled, in the *s* orbital of the *next higher* principal quantum level rather than the *d* orbitals of the *same* principal quantum level. When this *s* orbital is filled, electrons then go into the five underlying *d* orbitals until these are filled, before continuing to fill the outermost shell by entering *p* orbitals. The building-up of the atoms of successive atomic numbers may be represented by the following sequence: 1*s*, 2*s*, 2*p*, 3*s*, 3*p*, 4*s*, 3*d*, 4*p*, 5*s*, 4*d*, 5*p*, 6*s*, 5*d*, 4*f*, 6*p*, 7*s*, 6*d*, 5*f*. *The periodicity of atomic structure thus consists of the recurrent filling of successive outermost shells with from one to eight electrons that corresponds to the steady increase in nuclear charge.*

A period is considered to begin with the first electron in a new principal quantum shell and to end with the completion of the octet in this outermost shell, except, of course, for the very first period in which the outermost shell, having only one orbital, the *s*, is filled to capacity with only two electrons. From the order of orbital filling given above, it should be apparent that periods so defined cannot be alike in length. The first period, consisting of hydrogen and helium, has only two elements. The second period, beginning with lithium (3) and ending with neon (10), contains 8 elements, as does the third period that begins with sodium (11) and ends with argon (18). The fourth period begins with potassium (19), but following calcium (20), the filling of the outermost (fourth) shell octet is interrupted by the filling of the five *d* orbitals in the third shell. Thus 10 more elements enter this period before filling of the outermost shell is resumed, making 18 the total number of elements in this period, which ends with krypton (36). In the fifth period, the first two outermost electrons are added in rubidium (37) and strontium (38), but then this outer shell filling is interrupted by the filling of penultimate shell d orbitals, which again adds 10 elements before filling of the outermost shell is resumed; this period also contains 18 elements, ending with xenon (54).

The sixth period begins as before with first one, then two electrons in the outermost shell (cesium (55) and barium (56)), but then interruption at lanthanum (57) to begin filling the five $5d$ orbitals. Here, however, occurs an additional interruption, in which 14 elements are formed through filling of the $4f$ orbitals, before the remaining $5d$ orbitals can be filled, and in turn before the outermost shell receives any more electrons. Consequently here it takes 32 elements to bring the outermost shell to 8 electrons and thus end the period with radon (86).

The seventh period is similar but incomplete. In principle it would end with element 118, but artificial element 103 is the highest in atomic number known at the time of writing.

These elements which represent interruptions in the filling of the outermost s and p orbital octet are called "transitional elements" (where d orbitals are being filled), and "inner transitional elements" (where f orbitals are being filled). This is to distinguish them from the other, "major group" elements, in which underlying d or f orbitals are either completely empty or completely filled.

Physical properties of the elements that depend only on the electronic structure of the individual atom, such as the ionization potential and atomic radius, vary periodically with atomic number simply because of the recurrent filling of the successive outermost shells. Increasing the atomic number by increasing the nuclear charge while adding electrons to the outermost shell increases the attractive interaction between nucleus and outermost electrons more than it increases the repulsive forces among the electrons, with the result that the electronic clouds tend to be held closer (smaller radius) and more tightly (higher ionization energy), the greater the number of outermost shell electrons. For example, carbon (6) with half-filled octet has radius and ionization energy intermediate between the larger lithuim (3) atoms with low ionization energy and the smaller fluorine (9)

atoms with high ionization energy. Similar but smaller effects are observable for the addition of d or f electrons to underlying shells. Transitional elements differing in atomic number by one therefore are more alike than are corresponding neighboring major group elements. Changes in the number of underlying f electrons have an even smaller effect, resulting in still closer similarities among the inner transitional elements.

The bonding properties of elements also depend on the electronic structure of the individual atom and therefore likewise vary periodically. For example, each period, (except the first) begins with an alkali metal, lithium (3), sodium (11), potassium (19), rubidium (37), cesium (55), and francium (87), all of which show similar metallic bonding, crystallizing in a body-centered cubic lattice. Each has but one outermost electron per atom and can therefore form but one covalent bond. Each is very low in electronegativity and thus tends to become positive when bonded to another, more electronegative element. Crossing each period the elements become less metallic, higher in electronegativity, and able to form a greater number of bonds until this number becomes limited by the number of outer shell vacancies rather than the number of electrons. The halogens, fluorine (9), chlorine (17), bromine (35), iodine (53), and astatine (85), each of which is next to the end of its period, are all nonmetals, higher in electronegativity than any preceding element in their respective periods and thus tending to become highly negative when bonded to other elements. Having seven outermost electrons, each has but one vacancy, permitting but one covalent bond. At the end of each period is an element having no low-energy orbital vacancy in its outermost shell and therefore usually showing no covalent bonding ability. These elements, helium (2), neon (10), argon (18), krypton (36) xenon (54), and radon (86), all occur as monatomic gases, and compounds of the first three are unknown. The electronic shells of the last three are more polarizable and under the influence of the strongest electron-attracting element of all, fluorine, the integrity of the octet has recently been broken to produce fluorides, and from these, oxy-derivatives. Despite this violation of the sanctity of the "inert elements," they remain extraordinarily unreactive and as deserving as ever of their position as cornerstone of the periodic system.

Physical properties of the elements that are of greatest interest are usually properties that depend indirectly on the atomic structure but directly on the nature of the aggregate of atoms which results from the atomic structure. Such properties are melting point, density, and volatility. They may tend to vary periodically but the periodicity is not necessarily consistent or even evident, because of abrupt differences in the type of polyatomic aggregate. For example, the identical atoms of carbon may form soft, flaky, electrically conducting graphite or extremely hard, nonconducting diamond, depending on the kind of bonding and the arrangement of atoms. Nitrogen follows carbon in atomic number but because it forms N_2 molecules instead of giant 3-dimensional structures like diamond or graphite, it is a gas with physical properties strikingly different from those of either form of carbon.

Among the most useful applications of the periodic law is to an understanding of the differences among compounds, whose properties also vary in a periodic manner. For example, oxides of elements at the beginnings of periods tend to be very stable, high-melting, nonvolatile solids of strongly basic character and practically no oxidizing power. Oxide properties change progressively across each period until toward the end, the oxides tend to be unstable, low-melting, volatile compounds acidic in nature and of high oxidizing power. Such periodicity is recognizable throughout a very large part of chemistry.

In order to erect a framework upon which the myriad facts that are in accord with the Periodic Law can be organized, the chemical elements can be arranged in an orderly array called a "periodic table." The Periodic Law is fundamental, but the periodic table is merely an arbitrary attempt to arrange the elements to represent their periodicity most usefully. Any such arrangement can be satisfactory if it organizes the elements in some order of increasing atomic number, showing the separate periods and at the same time grouping elements of greatest similarity together—in other words, placing the

corresponding parts of the several periods together. Hundreds of variations, rectangular, triangular, circular, spiral, two-dimensional, and three dimensional, have been proposed with special merits claimed for each, but none has universal appeal. The form currently in widest use is shown in Figure 1. In it, elements are arranged in horizontal periods and in vertical groups bringing together corresponding parts of the periods. The groups are numbered by Roman numerals followed by A for the major groups elements and B for the transitional elements, or subgroups. Elements of each group have an electronic similarity that is reflected in their properties, affording a considerable degree of predictability of the properties of one element if the properties of other elements in the group are known.

Unfortunately, the periodic table of Figure 1 has serious defects, especially as a teaching aid, which are none the less serious because most experienced chemists have become too accustomed to this chart to be sensitive to its faults. First, world-wide consistency in designating the groups as A or B is lacking; for example, in writing of the IVB elements some chemists would be referring to the carbon group and others to the titanium group. Second, the transitional and inner transitional elements differ sufficiently from the major group elements as a class that it is both convenient and customary to treat them separately, and there is no advantage to disrupting the periodic arrangement of major group elements to include the transitional elements, thus introducing a meaningless and confusing space gap between beryllium and boron and between magnesium and aluminium. Third, the justification for separate treatment of the transitional metals lies in their use of inner d orbitals in bonding; zinc, cadmium, and mercury use only their outermost shell orbitals in bonding and have no basis for inclusion with the transitional elements. Fourth, the assignment of only one group number, VIII, to three distinct subgroups has no foundation except historical ignorance long since removed, and deprives the inert group of this number. Fifth, the chart offers no distinction between 8-shell and 18-shell elements within the major groups, leading to erroneous expectations concerning the similarity of

PERIODIC CHART OF THE ELEMENTS

IA	IIA	IIIB	IVB	VB	VIB	VIIB	VIII			IB	IIB	IIIA	IVA	VA	VIA	VIIA	INERT GASES
1 H 1.00797 ±0.00001																**1 H** 1.00797 ±0.00001	**2 He** 4.0026 ±0.00005
3 Li 6.939 ±0.0005	**4 Be** 9.0122 ±0.00005											**5 B** 10.811 ±0.003	**6 C** 12.01115 ±0.00005	**7 N** 14.0067 ±0.0001	**8 O** 15.9994 ±0.0001	**9 F** 18.9984 ±0.00005	**10 Ne** 20.183 ±0.0005
11 Na 22.9898 ±0.00005	**12 Mg** 24.312 ±0.0005											**13 Al** 26.9815 ±0.00005	**14 Si** 28.086 ±0.001	**15 P** 30.9738 ±0.00005	**16 S** 32.064 ±0.003	**17 Cl** 35.453 ±0.001	**18 Ar** 39.948 ±0.0005
19 K 39.102 ±0.0005	**20 Ca** 40.08 ±0.005	**21 Sc** 44.956 ±0.0005	**22 Ti** 47.90 ±0.005	**23 V** 50.942 ±0.0005	**24 Cr** 51.996 ±0.001	**25 Mn** 54.9380 ±0.00005	**26 Fe** 55.847 ±0.003	**27 Co** 58.9332 ±0.00005	**28 Ni** 58.71 ±0.005	**29 Cu** 63.54 ±0.005	**30 Zn** 65.37 ±0.005	**31 Ga** 69.72 ±0.005	**32 Ge** 72.59 ±0.005	**33 As** 74.9216 ±0.00005	**34 Se** 78.96 ±0.005	**35 Br** 79.909 ±0.002	**36 Kr** 83.80 ±0.005
37 Rb 85.47 ±0.005	**38 Sr** 87.62 ±0.005	**39 Y** 88.905 ±0.005	**40 Zr** 91.22 ±0.005	**41 Nb** 92.906 ±0.005	**42 Mo** 95.94 ±0.005	**43 Tc** (99)	**44 Ru** 101.07 ±0.005	**45 Rh** 102.905 ±0.0005	**46 Pd** 106.4 ±0.05	**47 Ag** 107.870 ±0.003	**48 Cd** 112.40 ±0.005	**49 In** 114.82 ±0.005	**50 Sn** 118.69 ±0.005	**51 Sb** 121.75 ±0.005	**52 Te** 127.60 ±0.005	**53 I** 126.9044 ±0.00005	**54 Xe** 131.30 ±0.005
55 Cs 132.905 ±0.0005	**56 Ba** 137.34 ±0.005	**57 ᴸLa** 138.91 ±0.005	**72 Hf** 178.49 ±0.005	**73 Ta** 180.948 ±0.005	**74 W** 183.85 ±0.005	**75 Re** 186.2 ±0.05	**76 Os** 190.2 ±0.05	**77 Ir** 192.2 ±0.05	**78 Pt** 195.09 ±0.005	**79 Au** 196.967 ±0.0005	**80 Hg** 200.59 ±0.005	**81 Tl** 204.37 ±0.005	**82 Pb** 207.19 ±0.005	**83 Bi** 208.980 ±0.0005	**84 Po** (210)	**85 At** (210)	**86 Rn** (222)
87 Fr (223)	**88 Ra** (226)	**89 ᴬAc** (227)															

*Lanthanum Series

58 Ce 140.12 ±0.005	**59 Pr** 140.907 ±0.0005	**60 Nd** 144.24 ±0.005	**61 Pm** (147)	**62 Sm** 150.35 ±0.005	**63 Eu** 151.96 ±0.005	**64 Gd** 157.25 ±0.005	**65 Tb** 158.924 ±0.0005	**66 Dy** 162.50 ±0.005	**67 Ho** 164.930 ±0.0005	**68 Er** 167.26 ±0.005	**69 Tm** 168.934 ±0.0005	**70 Yb** 173.04 ±0.005	**71 Lu** 174.97 ±0.005

ᴬActinium Series

90 Th 232.038 ±0.0005	**91 Pa** (231)	**92 U** 238.03 ±0.005	**93 Np** (237)	**94 Pu** (242)	**95 Am** (243)	**96 Cm** (247)	**97 Bk** (247)	**98 Cf** (249)	**99 Es** (254)	**100 Fm** (253)	**101 Md** (256)	**102 No** (253)	**103 Lw** (257)

Based on chart published by Fisher Scientific Co.

FIG. 1.

PERIODIC TABLE OF THE CHEMICAL ELEMENTS

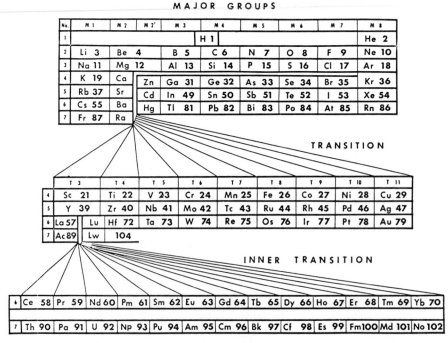

FIG. 2.

elements of the same group, or the trends down the group. Finally, the lack of extra vacant orbitals on the hydrogen atom disqualifies this element from membership with the alkali metals, and the lack of extra lone pairs disqualifies it from status as a halogen.

The periodic chart of Figure 2 eliminates the defects of Figure 1, as can be seen. The only radical change is in group numbers, the new chart designating the major groups by M and the transition groups by T, each followed by the arabic numeral corresponding to the number of electrons beyond the last completely filled sets of orbitals. Completely filled sets of orbitals correspond to the atomic numbers of the M8 elements and also the numbers 28, 46, 68, 78, and 100, corresponding to argon plus 10 d electrons, krypton plus 10 d electrons, xenon plus 14 f electrons, xenon plus 14 f electrons plus 10 d electrons, and radon plus 14 f electrons. The iron, cobalt, and nickel groups thus become T8, T9, and T10, instead of being lumped together as VIII or VIIIB, the copper group becomes T11, and the zinc group is placed where it belongs among the major groups, with designation M2′ to distinguish it from the beryllium group M2. Lutetium and lawrencium are similarly included with T3 rather than with the inner transitional elements because in these two elements the set of f electrons is complete.

The periodic table serves two main functions: prediction and organization. Prediction can be made on two bases, comparison with horizontal neighbors and comparison with vertical neighbors. Comparison with horizontal neighbors may not always be as precise but in general, it is more reliable, as the trend across a period tends to be more consistent than it may be down a group. In general, the differences between elements one apart in atomic number are greater for small atom numbers where the proportionate effect of unit change is greatest, and become progressively smaller as atomic number increases and the proportionate effect becomes less. For example bismuth differs much less from lead than nitrogen from carbon. However, disproportionately large differences must be expected to accompany abrupt changes in electronic type. Comparison with neighbors in the group may be useful provided that electronic differences are properly taken into account. In the major groups, the first member differs from the second in having a penultimate shell of two electrons instead of eight. From Group M3 on, the third member differs from the third in having a penultimate shell of 18 electrons instead of 8. Although the elements of these groups use the same kind of bonding orbitals, it would be unreasonable to expect the third member to follow necessarily the trends set by the first two, because associated with the electronic differences, its atoms tend to be more compact, more resistant to the removal of electrons, and more electronegative. In the transitional groups, $3d$ orbitals appear to be sufficiently different in behavior from $4d$ and $5d$ that the first member of each group is quite different from the other two.

As our understanding of the nature of individual atoms improves, we become less and less dependent on the periodic table as a basis for prediction, and one day soon we may dispense with it for this purpose. For no amount of organization or correlation will ever alter the fact that each chemical element is an individual and unique, nor will the properties of any element be changed one iota by placing that element in any special position in a periodic table. Nevertheless, there is enough consistency to the structure and behavior of atoms to make any reasonable form of the periodic table an extremely useful and durable framework upon which to organize and correlate an enormous quantity of chemical information. The periodic law is one of the truly great generalizations of science.

References

1. Magurs, E., "Types of Graphic Representation of the Periodic System of Chemical Elements," published by the author, 955 La Paz Road, Santa Barbara, Cal. 1957.
2. Rich, R., "Periodic Correlations," New York, Benjamin, 1965.
3. Sanderson, R. T., *J. Chem. Educ.*, **41**, 187 (1964).
4. Sanderson, R. T., "Chemical Periodicity," New York, Reinhold Publishing Corp., 1960.
5. Sanderson, R. T., "Inorganic Chemistry," New York, Reinhold Publishing Corp., 1967.

R. T. SANDERSON

PHOSPHORUS

Discovery and History

Phosphorus, atomic number 15, is the first element to which recorded history can attribute a known discoverer. In 1669, a German merchant named Hennig Brand distilled elemental phosphorus from urine, and claimed its discovery in a letter to von Leibniz. It seems quite likely that similar experiments by Arabian alchemists as early as the 12th Century may have produced the same results, but credit is given to the man who first claimed the discovery publicly—H. Brand. The name phosphorus was derived from the Greek φωσ (light) φερω (I bear) and indicated its property of glowing in the dark when exposed to air.

Subsequent investigations by other experimenters of this era showed that addition of sand or charcoal aided the liberation of phosphorus from urine. Approximately a hundred years after Brand's original work with urine, phosphorus was discovered to be an important component of bones; this formed the basis for a new method of preparation and, subsequently, a new industry.

Investigators soon found that digestion of bones with nitric acid or sulfuric acid produced phosphoric acid, which could be heated with charcoal in a retort to produce elemental phosphorus. This became the first commercial production method for elemental phosphorus. For the next 50 to 70 years, phosphorus was produced by treating degreased bones with sulfuric acid in large wood vats, filtering the by-product calcium sulfate from the phosphoric acid, and distilling phosphorus from a mixture of phosphoric acid and charcoal heated in clay retorts by coal-fired furnaces. Ultimately, phosphatic rock replaced animal bones in the acidulation step.

Toward the end of the Nineteenth Century, James Readman developed the first successful electric furnace process. Calcined phosphatic rock was mixed with tar and added to a small 80 kw electric furnace constructed of firebrick with carbon electrodes. Resistance heating between the two electrodes melted the charge and permitted the phosphate to be reduced to elemental phosphorus. Although many improvements have since been made in the design and operation of the electric furnace, the basic principles employed by Readman are still used in today's modern processes for producing elemental phosphorus.

The use of phosphorus in lucifer matches sustained the fledgling industry initially, but the next major use did not materialize until phosphoric acid became an important fertilizer material during the latter part of the Nineteenth Century. Wet-process acid could be produced by acidulation of phosphatic materials, however, and emphasis shifted from elemental phosphorus to phosphoric acid. In the 1920's, the need for higher purity phosphorus chemicals provided the impetus for increased phosphorus capacity; ultimately, this led to the use of phosphate builders in synthetic detergents—the major market for products derived from elemental phosphorus.

Prevalence, Sources, Distribution

Due to its important role in biological processes, phosphorus is one of the most widely distributed of all elements. It does not occur naturally in the free state; but in the form of phosphates it comprises about 0.10% of the earth's crust and is the crust's 12th most abundant element. It is estimated to be the 11th most abundant element in both igneous and sedimentary rocks.

Phosphorus is found in nearly all igneous rocks and undoubtedly was present originally in the volcanic eruptions that shook the infant Earth. In fact, a few large unaltered deposits of igneous phosphate are still important phosphate sources today. As many of the igneous rocks were leached by the waters of geologic ages, however, the dissolved phosphates were carried to the seas or were assimilated by prehistoric plants. Through ingestion, the leached phosphates also became part of the life cycles of the early marine life or mammals. Eventually, through accumulation of skeletal remains at the bottom of these ancient seas, today's important sedimentary phosphate deposits were formed; subsequent weathering upgraded the deposits by removing much of the associated carbonates. In some instances, phosphate was dissolved from sedimentary deposits by acidic waters and was reprecipitated as secondary deposits on the bottoms of rivers. Guano, another important type of deposit, was formed by the accumulation of seabird excrement on islands or coastal areas, or by similar deposition of bat dung in caves. Guano was probably the first fertilizer used by man, having been used for this purpose as early as 200 B.C.

Phosphorus is found in nearly 190 different minerals, but only the apatite series is important as a major source of phosphorus. This series is represented by the formula for the unit cell, $Ca_{10}(PO_4)_6$ (F, Cl, or $OH)_2$. Cationic substituents for calcium, such as Mg, Sr, Mn, Pb, and others, are common impurities, as are anionic substituents for the phosphate group, such as SiO_4, SO_4, VO_4, etc. Carbonate apatite, a common variation of the basic apatite structure, was thought originally to contain a carbonate group in place of the fluorine or hydroxyl group. Current theories, however, propose that carbonate is either substituted for the tetrahedral PO_4 groups or sorbed on the apatite surface by exchange with phosphate. Although phosphorus is present in bone and tooth tissue as hydroxyapatite, the large sedimentary deposits that constitute the major phosphate source are composed almost entirely of fluorapatite. Consequently, the conversion from hydroxy- to fluorapatite obviously resulted from the reaction of deposited bones, shells, teeth, etc., with fluorides in the seas.

The various known deposits of phosphate rock throughout the world have been estimated as comprising mineable reserves of about 50 billion tons. Of this, about 2/3 are in North Africa, with most of the remaining 1/3 divided between the United States and Russia. This does not include the many billions of tons of lower grade ore, particularly in the United States, that cannot be mined economically at present.

Derivation

Once the electric furnace route to elemental phosphorus was developed, emphasis was placed on factors related to its purity and subsequent use as an industrial chemical intermediate, while developments in wet-process phosphoric acid manufacture were directed primarily toward minimum cost and its use as an agricultural material. Both processes use phosphate rock as the phosphorus source, but the raw materials' specifications for each are quite different. The electric furnace process requires a phosphate charge in lump form to eliminate dusting and can tolerate a high percentage of silica as impurity; the wet process requires a phosphate rock that reacts rapidly with sulfuric acid and contains as few nonphosphatic impurities as possible.

The basic scheme for producing elemental phosphorus involves the carbon reduction of apatite in the presence of a silica flux. This may be represented by the following oversimplified equation;

$$4Ca_5(PO_4)_3F + 18SiO_2 + 30C \xrightarrow{\Delta}$$
$$3P_4\uparrow + 30CO\uparrow + \underline{14CaSiO_3 + 2Ca_3Si_2F_2O_6}$$
$$\downarrow$$
$$slag$$

This is an idealized equation that does not account for the many complex side reactions.

Fluoride reactions are numerous, as are reactions involving iron, aluminum, and other impurities in the furnace feed. Iron impurities, either as the oxide or the phosphate, are reduced to elemental iron. This, in turn, reacts with elemental phosphorus in the furnace to form ferrophosphorus, the phosphide of iron. Aluminum phosphate impurities are reduced to elemental phosphorus with the liberated alumina acting as a flux similar to the silica.

A well-known electric furnace design is shown in Fig. 1. In practice, the phosphate rock, coke, and silica are weighed accurately and added to the furnace by gravity feed. In the 1450–1550°C temperature zone at the electrode tips, the charge becomes molten and reaction takes place. Phosphorus vapors and other gaseous products leave continuously through the roof exits, and the molten by-products collect in the crucible bottom until removed through the tap holes at periodic intervals. The phosphorus vapors exit at about 300°C and are usually fed through electrostatic precipitators (to remove dust) to waterspray condensing towers. Elemental phosphorus is collected and stored under water. Most of the nearly 550,000 tons of elemental phosphorus produced annually in the United States is burned to P_2O_5 and converted to phosphoric acid.

The cost of producing elemental phosphorus is intimately tied to electric power

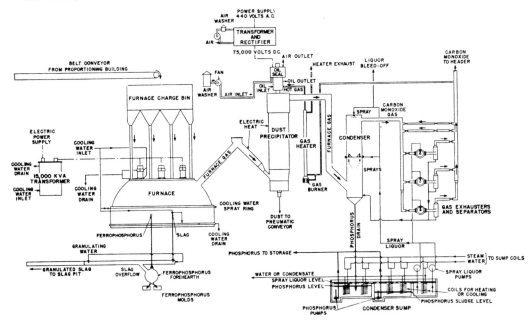

FIG. 1. Flow diagram of phosphorus furnace system for a Tennessee Valley Authority 15 Mw furnace.

costs. The electrical energy is utilized exclusively for heat, since electrolysis is not a factor in electric furnace operation, with roughly 50% of the current going to supply heat for the reaction. The remaining 50% of the heat goes to sensible heat in the reaction products or is lost to the environment. With this 50% electrical efficiency and an overall phosphorus recovery efficiency of roughly 90%, nearly 6000 KWH of electrical energy are required per ton of P_2O_5 produced, or roughly 13,000 KWH per ton of elemental phosphorus. This represents approximately 30% of the total production costs. The other major source of phosphorus for processing use, wet-process phosphoric acid, is produced in large vats by the reaction of phosphate rock with sulfuric acid, according to the equation:

$$Ca_5 (PO_4)_3F + 5H_2SO_4 + 10H_2O \longrightarrow$$
$$3H_3PO_4 + 5CaSO_4 \cdot 2H_2O + HF.$$

The gypsum, $CaSO_4 \cdot 2H_2O$, is removed by filtration, and the filtered phosphoric acid is then concentrated by evaporation. Although additional purification steps can be employed, this process does not remove most of the impurities normally associated with phosphate rock. Some of the fluorine is lost as HF

vapors during the acidulation step, but the major portion reacts with silica impurities to form SiF_4 or H_2SiF_6. Most of the wet-process acid produced is used in the manufacture of fertilizer materials.

Physical Properties

The presently accepted chemical atomic weight of phosphorus, 30.9738 on the Carbon-12 scale, is derived from the physical mass of the only naturally occurring isotope, $_{15}P^{31}$. Measurements based on chemical systems have been less precise. Each of the other isotopes of phosphorus ranging in mass numbers from 29 to 34 has been synthesized by appropriate nuclear reactions. All of the synthetic isotopes are radioactive and have relatively short half-lives. The isotope $_{15}P^{32}$ which decays with a 14.3–day half-life by a 1.7 MeV beta emission is particularly useful for chemical tracer studies involving phosphorus.

Elemental phosphorus is noted for the numerous allotropic forms in the solid phase and for the resultant complexities of the solid-liquid-vapor phase diagram. These allotropic and phase modifications of the element often are classified collectively on the basis of their colors—white, red-violet, and black. The method of classification is consistent with the respective nonmetallic-to-semimetallic properties and structural features of the various forms of the element.

The normal vapor of phosphorus consists of P_4 molecules. The four atoms of each molecule are positioned at the apices of a regular tetrahedron with each atom bonded equivalently at a 2.21 Å interatomic distance to the three other atoms of the molecule. Above 800°C, the P_4 molecules begin to dissociate to a diatomic species.

Atomic phosphorus has only a fleeting existence outside of the excitation of an electric discharge. Below the somewhat hypothetical boiling point, 280°C, the liquid and solid phases of white phosphorus are the condensed phases of the P_4 vapor. However, all of the forms of white phosphorus are

metastable with respect to other condensed forms of the element, and they can only be prepared by rapid condensation of the P_4 vapor. The wax-like transparent solid of pure white phosphorus has a normal melting point at 44.1°C as well as a solid-solid enantiotropic (i.e., reversible allotropic) transition between two crystal structures at − 79.6°C. Structural studies indicate that the liquid and two solid forms of white phosphorus consist of P_4 molecular species. All of these forms of phosphorus are quite soluble in organic-like solvents such as carbon disulfide, sulfur dioxide, and phosphorus trichloride. Molecular weight studies in solution confirm the existence of a P_4 molecular species for the solute form of the element as well.

A comparison of the properties of the various allotropes of phosphorus is given in Table 1.

TABLE 1. ALLOTROPIC FORMS OF PHOSPHORUS—PHYSICAL PROPERTIES

	β-white	α-white	red-violet	black
Crystal form	Hexagonal	Cubic	Amorphous, hexagonal, tetragonal triclinic and cubic	Amorphous or orthorhombic
Structure	Fixed orientations of P_4 molecules in lattice	P_4 molecules free to rotate in crystal lattice	Random-to-regular arrangement of atoms each bound to 3 neighbors	Laminar structure similar to graphite
Density g/cc	1.88	1.83	2.0 to 2.31	2.2 to 2.69
Transition temperature, °C	− 76.9 β ⇌ α	44.1 melt	590 melt	—
Heat of sublimation, kcal/mole	—	13.4	19.7 to 28.8	30.5
Method of preparation	Cooling α-white form below − 76.9°C	Condensation of vapor	Heating liquid from α-white form above 200°C	Heating to about 220°C, at 13,000 atmospheres
Solubility in organic solvents	—	Soluble in CS_2	Insoluble	Insoluble
Electrical resistivity	—	High	High	0.711 ohm-cm³ at 0°C
Reactivity to air	—	Ignites spontaneously at 35°C	Much less reactive than α-white	Less reactive than red, difficult to ignite

Physical properties of the α-white form of phosphorus are listed in Table 2.

TABLE 2. PHYSICAL PROPERTIES OF PHOSPHORUS
(α-white form)

Atomic number	15
Atomic weight	30.9738
Atomic radius, Å	1.09
Density, g/cc	
solid	1.83
liquid	1.74
Melting point, °C	44.1
Boiling point, °C	280.5
Heat of fusion, cal/g	5.03
Heat of vaporization, cal/g	130
Heat of sublimation, kcal/mole	13.4
Specific heat, cal/g	0.189
Critical temperature, °C	675
Critical pressure, atm	80
Coefficient of thermal expansion,	
0-44°C, per °C	125×10^{-6}
Viscosity, 50°C, centipoise	1.69
Hardness, Mohs' scale	0.5
Thermal neutron absorption	
cross-section, barns	0.20
Dielectric constant	3.6

The various forms of white phosphorus are quite reactive chemically. Despite a tendency to ignite spontaneously in air, white phosphorus is the principal industrial form of the element. It can be stored, fused, transferred and shipped safely as long as it is under a protective layer of water.

Frequently, white phosphorus may appear yellow or pink due to red phosphorus impurities. Since all of the condensed white forms of the element are metastable with respect to the red form, it is difficult to isolate pure white phosphorus. In the neighborhood of 200°C white phosphorus undergoes a slow monotropic (i.e., irreversible allotropic) conversion to a less volatile, amorphous red form of phosphorus. The transition can be accelerated by ultraviolet light or catalysts at moderate temperatures or by considerably elevated temperatures alone. Below 350°C, only the amorphous form of red phosphorus can be produced. At 460°C and above, monotropic and exothermic transitions lead through a series of two or three poorly defined but progressively more crystalline red states. The final product is a highly crystalline, red-violet form of the element which melts near 590°C. All of the forms of red phosphorus have a common structural feature in that each phosphorus atom is bound by its three nearest neighbors. The observed variety of red phosphorus forms can be explained by the polymeric modifications of this structure and the different terminal groups which are always present as impurities. The amorphous form of red phosphorus is used in the striking surface for safety matches and for the preparation of other phosphorus compounds when a less reactive form of the element is desired. Contrary to common opinion, however, the commercial form of red phosphorus is moderately unstable. Large quantities are subject to spontaneous combustion; and at even moderate temperatures it will react with water vapor or the oxgyen in air to produce phosphine and oxyacids of phosphorus.

A so-called high-pressure allotrope of phosphorus has been produced by applications of heat and very high pressures. More recently, this same black modification has been prepared at 200°C with the aid of a catalyst and without added pressure. This suggests that this black form of phosphorus may be the ultimate monotrope of the phosphorus series. Its properties, however, more nearly parallel those of the graphite form of carbon. Like graphite, it is a black, moderate electrical conductor having both amorphous and laminar crystal structures. No practical applications for black phosphorus have been established.

Chemistry

Phosphorus, like the other nitrogen group elements, has five potential valence electrons in its outer orbitals—three in p orbitals and two others in lower s levels. This electronic configuration and the three remaining unfilled p orbitals give rise to formal oxidation states of $+3$, $+5$, and -3. Unlike nitrogen, however, phosphorus often prefers the $+5$ state, since the energy difference between s and p electrons is reduced in second-row elements. Although phosphorus exhibits all of the indicated oxidation states, it generally does not exist as discrete monatomic ions. Instead, phosphorus generally prefers to be covalently bonded to the atoms surrounding it in a molecule or ion.

This propensity for covalent bonding is analogous to that of carbon and leads to a system of chemistry comparable to that of carbon. The chemistry of phosphorus is further complicated by the existence of several oxidation states, coordination numbers ranging from three to six, numerous possible orbital hybridizations, and the corresponding covalent geometrics. Phenomena common to organic chemistry, such as substitution series, isomerism, and polymerizations, are common to phosphorus as well. The possible substitutions of atoms or groups about phosphorus serve to extend the basis of this covalent system of chemistry.

Unlike carbon, phosphorus has only a limited ability to catenate (i.e., bond with itself). It has been indicated that the complicated allotropy of phosphorus is related in part to catenation structures. However, not many compounds are known to contain phosphorus-phosphorus bonding, and no extensive homologous series based on this type of bonding is known. Nevertheless, recent advances indicate that this is an area of investigation that may be expected to expand.

Phosphorus is able to form binary combinations with many of the chemically active elements. The well-established binary compounds of phosphorus are shown in Table 3.

The salt-like nature of phosphides obtained with the more electropositive elements is one of the few indications that a phosphide ion, P^{-3}, may exist.

The considerably more covalent phosphides of other metallic elements are generally classified as "hard-metal compounds" having some alloy-like properties but definite combining ratios. The metal phosphides are usually prepared by heating the metals with phosphorus in the absence of air. Unusual combining ratios and apparent anomalous oxidation states may be explained by phosphorus catenation or intermetallic bonding.

Many of the metalloids react directly with phosphorus. In some instances, however, it is necessary to synthesize these combinations by way of other chemical intermediates. In general, the metalloids form amorphous, laminar, or three-dimensional network structures in which phosphorus alternates with the other element in a polymeric structure.

Phosphorus combines spontaneously and exothermically with halogens and calcogens. The reactive products are usually simple volatile molecular species of pentavalent phosphorus—PX_5, P_4O_{10}, etc. If the reactions are controlled or modified, the lower oxidation state of phosphorus can be derived—PX_3, P_4O_6, etc. In the modified reaction with oxygen, the luminescence, from which phosphorus derives its name, may be observed. Appropriate synthetic sequences give rise to more complex halogen-calcogen compounds, such as $POCl_3$, and PF_2Cl_3. Pseudohalogens may replace halogens by substitution reactions. Many of the halogens and calcogen compounds of phosphorus are useful intermediates for the synthesis of organic or nitrogen derivatives of phosphorus. They may also serve as precursors to some of the more important phosphorus acids. Complete hydrolysis of phosphorus (V) halogen or calcogen compounds produces orthophosphoric acid,

$$\overset{\text{O}}{\underset{\|}{P}} (OH)_3.$$

Phosphoric anhydride, P_4O_{10}, is one of the common sources of this tribasic acid. Ionization of the acid or its many common salts produces the phosphate ion. Dehydration of the acid or its neutralization products causes polymerization of the phosphate structure through alternate phosphorus-oxygen arrangements. Linear, cyclic, and crosslinked homopolyphosphoric acids of their salts may be obtained. The use of such condensed phosphates as detergent builders and metal sequestering agents has led to extensive study of these systems. In addition, the phosphate group can be incorporated along with anhydrides of other acid systems into heteropolyacids. Other phosphorus (V) acids exist in which some or all of the oxy and hydroxy groups of phosphoric acid are replaced by fluorine atoms or organic groups,

e.g., $\overset{\text{O}}{\underset{\|}{F}}P(OH)_2$, $\overset{\text{O}}{\underset{\|}{F_2}}POH$, HPF_6, and $\overset{\text{O}}{\underset{\|}{R}}P(OH)_2$. Two other important acids of phosphorus may be viewed as similar substitution products—phosphorous acid, $\overset{\text{O}}{\underset{\|}{H}}P(OH)_2$, and hypophosphorous acid, $\overset{\text{O}}{\underset{\|}{H_2}}POH$. Dibasic phosphorous acid and its phosphite salts may

TABLE 3. RECOGNIZED BINARY COMPOUNDS OF PHOSPHORUS ARRANGED ACCORDING TO THE PERIODIC TABLE (HIGH-TEMPERATURE COMPOUNDS NOT STABLE AT ROOM TEMPERATURE ARE SHOWN IN BRACKETS).

1	2	3	4	5	6	7	8	9	10	11	12	13	14	15	16	17	18
H $[HP]$, P_2H, PO_2, P_4O_{10}, P_2O_5																	**He** Perhaps an interstitial compound
Li Li_2P_5, Li_3P	**Be** Be_3P_2											**B** BP, B_5P_3	**C** $[CP]$, C_2P	**N** $[PN]$, PN, P_3N_5	**O** $[PO]$, P_4O_6, PO_2, P_4O_{10}, P_2O_5	**F** PF_3, PF_5	**Ne** None
Na Na_2P_5, Na_3P	**Mg** Mg_3P_2											**Al** AlP	**Si** SiP	**P** $[P_2]$, black-P, red-P, P_4	**S** P_4S_3, P_4S_3, P_4S_7, P_4S_{10}	**Cl** PCl_3, PCl_5	**A** None
K K_2P_5	**Ca** Ca_3P_2	**Sc** ScP	**Ti** TiP_2, TiP, $TiP_{0.35}$, Ti_2P	**V** VP_2, VP, V_3P_2, V_2P, V_3P	**Cr** CrP_2, CrP, $CrP_{0.9}$, Cr_2P, Cr_3P	**Mn** MnP_3, MnP, Mn_3P_2, Mn_2P, Mn_3P	**Fe** FeP_2, FeP, Fe_2P, Fe_3P	**Co** $CoP_3(?)$, $Co_2P_3(?)$, CoP, $Co_3P_2(?)$, Co_2P, $Co_4P(?)$	**Ni** NiP, NiP_2, Ni_6P_5, Ni_2P, Ni_5P_2, Ni_3P	**Cu** CuP_2, $Cu_3P_2(?)$, $Cu_2P(?)$, Cu_3P	**Zn** ZnP_2, Zn_3P_2	**Ga** GaP	**Ge** GeP	**As** AsP	**Se** P_4Se_3, P_2Se_5	**Br** PBr_3, PBr_5	**Kr** None
Rb Rb_2P_5	**Sr** Sr_3P_2	**Y** YP	**Zr** ZrP_2, ZrP, $ZrP_{0.90}$, Zr_3P	**Nb** NbP_2, NbP, $NbP_{0.95}$	**Mo** MoP_2, MoP, Mo_3P	**Tc**	**Ru** RuP_2, RuP, Ru_2P	**Rh** RhP_3, RhP_2, Rh_5P_4, Rh_2P, Rh_3P	**Pd** PdP_2, Pd_5P_2, Pd_3P, Pd_5P	**Ag** AgP_3, AgP_2, Ag_3P	**Cd** CdP_2, Cd_3P_2	**In** InP	**Sn** SnP_3, Sn_3P_4, Sn_4P_3	**Sb**	**Te** Te_3P_2	**I** P_2I_4, PI_3	**Xe** None
Cs Cs_2P_5	**Ba** BaP_3, BaP_2, Ba_3P_2	**La*** LaP	**Hf**	**Ta** TaP_2, TaP	**W** WP_2, WP, W_2P, W_4P	**Re** ReP_3, ReP_2, ReP, Re_2P	**Os** OsP_2	**Ir** IrP_2, Ir_2P, Ir_3P	**Pt** PtP_2, $Pt_{20}P_7$	**Au** Au_2P_3, Au_3P	**Hg** $Hg_3P_2(?)$	**Tl** TlP_2, $Tl_3P(?)$	**Pb** Pb_3P_2, $PbP_2(?)$	**Bi**	**Po**	**At**	**Rn** None
Fr	**Ra**	**Ac****															

* Lanthanides:

Ce	Pr	Nd	Pm	Sm	Eu	Gd	Tb	Dy	Ho	Er	Tm	Yb	Lu
CeP	PrP	NdP		SmP	EuP	GdP	TbP	DyP	HoP	ErP	TmP	YbP	LuP

** Actinides:

Th	Pa	U	Np	Pu	Am	Cm	Bk	Cf	Es	Fm	Md	No	Lr
Th_3P_4, ThP		UP_2, U_3P_4, $U_2P_3(?)$, UP	Np_3P_4	PuP									

be derived from the hydrolysis of P_4O_6 or phosphorus (III) halides. Hypophosphites are derived, along with phosphine, PH_3, from the alkaline hydrolysis of phosphorus.

$$P + 4OH^- + 2H_2O \rightarrow 2H_2\overset{\displaystyle O}{\overset{\displaystyle \|}{P}}O^- + 2PH_3\uparrow$$

Phosphine, a highly toxic gaseous species, more closely resembles the phosphorus (III) halides than metal phosphides. Like ammonia and amines, phosphine and its organic-substituted derivatives form phosphonium ions with aprotic acids. In general, these are much stronger bases than PF_3, which forms metal complexes similar to the metal carbonyls.

Importance and Applications of Phosphorus and Its Compounds

Of the approximately 2,000,000 tons of phosphorus equivalent consumed each year in the United States—mostly in the form of phosphate derivatives—roughly 70% is consumed as phosphate fertilizers, 25% as industrial chemicals, and 5% as animal feed phosphate supplements. This total includes about 550,000 TPY (tons per year) of elemental phosphorus with the remainder divided between wet-process phosphoric acid and acidulated phosphate rock fertilizers.

Elemental Phosphorus. Less than 5% of the elemental phosphorus produced in the United States is consumed in elemental form. Roughly 22,000 TPY of P_4 are used in various pyrotechnic applications, such as tracers, incendiaries, fireworks, matches, etc. The remainder of the elemental phosphorus is used as an alloying agent (e.g., phosphor bronze), as a rodenticide, and for minor experimental purposes.

Another 30,000 TPY of elemental phosphorus are converted into simple, inorganic compounds by direct reaction of the elements. Roughly 14,000 TPY are converted to phosphorus sulfides for use in matches, insecticide manufacture, or as an oil additive, with another 9,000 TPY being used to produce various phosphorus halides, such as PCl_3, PCl_5, and $POCl_3$, for subsequent use in the synthesis of organophosphorus compounds, phosphate or phosphite esters, etc. Most of the remaining 7,000 TPY are burned to

phosphorus pentoxide for use in gas drying, conversion to organic phosphorus derivatives, and other applications.

The remainder and major portion of the elemental phosphorus is converted to the so-called "furnace grade," or high-purity, phosphoric acid. Because of its relatively high purity compared with the impure wet-process acid, it is used primarily in industrial applications that cannot tolerate the impurities found in wet-process acid. Almost 40,000 TPY of phosphorus equivalent are represented by direct uses of phosphoric acid, *per se*, in soft drinks, as a metal cleaner or phosphatizing agent, and other industrial applications. A growing application of furnace-grade phosphoric acid involves its use in liquid fertilizers.

Phosphate Salts. The largest consumer of phosphate salts is the fertilizer industry, with over 70% of the total phosphate rock tonnage going to supply needed phosphorus for the growth of crops, lawns, etc. The phosphorus in phosphate rock must be released from its fluorapatite structure in order to be available for assimilation by plants. The most inexpensive way to achieve this goal is to treat the fluorapatite with strong acid, such as sulfuric acid, phosphoric acid, or nitric acid, and convert it to water-soluble monocalcium phosphate, $Ca(H_2PO_4)_2$, as shown in the following oversimplified equations:

(1) $2Ca_5(PO_4)_3F + 7H_2SO_4 + 3H_2O \rightarrow$
$7CaSO_4 + 3Ca(H_2PO_4)_2 \cdot H_2O + 2HF$

(2) $Ca_5(PO_4)_3F + 7H_3PO_4 + 5H_2O \rightarrow$
$5Ca(H_2PO_4)_2 \cdot H_2O + HF$, or

(3) $2Ca_5(PO_4)_3F + 14HNO_3 + 3H_2O \rightarrow$
$7Ca(NO_3)_2 + 3Ca(H_2PO_4)_2 \cdot H_2O + 2HF.$

The products of reaction (1), monocalcium phosphate and calcium sulfate, are not separated but are sold and used as a fertilizer mixture termed "superphosphate;" (2) is known in the fertilizer trade as "triple superphosphate;" (3) the products of reaction are used as a fertilizer mixture termed "nitrophosphate." These products are often mixed with the other two important fertilizer ingredients—potash and ammonium salts—and sold as a complete "mixed fertilizer." Collectively, these products account for roughly two-thirds of the total phosphate fertilizer consumption of the United States. Much of the remaining one-third is accounted for by ammonium phosphates, primarily diammonium phosphate, produced by neutralizing phosphoric acid with ammonia.

The next largest application of phosphate salts is as a builder in synthetic detergents. This use represents nearly 60% of the total elemental phosphorus produced in the United States, with most of the market represented by a single product—sodium tripolyphosphate, $Na_5P_3O_{10}$. Other phosphate salts used in detergents, water softeners, and metal cleaners include tetrasodiumpyrophosphate, $Na_4P_2O_7$; tetrapotassium pyrophosphate, $K_4P_2O_7$; sodium metaphosphate, $(NaPO_3)_x$; trisodium phosphate, Na_3PO_4; and monosodium phosphate, NaH_2PO_4. Most of these phosphates are produced from furnace acid, but about 10% is produced from wet-process acid by special purification schemes. Certain phosphate salts are used as leavening agents in baking or as abrasives in dentifrices, and are produced from the high-purity furnace acid. Phosphate salts used as leavening agents include monocalcium phosphate, monosodium phosphate, and sodium acid pyrophosphate; the major phosphate salt used in toothpaste or tooth powder is dicalcium phosphate.

Another major application of calcium phosphate salts is as a phosphorus supplement to poultry and animal feeds to promote growth. This use represents about 5% of the total phosphate consumption of the United States and is supplied by neutralizing either furnace acid or defluorinated, wet-process acid with lime or limestone. The high fluorine content of regular wet-process acid would be toxic to animals and must be reduced to a P:F ratio of 100. This is generally accomplished by distilling HF from wet-process acid.

Biological Functions

Phosphorus is a basic requirement for the growth and health of plants and animals. Yet, in an outstanding example of nature's selectivity, phosphorus in the wrong form can be extremely toxic to the very life that depends on it. As hydroxyapatite, for example, phosphorus is a major constituent of teeth and bones; but elemental phosphorus is a very toxic material whose vapor is responsible for a dreaded tooth and bone disease known as phosphorus necrosis, or "phossy jaw." As adenosine triphosphate and other organic phosphates, phosphorus plays an indispensible role in the biochemical processes that govern life itself; yet many organic phosphorus compounds are among the most toxic substances known to man. These latter materials range from effective insecticides, such as parathion and malathion, to the dreaded "nerve gases" that inhibit choline esterace activity in the nervous system.

All biological processes that utilize phosphorus require it in the form of orthophosphate or a polyphosphate that hydrolyzes readily to the ortho form, such as pyrophosphate. This includes such processes as photosynthesis, glycolysis, fermentation, metabolism, and others. In photosynthesis, for example, adenosine triphosphate (ATP) is believed to be necessary for the fixation of carbon dioxide; ATP, in turn, is probably produced by the endergonic reaction of adenosine diphosphate (ADP) with an orthophosphate group coupled with the photolysis of water to provide the necessary oxidation. Although different mechanisms have been proposed to elucidate the photosynthetic cycle, the phosphate transfer step appears to have rather general acceptance. In the photosynthetic production of carbohydrates, carbon dioxide assimilation probably proceeds through the formation of phosphoglyceric acid; subsequent enzymatic reactions provide the necessary dephosphation steps leading to the carbohydrate end-products.

Phosphate transfer also plays a vital role in fermentation and glycolysis. Each of these anaerobic processes involves an enzyme-catalyzed phosphation of a 6-carbon entity and subsequent degradation to two, 3-carbon entities. Glycolysis, for example, proceeds through the initial reaction of glycogen with an orthophosphate to form glucose-1-phosphate; this is converted by a series of enzyme-catalyzed reactions, involving ATP phosphorylation, to fructose-1, 6-diphosphate. The remainder of the metabolic process involves cleavage and a series of phosphation-dephosphation reactions catalyzed by appropriate enzymes. Fermentation proceeds by an almost identical series of reactions, except that adenosine triphosphate provides the initial phosphation of glucose.

The metabolism of the higher forms of life requires fatty acids, amino acids, vitamins, etc., in addition to carbohydrates. In many instances, these more complex molecules are converted enzymatically to carbohydrates, and subsequent metabolic pathways involve phosphate transfers identical to those that occur in fermentation and glycolysis. In addition, however, substances known as phosphagens play an important role in the metabolic processes in muscle and other tissues. These are phosphoramidates contain-

$$\text{ing the } -N-\overset{\overset{\displaystyle NH_2^+}{\|}}{C}-\overset{\overset{\displaystyle O-}{|}}{N}-\overset{\overset{\displaystyle |}{P}}{=}O \text{ grouping and are}$$

formed by ATP phosphation.

In addition to its role in the biological reactions just described, the phosphate moiety is a critical ingredient in many other vital biological functions, such as aerobic metabolism, osmotic processes, and the synthesis of nucleic acids. Indeed, phosphate transfer is such a key step in so many biochemical reactions that phosphorus must be considered absolutely essential to life itself, comparable in importance to carbon, oxygen, hydrogen, nitrogen, and sulfur. It differs, however, in the manner in which it is supplied to these biological processes. Higher forms of life obtain phosphorus by ingestion of the lower forms of life, but a plant cannot obtain phosphorus from the atmosphere as it does carbon dioxide and water. Rather, it must be supplied by the soil in which the plants grow. The soil, in turn, is supplied with phosphorus by the by-products of the metabolic processes just described (e.g., the excrement of birds and animals) or by the end-products of still another biological process—the mineralization of tissue.

The mineralized tissues, teeth and bones, are formed in animals by the deposition of hydroxyapatite in an organic matrix that is composed principally of the protein, collagen. The exact mechanism by which this process occurs is not fully understood, but the initial step appears to be the accumulation of collagen in the form of a fibrous network. At certain locations in the body, called calcification sites, hydroxyapatite is apparently precipitated by the hydrolytic action of the enzyme phosphatase on a phosphate ester in the body fluid. The continuous deposition of hydroxyapatite in the collagen network, then, results in a mineralized tissue that becomes bones or teeth. (Tooth enamel involves a framework of keratin, instead of collagen.)

References

1. Gmelin "Handbuch der Anorganischen Chemie," Nummer 16, Achte Anflage, Teil A, B, and C, Weinheim/Bergstr., Verlag Chemie, Gmbh., 1965.
2. Grayson, Martin and Griffith, Edward J., "Topics in Phosphorus Chemistry," Vol. 1 and 2, New York, Interscience Publishers, Inc., 1964, 1965.
3. Kosolapoff, G. M., "Organophosphorus Compounds," New York, John Wiley and Sons, Inc., 1950.
4. Vam Wazer, John R., "Phosphorus and Its Compounds," Vol. 1 and 2, New York, Interscience Publishers, Inc., 1958.
5. Waggaman, William H., "Phosphoric Acid, Phosphates, and Phosphatic Fertilizers," ACS Monograph Series, New York, Reinhold Publishing Corp., 1952.

THOMAS P. WHALEY AND
JAMES W. CURRIER

PLATINUM

Platinum is a silvery white, soft, ductile metal highly valued because of its resistance to chemical attack and because of its considerable catalytic powers. It also gives its name to the group of six metals that occur together in the eighth group of the Periodic Table. These platinum metals occur together in varying proportions throughout the world and are to a large extent used together in a variety of valuable alloys. (See also **Palladium, Rhodium, Iridium, Ruthenium, Osmium**).

Discovery and History

The first known reference to what was undoubtedly native platinum occurs in the writings of Julius Caesar Scaliger (1557) as a substance found in mines in what is now Central America "which it has not hitherto been possible to melt by fire or by any of the Spanish arts". By the middle of the 18th

Century there were references to *platina* as an unwanted adjunct of gold in the mines of what is now Colombia. The name *platina* is thought to have been a derogatory diminutive of *plata*, silver. At about the same time specimens of this metal reached Europe. The first recorded experiments on it were conducted by the English physician, William Brownrigg and reported to the Royal Society in 1750. This publication stimulated other European scientists to investigate the new metal. As early as 1775 de l'Isle succeeded in melting platinum that had been freed from iron and sand by first dissolving native platinum with aqua regia, precipitating ammonium chloroplatinate, and then igniting this precipitate. Pierre-Francois Chabaneau developed and patented a process for producing malleable platinum in 1786. The first pure platinum appears to have been obtained in England in 1803 by W. H. Wollaston whose careful study of the solutions of crude platinum in aqua regia also led to the discovery of palladium and rhodium (q.v.). Wollaston's method for obtaining malleable platinum undoubtedly anticipated some of the techniques of modern powder metallurgy.

Occurrence

The three principal occurrences of platinum are in Canada, South Africa, and the U.S.S.R. In the Canadian deposits, which occur in the Sudbury district of Ontario, the platinum metals comprise about 0.5 ppm in copper-nickel sulfide ores associated with the igneous rock norite. Platinum and palladium are present in these in about the same proportions together with smaller amounts of the other platinum metals, as well as silver and gold. The principal South African deposits are in the Merensky Reef Horizon of the Bushveld Igneous Complex northwest of Johannesburg and west of Pretoria. Here the platinum metals comprise something of the order of 4 to 10 ppm in a rock that is predominately pyroxene, but invariably associated with chromite and sulfides of iron, copper, and nickel. The platinum is in the form of native metal alloyed with iron, or of sulfide, arsenide, or sulfarsenide. Platinum comprises 2/3 to 3/4 of the precious-metal content. In Russia enormous primary deposits of the platinum metals occur in highly basic rock formations such as peridotite in the Noril'sk region of Siberia, and in copper-bearing pentlandites (comparable to the Sudbury deposits) in the Kola peninsula. In addition, widespread secondary placer deposits principally of native platinum are found, with the greatest concentration of these in the Ural Mountains region.

Smaller deposits, chiefly placer, occur in Colombia, South America, and in the United States, especially in Alaska.

It has been estimated that the average abundance of platinum in the earth's crust is 0.01 gram per ton (which is about double that of gold).

Derivation

There are two aspects to the securing of pure platinum from these various raw materials. One, which applies to both Canadian and South African deposits, involves *extraction* of a concentrate of precious metals from a large body of ore. The other is the *refining* of the precious metals, which entails both separation and purification, from the concentrate or from native platinum, or even from scrap platinum (of which a considerable amount is treated annually for recovery of these valuable metals).

Extraction from the Canadian ores initially takes advantage of the strongly siderophile character of the precious metals. By controlling the oxidation of sulfur during preparation of a Bessemer matte a small amount of metallic nickel and copper is formed as a separate phase which acts as a collector of most of the precious metals. This metallic alloy is ground, and separated from the sulfides magnetically. It is treated with sulfur to produce a secondary matte and a secondary metallic phase that can be separated with considerable enrichment of the precious metal content. This concentrate is then subjected to electrolytic refining during which the platinum metals accumulate in the anode slimes. Leaching these sludges with acids to remove more base metals finally produces a concentrate containing about 50% platinum metals. Other residues from the refining of nickel also accumulate platinum metals, and these are also worked up for subsequent refining.

The South African ores are processed to

yield two products—a rich gravity concentrate, and a convertor matte which is worked up from the tailings from the gravity concentration. The former, containing about 22% platinum metals, is suitable for immediate refining. The latter must be smelted, the process employed resulting in nearly complete separation of copper and nickel. The platinum metals mainly accompany the latter. The nickel and copper are each refined electrolytically and the precious metals again collect in the anode slimes. The latter are roasted, leached with acids, and eventually produce a concentrate containing about 65% platinum metals and gold.

The refining of concentrates and other platiniferous materials is entirely a wet chemical operation. A preliminary separation of base metals may be required, and is achieved by smelting with litharge and fluxes to remove silica and base metals as a slag and to collect the precious metals in a lead button. Cupellation of this leaves a concentrated precious-metals alloy from which silver, if present, is removed by parting in nitric or sulfuric acid. All or part of the foregoing may be eliminated according to the composition of the material to be refined. The concentrate is then treated with aqua regia to bring most of the gold, platinum, and palladium into solution. Gold is then removed from the solution by precipitation with ferrous chloride, and purified.

Platinum is now separated from the chloride solution by the addition of ammonium chloride which produces a precipitate of ammonium chloroplatinate. Ignition of this leaves a crude platinum sponge which is again dissolved in aqua regia. A second precipitation of now purer ammonium chloroplatinate, followed by ignition, yields pure platinum sponge. Much valuable work has been done at the National Bureau of Standards in Washington in connection with refining the platinum metals to a very pure state for use as standards.

Melting

The melting point of platinum is 1769°C. Those who first encountered platinum from the Spanish colonies in South America were impressed with the difficulty involved in melting it. This difficulty was finally overcome by French scientists and goldsmiths from about 1775 onward. It is quite probable, however, that these early fusions of platinum were achieved with specimens containing sufficient impurity to lower the melting point to temperatures attainable with the available furnaces. Lavoisier in 1783 experienced greater success in melting this metal and a number of other substances regarded at that time as infusible by heating them on charcoal in a blast of oxygen gas.

Three principal phases have been recorded in the development of the technique of melting platinum. The first occurred following the invention, in 1801, of the oxyhydrogen blowpipe by Robert Hare in Philadelphia. The firm of J. Bishop, founded in Malvern, Pennsylvania, pioneered in the commercial fabrication of platinum apparatus in which the melting was done by the blowpipe. The second historical period began with the introduction by Deville and Debray in 1857 of a lime-block crucible or furnace in which platinum could be melted by an oxygas flame. From this time forward, melted platinum became readily available, and it assumed great importance following the introduction in 1862 of hardening of platinum by the addition of iridium. The third and contemporary period began in 1921 with the application to this work of the Ajax-Northrup high-frequency electric induction furnace.

Furnaces of this last type permit the attainment of high temperatures within the sample being melted without requiring a large surrounding thermal mass. Consequently, one may easily remove the crucible containing the melt, if packed within a silica sheath, for pouring. Mixing of alloys is accomplished automatically since electromagnetic forces in the melt bring about energetic stirring of the metal. Crucibles are mainly made of zirconia, or of silica or alumina lined with zirconia or thoria. The nature of induction heating is such that apparatus can easily be built in which the melting of metals can be carried out *in vacuo* or in an inert gas.

Physical Properties

A selection of physical properties of platinum is listed below. It is important to mention in connection with a number of these that, insofar as possible, they relate to the purest

TABLE 1. PHYSICAL PROPERTIES

Property	Units	Value
Symbol		Pt
Atomic number		78
Atomic weight	Cf. C–12	195.09
Stable isotopes		192 (0.78), 194 (32.8), 195
(with % relative abundance)		(33.7), 196 (25.4), 198,
		(7.23)
Density, 20°C	g/cc	21.45
Crystal lattice		Face-centered cubic
Lattice constant, a	Å	3.9231
Allotropic forms		None known
Melting point	°C	1769.3
	°K	2042.5
Boiling point (estimated)	°K	4100
Thermal conductivity	watts/cm/°C	0.73
Linear coefficient of thermal expansion		
20–100°C	per °C	9.1×10^{-6}
Specific heat, 0°C	cal/g/°C	0.03136
Heat capacity, C_p, 25°C	cal/mole/°C	6.18
Entropy, S, 25°C	cal/mole/°C	9.95
Latent heat of fusion	kcal/mole	4.7
Latent heat of evaporation	kcal/mole	135.0
Electrical resistivity, 0°C	μohm-cm	9.85
Temperature coefficient of resistance, 0–100°C	per °C	0.003925
Thermal neutron cross section	barns	9
Hardness (annealed)	Vickers units	40–42
Tensile strength (annealed)	tons/in²	9
Proportional limit (annealed)	tons/in²	2
Young's modulus (annealed)	tons/in²	1.2×10^4
Magnetic susceptibility, χ	cm³/g	0.9712×10^{-6}
Work function	ev	5.27
Thermionic function, A	amp/cm²/°K²	64

form of the metal that is available. In recent years it has been frequently shown that very minute traces of impurities, including the other platinum metals, cause significant changes in such properties as hardness, electrical resistance, etc. In view of the fact that the platinum metals have a marked tendency to pick up such gases as hydrogen and oxygen, it is not difficult to see how contamination may be overlooked. As with other metals it is also the case with platinum that physical properties often depend on the previous history of the specimen; hardness and other mechanical properties depend on the amount of cold working that has preceded the measurement.

The hardness of platinum is deliberately raised by the addition of alloying elements. Nickel, osmium, ruthenium, copper, gold,

silver, and iridium all produce considerable increase in hardness, the effect per unit weight of added element decreasing approximately in the order named. Rhodium and palladium produce much less increase in hardness than do the preceding metals. Because of their importance in producing thermocouples platinum and platinum alloys have been extensively studied from the point of view of producing thermal emf's, and numerous compilations of this data are published.

Platinum forms a number of alloys of commercial importance with copper, gold, iridium, rhodium, and ruthenium. Recently alloys of cobalt have received considerable attention because of their strong ferromagnetic properties. There is extensive, and in several instances complete, miscibility on the part of platinum with the elements of Groups VIII and IB. This is doubtless encouraged by the common crystal structure (face-centered cubic) and similar atomic size among many of these elements. Further ideas concerning the miscibility or otherwise among alloys of platinum and related metals have been recently summarized.[2] One unexpected feature among some of these alloys is that although complete miscibility may be found at high temperatures, appreciable miscibility gaps have been encountered in the same systems when prepared at lower temperatures.

Chemical Properties

Platinum is relatively inert to chemical attack by oxygen or many acids, and a number of its uses stem from this property. A factor governing chemical reactivity is the state of subdivision of the metal. Thus the sponge obtained by igniting ammonium chloroplatinate is more readily attacked than the compact metal; likewise, platinum dissolved in another metal like lead or silver is much more readily attacked. Platinum black is still more reactive and in addition displays remarkable catalytic properties.

Under usual conditions the metal is not attacked by single mineral acids, but it is dissolved by aqua regia with formation of H_2PtCl_6. Fluorine attacks hot platinum with formation of PtF_4; and chlorine forms a series of chlorides, $PtCl_2$, $PtCl_3$ and $PtCl_4$, when heated with platinum. Fused alkalis or alkaline salts, like cyanides or nitrites, attack the metal strongly. Also numerous elements like carbon, phosphorus, silicon, arsenic, etc., combine or alloy with platinum at elevated temperatures. Accordingly care must be taken in the laboratory to avoid heating compounds of these elements in platinum ware under reducing conditions. Also contact with sooty flames or unburned gas may lead to embrittlement of the platinum owing to formation of a carbide.

It has been known for a long time that platinum heated in air or oxygen to temperatures such as 1000°C loses weight, whereas if heated in a vacuum or in an inert gas such as argon no significant loss occurs. To account for this phenomenon various workers have postulated the formation of a volatile oxide of the metal, but this hypothesis has been questioned on the grounds that all known oxides of platinum have dissociation pressures of 1 atm at temperatures far below those at which the loss in weight occurs. Most recent work suggests that PtO_2, which probably exists as a thin film on platinum even at room temperature, is removed at high temperature partially by thermal decomposition and partially through evaporation of the oxide. There is evidence of a significant vapor pressure of PtO_2 molecules at high temperatures, and since the gaseous oxide (in contrast to the solid) is endothermic with respect to the elements it appears capable of surviving in equilibrium with platinum in the presence of oxygen.

Platinum metal, especially when heated, will absorb a considerable volume of gaseous hydrogen, and the gas will also diffuse through sheets of heated platinum. This phenomenon is exhibited to an even greater degree by palladium, and is discussed in greater detail under the entry for that element (q.v.).

The ground state of the gaseous atom is $5d^96s^1$. The first-stage ionization potential is 9.0 volts, only marginally higher than that of other transition elements. The standard electrode potential, E° (for $2e + Pt^{+2}(aq) = Pt(s)$) has been estimated to be +1.2 volts. The nobility of the metal, suggested by this value, can be linked mainly to the very high sublimation energy of the atoms.

Chemical Compounds

The principal valences of platinum are two and four, of which the second is more common. In the majority of its compounds platinum occurs in the form of complexes and there is scant evidence for the existence of simple aqueous metallic ions at all. In its complex ions bivalent platinum assumes a coordination number of 4 (square planar) and quadivalent platinum 6 (octahedral).

Chloroplatinic acid, H_2PtCl_6, is the compound formed by dissolution of the metal in aqua regia. It is a strong acid forming yellow or orange solutions. Both K_2PtCl_6 and $(NH_4)_2PtCl_6$ are sparingly soluble, and the former is sometimes used as a precipitating form in the analysis for potassium. Many organic amines also yield insoluble chloroplatinates which may be used for their characterization.

537

Platinic chloride, $PtCl_4$, is a red-brown crystalline mass formed by decomposing chloroplatinic acid by heat in a stream of HCl (165°C) or Cl_2 (369°C). It readily dissolves in water.

Platinous chloride, $PtCl_2$, is a brownish green solid formed by heating $PtCl_4$ in an atmosphere of chlorine (580°C). It is insoluble in water but dissolves in hydrochloric acid with formation of a dark brown solution of H_2PtCl_4.

Chloroplatinous acid, H_2PtCl_4, may be prepared in solution from $PtCl_2$ or by reduction of H_2PtCl_6 with sulfur dioxide.

Platinic oxide, PtO_2, may be prepared from H_2PtCl_6 by treating with Na_2CO_3, extracting the residue with acetic acid, and heating the yellow insoluble $H_2Pt(OH)_6$ below 100°C to yield the black dioxide. By heating PtO_2 more strongly the metal is obtained. The yellow "hydroxide" is known as platinic acid; it dissolves in either hydrochloric acid or alkali.

Platinous oxide, PtO, is obtained by careful heating of the black hydroxide formed when an alkali is added to a chloroplatinite. The gray oxide disproportionates if heated too strongly with formation of Pt and PtO_2. The hydroxide reacts with hydrochloric acid, disproportionating to give Pt and H_2PtCl_6.

Platinic sulfide, PtS_2, is obtained by treating hot acidified chloroplatinate solutions with H_2S. It is a black precipitate soluble in alkaline polysulfides. This is one form in which platinum may be precipitated for gravimetric analysis.

Barium platinocyanide, $BaPt(CN)_4 \cdot H_2O$, is of interest because of its use in making fluorescent screens for x-ray work.

The coordination chemistry of platinum possesses a number of interesting features of which perhaps the most striking is the remarkable stability of the bonds formed with many common ligands. Thus many substitution reactions are slow and proceed without the rearrangements that frequently accompany similar reactions of the more labile complexes of other metals. The integrity of these complexes has made possible many studies of geometrical isomerism and of the kinetics and mechanism of substitution reactions. The stability of platinum (II) complexes varies somewhat according to the donor atoms in the ligand; nitrogen (in aliphatic amines and in nitrite), halogens (except fluoride), cyanide, and heavy donor atoms, (e.g., phosphorus, sulfur, arsenic, selenium) give strong complexes, whereas oxygen and fluorine yield quite weak complexes. With platinum (IV) complexes maximum stability occurs where the ligand is bound through nitrogen atoms. The compounds are almost invariably diamagnetic, so that electron-spin pairing may be inferred for the platinum atoms in the complexes. The magnetic effects and the stereochemistry of the complexes suggest that the bonding orbitals are $5d6s6p^2$ and $5d^26s6p^3$ respectively; but in the complexes with the heavy donor atoms there is also evidence of π back-bonding from the metal to vacant orbitals in the valence shells of the heavy atoms. While the majority of platinum complexes contain one atom of this element per molecule or ion (mononuclear complexes), a number of polynuclear complexes have been characterized containing two or more atoms of platinum per structural unit.

Importance and Uses

In 1965 the annual world production of platinum metals amounted to almost 100 tons, of which platinum itself accounted for about 43 per cent. However, in most of its applications platinum is not consumed and, because of its high intrinsic value, considerable quantities are recovered annually from scrap, used appliances, spent catalysts, and the like. The price of platinum in recent years has been about $110 per troy ounce, though this figure has fluctuated somewhat according to demand.

The following figures show the distribution of sales of platinum to the principal consuming industries in the United States for the year 1965: chemical 32.0%, petroleum 19.7%, electrical 26.0%, glass 4.8%, jewelry and decorative 8.6%, dental and medical 6.5%, miscellaneous 2.5%. (Total sales 411,435 troy oz.)

Platinum is used mainly as the free metal. In finely divided form on a suitable carrier it serves as a catalyst for hydrogenation and dehydrogenation reactions in organic chemistry, for reforming of gasoline to improve the octane rating by isomerization, for the contact process for the manufacture of sulfuric acid (although this use is yielding to the less expensive vanadium pentoxide), and for the purification of gases by catalytic oxidation or hydrogenation. In the form of a gauze, and alloyed with rhodium, the metal catalyzes the oxidation of ammonia to nitric oxide for the manufacture of nitric acid, and also the synthesis of hydrogen cyanide from air, ammonia, and methane.

Very pure platinum is used in resistance thermometers and in thermocouples. An alloy with 10% (sometimes 13%) rhodium forms the second element in the latter. The same alloy is also used in windings for high-temperature electric furnaces, and for the spinnerets and bushings used in the production of rayon and glass fiber. Other applications in the chemical industry include the lining of small pressure vessels, or for the fabrication of larger reaction vessels from platinum-clad nickel or copper.

Alloyed usually with iridium the metal is used for jewelry, laboratory ware, electrodes (especially anodes for electrolytic oxidations), and electrical contacts. Some platinum is used in dental alloys with palladium. An alloy with 4% tungsten is used in certain spark electrodes and for the grids of radar tubes. In recent years certain alloys with cobalt have proven capable of providing powerful permanent magnets, and these have found application in hearing aids, self-winding watches, and so forth.

References

1. Platinum Metals Review. A quarterly survey of research on the platinum metals and of developments in their application in industry. Johnson, Matthey and Co. Ltd., Hatton Garden, London, E.C.1, England, 1957.
2. Hume-Rothery, W., *Ibid*, **10**, 94, (1966).
3. Weeks, M. E., "The Discovery of the Elements," 6th Edition, pp. 407–453, Easton, Penna., Journal of Chemical Education, 1957.
4. McBryde, W. A. E., "Platinum Metals," pp. 304–335 in "Rare Metals Handbook," 2nd Edition, C. A. Hampel, Editor, New York, Reinhold Publishing Corporation, 1961.
5. Cotton, F. A., and Wilkinson, G., "Advanced Inorganic Chemistry," pp. 845–860, New York, Interscience Publishers, 1962.

W. A. E. McBRYDE

PLATINUM METALS

The platinum metals are members of the transition or *d*-block elements and their relationship to each other and to neighboring elements in the periodic classification is shown in the table on the next page. Group relationships are not as clear-cut in this region of the Periodic Table as they are for the regular or *s*- and *p*- block elements.

Among the platinum metals the most significant kinship is seen in the vertically arranged pairs, though a number of important differences are seen between these and the ferrous metals of the first long period which lie above them. Certain evident trends among each horizontal triad in Group VIII are carried along to the corresponding coinage metal in Group IB. In general the platinum metals have high melting points and small atomic volumes. Melting points, hardness, and mechanical strength tend to peak among the transition elements at Group VI (Cr, Mo, W) and with exceptions for manganese and technetium, to decrease progressively in each period until the end of the transition series at Group IIB (Zn, Cd, Hg). These differences have been attributed to a progressive decrease in the number of electrons that are available for bonding among the atoms in the solid state. The bonding electrons are in orbitals that have been hybridized from *s*, *p*, and *d* states. The amount of *d* character that can be contributed to these bond orbitals presumably falls off as electrons become paired in atomic *d* orbitals or otherwise fail to participate in metallic bonding. The trend in properties within each triad of platinum metals accords

	Fe	*Co*	*Ni*
M. P.	1528°C	1493°C	1452°C
Hardness	~50	124	~70
Ox. State	**2,3,6**	**2,3**	2
	Ru	*Rh*	*Pd*
M. P.	2310°C	1960°C	1552°C
Hardness	200-350	100-120	40-42
Ox. State	**2,3,4,6,7,8**	3	**2,4**
	Os	*Ir*	*Pt*
M. P.	3050°C	2443°C	1769°C
Hardness	300-670	200-240	40-42
Ox. State	**2,3,4,6,8**	**2,3,4,6**	**2,4**

	Group VII	Group VIII			Group IB
	Manganese	*Iron*	*Cobalt*	*Nickel*	*Copper*
Atomic Number	25	26	27	28	29
Atomic Weight	54.938	55.847	58.933	58.71	63.54
	Technetium	*Ruthenium*	*Rhodium*	*Palladium*	*Silver*
Atomic Number	43	44	45	46	47
Atomic Weight	—	101.07	102.905	106.4	107.870
	Rhenium	*Osmium*	*Iridium*	*Platinum*	*Gold*
Atomic Number	75	76	77	78	79
Atomic Weight	186.2	190.2	192.2	195.09	196.967

with these ideas in that platinum or palladium are the softest and lowest melting and osmium or ruthenium the hardest and highest melting. Hardness refers to annealed metal in Vickers units. The most common oxidation states are shown in heavy type. A number of other oxidation states are known but are all considered rare.

Similar considerations lead to the inference that among the Group VIII elements there is a trend to a greater effective number of valency electrons in each succeeding period. Thus there is evidence of increasing atomic cohesion in passing down each vertical triad manifest in such properties as melting point and hardness. Complementary evidence to the same effect is provided by the common oxidation states assumed by these elements in their compounds. Higher oxidation states assume greater importance among those elements that lie to the left or lower in the foregoing table.

The platinum metals are all "noble" in the sense that the massive metal resists oxidation, particularly into aqueous solution. The nobility is believed to be due mainly to the very strong cohesion of the atoms in the solid state. The metals show much increased activity in finely divided form, and in highly dispersed condition such as the "blacks" they exhibit remarkable catalytic powers. The chemical compounds of the platinum metals are distributed over a wide variety of oxidation states of which the more common are listed in the table given previously. The aqueous solution chemistry is characterized by a marked tendency to form stable complex ions, and in fact simple aqueous ions are uncommon, and for some of the elements unknown.

W. A. E. McBryde

PLUTONIUM

Plutonium (Pu), atomic number 94, is one of the radioactive man-made elements. Although it was not the first element to be created by man (technetium was produced in 1937 and astatine and neptunium in 1940), it was the first to be produced synthetically in amounts large enough to be visible to the unaided eye.

Plutonium has a number of remarkable properties. For example, it is the only element known to have as many as six different crystalline forms; two of these allotropes contract rather than expand when heated. The metal's thermal and electrical conductivities, which are exceptionally low, increase with increasing temperature over a considerable temperature range. Natural radioactivity causes self-heating, so that large pieces of the metal may have to be cooled to be kept from overheating or even melting. Plutonium is fissionable by both high and low-energy neutrons, and thus has the potential of being an important nuclear fuel—possibly the most important, since its use could have the effect of greatly extending the world's energy resources. Plutonium is also one of the most dangerous substances known, its permissible contamination levels being lower than for any other substance. In spite of the difficulties of working with plutonium, however, this unusual element has been the object of intensive study since it was first produced, and a large amount of information about it has been amassed in only a few years.

History

Plutonium was discovered in February, 1941, when A. C. Wahl, G. T. Seaborg and J. W. Kennedy first isolated and identified

540

the isotope plutonium-238 at the University of California. With the added collaboration of E. Segrè, the fissionable isotope plutonium-239 was soon found, and later in 1941 a project to develop a production method for plutonium to be used in a nuclear weapon was established at the University of Chicago. By August, 1942, only about 50 micrograms of plutonium-239 in combination with uranium and fission products had been produced by cyclotron bombardment, and about one microgram was isolated. Within a few months, in November, 1943, some plutonium trifluoride was reduced to form the first plutonium metal, a few micrograms of metallic beads.

Cyclotron bombardment was obviously incapable of producing enough plutonium to make a nuclear weapon. The solution to this problem came in December, 1942, when E. Fermi and his associates achieved a self-sustaining nuclear chain reaction in a pile or reactor of uranium and graphite at the University of Chicago. Soon, plutonium-producing reactors were constructed at Oak Ridge, Tennessee and at Richland, Washington, and the secret Project Y, to build the atomic bomb, was established at Los Alamos, New Mexico. That project led to the successful explosion of the first atomic bomb in the desert 60 miles northwest of Alamogordo, New Mexico, on July 16, 1945.

Formation

The principal sources of plutonium in the United States have been the Richland reactors and the more recent reactors of the Savannah River Plant near Aiken, South Carolina. In such nuclear reactors fueled with natural uranium (99.3% uranium-238 and 0.7% uranium-235), neutrons produced by fission of uranium-235 are captured by the uranium-238 to yield plutonium-239 by the "pile reactions":[7]

$$_{92}U^{235} + n \rightarrow \text{Fission Products} + 2.5n + 200 \text{ MeV}$$

$$_{92}U^{238} +$$
$$n \rightarrow _{92}U^{239} \xrightarrow[23.5m]{\beta-} _{93}Np^{239} \xrightarrow[2.35d]{\beta-} _{94}Pu^{239}$$

After the plutonium-239 has been formed, continued neutron bombardment converts some of that isotope to plutonium-240 and some of the 240 to 241 or higher isotopes. The amounts of higher isotopes thus produced with the plutonium-239 depend on the type of reactor and how it is operated but rarely make up more than a few per cent of the total plutonium.

Plutonium has 15 known isotopes ranging in atomic weight from 232 to 246. Plutonium-239 is currently the isotope of greatest importance, because it is readily fissionable, has the relatively long half-life of 24,360 years, and can be produced in amounts large enough to be of practical use.

The known isotopes of plutonium with their radioactive decay characteristics, and some methods of production, are given in page 745 in the article on **Transuranium Elements.**

Extremely minute amounts of plutonium have been found in some concentrated ores of uranium, to the extent of a few parts of plutonium-239 per trillion or more parts of the concentrate. This plutonium must have been formed by the natural nuclear reactions that go on continuously,[10] since the half-life of plutonium-239 is so short as compared with the estimated age of the earth that any plutonium-239 which existed when the earth was young could hardly still exist today.

Derivation

Approximately one atom of plutonium-239 can be formed for each atom of uranium-235 undergoing fission. Thus it is clear, from the relative amounts of uranium-238 and -235 in natural uranium, that a very small amount of plutonium will be present with a very large amount of uranium. Actually, grams of plutonium are recovered from tons of uranium. The intense radiation from the fission products that are formed with the plutonium (see the pile reactions above) further complicates the recovery process by dictating that the operations be performed remotely from behind thick shielding.

When the reactor fuel has been irradiated for a sufficient time to form an appreciable amount of plutonium-239, the irradiated fuel elements, consisting of uranium, plutonium, and fission products, are removed from the reactor and stored under water for 2 to 4 months. During this "cooling period," the highly radioactive fission products (mainly xenon-133 and iodine-131) decay and most of the neptunium-239, which was initially formed from the uranium-238, is transformed to plutonium-239.

Any of a number of methods or combination of methods may then be used to recover the plutonium from the fission products and uranium. Chemical methods, now generally used in large-scale operations, involve separation and recovery of a plutonium salt, usually by selective precipitation or solvent extraction. Such methods are possible because plutonium and uranium can exist in different oxidation states—and thus have different chemical properties—in the same solution. Pyrometallurgical processes, which include distillation, molten-metal extraction, and salt extraction, are possible and do not involve the handling of large volumes of solutions but must be performed at high temperatures. They appear to hold promise for processing the highly irradiated fuels which are likely to be associated with the high-power-density reactors of the future.

Metal Preparation

The plutonium salt, which is the product from most of the separation processes currently in use, must be further processed before the element can be obtained in metallic form. Generally the metal is produced by the reduction of plutonium fluoride with calcium metal in an inductively heated pressure chamber (bomb reduction process), and is typically 99.87% pure. Higher purity material, 99.98 or 99.99%, is produced by electrorefining the bomb-reduced metal.

Plutonium metal must be melted in vacuum or an inert atmosphere because of its reactivity in air at high temperature. Furthermore, plutonium has strong reducing properties which limit the choice of crucible materials to the more stable oxide, carbide, nitride, boride, and silicide compounds, or such refractory metals as tantalum and tungsten. Arc melting is satisfactory for producing small ingots of plutonium and its alloys, and eliminates the problem of selecting a suitable crucible material. Graphite or metal molds that have been coated with calcium fluoride are often used in casting plutonium.[1]

Unalloyed plutonium (alpha phase) is hard and brittle at room temperature and has machining characteristics similar to those of cast iron. At slightly higher temperatures, the unalloyed metal transforms to beta phase, which is sufficiently plastic to be worked. Delta phase, the allotropic form in which unalloyed plutonium normally exists between 310 and 452°C, is stabilized to room temperature and below by the addition of small amounts of any of several alloying elements; gallium, aluminum and cerium are examples. Such alloys are soft and ductile at room temperature and have machining characteristics similar to those of aluminum. Unalloyed plutonium is riveted, threaded, interlocked, and shrink fitted but cannot be welded successfully by current techniques because of the large volume changes that accompany the allotropic transformations. The alloyed delta phase, however, may be fusion welded by resistance or tungsten-inert-gas methods without appreciable loss of strength.[5]

Physical and Mechanical Properties

Data concerning some physical constants and properties of plutonium are given in Tables 1 through 3.

TABLE 1. SOME PHYSICAL CONSTANTS OF PLUTONIUM

Atomic number	94
Isotopic mass, Pu-239 (physical scale)	239.13
Isotopic mass, Pu-239 (chemical scale)	239.06
Atomic weight (chemical scale)	239.11†
Melting point	641°C
Boiling point	3327°C
Vapor pressure, 1120-1520°C	$\mathrm{Log_{10}Pmm} = (-17{,}420/t + 273.18) + 7.794$
Average heat of vaporization, 1120-1520°C	79.7 kcal/g-atom
Heats of transformation (ΔH):	$\alpha \rightarrow \beta$ 900 ± 20 cal/g-atom
	$\beta \rightarrow \gamma$ 160 ± 10 ,,
	$\gamma \rightarrow \delta$ 148 ± 15 ,,
	$\delta \rightarrow \delta'$ 10 ± 10 ,,
	$\delta' \rightarrow \epsilon$ 444 ± 10 ,,
	$\epsilon \rightarrow$ liquid 676 ± 10 ,,

† Computed weight for plutonium containing 95.37 (atomic) % Pu-239, 4.43% Pu-240, and 0.20% Pu-241.

TABLE 2. CRYSTAL STRUCTURES OF THE PLUTONIUM ALLOTROPES

Allotrope	Stability range, °C	Crystal Structure	Unit-cell dimensions, Å (at the indicated temperature)	Number of atoms/unit cell	Calculated density, g/cc
Alpha	< 115	Simple monoclinic	at 21°C a = 6.183 ± 0.001 b = 4.822 ± 0.001 c = 10.963 ± 0.001 β = 101.79° ± 0.01°	16	19.86
Beta	~ 115–~ 200	Body-centered monoclinic	at 190°C a = 9.284 ± 0.003 b = 10.463 ± 0.004 c = 7.859 ± 0.003 β = 92.13° ± 0.03°	34	17.70
Gamma	~ 200–310	Face-centered orthorhombic	at 235°C a = 3.159 ± 0.001 b = 5.768 ± 0.001 c = 10.162 ± 0.002	8	17.14
Delta	310–452	Face-centered cubic	at 320°C a = 4.6371 ± 0.0004	4	15.92
Delta-prime	452–480	Body-centered tetragonal	at 465°C a = 3.34 ± 0.01 c = 4.44 ± 0.04	2	16.00
Epsilon	480–641	Body-centered cubic	at 490°C a = 3.6361 ± 0.0004	2	16.51

TABLE 3. SPECIFIC HEATS, C_p, OF PLUTONIUM (after Kay and Loasby[9])

Phase	C_p, cal/g-atom	Temperature, °K	Phase	C_p. cal/g-atom	Temperature, °K
Alpha	8.0	260	Delta	9.0	600
	8.84	340		9.0	700
			Delta-prime	No true value	—
Beta	8.20	413			
	8.46	463	Epsilon	8.4	773
				8.4	873
Gamma	8.58	503	Liquid†	9.9	923
	8.85	543		10.0	948

† Values for the liquid reported by Loasby.[11]

The unusual expansion and contraction behavior of plutonium is illustrated in the idealized curve of Fig. 1, where it may be

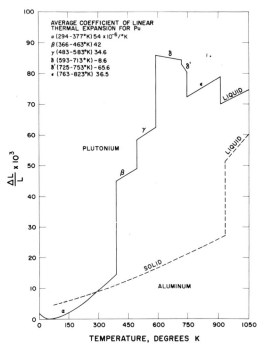

FIG. 1. The idealized expansion behaviors of plutonium and aluminum.

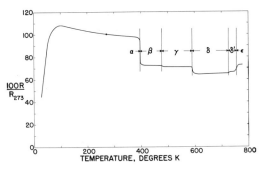

FIG. 2. The electrical resistivity of plutonium between 26° and 774°K. (For the data in the figure, the resistivity at 273°K is 146.45$\mu\Omega$-cm.)

compared with the simpler behavior of aluminum. Notably, the delta and delta-prime allotropes contract rather than expand when heated. When plutonium melts, its density increases about 2.5%, changing from 16.24 g/cc for the solid phase to 16.66 g/cc for the liquid phase. Then as the liquid metal is heated its density decreases linearly[14] according to the expression: $\rho = (17.63 - 1.52 \times 10^{-3}t) \pm 0.04$, where t is in °C.

The electrical resistivity of plutonium at room temperature is exceptionally high for a metal and decreases with increasing temperature over a considerable range, as shown in Fig. 2. Below the resistivity maximum, near 100°K, the resistivity decreases rapidly with decreasing temperature. The residual resistivity at 3°K of crack-free, high-purity (99.99%) plutonium has been found to be about 8 $\mu\Omega$-cm.[3] At temperatures in the

vicinity of 20°K or lower, the accumulation of radiation damage due to the alpha activity causes the resistivity of plutonium to increase with time. The rate of resistivity increase at constant low temperature varies with the isotopic composition of the metal, but for plutonium containing 94.58% plutonium-239 5.10% plutonium-240, and 0.32% plutonium-241, a rate of about 0.07 microhm-cm per hour has been observed. When the radiation-damaged metal is heated, the damage is annealed in at least two stages, roughly at 80 and 160°K, so that at room temperature the resistivity has regained its normal value.[4] Plutonium has not been found to be superconducting down to 0.5°K.[12]

The thermal conductivity of plutonium is low. Values as low as 0.03 watt/cm/°K[13] and as high as 0.08 watt/cm/°K[8] have been reported for alpha phase, but recent work[2] suggests that the value is 0.065 at room temperature and decreases to 0.030 at 80°K. The corresponding Lorenz numbers are 3.13 and 5.51×10^{-8} watt-ohm per °K.[2]

The viscosity of plutonium in the range 645-950°C may be calculated from the expression: $\text{Log}_{10}\ \eta = 0.672\ (1/T) + 0.037$, where η is in centipoises and T is in $°K \times 10^{-3}$. At its melting point, plutonium has a viscosity of 6.0 centipoises.[6]

The surface tension of plutonium has been predicted from the known physical constants of the metal to be in the range 490-580 dynes per cm.[15]

Typical values for some mechanical and elastic properties of plutonium at room temperature are presented in Table 4.

TABLE 4. TYPICAL VALUES FOR SOME ELASTIC AND MECHANICAL PROPERTIES OF PLUTONIUM AT ROOM TEMPERATURE

Young's modulus	14×10^6 psi
Shear modulus	6×10^6 psi
Poisson's ratio	0.17
Compressibility	2×10^{-6}/bar
Hardness, DPN	~ 290 kg/mm²
Tensile properties:	
Yield strength	40,000 psi
Ultimate strength	60,000 psi
Elongation	0.1%
Compressive properties:	
Yield strength	107,000 psi
Ultimate strength	175,000 psi
Decrease in length	23%

Chemical Properties and Compounds

Plutonium has four valence states: (III), (IV), (V), and (VI). States (III) and (IV) are the ones most commonly observed, both in solution and in solid compounds, and are more stable than the corresponding states in uranium and neptunium. In work with aqueous solutions, precautions must be taken to ensure that only one valence state is present, since all four can coexist in equilibrium. State (V) is relatively unstable, tending to disproportionate to (IV) and (VI). State (VI) exists in strongly oxidizing solutions as plutonyl ion, PuO_2^{++}; only a few compounds such as PuF_6 have been made.

Metallic plutonium dissolves readily in concentrated hydrochloric, hydroiodic, and perchloric acids. It does not react readily with strong sulfuric and nitric acids or with aqueous bases such as sodium hydroxide solutions. Dilute acids attack the metal, but an insoluble residue, thought to consist of polymeric plutonium hydroxides or hydrous oxides, is formed.

At high temperatures, all the common gases react with plutonium metal: oxygen forms various oxides; carbon monoxide, carbides; carbon dioxide, carbides and oxides; ammonia and nitrogen, nitrides; the halogens and halogen acids, halides; and hydrogen forms hydrides. Water vapor in excess forms PuO_2, and in limited amounts forms mixtures of PuO_2 and plutonium hydride.

Plutonium forms stable compounds with all the nonmetallic elements, except the rare gases. Most of the simple, inorganic compounds of plutonium are more stable than the analogous compounds of other metals. Nearly all the solid plutonium compounds can be converted to PuO_2 by ignition in air at 1000°C.

Alloying Behavior

Plutonium forms alloys and intermetallic compounds with most of the metals. Exceptions are lithium, sodium, and potassium (perhaps rubidium and cesium) of the alkali metals; calcium, strontium, and barium of the alkaline earth metals; and europium and ytterbium of the rare earth metals, all of which are immiscible with both solid and liquid plutonium. The refractory metals, tungsten, tantalum, molybdenum, niobium, chromium, and vanadium are soluble in liquid plutonium but are insoluble or only slightly soluble in solid plutonium.

Applications

Plutonium, besides providing the destructive force of atomic weapons, has the constructive capability of supplying much of the power that man finds so increasingly important. Fast reactors operating on plutonium-bearing fuels, and producing as much or more plutonium than they consume, appear to hold promise for the future. Ways to harness plutonium efficiently for this use are being developed.

Nuclear explosives are being considered for excavating large amounts of earth economically, as might be necessary in constructing large, sea-level, interoceanic canals. Although the actual work would likely be done by the hydrogen fusion reaction, because of the immense amounts of power required, it is possible that fissioning of plutonium would be used to trigger the fusion reaction.

The isotope plutonium-238, because of its high alpha activity (half-life 86.4 years) and availability, is being considered for use as the power source in some of the isotope power generators now being developed, and is the source of power in a small navigational satellite which was placed in earth orbit in June, 1961. The heat from the radioactive disintegration of plutonium-238 is also being utilized in an isotope-heated SCUBA suit currently under development, and a plutonium-238 fueled pacemaker that can be implanted in the bodies of heart patients has been proposed.

The large fission cross section of plutonium makes the metal useful as a threshold detector for determining the spectra of neutrons having energies greater than 4 kv. The large neutron-capture cross section is also utilized in the production of transplutonium elements and higher isotopes of plutonium. Irradiating plutonium in a nuclear reactor has resulted in the production of modest amounts of elements having atomic numbers as high as 100.

The compound $PuBe_{13}$ is an excellent, relatively stable, low-flux source of neutrons.

Precautions in Handling

Two special types of precautions must be taken by those who work with plutonium. One is a consequence of the element's fissionable nature and concerns criticality; the other arises mainly from the alpha-emitting property and relates to toxicity.

If a sufficient amount of plutonium is brought together, a critical mass is formed which emits lethal amounts of neutrons and gamma rays. In addition, the large amount of heat generated in a short time may cause the reaction to approach explosive proportions, depending on the rapidity with which the critical mass is formed and the closeness of its confinement.

The amount of plutonium necessary to form a critical mass depends on the shape of the mass and the proximity of any neutron reflecting or neutron absorbing substances, but is only a few pounds for a solid block of metal and about one-tenth that amount for plutonium in aqueous solution. Therefore, in a plutonium production plant, or wherever large quantities of plutonium are handled, elaborate precautions are taken to prevent the unintentional formation of a critical mass. Tanks and tubing are of such dimensions and capacities that a critical mass cannot be formed in them. Batch processing, in which considerably less than a critical amount of plutonium is carried completely through one operation before another batch is admitted to the same operation, may be utilized. Careful attention is paid to the sizes and shapes of plutonium pieces being worked with

or assembled in storage areas, strict accounting shows the amount of plutonium on hand at any given time in various areas of the plant, and gamma radiation detectors provide automatic warning of the presence of any above-normal gamma-ray activity.

In addition to the criticality hazard, the highly toxic nature of plutonium must also be considered. This toxicity arises from the element's alpha radioactivity and its tendency to concentrate chemically and remain in the liver and in the blood-forming sections of the bones where it can cause serious body damage. The alpha radiation given off by plutonium cannot penetrate unbroken human skin, but particles of plutonium can enter the body through abrasions or cuts in the skin, through ingestion, and through inhalation, and plutonium in solution may be absorbed through the skin.

The maximum permissible body burden of plutonium, or that amount which an adult is thought to be capable of maintaining indefinitely in his body without suffering significant body damage, is now set at 0.04 microcurie (0.6 microgram). The corresponding limit on the amount of plutonium that can be safely allowed in the air people breathe (maximum allowable concentration) is 0.00003 microgram per cubic meter of air.

The toxicity hazard, which is aggravated by plutonium's reactivity and tendency to produce fine particles of oxide, makes strict control of radioactive contamination imperative in a plutonium operation. This control is usually achieved by confining the plutonium, and the equipment used in working with it, in glove boxes or other types of enclosures and by providing special alpha detection equipment and health physics personnel to search continually for overtolerance plutonium contamination.

References

1. Anderson, J. W., and Maraman, W. J., *Trans. Am. Foundrymen's Soc.*, **70**, 1057 (1963).
2. Andrew, J. F., *J. Phys. Chem. Solids,* **28**, 577 (1967).
3. Elliott, R. O., Unpublished data, Los Alamos Scientific Laboratory, 1966.
4. Elliott, R. O., and Olsen, C. E., *J. App. Phys.*, **35**, 1925 (1964).

5. Henry, C. R., "Plutonium and Uranium as Engineering Materials," Paper 65-MET-20, presented at the Metals Engineering and Production Engineering Conference, Berkeley, Calif., June 9–11, 1965 of the American Society of Mechanical Engineers, New York, The American Society of Mechanical Engineers, 1965.
6. Jones, L. V., Ofte, D., Rohr, W. G., and Wittenberg, L. J., *Trans. ASM*, **55**, 819 (September 1962).
7. Katz, J. J., and Seaborg, G. T., "The Chemistry of the Actinide Elements," Chap. 7, pp. 239–330, New York, John Wiley and Sons, Inc., 1957.
8. Kay, A. E., in "Discussion, Replies and Comments," p. 107 in "Plutonium 1960," E. Grison, W. B. H. Lord, and R. D. Fowler, (Eds.), London, Cleaver-Hume Press Ltd., 1961.
9. Kay, A. E., and Loasby, R. G., *Phil. Mag.*, **9**, 37, (1964).
10. Levine, C. A., and Seaborg, G. T., *J. Am. Chem. Soc.*, **73**, 3278 (1951).
11. Loasby, R. G., in "Discussion, Replies and Comments," p. 98 in "Plutonium 1960," E. Grison, W. B. H. Lord, and R. D. Fowler, (Eds.), London, Cleaver-Hume Press Ltd., 1961.
12. Meaden, G. T., and Shigi, T., *Cryogenics*, **4**, 90 (1964).
13. Sandenaw, T. A., and Gibney, R. B., *J. Phys. Chem. Solids*, **6**, 81 (1958).
14. Serpan, C. Z., Jr., and Wittenberg, L. J., *Trans. Met, Soc. AIME*, **221**, 1017 (1961).
15. Taylor, J. W., private communication, Atomic Energy Research Establishment, Harwell (1956).

W. N. MINER AND F. W. SCHONFELD

POLONIUM

Polonium, atomic number 84, was discovered in 1898 by Pierre and Marie Curie and named after Mme. Curie's native land, Poland. It was the first element to be discovered as a direct result of its radioactivity, and at the time there was some question as to whether it was indeed a new element. In their first attempt the Curie's separated polonium from about a ton of pitchblende and succeeded in concentrating it to such an extent that its specific radioactivity was some 400 times that of uranium, showing that it was not uranium or thorium. They showed that while it coprecipitated with bismuth sulfide, it was more volatile than the latter on vacuum sublimation. Marckwald (1902-03) noted the chemical similarity to tellurium and suggested the name "radiotellurium."

Radium was also discovered by the Curie's later in 1898 and during the first few years of this century radiochemists and physicists worked on the genealogy of radium decay products. Polonium was shown to be the last radioactive member of the radium series and Rutherford designated it radium F(RaF). About this same time radium was shown to be a new element distinct from barium (whose chemistry it followed), both by chemical means and by its different atomic spectrum. Mme. Curie measured an atomic weight for radium of about 225 (now known to be 226.05), and from this value and the known decay sequence the approximate atomic weight of polonium could be deduced. Thus it was not until about 1905 that polonium was generally recognized as a new element and the homolog of selenium and tellurium predicted by Mendeleev in 1889. It has no known stable isotopes and is one of the rarest naturally occurring elements.

It was the isotope Po^{210}, a 138.4-day α-emitter, which led to the discovery of the element. This isotope is a member of the uranium $(4n + 2)$ natural radioactive decay series. Some 27 isotopes (masses 192 through 218) of polonium are now known, seven of which are found in nature in the three naturally occurring $(4n, 4n + 2$ and $4n + 3)$ radioactive decay series: Po^{210} (RaF), Po^{211} (AcC'), Po^{212} (ThC'), Po^{214} (RaC'), Po^{215} (AcA), Po^{216} (ThA) and Po^{218} (RaA). While Po^{210} is the longest lived naturally occurring isotope (the others having half-lives of from minutes to microseconds) two longer lived isotopes have been produced artificially. These are the 2.9-year α-emitter Po^{208} which may be produced by a (p,2n) reaction on Bi^{209} and the 103-year α-emitter Po^{209} which may be produced by a (d,2n) reaction on Bi^{209}.

Interest in Po^{210} for Neutron and α-Particle Sources

In the early 1940's members of the Manhattan Project asked the Monsanto Chemical Company to investigate various alpha and neutron sources and their means of production in connection with the atomic energy program. This it did at its Dayton (Ohio) facility. It soon became apparent that Po^{210} is almost a unique α-emitter in that: (1) it is relatively free of other types of radiation (only one 0.8 MeV γ-ray per 100,000 α-particles plus some x-rays of much lower energy); (2) it decays directly to a stable isotope; (3) it is found in nature and it can be produced artificially by neutron irradiation; (4) it has a decay half-life short enough to provide a high specific activity and long enough that it does not decay excessively rapidly for certain purposes; (5) it has a high relative volatility which facilitates purification of the element and preparation-by-volatilization of neutron sources and alpha sources; and (6) it emits a sufficiently energetic α-particle (5.305 MeV) to allow a reasonably high rate of (α,n) reactions on light elements.

Two general large-scale sources of Po^{210} were considered by the Dayton Project in 1943:

(a) the lead fraction (containing RaD) in the extraction of radium from uranium ore

$$Pb^{210} \xrightarrow{\beta} Bi^{210} \xrightarrow{\beta} Po^{210} \xrightarrow{\alpha} Pb^{206} \text{ (stable)}$$
$$\text{(RaD) 22y (RaE) 5.0d RaF 138d (RaG)}$$

(b) neutron irradiation of natural bismuth (Bi^{209}) in a reactor in which RaE and a 2.6×10^6-year α-emitting isomer of Bi^{210} are made in nearly equal amounts.

In nature the equilibrium atom ratio of uranium to Po^{210} is about 1.2×10^{10} or about 0.02 mg Po per metric ton of ore containing 30% uranium. By contrast the lead dioxide residues from radium production in the Belgian Congo were estimated to contain some 10 to 30 times as much polonium.

Some 37 tons of the lead residues were purchased by the Dayton Project and from these some 40 curies of Po^{210} (0.22 mg/curie) were extracted.

Although work continued for awhile on recovery of polonium from the ore residues it was soon generally agreed that irradiated bismuth was the most promising ultimate source. As a result the recovery from natural sources was abandoned before a satisfactory method of Po recovery was developed.

RaE is formed from Bi^{209} with a thermal neutron reaction cross section of 0.015 barns. When the graphite reactor at the Clinton Laboratories (which was a pilot reactor for those at Hanford, Washington) reached its full power of one megawatt as originally designed, its maximum thermal flux was about 5×10^{11} neutrons/cm^2/sec. Thus in this reactor a maximum production of Po^{210} of about 0.02 mg (0.1 c) per kg of Bi was possible in a 30-day irradiation in 1944. In subsequent years when fluxes of some 10^{14} became available elsewhere this production rate could be increased by a factor of 200 (or more in longer irradiations).

The first irradiated bismuth received by the Dayton Project from Clinton Laboratories was found to contain from 0.03 to 0.08 c per kg or an average of about 50 c per ton. This represented a large enhancement compared to the lead dioxide residues and involved a separation from essentially only one element (bismuth) rather than the many elements present in ore residues.

Commercial Po^{210} Production by Neutron Irradiation

For neutron irradiations bismuth metal slugs (solid cylinders) are canned in aluminum jackets. After irradiation and jacket removal the slugs are dissolved in a mixture of hydrochloric and nitric acids, or if a positive potential is applied to the bismuth (making it an anode) it is dissolved in hydrochloric acid. When the acid mixture is used the excess nitrate ion is removed by addition of such reducing agents as urea, formaldehyde or formic acid.

The Po could be concentrated with respect to bismuth in a number of ways. For example, it could be allowed to deposit spontaneously on a less noble metal such as silver, bismuth, copper or nickel. If bismuth is used, it may be dissolved in acid and the process repeated one or more times whereby a further factor of 100 per cycle may be achieved in concentration. The concentration step has also been achieved by coprecipitation with tellurium, i.e., by the addition of Te(VI) or Te(IV), followed by addition of stannous chloride, which reduces both tellurium and polonium to the metal. Polonium may also be removed from bismuth by first heating in oxygen at 650°C to convert the metals to the oxides, which decreases the volatility of the Bi. Subsequent heating at some 20° below the melting point, 820°C, of Bi_2O_3 at reduced pressure, reduces polonium to the metal which is then removed by volatilization.

The final step in the separation and purification of Po is usually accomplished by electrodeposition onto Au, Pt, Ta, Mo, carbon or Ni, usually from HNO_3 solutions. Spontaneous deposition onto copper or nickel has also been used, as has precipitation of the sulfide followed by thermal decomposition.

During chemical processing Po is usually assayed by alpha counting, with low-geometry (low solid angle) counters being used for large amounts of Po. Counting of the 0.8 MeV γ-rays has also been used. When the quantity present exceeds 0.1 mg it is often more convenient to assay it by measuring the total energy emitted with a calorimeter. Basic purity assay may be accomplished by counting a "microfoil" followed by weighing on a microbalance.

Physical Properties

Two crystalline forms of metallic polonium have been recorded: α-Po, a simple cubic low-temperature form, and β-Po, a simple rhombohedral high-temperature form. It appears to change phase at about 36°C although both phases seem to co-exist between about 18 to 54°C, perhaps due to radiation damage effects. The metal is silvery-white in bulk, brownish in thin films, and black when precipitated from solution. It melts at 254°C and boils at 962°C to form an apparently colorless vapor containing Po_2 molecules. Table 1 lists polonium's physical properties.

TABLE 1. PHYSICAL PROPERTIES

Atomic number	84
Atomic weight	210
Melting point	254°C
Boiling point	962°C
Density	9.4 ± 0.5 g/cc for either the α or β phase
Atomic volume	22.53 cc/g-atom
Atomic radius	1.64 Å
Heat of vaporization	24.597 ± 0.031 kcal/mole
Heat of sublimation at 298°K	34.5 kcal/g-atom
Ionization potential	8.43 ev
Linear coefficient of thermal expansion	$23.0 \pm 1.5 \times 10^{-6}$ cm/cm/deg
Electrical resistivity at 20°C of α-phase	140 ± 10 μohm-cm
Thermal coefficient of electrical resistivity	0.0046 ohm/ohm/°C (α-phase)
	0.0070 ohm/ohm/°C (β-phase)

Vapor pressure (meas. in the range 438–745°C)

$$\log p = \frac{-5377.8 \pm 6.7}{T} + 7.2345 \pm 0.0068$$

(p in mm, T in °K)

The following are *estimated* values:

Young's (elastic) modulus	0.26×10^6 kg/cm²
Shear modulus	0.97×10^6 kg/cm²
Poisson's ratio	0.338
Bulk modulus	0.27×10^6 kg/cm²
Heat of fusion	0.91 kcal/g-atom
Debye temperature, θ	81°K
C_p	6.30 cal/g-atom/deg
C_v	6.09 cal/g-atom/deg
Entropy of fusion	1.76 e.u./g-atom
Entropy of vaporization	23.8 e.u./g-atom

Chemical Properties

Although the physical properties of the metal resemble those of elements in the same period (thallium, lead and bismuth) more than those of selenium and tellurium, its chemistry shows much similarity to that of tellurium. Polonium oxidizes slowly in air at room temperature forming mainly the basic dioxide. It dissolves in concentrated sulfuric or selenic acid. Both concentrated nitric acid and aqua regia dissolve it by oxidation to Po(IV). It also dissolves in dilute (2N) hydrochloric acid to form the red or pink Po(II) which rapidly oxidizes to the yellow Po(IV) due to radiolysis reactions.

In solution Po may be separated from Se and Te by virtue of the fact that sulfur dioxide reduces the latter two to the (insoluble) elements and Po to Po(II). The Po(II) may be precipitated subsequently as the sulfide (e.g., by adding H_2S or ammonium polysulfide) which decomposes to the metal on heating to 275°C.

Polonium exhibits the valences $-2, 0, +2, +4, +6$ and there is evidence for the existence of the $+3$ valence state; however, this evidence involves small amounts or low concentrations of Po where radiolysis effects are small but where interpretations are difficult.

As expected, polonium salts are more basic than the corresponding selenium and tellurium compounds. For example, as shown in Table 2, polonium forms a disulfate and tetranitrate while the other two elements do not.

Health Hazards and Radiolysis Problems

The high specific activity of Po^{210} creates both a serious health hazard and a chemical problem due to radiation damage. Polonium when ingested tends to concentrate in certain organs, e.g., the kidneys, spleen and liver, where irreversible radiation damage is done by the α-particles. In addition polonium has a notorious reputation for migrating and getting spread all around a laboratory. It is not clear to what extent this behavior is due to its peculiar chemistry, to its radiolysis effects or to its high specific activity.

Because of the very high specific activity and consequent serious health hazard, the maximum permissible body-burden has been set at 0.03 μc or about 2×10^{10} atoms. Consequently any work with weighable amounts of polonium must be carried out under strict control in a totally enclosed system. Because of the short range of α-particles and the relative freedom of Po^{210} from β- and γ-radiations, glove boxes provide adequate protection at least for moderate amounts (milligrams) of Po, if the glove material is impenetrable to polonium. The boxes should be well-ventilated and maintained at a pressure such that any air leak is into the box to prevent any radioactive dust or vapor from escaping. At higher levels of activity γ-ray shielding is required and, if the Po^{210} α-particles are allowed to come into direct contact with certain light elements, the material also becomes a fast neutron source. Since neutrons (particularly fast neutrons) are highly penetrating, such high-level operations must be carried out by mechanical means in cells behind thick neutron shields.

Because of radiation damage the concentration of Po^{210} has a marked effect on the chemical procedures which can be used in its separation as well as the equipment which can be used. At tracer levels (sub-μg amounts) polonium may be extracted into such solvents as diisopropyl carbinol, diisopropyl ketone,

TABLE 2. PREPARED SIMPLE OXO-ACID SALTS

Anion	Se	Te	Po
Nitrate	**	$Te(NO_3)_2$ (?) $2TeO_2 \cdot HNO_3$	$4PoO_2 \cdot N_2O_5$ $4PoO_2 \cdot 3N_2O_5$ $Po(NO_3)_4 \cdot N_2O_4$
Sulfate	$SeO_2 \cdot SO_3$	$2TeO_2 \cdot SO_3$	$2PoO_2 \cdot SO_3$ $Po(SO_4)_2$

** Preparation attempted but unsuccessful.

methyl di-*n*-octylamine and tri-*n*-butylphosphate. Ion-exchange and paper chromatography have also been used in separations. On the other hand, aqueous solutions of even millimolar concentrations (about 1 curie/ml) exhibit a visible evolution of gas and the formation of oxidizing and reducing radiolysis products. These render difficult any studies concerning the (II) or the questionable (VI) valence states. In addition the α-particles and their radiolysis products decompose other ionic or neutral polyatomic species present, particularly organic matter. Thus separations involving solvent extraction or ion exchangers are not feasible at higher concentrations of Po^{210}, where glassware is crazed at the surface and made fragile if the walls are thin.

Solid compounds are very difficult to study at the curie (220 μg) level. When this amount of Po is concentrated into a single piece of pure compound most of the α-particle energy is absorbed within the compound itself causing considerable radiation damage. Under these conditions salts of organic acids char within a short time, the iodate evolves iodine, and in any of its crystalline compounds every atom is displaced at least once a day.

Thus in the work on the recovery of Po from irradiated bismuth conducted at the Dayton Project and later at the Mound Laboratory at Miamisburg, Ohio, and at other installations, procedures had to be developed which would allow isolation of large quantities of Po^{210} without excessive decomposition of reagents, equipment or containers and without excessive exposure of the workers.

Uses: Neutron Sources, α–Sources and Power Sources

All the uses of polonium depend on its α radioactivity, which makes it interesting as an α-source, a neutron source and an energy source.

The most common small neutron sources have consisted of Ra-Be or Po-Be, although other α-emitters have been used in more recent years. Radium has the advantages of a longer half-life (1620 years compared to 138 days) and higher energy α-particles in its decay chain, while Po has the advantage of having much less γ-activity associated with it.

The probability of an α-particle entering a nucleus is limited by the α-particle energy and the coulomb barrier, which depends on the nuclear charge. Although the coulomb barrier is smaller the lower the atomic number, the overall reaction rate in which the neutron is emitted also depends on the particular reaction energetics. Be, B and F give the best theoretical yields of about 65, 20 and 10 neutrons/10^6 α-particles of Po^{210}, respectively, assuming perfect mixing and a low concentration of Po. Sources can be prepared readily which give neutron yields within 75 to 95% of the theoretical value (depending on Po concentration) and which emit greater than 10^8 neutrons/sec. A satisfactory method of preparing Po-Be sources involves volatilizing the Po into a metal container, adding powdered Be, capping the container and sealing it by means of tungsten-inert gas fusion welding, and heating to about 600°C to distribute the Po throughout the Be. The Mound Laboratory has supplied sources consisting of Po^{210} plus any of several other light elements, each giving neutrons of different energy spectra. Mock-fission neutron sources have been made with a mixture of Po, LiF, B and Be.

The major uses of neutron sources are for instrument calibration, reactor start-up, reactivity measurements of critical and subcritical nuclear fuel assemblies, oil well logging and moisture determination in bulk materials.

Because Po is notorious for migrating readily and causing serious contamination problems, uncovered Po^{210} α-sources are supplied only to those experienced in handling polonium. The α-particles of Po^{210} have a range of 3.83 cm in air and less than 0.0025 cm in metals. Thin layers of mica, tantalum and gold have been used successfully as covers, although for the last few years the favorite has been thin-rolled (as low as 0.0001 inch thick) stainless steel.

The first demonstration of converting radioactive decay energy into electrical energy was conducted by J. H. Birden and K. C. Jordon at Mound Laboratory in the early 1950's using Po^{210} and chromel-constantan thermocouples. The first demonstration of conversion via a steam engine was also carried out at Mound Laboratory (1954), although the latter type of device appears to have fewer practical potential uses.

In 1956 studies of the feasibility of using radioactive sources for direct conversion of decay heat into electrical energy were begun under the USAEC SNAP (Systems for Nuclear Auxiliary Power) Program. Several longer lived β-emitters as well as α-emitters, including Po^{210}, have been considered for power sources for satellites, out-of-the-way places on earth, navigation buoys at sea and in undersea vehicles. The usual method considered for this direct conversion, based on the thermocouple principle, involves the use of such semiconductor thermoelectric elements as lead telluride or cobalt silicide. The inner container of the radioisotope acts as the hot junction while an outer metal can, thermally insulated from the inner container, serves as the cold junction. The heat output of Po^{210} is about 140 watts per gm. Here again the near lack of γ-rays is an advantage.

References

1. Bagnall, K. W., "Chemistry of the Rare Radioelements—Polonium-Actinium," London, Butterworths Scientific Publications, 1957.
2. Bagnall, K. W., "The Chemistry of Selenium, Tellurium and Polonium," Amsterdam, London, and New York, Elsevier Publishing Company, 1966.
3. Corliss, William R., and Harvey, Douglas G., "Radioisotopic Power Generation," Chapter 6, Englewood Cliffs, N.J., Prentice-Hall, Inc., 1964.
4. Figgins, P. E., "The Radiochemistry of Polonium," NAS-NS 3037, January 1961, Washington, Office of Technical Services, Dept. of Commerce.
5. Haissinsky, M., "Polonium," Translated by Lange, Robert C., AEC Research and Development Report MLM-1165 (Tr), TID-4500 (23rd Ed.), Jan. 7, 1964.
6. Lange, Robert C., Chapter 5 in "Analytical Chemistry," Series IX, Volume 6, "Progress in Nuclear Energy," Edited by Stewart, D. C., and Elion, H. A., Oxford, Pergamon Press Ltd., 1966.
7. TID-5221, "Polonium," Edited by Moyer, Harvey V., U.S.A.E.C. Technical Information Service Extension, Oak Ridge, Tennessee, July 1956.
8. O'Kelley, G. D., Chapter 3.1, "Radioactive Sources" in "Methods of Experimental Physics," Volume 5, "Nuclear Physics," Part B, New York, Academic Press, 1963.
9. Seitz, Frederick, and Turnbull, David, "Solid State Physics," Vol. 16, New York, Academic Press, 1964.

R. W. STOUGHTON AND M. H. LIETZKE

POTASSIUM

History

Potassium, one of the alkali metals, was first recognized as an element by Sir Humphry Davy, who in 1807 electrolyzed potash and produced silvery metal droplets. Potassium was the first element discovered by electrolytic separation. Potash, or potassium carbonate, had been produced by leaching wood ashes and was well known, being commonly used for soap making.

The preparation of potassium carbonate or "potash" by leaching and concentrating wood ashes was the subject of the first United States patent, issued to Samuel Hopkins. However, Jeremiah in the Old Testament refers to "wash yourself with lye and use much soap." Here the lye is potassium carbonate and soap a product of this potash and fats, indicating that potassium carbonate was known from quite early times. Job also refers to "cleanse my hands with lye."

Beginning in the early years of colonization of the American continent large areas of woods were burned to secure the ashes, which contained potassium carbonate. By leaching with water, the potassium carbonate was removed, and concentrated to the lye solution by boiling. Potassium carbonate was an important export from the United States and Canada, beginning in 1635 and continuing through 1865.

Potassium salts were found in Germany in the Stassfurt deposits in 1839 and became the basis for much of the early German chemical industry. Sodium, however, has replaced potassium in most salts in industrial use, except where the potassium salt has some specific desired properties. The demand in fertilizers quickly became the backbone of the potash industry.

In 1914 at the start of the first World War the only deposits being worked and the only ones of any extent known were in Germany. As shipments from Germany were cut off, potassium was recovered in the United States from lake waters, from plant residues, from green sand silicates, and from other types of deposits, but the severity of the shortages was shown by skyrocketing prices. This evidence of dependence on one source of supply led to an intensive search for other potash deposits.

In the United States, Searles Lake, California, a mixed crystalline mass, was the first large deposit worked. A plant was completed in 1914 but did not begin operation until 1916. Through an extensive research program, methods for producing several salts from the brine were developed and the plant was operated successfully. Oil well cores in New Mexico in 1925 revealed potassium salts, and several deposits at Carlsbad were later developed. This major discovery made the United States independent for the first time of foreign sources. These deposits are at the west edge of the larger Permian salt basin extending from West Texas to Kansas.

The first beneficiation plant in New Mexico used the classical recrystallization process. However, the second plant used a flotation process for separation of the potassium chloride of the ore, and later other plants also used the flotation separation. During the same period, potash deposits were discovered in the Soviet Union, and a parallel development of flotation occurred there.

More recently, deposits have been found in several other areas. Large deposits, but at considerable depth were found in Saskatchewan, Canada. Mines and concentration plants have been developed along the northern edge of the deposit. Other potash deposits have been found in various parts of the world.

Occurrence

Potassium is widely distributed in nature and ranks 7th of the elements in abundance, contributing 2.59% of the weight of the lithosphere. Water of the oceans contains 0.07% of potassium chloride, and on evaporation 98% of the water must be removed before the potassium salts start to crystallize.

Potassium is found in many igneous rocks, which by disintegration furnish potassium to the soil and water. Leucite and glauconite are silicates which have been considered as commercial sources of potassium. Clays may absorb potassium and thus retain it for plant use.

The main deposits worked for potassium are salt beds, and many sodium chloride beds have deposits of potassium chloride associated with them. The minerals of importance are sylvite, KCl; carnallite, $KCl \cdot MgCl_2 \cdot 6H_2O$ langbeinite, $K_2SO_4 \cdot 2MgSO_4$; and polyhalite, $K_2SO_4 \cdot MgSO_4 \cdot 2CaSO_4 \cdot 2H_2O$.

Some lakes and crystal masses in dried lake beds are worked. Searles Lake is an important source, Great Salt Lake in Utah provides commercial production, and the Dead Sea, one of the richest of these deposits, has been estimated to contain two billion tons of potassium chloride. For comparison, the Canadian underground deposit has been estimated to have 10 billion tons of potassium chloride recoverable under conventional mining methods.

Evaporite deposits are now known in many parts of the world, and they were deposited in various geologic periods. Deposits in Saskatchewan, Canada were laid down in the Devonian period, those in Utah in the Pennsylvanian, those in New Mexico, England and the Ural deposits in Russia were developed in the Permian, some of those in France in the Triassic, others in France, Spain, and Germany in the Oligocene epoch, and the Ukraine deposits in Russia and those in Sicily in the Miocene period.

Other large deposits are under development in the Congo and Ethiopia in Africa, and in Brazil and Bolivia in South America.

Preparation of Potassium

Potassium metal can be prepared by several methods, but the electrolysis of molten potassium chloride cannot be used to produce the metal although sodium metal is easily produced by the electrolysis of molten sodium chloride. An electrolytic process using potassium hydroxide with added carbonate and chloride was used in Germany but has been discontinued.

Potassium and potassium chloride are fully miscible at temperatures just above the melting point of potassium chloride. This behavior contrasts with that of sodium and sodium chloride, in which the metal separates and floats on the molten sodium chloride in the electrolysis of the fused salt.

Thermal methods of preparation have been used, such as the reduction of potassium compounds with calcium carbide, carbon, silicon, and metallic sodium. In the United States potassium is made chiefly by reaction of sodium on potassium chloride.

Physical Properties

Potassium is a silvery white metal, quite soft, and must be kept out of contact with air or water, and in the laboratory is stored under oil, such as kerosene. Potassium is a highly active metal in Group I of the Periodic Table. It has a specific gravity of 0.85 and a melting point of 63.2°C. Due to the violence of its reaction with water, indirect methods are required for determination of its electrode potential, which is about −2.95 volts.

The following physical properties have been assembled from several sources. For several properties a wide range of values have been reported, but in general these represent more recent values and are approximate averages of determinations.

Potassium consists chiefly of three isotopes of atomic weight 39, 40, and 41 which comprise 93.1, 0.0118, and 6.88%, respectively, in natural potassium. Isotope 40 is radioactive and has a half-life of 1.2×10^9 years. About 89% of its radioactivity is by beta emission to give an atom of calcium, and the rest is by electron capture and gamma ray emission to give an atom of argon.

The radioactivity of potassium, though very small, accounts in large measure for the accumulation of heat in the earth. It also provides a possibility of dating geological specimens, and a means for the analytical determination of potassium. Its radioactivity is about one-thousandth of that of uranium and therefore offers no hazard. Analytical applications, however, require large samples, long counts or heavy shielding from background radiation.

Elemental potassium shows a body-centered cubic lattice at room temperature and below, and the lattice constant of 5.31Å has been reported. The ionic radius of 1.33Å is exhibited in its compounds.

TABLE 1. PHYSICAL PROPERTIES OF POTASSIUM

Atomic number	19
Atomic weight	39.102
Isotopes and abundance	
K^{39}	93.09%
K^{40}	0.0118%
K^{41}	6.90%
Radioactivity of K^{40}	
Half-life	1.4×10^9 years
Energy of beta	1.33 MeV
Energy of gamma	1.47 MeV
Color	silvery
Crystal structure	body-centered cubic
Atomic radius	2.31 A°
Ionic radius	1.33 A°
Density, g/cc	
solid 18°C	0.856
liquid 100°C	0.819
300°C	0.771
500°C	0.723
Melting point	63.4°C
Latent heat of fusion, cal/g	14.67
Boiling point	757.°C
Latent heat of vaporization, cal/g	496
Vapor pressure, mm Hg	
587°C	123
686°C	392
763°C	806
Specific heat, solid, cal/g/C°	
0°C	0.176
63°C	0.200
200°C	0.1887
Electrode potential, volts ($H_2 = 0.0$ volts)	−2.95
Surface tension, dynes/cm 62°C	411
100-150°C	86
Electrical resistivity, microhm-cm, 0°C	6.1
100°C	15.31
250°C	25.0
Thermal conductivity, cal/sec/cm/°C	
21°C	0.232
200°C	0.1073
400°C	0.0956
Viscosity, centipoises 69.6°C	0.515
167.4°C	0.331
250°C	0.258
400°C	0.191
Thermal neutron absorption cross section, barns	2.07

Chemical Properties

Potassium will form four oxides, potassium monoxide, K_2O; potassium peroxide, K_2O_2; potassium superoxide, KO_2; and potassium ozonide, KO_3; indicating a variety of oxides not shown with sodium. Potassium superoxide is used to produce oxygen in gas masks.

Potassium reacts with water vigorously to form the hydroxide, reacts with hydrogen at about 350°C to form potassium hydride, and reacts with nitrogen to form azides under an electric charge. It reacts with sulfur to form six different sulfides.

Because of its high reactivity, its compounds are very stable. However, because of its high reactivity it will also undergo reactions to form some unstable compounds. The azides are examples of such behavior.

Potassium, on contact with liquid bromine, reacts with explosive violence, and similar behavior is exhibited with several halogen compounds. Copper and iron halides react with potassium with explosive violence on mechanical shock, as do many other halide salts.

Carbon monoxide and potassium can form an explosive carbonyl. Graphite will react with potassium to form a series of carbides. Solid carbon dioxide and potassium will react with an explosion if subjected to shock and at higher temperatures potassium will reduce carbon dioxide to carbon monoxide and carbon.

Potassium reacts with many organic compounds. Alkyl or aryl compounds of potassium can be produced which are stable at room temperature. Carbon tetrachloride at room temperature undergoes no reaction with solid potassium, but on reaching the melting point of potassium, explosive reaction occurs. Compounds carrying the carbon-potassium bond and adjacent aromatic or conjugated double bonds exhibit high color.

Potassium has an electrode potential intermediate between lithium and sodium. In most reactions the greater activity of potassium over sodium is quite pronounced. The electrode potentials of lithium, potassium, and sodium are -3.05, -2.95, and -2.71 volts, respectively. The molar heat of formation of their compounds do not all follow the same order. For example, the molar heats of formation of the chlorides for lithium, potassium, and sodium are 98.7, 97.8, and 104.0 kcal/g-mole. An additional factor influencing the comparative rates of reactions in aqueous media is the extent of hydration of their ions.

It forms alloys with many metals, and forms distinct compounds with many metals. It has, however, found little use as a metal. Alloys of sodium and potassium have recieved considerable attention, and the application as a heat transfer medium in nuclear reactors has led to commercial production. The alloy is prepared by heating potassium chloride with metallic sodium. Potassium can then be prepared by fractional distillation of the alloy.

The eutectic with sodium of about 77% potassium has a melting point of -12.3°C. The alloys are more reactive than sodium. It is of interest that at room temperature, oxygen reacts with the alloy to form sodium monoxide and potassium superoxide, KO_2, while at higher temperatures sodium peroxide, Na_2O_2, and KO_2 are formed.

Compounds

Potassium Chloride. Most of the potassium salts are produced from the chloride, the form in which most of the commercial deposits are found.

Potassium chloride has a specific gravity of 1.98, is generally cubic in crystal form, and melts at 772°C. Its solubility is 31.0 g/100 g of water at 10°C and 56.7 g at 100°C, which is the basis of the crystallization process for producing the salt.

The methods of preparation and uses will be described under technology.

Potassium Hydroxide. Potassium hydroxide is produced by electrolysis of aqueous solutions of potassium chloride. Several types of cells are used. The cells used for potassium hydroxide are similar to those used for the sodium caustic, but the slightly higher potential required can make large differences in the operation of different cells. In potassium hydroxide preparation, danger of hydrogen evolution is apparently greater than in sodium hydroxide production. The diaphragm cells have been standard in the industry, but several mercury cell plants are now in use.

555

The mercury cells have a layer of mercury as the cathode. Cell brine flows above it around graphite anodes at which the chlorine is generated. Metallic potassium produced at the cathode dissolves in the mercury. The potassium amalgam is removed continuously to a decomposer where the potassium reacts with water to produce hydrogen and potassium hydroxide. The mercury cells require a higher purity of feed than the diaphragm cells since minute traces of metallic impurities can lead to difficulty, probably through the generation of hydrogen at local points of metal deposition on the mercury.

In the diaphragm cell, chlorine is produced at the anode but at the cathode hydrogen and potassium hydroxide are produced. The diaphragm separates the cell into anode and cathode compartments. The solution discharged from the diaphragm cell contains about 15% potassium hydroxide and about 10% potassium chloride. This solution must be concentrated by evaporation. As the potassium hydroxide increases in concentration the potassium chloride decreases in solubility and precipitates out. A method has also been described for removing the potassium chloride by flotation from the strong caustic solutions. The potassium hydroxide may be marketed as a solid or as a 50% solution. To produce the crystalline material, the solutions are heated nearly to the melting point of the caustic.

The melting point of potassium hydroxide is about 405°C. It absorbs water vigorously and several hydrates are known having one, two, and four molecules of water per molecule of potassium hydroxide. Other hydrates have been described.

Electrolysis of potassium hydroxide solutions can produce oxygen and hydrogen. Potassium hydroxide is the electrolyte in some alkaline storage batteries, and is used in some fuel cells. It is preferred over sodium hydroxide because of its greater conductivity.

Potassium hydroxide is also used as an absorbent for carbon dioxide, and for hydrogen sulfide. Other uses in organic reactions as well as in inorganic usually depend on solubility advantages over sodium hydroxide. It is of course used in preparing many potassium salts.

Potassium Sulfate. Potassium sulfate is prepared either from a naturally occurring sulfate, such as langbeinite, or by reaction of potassium chloride either with sulfuric acid in Mannheim furnaces or with sulfur dioxide, air and water by the Hargreaves process.

Potassium sulfate is used with calcium sulfate to control rate of set and to improve the strength of gypsum cements. However, its chief use is for fertilizer with crops, such as tobacco and citrus, where the chloride is considered objectionable.

Langbeinite, a double salt of potassium and magnesium sulfates, is also used as fertilizer for chloride-sensitive crops. It is prepared from ores by washing out the sodium chloride with which it is associated.

Potassium Carbonate. Potassium carbonate is generally prepared by carbonation of potassium hydroxide although many methods have been described for its preparation.

The Solvay process for making sodium carbonate from sodium chloride, ammonia, and carbon dioxide has made sodium carbonate available at low cost. The corresponding process using potassium chloride fails because of the high solubility of potassium bicarbonate. The solubility of potassium bicarbonate in water is about 53 g/100 g of saturated solution at 20°, while sodium bicarbonate under the same conditions will dissolve to 25 g.

Many methods have been suggested to produce potassium carbonate at low cost, but its comparative price indicates a high cost of production.

The Engel-Precht process uses magnesium oxide, potassium chloride, and carbon dioxide, separating the Engels salt, $MgCO_3 \cdot KHCO_3 \cdot 4H_2O$, which on decomposition precipitates magnesium carbonate for recycling and leaves potassium bicarbonate in solution, which can then be processed to potassium carbonate.

Alkyl amines or ion exchange resins can be used, with potassium chloride and carbon dioxide, to produce potassium bicarbonate and by calcining, potassium carbonate. This is actually a variation of the Solvay process for sodium carbonate in which the ammonia of the Solvay process is replaced by the alkyl amines.

Potassium carbonate is used in making ceramics and glass of particular qualities, such as glass used in fine tableware, the glass of television tubes, and optical glass.

Potassium Nitrate. The name saltpetre was applied to potassium nitrate which was found in limited amounts in many areas. It was found associated with guano deposits, in caves, and as a surface deposit in other areas. Extensive deposits of sodium nitrate are found in Chile and in some areas show an appreciable proportion of potassium nitrate.

Its early use in gunpowder led to its manufacture. Preparation of potassium nitrate and potassium-sodium nitrate from Chilean deposits led to limited use as fertilizer. Since the potassium and the nitrogen are in forms that are more expensive to produce, the cost is higher than for potassium in muriate and the nitrogen in ammonia. Its use as fertilizer is therefore limited but it will be in demand for specialty uses as fertilizer.

Various methods have been described for making potassium nitrate from potassium chloride and nitric acid, and some plants are in production. Methods for production from sea water using organic compounds such as dipicrylamine and ion exchange resins using highly nitrated compounds which have a high selectivity for potassium have been described.

Potassium Chloride Technology

Since potassium chloride is the compound of potassium found in largest amounts and the compound used most generally for fertilizers, its discovery, mining and concentration have received much attention. Sulfates are produced in considerable tonnages also.

Deposits. The underground deposits furnish by far the largest part of the potassium salts produced today. The chief ore being mined is sylvite, or potassium chloride. It is found with halite, sodium chloride, as the main constituent. Typical ores may carry from 20 to 35% sylvite. Generally small amounts of other salts are present, including calcium sulfate, magnesium chloride and magnesium sulfate, as well as clay.

Deposits worked are generally from 600 to 3500 feet underground. Deposition usually shows interruption so several strata are usually shown, but deposits less than three feet in thickness would barely be considered commercial.

Horizontal deposits are naturally ideal to work, but some deposits are found at the edge of salt domes and may be vertical, or others may be folded due to earth movements after deposition.

Mining. Deposits in the New Mexico area lie generally horizontal and from 600 to 1800 feet in depth. Deposits worked in Saskatchewan, Canada are around 3500 feet in depth and, though horizontal, offer severe problems in mining due to depth and to the nature of overlying deposits.

Mining is usually carried out using a room and pillar extraction pattern. While undercutting, blasting, and loading at the face was the general method of mining, mining machines with which the ore is cut from the face have been replacing the blasting procedure. In planning the mining pattern, the strength of the ore and its ability to support the overburden must be considered. The salts tend to be plastic, and deformation will be slow if the pressure is held within limits.

Mining by removal of pillars has been carried out in the New Mexico area, and when the retreat is properly related to character of the salt and overburden, the back will settle slowly and close the area.

Since the deposits were generally laid down intermittently, layers of clay are frequently found. These become good markers in mining but also constitute hazards, since they represent weakness in the strata. Rockfalls will generally occur from a clay seam. These have been very infrequent in room and pillar mining but in pillar extraction may be very dangerous. Mining in the New Mexico area has had an excellent safety record.

Since potash is essentially a sedimentary deposit, oil and gas will often be found in the same general area. In horizontal deposits the salt is generally undisturbed and the oil and gas constitute no hazard, but in areas showing earth movement they may be a serious hazard.

Production by leaching underground deposits is probably more suited to deposits of greater depth than would be feasible with conventional mining procedures. One plant in Canada is based upon leaching a deep deposit from wells drilled into the deposit.

In the New Mexico area, gas pockets filled with nitrogen have been found. In these, the slow diffusion and evaporation of the brines have led to the formation of large potassium chloride crystals often showing octahedral faces. These are rare and really only museum specimens, but some have measured as much as 18 inches across.

Concentration by Crystallization. Concentration of the potassium chloride ore was carried out by the fractional crystallization system, until about 1935 when flotation was developed as a separation method. The crystallization method is based on the presence of potassium chloride and sodium chloride as the main constituents of the ore. Sodium chloride solubility in water changes very little with rise of temperature while potassium chloride solubility increases quite rapidly with increasing temperature.

The ore is crushed to permit faster dissolution, and is then leached in hot water to bring all the potassium chloride into solution. Undissolved sodium chloride and insoluble matter settle out and the clear hot brine is cooled to crystallize the potassium chloride.

In Germany and in Russia evaporation has been carried out in many stages for high efficiency. However, development of larger crystal products has largely occurred in the United States. Production by crystallization of granular size products at 8 and 10 mesh has been achieved.

Sodium chloride and potassium chloride will form mixed salts at high temperatures, but these are not stable at crystallizing temperatures. Nevertheless, pure potassium chloride cannot be produced in a brine containing sodium chloride. Some commercial industrial potassium chloride is crystallized from brines containing low concentrations of sodium, and contains less than 100 ppm of sodium and carries more than 99.95% potassium chloride.

Brine saturated with potassium chloride and sodium chloride carries about 33% solids and while at 70°F contains about 21% NaCl and 10% KCl, at 200°F will contain about 21% NaCl and 17% KCl. A brine saturated with potassium chloride alone at 70°F contains about 25.5% KCl and at 200°F 35% potassium chloride.

Concentration by Flotation. The first flotation of potassium chloride crystals from brine as medium was carried out by L. D. Anderson of Potash Company of America working with ores of the Carlsbad, New Mexico district. In attempting to apply flotation procedures to these soluble salts he used a brine prepared from ore which contained considerable magnesium chloride. Cottonseed oil was saponified with caustic and used as the flotation agent. A concentrate of 67% potassium chloride was floated. Magnesium had reached a fairly high concentration in the brine of the early tests and magnesium and oleic acid combined to produce flotation. This led to intensive testing to develop a commercial separation of the salts in brine. Flotation was of particular interest because of the scarcity of water in the area.

A combination of lead and fatty acid as flotation reagent floated the sodium chloride and became a commercial method. The discovery of fatty amines as a collector for potassium chloride led to wide acceptance and further American development used this process. The process was easily applied where the ores consisted chiefly of sodium and potassium chloride. The presence of sulfate minerals led to difficulty of application. For economical use, clay which is present in most ores had to be removed. Clay having appreciable exchange value would absorb amines to saturation before flotation of the potash would occur. Desliming, or removal of clay, thus became an important step in preparation for flotation.

Flotation separation includes crushing the ore to flotation size, scrubbing the ore by agitation in brine, washing to remove released clay (desliming), conditioning the ore with reagents, carrying out the flotation process for separation of values, then dewatering and drying the concentrates. The medium is a brine saturated with sodium chloride and potassium chloride. Appreciable concentrations of magnesium chloride or calcium chloride can be tolerated without affecting flotation and may even be of advantage in reducing the potash values in the brine of the system.

Flotation with the amine reagents is very effective and flotation can be carried out at relatively large particle size, 14 mesh being rather standard. By the use of special techniques and auxiliary reagents it is possible to float 6 mesh particles.

Analysis

Earlier methods of analysis used the potassium cobaltinitrite, the perchlorate, the tartrate, and the potassium chloroplatinate precipitation and various volumetric variations.

Flame photometric techniques have been developed to make very quick analysis possible. A solution of the sample is sprayed or pumped into a flame, in which the potassium salt is vaporized. The potassium salt gives the flame a violet color which can be detected by phototubes and the signal measured for intensity. This has been used for plant control. Flame photometers of considerable sophistication have been developed.

Atomic absorption instruments have also found application. In atomic absorption, a beam of light characteristic of an element is passed through a flame in which a sample has been introduced. Atoms at lower temperatures will absorb light of the same wave length which they emit at higher temperatures. Absorption by the element in the flame is measured as the difference in the intensity of the light at the appropriate wave length before and after absorption. Atomic absorption is therefore particularly applicable to elements requiring a higher temperature for emission, but it has also been applied to potassium where lower temperatures can be used.

The potassium salt of tetraphenylboron is relatively insoluble and has become the basis of then ewer procedures. This analysis can be carried out gravimetrically, or with very dilute samples volumetrically. The volumetric method is rapid, accurate, and dependable. The reagent is unstable in acid conditions, but very stable in basic solutions.

The radioactivity can be used for determination of potassium, but because of the very low level of radioactivity, has not been widely used. Beta activity can be used on small samples with good shielding and long counts. Gamma activity, which has greater penetration, can be used with large samples and in spite of the lower ratio of gamma disintegrations, large counts can be secured. Single channel analyzers can be used to reduce background. However, the difficulty of preparing samples to secure uniform densities, and arranging samples to assure uniform geometry, as well as the presence of variable background limit the accuracy and the application of the method.

Potassium, the Vital Need

Potassium in Soils. Potassium, an essential constituent for plant growth, is found in all soils. It exists in several forms, in different degrees of solubility. It may be soluble and exist in the soil water solution. It may be in clay or other materials subject to ion exchange, readily released for plant use; or it may be fixed in different chemical compounds, chiefly silicates, and be released only by slow processes of weathering.

Potassium is absorbed by various ion exchange materials in the soil such as humus compounds, clays, and natural zeolites. These provide the potassium for growing plants. Clays differ as to exchange capacity, which is a measure of the amount that can be absorbed. These compounds absorb potassium as well as other ions from solution and the character of the soil depends to a large measure on the ions absorbed. High sodium absorption leads to "black soils," and these can be recovered by replacement of the sodium with calcium and potassium. Some clays such as illite tend to bind potassium so tightly that it is not available for plant use.

Humus materials may have several types of structures which can act as ion exchange sites, hydroxyl, carboxyl, amine, and these will have varied ability to hold metals but they probably hold calcium better than potassium. On addition of potassium in fertilizers, it will be incorporated into the soil structure, soils with high clay and humus content holding the potassium best. In sandy soils a larger share of the potassium will be lost to water leaching. Potassium is continually leached into the rivers and must be replaced by weathering of potash containing rocks, or by addition in fertilizers.

Plants differ in their ability to remove potassium from the soil complex. Potassium available to plants can therefore not be measured by simply leaching the soil with water. Extracting solutions of various kinds have been used, and biological determinations have been devised in which plants are grown in the soil, and after a period of growth, their potassium content determined. Leaf analysis has been a valuable tool in noting deficiencies of potassium in the soil. Plants also differ in level of potassium required for good growth. In tests on plants grown by solution techniques, plants varied from one half to 40 ppm of potassium for optimum growth.

Potassium in Living Matter. Potassium is the characteristic metal in both plant and animal cells, but the extracellular fluid in animals has sodium in higher concentration. Because of this, potassium has often been considered the more important metal in plants and sodium the more important metal in animals.

Potassium as an essential element in plant growth was recognized by von Liebig who published his theory on mineral nutrition of plants in 1840. Its necessity in animal growth was recognized later. A great deal of work has defined the activity of potassium in many biological functions.

Potassium has not been found in any organic compounds in living tissue. Potassium is found in plants only as the free ion, 70% is found in the cell juice, and the remainder absorbed by proteins. This is essentially true in animals also. Life reactions occur in a medium in which potassium has very important functions to perform. Function has been defined in nerve cell, in heart muscle, in enzyme action, and in almost every life function. Disturbance in the ratio of potassium and sodium will lead to serious effects.

Man is not likely to suffer from potassium deficiency when fed a normal diet, since plants have such a demand for potassium. Deficiencies in animals are therefore generally due to some malfunction rather than deficiency in diet. However, with the extensive use of prepared foods, potassium may be leached out and potassium deficiency has been associated with many common ailments.

The exact means of absorption of potassium into the plant is uncertain. However, potassium is absorbed selectively over other ions, such as sodium, calcium, and magnesium. There may be some carrier which assists in transfer in the plant, and some phosphate compounds have been proposed as carrier. Potassium participates directly in photosynthesis, and in respiration. Deficiencies lead to specific symptoms in each species and excellent reports are available describing the effects. The deficiencies show as yellow or brown areas, curling of the leaves, or weak stalk, and appear early. A deficiency in plants leads to failure to polymerize the high molecular weight carbohydrates and proteins, while the sugars and amino acids increase in concentration. Since the metabolism of the plant is so involved, the quality and yield of crop are influenced. Root growth is severely diminished.

Plants appear to maintain the level of potassium in the fruit or seed, so the size and yield is sometimes determined by the available potassium.

Potassium is one of the big three elements required in crop growth, nitrogen and phosphorus ranking at about the same level.

Fertilizer Requirements. In fertilizer terminology potassium is measured as a percentage of potash (K_2O). Muriate of potash of fertilizer grade is usually about 95% potassium chloride, or 60% K_2O content. Prices are based on units. A unit represents 1% K_2O per ton of fertilizer, or 20 pounds of K_2O.

There has been considerable agitation to change the system to elemental percentages, but the practice of measuring fertilizers as percentages of N, P_2O_5, and K_2O is widespread and there has been strong resistance to change.

World Production

World production and use of potash has been estimated for 1965 at about 13.5 million metric tons of K_2O. In the year ending June 30, 1966, the United States produced and used over 3 million metric tons. By 1970 world production capacity will probably be over 20 million tons. Whereas food production would profit from such use, it is unlikely that use will expand as rapidly as production capacity.

Farming practices leading to use of adequate fertilizers developed slowly in Europe and in the United States. Much increased use will come from Asia, Africa, and South America. Increased world food demands will require large tonnages of fertilizers, and the rate of increase in the use of potash may therefore be accelerated.

Production in the United States has been largely used in the United States. With the development of potash in Canada both countries have entered the world markets, and will undoubtedly extend their influence. The following tables show the production and use in the United States, and a brief summary of world production.

TABLE 2. PRODUCTION AND USE IN UNITED STATES (IN SHORT TONS K₂O) YEAR ENDING JUNE 30, 1966

Production in U.S.		3,216,000
Sales by U.S. Producers		3,039,000
Imports to U.S.		1,324,000
from		
Canada	1,119,000	
France	71,000	
West Germany	89,000	
Italy	6,000	
Spain	18,000	
Exports from U.S.		685,000
Consumption in U.S.		3,678,000

TABLE 3. WORLD PRODUCTION OF POTASH (IN METRIC TONS K₂O) (FROM DATA AND ESTIMATES)

	1961	1965
United States	2,478,962	2,848,545
Canada	—	1,297,267
South America	14,065	14,200
France	1,709,856	1,879,000
East Germany	1,675,000	1,900,000
West Germany	2,044,000	2,400,000
Italy	135,340	210,000
Spain	262,210	387,600
U.S.S.R.	1,322,000	2,300,000
Israel	84,900	310,000
Total	9,700,000	13,500,000

Potassium is a large tonnage chemical in the form of salts for fertilizer use. Expansion in production has been phenomenal and there will be several new plants in operation by 1975, which should assure adequate supplies for fertilizer use in the world war against hunger.

References

1. "Second Symposium on Salt," Northern Ohio Geological Society, Inc., Cleveland, Ohio, 1966.
2. "Potassium Symposium," International Potash Institute, Zurich, 1954.
3. Lotze, Franz, "Steinsalz and Kalisalze," Berlin, Gebruder Borntraeger, 1957.
4. "Saskatchewan Potash Show Proceedings," Regina, Saskatchewan Department of Industry and Commerce, 1965.
5. "Hunger Signs in Crops, A Symposium," Washington, D.C., National Fertilizer Association, 1941.
6. Eckstein, O., Bruno, A., and Turrentine, J. W., "Potash Deficiency Symptoms," Leipzig, Buchgestaltung F. Winnegar, 1937.
7. Mellor, J. W., "Comprehensive Treatise on Inorganic and Theoretical Chemistry," Vol. II, 1963 Supplement, New York, John Wiley and Sons, Inc., 1963.
8. Anderson, L. D., (to Potash Company of America), U.S. Patent 2,046,312 (July 7, 1936).
9. Kirby, J. E., (to E. I. duPont de Nemours & Co., Inc.), U.S. Patent 2,088,325 (July 27, 1937).
10. Weinig, A. J. (to Potash Company of America), U.S. Patent 2,188,933 (Feb. 6, 1940)
11. Tartaron, F. X., Cole, Allen F., and Duke, James B. (to Phosphate Recovery Corp.), U.S. Patent 2,288,497 (June 30, 1942).
12. Schoeld, E, A. (to Potash Company of America), U.S. Patent 2,931,502 (April 5, 1960).

EDMUND A. SCHOELD

PRASEODYMIUM

Praseodymium, Pr, has an atomic number 59 and atomic weight 140.907. It exists in nature as isotope Pr^{141} only.

History

Baron Auer von Welsbach separated didymia (twin) into praseodymia and neodymia (green twin and new twin), and announced it on June 18, 1885, having achieved the separation by fractional crystallization of the double ammonium nitrates.

Occurrence and Abundance

Along with other rare earths, praseodymia occurs in relatively high proportions in the minerals monazite, a thorium-rare earth phosphate; cerite, a hydrated rare earth silicate: and allanite, a hydrated aluminum silicate of rare earths, calcium and iron. It is also a fission product of uranium, thorium and plutonium.

Monazite minerals are found principally in

India, Brazil, and in Florida and South Carolina in the United States. Cerite occurs principally in Sweden and allanite in the western United States.

The relative "cosmic" abundance of Pr is about the same as Rh, Ag, Sb, Tl, and Bi, less abundant than Ce and Nd by almost a factor of ten, and only slightly more abundant than gold. Neither the volatile substances nor those of the heavy radioactive series are considered in this classification. The picture changes if abundances in the earth's crust are considered where the relative amounts of the rare earths are significantly higher.

Preparation

The discovery of the rare earth elements was actually the discovery of their oxides; the term "rare earth" refers to the oxides of the elements. As with the alkaline earth elements, reduction to the metal was difficult at first and it was not always known that the oxides were actually compounds. The rare earth oxides are among the most refractory substances known.

Praseodymium metal has the color and luster of iron and is prepared either by reduction of the trifluoride with alkali or alkaline earth metals, or by the electrolysis of the fused halides. The metals thus prepared are purified by distillation, remelting, amalgam formation or by other means and are routinely available in relatively high purity (99.9%) so far as the other rare earth elements are concerned. The major impurities are usually silicon, calcium and the nonmetals oxygen and nitrogen.

Physical Properties

The electronic configuration of the metallic state, beyond the xenon core, is $6s^2 5d^1 4f^2$; whereas, the gaseous atom is $6s^2 4f^3$. The chemical behavior of praseodymium indicates that the $4f$ electrons are relatively localized. The metallic valence has been estimated as three.

There are two crystalline forms of praseodymium metal. α-Pr is hexagonal closest packed (A3′, La-type) with a stacking sequence of A B A C A B A C... with a stacking fault every fourth layer. The lattice parameters are $a = 3.6725 \pm 7$ and $c = 11.8354 \pm 12$ Å. The

x-ray density is 6.769 while the pycnometric density is 6.475 g/cc. A transformation occurs at 792°C and β-Pr is formed. The heat of transformation is 760 cal/mole. It has an open body-centered cubic structure (A2, tungsten type) with $a = 4.13 \pm 1$ Å. The x-ray density is 6.64 g/cc. The molar volume of α-Pr is 20.82 and that of β-Pr is 21.2 cc/mole.

Praseodymium metal melts at 935 ± 5°C absorbing 1650 cal/mole. This gives an entropy of fusion of 1.76 cal/deg comparable to other rare earths, but somewhat lower than is usually observed. In the temperature range 1150-1420°C the vapor pressure may be represented as $\log P_{mm} = 17188/T + 8.098$ yielding a heat of vaporization of $\triangle H_v = 79.5 \pm 1.1$ kcal/mole. The boiling point is 3017°C. For α-Pr at 300°K, $S_o = 17.49$ cal/deg-mole, while the enthalpy function is $H_T^0 - H_0^0/T = 5.69$ cal/deg-mole; the free energy function $F_T^0 - H_0^0/T = 11.80$ cal/deg-mole. The heat capacity curve up to about 200°K indicates no anomolies. The Debye temperature for α-Pr is 144°K, and the heat capacity between 0 and 792°C may be represented as $C_p = 6.38 + 2.86 \times 10^{-3} t + 2.19 \times 10^{-6} t^2$ ($t = $ °C). For β-Pr the heat capacity is essentially constant at 9.19 cal/deg between 792°C and the melting point.

Praseodymium is paramagnetic at room temperature. The ground state of Pr^{+3} is $^3H_4$ and for Pr^{+4} is $^2F_{5/2}$; the calculated effective magnetic moments are 3.62 and 2.56 Bohr magnetons per atom, respectively. Magneto-chemical studies of the highest oxides of praseodymium indicate that probably only Pr^{3+} and Pr^{4+} ions are present, although Pr^{5+} is not completely ruled out. The magnetic susceptibility at 25°C for α-Pr is $5,320 \times 10^{-6}$ emu/mole. The Curie-Weiss constants are $C = 119.8 \times 10^{-4}$ emu-°K/gm, and $\theta = -21$°K in the temperature range -195 to $+230$°C.

The thermal neutron absorption cross section is 11.6 barns.

Superconductivity is not observed in Pr down to 0.25°K. For α-Pr the electrical resistivity at 25°C is 68.0×10^{-6}; whereas, for β-Pr at 820°C it is 132×10^{-6} ohm-cm. The Hall coefficient for α-Pr is $+0.709 \pm 0.008 \times 10^{-12}$ volt-cm/amp-oersted at 25°C; the work function is 2.7 ev; the electronegativity is 1.19; and the first ionization potential is 5.76 ev, while the sum of the first three ionization potentials is 37.5 ev.

In the pressure range 0-100,000 kg/cm^2, the coefficient of expansion, $\triangle V/V_o = -3.401 \times 10^{-6}$ (P-P$_o$) $+ 2.186 \times 10^{-11}$ (P-P$_o$)$^2 - 0.699 \times 10^{-16}$ (P-P$_o$)^3 when P is in kg/cm^2.

The lattice parameters of α-Pr increase with temperature according to the equation $a = 3.6702 + 1.66 \times 10^{-5}t$, and $c = 11.828 + 13.3 \times 10^{-5}t$ in the range 20-449°C. The rare earth metals have thermal conductivities about one-tenth that of the common metals. For α-Pr it is 0.028 ± 0.003 cal-cm/sec-cm^2-°C between 26-30°C. The isothermal compressibility for α-Pr is 3.16×10^{-6} cm^2/kg. The coefficient of thermal expansion is $4.8 \pm 0.6 \times 10^{-6}$ per °C, whereas, the average value in the temperature range -173 to $+800$ is 6.5×10^{-6} per °C.

The rare earth metals are almost uniformly soft; on the Vickers scale the hardness of α-Pr is 43 kg/mm^2. The yield strength is 10.0×10^8 dynes/cm^2; the ultimate tensile strength is $8.7 - 11.2 \times 10^8$ in tension and 32.4×10^8 dynes/cm^2 in compression. Young's modulus is 3.25×10^{11} dynes/cm^2 from sound velocity measurements and $4.8 - 9.6 \times 10^{11}$ dynes/cm^2 from stress strain observations. The shear modulus is 1.35×10^{11} dynes/cm^2, while Poisson's ratio is 0.305.

Chemical Properties

The preparation of praseodymium by reduction using another metal usually results in alloy formation; hence, the need for subsequent separation. Alloys of praseodymium with Al, Cu, Ga, Au, In, Pb, Mg, Ni and Ag have been prepared, their properties determined, and plausible phase diagrams proposed. Alloys have been observed with a very large number of other elements.

Of the rare earth metals, except cerium, praseodymium reacts most rapidly with dry oxygen. The parabolic law is observed for its oxidation. It would appear that the complex oxide system, to be described below, is less protective than the sesquioxide. The metal is very reactive towards almost any substance; hence, must be handled in inert atmospheres or in vacuum.

Praseodymium reacts to yield solid compounds containing essentially all the known

anions. Some of the specific compounds of praseodymium are discussed below.

Nitrates. Pr(NO$_3$)$_3$.6H$_2$O can easily be prepared either by reaction of the metal or oxide with nitric acid. The ignited compound decomposes to form PrONO$_3$ at 250°C in vacuum further decomposing to the oxide at 420°C.

Halides. The trihalides of praseodymium are prepared by dissolving the oxide in the appropriate halogen acid. Except for the fluoride the hexahydrate crystallizes from concentrated solution but is very soluble in water. The halide solution hydrolyzes readily forming the extremely insoluble oxyhalide. The tetrafluoride of praseodymium has been made in poor yield from the mixed alkali fluoride salt. This is the only tetravalent compound of praseodymium known except for the dioxide.

Sulfates. Anhydrous Pr$_2$(SO$_4$)$_3$ can be prepared. This salt has a negative temperature coefficient of solubility, a fact which is useful in gross separations.

Carbonates. Praseodymium carbonates of three kinds can be prepared by several methods. The normal carbonate, Pr$_2$(CO$_3$)$_3$·8H$_2$O, is conveniently prepared by the hydrolysis, under CO$_2$ pressure, of salts of the lower molecular weight organic acids—mainly acetates and butyrates. Without CO$_2$ pressure some carbonate is formed having a ratio CO$_2$·Pr$_2$O$_3$ close to two. This is a basic carbonate of possible formula, Pr$_2$(OH)$_2$(CO$_3$)$_2$·H$_2$O. When this compound or praseodymium oxalate is thermally decomposed a third carbonate, Pr$_2$O$_2$CO$_3$ with a ratio Pr$_2$O$_3$:CO$_2$ of one, is formed.

Oxalates. One of the most useful insoluble salts (K$_{SP} \cong 10^{-30}$) for precipitating praseodymium from solution for further treatment is the oxalate, Pr$_2$(C$_2$O$_4$)$_3$·10H$_2$O, which decomposes to the oxide at 850°C or above. All the compounds of the oxyacids thermally decompose at high temperature to yield the oxide.

Silicates. When praseodymium oxides are heated together with silica, compounds of the type, Pr$_2$O$_3$·SiO$_2$ and Pr$_2$O$_3$·3SiO$_2$, are formed. Numerous other oxysalts such as the sulfates, thiosulfates, hydroxides, chromates, molybdates, tungstates, and borates have been studied.

Pnictides (compounds with the Group VA

TABLE 1. PRASEODYMIUM COMPOUNDS

Compound	Structure	a(Å)	b(Å)	c(Å)	ρ, g/cc	χ × 10⁶ emu/mole	μeff	Curie temp., °K	Melting point, °C	Boiling point, °C	Note:
PrSb	cubic, NaCl	6.366			(6.761)		3.63				
PrAs	cubic, NaCl	6.009			(6.606)		3.80				
PrBe₁₃		10.367									
PrBi	cubic, NaCl	6.461					3.52				
PrB₃	pseudocubic	3.81			(5.20)						
PrB₄	tetragonal	7.20		4.11	(5.74)						
PrB₆	cubic	4.130			(4.851)	4800	3.37				
PrC	cubic, NaCl	5.131									
Pr₂C₃	b.c.c., Pu₂C₃	8.6072			(6.621)						
PrC₂	b.c. tetragonal, CaC₂	3.855		6.434	(5.73)	4500	(3.15)	5.2	2535		
PrGe	orthohombic	4.474	11.098	4.064	(6.78)						
PrGe₂	tetragonal, α-ThSi₂	4.253	13.940	7.48	7.24						
PrBr₃	hexagonal, UCl₃	7.422		4.275					693	1550	
PrCl₃	tetragonal	4.051		6.810					786	1710	
PrOCl	hexagonal, UCl₃	7.061		7.218							
PrF₃	rhombohedral	7.016			6.18				1395	2327	
PrOF					6.39						β = 33.03
PrI₃	orthohombic, PuBr₃	13.9	4.3	10.0					738	1380	
PrF₄											
PrH₂	f.c.c., CuF₂	5.517			5.65						
PrH₃	f.c.c., CaF₂				5.56						
PrN	cubic, NaCl	5.165			(7.467)	5616	3.66				
Pr₂O₃	cubic, Mn₂O₃	11.152				4410	3.6		2200		
	hexagonal (A type)										

Compound	Structure										
Pr_7O_{12}	rhombohedral	6.741			$\alpha = 99.28°$						
Pr_9O_{16}	triclinic	5.478	5.482	5.496	$\alpha = 90.15°$ $\beta = 90.50°$ $\gamma = 90.91°$						
$Pr_{10}O_{18}$	triclinic	5.482	5.482	5.482	$\alpha = \beta = 90.28°$ $\gamma = 90.09°$						
$Pr_{11}O_{20}$	triclinic	5.473	5.474	5.475	$\alpha = \beta = \gamma = 90.09°$						
$Pr_{12}O_{22}$	triclinic	5.466	5.466	5.465	$\alpha = \beta = \gamma = 90.08°$						
PrO_2	cubic, CaF_2	5.3932									
PrP	cubic, NaCl	5.872									
$PrSe$	cubic, NaCl	5.950				(6.932)	2540	2.8			
$PrSe_2$	hexagonal	8.39		8.46		6.66	1910	2.51			
Pr_2Se_3	b.c.c., Th_3P_4	8.909					4611	3.77			
Pr_3Se_4	b.c.c., Th_3P_4	8.927				6.89	4631	3.3			
Pr_2O_2Se	H.C.P.	4.01		7.04		6.65	4465	3.3			
$\alpha PrSi_2$	orthorhombic, α-VSi_2	4.23	4.40	13.68		(5.38)		3.38	10.5		$\alpha \rightarrow \beta$ at 153°K
$\beta PrSi_2$	tetragonal, α-$ThSi_2$	4.140		13.65		(5.64)					
PrS	cubic	5.747				(6.07)	4730			2230	
PrS_2	cubic	8.08				(4.90)	4800			1780	
γPr_2S_3	cubic	8.611				(5.27)	4640			1795	
Pr_3S_4	cubic	8.611				(5.77)				2100	
Pr_2O_2S	hexagonal	3.974		6.825		6.16					
$PrTe$	cubic, NaCl	6.322									
$PrTe_2$	tetragonal, Fe_2As	4.46		9.05							
Pr_2Te_3		9.482									
Pr_2O_2Te	hexagonal	4.06		12.83		6.6					

elements). The monopnictides all have the rock salt structure and interesting magnetic properties. They are all prepared by the direct reaction of the elements. Table 1 gives some structural, magnetic and other properties of many important binary compounds of praseodymium.

Oxides. The most thoroughly studied binary system of praseodymium is that of PrO_x-O_2. Praseodymium reacts with oxygen to form a large number of oxide phases in the composition range PrO_x, $1.5 \leq x \leq 2.0$. A projection of the phase diagram is shown in Fig. 1.

Praseodymium sesquioxide exists either in the hexagonal A-form or in the body-centered cubic C-form. The C-form sesquioxide and the fluorite-type dioxide, together with the intermediate phases (designated β, δ, ε, ζ, and ι), belong to an homologous series of narrow composition range having the formula, Pr_nO_{2n-2}, where n is 4, 7, 9, 10, 11, 12, ∞ for the stable phases observed. In addition, there are disordered phases designated α and σ existing over the entire composition range at higher temperature and pressure except for a narrow miscibility gap at a composition

of approximately $PrO_{1.7}$. When any of the oxides or salts of the oxyacids are ignited in air and cooled slowly the β phase Pr_6O_{11} is always formed. It can be seen from the diagram that this phase has a narrow composition limit. PrO_2 may be prepared by heating a lower oxide in oxygen at one atmosphere pressure and 300°C for many hours. It is also formed when $PrO_{1.833}$ is leached with dilute acids dissolving the Pr^{3+} fraction of the oxide.

All the phases shown in the figure are fluorite-related in the sense that the metal atoms show only slight shifts from the fluorite positions. The ordering in the oxide sublattice is unique to each phase.

In addition to the complex phase relationships illustrated in the phase diagram, there are order-disorder transformations and chemical hysteresis effects demonstrated by the system. The properties of these binary oxides and the transformations between them have important implications for solid state chemistry. See Table 1 for some properties of these compounds.

Chalcogenides. The remaining praseodymium chalcogenides (sulfides, selenides and

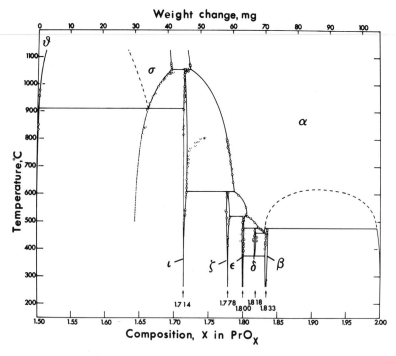

FIG. 1. Projection of the praseodymium oxide-oxygen phase diagram on the T,X plane. The experimental points are shown as small circles.

tellurides) may be prepared by direct reaction of the elements. See Table 1 for some properties.

Hydrides. Praseodymium reacts directly with hydrogen to form compounds in the composition range PrH_x, $0 \leq x \leq 3$. Equilibrium dissociation pressure measurements reveal that at moderate temperatures the metal takes up hydrogen to about $PrH_{0.1}$, then with increased hydrogen content transforms to PrH_2. This fluorite phase takes up hydrogen approaching PrH_3 at 200°C and 400 mm Hg hydrogen pressure (See Table 1).

Solution Chemistry. The formal oxidation potential for the $Pr^{3+} \longrightarrow Pr^{4+} + e^-$ couple has been estimated at -2.86v; for the reaction $Pr \longrightarrow Pr^{3+} + 3e^-$ a value of 2.47v is given.

The trivalent praseodymium ion occurs as $[Pr(H_2O)_n]^{3+}$ and is only weakly hydrolyzed in aqueous solution. Pr^{4+} is not stable in water but oxidizes it immediately yielding oxygen and the trivalent ion.

The trivalent ion is complexed in solution only by the strongest chelating agents. This is in contrast to the *d*-transition metal ions. Although weak associations are made by Pr^{3+} with many ligands, solid compounds can be separated from solution for only a few. The common logarithms of the stability constant for 1:1 complexes with praseodymium ion are: nitrilotriacetic acid, 11.07; *n*-hydroxyethylethylenediaminetriacetic acid 14.61; ethylenediaminetetraacetic acid, 16.40; 1,2-diaminocyclohexanetetraacetic acid, 17.23; and diethylenetriaminepentaacetic acid, 21.07.

Uses

Along with other rare earths praseodymium finds uses in catalysts, in a wide variety of metalurgical applications, in phosphors, lasers, in masers and in glass manufacture, both as a constituent and in polishing, and in electronic and thermoelectric materials. There are no extensive commercial uses of pure praseodymium or its salts.

References

1. Eyring, L., Editor, "Progress in the Science and Technology of the Rare Earths," Oxford, Pergamon Press, Vol. I 1964, Vol. II 1966.

2. Gschneidner, Karl A., Jr., "Rare Earth Alloys," Princeton, New Jersey, D. Van Nostrand Company, Inc., 1961.

3. Kleber, Eugene V., and Love, Bernard, "The Technology of Scandium, Yttrium and the Rare Earth Metals," New York, The Macmillan Company, 1963.

4. Moeller, Therald, "The Chemistry of the Lanthanides," New York, Reinhold Publishing Corporation, 1963.

5. Samsonov, Grigorii Valentinovich, "High-Temperature Compounds of Rare Earth Metals with Nonmetals," Authorized Translation, New York, Consultants Bureau, 1965.

6. Topp, N. E., "The Chemistry of the Rare-Earth Elements," Amsterdam, Elsevier Publishing Company, 1965.

7. Trifonov, D. N., "The Rare Earth Elements," translated by Prasenjit Basu, translation edited by R. C. Vickery, New York, The Macmillan Company, 1963.

8. Weeks, Mary Elvira, "Discovery of the Elements," 6th Edition, Published by the Journal of Chemical Education, Easton, Pennsylvania, 1956.

LeRoy Eyring

PREVALENCE OF THE ELEMENTS

"The chemical elements and their compounds have most complicated and varied properties which can not be described in terms of manageable theories and they are independent of the wills and arbitrary assumptions of chemists and astrophysicists." (Urey, 1966).

Much of the early data on elemental abundances was derived from geochemical investigations of the crust, ocean, and atmosphere of the earth. It was soon realized, however, that the earth is a highly differentiated cosmic body. We can analyze sea water, the gases of the air, and selected composites of crustal rocks and build up a compilation of abundances fairly representative of the surface of the earth. Yet, we can say little about the composition of the earth's mantle or core. Certainly, crustal abundances can not be taken as representative of the entire earth, and much less as representative of the solar system, or the cosmos.

Some of the best estimates for the primordial abundances (composition of the dust cloud from which the sun and the planets

TABLE 1. ATOMIC ABUNDANCES OF THE CHEMICAL ELEMENTS, RELATIVE TO SILICON = 10^6 ATOMS

Atomic number	Element	(1) Atomic weight	(2) Solar	(3) Ordinary chondrites	(4) Type I Carbonaceous chondrites	(5) Crustal abundances
1	H	1.0080	$10^{10.5}$	—	5,900,000	—
2	He	4.0026	—	0.11	—	—
3	Li	6.939	1.1	(45) (61)	50	290
4	Be	9.01	6.9	0.69	—	31
5	B	10.81	—	6.2	—	93
6	C	12.01	17,000,000	2,000	820,000	1,700
7	N	14.01	3,000,000	90	50,000	140
8	O	16.00	29,000,000	3,700,000	7,500,000	2,900,000
9	F	19.00	—	(260) (1100)	4,000	3,300
10	Ne	20.18	—	0.0015	—	—
11	Na	22.99	63,000	46,000	64,000	100,000
12	Mg	24.31	790,000	940,000	1,050,000	96,000
13	Al	26.98	50,000	60,000	85,100	300,000
14	Si	28.09	1,000,000	1,000,000	1,000,000	1,000,000
15	P	30.97	6,900	5,300	11,000	3,400
16	S	32.06	630,000	110,000	505,000	810
17	Cl	35.45	—	700	2,240	370
18	Ar	39.95	—	0.4	—	—
19	K	39.10	1,600	3,500	3,550	53,000
20	Ca	40.08	35,000	49,000	73,600	100,000
21	Sc	44.96	20	29	35	49
22	Ti	47.90	1,200	(2100) (3100)	2,300	12,000
23	V	50.94	420	200	298	260
24	Cr	52.00	2,500	6,600	11,900	190
25	Mn	54.94	2,000	7,400	8,820	1,700
26	Fe	55.85	120,000	690,000	890,000	100,000
27	Co	58.93	1,600	1,300	2,360	42
28	Ni	58.71	26,000	40,000	49,100	130
29	Cu	63.54	100	250	1,000	87
30	Zn	65.37	200	130	1,500	110
31	Ga	69.72	18	12	51	22
32	Ge	72.59	10	20	135	2.1
33	As	74.92	—	4.6	—	2.4

No.	El.	At. wt				
34	Se	78.96	—	19	89	0.063
35	Br	79.91	—	5	18.6	3.1
36	Kr	83.80	9.5	—		
37	Rb	85.47	150	(4.3) (5.9)	6.5	110
38	Sr	87.62	5	20	24	430
39	Y	88.91	14	3.4	4.6	37
40	Zr	91.22	6.3	(16) (58)	32	180
41	Nb	92.91	6.3	1	—	22
42	Mo	95.94	—	2.5	—	1.6
43	Tc	(99)		—	—	
44	Ru	101.07	2.1	1.5	4.2	—
45	Rh	102.91	0.7	0.25	0.96	—
46	Pd	106.4	0.6	(0.57) (1.3)	2.1	—
47	Ag	107.87	0.2	(0.05) (0.13)	1.6	0.065
48	Cd	112.40	1.4	0.079		0.18
49	In	114.82	0.9	0.0011		0.087
50	Sn	118.69	5.6	0.56	0.40	1.7
51	Sb	121.75	0.08	0.11		0.16
52	Te	127.60		0.60	2	
53	I	126.90		0.051		0.39
54	Xe	131.30		0.000007	—	
55	Cs	132.91	10	0.14	0.37	2.3
56	Ba	137.34		5	12	310
57	La	138.91		0.39	0.36	22
58	Ce	140.12		1.2	1.17	43
59	Pr	140.91		0.14	0.17	5.8
60	Nd	144.24		0.64	0.77	19
61	Pm	(147)				
62	Sm	150.35		0.23	0.23	4.0
63	Eu	151.96		0.082	0.091	0.79
64	Gd	157.25		0.34	0.55	3.4
65	Tb	158.92		0.051	0.037	0.57
66	Dy	162.50		0.33	0.36	1.8
67	Ho	164.93		0.076	0.09	0.73
68	Er	167.26		0.23	0.22	1.7
69	Tm	168.93		0.031	0.035	0.28
70	Yb	173.04	1	0.18	0.21	1.7
71	Lu	174.97		0.031	0.035	0.29
72	Hf	178.49		0.17	—	1.7

TABLE 1—*continued*

Atomic number	Element	(1) Atomic weight	(2) Solar	(3) Ordinary chondrites	(4) Type I Carbonaceous chondrites	(5) Crustal abundances
73	Ta	180.95	—	0.016	—	1.1
74	W	183.85	—	0.12	—	0.82
75	Re	186.2	—	0.046	0.05	—
76	Os	190.2	—	0.54	0.62	—
77	Ir	192.2	—	0.35	0.49	—
78	Pt	195.09	—	1.3	—	—
79	Au	196.97	—	0.18	0.22	0.002
80	Hg	200.59	—	0.1	29	0.04
81	Tl	204.37	1.4	0.001	0.18	0.22
82	Pb	207.19	—	0.14	3.8	6.0
83	Bi	208.98	—	0.002	0.17	0.08
84	Po	(210)	—	—	—	—
85	At	(210)	—	—	—	—
86	Rn	(222)	—	—	—	—
87	Fr	(223)	—	—	—	—
88	Ra	(226)	—	—	—	—
89	Ac	(227)	—	—	—	—
90	Th	232.04	—	0.027	0.070	4.1
91	Pa	(231)	—	—	—	—
92	U	238.03	—	0.009	0.026	1.1

(1) 1961 International Atomic Weights based on C^{12}. "*Handbook of Chemistry and Physics*," 44th Edition, Sandusky, Ohio, Chemical Rubber Publishing Co., 1962–1963.

(2) Based on Goldberg, *et al* (1960) and Aller (1964).

(3) Based on compilations by Ehmann (1961), Wood (1963), and largely on Urey (1964), supplemented by recent determinations for several elements. The SiO_2 content of ordinary chondrites is taken to be 38.5 %, as in Urey (1964). The approximate chondritic abundances in units of parts per million by weight may be obtained from the atomic abundances listed by use of the equation:

$$\text{(ppm by weight)} = 6.32 \times 10^{-3} \text{ (Atomic Weight) (Atomic Abundance)}$$

(4) Based on the compilation of Ringwood (1966) and supplemented by various recent determinations. The SiO_2 content of the Type I carbonaceous chondrites is approximately 31.5 % on a water- and carbon-free basis. On this basis abundances in units of ppm by weight may be obtained from the atomic abundances listed by use of the equation:

$$\text{(ppm by weight)} = 5.24 \times 10^{-3} \text{ (Atomic Weight) (Atomic Abundance)}$$

(5) Derived from the compilation of Taylor (1964), assuming a 1:1 weight mixture of granitic and basaltic (Mohole and Atlantic Ridge) components. On this basis the SiO_2 content of the crust is 60.3 %. The atomic crustal abundances listed may be converted to units of ppm by weight by use of the equation:

$$\text{(ppm by weight)} = 1 \times 10^{-2} \text{ (Atomic Weight) (Atomic Abundance)}$$

condensed) of the elements are derived from the analyses of spectra of light emitted by gaseous nebulae and the atmospheres of the sun and the stars. These sources are probably little affected by the loss of volatile elements, as are the meteorites and the earth. The light emitting regions of the sun and the stars, however, may not be truly representative of the composition of the interiors of these objects. Any compilation of elemental abundances for objects as large as the earth or the sun must involve many assumptions and the derivation of any scale of primordial abundances from available experimental measurements is subject to even more uncertainties.

Our sun appears to be a "typical" star and an enormous amount of effort has been placed in the analysis of its atmospheric spectrum. A compilation of recent solar abundances in terms of atoms per 10^6 atoms of silicon is given in Table 1. Unfortunately, these spectral observations are very difficult to make and to interpret. Therefore, many elements are as yet undetermined in the solar atmosphere.

It was suggested by Urey and Craig (1953) that a certain class of the stony meteorites called the chondrites (derived from the fact that they contain abundant spherical mineral inclusions known as chondrules) might be a good average sample for the determination of the relative solar system abundances of the nonvolatile elements. This postulate was supported by the generally good agreement obtained in the comparison of chondritic abundances with many of the spectrographic solar abundances. Chondrites make up approximately 85% of all observed meteorite falls and according to some theories may be fragments of the mantle of parent meteorite bodies once present in the asteroid belt between Jupiter and Mars. Urey (1959) has suggested that the chondrites may have derived from the surface of the moon. In any case, these objects must be far more primitive, and hence more representative of primordial cosmic abundances, than any terrestrial material. A compilation of recently determined atomic abundances in the chondrites relative to silicon = 10^6 atoms is also given in Table 1.

Where widely different analytical data appear in the literature, the values are given

in parentheses. No attempt is made in a brief presentation such as this to list individual references for the data.

Using compilations of abundance data largely from analyses of chondritic meteorites, Suess and Urey (1956) plotted the logarithm of the relative atomic abundances versus atomic weights for the stable nuclei (Fig. 1).

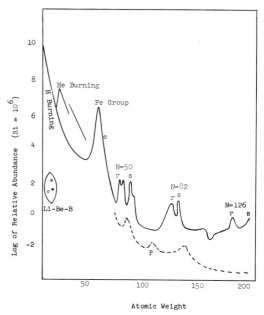

FIG. 1. Schematic abundance curve *(Suess and Urey, 1956)*.

From this plot it is obvious that there is an approximately exponential decrease in abundance with an increase in atomic weight until approximately mass 100. After this, there is a much slower decrease on which are superimposed rather distinct fluctuations. In addition, it is noted that there is a distinct depletion of Li, B, Be, and deuterium relative to neighboring elements, a large abundance peak in the region of Fe, enrichment of nuclei that are simple multiples in atomic number and mass number of the alpha particle, and a tendency for the heavy nuclei to be neutron-rich.

Observations of this type coupled with calculations using the data of nuclear physics have led to the development of theories of nucleosynthesis. Burbidge, *et al* (1957) assumed that the elements are all synthesized from hydrogen and that this process is still

571

taking place today in the sun and the stars. To account for the observed features of the experimental abundances curves, Burbidge *et al* postulated eight different processes in nucleosynthesis. These are listed below:

(1) Hydrogen burning to produce helium.

$$H^1 + H^1 \rightarrow H^2 + \beta^+ + \nu$$
$$H^2 + H^1 \rightarrow He^3 + \gamma$$
$$He^3 + He^3 \rightarrow He^4 + 2H^1, \text{ etc.}$$

(2) Helium burning to produce carbon, oxygen and neon.

$$3He^4 \rightarrow C^{12}$$
$$C^{12} + He^4 \rightarrow O^{16}, \text{ etc.}$$

(3) Alpha capture processes to produce the "alpha particle nuclei," such as Mg^{24}.

$$Ne^{20} + He^4 \rightarrow Mg^{24} + \gamma$$

(4) An equilibrium process, involving a variety of simple nuclear reactions. Free protons and neutrons interact with the lighter elements produced above leading to the formation of elements principally in the region of iron. Stellar temperatures at this point would exceed $10^9 °K$.

(5) Neutron capture reactions on a slow time scale (s-process) in which neutrons are captured by seed nuclei in the iron region to form radioactive nuclei which decay by negatron emission. Many nuclei in the region between iron and bismuth are produced by this process. The rate of neutron capture is slow enough that the radioactive product nuclei have time to decay on the average before another neutron capture takes place.

$$Co^{59} + n \rightarrow Co^{60} + \gamma$$
$$Co^{60} \rightarrow Ni^{60} + \beta^- + \gamma, \text{ etc.}$$

(6) Neutron capture reactions on a fast time scale (r-process) in which a number of neutrons are captured in succession by seed nuclei before a negatron decay can take place. This process probably takes place in supernovae and leads to the formation of many heavy nuclei, including thorium and uranium.

(7) Processes probably involving spallation reactions to produce the light elements lithium, beryllium, and boron from heavier nuclei.

(8) Addition of protons to various heavy nuclei to produce certain proton-rich nuclei.

While these theories of nucleosynthesis predicted the main features of the chondritic abundance curve, there were several severe discrepancies for certain volatile elements, such as Bi, Tl, Hg, Pb, and In. Experimental abundances of these elements in the chondrites were much lower than would be predicted by theory. Several investigators suggested that a rare type of chondrites called the Type I carbonaceous chondrites are better average samples of solar system matter than the ordinary chondrites. These meteorites contain significant amounts of water, sulfur, and various volatile organic compounds. Even if they are not, in fact, the primitive matter from which the solar system evolved, they certainly exhibit less differentiation than either the chondrites as a whole, or the earth. Indeed, the experimental abundances of the volatile elements in the Type I carbonaceous chondrites have been found to agree quite closely with the predictions of theories of nucleosynthesis. The relative atomic abundances of elements in this class of meteorites are also listed in Table 1.

While there are many points of general agreement of solar abundances with the chondritic values, several serious discrepancies may be noted. These discrepancies, such as in the case of iron, have not yet been satisfactorily explained.

In discussing the prevalence of the elements in the earth's crust, it is recognized that wide-scale chemical differentiation processes have altered the distribution of abundances in the original dust cloud from which the earth formed. Factors such as ionic size, valency, and bond type are important in controlling the distribution of the elements in mineral lattices. Taylor (1966) has divided the elements into eight groups based on their geochemical association in common rocks and minerals (Table 2.) The principal advantage of such a classification is that elements whose geochemical behaviors are similar and whose ratios are significant in geological processes are brought together.

The crust of the earth makes up only about 0.4% by mass of the entire mass of the earth. It is a difficult task to select a group of samples that would best represent the composition of the earth's crust. Clarke and Washington (1924) compiled a table of crustal abundances

TABLE 2. GEOCHEMICAL ASSOCIATION OF THE ELEMENTS IN COMMON ROCKS AND MINERALS (Taylor, 1966)

Geochemical Group	Ions
Large cations (potassium type)	Cs^+, Rb^+, Tl^+, Ba^{2+}, K^+, Eu^{2+} Pb^{2+}, Sr^{2+}, Ca^{2+}, Na^+
Large highly charged cations (zirconium type)	Th^{4+}, U^{4+}, Ce^{4+}, Zr^{4+}, Hf^{4+} Sn^{4+}, Nb^{5+}, Ta^{5+}, Ti^{4+}, Mo^{6+}, W^{6+}
Rare earths	La^{3+}, Ce^{3+}, Pr^{3+}, Nd^{3+}, Sm^{3+}, Eu^{3+}, Gd^{3+}, Tb^{3+}, Dy^{3+}, Ho^{3+}, Er^{3+}, Tm^{3+}, Yb^{3+}, Lu^{3+}, Y^{3+}
Ferromagnesium elements	Mn^{2+}, Fe^{2+}, Zn^{2+}, Cu^{2+}, Co^{2+}, Ni^{2+}, Li^+, Mg^{2+}, Sc^{3+}, V^{3+}, Ti^{4+}, Fe^{3+}, Cr^{3+}, Ga^{3+}, Al^{3+}
Small cations (silicon type)	Al^{3+}, Ge^{3+}, Si^{4+}, P^{5+}, Be^{2+}, B^{3+}
Chalcophile elements	Tl^+, Ag^+, Pb^{2+}, Hg^{2+}, Cd^{2+}, Bi^{3+}, In^{3+}, Sb^{3+}, Fe^{2+}, Zn^{2+}, Cu^{2+}, Co^{2+}, Sn^{4+}, Ni^{2+}, Mo^{6+}, As^{3+}, Ga^{3+}, Te^{6+}, Ge^{4+}, Se^{6+}
Platinum elements	Rh^{3+}, Os^{4+}, Ir^{4+}, Ru^{4+}, Pt^{2+}, Pd^{2+}, Au
Anions	Te^{2-}, Se^{2-}, I^-, Br^-, S^{2-}, Cl^- O^{2-}, F^-

based on extensive analyses of igneous rocks. The results of the former work were found to agree well with abundance data obtained from the analyses of glacial clays by Goldschmidt (1933). The erosional processes forming these clays had therefore resulted in a type of natural averaging process. There is still not widespread agreement on the best materials to select for computing crustal abundances. One recent proposal by Taylor (1964, 1965) uses a 1:1 weight mixture of granitic and basaltic rocks. The basalts chosen are those from the Atlantic Ridge and the preliminary Mohole experiments. Calculated atomic abundances relative to silicon as 10^6 based on this proposal are given in Table 1.

The order of abundance of the chemical elements in the continental crust is listed in Table 3.

In the common usage concerning the earth's crust the majority of the chemical elements are referred to as "rare elements." This is certainly a relative term and the classification of a given element as "rare" in the earth's crust depends on several factors. First, of course, the element may have a low absolute abundance in the earth's crust, such as the rare gases. Second, the element may not form any minerals of its own and may appear among the "left-over" elements at the end phase of magmatic crystallization. Rubidium is much more abundant than copper, but forms no minerals of its own and its resultant dispersion in the crust accounts for its common inclusion among the "rare" elements. Finally, certain elements have little current economic importance and are classified as "rare" merely because they are rarely re-

TABLE 3.   ORDER OF ABUNDANCE OF ELEMENTS IN THE CONTINENTAL CRUST IN PARTS PER MILLION OR GRAMS PER TON

Element	Ppm	Element	Ppm	Element	Ppm
O	464,000	La	30	Ge	1.5
Si	281,500	Nd	28	Eu	1.2
Al	82,300	Co	25	Ho	1.2
Fe	56,300	Sc	22	Tb	0.9
Ca	41,500	Li	20	Lu	0.5
Na	23,600	N	20	I	0.5
Mg	23,300	Nb	20	Tm	0.48
K	20,900	Ga	15	Tl	0.45
Ti	5,700	Pb	12.5	Sb	0.2
H	1,400 (1)	B	10	Cd	0.2
P	1,050	Th	9.6	Bi	0.17
Mn	950	Pr	8.2	In	0.1
F	625	Sm	6.0	Hg	0.08
Ba	425	Gd	5.4	Ag	0.07
Sr	375	Dy	3.0	Se	0.05
S	260	Yb	3.0	Ar	0.04 (1)
C	200	Hf	3.0	Pd	0.01 (1)
Zr	165	Cs	3.0	Pt	0.005 (1)
V	135	Be	2.8	Au	0.004
Cl	130	Er	2.8	He	0.003 (1)
Cr	100	U	2.7	Te	0.002 (1)
Rb	90	Br	2.5	Rh	0.001 (1)
Ni	75	Sn	2.0	Re	0.001 (1)
Zn	70	Ta	2.0	Ir	0.001 (1)
Ce	60	As	1.8	Os	0.001 (1)
Cu	55	Mo	1.5	Ru	0.001 (1)
Y	33	W	1.5		

(1) Data for concentration in the earth's crust from Mason, B., "Principles of Geochemistry," New York, John Wiley & Sons, Inc. 1952.
All other data from Taylor, S. R., *Geochim. et Cosmochim. Acta,* **28,** 1273–1285 (1964).

covered. Until recently, titanium was among this group of elements.

The oceans of the world comprise the largest aqueous chemical system we know of. The oceans contain chemical species of all the elements found on the earth, yet only 12 have concentrations equal to or greater than one part per million by weight. Most of the chemical reactions occurring in the ocean system occur at the water-atmosphere, water-biosphere, or water-sediment interfaces. Over the long geologic lifetime of the oceans it might be expected that chemical equilibration would have been reached. However, large masses of the ocean are out of contact with one or the other of these interfaces and unstable chemical species are, indeed, present in varying amounts. A recent compilation of elemental abundances in sea water in units of microgams per liter of sea water is given in Table 4.

Two suggestions have been made relating to the evolution of the oceans. The first suggests that they have accreted continuously, but not necessarily uniformly, through geologic time. The second suggests the oceans and the atmosphere are residual from a primitive atmosphere that surrounded the earth during the early stages of its formation. Certain elements, such as the halogens seem to be too abundant in the atmosphere-biosphere-ocean system to have been derived from the mere weathering of crustal rocks. Possibly some of these elements were released from instrusive and extrusive rocks that have continuously risen from the interior of the earth. Table 5 lists the ratios of the concentration of selected elements in average crustal

TABLE 4. CHEMICAL COMPOSITION OF SEA WATER (Goldberg, 1961)

Element	Order of Abundance	Micrograms/liter	Element	Order of Abundance	Micrograms/liter
H	2	1.08×10^8	Ge	51	0.07
He	58	0.005	As	31	3
Li	17	200	Se	27	4
Be	60	0.0006	Br	9	65,000
B	12	4,600	Kr	44	0.3
C	10	28,000	Rb	18	120
N	16	500	Sr	11	8,000
O	1	8.57×10^8	Y	41	0.3
F	13	1,300	Nb	56	0.01
Ne	50	0.1	Mo	26	10
Na	4	1.05×10^7	Ag	42	0.3
Mg	5	1.35×10^6	Cd	46	0.11
Al	23	10	In	22	< 20
Si	13	3,000	Sn	29	3
P	19	70	Sb	39	0.5
S	6	8.85×10^5	I	20	60
Cl	3	1.9×10^7	Xe	49	0.1
Ar	15	600	Cs	37	0.5
K	8	3.8×10^5	Ba	21	30
Ca	7	4.0×10^5	Ta	43	0.3
Sc	53	0.04	Ce	41	0.4
Ti	35	1	W	48	0.1
V	34	2	Au	59	0.004
Cr	52	0.05	Hg	54	0.03
Mn	32	2	Tl	57	< 0.01
Fe	24	10	Pb	47	0.1
Co	38	0.5	Bi	45	0.2
Ni	33	2	Rn	62	6×10^{-16}
Cu	28	3	Ra	61	1×10^{-10}
Zn	25	10	Th	36	0.7
Ga	55	0.03	U	30	3

Note: Atomic Abundance $(Si = 10^6) = \dfrac{9362\,(\mu\,g\,element/liter)}{Atomic\ Weight}$ based on silicon content of average sea water $= 3000\,\mu\,g/liter$.

TABLE 5. RATIOS OF CONCENTRATION OF CERTAIN ELEMENTS IN AVERAGE CRUSTAL MATERIAL TO THEIR CONCENTRATION IN AVERAGE SEA WATER NORMALIZED TO SILICA (Schutz and Turekian, 1965)

Al	700	P	0.1
Zr	150	Ni	0.1
Fe	70	Mo	0.0009
Ti	40	K	0.0008
Mn	3	Ag	0.0007
Pb	1	Sr	0.0004
Cr	1	Mg	0.00009
Si	1	I	0.00008
V	0.5	Na	0.00002
Ba	0.5	S	0.00001
Co	0.4	Cl	7.5×10^{-9}

material to their concentration in average sea water normalized to silica. The high ratios are common for elements that form hydrous precipitates in sea water and, hence, are selectively removed as sediments. The great enrichment of chlorine in the oceans is evident.

The study of elemental abundances is continuing today at a rapid pace. Modern sensitive techniques of analysis, such as activation analysis, x-ray analysis, and spark source mass spectrometry are playing a major role in these studies. New and important materials such as Mohole cores and lunar surface rocks may soon be available for study. Data on elemental abundances are essential in the development of theories for nucleo-synthesis, the evolution of the solar system, and the differentiation processes operative in the formation of the earth.

References

1. Aller, L. H., "Advances in Astronomy and Astrophysics," Vol. III, New York, Academic Press, 1964.
2. Aller, L. H., "The Abundance of the Elements," New York, Interscience Publishers, 1961.
3. Burbidge, E. M., Burbidge, G. R., Fowler, W. A., and Hoyle, F., *Rev. Mod. Phys.*, **29**, 548–650 (1957).
4. Cherdyntsev, V. V., "Abundance of Chemical Elements," Chicago, University of Chicago Press, 1961.
5. Clarke, F. W., and Washington, H. S., Washington, D.C., U.S. Geological Survey Prof. Paper 127, 1924.
6. Ehmann, W. D., *J. Chem. Education,* **38**, 53–57 (1961).
7. Goldberg, E. D., *Ann. Rev. Phys. Chem.,* **12**, 29–48 (1961).
8. Goldberg, L., Muller, E., and Aller, L. H., *Ap. J. Suppl.,* **5**, No. 45 (1960).
9. Goldschmidt, V. M., "Geochemistry," London, Oxford University Press, 1954.
10. Goldschmidt, V. M., *Fortsch. Min. Krist. Petrog.,* **17**, 112 (1933).
11. Rankama, K., and Sahama, S., "Geochemistry," Chicago, University of Chicago Press, 1950.
12. Ringwood, A. E., *Rev. Geophys.*, **4**, 113–175 (1966).
13. Schutz, D. F., and Turekian, K. K., *Geochim. et Cosmochim. Acta*, **29**, 259–313 (1965).
14. Suess, H. E., and Urey, H. C., *Rev. Mod. Phys.,* **28**, 53–74 (1956).
15. Taylor, S. R., *Geochim. et Cosmochim. Acta,* **28**, 1273–1285 (1964); ibid., **29**, 145–146 (1965).
16. Taylor, S. R., Preprint, Australian National University, 1966.
17. Urey, H. C., *Rev. Geophys.,* **2**, 1–34 (1964).
18. Urey, H. C., and Craig, H., *Geochim. et Cosmochin. Acta,* **4**, 36–82 (1953).
19. Urey, H. C., *J. Geophys. Res.,* **64**, 1721–1737 (1959).
20. Urey, H. C., *Monthly Notices Roy. Astron. Soc.,* **131**, 199–223 (1966).
21. Wood, J. A., "The Moon, Meteorites, and Comets," pp. 337–401, Chicago, University of Chicago Press, 1963.

WILLIAM D. EHMANN

PROMETHIUM

Promethium, symbol Pm, atomic number 61, is named after Prometheus, who, according to Greek mythology, brought fire to man.

Discovery

According to Moseley's law, there should be 14 elements in the lanthanide series, 13 of which are known to occur in nature in sufficient abundance to allow their isolation in substantial quantities. From evidence of x-ray emission spectra, the 14th, missing element of this series should occupy position No. 61 in the Periodic Table, intermediate between neodymium (No. 60), and samarium (No. 62). Many attempts have been made to isolate and identify the missing element in natural sources; however, no positive proof of natural occurance was given until 1965, when O. Erämetsä found traces of element 61 in nature. In working up 6,000 tons of apatite, he recovered 20 tons of rare earths. From this material, 350 mg of a fraction was obtained, which showed a 220 KeV β^- activity, which is believed to originate in traces of 61^{147} contained in that fraction, thus giving an abundance of 45×10^{-20} for element 61 in natural lanthanide mixtures.

Of the earlier attempts to discover element 61 in nature, the most important ones are those of Harris, Hopkins, and Yntema (claim for "Illinium" after the state of Illinois) and of Rolla, Fernandes, and Brunetti (claim for "Florentium," after the city of Florence), none of which could be substantiated.

Discovery is now credited to J. A. Marinsky and L. E. Glendenin, who identified long-lived 61^{147} in uranium fission products in 1945. They suggested the name promethium (originally: prometheum), symbol Pm. This name was accepted by the IUPAC committee on new elements in 1949.

Nuclear Properties

Table 1 gives a survey of the promethium isotopes known to date, with their half-lives and principal modes of decay.

As can be seen from Table 1, the longest-lived species is Pm^{145}, half-life 18 years. This excludes a natural occurance of promethium in nature, because there is no known source with which any of the long-lived promethium

TABLE 1. NUCLIDES OF PROMETHIUM

Mass	Half-life	Mode of Decay	Mass	Half-life	Mode of Decay
140	5.8 minutes	β^+, γ	148	42 days	β^-, γ
141	20.9 minutes	β^+, γ	149	54.4 hours	β^-, γ
142	34 sec	β^+, E.C., γ	150	161 minutes	β^-, γ
143	265 days	E.C., γ	151	27.5 hours	β^-, γ
144	377 days	E.C., γ	152	6.5 minutes	β^-
145	18 years	E.C., γ	153?	5.5 minutes	β^-, γ
146	1.94 years	β^-, γ, E.C.	154	2.5 minutes	β^-
147	2.64 years	β^-, γ	155?	< 5 minutes	β^-
148m	5.3 days	β^-, γ	156?	< 5 minutes	β^-

isotopes Pm^{145}, Pm^{146}, or Pm^{147} is in secular equilibrium. The traces allegedly found in nature probably have their origin in nuclear reactions excited by cosmic radiation or natural neutrons. Artificial promethium only has become available in substantial quantities, Pm^{147} being the only isotope isolated by 1966 in major amounts.

Isolation

Pm^{147} was first isolated in 1948 at Oak Ridge National Laboratory by G. W. Parker, and P. M. Lantz, who obtained 4.5 mg from fission product waste, and prepared the first compounds (oxalate, hydrated chloride, hydrated nitrate, oxide). Ever since, increasing quantities have been isolated from fission product waste. The first separations yielding gram quantities of promethium-147 were carried out in 1962 by P. B. Orr at Oak Ridge, and by E. J. Wheelwright and F. P. Roberts at Hanford. In 1966, the latter group isolated, an additional large quantity (about 1 kg). The method used in isolation of the promethium consists of elution from Dowex 50 using either ethylenediaminetetraacetic acid (EDTA), or diethylenetriaminepentaacetic acid (DTPA) as complexing agents. A product with 99% pure Pm^{147} is obtained immediately upon purification. However, on standing, Sm^{147} grows into the promethium by radioactive decay at a rate of 0.07%/day, requiring periodic "cleanup" operations, if chemically pure promethium is desired. On the milligram scale, α-hydroxy-isobutyric acid may be used successfully for this purpose. Large-scale isolation of promethium-147 is a hot cell operation; quantities up to 100 mg may be handled safely in a glovebox.

Spectroscopic Properties

Various spectroscopic properties of promethium are known. X-ray emission spectra were obtained by Peed and coworkers at Oak Ridge in 1948. Values of 319.02 XU for Pm K_{a1} and 323.68 XU for Pm K_{a2} were found. The line positions gave definite proof that promethium is identical with element 61. The arc emission spectrum was studied by C. Feldman at Oak Ridge; his results showed the absence of "Illinium" lines. The spark spectrum was taken by D. L. Timma in 1949; later, Meggers at the National Bureau of Standards made a more detailed study of the emission spectra. For analytical purposes, the following lines in the spark spectrum may be used: 3980.73 Å, 3957.74 Å, 3910.26 Å, 3711.77 Å. More recently, Orr and coworkers at Oak Ridge have established a primary spectrographic standard for promethium.

The absorption spectra of Pm have been studied by many workers. The solutions of promethium (III) show colors from bright yellow to purplish-pink. Sometimes, lavender, crimson or scarlet colors are observed. Due to their high radioactivity, promethium salts luminesce in the dark with a pale blue or greenish glow. The spectrum of this glow was studied by Conway on the solid chloride. The hyperfine structure of the promethium-147 levels was studied by R. F. Marrus and coworkers at Berkeley. The electronic configuration of the Pm atom is $4f^5 6s^2$ ($^6H_{5/2}$) from spectroscopic data.

Metallic Promethium

Very little is known about the properties of metallic promethium. The metal was first prepared by F. Weigel at the University of

577

Munich in 1963. Reduction of promethium (III) fluoride with lithium metal at 700-800°C in a vacuum of better than 10^{-6} mm Hg and subsequent heating to 1100°C in a double tantalum crucible system yields small, shiny globules of promethium metal. The color is silvery white, sometimes with a golden cast (probably nitride or lower oxide skin). From a major series of reduction experiments, a m.p. of ~1080°C is inferred. Attempts of a direct determination of the m.p. using the solder-rupture method of Cunningham and McWhan yielded an apparent m.p. of 850 ± 40°C. From recent (1965) experiments, this is now believed to be an allotropic transformation point at which the metal softens. The existence of at least two allotropic modifications is therefore probable. X-ray data on the metal could not yet be fully interpreted. At 1200°C, in a vacuum of 10^{-6} mm Hg, Pm metal is somewhat volatile.

Solid State Chemistry

Prior to 1965, only five compounds of the element had been reported: the four compounds prepared by Parker in 1948, and the fluoride. In 1965 and 1966 Weigel and V. Scherer made the first detailed study of solid promethium compounds and identified some 30 different compounds by comparison of their x-ray powder patterns with those of the corresponding Nd and Sm compounds. Table 2 is a survey of all compounds known prior to June 1966.

The data are definite proof for the intermediate position of promethium between neodymium and samarium. In general, they fit satisfactorily into the corresponding isomorphic series of lanthanide compounds. No valence except Pm^{3+} could be identified with certainty until 1966.

Ionic Radius

From x-ray data, the ionic radius of Pm^{3+} has been determined to be, $r(Pm^{3+}) = (0.981 ± 0.002)$ Å, in good agreement with D. H. Templeton's calculated value of 0.979 Å.

Applications

Several applications for promethium have been considered, some have been made in practice. All of them utilize the radioactive properties of the long-lived Pm^{147}. With a half-life of 2.64 years, this species has a specific activity of 940 curies per gram, corresponding to $(2.026 ± 0.048) \times 10^{15}$ dis/min/g. Wheelwright and coworkers, by means of calorimetric methods, determined the power density of Pm^{147} to be 0.33 watts/g. Therefore, Pm^{147} seems to be a useful source material for space power sources (SNAP generators). Large quantities of Pm^{147} are used in luminescent paint for watch dials. In 1964, Weigel and Scherer found evidence that certain compounds of Pm^{147}, like the tungstate or molybdate, may be used as homogenous x-ray sources. The 223 KeVβ's of the promethium were found to excite the x-ray spectra of Mo, and W, the x-ray intensity depending on the ratios Pm:Mo and Pm:W, respectively.

A novel application of promethium-147 has been studied recently by Russell H. Barnes and coworkers[10]. It is what is called a betavoltaic battery. A betavoltaic battery consists of a thin layer of Pm^{147} sandwiched between two n-on-p silicon solar cells, and encapsulated in a stainless steel case. The batteries operate as follows: The region in the vicinity of the semiconductor junction is ionized by the beta particles of the promethium. This ionization increases the minority carrier concentration over the normal equilibrium values on both sides of the junction. The carriers generated within a diffusion length of the junction can move to the junction and can flow across it under the influence of the junction potential. The current thus produced is proportional to the energy absorbed within the junction, and is available to drive an external load. With a Pm^{147} charge of 2 curies as Pm_2O_3, 713 mw of beta-energy are primarily generated, corresponding to a beta-current of 1.2×10^{-8} amp, ~1.1% of which is converted into useful electrical energy.

Precautions in handling

Promethium-147, the isotope with the most widespread use, requires stringent precautions in its handling because of its high radioactivity. In large-scale separations work, hot cells with primary enclosures should be used, for larger quantities of highly purified Pm^{147} shielded gloveboxes are recommended; amounts up to ~100 mg may be safely

TABLE 2. PHYSICAL PROPERTIES OF PROMETHIUM COMPOUNDS

No.	Compound (Formula)	Color	Crystal system	a[Å]	b[Å]	c[Å]	β[°]	v[Å³]	X-ray density [gcm⁻³]
1	PmF_3	pink	hexag'l	6.97	—	7.19	—	302.4	6.72
2	$PmCl_3$	lavender	hexag'l	7.40	—	4.21	—	199.5	4.19
3	$PmBr_3$	coral-red	orthorh	12.65	4.08	9.12	—	470.7	5.45
4	$PmCl_3 \cdot xH_2O$	yellow	?			yet unknown			
5	$PmOF$	purplish-pink	fcc or	5.50	—	—	—	172	7.03
			tetrag'l	5.95	—	5.58	—	87.1	6.94
6	$PmOCl$	pale pink	tetrag'l	4.02	—	4.74	—	109	6.03
7	$PmOBr(?)$	pale pink	tetrag'l	3.98	—	7.56	—	120	6.72
8	$PmOI$	pale lav	tetrag'l	4.01	—	9.18	—	147.6	6.52
9	$Pm(IO_3)_3 \cdot xH_2O$	yel-pink	?		pattern taken, not yet interpreted				
10	$PmO(PmN?)$	metallic?	fcc	5.05	—	—	—	129	
11	Pm_2O_3(A-type)	lavender	hexag'l	3.80	—	5.95	—	74.5	7.62
12	Pm_2O_3(B-type)	purp-pink	monoc'l	14.26	3.65	8.94	100.5	458.5	7.45
13	Pm_2O_3(C-type)	coral-red	cubic	10.99	—	—	—	1327	6.84
14	$Pm(OH)_3$	purp-pink	hexag'l	6.39	—	3.68	—	130.1	5.1
15	$Pm(NO_3)_3 \cdot xH_2O$	purp-pink				yet unknown			
16	$PmPO_4[0 \cdots 0.5]H_2O$	pale lav	hexag'l	6.99	—	6.35	—	268.7	4.49 -4.65
17	$PmPO_4$	garnet-red	monoc'l	6.72	6.89	6.37	104.3	285.8	5.62
18	$PmAsO_4$	pink	tetrag'l	7.31	—	6.43	—	343.7	5.53
19	$PmCrO_4(?)$	green(?)	tetrag'l	7.28	—	6.37	—	338	5.17
20	$PmVO_4$	coral-red	tetrag'l	7.31	—	6.41	—	342.5	5.91
21	$PmCrO_3$	green(?)	orthorh	5.40	5.49	7.69	—	228	7.20
22	$PmBO_3$	pale lav	orthorh	5.70	8.07	5.02	—	230.9	5.91
23	$PmScO_3$	pale lav	orthorh	5.56	5.79	7.94	—	255.6	6.24
24	$PmInO_3$	lavender	orthorh	5.70	8.20	5.90	—	—	—
25	$Pm_2(CrO_4)_3 \cdot xH_2O$	yellow				yet unknown			
26	$Pm_2(MoO_4)_3$	coral-red	monoc'l	9.55	11.68	11.77	120.8	890.3	—
27	$Pm_2(WO_4)_3$	coral-red	monoc'l	7.73	11.55	11.44	109.7	961.6	7.17
28	$Pm_2(CO_3)_3 \cdot 2H_2O$	pale pink	pseudoc	14.77	—	—	—	—	—
29	$Pm_2(C_2O_4)_3 \cdot 10H_2O$	purp-pink	monoc'l	11.14	9.64	10.19	114.4	996.5	2.46
30	$Pm(HCOO)_3$	pale lav	hexag'l	10.57	—	4.04	—	390.0	—
31	$Pm(CCl_3 \cdot COO)_3$	pink			pattern taken, not yet interpreted				

handled in light standard gloveboxes. Lucite or homalite effectively shield Pm [147] sources; for large quantities lead or depleted uranium should be used. Particular care should be taken, when Pm[147] compounds containing heavy elements are being handled, because penetrating x-rays may be emitted. Lead rubber gloves (Rad Bar) are recommended in that case and palm films should be worn. Standard portable radiation monitors are rather insensitive to Pm[147] betas, because of the low energy. Highly sensitive β-probes of the type used for C[14] monitoring have been found to be extremely useful.

References

1. Marinsky, J. A., and Glendenin, L. E., "The Separation and Identification of Nd and Element 61 Fission Activities by Specific Elution from Amberlite Resin," CC-2829 (June 1, 1945).
2. Parker, G. W., and Lantz, P. M., "The Separation of Milligram Quantities of Element 61 from Fission," ORNL-75 (AECD-2160) (1948).
3. Orr, P. B., "Ion Exchange Purification of Promethium-147 and its Separation from Americium-241 with Diethylenetriaminepentaacetic acid as the Eluant," ORNL-3271 (January 21, 1962).

4. Wheelwright, E. J., and Roberts, F. P., "Development and Demonstration of an Ion Exchange Process for Kilogram Production of High-Purity Promethium," HW-78651 (Rev.) (October, 1963).

5. Meggers, W. F., Scribner, B. F., and Bozman, W. R., "Absorption and Emission Spectra of Promethium," *J. Res. Nat'l Bur. Standards*, **46**, 85 (1951).

6. Erämetsä, O., "Separation of Promethium from a Natural Lanthanide Mixture," *Acta Polytechnia Scandinavica, Chemistry Including Metallurgy*, Series No. 37, 1965.

7. Weigel, F., "Darstellung von metallischem Promethium," *Angew. Chem.*, **75**, 451 (1963).

8. Weigel, F., "Preparation and Properties of Promethium and some of its Compounds," Proc. 5th Rare Earth Research Conference, Aug. 30, 31, Sept. 1, 1965, Ames, Iowa, Book 3, Chemistry Session, pp. 107–118, CONF-650804-7, 1965.

9. Scherer, V., "Zur Chemie des Promethiums," Ph.D. Thesis, University of Munich, 1966.

10. Barnes, R. H., Ritzmann, R. I., Kircher, J. F., and Sunderman, D. N., "Fabrication Studies on Pm^{147} Betavoltaic Batteries," Report BMI-1709 (Jan. 25, 1965).

FRITZ WEIGEL

PROTACTINIUM

Discovery

The first isotope of protactinium, the element of atomic number 91, to be discovered was Pa^{234m}, also called UX_2, a short-lived member of the naturally occurring $4n + 2$, or U^{238}, decay series. (See **Uranium**.) It was identified by Fajans and Göhring in 1913 and the element called *brevium*. However, when the longer-lived isotope Pa^{231}, the parent of actinium in the $4n + 3$, or U^{235}, decay series, (see Fig. 1 under **Actinium**) was identified, independently and almost simultaneously, by Hahn and Meitner and by Soddy and Cranston in 1918, the name protoactinium, more recently contracted to *protactinium*, was adopted.

Three years later Pa^{234}, the isomeric ground state of UX_2, was also identified by Hahn and Meitner. This species, also known as UZ, was the first example of nuclear isomerism.

Occurrence

Because of their very short half-lives the natural abundances of UX_2 and UZ are very

TABLE 1. PROTACTINIUM ISOTOPES

Mass No.	Mode of Decay	Half-life	Decay Characteristics	Origin
225	α	2 s	7.3	Th^{232} (d, 9n.)
226	α	1.8 m	~6.81	Th^{232} (d, 8n.)
227	α (85%)E.C.(15%)	38.3 m	α: 6.460(50.7%)6.418(11.8%) 6.410(15.2%) *et al* γ: 42.4, 50.5, *et al*	Th^{232} (p, 6n.)
228	α (2%)E.C.(98%)	22 h	α: 6.114(10.5%)6.101(12.0%) 6.074(20.7%)5.795(11.3%) *et al* γ: 57.5, 95, 129, 240, 280, 310, 410, 912, 966, 970 and many others.	Th^{232} (p, 5n.)
229	α (0.25%)E.C.(99%)	1.4 d	α: 5.665(19.1%)5.610(13.4%) 5.575(36.8%) *et al* γ: 42 *et al*	Th^{230} (d, 3n.)
230	$β^-$(9%)E.C.(91%) α (0.003%)	17.0 d	$β$:$_{max}$410. γ: 53, 444, 508, 901, 920, 954 and many others.	Th^{232} (p, 3n.)
231	α	3.28. 10^4 y	α: 5.017(23%)5.001(24%) 4.938(22%) *et al* γ: 11, 16.5, 25.4, 27.4, 29.4, 34.0, 38.2, 57.0, 63.3, 300, 330 and many others. All above 60 weak.	Natural $4n + 3$ series.

TABLE 1—*continued*

Mass No.	Mode of Decay	Half-life	Decay Characteristics	Origin
232	β^- (100%)E.C.?	1.32 d	β_{max}: 320 (98%) (small proportion up to 1245) γ: 47.6, 109, 150, 895, 791, *et al*	Pa^{231} (n, γ)
233	β^-	27.4 d	β_{max}: 256(57%). Some β up to 568 γ: 28, 40, 75, 87, 312, 340, 399, *et al*	decay of Th^{233}
234^m	β^-, I.T.(0.13%)	1.17 m	β_{max}: 2310. γ: weak. I.T. 69 Internally converted.	Natural 4n + 2 series.
234	β^-.	6.7 h	β_{max}: 790 (Small proportion of harder β's). γ: 920, 565, 123 and many others.	Natural 4n + 2 series.
235	β^-	23.7 m	β_{max}: 1400. No. γ, ?	^{238}U (d, αn)
236	β^-	~ 10–13 m	β_{max}: 3300. Several γ.	^{238}U (d, α.)
237	β^-	39 m	β_{max}: 2300. Several γ up to 1420	^{238}U (γ, p.)

EC. = electron capture, I.T. = isomeric transition, α energies in MeV; and γ energies in KeV. The softer γ radiations are often partially, or even substantially, internally converted. Data on Pa^{236} are conflicting and uncertain. For detailed decay schemes see "The Nuclear Properties of the Heavy Elements," by E. K. Hyde, I. Perlman and G. T. Seaborg. Vol. II, New Jersey, Prentice Hall, 1964.

TABLE 2. NUCLEAR PROPERTIES

Mass number	Spin	Mass on C_{12} scale	Neutron Separation Energy, MeV	Proton Separation Energy, MeV	6_c, barns	Approx. Fission Threshold, MeV	6_f, barns
Pa^{230}	2	230.03434	5.85	4.77	—	Thermally fissile	1500
Pa^{231}	3/2	231.03587	6.65	4.62	293	0.4	0.01
Pa^{232}	3	232.03844	5.67	5.27	760	Thermally fissile	700
Pa^{233}	3/2	233.04011	6.51	5.38	140	0.9	
Pa^{234}	4	234.04323	5.16	5.61			

The spontaneous fission half-life of Pa^{231} is about 10^6y.

small. But the longer-lived Pa^{231} is of comparable abundance to radium. Thus an unchanged uranium ore containing 1 ton of uranium also contains in radioactive equilibrium about 340 mg of protactinium–231.

Altogether 12 isotopes of the element have now been identified and their principal properties are summarized in Tables 1 and 2.

Derivation

Protactinium-233. The most important of the synthetic species is Pa^{233}, the parent of U^{233}. It is produced by the decay of the short-lived Th^{233} (see **Thorium**) which is obtained by radiative neutron capture by

natural thorium, Th^{232} (n, γ) $Th^{233} \xrightarrow{22.1m}$ Pa^{233}. It has been made and separated in amounts up to a substantial fraction of one gram. Submicroscopic, but detectable, amounts of the same isotope can be found in uranium and thorium minerals, being produced by naturally formed neutrons (see **Actinium**).

Protactinium-233 is separated from irradiated thorium nitrate after decay of Th^{233}. The salt is dissolved in 3M nitric acid and the Pa^{233} codeposited on manganese dioxide by addition of a manganous salt and permanganate to the hot solution. The washed precipitate is dissolved in 6M HCl and the Pa^{233}

extracted into di-isopropyl ketone. After washing the extract with $6M$ HCl the Pa^{233} is re-extracted into $6M$ HCl $+ 0.1$ M HF.

Protactinium-231. Various residues from uranium and radium refineries have been the main source of naturally occurring Pa^{231}, but before 1960 the amount of pure protactinium available in the world was less than 1 gram. Since then much larger amounts, 100 g in 1960, have been isolated as a result of research directed to the recovery of it from the "ethereal sludge" formed in the older uranium recovery processes. In addition to the natural source, protactinium-231 is made synthetically by the neutron bombardment of thorium-230.

To separate protactinium-231 from uranium refining residues, the Pa^{231} is taken into solution in $8M$ HCl and 0.1 M HF. The fluoride is then complexed by aluminum or boric acid and the Pa^{231} extracted into di-isopropyl ketone. After washing it is re-extracted into an HF-HCl mixture and the cycle of extraction repeated. An oxalic acid strip, replacing the fluoride solution, reduces iron contamination. Finally the Pa^{231} is precipitated as K_2PaF_7, the precipitate dissolved in sulfuric acid and the Pa^{231} precipitated as peroxide, to separate niobium. The peroxide can be ignited to Pa_2O_5.

Physical Properties

The element is a hard white metal. At room temperature it has a body-centered tetragonal structure, a $= 3.925$; c $= 3.238$ Å. The calculated density is 15.37 g/cc and the structure gives a radius of 1.63 Å for 12-coordinate protactinium. The coefficient of linear expansion in the range 0-700°C is $9.9 \times 10^{-6}/°C$. The melting point is less than 1600°C, but is not accurately known. An indirect measurement gives a vapor pressure of 5.1×10^{-5} atm at 2200°K. It is superconducting below 1.4°K.

The emission spectrum has been recorded between 2000 and 25000 Å but no detailed term analysis has been attempted. The most sensitive and distinctive lines appear at 3957.8, 3054.6 and 3053 Å. The ground state electronic configuration is unknown, evidence both for and against the presence of 5 f electrons being available. The x-ray spectrum has also been examined.

Electron binding energies in KeV for protactinium are K, 112.6; L_I 21.1; L_{II} 20.2; L_{III} 16.71.

Chemical Properties

Solution chemistry Pa(V). In solution the element is found in oxidation states five and four. The latter solutions suffer atmospheric oxidation so that protactinium is generally handled as its pentavalent compounds. In this state it is quite similar to niobium and tantalum. No simple cationic or anionic species can be obtained at appreciable concentrations. Many of the complex ions, nearly all anionic, are liable to hydrolytic condensation reactions. These yield ill-defined products of increasing molecular weight giving rise first to colloidal systems and ultimately to precipitates. These processes take place more rapidly the higher the concentration of protactinium. Fluoride, sulfate and selenate solutions, as well as those of organic acids like oxalate, citrate, tartrate etc., appear to be stable with respect to the above reactions. These properties make the analytical chemistry and handling of protactinium difficult, especially at tracer concentrations.

Except in the presence of the above organic acids trace concentrations of the element will codeposit with varying efficiencies on most precipitates formed at or above pH 3.0. Zirconium precipitates usually carry protactinium very efficiently, as do the phosphate, hypophosphate and iodate in acid solutions (1-4M) and the phenylarsonate and mandelate in less acid solution. In nitric and acid solution ($\sim 3M$) a precipitate of manganese dioxide carries the protactinium very effectively. However, such nitrate solutions are metastable at higher protactinium concentrations and the efficiency falls in the more stable sulfate solutions. At macroscopic concentrations in sulfate solution protactinium can be precipitated as hydroxide by alkali, as K_2PaF_7 by potassium hydrogen fluoride, as an ill-defined peroxide by hydrogen peroxide and as a sparingly soluble potassium sulfatoprotactinate by potassium sulfate. The iodate, phosphate and hypophosphate can be precipitated in 4M mineral acid. All these precipitates, except K_2PaF_7, dissolve in hydrofluoric acid.

Solutions in inorganic acids are colorless and transparent at >300 mμ. At lower wave lengths there is an intense charge transfer band (~ 210 mμ in 6M HCl; ~ 206 mμ in 4M H$_2$SO$_4$). In both solutions increase of pH and consequent onset of the hydrolytic condensation is associated with a broader band in the region 250-290 mμ.

Polarographic reduction of the fluoride solution (3.8 M NH$_4$F, pH 7.2) gives a wave at -1.29 volts versus the SCE, whose height is proportional to the protactinium concentration. It is doubtful if electrochemical deposition of the element is possible from aqueous solution, but both cathodic and anodic deposition as unidentified compounds, probably by electrode reactions followed by electrophoresis, is possible.

The successive stability complexes of the fluoro-complexes, PaF$_3^{2+}$aq $+$ F$^-$ $\xrightarrow{k_4}$ PaF$_4^+$ aq, etc., are log k$_4$ = 4.8 $\pm$ 0.3; log k$_5$ = 4.5 $\pm$ 0.2; log k$_6$ = 4.4 $\pm$ 0.2; log k$_7$ = 3.7 $\pm$ 0.2; log k$_8$ = 1.7 $\pm$ 0.5.

Solvent extraction and ion exchange. Protactinium (V) can be extracted from acidic nitrate, chloride, bromide, oxalate, thiocyanate and sulfate solutions by donor solvents, probably as ion pair complexes of the anionic Pa (V) species. Carbinols and ketones, especially di-isopropyl ketone, are suitable. In the presence of fluoride ($>10^{-2}$

M) the protactinium remains in, or returns to, the aqueous phase. Similar separations can be made using solutions of the higher amines, such as trioctylamine, in benzene. These extractions can also be conducted by the technique of partition chromatography for analytical purposes.

Extractable chelate complexes are formed with β diketones, alkyl phosphoric acids, nitrosophenylhydroxylamine and its derivatives as well as derivatives of the arsonic acids. With the exception of the diketonates these complexes can be extracted from very acid solutions (e.g., 4M H$_2$SO$_4$).

Anion exchange is possible from sulfate, fluoride and oxalate solutions. The data show that in $<1M$ sulfuric acid the Pa (V) complex carrier charge -1, but at $>2M$ it becomes -3, as in the fluoride solutions.

Solution chemistry Pa (IV). Pa (V) solutions can be reduced to Pa (IV) by Zn amalgam. Their most distinctive reaction is the precipitation of PaF$_4$.nH$_2$O. Pa (IV) solutions show three absorption bands with maxima near 225, 257 and 280 mμ.

Crystal chemistry. Covalent single bond radii are Pa (IV) 1.64, and Pa (V) 1.52 Å.

Analytical chemistry and separation. Radioactive assay of Pa^{233}: The 312 and 340 KeV photon emissions are convenient for measurement but discrimination against other nuclides is poor, so that measurement must be preceeded by chemical separation. It should

TABLE 3. Pa (IV) COMPOUNDS

Compound	Color	Symmetry	Isostructural with	Preparation
PaF$_4$	Tan	Monoclinic	ZrF$_4$, UF$_4$	Pa$_2$O$_5$ +H$_2$ +HF at 500°C
PaCl$_4$	Yellow-green	Tetragonal, a = 8.377, c = 7.482	UCl$_4$	PaCl$_5$ +H$_2$ at 900°C
PaO$_2$	Black	Cubic, a = 5.505	UO$_2$	Pa$_2$O$_5$ + H$_2$ at 1500°C
Cs$_2$PaCl$_6$			Cs$_2$ZrCl$_6$	
PaOS	Pale yellow	Tetragonal, a = 3.832, c = 6.704	UOZ	PaCl$_5$ + H$_2$S/CS$_2$ at 900°C
LiPaF$_5$	Pale pink	Tetragonal, a = 14.96, c = 6.58	LiUF$_5$	Reduce LiPaF$_6$ with H$_2$ at 450°C
(NH$_4$)$_4$PaF$_8$		?	(NH$_4$)$_4$UF$_8$	NH$_4$F + PaF$_4$ at 90°C

The metal reacts with hydrogen at 300°C to give PaH$_3$, isostructural with UH$_3$.
The above compounds are paramagnetic and the e.s.r. spectrum of Cs$_2$PaCl$_6$ suggests Pa (IV) has one 5f electrons.

TABLE 4. SOME Pa (V) COMPOUNDS

Compound	Color	Symmetry	Preparation
PaF_5	White	Tetragonal, $a = 11.53$, $c = 5.19$	$PaF_4 + F_2$ at 500°C
$PaF_5 2H_2O$	White	—	Evaporate solution of PaF_5 in HF
Pa_2OF_8	White	Body-centered cubic, $a = 8.4065$	Heat PaF_5 with O_2
$KPaF_6$	White	Orthorhombic	F_2 on $KF + PaF_4$ at 300°C
K_2PaF_7	White	Monoclinic, $\beta = 125.5°$ $a = 13.94$, $b = 6.76$, $c = 8.24$	Solution of $PaF_5 + KF$ in stoichiometric amounts
Na_3PaF_8	White	Tetragonal, $a = 5.487$, $c = 10.89$	Solution of $PaF_5 + NaF$ in stoichiometric amounts
$PaCl_5$	Very pale yellow	Monoclinic, $\beta = 111.8°$ $a = 10.25$, $b = 12.31$, $c = 8.82$	Chlorinate Pa_2O_5 with $SOCl_2$
NMe_4PaCl_6	Pale yellow		$PaCl_5 + NMe_4Cl$ in $SOCl_2$
$(NMe_4)_3PaCl_8$	Bright yellow		,, ,, ,, ,,
$PaBr_5$	Orange-red	Orthorhombic, $a = 7.25$, $b = 12.12$, $c = 9.13$	Br_2 on $Pa_2O_5 + C$ at 600°C
$PaOBr_3$	Yellow-green	—	By-products action of bromination of $Pa_2O_5 + C$
$PaOBr_2$	White		
PaI_5	Black	Orthorhombic, $a = 7.22$, $b = 21.2$, $c = 6.85$	$Pa_2O_5 + AlI_3$ at 350°C
Pa_2O_5	White	Tetragonal (?), $a = 5.433$, $b = 5.488$ Hexagonal form also known. $a = 3.817$, $c = 13.22$	Ignite precipitated hydroxide
$H_3PaO(SO_4)_3$	White	Hexagonal, $a = 9.439$, $c = 5.506$	Evaporation of sulfuric acid solution of Pa
$H_3PaO(SeO_4)_3$	White	$a = 9.743$, $c = 5.679$	Evaporation of selenic acid solution of Pa

† Several mixed oxide lattices have been identified.

be noted that Pa^{231} also gives photons in this energy region. Pa^{231}: The photon emission near 300 KeV is useful for measuring pure Pa^{231} preparations. Alpha spectrometry provides the most reliable method of assay but it is inconvenient at very low specific activities, when prior chemical separation of protactinium again becomes necessary. An activation analysis, measuring the Pa^{232}, appears promising.

Chemical assay: At present protactinium is almost always weighed as the ignited oxide, Pa_2O_5, after chemical separation. A spectrophotometric determination using the absorption of the arsenazo (III) complex at 630 mμ is also possible.

Separation: The most satisfactory procedures depend on solvent extraction and anion exchange. The use of sulfate solutions to avoid losses by hydrolytic condensation is advisable.

Toxicity

Pa^{231} is a long-lived alpha emitter and not readily excreted. It is therefore a dangerously toxic material. Work with Pa^{231} demands much the same precautions as work with Pu^{239}.

References

1. Brown, D., and Maddock, A. G., "Comprehensive Review of Protactinium," *Quarterly Reviews*, **17**, 3 (1963).

2. Hyde, E. K., Perlman, I., and Seaborg, G. T., "The Nuclear Properties of the Heavy Elements," Vol. II, New Jersey, Prentice-Hall, 1964.

3. Kirby, H. W., "The Radiochemistry of Protactinium," U.S.A.E.C., NAS-NS 3016, Dec. 1959.

4. Goble, A., Golden, J., Maddock, A. G., and Toms, D. J., "Progress in Nuclear Energy," Series 3, 1959, Vol. II, p. 86, Bruce, F. R., Fletcher, J. M., and Hyman, H. H., Eds., London, Pergamon, 1958

5. Haissinsky, M., and Bouissières, G., "Nouveau Traité de Chimie Mineral," Ed., Pascal, P., Vol. XII, Paris, Masson et Cie, 1958.

6. Bouissières, G., and Muxart, R., "Physico-Chimie du Protactinium," C.N.R.S. Colloquium No, 154. Paris, 1966.

ALFRED G. MADDOCK

R

RADIUM †

Radium, symbol Ra, is the heaviest known alkaline earth, Group IIA, element. Its atomic number is 88 and the atomic weight of the only prevalent isotope is 226.05. About fourteen isotopes of Ra are known but only Ra^{226} has a half-life (1620 years) greater than a few weeks. It is present in nature due to the fact that it is continuously formed by the decay of U^{238}.

History

In 1898, Pierre and Marie Curie and G. Bémont found that the major part of the radioactivity in pitchblende was due to a new radioactive substance. In the next few years, they managed to concentrate the substance in the barium fraction of their residues and gradually to separate it from barium by fractional crystallization. Examination of the spectrum of the fractions by Demarcay showed that new lines in the ultraviolet became more intense with respect to Ba as the purification continued; simultaneous measurements of the apparent atomic weight of the Ba fraction as the radioactivity was enriched showed a decided increase indicating the presence of an element heavier than Ba. This was named radium. The final atomic weight, obtained by Marie Curie, of the purest fraction was 225.18 which was very close to our present value.

For the early work on radium and the studies of radioactivity that grew from this, Marie Curie received several prizes from the French Academy of Science in 1902 and Pierre Curie was elected to membership in

† Based on work performed under the auspices of the U. S. Atomic Energy Commission.

the Academy in 1905. Both later received the Nobel Prize for their work.

A commercial radium industry was soon set up in Europe and by 1920, the Standard Chemical Co., American Radium Co., the U.S. Radium Corp., and the National Radium Institute were all producing it commercially in the United States.

Occurrence

Radium occurs in all uranium ores, being supported by radioactive decay. Since it forms many water-soluble compounds it is leached from the ores by ground water and is widespread over the earth's surface. In pitchblende radium is present to about 300 milligrams per 10^6 g of uranium. In the earth's surface there is about 1.8×10^{13} g of radium. In normal ocean water there is about 10^{-13} grams per liter and in the earth's ground water it varies from 10^{-12} to 10^{-11} gpl depending on the locations.

Production

Radium is coprecipitated with silica, barium, and lead from uranium ores by an acid sulfate treatment. The resultant precipitate (called white cake) is then treated with excess carbonate to convert the radium and barium salts to the carbonates. These are then treated with HCl to remove the lead and silica and the process is repeated several times. The final product of pure mixed $BaCO_3$ and $RaCO_3$ is then converted to $BaBr_2$ and $RaBr_2$ which are separated from each other by fractional crystallization and can give a final product of up to 90% $RaBr_2$. For further purification ion exchange techniques are used.

Radium metal can be prepared from its salts by electrolytic reduction. This was first done by M. Curie and A. Debienes. A mercury cathode is used; and after drying, the mercury-radium amalgam is placed in an iron crucible in a hydrogen atmosphere and heated to distill the mercury. The mercury selectively distills until a temperature of 700°C is reached. At that point the radium begins to distill also.

Physical Properties

The most important property of radium is its intense radioactivity. One gram of Ra^{226} will undergo 3.7×10^{10} disintegrations per second. In fact, the most common unit of radioactivity, the curie, is defined as that amount of any radioactive material which has the same disintegration rate as 1 gram of Ra^{226}. Since Ra^{226} emits alpha particles of about 4.8 MeV of energy, this will correspond to 6.8×10^{-3} cal/sec/gram of Ra^{226}. However, since there are a large number of short-lived radioactive daughter isotopes of Ra^{226}, the total radio-activity of a pure Ra^{226} sample would increase to about 17×10^{-3} cal/sec/gram in about 4 days and to about 28×10^{-3} cal per gram in about 20 days. Thereafter it would increase slowly to about 35×10^{-3} cal per gram after about 50 years. If the specific heat of Ra is about the same as Ba, or 0.068 cal/g/deg., then a well insulated pure Ra^{226} sample would raise its own temperature 0.1°C/second. Additional physical properties are listed in Table 1.

TABLE 1. PHYSICAL PROPERTIES OF RADIUM

Atomic weight	226.0254
Density, g/cc	5 (?)
Ionic radius	$Ra^{+2} = 1.43$ Å
Melting point, °C	700
Boiling point, °C	1140
Color	silver-white
Half-life (Ra^{226})	1620 years

Chemical Properties

The chemical properties of radium are indicated by its position in the Group II elements in the Periodic Table. Its electron configuration is $5s^2\, 5p^6\, 5d^{10}\, 6s^2\, 6p^6\, 7s^2\, (^1S_0)$ and the oxidation states are 0 and +2. Its oxidation potential, 2.916 volts, is similar to those of calcium, strontium, and barium, and the chemical behavior of radium is also similar to that of those elements. However, the intense radioactivity associated with radium compounds causes a large amount of radiation damage in crystals containing radium. In solutions, it leads to the formation of peroxides and oxygen which can cause unusual chemical behavior of radium solutions. As an example of these properties one might notice the behavior of $Ra(IO_3)_2$. As is the case with $Ba(IO_3)_2$ this salt is easily precipitated from solution and is colorless. After a period of time the $Ra(IO_3)_2$ crystals turn brown due to the presence of free iodine formed by radiation reduction and the supernatant will show traces of I_3^- ions. This, however, is due to the radioactivity and is not a property of the chemical behavior of radium.

Some typical reactions of metallic radium are:

$$Ra + 2H_2O \longrightarrow Ra^{++} + 2OH^- + H_2$$
$$Ra + 2HX \longrightarrow Ra^{++} + H_2 + 2X^-$$
$$2Ra + O_2 \longrightarrow 2RaO \quad \triangle H = -130$$
$$\text{kcal/mole}$$
$$3Ra + N_2 \longrightarrow Ra_3N_2 \text{ (unconfirmed)}$$

Principal Compounds

The halides are quite stable with the exception of RaI_2. The hydrated halides, generally dihydrates, can be made by evaporating to dryness $RaCO_3$ solutions in the corresponding acids. However, they all will decompose in time due to radiation decomposition. $RaCl_2$ can also be formed in the unhydrated state by heating $RaSO_4$ with CCl_4 and HCl gas at red heat; its density is 4.9 and melting point about 900°C. It is soluble to 24.5 g/100 g of water at 20°C, and the heat of formation is about -230 kcal/mole.

$RaBr_2$ (anhydrous) can be formed from $RaCl_2$ by heating with HBr at red heat. It melts at 730°C and sublimes at 900°C. It has a density of 5.78 and is soluble in water to 70.6 g/100 g of H_2O at 20C°.

There are several insoluble salts of radium. $RaCO_3$ can be precipitated from neutral solutions of Ra salts by $(NH_4)_2CO_3$ and is slightly more soluble in excess $CO_3^=$ solutions than $BaCO_3$.

$Ra(IO_3)_2$ can be precipitated from solution by the addition of KIO_3. Its solubility is 437 mg/liter at 25°C.

$RaSO_4$ can be precipitated by dilute H_2SO_4. Its solubility is 2.1×10^{-3} gpl at $20°C$.

Commercial Uses of Radium

Neutron Sources. The alpha particles emitted by radium and its daughters are sufficiently energetic to cause nuclear reactions in light elements. The most important of these is the $_4Be^9 + _2He^4 = _6C^{12} + _0n^1$ which is the basic reaction of commercial Ra-Be neutron sources. In practice, the beryllium is in the form of finely divided powder (less than 300 mesh) which is intimately mixed and compressed with particles of $RaSO_4$ or a $RaSO_4$, $BaSO_4$ mixture of less than 30 micron diameter. This type of source can give about 1.7×10^7 neutrons/g of radium.

However, the neutron yield depends on the Be/Ra ratio and in general a ratio of 8/1 is used which gives about 10^7 n/g of Ra. The yield also depends on the packing density and, thus, will vary from source to source.

A more constant, although weaker, source can be made by using the compound $RaBeF_4$ which may be prepared with a constant Be ratio. This will yield 1.84×10^6 n/sec/g of $RaBeF_4$ and is constant to 0.5%.

These Ra-Be sources emit neutrons having a broad spectrum with maximum energy of 13.0 MeV and the greatest intensity at about 5 MeV. If one uses the gamma rays emitted by the Ra (actually by its daughters) by enclosing the radium in a capsule in the Be so that none of the alpha particles will penetrate, then the neutrons are formed by the reactions $\gamma + _4Be^9 = _0n^1 + 2_2He^4$. The neutrons then will have an energy of less than 0.6 MeV and yield of about 2×10^5 n/sec/g of Ra.

Luminous Paints. An important commercial application of radium was in the manufacture of luminous paints. In these an alpha emitter such as radium is uniformly dispersed in an inorganic phosphor. Since the phosphorescence is excited by the alpha particles, no external source of energy is required. These paints were widely used for watch dials and instrument dials until the early 1950's. The availability of other, less hazardous alpha emitters has since then reduced the use of radium for this purpose.

Radon Sources and Radiotherapy. Although Ra^{226} itself does not emit very intense γ

radiation, the radioactive daughters in equilibrium with it are intense gamma emitters. For this reason radium sources have long been used in medicine for the treatment of tumors by irradiation. Although the use of Ra^{226} for this purpose has been supplanted by the general availability of other radioactive isotopes, especially Co^{60}, it is still used in medicine, primarily for interstitial irradiations. In this method the Ra^{226} is sealed in small capsules or "needles" which are surgically implanted in the area to be irradiated and are removed after the treatment is ended.

A more usual technique is to fill the needles with the first daughter of Ra^{226}, *i.e.,* Rn^{222} (See p. 593). This has all of the original gamma emitting daughters in equilibrium with itself and has a half-life of 3.8 days. Since the total activity of the radon needles will decay to a safe level within a few weeks, there is no need to remove the Rn needles at the end of the treatment, and the surgical procedure is much less complex than in the case of treatment with Ra^{226} itself. The use of Ra^{226} for production of Rn^{222} is probably the most important medical use of radium at the present time.

Radium is the chief source of radon (q.v.), the heaviest of the noble gases; see page 590 for details of radon collection.

Toxicology of Radium

The general problem of radium poisoning was brought to public attention by the disastrous effects of radium on a number of women who had been employed in a factory making luminous dials during the First World War. They had been in the habit of wetting the points of their brushes on their lips and had thus accumulated a large amount of radium internally. During a 10-15 year period about 24 of them died from osteogenic sarcoma or aplastic anemia. It was found that from 1.2 to $50/\mu g$ of radium remained in their bodies at the time of death. On the basis of physical and medical evidence of these and other cases the maximum permissible limit of fixed Ra^{226} in the body has been set at $0.1/\mu g$ at any time.

Due to its chemical similarity to calcium, radium tends to concentrate in the bone where the alpha radiation can cause breakdown of the red cell producing centers in the marrow, and also can lead to cancer of the bone. Fortunately, very sensitive tests, such as detection of exhaled radon can be used to detect amounts of radium that are even one tenth of the maximum permissible dosage. Most countries now require tests of this type to be made of all workers handling large amounts of radium.

References

1. Curie, M., "Recherches sur les Substances Radioactives," Thesé, Faculté des Sciences de Paris, Paris, Gauthier-Villars, 1904.
2. Curie, P., Curie, M., and Bemont, G., *Compt. Rend.* **127**, 1215 (1898).
3. Baganall, K. W., "Chemistry of the Rare Radioelements, Polonium-Actinium," New York, Academic Press Inc., 1957.
4. Soddy, F., "The Chemistry of the Radioelements," London, Longmans Green and Co., 1914.
5. Adams, J. O., and Lander, W. M., "The Natural Radiation Environment," Chicago, University of Chicago Press, 1964.
6. Gmelin, "Handbuch der Anorganischer Chemie," System No. 31, Berlin, G.m.b.H., 1928.
7. Rajewsky, "Review of Radium Poisoning," *Radiology*, **32**, 57 (1939).
8. National Bureau of Standards, "Radium Protection," National Bureau of Standards Handbook, H. 23.
9. "Thorpe's Dictionary of Applied Chemistry," Vol. X, 4th Edition, London, Longmans Green and Co., 1950.
10. Kirk, R. E., and Othmer, D. F., Eds., "Encyclopedia of Chemical Technology," Vol. 1, New York, Interscience, 1953.

A. M. Friedman

RADON †

Element 86, symbol Rn, is the heaviest of the noble gases; the atomic weight of isotope $Rn^{222} = 222.02$.

Discovery and Early History

In 1899 R. B. Owens noted that the radioactivity of thorium compounds could be reduced by flushing the compounds with air. E. Rutherford studied the phenomenon and found that thorium continuously evolved a

† This entry prepared under the auspices of the U. S. Atomic Energy Commission.

gaseous radioactive daughter, "Thorium Emanation," which was swept away by the stream of air. F. E. Dorn (1900) showed that radium also evolved a gaseous daughter, "Radium Emanation." This explained the growth of radioactivity in air in contact with radium compounds which had been noted earlier by P. Curie and M. Curie. A third radioactive gas, "Actinium Emanation," was found by A. Debierne (1900) and F. O. Giesel (1903) among the products of actinium decay.

The similarity of the spectrum of radium emanation to that of argon, krypton, and xenon and the chemical inertness of radium and thorium emanations to acids, alkalies, metals, and many oxidizing and reducing agents indicated that the emanations were new members of the noble gas family of elements. Rutherford predicted an atomic weight of approximately 222 for radium emanation, since it was known to be formed from radium-226 by loss of an α-particle. On confirmation of this atomic weight by W. Ramsay and W. R. Gray (gas density measurements, 1910) and A. Debierne (effusion measurements, 1910), radium emanation was assigned atomic number 86 and placed in the vacant space below xenon in the zero subgroup of the Periodic Table. (See article on **Noble Gases**).

Isotopes were unknown at the time of these discoveries. Only in later years was it recognized that all three emanations were isotopes of element 86.

The name "Radon" for the element was adopted in 1923, superseding the older names "Emanation" and "Niton." The natural isotopes (Rn^{222}, Rn^{220}, and Rn^{219}) were once called "Exradio," "Exthorio," and "Exactinio" by Ramsay and co-workers but are now designated by the names "Radon," "Thoron," and "Actinon," respectively.

Isotopes

Eighteen isotopes of radon, all radioactive, are known at the present time. The half-lives, modes of decay, and emission energies are shown in Table 1. Atomic weights on the carbon-12 scale (calculated from known masses and emission energies) are also included, where known.

The natural isotopes are found in very low concentrations in soil, the oceans, lake and

TABLE 1. ISOTOPES OF RADON (from Reference 1)

Mass Number	Atomic Weight	Half-life		Mode of Decay	Emission Energy, MeV
204	——	3	m	α	α, 6.28
206	——	6.5	m	α, E.C.	α, 6.25
207	——	11	m	E.C., α	α, 6.12
208	——	23	m	E.C., α	α, 6.15
209	——	30	m	E.C., α	α, 6.04
210	209.9897	2.7	h	α, E.C.	α, 6.04
211	210.9906	16	h	E.C., α	α, 5.78, 5.85, 5.61
					γ, 0.069, 0.032, 1.82
212	211.9907	25	m	α	α, 6.27
215	214.9987	<1	m	α	α, 8.6
216	216.0002	45	μs	α	α, 8.04
217	217.0039	500	μs	α	α, 7.74
218	218.0086	0.035	s	α	α, 7.13, 6.52
					γ, 0.61
219 (Actinon)	219.0095	4.0	s	α	α, 6.82, 6.55, 6.42
					γ, 0.27, 0.40
220 (Thoron)	220.0114	56	s	α	α, 6.29, 5.74
					γ, 0.54
221	——	25	m	β^-, α	α, 6.0
222 (Radon)	222.0175	3.823	d	α	α, 5.49, 4.98
					γ, 0.51
223	——	43	m	β^-	——
224	——	1.9	h	β^-	——

well waters, and the atmosphere. Concentrations of Rn^{222} in the atmosphere have been measured most frequently and found to vary greatly with geographic location and time. Among the factors influencing the concentrations in air are: proximity to emanating ore bodies; porosity of soil; height of sampling station above ground; presence or absence of waste gases from the combustion of coal, natural gas, and other fuels; meteorological conditions. After rainfall, abnormally low levels of radon have been observed due to the low rate of diffusion of the gas through wet soil. The concentrations of Rn^{222} observed in many European and North American cities generally fall in the range of 2 to 80×10^{-14} curie per liter of air; occasionally, during temperature inversions and conditions of dense smoke or fog, higher concentrations have been observed. The lowest concentrations of radon, 0.3 to 2.6×10^{-15} curie per liter, have been noted in air over the oceans.

Collection and Purification

Most solid radium compounds release radon only partially at room temperature. The compounds must be heated, generally to at least 600°C, to promote rapid diffusion of the radon through the solid into the gas phase. Exceptions are mixed barium-radium salts of caproic, lauric, and palmitic acids, and gels of radium and ferric hydroxide, which liberate 90% or more of their radon at room temperature. The latter have been used, particularly by O. Hahn and co-workers, as efficient "emanating sources."

Radon is most often obtained for medical and experimental purposes by boiling or pumping on a solution of a radium salt. In a typical "radon plant," a slightly acid solution of radium chloride, bromide, or other soluble salt is contained in a soft-glass vessel behind lead shielding. Radon is pumped off as required, collected in a small volume by means of a Toepler pump or frozen into a cold trap at −195°C, and purified. Hydrogen and oxygen (formed by radiolytic decomposition of the solution at a rate of approximately 50 cc, STP, per day per curie of radium) are the principal impurities. The radiolytic gases are either recombined by sparking or by a hot-wire technique[2] or are pumped off while the radon is frozen. Helium, from emitted α-particles, is also removed by the latter method. Other impurities, such as water vapor, acid vapor, carbon dioxide, and hydrocarbons (from stopcock greases, which decompose rapidly under α-particle bombardment) are removed by chemical methods.

One curie of Rn^{222} has a volume of 0.66 mm^3 and a weight of 6.5 micrograms. The isotope decays by α-emission and exhibits only slight γ-activity when freshly separated from radium. However, short-lived β and γ-emitting daughters (chiefly Bi^{214} and Pb^{214}) as well as α-emitting daughters (chiefly Po^{218} and Po^{214}) grow into equilibrium with the parent within 4 hours, as shown by the following decay scheme:

Radon, xenon, and other noble gases are released at different temperatures when the adsorbant is heated, therefore can be separated by this method. The enthalpy of adsorption varies from 6.0 to 9.5 kcal/mole for radon on different types of charcoal or silica gel. Separations of noble gases can also be achieved by gas chromatographic methods. A small column packed with synthetic hydroxyapatite has been reported to give a separation factor of 10^6 for xenon and radon.

The concentration of radon in air and other gases is often determined indirectly by collecting and counting the radioactive daughters (active deposit) on paper or fiberglass filters. It is assumed that the daughters

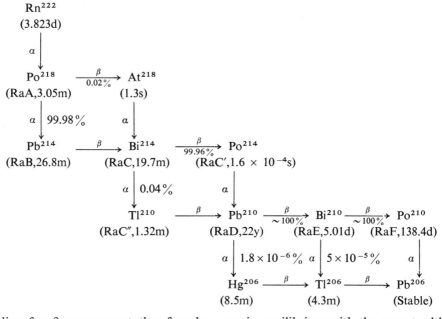

Shielding for β-γ rays must therefore be provided when large amounts of radon are stored. All surfaces in contact with the gas rapidly become contaminated with the radioactive daughters, which are solids and are referred to as the "active deposit."

Radon is frequently collected and purified by adsorption on activated charcoal or silica gel. The method is particularly useful for the extraction of traces of radon in large volumes of other gases (i.e., in the atmosphere, in the breath of persons with body burdens of radium, etc.). Adsorption is most efficient at low temperatures (−80 to 0°C) but also occurs to a measurable extent up to 120°.[3]

are in equilibrium with the parent, although under some circumstances this may not be true. Scintillation counting of radon and its daughters (after an elapsed time of about 4 hours) in a zinc sulfide-coated chamber is probably the most reliable method for analysis of small samples. Methods of collecting and counting radon isotopes are described in detail by Sedlet.[11]

Physical Properties

Radon is a colorless monatomic gas at 25°C and one atmosphere pressure. When cooled or compressed, it condenses to a colorless liquid, which fluoresces in blue, blue-green, or lilac colors in different types of glass (effect of the intense α-bombardment of the glass). The solid fluoresces in blue, yellow, and orange-red colors (in succession) when cooled slowly to liquid air temperature in glass. Some physical properties of the element are listed in Table 2.

TABLE 2. SOME PHYSICAL PROPERTIES OF RADON

Melting point	$-71°C$
Boiling point	$-61.8°C$
Critical temperature	$104.4°C$
Critical pressure	62.4 atm
Density (liq., $\sim 20°C$)	5 g/cc
$\triangle H$ vaporization	3.94 kcal/mole
$\triangle H$ fusion	†0.65 kcal/mole
Heat capacity, C_P	†4.97 cal/degree/mole
Heat capacity, C_V	†2.98 cal/degree/mole
Viscosity, 0°C	†2.13×10^{-4} poise
Surface tension	†29 dyne/cm
Atomic diameter	†3.64 Å
Magnetic susceptibility,	
χ_A	†-57.4×10^{-6}
Ionization potential	10.7 volt

† Estimated value.

The vapor pressure of liquid radon is given approximately by

$$\log P \text{ (mm)} = \frac{-862}{T} + 4.08,$$

where T is the temperature in degrees Kelvin. This equation is derived from vapor pressure data of Gray and Ramsay[4] from 202.6 to 377.5°K. Measurements of the vapor pressure of the solid by others appear to be much less reliable.

The emission spectrum of radon has been reported by many investigators. The strongest lines occur at 7055.42 and 7450.00 Å. The most complete spectrum, containing 172 lines from 3316 to 10161 Å, is that of Rasmussen.[5] In the ultraviolet region, Wolf[6] has observed 122 lines from 2378 to 3761 Å.

Radon is slightly soluble in water and appreciably soluble in organic liquids. Jennings and Russ[8] and Bagnall[9] give the coefficient of solubility (ratio of concentration in the liquid phase to that in the gas phase) for a number of liquids. The following are a few coefficients at 18° selected from their tables: water, 0.285; acetone, 6.30; benzene, 12.82; carbon disulfide, 23.14; ethyl alcohol, 6.17. The solubility coefficient of radon in water decreases regularly from 0.507 at 0°C to 0.106 at 100°C. The enthalpy of solution is 6.7 kcal/mole at 0°C and 4.7 kcal/mole at 35°C.

Chemical Properties

In the early experiments, Rutherford, Ramsay, and Soddy showed that radon (either Rn^{222} or Rn^{220}) remained uncombined when treated with the following substances: alkali metals; alkali hydroxides; sulfuric, hydrochloric, and nitric acids; air, hydrogen, and carbon dioxide at high temperatures; phosphorus pentoxide; burning phosphorus; platinum black, palladium black, zinc powder, magnesium powder, calcium oxide, and lead chromate, each at red heat. J. J. Thomson and F. Himstedt also found no evidence that radon reacted with common acids and bases or with copper and platinum heated to incandescence. More recently, H. Kading and N. Riehl have attempted to prepare radon compounds by photochemical and electrical discharge methods in mixtures of the element with water and air, bromine, and water, air, and iodine, but without success.

B. Nikitin and co-workers have found evidence that radon forms clathrate compounds similar to those known for xenon, krypton, and argon. In such compounds, the noble gas atoms are trapped in the lattice of the host substance during crystallization. There are no chemical bonds between the noble gas atoms and surrounding atoms in the usual sense but only weak Van der Waal forces, and the trapped atoms escape when the host crystal melts or dissolves. From phase studies with tracer amounts of radon and macro amounts of sulfur dioxide, hydrogen sulfide, phenol, p-chlorophenol, and water, Nikitin has inferred the existence of such clathrates as $Rn \cdot 6H_2O$, $Rn \cdot 3C_6H_5OH$, and $Rn \cdot 3p\text{-}ClC_6H_4OH$.

In 1962, after the discovery of xenon fluorides, the reaction of radon and fluorine was examined, and evidence for the existence of a radon fluoride was obtained.[7] Tracer amounts of radon (5 microcuries to 2 millicuries) were shown to form a stable compound of very low volatility when heated to 400°C with fluorine in a nickel vessel. Although elemental radon distills in vacuum at $-78°C$ and even lower temperatures, the compound prepared in this manner does not distill at room temperature and 2×10^{-6} mm Hg pressure; it moves from a heated vessel only at about 230 to 250°C and recondenses in a cooler region. The compound is reduced by hydrogen at 500°C, with the liberation of elemental radon.

By analogy with xenon, radon may be expected to form the simple fluorides RnF_2, RnF_4, and RnF_6, as well as oxyfluorides and oxides. Complex salts may also be formed in reactions of the simple fluorides with metal fluorides. Recently, evidence for the existence of volatile radon fluorides has been obtained in experiments with vessels made of Pyrex, quartz, and Kel-F plastic rather than nickel. However, none of the products have yet been identified at tracer levels, even by sensitive mass spectrometric methods.

The electron configuration of a neutral radon atom in the ground state is $5s^2 5p^6 5d^{10} 6s^2 6p^6$ (^1S_o). Previously this was considered to be too stable to be altered by chemical bond formation. The new chemistry of krypton, xenon, and radon indicates that charge transfer processes can occur, however, even with filled s and p orbitals, and that heavy noble gas atoms can behave as electron donors to highly electrophilic substances, such as fluorine.

Behavior in Electrical Discharges

In electrical discharges, radon is frequently ionized and driven into the walls of glass or metal vessels by the electric fields. Rutherford, Rasmussen, and others have noted the disappearance of radon from discharge tubes during spectral measurements due to this effect. Radon fixed in quartz by a microwave discharge is retained even when the quartz is heated in vacuum to 970°C, although β-γ emitting daughters distill at about 600°C. Probably the first daughter, Po^{218}, is the volatile species, and subsequent daughters appear at the site on which the polonium condenses.

Biological Effects

In past years, a high incidence of lung cancer has been noted among miners in the Schneeberg region of Germany and the Joachimsthal

region of Czechoslovakia. This has been attributed to prolonged inhalation of high concentrations of radon and its daughters, although arsenic and other tumor-producing agents may also have been present in the air of the mines. It has subsequently been shown that radon concentrations may exceed 1×10^{-9} curie/liter in unventilated uranium mines. Greatly improved ventilation methods have been introduced in recent years to lower the concentrations of the gas in operating mines. The maximum concentration of radon now considered safe for long term exposure is approximately 1×10^{-11} curie/liter.

In numerous laboratory experiments, mice which have been made to inhale large amounts of radon have developed pulmonary tumors (adenomas or carcinomas of the bronchus). It has been found that such exposure lowers the number of red blood cells and shortens the life span of the experimental animals. A single exposure to more than 6 millicurie-hr./liter causes death within 30 days.

Radon has germicidal action on *Brucella Actinomycetales* and induces a high rate of mutation in *Drosophila*. It also causes alterations in barley, bean, and other crop seeds.

Medical and Other Uses

Both radium and radon have been widely used as radiation sources for the treatment of cancer. The β-γ radiation is the same with either element, since it is produced by daughters in the decay chain, chiefly Bi^{214} and Pb^{214}. However, radon can be used with greater safety than radium since its activity decays to a small fraction of the initial value within several weeks. Measured amounts of radon are sealed into very small glass, gold, or platinum capillary tubes, called "seeds" or "needles," for therapeutic use. The "seeds" are implanted in patients and left in place for extended periods of time (sometimes permanently). In the treatment of skin diseases an ointment consisting of a solution of radon in petroleum jelly is also used by some practitioners. The medical use of radon and the methods of preparation of "seeds" and ointment are described at length by Jennings and Russ.[8]

Radon has been used as a gaseous tracer in leak detection and in the measurement of flow rates. Compressed into a small capsule, it has also been used as a "point source" of γ-rays in the radiography of metal welds and castings. Neutron sources have sometimes been prepared from radon-beryllium mixtures. Since α-particles emitted by radon and its daughters ionize gases effectively and promote chemical change, many kinetic studies have been made of radon-induced reactions, such as the synthesis and decomposition of ozone, ammonia, water, and hydrogen bromide; oxidation of methane, ethane, and cyanogen; polymerization of actylene, ethylene, and cyanogen.[10]

References

1. "Chart of the Nuclides," Schenectady, New York, Knolls Atomic Power Laboratory, Eighth Edition, 1965.
2. Rudolph, P. S., *Rev. Sci. Instr.*, **36**, 75 (1965).
3. Gübeli, O., and Störi, M., *Helv. Chim. Acta*, **37**, 2224 (1954); *ibid*, **38**, 180 (1955).
4. Gray, R. W., and Ramsay, W., *J. Chem. Soc.*, 1073 (1909).
5. Rasmussen, E., *Z. für Physik*, **62**, 494 (1930); *ibid*, **80**, 726 (1933).
6. Wolf, S., *Z. für Physik*, **48**, 790 (1928).
7. Fields, P. R., Stein, L., and Zirin, M. H., "Noble-Gas Compounds," H. H. Hyman, Editor, pp. 113–119, Chicago, The University of Chicago Press, 1963; *J. Am. Chem. Soc.*, **84**, 4164 (1962).
8. Jennings, W. A., and Russ, S., "Radon: Its Technique and Use," London, John Murray, 1948.
9. Bagnall, K. W., "Chemistry of the Rare Radioelements," pp. 105–113, London, Butterworths Scientific Publications, 1957.
10. Lind, S. C., Hochanadel, C. J., and Ghormley, J. A., "Radiation Chemistry of Gases," New York, Reinhold Publishing Corporation 1961.
11. Sedlet, J., "Treatise on Analytical Chemistry," I. M. Kolthoff, P. J. Elving, and E. B. Sandell, Editors, Part II, Vol. 4, pp. 219–366, New York, Interscience Publishers, 1966.

LAWRENCE STEIN

RHENIUM

Rhenium, symbol Re, atomic number 75, atomic weight 186.2, is located in Group VIIB of the Periodic Table with manganese, element number 25, and technetium, element number 43. Until the discovery of rhenium in 1925, manganese was the only known member of Group VIIB; technetium was not discovered until 1937.

Discovery

Despite the many claims and counterclaims regarding the discovery of element number 75, the long-sought homolog of manganese, credit for the actual discovery is given to Walter Noddack, Ida Tacke (later Ida Noddack) and O. Berg. In 1925 they announced the detection of the element in platinum ores and in columbite. Their name of rhenium for the new element, derived from the Latin *Rhenus* for the German Rhine, has been accepted.

The existence of rhenium was based on x-ray examination of the above ores, and in 1929 Ida and Walter Noddack described the preparation of 1 g of rhenium metal from 600 kg of a Norwegian molybdenite.

Occurrence

Rhenium does not occur free in nature nor as a compound in a distinct mineral. Instead it is widely distributed in minor amounts in other minerals. The average concentration in the earth's crust is estimated to be 0.001 ppm or 1×10^{-9}.

In view of the position of rhenium in the same group as manganese in the Periodic Table, it is rather surprising that it is not found associated with manganese minerals. Rather, it is found in molybdenites, ores of MoS_2, some of which contain rhenium in concentrations of 0.002 to 0.02%. In the United States two sources of rhenium-bearing molybdenites have been used for the preparation of rhenium and its compounds. They are the copper sulfide ores in the vicinity of Miami, Arizona, formerly mined by the Miami Copper Co., and those from the Utah and New Mexico mines of Kennecott Copper Corp. Flue dusts and effluent gases from the molybdenite roasting operations conducted in the processing of these ores are the raw materials for rhenium production.

Of interest, the above two commercial sources of rhenium are molybdenites originally associated with copper sulfide ores. It is thus probable that the rhenium occurs as a sulfide, either ReS_2 or Re_2S_7, in these ores.

Derivation

The flue dusts and gases from the roasting of molybdenites which contain rhenium are leached and scrubbed, respectively, with water to dissolve the rhenium oxide, Re_2O_7, the anhydride of perrhenic acid, $HReO_4$. The acidic filtrate containing perrhenic acid can be treated with solid potassium chloride to precipitate potassium perrhenate, $KReO_4$. The latter is purified by repeated recrystallizations from water solutions; the solubility of $KReO_4$ is 14 g/100 g water at 100°C and 0.55 g/100 g water at 7°C.

Alternatively, the acidic extract can be treated with ammonia to yield ammonium perrhenate, NH_4ReO_4, which is also purified by repeated recrystallizations. This salt can also be made by passing the acidic extract, crude $HReO_4$, through a bed of anionic exchange resin, eluting the column with perchloric acid, and treating the effluent with H_2S and then ammonia to form NH_4ReO_4.

Rhenium metal is made in powder form by the reduction of $KReO_4$, or more commonly NH_4ReO_4, with hydrogen. The latter salt yields the higher purity metal. It is reduced to metal according to the reaction:

$$2NH_4ReO_4 + 7H_2 \rightarrow 2Re + 8H_2O + 2NH_3.$$

The reaction is conducted by placing finely divided, high-purity ammonium perrhenate in 8″ long molybdenum or quartz boats to a depth of $\frac{5}{8}″$ or so. The boats are loaded into an externally heated furnace of horizontal stainless steel pipe 2″ diameter × 12′ long, and purified dry hydrogen is passed into the furnace whose temperature is gradually raised to 700–800°C to complete the reduction. The product is high-purity rhenium metal powder which is cooled to room temperature under a stream of nitrogen.

The removal of all hydrogen from the finely divided rhenium powder is most important since the catalytic activity of the powder is such that any hydrogen is oxidized in air or oxygen and sufficient heat is liberated to ignite the metal.

Powder metallurgy techniques are used to consolidate the rhenium into bars. Powdered metal is pressed into compacts at 25 to 30 tons/sq. in., vacuum presintered at 1200°C for 2 hours and then sintered with hydrogen at 2850°C, usually by passing an electric current through the bar. This yields a bar whose density is over 90% of theoretical and which is shaped by alternate cold working and annealing. The metal can also be melted in vacuum or inert atmosphere consumable electrode arc melting furnaces.

Physical and Mechanical Properties

The melting point of rhenium, 3170°C, is exceeded only by those of tungsten and carbon among the elements; its density of 21.04 g/cc is above that of every element except iridium, osmium and platinum; and its modulus of elasticity is exceeded only by those of osmium and iridium. Further, the modulus of elasticity decreases from about 68×10^6 psi at zero degrees to about 54×10^6 psi at 800°C, at which temperature it is still higher than that of tungsten.

The ultimate tensile strength of annealed rhenium sheet is about 168,000 psi and after a reduction of 31% by cold rolling, this value increases to 322,000 psi. Even at elevated temperatures, the ultimate tensile strength of annealed rhenium is very much higher than that of other refractory metals, such as tungsten, tantalum, niobium, molybdenum and chromium. At 580°C it is about 120,000 psi, at 800°C about 99,000 psi, at 1200°C about 64,000 psi, at 1600°C about 32,000 psi, at 2000°C about 16,000 psi, and at 2400°C about 8,000 psi.

The stress-rupture strength of rhenium is very high at elevated temperatures. Data obtained at 1000°C on 50 mil wire show a time for rupture of 30 sec at 80,000 psi stress, 5 min at 60,000 psi, 16.5 hr at 40,000 psi, and 100 hr at 20,000 psi. The 100-hour value at 2000°C is 800 psi. The elongation during the test was only 3% in 2″ at stresses of 50,000 to 80,000 psi.

Table 1 contains a summary of values of physical and mechanical properties of rhenium.

Chemical Properties

Rhenium is characterized by its range of valence states: −1, 2, 3, 4, 5, 6 and 7, the latter being its most stable valence. The 4, 6 and 7 are the most common valences, but there is a tendency for rhenium in the valence

TABLE 1. PHYSICAL AND MECHANICAL PROPERTIES OF RHENIUM

Atomic number	75
Atomic weight	186.2
Isotopes (% natural abundance)	185 (37.07)
	187 (62.93)
Atomic radius, Å	1.3777
Crystal structure	Hexagonal close-packed
Lattice constants, Å	a = 2.758
	c = 4.454
	c/a = 1.615
Color	Typically metallic in massive form; black to metallic in powder or electrodeposited form
Allotropic transition	None
Recrystallization temperature, °C	1400
Density, g/cc	21.04
Melting point, °C	3170
Boiling point, °C (est.)	5630
Coefficient of linear thermal expansion, 20–1000°C, per °C	6.6 to 6.8×10^{-6}
Latent heat of fusion, kcal/g-atom	7.9
Latent heat of vaporization, kcal/g-atom	152
Heat of sublimation (calc.), kcal/g-atom	152 to 187
Specific heat, C_p, 0–20°C, cal/g/°C	0.03262
0–1200°C	$C_p = 0.03256 + 0.6625 \times 10^{-5}t$
Thermal conductivity, cal/sec/cm/°C	0.17
Electrical resistivity, microhm-cm	19.14
Temperature coefficient of electrical resistance, 0–100°C, per °C	3.11×10^{-3}
0–2700°C, per °C	1.98×10^{-3}
Superconductivity transition temperature, °K	1.7
Vapor pressure, 2221°C, atm	1.24×10^{-9}
2500°C, atm	6.11×10^{-8}
2726°C, atm	7.37×10^{-7}
Molal entropy, 298.16°K, cal/mole/deg	8.887
Spectral data	Persistent spectral lines at 3000, 3425, 3452, 3462 and triplet at 3640 Å
Photoelectric threshold (long wave limit), Å	
not in vacuum	2671–2677
partial vacuum	2810–2830
completely outgassed	2480 and 2662
Photoelectric work function, electron volts	~5.0
Magnetic moment in nuclear magnetons	3.1433 for Re^{185}
	3.1755 for Re^{187}
Specific magnetic susceptibility	0.369×10^{-6}
Atomic paramagnetism	68.7×10^{-6}
Parachor, from ReO_2Cl_3	78.9
from Re_2O_7	68.9
from ReO_3Cl	76.4
Thermal neutron absorption cross section, barns/atom	86
Modulus of elasticity, 20°C, psi	67×10^6
Tensile strength, pure, annealed, room temp., psi	1.68×10^5, 28% elong.
pure, worked, room temp., psi	3.22×10^5, 2% elong.
pure, worked, 1010°C, psi	1.24×10^5, 1% elong.
pure, worked, 1482°C, psi	0.40×10^5, 1% elong.
Hardness, Brinell	250

states of 1 to 6 to disproportionate into products one of which is almost invariably the +7 valence. For example, when heated: $3ReO_3 \rightarrow ReO_2 + Re_2O_7$. However, the perrhenate ion containing Re(VII) is unlike the permanganate ion and is only a weak oxidant, comparable to ferric ion.

Rhenium metal is quite stable at ordinary temperatures in massive or compact form, but is severely oxidized when heated in air to about 350°C or above. The Re_2O_7 which forms melts at 279°C and boils at 363°C. Two other rhenium oxides are the red ReO_3 and the black ReO_2. The metal is not affected by nitrogen or hydrogen even at elevated temperatures.

All of the halogens react with rhenium (even iodine which formerly was not thought to react), but in no case is the maximum of seven halogen atoms per Re atom obtained, undoubtedly because of steric effects, even in the case of fluorine. Among the halides reported are ReF_6, $ReCl_5$, ReF_4, $ReCl_3$, $ReBr_3$, ReI_3 and ReI.

The rhenium halides hydrolyze in water to form oxy compounds and frequently also undergo disproportionation. Among the derivatives are: ReO_3Br, $ReOCl_4$, ReO_3Cl, $ReOF_4$, and ReO_2F_2. Rhenium trichloride, $ReCl_3$, is a red solid that behaves as a non-electrolyte in solution; when heated it emits a green vapor ($ReCl_5$?) from which metal may be deposited by thermal decomposition. Complex rhenium (IV) halides of the type K_2ReX_6 have been reported for all four halides.

Hydrochloric acid attacks rhenium at a minute rate, if at all, and the metal is also very resistant to cold sulphuric acid and to hydrofluoric acid. Strong oxidizing agents, like nitric acid and hot sulphuric acid, vigorously attack the metal and convert it to perrhenic acid. Hydrogen peroxide in ammoniacal solution oxidizes rhenium, as well as its oxides and sulfides, to ammonium perrhenate. The metal is affected very little by sea water and other nonoxidizing saline solutions.

At elevated temperatures rhenium combines with sulfur, phosphorus, silicon, selenium, tellurium and arsenic to form binary compounds. Rhenium is resistant to attack by molten tin, zinc, copper and silver, is attacked slowly by aluminum and is dissolved readily by nickel and iron.

While the existence of a rhenium carbide is not settled, rhenium does absorb carbon when heated at very high temperatures with carbon monoxide or methane to give a rhenium: carbon ratio of 1:0.7.

The metal is stable in contact with alumina at elevated temperatures (7000 hr at 1600°C) and so might be used as a resistance winding on aluminum oxide furnace cores for exposure in inert atmospheres.

Fabrication Techniques

Rhenium cannot be hot worked successfully in air because to the rapid formation of the volatile Re_2O_7, so it must be formed by cold working techniques. However, rhenium work hardens more rapidly than does any other metal; e.g., the hardness is doubled for a 10% reduction in area. Thus, cold working operations must include frequent annealing in hydrogen for periods up to 2 hours at 1700–1800°C. Annealed metal is very ductile and may be swaged, bent, rolled and drawn into forms such as rod, wire, strip, sheet and foil.

Rhenium may be electrodeposited as bright coherent deposits on a variety of metal surfaces and on graphite from a bath containing $KReO_4$ in sulfuric acid. One bath contains 11 gpl $KReO_4$ and 12 gpl concentrated H_2SO_4 and is operated at 28–50°C and a current density of 100 to 200 amp/sq ft.

Vapor phase deposition of rhenium on filaments of high-melting-point metals is accomplished by heating the filament in the presence of a volatile rhenium halide which is thermally decomposed at the filament surface to deposit rhenium thereon.

Applications

The scarcity and high price (about $2 per g) of rhenium limit its applications to those where its high melting point and good strength at high temperatures are advantageous. One such outlet is high-temperature thermocouples of rhenium-tungsten, rhenium-molybdenum, rhenium-iridium and rhenium-platinum. The rhenium-tungsten thermocouples are capable of measuring and controlling temperatures up to 2500°C in nonoxidizing atmospheres.

In electrical contacts rhenium outperforms both tungsten and platinum-ruthenium contacts by a wide margin and withstands the mechanical effects of electrical erosion. Rhenium has been put to limited use as a contact metal in magnetos for marine engines. In this application its resistance to sea water as well as its resistance to electrical erosion make rhenium especially attractive.

Electronic tube components offer another field of application for rhenium, as do the refractory alloys of rhenium with tungsten, tantalum, niobium, molybdenum, etc. which have been studied. For example, the hardening effect of rhenium on platinum is greater than the hardening effect of such metals as nickel, osmium, iridium and rhodium on platinum.

Rhenium and some of its compounds have interesting catalytic activity. Colloidal rhenium or active rhenium metal powder are effective in the dehydrogenation of alcohols; the synthesis of ammonia; the hydrogenation of coal, coal tar and mineral oil; the oxidation of ammonia; and the oxidation of sulfur dioxide to sulfur trioxide.

In addition to the above uses, rhenium and its alloys have found limited application as fountain pen points, instrument bearing points and electrical components.

Biological and Toxicological Aspects. No data appear to be available regarding the biological, biochemical and toxicological effects of rhenium.

References

1. Melaven, A. D., "Rhenium," chapter in "Rare Metals Handbook," C. A. Hampel, Editor, 2nd Ed., pp. 418–433, New York, Reinhold Publishing Corp., 1961.
2. Sims, C. T., *J. Metals*, 7, 168–179 (Jan. 1955); also, *ibid.*, 8 (1956).
3. Sims, C. T., *et al.* "Investigations of Rhenium," *WADC Technical Report, 54–371, Supplement 1*, ASTIA Document No. AD-97301, p. 57, Washington, D.C., Office of Technical Services, Sept. 1956.
4. Davenport, W. H., "Novel Recovery Puts Rhenium Within Industry Reach," *Chem. Eng.*, 70, 86–88 (June 24, 1963) (includes flowsheet).
5. Eilertsen, D. E., "Rhenium," chapter in "Mineral Facts and Problems," U.S. Bur. Mines Bull. 585, 1960.
6. Pugh, J. W., "Refractory Metals: W, Ta, Cb, Re," *J. Metals*, 10, 335–339 (May 1958).

CLIFFORD A. HAMPEL

RHODIUM

Rhodium is a member of the platinum group of metals, among which it ranks third, after platinum and palladium, in economic significance. Some general comments about the platinum metals and their properties are given under the entry for **Platinum Metals** (q.v.). Within this group of six elements rhodium has certain properties of special interest. It is much harder and considerably higher in melting point than platinum or palladium. It has the highest electrical and thermal conductivity among the platinum metals, as well as the highest specular reflectivity. It is more resistant to chemical attack than either platinum or palladium; and within the platinum group it shows the least tendency to multiple valency, being terpositive in the great majority of its compounds.

Discovery and History

Rhodium was discovered in 1803–04 by W. H. Wollaston working in London. He had entered into a loose partnership with Smithson Tennant in 1800 primarily for the purpose of developing and improving the technology for the refining and fabrication of platinum. Some 7000 ounces of native platinum from South America had been dissolved in aqua regia, and from the resulting solutions platinum had been removed as $(NH_4)_2PtCl_6$. In the filtrate from this Wollaston discovered palladium when he decomposed the yellow substance precipitated by the addition of mercurous cyanide. When the palladous cyanide had been removed he evaporated the remaining solution with hydrochloric acid to decompose the excess mercurous cyanide. The residue was washed with alcohol, which dissolved everything except a dark red material which proved to be a double chloride of sodium and a new metal. The salt today would be called sodium chlororhodite, $Na_3RhCl_6 \cdot 18H_2O$. When this was reduced by heating in hydrogen, and then leached with water to remove sodium chloride, the residue was rhodium powder.

Wollaston chose the name rhodium (from the Greek *rhodon*, rose) in recognition of the beautiful color of the chloro salt and its aqueous solutions. It is evident that as early as 1803 in France N. L. Vauquelin and A. F. deFourcroy had observed the production of a rose color during experiments on the mother liquor remaining after precipitation of ammonium chloroplatinate, but they did not attribute this to a new element.

Another item of historical interest concerning rhodium was the development by H. LeChatelier between 1885 and 1887 of the rhodium-platinum thermocouple. The first suggestion for using the recently discovered thermoelectric effect for the measurement of high temperature was made by A. C. Becquerel in 1826, and the most suitable combination of metals for this purpose was stated to be platinum and palladium. The use of palladium in this application led to erratic results, and after LeChatelier introduced the 10% rhodium-platinum alloy the latter came to displace palladium and other platinum alloys in thermocouples.

Occurrence

Rhodium is invariably found associated with the other platinum metals. The occurrence of these has been described under the entries for platinum (q.v.) and palladium (q.v.), and will be dealt with only briefly here. Most of the platinum metals being produced today come from primary deposits in three main areas: northern Siberia, U.S.S.R.; northern Ontario, Canada; and the Transvaal, South Africa. The Canadian source is the rich nickel-copper sulfide ores found especially in the Sudbury area. The South African deposits occur in an igneous mass, mainly of pyroxene, but associated with chromite and some sulfides.

Secondary deposits or placers, which have resulted from the weathering of certain primary deposits, occur in a number of places, especially in Russia, Colombia, and Alaska. These deposits are generally alloys in which platinum, or less commonly palladium, predominates.

The rhodium content of all these sources is low. In the precious metals concentrate from Canadian ores rhodium may amount to 1%, and this is about one-tenth of the platinum or palladium content. The South African material generally contains an even lower proportion of rhodium.

The estimated abundance of rhodium in the earth's crust is 0.001 g/ton (one-tenth that of platinum).

Derivation

The isolation of pure rhodium from the raw ores in which it occurs is a lengthy and complicated operation. Concentrates of the precious metals are obtained by working up the anode slimes that accumulate in the electrolytic refining of nickel and copper, or by an acid leaching of the residue from the refining of nickel by the Mond carbonyl process. In the case of South African ores a rich gravity concentrate is obtained by treatment of the ground ore on tables and corduroys. These concentrates are then smelted with fluxes and/or treated with acids as appropriate for the removal of base metals. The residual precious metal is then treated with aqua regia to bring gold, platinum, and palladium into solution.

Rhodium, then, makes up part of the residue undissolved by aqua regia; along with it will be iridium, ruthenium, osmium, and generally silver. The procedures for handling this insoluble material vary somewhat, but the following summarizes the practice in one major refinery according to a recent publication.[5] The material is smelted with appropriate amounts of soda ash, borax, lead carbonate, and carbon to produce a slag, and a lead alloy containing 20% precious metals. The granulated lead alloy is dissolved in dilute nitric acid, into which any silver passes, and the platinum metals form an insoluble residue. The latter is fused with sodium bisulfate in silica vessels at 500°C. This treatment converts the rhodium to a water-soluble sulfate, but scarcely attacks the other metals.

From its aqueous sulfate solution rhodium is precipitated as hydroxide; this is separated and dissolved in hydrochloric acid. By this step rhodium sulfate is converted to chloride and the metal content of the solution is increased. Impurities with the rhodium are carried through this step, but are subsequently separated by hydrolytic precipitation in the presence of nitrite. The nitrite complex of rhodium, $Rh(NO_2)_6{}^{3-}$ (cf. cobaltinitrite), is very stable over a wide range of pH, and in this form rhodium is kept in solution under conditions where hydrous oxides of many base metals are precipitated. The metal is subsequently precipitated as ammonium hexanitritorhodite, $(NH_4)_3Rh(NO_2)_6$.

This last compound is digested with hydrochloric acid to produce the chlororhodite, $RhCl_6^{3-}$. Final purification is effected by passing the chlororhodite solution through a column of cation exchange resin, which serves to remove traces of lead, iron, copper, and other elements. The purified solution is then boiled with formic acid to precipitate rhodium black which is then further reduced with hydrogen to yield rhodium powder of high purity.

Melting and Fabrication

Rhodium is produced in the refinery in the form of powder. This may be converted to compact metal either by melting and casting into ingots, or by the technique of powder metallurgy followed by forging and rolling. Molten rhodium has a pronounced tendency to dissolve oxygen gas, but much of this is liberated as the metal solidifies, with "spitting" and rupture of the crust; consequently, melting is best carried out in an atmosphere of argon. Reducing atmospheres must be avoided in melting any of the platinum metals owing to risk of contamination by products of reduction of the refractory crucibles. Melting may be done in an induction furnace, usually in a zirconia crucible, or in an argon arc furnace on a water-cooled copper hearth.

The metal can be forged at temperatures above 800°C but an initial temperature of 1200°C is commonly used. By decreasing the temperature while continuing to work the metal, improved ductility is obtained. In thin sheets rhodium may be cold-worked, but periodic annealing is required during cold work to relieve stresses in the metal.

Physical Properties

A selection of physical properties of rhodium are given in Table 1. Insofar as possible they refer to the metal in the purest available state.

The hardness of pure annealed rhodium

was shown in one study to increase from 110 Vhn to 300 during a 15% reduction in cross section through rolling. This is an uncommonly rapid rate of work-hardening, the cause of which is as yet unknown. The tensile strength can be doubled by cold-drawing.

The reflectivity of rhodium surfaces is very high, exceeding 80% in most of the visible region of the spectrum. This is not as high as that of polished silver, which has a reflectivity averaging about 90% for visible radiation. However, since silver tends to become tarnished in normal atmospheres, its reflectivity soon falls below that of rhodium. Accordingly rhodium finds numerous uses as a durable, highly reflecting surface material.

Rhodium forms continuous series of solid solutions with platinum, palladium, and iridium within the platinum group of metals. A brief discussion of the alloying characteristics of these metals is given under the entry for palladium (q.v.). In agreement with the principles discussed there, rhodium does not show complete miscibility with ruthenium or osmium, although extensive dissolving of rhodium and ruthenium in one another does occur. Complete miscibility is also shown with iron, cobalt, nickel, and copper; but there is remarkably little mutual dissolving of rhodium with either silver or gold. In the case of iron, rhodium acts as platinum does to stabilize the γ-modification, so that alloys with only small percentages of rhodium crystallize in the face-centered cubic form. At lower temperatures, the alloys with palladium or copper (and possible iridium as well) show miscibility gaps; for instance, binary alloys prepared with palladium below 850°C reveal miscibility limits, though the compositions at these have not yet been precisely established.

Alloys containing about 50 atomic-% iron display an unusual property. They are practically nonmagnetic at room temperature, but become suddenly ferromagnetic when heated to 60°C. Above this temperature they behave as normal ferromagnetic materials do, showing a sharp drop in saturation intensity just below the Curie point, which occurs at 400°C. The 50 atomic-% alloy at these temperatures possesses an ordered "superlattice" structure of the CsCl type, and recent work has shown that the lattice dimensions undergo

TABLE 1. PHYSICAL PROPERTIES OF RHODIUM

Property	Units	Value
Symbol		Rh
Atomic number		45
Atomic weight	Cf. C–12	102.905
Stable isotopes		103 (100%)
Density, 20°C	g/cc	12.41
Crystal lattice		Face-centered cubic
Lattice constant, a, 20°C	Å	3.8031
Allotropic forms		None known
Melting point	°C	1960
	°K	2233
Boiling point (estimated)	°K	4000
Thermal conductivity, 0–100°C	watts/cm/°C	1.50
Linear coefficient of thermal expansion, 20–100°C	per °C	8.3×10^{-6}
Specific heat, 0°C	cal/g/°C	0.0589
Heat capacity, C_p, 25°C	cal/mole/°C	5.98
Entropy, S, 25°C	cal/mole/°C	7.53
Latent heat of fusion	kcal/mole	5.15
Latent heat of evaporation, 25°C	kcal/mole	133.1
Electrical resistivity, 0°C	μohm-cm	4.33
Temperature coefficient of resistance, 0–100°C	per °C	0.00463
Thermal neutron absorption cross section	barns	156
Hardness, annealed	Vickers units	100–120
Hardness, electrodeposited	do	800
Tensile strength, annealed	tons/in²	50
Young's modulus, annealed	tons/in²	2.3×10^4
Magnetic susceptibility, χ	cm³/g	0.9903×10^{-6}
Work function	eV	4.90
Thermionic function, A	amp/cm²/°K	100

rapid, uniform expansion at the temperature at which the magnetic transformation occurs.

Chemical Properties

Rhodium is superior to platinum in its resistance to attack by acids and other aqueous reagents. The compact metal is attacked only by boiling sulfuric or hydrobromic acid. Aqua regia does not dissolve rhodium in massive form; but, as the method of its discovery suggests, when dispersed as a dilute constituent of an alloy that is dissolved by aqua regia rhodium is at least partially brought into solution by this reagent. Aqueous solutions of sodium hypochlorite also slowly attack the element.

Fused alkalis will attack rhodium, especially under oxidizing conditions, as also will fused alkali cyanides and fused sodium bisulfate.

Rhodium is oxidized by the halogens at elevated temperatures. At 500–600°C fluorine forms mainly RhF_3 but also some RhF_4. Chlorination yields $RhCl_3$. One excellent method for bringing rhodium into solution is to heat the metal in a sealed tube with hydrochloric acid and an oxidizing agent such as chlorine or sodium chlorate.

At room temperature rhodium does not tarnish in air, but above about 600°C it undergoes superficial oxidation which may be apparent as a dark discoloration. The oxide formed in this way, Rh_2O_3, is decomposed to the elements above 1100°C. At still higher temperatures rhodium (like platinum) loses weight when heated in air or oxygen, and the loss is attributed to a volatile oxide, RhO_2. The tendency of the molten metal to absorb much gaseous oxygen has been mentioned previously.

601

Rhodium powder, when heated, will absorb considerable hydrogen or carbon monoxide.

The ground state of the gaseous atom, as deduced from spectroscopic evidence, is $4d^8 5s^1$. The first-stage ionization potential is 7.46 volts. The standard electrode potential $E°$ (for $3e + Rh^{3+}$ $(aq) \rightarrow Rh(s)$), is not directly measurable but has been estimated by Latimer to be +0.8 volt.

Chemical Compounds

Rhodium shows a marked preference for the oxidation state +3 in its compounds. Quadrivalence is observed in RhF_4, a poorly characterized hydrous dioxide, and a few chloro- and fluoro- complexes such as Cs_2RhCl_6. A hexafluoride is the sole example of the +6 oxidation state. Oxidation states lower than +3 are exhibited by a number of esoteric complexes, and by the carbonyls and carbonyl halides. Rhodium is said to be the only element in the second or third transition series which possesses a definite, well-characterized aquo-ion; this is the yellow $Rh(H_2O)_6^{3+}$, found in aqueous sulfate or perchlorate solutions.

The oxide, Rh_2O_3, is obtained by heating the metal to red heat in air, or by igniting rhodium (III) nitrate. It is a gray crystalline solid with the same crystal structure as corundum. It is insoluble in acids. Careful addition of alkali to rhodium (III) solutions yields a yellow precipitate, said to be $Rh_2O_3 \cdot 5H_2O$. This will dissolve in acids or in excess alkali, and can be ignited to the anhydrous oxide. If too much alkali is used a black precipitate, said to be $Rh_2O_3 \cdot 3H_2O$, is produced; this does not dissolve in acids.

Rhodium trifluoride is a red powder unreactive toward water or aqueous acids or alkalis. It is produced by the action of fluorine on metallic rhodium or $RhCl_3$ at 500–600°C. A small amount of RhF_4, a blue solid is produced at the same time.

The properties of rhodium (III) chloride depend on its preparation. Direct union of the elements at 250°C yields a red powder insoluble in water or acids. Treatment of the yellow hydrous oxide with hydrochloric acid, followed by careful evaporation, produces $RhCl_3 \cdot 4H_2O$, dark red and water-soluble. When this is dehydrated in a stream of HCl at 180°C a water-soluble anhydrous salt is formed.

Several rhodium (III) salts containing the aquo-ion, $Rh(H_2O)_6^{3+}$, have been prepared by dissolving the yellow hydrous oxide in the appropriate acid. The salts that have been characterized are formed with oxy-acids. $Rh(ClO_4)_3 \cdot 6H_2O$ has been characterized crystallographically, and rhodium alums such as $KRh(SO_4)_2 \cdot 12H_2O$ have long been known. Two forms of rhodium sulfate are known; one is a yellow crystalline solid, $Rh_2(SO_4)_3 \cdot 14H_2O$, and the other is red, with the formula $Rh_2(SO_4)_3 \cdot 6H_2O$. The yellow sulfate is a normal ionic salt from solutions of which $BaSO_4$ can be precipitated. The red salt is obtained by evaporating the yellow solution to dryness at 100°C, and from its solution no $BaSO_4$ can be precipitated; the inference here is that three sulfates are coordinated to the metal in a nonlabile complex.

There are a great many rhodium (III) complexes; they are characterized by co-ordination number 6 (octahedral shape) and rather slow rates of ligand exchange. A number of these with nitrogen basis as ligands are cationic, e.g., $Rh(NH_3)_6Cl_3$. In these rhodium displays considerable similarity to cobalt (III), but there are many anionic complexes that have no counterparts in cobalt chemistry, e.g., RhX_6^{3-} or $RX_5(H_2O)^{2-}$, in which $X = Cl$, Br, or CNS. Of these the best known is the hexachlororhodite ion, $RhCl_6^{3-}$, whose beautiful rose color led to the name of the element. Aqueous solutions of this complex turn brown slowly on standing as a result of hydrolysis in which one or more chloride ions are replaced by water molecules.

Importance and Uses

The world annual production of new rhodium is only of the order of 2 or 3 tons, although the supply is increased somewhat by the metal recovered and refined from scrap, spent catalyst, and so forth. The current (1967) price of rhodium is $210.00 per troy ounce.

Some idea of the qualitative distribution of the uses of rhodium is given by the following data based on sales of the metal to the principal consuming industries in the United States during 1965: glass 26.4%, chemical

32.1%, jewelry and decorative 19.3%, electrical 20.4%, petroleum 1.0%, miscellaneous 0.8%. (Total sales 38,910 troy oz.)

Rhodium is used principally as an alloying element for platinum. Its effect is to raise the melting temperature, hardness, and ultimate tensile strength of platinum—most markedly for the first 20% of rhodium added. Although it is inferior to iridium or ruthenium in increasing the hardness of platinum, rhodium is nonetheless extensively used as a hardening agent, particularly for applications at high temperatures. The rhodium alloys undergo the least loss in weight resulting from oxidation at high temperatures.

The glass industry uses large amounts of platinum-rhodium alloys for electrically heated glass furnaces, and for bushings required in the production of glass fiber. Molten glass wets the platinum-rhodium alloy less than it does pure platinum. A more recent application in the glass industry has been as an additive for prolonging the life of iridium vessels in which materials for laser crystals are melted.

The 10% rhodium alloy with platinum is used extensively for windings for furnaces designed to operate at high temperatures and to withstand corrosive atmospheres. For still higher temperatures alloys containing up to 40% rhodium may be used.

For a number of high-temperature catalytic applications the 10% rhodium-platinum alloy is preferred. For instance, the gauze catalyst for the oxidation of ammonia to nitric oxide in the manufacture of nitric acid is fabricated with this alloy because of both greater mechanical strength and higher catalytic activity as compared to pure platinum. Similarly in the Andrussow process for producing hydrogen cyanide from methane and ammonia the rhodium alloy catalyst is chosen for its high mechanical strength at the prevailing operating temperatures (1000 to 1200°C). Glow plugs for aircraft gas turbines, and igniters in the reheat systems of these engines are made of the same 10%-rhodium alloy; these must perform under conditions of high temperature, thermal shock, mechanical stress, and chemical corrosion.

Mention has been made of the platinum *vs* 10% rhodium-platinum thermocouple. This has been used since 1927 to define a portion of the International Temperature Scale (between 660 and 1063°C). In recent years thermocouples have been developed and calibrated in which both limbs are rhodium-platinum alloys but differing in rhodium content. Although these generate slightly smaller thermoelectric potential differences, this limitation is offset by greater stability, increased mechanical strength, and higher ranges of operating temperatures. Combinations that have come into general use (the numbers referring to percentages of rhodium in the two limbs) are five-twenty, six-thirty, and for very high temperatures twenty-forty. Thermocouples consisting of pure iridium in one limb and either 40% or 50% rhodium with iridium in the other are now regarded as advantageous for use in oxidizing atmospheres at very high temperatures.

Among the platinum metals rhodium apparently lends itself most readily to electrodeposition. The deposited metal has a hardness of 800 Vhn or greater, but the great hardness is apparently achieved at the cost of high internal stress which may lead to cracking, especially in thicker deposits. The plating solutions usually contain rhodium sulfate or phosphate in the corresponding acid. Additions such as selenic acid or magnesium sulfate and sulfamate are used to diminish stress and enable thicker coatings to be applied. Rhodium has been used in flash deposits to coat silver jewelry; it is said to preserve the distinctive luster of silver itself while eliminating the objectionable tarnish. In thicker deposits it is used on table silverware and on high-grade reflectors for searchlights and projection lanterns.

Electrical contacts plated with rhodium are extremely free from contact resistance, and find application in components for radio- and audio-frequency circuits. Sliding electrical contacts are also commonly rhodium-plated to take advantage of the great hardness of the electrodeposited metal.

By the recently developed technique of vacuum deposition, rhodium can be sublimed onto glass for mirrors or, in thinner layers, for interference filters for light.

Rhodium has not yet been used as extensively as platinum or palladium for catalysis, but a number of special applications have been developed in recent years. For instance, rhodium on alumina shows a high degree of specificity as a catalyst for the hydrogenation of certain categories of organic compounds. It also has been applied for the oxidation of hydrocarbons, especially unsaturated ones, in air or other oxygen-bearing gases.

References

1. Platinum Metals Review. A quarterly survey of research on the platinum metals and of developments in their application in industry. Johnson, Matthey and Co. Ltd., Hatton Garden, London E.C.1, England, 1957.
2. Hampel, C. A., Editor, Rare Metals Handbook," 2nd Edition, pp. 304–335, New York, Reinhold Publishing Corporation, 1961.
3. "Rhodium—the metal, its alloys, chemical compounds, and catalytic properties," International Nickel Co. Inc., 67 Wall St., New York, 1966.
4. Cotton, F. A., and Wilkinson, G., "Advanced Inorganic Chemistry," pp. 832–845, New York, Interscience Publishers, 1962.
5. Clements, F. S., *Industrial Chemist* (*London*), **38**, 345–354 (1962).

W. A. E. McBryde

RUBIDIUM

Discovery and History

Rubidiumis an alkali metal located in Group IA of the Periodic Table. It was discovered by Kirknoff and Bunsen in 1861 when new lines were found in the dark red region of the spectrum of a sample of lepidolite, from Saxony. The element was named rubidium from the Latin *rubidus,* meaning dark red. The extract from 150 kg of lepidolite was treated with platinic chloride to isolate the alkali metal concentrate. The particular lepidolite that was the original source was found to contain 0.24% Rb_2O.

Further investigations led to the isolation of pure rubidium compounds. The carbonate, chloride, tartrate, and other salts were prepared and their properties studied. Bunsen tried to prepare rubidium metal but was unsuccessful in his early attempts. In later years he achieved an 18% yield of metal by heating rubidium hydrogen tartrate with carbon. The first successful metal preparation was carried out by Hevesy. His method consisted of electrolyzing a melt of rubidium hydroxide in a nickel reactor. An iron wire was used at the cathode. A current density of 0.5 amp/mm^2 was used to reduce the rubidium hydroxide to rubidium metal. The current efficiency was 28.6–32.7%. The major reason for the low yields was that oxygen produced by the reduction was transferred to some degree to the cathode and reacted with the rubidium metal to form oxide.

Hevesy later prepared rubidium by reducing rubidium hydroxide with sodium or potassium. The hydroxide was first fused under nitrogen to effect dehydration and then the sodium or potassium metal was added. The reaction can produce 80% yields of rubidium metal if care is used.

The earliest reported rubidium metal preparation was by Beketov in 1888. He succeeded in reducing rubidium hydroxide with aluminum at red heat. The reaction can be written:

$$(1) \quad 4RbOH + 2Al \longrightarrow Rb_2O + Al_2O_3 + 2Rb + 2H_2$$

The hydrogen acts as a protective blanket for the metal as it is formed. A maximum yield (Rb) is 50% since 50% converts to oxide. Beketov obtained yields of 28–33%.

For many years there was very little interest in rubidium due to its scarcity and difficult extraction and purification procedures. As a result, the metal remained a laboratory curiosity since few uses were developed.

Occurrence

Rubidium is widely distributed in the earth's crust. The element is actually more abundant than either lead, copper, or zinc. It is about ten times as abundant as cesium. (See **Cesium.**)

The original source of the mineral containing rubidium from which it was eventually recovered was lepidolite from Saxony. The mineral contained 0.24% Rb_2O. In the ensuing years, rubidium was found in many minerals and mineral waters but in low concentrations. There are no known minerals where rubidium is a major constituent. It exists in some potassium minerals, such as petalite, biotite, feldspars, beryl, lepidolite,

TABLE 1. RUBIDIUM SOURCES

Mineral	Locality	% Rb$_2$O	% Cs$_2$O
Pollucite	Bikita, S. Rhodesia	0.44	29.0
Pollucite	Bernic Lake, Manitoba	1.15	28.2
Pollucite	Maine, USA	0.065	22.4
Amazonite	Colorado, USA	1.13	0.003
Amazonite	Saxony	0.87	—
Muscovite	Norway	0.40	0.015
Lepidolite	Mass., USA	3.73	0.72
Leucite	Mt. Vesuvius, Italy	0.9	0.9
Amazonite	Madagascar	1.0	0.15
Lepidolite	Southwest Africa	1.73	—
Lepidolite	Bikita, S. Rhodesia	4.60	0.50

leucite, amazonite, and pollucite. Table 1 lists some of the various minerals and their rubidium and cesium contents.

Rubidium is also found in many rocks such as granites, basalts, clay shales, limestones, etc. It will range usually from 0.02–0.09%. In meteorites where the potassium level was found to be 0.05–0.13%, rubidium was found to be present to the extent of 0.0009%. Data have shown that the K/Rb ratio is usually 90.

Rubidium occurs also in sea water and mineral springs. The north Pacific contains 350 micrograms/l Rb, the North Atlantic about 120 micrograms/l, the Black Sea 450 micrograms/l, and 5700 micrograms/l in the Caspian Sea. Mineral springs in Germany contain as much as 1.1 mg/l Rb, and in Japan 0.4 mg/l.

Rubidium and cesium have been deposited from mineral waters along with other minerals to form the potash and saltpeter deposits. Both alkali metals are preferentially concentrated in carnallite deposits. The Strassfurt (Germany) carnallites contain 0.037 to 0.15% rubidium and up to 0.0003% cesium.

The disperse occurrences of rubidium in nature plus its difficult extraction procedures are the main reasons for its limited availability and high cost. There are no major rubidium minerals such as one finds for cesium. Rubidium occurs as an impurity and hence as a constituent of low concentration. The use of carnallites as the rubidium source material in the near future is very probable if uses develop for the element. It could also be obtained as a by-product of cesium extraction from pollucite.

The extraction of lithium from lepidolite produced a rubidium rich by-product known as *Alkarb* (mixed-alkali carbonate); however, the economics of this method of lithium production were not advantageous and the processing of lepidolite ceased. *Alkarb* has been one of the largest sources for rubidium. Its approximate analysis was K$_2$CO$_3$ − 68%, Rb$_2$CO$_3$ − 25%, Cs$_2$CO$_3$ − 2%. This material has virtually been exhausted and no longer constitutes a continuing raw material supply.

Derivation

The extraction and refining of rubidium has been solely from two sources. *Alkarb*, the by-product from lepidolite refining, has been used in the United States since 1956–1957 when an African lepidolite was processed by San Antonio Chemicals for its lithium values. The other source of rubidium is the residues from carnallite processing.

The methods for opening lepidolite ores fall into two categories:

(1) Fusion with gypsum, potassium sulfate, or a mixture of barium carbonate and sulfate.

(2) Leaching with hot sulfuric acid or sulfuric acid plus fluorspar.

The first method, gypsum fusion, is the most widely used. The mass is leached with hot water to extract the alums of cesium, rubidium, and potassium. About 25 recrystallizations of these alums eventually lead to a pure rubidium aluminum sulfate. The rubidium alum solubility lies between that of potassium and cesium.

The fusion of lepidolite with potassium sulfate has been used in Germany on a commercial scale for lithium recovery. The lepidolite is mixed with an excess of potassium sulfate and the mixture heated to a moderate red temperature. The reaction produces soluble sulfates of the alkali metals. The addition of ammonium or potassium carbonate, or carbon dioxide produces an insoluble Li_2CO_3, leaving the potassium, sodium, rubidium, and cesium carbonates in solution. Evaporation of this liquor will result in a mixed alkali metal carbonate. The carbonates can be converted to alums and fractionally crystallized to obtain pure rubidium alum.

The sulfuric acid decomposition process involves heating the finely ground ore with concentrated sulfuric acid. The use of calcium fluoride in the reaction will lead to silicon removal. The alkali metals are solubilized as sulfates. A carbonate addition removes lithium leaving the other alkalies in solution. The rubidium must be isolated by fractionation of the alums.

The use of the inefficient, expensive alum fractionation method has in recent years been supplanted by either chlorostannate or ferrocyanide fractional precipitation.

The chlorostannate method requires that the large amount of potassium in the mixed carbonates be removed for the greater part. This can be accomplished by utilizing the relative insolubility of potassium bicarbonate. The solution of mixed carbonates is treated with CO_2 precipitating 70% of the potassium as potassium bicarbonate. After upgrading the cesium and rubidium contents, the carbonates are converted to the chlorides by addition of HCl. The precipitation of rubidium and cesium chlorostannate is accomplished by adding stoichiometric quantities of stannic chloride. Reactions are given in the following equations:

(2) $\quad 2KHCO_3 + Rb_2CO_3 + 0.1Cs_2CO_3$
$\qquad + 4.2HCl \longrightarrow 2KCl + 2RbCl$
$\qquad + 0.2CsCl + 3.1H_2O + 3.1CO_2$

(3) $\quad 2KCl + 2RbCl + 0.2CsCl + 1.1SnCl_4 \longrightarrow$
$\qquad \underline{Rb_2SnCl_6 + 0.1Cs_2SnCl_6} + 2KCl$

The chlorostannate precipitation must be carried out at a pH just below 7 in order not to hydrolyze the precipitate. Cesium chlorostannate is more insoluble than the rubidium

salt, hence by careful control of stannic chloride additions a reasonably pure rubidium fraction can be obtained. By reducing the tin from $+4$ to $+2$ with iron powder, the complexes can be solubilized. Oxidation of the tin back to $+4$ with chlorine will reprecipitate a portion of the least soluble alkali metal. Equations for these reactions are:

(4) $\quad Rb_2SnCl_6 + Fe \xrightarrow{HCl} 2RbCl$
$\qquad\qquad\qquad\qquad + FeCl_2 + SnCl_2$

(5) $\quad 2RbCl + SnCl_2 + FeCl_2 + Cl_2 \longrightarrow$
$\qquad\qquad\qquad\qquad Rb_2SnCl_6 + FeCl_2$

The rubidium chlorostannate can be converted by thermal decomposition to rubidium chloride and stannic chloride vapor which can be condensed and recycled to the precipitation step.

Another method to decompose the chlorostannate is to dissolve the complex and reduce the tin with iron powder. The addition of a perchlorate will precipitate rubidium perchlorate. The decomposition of rubidium perchlorate to rubidium chloride is effected by heat. Tin values are recovered by chlorination of the solution.

(6) $\quad 2RbCl + SnCl_2 + FeCl_2 + 2NaClO_4 \longrightarrow$
$\qquad 2RbClO_4 + 2NaCl + SnCl_2 + FeCl_2$

(7) $\quad 2RbClO_4 \xrightarrow{\triangle} 2RbCl + 4O_2\uparrow$

(8) $\quad SnCl_2 + FeCl_2 + 2NaCl + Cl_2 \longrightarrow$
$\qquad\qquad\qquad SnCl_4 + FeCl_2 + 2NaCl$

The main disadvantage of this route is that rubidium chloride is more difficult to convert to other rubidium salts.

The rubidium zinc ferrocyanide method will yield pure carbonate salt. The order of decreasing solubility is cesium, rubidium, potassium. The zinc ferrocyanide complexes are precipitated by the addition of sodium zinc ferrocyanide to a mixed alkali carbonate solution as shown in the following equation:

(9) $\quad Na_xZn_yFe(CN)_6 + Rb_2CO_3 \longrightarrow$
$\qquad\qquad Rb_2ZnFe(CN)_6 + 1/2xNa_2CO_3$
$\qquad\qquad\qquad\qquad + (y\text{-}1) ZnCO_3$

The controlled fractional precipitation yields 98% plus rubidium carbonate. The rubidium zinc ferrocyanide is decomposed by heating in air as shown.

$$(10) \quad Rb_2ZnFe(CN)_6 + 7.75O_2 \longrightarrow$$
$$Rb_2CO_3 + 0.5Fe_2O_3 + 4CO_2 + 3N_2$$
$$+ ZnCO_3$$

Leaching the roasted mass solublizes the rubidium carbonate which can be separated from the other decomposition products by filtration.

Carnallites from the Strassfurt, Germany area have been treated to recover rubidium values. This process is based on the multiple fractional crystallizations of a mixture of potassium, magnesium, and rubidium chlorides and the use of silicomolybdates as intermediates. The natural carnallite contains 0.02% rubidium chloride. The manufacture of potassium chloride from the carnallite results in a synthetic intermediate of much higher rubidium values, which is used in this process.

The recent development of a liquid ion exchange process by researchers at Oak Ridge National Laboratory may possibly be used to extract and purify rubidium from alkaline liquors. The use of controlled extraction conditions with 4-sec-butyl-2-(α-methyl benzyl) phenol (BAMBP) in a kerosene diluent can conceivably effect a separation of potassium, rubidium, and cesium. Extraction coefficients for the three-element partition are favorable. This procedure would lead to the preparation of rubidium carbonate. It appears to be feasible to utilize this interesting technique for rubidium and cesium recovery from carnallite, pollucite, or lepidolite liquors.

Other method which have been tried for separation of the mixed alkali metals are fractional crystallization or precipitation of alums, oxalates, acid tartrates, alkali magnesium phosphates, and alkali-halogen complex salts of elements such as antimony, lead, platinum, iridium and bismuth. Silicotungstates, cobaltinitrites, and organic compounds of picrates, hexanitrodiphenylamine and tetraphenylboron have all been used with varying degrees of success.

Preparation of Rubidium Metal

As described previously, Bunsen and Beketov attempted various methods of preparation of rubidium metal.

Reduction of rubidium carbonate with magnesium in a hydrogen atmosphere was tried successfully in 1906. Nearly theoretical yields were obtained.

Hackspill developed the method of reduction of rubidium chloride with calcium, and it became the standard means of preparing rubidium metal. Dry rubidium chloride is thoroughly mixed with calcium chips and placed in an iron, stainless steel, or nickel tube which is then inserted into a Pyrex tube with the end closed. The open end is attached to a vacuum system and a receiver is attached to the reaction tube between the vacuum outlet and reaction chamber. The system is evacuated and heat applied to the reactants. After 3–4 hours of slow heating, the temperature is raised to 700–800°C. The rubidium distills and is collected in the receiver. The receiver is sealed off at the end of the run and the rubidium kept in this glass ampoule. Nearly theoretical yields can be obtained.

Many metals have been found that will reduce rubidium chloride. Sodium, aluminum, magnesium, iron, silicon, zirconium, thorium, titanium, and hafnium are all reported to be capable of reducing various rubidium salts. Iron can reduce the sulfate and carbonate at temperatures over 1100°C.

One of the methods used to prepare rubidium in the production of photoelectric cells is to reduce rubidium chromate with zirconium powder. This method has the advantage that no gases result from the reaction. The reaction is represented in the following equation:

$$(11) \quad 2Rb_2CrO_4 + Zr \longrightarrow 4Rb + Zr(CrO_4)_2$$

The reaction begins at 700°C and a yield of almost 100% is obtained.

A method for producing rubidium metal with low gas content is by thermally decomposing rubidium azide according to the following reaction:

$$(12) \quad 2RbN_3 \longrightarrow 2Rb + 3N_2$$

The decomposition temperature of the azide is 395°C. The reaction is carried out at 500°C under very high vacuum. The temperature must be raised slowly to avoid violent decomposition. Yields of rubidium never exceed 60% due to the formation of rubidium nitride, Rb_3N.

Rubidium metal was prepared by Hevesy utilizing an electrolysis of rubidium hydroxide as described previously.

Physical Properties

Rubidium, next to cesium, has the lowest ionization potential of all the elements. This property coupled with its low melting point and its low boiling point, high vapor pressure, large ionic radius, low density and low electron work function makes the element a secondary candidate for use in the ion engine, photoelectric tubes, and other applications. Its properties of low melting point, high heat capacity and high heat transfer coefficient make the element a possible choice as a heat transfer medium for space vehicles. Rubidium is the second most electropositive element and the second most alkaline.

Approximately 27% of naturally occurring

TABLE 2. PHYSICAL PROPERTIES OF RUBIDIUM

Atomic number	37
Atomic weight	85.47
Crystal form	Body-centered cubic
Atomic radius	2.43 Å
Ionic radius	1.48 Å
Atomic volume	55.9 cc/g-atom @ 20°C
Lattice constant	$a = 5.62$ Å @ -173°C
Density, solid	1.532 @ 20°C
liquid	1.475 @ 39°C
Melting point	39°C
Boiling point	688°C
Latent heat of fusion	6.1 cal/g
Latent heat of vaporization	212 cal/g
Specific heat	0.080 cal/g/°C @ 0°C
	0.0907 cal/g/°C @ 50°C
Vapor pressure, temperature for	°C
1 mm Hg	294
10 mm Hg	387
100 mm Hg	519
200 mm Hg	569
400 mm Hg	628
Thermal conductivity	0.075 cal/sec/°C/cm @ 50°C
Ionization potential of gaseous atoms	4.16 volts
Electron work function	2.09 eV
Electrical resistivity	11.6 microhm-cm @ 0°C
	23.15 microhm-cm @ 50°C
	27.47 microhm-cm @ 100°C
Magnetic susceptibility	0.09×10^{-6} cgs units @ 18°C
Coefficient of linear thermal expansion	90×10^{-6}/°C @ 20°C
	340×10^{-6}/°C in a range from 40–100°C
Viscosity	0.6734 centipoises @ 38°C
	0.6258 centipoises @ 50°C
	0.4844 centipoises @ 99.7°C
	0.3234 centipoises @ 220.1°C
Temperature coefficient of electrical resistivity	0.006/°C @ 0°C
Electrode potential	
$Rb \longrightarrow Rb^+ + e$	2.926 volts
Thermal neutron absorption cross section	0.73 barns
Important spectral lines	7947.60 Å
	7800.23 Å
	4215.556 Å
	4201.85 Å
Mohs hardness	0.3

rubidium is rubidium-87, a beta emitter with a half-life of 6.3×10^{10} years. The age of rubidium containing rocks can be determined by the amount of the rubidium-87 isotope which has decomposed to strontium.

The physical properties are given in Table 2.

Chemical Properties

Rubidium is a very reactive metal with a silvery-metallic surface. It melts at 39°C and boils at 688°C. Its properties are similar to those of the other alkali metals. Rubidium reacts vigorously with air and water and this reactivity requires that special techniques be used to prepare and handle the metal.

Rubidium forms four oxides: Rb_2O, Rb_2O_2, Rb_2O_3, Rb_2O_4. The metal reacts with hydrogen and nitrogen to form rubidium hydride and nitride, respectively. Rubidium hydroxide can be formed by the reaction of the metal with water. Rubidium hydroxide is a very strong base.

The halides of rubidium can form double halide complexes with other metals, such as antimony, nickel, cobalt, thorium, bismuth, cadmium, manganese, mercury, etc. Many can be used as intermediates in the purification and separation of rubidium from the other alkali metals. Polyhalides can also be formed.

Many of the more common salts, such as the hydroxide, fluoride, and carbonate, are extremely hygroscopic and corrosive, and must be handled in an appropriate fashion.

A number of organic rubidium compounds are known. Rubidium will alloy with the other alkali metals, alkaline earths, bismuth, gold, antimony, mercury, and lead.

Principal Compounds

Rubidium Chloride. Rubidium chloride crystallizes from water in well-defined colorless cubic crystals. It has a solubility of 77 g in 100 ml of water at 0°C and 139 at 100°C. Its solubility in alcohol is only 0.03 g per 100 g at 20°C. Rubidium chloride can be heated to its boiling point without dissociation. It is easily prepared by adding hydrochloric acid to a solution of rubidium hydroxide or carbonate. Evaporation produces crystalline rubidium chloride. This salt is the one most commonly used for preparing rubidium metal.

Rubidium Carbonate. Rubidium carbonate is isolated as colorless crystals. It can be made by adding carbon dioxide gas to a solution of rubidium hydroxide. It can also be prepared by adding ammonium carbonate to a rubidium hydroxide solution and evaporate to dryness to expel the ammonia. The carbonate is extremely soluble, 450 g in 100 ml of water at 20°C. It is stable when heated to its melting point of 837°C but begins to dissociate at temperatures above 900°C. The carbonate can be converted to bicarbonate by addition of carbon dioxide to a concentrated aqueous solution. The carbonate is extremely hygroscopic and forms the monohydrate very readily.

Rubidium Nitrate. Rubidium nitrate is formed from aqueous solution by the addition of nitric acid to a solution of rubidium carbonate or hydroxide. It can also be prepared by the reaction between solutions of barium nitrate and rubidium sulfate. The solubility of the nitrate is 19.5 g per 100 ml at 0°C and 452 at 100°C. The nitrate crystallizes in the cubic system. The salt melts at 294°C and then boils and decomposes at its dissociation temperature 881°C.

Rubidium Hydroxide. Rubidium hydroxide can be prepared by adding barium hydroxide to a boiling solution of rubidium sulfate. The precipitated barium sulfate is removed by filtration. The rubidium hydroxide can be isolated by evaporation to dryness. The anhydrous hydroxide can be obtained from the monohydrate by passing N_2 through molten hydroxide at 400°C in a silver vessel. The hydroxide is a very strong base which will attack glass at room temperature. Rubidium hydroxide is extremely hydroscopic and readily absorbs carbon dioxide from the air.

Rubidium Sulfate. Rubidium sulfate can be prepared by neutralizing a rubidium carbonate or hydroxide solution with sulfuric acid. It can be prepared by adding ammonia to a hot solution of rubidium aluminum sulfate. The removal of the precipitated aluminum hydroxide by filtration results in a rubidium sulfate solution that can be evaporated to crystallize the salt. The sulfate has a solubility of 36 g per 100 ml of water at 0°C and 82 at 100°C.

Applications of Rubidium and its Compounds

The present industrial uses of rubidium metal and its compounds are largely limited at present to research and development applications. The availability of the element is limited since no specific minerals containing rubidium are known. All production must come from residues and concentrates that are by-products of the various other alkali metal processing industries.

Significant developments for use of rubidium did not materialize until the discovery of its photoelectric properties. The use of rubidium in vacuum tubes and photocells has been the major outlet for the metal. Certain compounds such as the carbonates have been used in special glasses.

Rubidium metal has been investigated as a possible fuel for the ion propulsion engine, but results have indicated that cesium is the most desirable alkali metal for this application because of its ionization properties.

The field of heat conversion to electricity utilizing the thermoionic mechanism, a magnetohydrodynamic system, has received wide attention. Rubidium has been tested in both areas; however, results to date show cesium to be the favored alkali metal.

Rubidium is being investigated as a heat transfer medium in space vehicles. Its properties of low melting point, heat capacity, and high heat transfer coefficient are the properties which are of interest in this application.

Rubidium hydroxide has been suggested as an electrolyte in alkaline storage batteries for use in low-temperature applications. Rubidium di-acid phosphates possess piezoelectric properties. Other rubidium compounds have been used as soporifics, sedatives, and for the treatment of epilepsy.

Toxicity of Rubidium

There is little evidence that rubidium is toxic to humans. Large amounts added to a diet low in potassium causes symptoms of neuro-muscular hyperirritability with an unfavorable effect on reproductive function; violent tetanic spasms, followed by death in several weeks results from such a supplemented diet. No hystological changes have been found in the nervous system. These studies were conducted on animals.

The hazard of rubidium metal as well as some of its salts are due to the chemical properties of the metal and salts. Rubidium metal will cause serious burns of the skin and a number of the compounds are capable of producing burns and skin irritation. The main hazard of rubidium compounds is usually due to the metal or radical that is combined with the rubidium. Examples of this are fluoride, hydroxide or cyanide.

References

1. Brauer, G., "Handbook of Preparative Inorganic Chemistry," Volume I, 2nd Edition, pp. 950–992, 1963.
2. Eilertsen, D. E., "Rubidium," a chapter from "Mineral Facts and Problems," 1965 Edition, Bulletin 630, Washington, D.C., U.S. Bureau of Mines.
3. Hampel, C. A., "Rare Metals Handbook," 2nd Edition, pp. 434–440, New York, Reinhold Publishing Corp., 1961.
4. Hopkins, B. S., "Chapters in the Chemistry of the Less Familiar Elements," Volume I, Chapter 3, Champaign, Ill., Stipes Publishing Co., 1938.
5. Lam, H., and Foster, H. R., Jr., "Preparation of Cesium and Rubidium Metals," paper presented before the Division of Industrial and Engineering Chemistry, ACS Meeting, San Francisco, Calif., April 17, 1958.
6. Mellor, J. W., "Comprehensive Treatise on Inorganic and Theoretical Chemistry," Volume II, Supplement III, "The Alkali Metals," New York, Longmans, Green & Co., 1963.
7. ORNL-3454, Chemical Technology Division, "Annual Progress Report for Period ending May 31, 1963," Oak Ridge National Laboratory, pp. 175–177, 189–192.
8. Perel'man, F. M., "Rubidium and Cesium," New York, Macmillan Co., 1965.

C. EDWARD MOSHEIM

RUTHENIUM

This element is a member of the platinum group of metals (q.v.). It is situated in Mendeléev's Table below iron and above osmium, and bears strong resemblances to the latter. It is characterized physically by a high melting point, great hardness, and low workability. Chemically its most distinctive features are a volatile tetroxide, a great variety of oxidation states, and a marked disposition to form complex ions of which numerous are polynuclear.

Discovery and History

Ruthenium was the last of the platinum metals to be discovered. In 1824–5 extensive alluvial deposits of native platinum were discovered in the Ural Mountains region of Russia. Very soon thereafter Russia was to become the principal source of platinum metals for the entire world, a position that was maintained until early in the present century. (By the 1960's Russia had again become the leading producer of platinum metals, although the source had changed and a different type of deposit was involved). In 1828 platinum coins were issued by the government mint in St. Petersburg, under whose auspices refining of the metal was carried out. Various scientists began to investigate the insoluble residues arising from this refining, and among these was G. W. Osann at the University of Dorpat (now Tartu). He announced in 1828 that this material contained three new elements which he named pluran, ruthen, and polin. His work was discredited by Berzelius, but later was a stimulus to the real discovery of ruthenium in 1844 by K. K. Klaus at the University of Kazan.

Klaus fused the insoluble material with potassium hydroxide and nitrate in a silver crucible. The cooled melt yielded on treatment with water an orange-colored solution (of osmate and ruthenate). When this was treated with nitric acid he obtained a black precipitate of the oxides of these metals. Distillation of this with aqua regia yielded osmium tetroxide. The remainder of the solution, after removal of the osmium, was treated with ammonium chloride which resulted in the formation of crystals of ammonium chlororuthenate. This salt could be ignited to a residue of the new metal ruthenium. Klaus adopted the name ruthenium, a latinized name for Russia, partly for patriotic reasons and partly in recognition of the earlier work of Osann.

Occurrence

Ruthenium is always found associated with the other platinum metals, and its abundance is about comparable to that of the minor metals rhodium and iridium. Since the occurrence of the platinum metals has been described in some detail under the entries platinum (q.v.) and palladium (q.v.) the information will not be repeated here. The abundance of the element in the earth's crust has been estimated as 0.001 g/ton.

Derivation

The refining of platinum metals begins with concentrates produced in a variety of ways from the ores in which these metals occur at very low concentration. For instance, in the electrolytic refining of nickel or copper from Canadian and (in part) South African ores, precious metals accumulate in the anode sludges. The latter may be worked up by acid leaching and smelting to give a rich concentrate. In the same way, the residue from the Mond carbonyl refining of nickel contains precious metals which may be concentrated for the extraction of the latter. Most of the platinum metals in South African deposits are found in a gravity concentrate from the ground ore. The concentrates are stripped of any residual base metals by smelting with suitable fluxes, and by acid treatment. The isolation and separation of the platinum metals involves a lengthy sequence of wet chemical operations. The first of these is the dissolving of gold, platinum and palladium by aqua regia, leaving a residue of silver and the other four metals of the platinum group.

The treatment of this insoluble residue evidently varies among the major refiners, but at some stage it is subjected to an alkaline oxidizing fusion, e.g., with sodium peroxide. This converts ruthenium and osmium to water-soluble ruthenate and osmate. Solutions of the latter are then treated so as to distill out the volatile tetroxides of these metals. The manner of doing this so as to achieve a separation of osmium and ruthenium varies somewhat according to the relative proportions of these two elements. In Canadian deposits osmium generally amounts to less than 1% of the ruthenium content. The aqueous extract from the peroxide fusion then contains mainly sodium ruthenate. This is treated with chlorine gas and heated, and the ruthenium tetroxide is distilled out and caught in receivers containing hydrochloric acid. The resulting ruthenium chloride solution is boiled with nitric acid to remove traces of osmium, and then treated with ammonium chloride to precipitate ammonium chlororuthenate. These brown crystals are separated, washed, dried, and ignited to a ruthenium black. This is reduced in an atmosphere of hydrogen at 1000°C to give very pure ruthenium powder.[5]

The separation of osmium from ruthenium is generally based on the fact that nitric acid will oxidize osmium compounds to OsO_4, but converts ruthenium to nitric oxide (nitrosyl) complexes which remain in solution during distillation of the volatile osmium tetroxide.

Melting and Fabrication

The powdered metal from the refinery is converted to massive form either by melting in an argon arc furnace, or by the methods of powder metallurgy. The molten metal has a tendency, like rhodium or palladium, to dissolve a good deal of oxygen and then upon solidification to reject this with disruption of the crust. Melting is on this account best carried out in a vacuum or in an argon atmosphere. To get high-purity ruthenium in this way special pains should be taken to minimize the presence of reactive gases in the furnace by means of scavengers.

Investigation of the consolidation of ruthenium by powder metallurgy has shown the influence of purity, and even of powder size, on the mechanical properties of the metal.[6] Compacts pressed under high pressure are sintered, either in hydrogen or in a vacuum, at about 1500°C. The sintered material is then subjected to hot forging, swaging, or rolling. From an extensive study of the workability of the compact metal, it has been concluded that it is not intrinsically brittle but normally it is not very ductile owing to traces of impurities.

Single-crystal ruthenium, prepared by electron-beam zone refining proved to be quite ductile. When these specimens were cold-worked and then annealed, they reverted to a polycrystalline state and became very brittle at room temperature.

Physical Properties

A compilation of physical properties of the pure metal is given in Table 1.

Over a period of years there has been some uncertainty concerning the existence of allotropic modifications of ruthenium. On the basis of measurements of heat capacity and of the temperature coefficient of electrical resistance, it was concluded that four, and possibly even five, polymorphic modifications of ruthenium exist. The values reported for the transition temperatures were 1035°, 1190°, and 1500°C. However, high-temperature x-ray diffraction measurements made in 1957[7] indicate no change in crystal structure or discontinuities in lattice parameters at least up to 1300°C. In view of this structural evidence it has been concluded[8] that the anomaly at 1035°C is due to a second-order transition.

When the axial ratio, c/a, in a hexagonal close-packed crystal lattice is not 1.633, two different interatomic distances are obtained from the structural analysis. The atoms lying in the basal (0010) plane are separated by the distance a, but the closest neighbors in the layers above and below a given atom may be at a greater or smaller distance according to the value of c/a. In the case of ruthenium the interatomic distances indicated are 2.7056 Å and 2.6496 Å. A mean atomic diameter for 12-coordination according to Goldschmidt is 2.68 Å.

A number of the mechanical properties of ruthenium vary in magnitude according to the orientation of their measurement with respect to the crystal faces. For instance, measurements on single crystals show a hardness of 200 Vhn on the basal (0010) plane, and as high as 480 Vhn in the prismatic (10$\bar{1}$0) plane. Likewise tensile properties also vary considerably according to the orientation of the crystal faces. Thus in single crystals little or no elongation is possible in the direction of the hexagonal axis, but at right angles to this elongations up to 30% are possible.

Alloys with ruthenium have not been as well investigated as those of the face-centered cubic platinum metals. Alloys with platinum and palladium have been examined from the point of view of the use of ruthenium as a hardening and strengthening agent for these metals. Palladium and ruthenium show a solubility of one in the other amounting to about 15 atomic–% at the solidus temperature

TABLE 1. PHYSICAL PROPERTIES OF RUTHENIUM

Property	Unit	Value
Symbol		Ru
Atomic number		44
Atomic weight	*cf* C–12	101.07
Stable isotopes (with % abundance)		96 (5.7), 98 (2.2), 99 (12.8), 100 (12.7), 101 (17.0), 102 (31.3), 104 (18.3)
Density, 20°C	g/cc	12.45
Crystal lattice		Hexagonal close-packed
Lattice constants, 20°C, *a*	Å	2.7056
c/a		1.5820
Allotropic forms		probably none
Melting point	°C	2310
	°K	2583
Boiling point (estimated)	°K	4392
Thermal conductivity, 0–100°C	watts/cm/°C	1.05
Linear coefficient of thermal expansion, 20–100°C	per °C	9.1×10^{-6}
Specific heat, 0°C	cal/g/°C	0.0551
Heat capacity, C_p, 25°C	cal/mole/°C	5.75
Entropy, S, 25°C	cal/mole/°C	6.82
Latent heat of fusion	kcal/mole	6.2
Latent heat of evaporation, 25°C	kcal/mole	155.0
Electrical restitivity, 0°C	μohm-cm	6.71
Temperature coefficient of resistance, 0–100°C	per °C	0.0042
Thermal neutron absorption cross section	barns	2.6
Hardness (annealed)	Vickers units	200–350
Young's modulus	tons/in²	3.0×10^4
Magnetic susceptibility, χ	cm³/g	0.427

(1575°C).[9] Rhodium and ruthenium dissolve in one another to a slightly greater extent. Even greater dissolving of ruthenium in platinum, and of iridium in ruthenium is recorded. Complete miscibility is found for the two hexagonal close-packed metals, osmium and ruthenium. Several workers have studied the effect of additions of ruthenium on the mechanical properties and corrosion resistance of the Group VI transition elements; in general the effects are beneficial.

Chemical Properties

Ruthenium is superior to platinum in its resistance to attack by acids. Cold or hot acids, including aqua regia, are without effect on the metal. However, it is considerably more susceptible to attack by alkaline oxidants such as sodium hypochlorite solution or concentrated aqueous sodium hydroxide or peroxide. Fused alkaline hydroxides, carbonates, cyanides, and especially peroxides attack the metal, especially when finely divided. (Advantage is taken of this in the refining operations described previously).

Although ruthenium forms a volatile tetroxide as osmium does, it differs from the latter in that the tetroxide does not form directly from the elements. Thus, although the pungent odor of osmium tetroxide is quickly detected when osmium is heated in air, no evidence of tetroxide formation is observed with ruthenium under these conditions. However, when ruthenium is heated in oxygen at temperatures above 1000°C a significant loss in weight is detected. This loss, incidentally, is much greater than that sustained by platinum under the same conditions (q.v.). A trioxide, RuO_3, the vapor pressure of which attains 10^{-3} atm at a little above 1100°C, is

613

believed to account for the disappearance of the metal. When ruthenium is heated in air or oxygen it becomes coated with a very thin layer of dioxide, RuO_2, and this is believed to persist up to 1540°C, at which temperature its dissociation pressure attains 1 atm.

The halogens all attack ruthenium fairly easily. Saturated chlorine water or bromine water, or alcoholic iodine solutions will corrode the metal. Fluorination at 300°C converts ruthenium to a pentafluoride, RuF_5. Chlorine at 450°C or higher temperatures forms the trichloride, $RuCl_3$.

The metal shows excellent resistance to attack by a number of molten metals when heated in argon atmospheres. Lithium, sodium, potassium, silver, copper, gold, cadmium, mercury, indium, tin, lead, and tellurium fail to attack ruthenium at all. Calcium, gallium, and bismuth cause only slight attack; the most severe corrosion is caused by zinc.

The ground state of the gaseous atom is deduced from spectroscopic evidence to be $4d^7 5s^1$. The first-stage ionization potential is 7.36 volts. Because of the lack of reliable thermodynamic data for aqueous ruthenium species, standard electrode potentials for ruthenium couples have all had to be estimated. Of such values the following is probably the most reliable: for $3e + RuCl_5{}^{2-}$ $(aq) \rightarrow Ru\ (s) + 5\ Cl^-$, $E° = 0.601$ volt.

Chemical Compounds

Ruthenium compounds show a marked resemblance to those of osmium, which the element resembles much more than it does iron. Compounds in at least eight oxidation states have been characterized, but of these $+2$, $+3$ and $+4$ are the most common. The solution chemistry of ruthenium received considerable study from 1945 onward because of the common appearance of this element among the products of nuclear fission of heavy-atom elements. This study has disclosed the great variety in oxidation states assumed by this element, and the pronounced tendency toward formation of polynuclear complexes.

The tetroxide has already been mentioned; it is a yellow molecular solid (m.p. 25°C, b.p. 100°C), and like osmium tetroxide it is highly toxic. It is formed when acidic solutions of ruthenium compounds are heated with powerful oxidizing agents. It is not formed by the reaction of nitric acid on ruthenium compounds, nor by direct union of the elements (difference from osmium). On dissolution in alkali RuO_4 is immediately reduced, first to a green perruthenate (VII), and subsequently to an orange-colored ruthenate (VI).

The dioxide, RuO_2, is produced when the metal is heated in air at 500–700°C. It is a black crystalline solid with the structure of rutile. It is not dissolved by acids, but may be reduced to the metal by heating in hydrogen. Dark-colored hydrous oxides are precipitated from ruthenium (III) solutions by the addition of alkali, and from alkaline solutions of RuO_4 by the addition of alcohol and by boiling. Neither preparation has been well characterized.

Ruthenium disulfide, RuS_2, is a gray-blue crystalline solid known as a mineral called laurite. It can also be prepared by the action of hydrogen sulfide on hot $RuCl_3$. It is chemically unreactive.

Fluorination of the element gives RuF_5, a green solid (m.p. 107°C, b.p. ca.270°C) with a colorless vapor. It is very reactive, is hydrolyzed by water, and reduced by iodine to brown solid RuF_3.

Chlorination at 700°C yields $RuCl_3$, a black solid almost insoluble in water. A hydrated form, prepared by the evaporation of a solution of RuO_4 in hydrochloric acid in a stream of hydrogen gas, is formulated $RuCl_3 \cdot H_2O$. It is water-soluble, but the fresh solution contains no chloride ion and should properly be formulated as a complex. The aqueous solution undergoes hydrolysis with precipitation of a hydrous oxide.

Ruthenium tetrachloride, $RuCl_4$, and a hydroxychloride $RuOHCl_3$, are formed when hydrochloric acid solutions of RuO_4 are evaporated. There is reason to believe that these compounds are structurally much more complex than these formulas suggest.

Perruthenate, $RuO_4{}^-$, and ruthenate, $RuO_4{}^{-2}$, are formed when RuO_4 dissolves in alkali, and also when the element or certain compounds are fused with alkali in the presence of an oxidizing agent. There is no analogue of the osmate (VIII) ion (q.v.), and the ruthenate (VI) ion is tetrahedral and accordingly different from osmate (VI) (q.v.).

The element forms a large number of

complex ions. Some of these are known to be mononuclear and 6-coordinate, and involve the element in various oxidation states; e.g., $Ru(CN)_6^{-2}$, $Ru(phenanthroline)_3^{+2}$, $Ru(NH_3)_4Cl_2^{+}$, $RuO_2Cl_4^{-2}$. A number of complexes have been shown to be polynuclear; for instance an ion long formulated as $RuCl_5OH^{-2}$ has been shown to be $Ru_2Cl_{10}O^{-4}$. A striking feature of the coordination chemistry of ruthenium is the large number of nitric oxide or nitrosyl complexes formed by this element. Thus $RuNOCl_3 \cdot 5H_2O$ is identified in solutions in which ruthenium chloride has been treated with nitric acid (e.g., aqua regia); this is a dark red color. These complexes are reminiscent of the species $FeNO^{+2}$ associated with the well known "brown ring test" for nitrates.

Ruthenium forms a pentacarbonyl, $Ru(CO)_5$, when the finely divided metal is heated with carbon monoxide under 200 atm pressure. It is a colorless liquid (m.p. $-22°C$) which decomposes on heating with formation of $Ru_2(CO)_9$, a yellow crystalline solid. Ruthenium also forms a yellow crystalline addition compound with cyclopentadiene, $Ru(C_5H_5)_2$, known as ruthenocene.

Importance and Uses

Ruthenium is produced on about the same scale as iridium. Its importance as an industrial metal can be judged from the following information concerning sales to the principal consuming industries in the United States during 1965. Of 8083 troy ounces sold, 38.4% went to the chemical industry; 32.7% was used in electrical goods, 1.8% in dental and medical wares, and 10.6% in jewelry and decorative uses; the remainder was unclassified. The current (1967) price for ruthenium is $55 to $60 per troy ounce.

Ruthenium is used as a hardening element for platinum or palladium. A number of applications of these alloys are in the field of electrical contacts for which their high wear resistance and freedom from oxidation and corrosion are advantageous. The palladium alloys with 4.5% ruthenium are used considerably for jewelry; and a number of dental alloys are also based on palladium hardened with ruthenium. Small additions of ruthenium, like the other platinum metals, markedly increase the corrosion resistance of titanium.

A number of alloys have been developed with relatively high content of ruthenium together with other platinum metals or base metals. These are very hard, wear-resistant, and nonmagnetic, and find applications for electrical contacts, tips for fountain pen nibs, and instrument pivots.

Thin coatings of ruthenium may be electrodeposited on a suitable base coat. Plating on silver, copper, or nickel is preceded by a flash deposition of gold. The electrodeposited metal is very hard (900 Vhn or greater) and with lower internal stress than rhodium. Plating baths based on nitrosyl chlorides or nitrosyl sulfamates have been developed, from which the metal is deposited often at elevated temperatures and low current efficiency.

A number of catalytic applications have been proposed, but of these special mention is made of the highly selective catalysis of the hydrogenation of carbonyl groups. These in aldehydes and ketones may be reduced to alcoholic groups; and in favorable cases this functional group may be selectively reduced in the presence of an olefinic linkage.

References

1. Platinum Metals Review. A quarterly survey of research on the platinum metals and of developments in their application in industry. Johnson, Matthey and Co. Ltd., Hatton Garden, London, E.C.1, England, 1957.
2. Hampel, C. A., Editor, "Rare Metals Handbook," 2nd Edition, pp. 304–335, New York, Reinhold Publishing Corporation, 1961.
3. Cotton, F. A., and Wilkinson, G., "Advanced Inorganic Chemistry," pp. 811–832, New York, Interscience Publishers, 1962.
4. "Ruthenium, The Metal, its alloys, chemical compounds, and catalytic properties," The International Nickel Co. Inc., 67 Wall St., New York, 1963.
5. Clements, F. S., *The Industrial Chemist*, **38**, 345–354 (1962).
6. Rhys, D. W., *J. Less Common Metals*, **1**, 269–291 (1959).
7. Hall, E. O., and Crangle, J., *Acta Cryst.*, **10**, 240–1 (1957).
8. Hultgrew, R., Orr, R. L., Anderson, P. D., and Kelley, K. K., "Thermodynamic Properties of Metals and Alloys," pp. 242–246, New York, J. Wiley and Sons, Inc., 1963.
9. Darling, A. S., and Yorke, J. M., *Platinum Metals Review*, **4**, 104–110 (1960).

W. A. E. McBryde

S

SAMARIUM

Samarium is one of the group of 15 elements in Group III of the Periodic Table having atomic numbers from 57 to 71 and known as the rare earth metals, or as lanthanons or lanthanides. (See **Lanthanide Elements.**) Samarium, atomic number 62, is the sixth member of the lanthanum series falling between promethium, number 61, and europium, number 63. Its discovery generally is credited to Boisbaudran who in 1879 isolated "samaria" from Mosander's "didymia", a mixture of rare earths from which the cerium and lanthanum had been extracted, and identified it by its spectrum. Actually, Boisbaudran's "samaria" was a mixture of samarium and europium which Demarcay resolved in 1901. The name samarium was taken from the mineral samarskite, in turn named in honor of a Russian mine official, Colonel Samarski.

The rare earths as a group constitute about 0.008% of the earth's crust and samarium generally comprises about 1 to 2% of the rare earth mixtures, although in some minerals in which the "heavier" rare earths predominate, the abundance of samarium may run as high as 7%. The principal commercial ores from which rare earths are extracted are monazite and bastnasite and in each of these, the Sm_2O_3 normally is about 2% of the total equivalent rare earth oxides present.

The lanthanides are characterized by the successive filling-in of the well-shielded $4f$ electron shell while maintaining (ideally) the same $5d^16s^2$ outer electronic configuration in each element. Because of its position in the series, samarium would have ideally the electronic configuration $4f^55d^16s^2$. However, the more probable configuration is $4f^66s^2$ for

the neutral atom and $4f^55s^25p^6$ for the Sm^{3+} ion. A consequence of this configuration is that samarium exhibits valences of $2+$ and $3+$. As expected from its configuration, the trivalent state is the more stable.

Natural samarium has 7 stable isotopes having whole number masses 144, 147, 148, 149, 150, 152, and 154 and respective relative natural abundances of 3.16, 15.07, 11.27, 13.84, 7.47, 26.63, and 22.53%. All are stable except Sm^{152} which is an α-emitter with a half-life of 2.5×10^{11} years. The thermal neutron cross section of the natural mixture is 5600 barns. This is sufficiently high to make samarium useful in nuclear technology for control rod and shielding applications.

Occurrence and Extraction

The two most important ores from which rare earths are extracted are monazite and bastnasite. Monazite is an orthophosphate of the rare earths and thorium forming monoclinic crystals with a hardness of about 5.0–5.5 (Mohs' scale), and a specific gravity of 5.0–5.5. The mineral generally is a light brown to a hyacinth red color. It usually concentrates as a sand along with magnetite, ilmenite, rutile, garnet, and other minerals in stream and beach placers in such countries as India, Ceylon, Brazil, Australia, Southeastern United States, etc., but also occurs in massive lodes, the largest of which is in South Africa. Because of its thorium content (5–9% ThO_2) monazite is radioactive. Bastnasite is a rare earth fluocarbonate, the largest massive lode of which occurs in the Mountain Pass region of Southeastern California. Like monazite it is composed chiefly of the light rare earths, but contains only about 0.1% ThO_2. Both ores after beneficiation contain from 50 to

70% equivalent rare earth oxide, of which the samarium content (Sm_2O_3) is about 2%.

The ores generally are cracked by acid attack (H_2SO_4 or HCl) which converts the rare earth values to the soluble sulfates or chlorides. In the case of monazite a mixture of sand and sulfuric acid is heated to a temperature of from 120 to 170°C in cast iron pots fitted with cast iron covers and heavy anchor stirrers. The reaction is exothermic and the temperature rises to about 200 to 250°C. After reaction, the mixture is added to cold water to dissolve the anhydrous rare earth sulfates. Thorium is then removed by addition of sodium pyrophosphate or by fractionally precipitating basic thorium salts. After thorium removal the rare earths may be recovered by treatment with sodium sulfate to precipitate rare earth sulfate-sodium sulfate double salts. These are converted to rare earth hydroxides by heating with sodium hydroxide. If the rare earth hydroxide is dried, the cerium is oxidized to $Ce(OH)_4$ which then may be leached with hydrochloric or nitric acids to solubilize the rare earths other than cerium (didymium). Fractional crystallization of the didymium ammonium or magnesium nitrates may be used to separate lanthanum and the other components of didymium, but as the series is ascended recovery by this method becomes increasingly more difficult. A fraction enriched in samarium and europium is recovered by continuing the crystallization of the soluble side of the neodymium magnesium nitrate separation. The enriched Sm-Eu mixture may then be separated by making use of the fact that these elements are relatively easily reduced by treating a solution (usually the acetate) with sodium amalgam. The reduced europium and samarium are recovered from the amalgam by treatment with dilute acid. Proper adjustment of this technique developed by Marsh and more recently modified by Onstott allows separation of both the samarium and europium in high purity. The overall method, however, is cumbersome and present commercial practice is to effect the separations by ion exchange or solvent extraction methods. After separation by these methods, the purified samarium is usually recovered from solution by precipitation of the insoluble oxalate which may then be converted to the oxide by calcination.

Samarium Metal

Samarium metal cannot be prepared by the usual method for the lanthanons, i.e., metallothermic reduction of the trihalides. When SmF_3 or $SmCl_3$ is reacted with calcium or barium, a very exothermic reaction occurs in which the trihalides are reduced to the dihalides, but no metal is obtained. However, because samarium has a relatively high vapor pressure compared to lanthanum, a method was devised by Daane and coworkers in which lanthanum turnings in excess of 10% are mixed with Sm_2O_3 and the charge is heated in a tantalum crucible in a high vacuum. The reduced samarium metal volatilizes and is recovered as a bright crystalline condensate on the walls of the upper part of the crucible or on a cooled (300–400°C) copper condenser painted with an alcoholic wash of Sm_2O_3 to prevent contamination of the metal deposit. If the condenser is too cool, the metallic deposit is so powdery that it is pyrophoric and difficult to handle in air.

Cerium may also be used as the reductant in this procedure and good results have been obtained with misch metal although in the latter case, the commercial product must be vacuum melted before use to remove volatile impurities such as magnesium and aluminum. Samarium metal crystals may be induction melted and cast into graphite molds with only a small (0.02%) amount of carbon pickup.

Physical Properties

Samarium resembles steel in appearance. At room temperature it crystallizes in the rhombohedral form (α-Sm) having the respective lattice constants of $a_0 = 8.996$ Å and $\alpha = 23°13'$. The nonprimitive hexagonal unit cell has the respective lattice constants of $a_0 = 3.621$ Å and $c_0 = 26.25$ Å. The density of α-Sm is 7.536 g/cc. At 917°C it transforms to the body-centered cubic form (β-Sm) having a lattice constant of 4.07 Å and a density of 7.40 g/cc. The heat of transition is 0.744 kcal/mole. The atomic radius in the rhombohedral form is 1.802 Å and the ionic radius 1.13 Å. Samarium melts at 1072°C and boils at 1900°C. The heat of vaporization is 46 kcal/mole. Table 1 summarizes the physical properties of samarium.

TABLE 1. PHYSICAL PROPERTIES OF SAMARIUM

Symbol	Sm
Atomic number	62
Atomic weight	150.35
Density	7.536 g/cc
Melting point	1072°C
Heat of fusion	2.061 kcal/mole
Boiling point	1900°C
Heat of vaporization, 25°C	46 kcal/mole
Vapor pressure, 885–1222°K	$Log\ P_{mmHg}$ $= 8.781 - \dfrac{10784}{T}$
Specific heat, 25°C	6.76 cal/mole/°C
Heat of combustion	216.94 kcal/g-atom
Heat of sublimation, 25°C	49.3 kcal/mole
Work function	3.2 eV
Debye temperature	166°K
Thermal neutron absorption cross section	5600 barns

Chemical Properties

Samarium metal is an active reducing agent. It will reduce carbon monoxide and decompose carbon tetrachloride, as well as the oxides of many metals including iron, manganese, chromium, silicon, tin, lead, and zirconium. The electrode potential, $E°$, of $Sm(s) = Sm^{+3} + 3e$ is $+ 2.2$ volts. While samarium metal is an active reducing agent, it is moderately stable in dry air, but in moist air an oxide coating develops. The metal burns in air at about 150–180°C and in halogen vapors at about 200°C. Many compounds such as nitrides, sulfides, carbides, silicides, phosphides, and hydrides may be formed directly by reacting the metal and corresponding nonmetal at high temperature.

Principal Compounds

The principal compounds of samarium are the trivalent oxide, hydrous oxide, oxalate, nitrate, chloride, sulfate, carbonate, and sulfide. The divalent salts are at present of little commercial value. Prior to the advent of ion exchange and solvent extraction methods, samarium double salts with sodium, potassium, or ammonium sulfate and ammonium or magnesium nitrate were extensively used

for purification by crystallization. Other compounds used for this purpose were acetate, acetylacetonate, bromate, dimethyl phosphate, ethyl sulfate, and many more. Such compounds are used only infrequently in modern purification schemes.

The oxide, Sm_2O_3, is probably the most important salt. It is insoluble in water, but dissolves readily in mineral acids. Preparation is accomplished by calcination of various other salts, some of which are the carbonate, hydrous oxide, oxalate, nitrate, and sulfate, or by air oxidation of the metal. The oxide is a convenient compound for preparation of other salts and the metal.

Samarium oxalate, $Sm_2(C_2O_4)_3 \cdot 10H_2O$, is precipitated from aqueous salt solutions by the addition of oxalic acid or ammonium oxalate. The oxalate is virtually insoluble in water, the solubility being less than 0.01 gpl at 25°C. The solubility in acid increases with acid concentration, reaching a value of approximately 0.7 gpl in $1.0N$ HCl and 2.3 gpl in $6N$ HCl at 25°C. Complete thermal decomposition of the oxalate to the oxide is accomplished via one or more carbonate intermediates at about 800°C.

Samarium carbonate, $Sm_2(CO_3)_3 \cdot 3H_2O$, is prepared by precipitation of aqueous solutions with solutions of alkali bicarbonates saturated with carbon dioxide or by hydrolysis of a solution of the trichloracetate. The use of normal alkali carbonates results in mixtures of the normal, basic, and double carbonates. The normal carbonate will expel carbon dioxide from a heated slurry to form the basic carbonate, $SmOHCO_3$. The carbonates are insoluble in water, but are readily soluble in acids. Thermal decomposition to the oxide proceeds stepwise through oxycarbonate stages and finally to the oxide at about 800°C.

Samarium chloride, $SmCl_3 \cdot 6H_2O$, is prepared by dissolving the oxide, hydrous oxide, or carbonate in hydrochloric acid, evaporating to a syrup and cooling. The salt is very soluble in water. The anhydrous salt is prepared by heating the hydrated salt in a stream of dry hydrogen chloride or by heating ammonium chloride with the oxide and subliming the excess ammonium chloride. The water-insoluble oxychloride is formed by heating the hydrated salt in air. Divalent samarium chloride forms upon reduction of the trivalent salt with hydrogen at about 270°C. The divalent chloride reoxidizes easily in the presence of air.

Samarium fluoride, $SmF_3 \cdot H_2O$, is formed as a gelatinous precipitate by the addition of hydrofluoric acid to an aqueous solution of a samarium salt. It can also be prepared by treating the oxalate, hydrous oxide, or carbonate with HF. The fluoride is insoluble in water or acid. The oxyfluoride is formed by heating the hydrated fluoride in an atmosphere of air. Anhydrous SmF_3 is prepared by heating Sm_2O_3 in a current of HF.

Samarium bromide and iodide have been studied much less than the chloride and fluoride. The iodide is especially unstable in moist air and difficult to prepare.

Samarium hydrous oxide (hydroxide), Sm $(OH)_3$, is formed by the addition of an alkali or ammonium hydroxide to an aqueous solution of a samarium salt or by metathesis of samarium salts, such as the double sulfate, oxalate, or fluoride, with an alkali hydroxide. The solubility product in water is about 10^{-22} at 25°C. Accordingly, only very low concentrations of OH^- ions are produced in solution even though samarium metal is moderately basic. The hydrous oxide dissolves readily in acid and is thermally decomposed to the oxide at about 350–400°C.

Samarium nitrate, $Sm(NO_3)_3 \cdot 6H_2O$, is prepared with nitric acid in the same general manner as the chloride is with hydrochloric acid. It is very soluble in water and moderately soluble in some alcohols, ketones, and ethers. It is extracted by tributyl phosphate as are other lanthanon nitrates. Such a method is used for purification of the lanthanon series owing to the difference in distribution coefficients between the members of the series. Double salts with ammonium and magnesium nitrates are well known, having been used for purification by crystallization of the various lanthanons. Samarium nitrate can be thermally decomposed to the oxide.

Samarium sulfate, $Sm_2(SO_4)_3 \cdot 8H_2O$, can be prepared by dissolving the oxide, hydrous oxide, or carbonate in sulfuric acid and is crystallized by evaporation. It can also be prepared by precipitation by the addition of sulfuric acid to a concentrated solution of a salt such as the chloride or nitrate. Water solubility of the hydrated sulfate is quite low, being 2.67 g/100 g H_2O at 20°C. Contrary to normal behavior, the solubility decreases with increasing temperatures, being 1.99 g/100 g H_2O at 40°C. Anhydrous samarium sulfate is formed by heating to about 400°C. Difficultly soluble basic sulfates form at higher temperatures and finally proceed to the oxide at a temperature in excess of 1000°C. Addition of alkali or ammonium sulfates to a solution of samarium sulfate results in the precipitation of double sulfates. Divalent samarium sulfate can be precipitated from the trivalent sulfate solution by reduction with magnesium amalgam. The divalent sulfate is easily oxidized by air or dilute nitric acid.

Samarium sulfides, SmS_2, Sm_2S_3, and Sm_3S_4, are formed under a variety of conditions at elevated temperatures by conversion of solid samarium salts such as the oxide, carbonate, sulfate, or chloride with agents such as sulfur, carbon disulfide, hydrogen sulfide, and ammonium sulfide. Sm_2S_3 cannot be prepared by precipitation with ammonium or alkali sulfides inasmuch as the hydrous oxide is precipitated. The sulfides are insoluble and fairly stable in water. In acid, decomposition takes place with the evolution of hydrogen sulfide.

Analysis

Analysis of samarium is carried out mainly by spectrographic and spectrophotometric methods. The bivalency of samarium cannot be taken advantage of by polarographic methods because of certain trivalent cation interference at the reduction potential of Sm^{3+} to Sm^{2+} ($E_{\frac{1}{2}} = -1.80$ v). Spectrographic analysis is well established for the determination of impurities, both lanthanon and others, in samarium and for samarium in other compounds. Useful arc spectrum lines for samarium are found at 3568.26, 3592.59, and 3634.27 Å. In solution both valence states show light absorption at various wavelengths. Divalent samarium is characterized by intense absorption bands in the ultraviolet. Because of its instability, the divalent state is not particularly useful for analysis. The trivalent ion exhiibts absorption at 3625, 3475, and 4020 Å in addition to other less intense bands. Light absorption enables analyses to be carried out rapidly by spectrophotometric methods. The absorption bands of samarium and most trivalent lanthanons are very sharp in contrast to broad absorption bands of the transition-metal ions. Such analysis can be utilized with fairly high purity materials, (99.9%) and can also be used effectively in crude mixtures. A particularly important use is in following purification processes.

Other methods of instrumental analysis such as atomic absorption and neutron activation offer promise as development of these methods progresses. Wet chemical analyses relying on solubility differences, complex formation, etc., are of essentially no value.

Importance and Use

As yet, only relatively few uses of much importance have been found for samarium and its compounds. Expanded research in rare earth chemistry in recent years has developed major uses for various rare earth elements and the future may also hold promise for samarium.

Samarium oxide has been used in optical glass filters, sunglasses, etc., for increasing the infrared absorption. Catalytic activity has been shown by samarium oxide for the dehydration of acyclic primary alcohols to aldehydes and ketones. Various samarium compounds have shown promise as phosphor activators and also thermionic emitters. Samarium titanate has been used to stabilize the performance of capacitors and the sulfide salt has been studied for use in thermoelectric generating devices. Because of its high thermal neutron absorption cross section, 5600 barns, samarium may have nuclear application in control rods, as burnable poisons, and as shielding.

The industry's production capacity far exceeds the demand. The estimated yearly consumption of samarium metal is 50 lb and 500 lb of its salts on the basis of the oxide. Current prices are about $225/lb for samarium metal (99%) and $50/lb for 99.9% samarium oxide.

Safety

The toxicity of samarium is unknown. Some care must be exercised in machining the metal to prevent hot chips from igniting.

References

1. Eyring, L., Ed. "Progress in the Science and Technology of the Rare Earths," Vol. 1, New York, The Macmillan Co., 1964.
2. Gibson, J. A., and Harvey, G. S., "Properties of the Rare Earth Metals and Compounds," Technical Report AFML-TR-65-430, p. 71, 185–203, (Battelle Memorial Institute), Air Force Materials Laboratory, Wright-Patterson Air Force Base, Ohio, 1966.
3. Kremers, H. E. in "Rare Metals Handbook," Hampel, C. A., Ed., Chapter 19, 2nd Edition, New York, Reinhold Publishing Corp., 1961.
4. Moeller, T., "The Chemistry of the Lanthanides," New York, Reinhold Publishing Corp., 1963.
5. Spedding, F. H., and Daane, A. H., "The Rare Earths," New York, John Wiley & Sons, Inc., 1961.
6. Topp, N. E., "The Chemistry of the Rare Earth Elements," New York, Elsevier Publishing Company, 1964.
7. Vickery, R. C., "The Chemistry of the Lanthanons," London, Academic Press, Inc., 1953.
8. Woyski, M. M., and Harris, R. E., in "Treatise on Analytical Chemistry," Kolthoff and Elving, Eds., Part 2, Vol. 8, New York, Interscience Publishers, 1963.
9. Yost, D. M., Russell, H., and Garner, C. S., "The Rare Earth Elements and Their Compounds," New York, John Wiley & Sons Inc., 1947.

W. L. SILVERNAIL

SCANDIUM

Mendeléev, in 1871, predicted a new element in his Periodic Table and, along with some properties of the element, gave its position in the Periodic Table as under boron (eka-boron) in Group III. Lars Nilson, an agricultural chemist in Sweden, discovered this new element in 1876, while carefully analyzing the ore euxenite, and named it scandium after his homeland. Little scandium has been available for study, so, for lack of detailed information about the properties of this element, it has been grouped with the rare earths in many treatments because of their common Group-III position. This has generally been satisfactory, although, as the chemical and physical properties of scandium are becoming known, it is apparent that this element deserves a treatment separate from the rare earths. Scandium is the first element of the first transition group with one $3d$ electron, and exhibits the enhanced binding in the metallic state characteristic of "d" electron metals.

Occurrence

Scandium is present in the earth's crust in a concentration of about 5 ppm and is, accordingly, about as abundant as beryllium and some of the rare earth elements. It is very widely dispersed, occurring in low concentrations in the minerals wolframite, wiikite, and cassiterite, and may be detected in most soils. Although scandium is chemically similar to the rare earths, its ion size places it with aluminum, magnesium, hafnium, and zirconium in geochemical equilibria, so that it is not found to a great extent in rare earth ores. Goldschmidt[6] has described the geochemistry of scandium in detail.

In 1911 Schetelig, in Norway, discovered a new mineral, thortveitite, which contained the startling amount of 30 to 40% Sc_2O_3, and this mineral was subsequently found in Madagascar also. Thortveitite occurs in very small amounts as protruding or residual prismatic crystals from the weathering of pegmatite dykes such as the black Norwegian uranite, and, because of its light tan color and prismatic needle form, the thortveitite can be recognized and recovered. Perhaps partially because of lack of need for it, but primarily because of its scarcity, less than 50 lb of this mineral had been removed from quarries in Norway from the time of its discovery in 1911 to 1952.

A considerable amount of scandium has recently become available from the processing of uranium ores that contain only a few ppm of scandium. Lash and Ross[9] have described these operations (see "Ore Treatment").

Ore Treatment

A detailed analysis of thortveitite has been given by Marble and Glass,[12] showing this mineral to contain 46% SiO_2, 34% Sc_2O_3, 9.5% heavy rare earths, 5% Al_2O_3, 3% Fe_2O_3, 1.5% light rare earths, 0.5% MnO, and smaller amounts of CaO, MgO, ThO_2, and little hafnium or zirconium, although Goldschmidt suggests distinct amounts of these latter two elements to be in some samples of thortveitite. Marble and Glass accomplished the degradation of thortveitite by a series of sodium carbonate fusions or by hydrofluoric acid treatment. In either case, the resulting solution is subjected to a series of oxalate or hydroxide precipitations under carefully controlled conditions, resulting in a relatively low yield of scandium oxide.

Recently, Spedding et al.[17] have described a treatment of thortveitite that recovers the scandium in much higher yields. The powdered thortveitite is mixed with three times its weight of ammonium hydrogen fluoride and heated at 375–400°C (708–752°F) for 12 hr in a platinum boat while passing a stream of dry air over the charge. This removes all of the SiO_2 as the volatile SiF_4, which results in a salt containing 65 to 70% ScF_3, plus the fluorides of the other elements in the ore that do not volatilize under these conditions. Although this mixed fluoride may be dissolved in concentrated H_2SO_4, the process is quite tedious, and the solution is effected by first mixing the salt with 62% of its weight of calcium metal and heating this charge in a tantalum crucible to 1400°C (2552°F) in an inert atmosphere, producing a scandium-rich alloy phase (70% Sc) and calcium fluoride slag. This metallic phase is readily soluble in hydrochloric acid to give a solution from which pure Sc_2O_3 is obtained by a combination thiocyanate-ether extraction, ion exchange process.

In the solvent extraction processing of uranium ores containing only a few ppm of scandium, the scandium follows the uranium into the dodecyl phosphoric acid solution, but does not strip out with the uranium into the hydrochloric acid wash solution. A hydrofluoric acid strip of the organic phase does remove the scandium and is the basis of the separation and recovery method described by Lash and Ross.[9]

Preparation of Metal

Scandium metal was first prepared by Fischer and co-workers,[4] in 1937, by the electrolysis of scandium chloride in a molten salt bath, but the product contained about 5% impurities, mostly iron and silicon, so that the physical properties of the element could not be given from this work. Subsequent preparations of scandium have also been either impure, or of unstated purity,[13] so that the data on the phsyical properties of the metal have been somewhat inconsistent as well as scarce.

As part of a program of study of the rare earth elements in the Ames Laboratory at Iowa State University, Wakefield, Spedding, and Daane[18] have devised methods of preparing scandium metal and have also examined some of its properties. These preparative methods, given below, all utilize scandium fluoride as a reactant, which may be prepared by either of the following methods:

Preparation of Scandium Fluoride

Ammonium Hydrogen Fluoride Process. Ammonium hydrogen fluoride and scandium oxide are mixed together in stoichiometric amounts (2.5:1 weight ratio of ammonium hydrogen fluoride to Sc_2O_3) corresponding to:

$$Sc_2O_3 + 6NH_4HF_2 \rightarrow$$
$$2ScF_3 + 6NH_4F + 3H_2O.$$

It is to be noted that only half of the fluoride in the ammonium hydrogen fluoride is assumed to enter into the reaction; undoubtedly, some of the ammonium fluoride dissociates

$$NH_4F \rightarrow NH_3 + HF.$$

to present additional HF in the reaction, but, since the amount is uncertain, it is neglected. The mixture is placed in a platinum or "Monel" boat and heated for 8 to 12 hr in a "Monel" tube to 300°C (572°F) in a stream of dry air. This treatment provides a 95% conversion of Sc_2O_3 to ScF_3, with the last 5% being difficult to convert because of a crust of ScF_3 formed around the unreacted Sc_2O_3. If this product is ground and mixed with another quantity of ammonium hydrogen fluoride in the same weight ratio of 2.5:1 and heated as before, a good grade of ScF_3 is obtained that reduces well to give metal as described below.

Hydrogen Fluoride Process. Scandium oxide may be converted to ScF_3 by heating it to 700°C (1292°F) in a stream of HF gas in a "Monel" tray and tube:

$$Sc_2O_3 + 6HF \rightarrow 2ScF_3 + 3H_2O.$$

As the efficiency of the HF gas decreases as it has to diffuse through a layer of ScF_3 to reach the unreacted Sc_2O_3 (as in the ammonium hydrogen fluoride process above), approximately a 200% excess quantity of HF is passed through the furnace to achieve a good quality ScF_3.

The ammonium hydrogen fluoride process is generally preferred for small-scale work and is preferable for laboratories not equipped to handle tank HF.

Preparation of Scandium Metal

Direct Reduction of ScF_3. Following the general method used for preparing rare earth metals as described by Spedding and Daane,[15,16] scandium metal has been prepared by the direct reduction of scandium fluoride with calcium.[18] Pulverized ScF_3 is mixed with 10% more granular calcium (redistilled) than required by the stoichiometry of the reaction:

$$2ScF_3 + 3Ca \rightarrow 3CaF_2 + 2Sc.$$

The charge is placed in a tantalum or tungsten crucible in a silica tube induction furnace which is evacuated and filled with purified argon gas to 1 atm pressure. The charge is heated to 1600°C (2912°F) to melt the slag and the metal, which separate cleanly into two layers, with the metal layer on the bottom. This clean separation of slag appears somewhat surprising at first, in view of the fact that the room-temperature densities of scandium metal and calcium fluoride are such that a reverse layering would be expected (Sc 3.0 g/cc, CaF_2 3.2 g/cc). The expansion of salts on melting, however, is very much larger than that of metals, and is undoubtedly the prime factor in relegating the slag to the upper layer at the freezing point of scandium. The excess calcium from the reaction is largely concentrated in the slag layer, and this, too, lowers the density of the slag to promote the separation.

After breaking away the slag, the scandium ingot is remelted in the tantalum crucible in a vacuum to remove the 0.5 to 2% calcium remaining after the reduction. The resulting scandium contains from 3 to 5% tantalum as the one big impurity, with carbon, nitrogen, silicon, iron, calcium, and other rare earths present to the extent of less than 300 ppm each. This large tantalum content is highly undesirable in a process designed to prepare a pure metal, but as this impurity is present as primary tantalum dendrites uncombined with any scandium, it does not interfere with the use of this material in some studies.

Zinc-Alloy Process. To carry out the reduction of ScF_3 at a lower temperature than that required in the above process, and thus eliminate much of the tantalum content of the final product, a zinc-alloy reduction process may be used. This is similar to the Ames Laboratory process for preparing thorium, devised by Wilhelm *et al.*, described in the article on thorium in this book. As used to prepare scandium, pulverized ScF_3, redistilled calcium, zinc, and lithium fluoride are mixed in the quantities corresponding to the reaction:

$$2ScF_3 + 3Ca \text{ (10% excess)} + \\ 8Zn + 12LiF \rightarrow \\ 3(CaF_2 \cdot 4LiF) + 2(Sc \cdot 4Zn) \text{ alloy.}$$

The charge is placed in a tantalum crucible and is welded shut under a partial atmosphere of helium (150 mm Hg). This bomb is then heated to 1100°C (2012°F) in an inert atmosphere, and, at this temperature, both the scandium-zinc eutectic alloy and the calcium fluoride-lithium fluoride eutectic are liquids, allowing clean separation of the two phases. Since the liquid alloy is in contact with tantalum at a much lower temperature than is the scandium metal in the direct reduction process described above, much less tantalum is dissolved into the scandium alloy.

After cooling, the brittle alloy is crushed to pea-size chunks and is then heated in a vacuum to 1200°C (2192°F) to distill away the zinc, leaving behind a porous sponge of pure scandium metal. This sponge may then be consolidated into solid metal by conventional inert atmosphere arc melting processes, although the vapor pressure of scandium is sufficiently high that about 10% of the charge is dispersed around on the inside of the furnace as "fog" in this operation.

The product of this method contains only a trace of tantalum and less than 500 ppm zinc, with other impurities essentially the same as the metal prepared by the direct reduction process. It is believed that, in most cases, these figures given for impurities are conservatively higher than the actual amounts. With only small amounts of metal available,

it has not been possible to divert samples to permit development of analytical methods to the desired accuracy.

One disadvantage of this process is that the zinc and the lithium fluoride added to achieve the convenience of working at a lower temperature require a crucible volume three times that needed to produce the same quantity of scandium by the direct reduction process. In addition, these additives undoubtedly contribute some of their own impurities to the final product.

Magnesium Alloy Process. Habermann *et al.*[7] have described a magnesium alloy process for preparing scandium. This is similar to the zinc alloy process described above, but has a minor complication in that the densities of the slag and the alloy are nearly equal. Separation of slag and alloy is not as clean as in the zinc alloy process, but yields of 90% were obtained.

Purification of Scandium

From Wakefield's vapor-pressure data,[18] it is apparent that distillation is an obvious technique to use in combination with either of the above preparative methods to obtain high-purity metal. The preferred combination is first to utilize the direct reduction process to obtain metallic scandium in good yields, with tantalum the only impurity present in large quantities. Distillation of this material effectively eliminates this impurity as well as the major portion of the other impurities present in smaller amounts.

The distillation of scandium is accomplished by heating the metal to 1650–1700°C (3002–3092°F) in a vacuum of 10^{-5} mm Hg or better in the apparatus shown in Fig. 1. The tantalum crucible extends to within 2 in. of the top of the heated zone of the furnace, and the condenser, consisting of a sheet of 0.005-in. tantalum wrapped around the crucible and held in place with a band of tantalum wire, extends out of the heated zone. The condenser is capped with a press-fitted tantalum lid with a $\frac{1}{8}$-in. hole in its center to allow rapid pumping out of the system at the start. When the distillation is taking place, the bottom of the crucible from which the vapor moves is at a temperature of 1650–1700°C (3002–3092°F), and the top of the condenser is at 800–1000°C (1472–1832°F). The two collimators are an

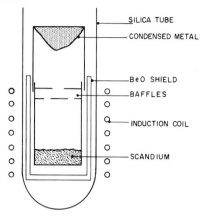

FIG. 1. Apparatus for distilling scandium.

inch apart, with the lowest one about 2 to 3 in. above the surface of the liquid scandium. These baffles serve to direct the vapor to the upper portion of the condenser section, so that the major portion of the condensate is on the underside of the lid. The condensate is a conically shaped fibrous deposit of bright metal with the tip essentially fused metal. The condenser may be disassembled, peeled away from the condensate, and reused. This compact, partially fused mass of metal may be consolidated by arc melting with recoverable losses by vaporization of up to 10%, as previously mentioned.

Analysis of the distilled metal shows it to contain no detectable tantalum, with other impurities as follows: Fe, $< 0.05\%$; Ca, $< 0.02\%$; Mg, $< 0.03\%$; Cr, $< 0.06\%$; and C and N, about 100 ppm each.

Physical Properties

Scandium metal has a silver metallic luster with a slight yellowish cast after exposure to air. The metal is soft and is easily fabricated if pure. Table 1 lists the physical properties of scandium.

Chemical Properties

Scandium reacts rapidly with acids, but it does not tarnish rapidly in air and is not attacked rapidly by water. At higher temperatures [500–800°C (932–1472°F)] scandium may be oxidized in air. Scandium shows a remarkable property in common with some of the heavy rare earth metals and yttrium: it is not attacked by a 1:1 mixture of concentrated nitric acid and 48% hydrofluoric acid, and as a consequence, this mixture may

TABLE 1. PHYSICAL PROPERTIES OF SCANDIUM

Atomic number	21
Atomic weight	44.956 (100% isotope 45)
Melting point	1539°C (2802°F)
Boiling point	2727°C (4941°F)
Transformation temperature	1335°C (2435°F)
Density	2.99 g/cc
Crystal structure, to 1335°C (2435°F)	Hexagonal close-packed,
	$a = 3.308 \pm 0.001$ Å
	$c = 5.267 \pm 0.003$ Å
	$c/a = 1.59$
above 1335°C	Body-centered cubic
Atomic volume	15.0 cc/mole
Metallic radius	1.64 Å
Heat capacity, 25°C (77°F)	6.01 cal/mole/°C
Heat of fusion	3.85 kcal/mole
Heat of vaporization at 1630°C (2966°F)	87.6 ± 0.4 kcal/mole
Linear coefficient of expansion, 0–900°C (32–1652°F)	12×10^{-6}/deg
Electrical resistivity, room temperature	66×10^{-6} ohm-cm
Temperature coefficient of resistivity	
[room temperature to 100°C (212°F)]	5.4×10^{-8} ohm-cm/deg
Ultimate compressive strength, psi	57,000
Hardness	Rockwell F 98 (severely cold rolled and unannealed)
Thermal neutron absorption cross section	24.0 ± 1.0 barns/atom

be used to dissolve tantalum away from scandium.

Since scandium is a very electropositive metal, its oxide is basic and is soluble in acids to give colorless solutions of the trivalent ion; no other valence state has been observed for this metal. Scandium hydroxide may be precipitated from solutions on addition of bases, and oxalate ion precipitates the oxalate, although this substance is not as insoluble as the rare earth oxalates. Fluoride ion precipitates the hydrated $ScF_3 \cdot \frac{1}{2}H_2O$. Pokras and Bernays[14] have described gravimetric methods that may be used to determine scandium, but these generally require preliminary separations to be effective. Recently, Fritz and Pietrzyk[5] have reported an ethylenediaminetetraacetic acid (EDTA) titrimetric procedure for scandium that has been shown to be effective in the presence of a number of ions commonly encountered with scandium.

Neutron activation[2,10] and emission spectrographic[3] techniques have been developed for scandium.

Fabrication

Scandium containing oxygen and other non-metallic elements as impurities is quite difficult to fabricate, and, like yttrium, appears to have greatly improved fabricability when pure. Although it has not as yet been available in quantities that would permit studies of fabrication by extrusion, scandium has been rolled and swaged successfully. It may be welded by inert atmosphere arc welding, and may be spot welded.

Alloys

As little scandium metal has been available, scarcely any work has been done on alloy systems of this element. The similarity of scandium to yttrium and the rare earth metals appears to extend to alloying behavior in the few cases where data exist to permit comparison. Consequently, in the absence of experimental evidence, a corresponding rare earth alloy system may be used as a first approximation for the case with scandium. This assumption is not likely to be universally valid, for cases are known where there are distinct differences between the behavior of two rare earth metals with another element. In addition, the metallic radii of the rare earths are quite large (1.73 to 1.87 Å) compared to that of scandium (1.64 Å), so that scandium would be much more likely than the rare earths to form solid solution alloys with some of the metals having radii nearer this smaller value, such as hafnium (1.59 Å), magnesium (1.60 Å), plutonium (1.64 Å), uranium (1.56 Å), and zirconium (1.60 Å).

The following outline of the behavior of scandium toward other metals includes a few cases of actual experimental observations, but, mostly, it represents predictions based on a degree of similarity of scandium to yttrium and the rare earths.

Group IA (Alkali Metals). There is little or no alloying tendency. Possibly there is liquid immiscibility, as evidenced by behavior in reduction processes.

Group IIA (Alkaline Earth Metals). Scandium is soluble enough in magnesium to harden it. There appear to be no intermetallic compounds between magnesium and scandium and between calcium and scandium.

Group IIIB (Yttrium and the Rare Earths). Considerable solid solubility occurs with no intermetallic compounds.

Group IVB (Ti, Zr, Hf). Complete solid solubility between the high temperature forms of titanium and scandium has been observed by Beaudry;[1] this is the best evidence available that scandium is body-centered cubic above 1335°C. Attempts to confirm this by high temperature x-ray studies and by quenching have not been successful. The hexagonal forms of titanium and scandium are soluble in each other to the extent of about 10%; some solid solubility has been observed by other workers.[8,11]

Group VB (V, Cb, Ta). There is essentially no solid solubility, but there is increasing liquid solubility of Ta, Cb, V in Sc. There are no intermetallic compounds.

Group VIB (Cr, Mo, W). No intermetallic compounds or solid solubility are likely. (This is known to be the case for W). Liquid solubility of these metals in liquid scandium is less than in the V, Cb, Ta group.

Groups VIIB, VIIIB, IB, IIB, IIIA, IVA. Compounds of these elements with scandium are likely or known (Sc-Au, ScC, ScN, Sc_2O_3, ScH_3, Sc-Cd, Sc-Zn). Some compounds are easily decomposed in vacuum on heating (Sc-Zn, Sc-Cd).

Th, U, Pu. Some solid solubility is possible. Intermetallic compounds are unlikely.

Toxicity

No toxicity data are available on scandium at the present time. Based on analogy with yttrium and the rare earths, it would not be expected that scandium would present a serious health hazard, but it should be treated with respect until its toxic character is established.

References

1. Beaudry, B. J., and Daane, A. H., *Trans. AIME*, **227**, 865 (1963).
2. Desai, H. B., Iyer, R. K., and Das, M. S., *Talenta*, **11**, 1249 (1964).
3. Fassel, V. A., D'Silva, A. P., Kniseley, R. N., Curry, R. H., and Myers, R. B., *Anal. Chem.*, **36**, 532 (1964).
4. Fischer, W., Brunger, K., and Grieneisen, H., *Z. anorg. Chem.*, **231**, 54 (1937).
5. Fritz, J. S., Pietrzyk, D. J., *Anal. Chem.*, **31**, 1157 (1959).
6. Goldschmidt, V. M., "Geochemistry," Oxford, Clarendon Press, 1954.
7. Habermann, C. E., Daane, A. H., Palmer, P. E., *Trans. AIME*, **233**, 1038 (1965).
8. Kornilov, I. I., *Izvest. Akad. nauk SSSR, Otdel. Khim. nauk*, **1954**, 392 (1954).
9. Lash, L. D., and Ross, J. R., *J. Metals*, **13**, 555 (1961).
10. Leddicotte, G. W., Private communication (1967).
11. Love, B., WADC Report RC 106 (1958).
12. Marble, J. P., and Glass, J. J., *Am. Mineralogist*, **27**, 696 (1942).
13. Petru, F., Prochazka, V., and Hajck, B., *Czechoslov. Chem. Commun.*, **22**, 1534 (1957).
14. Pokras, L., and Bernays, P. M., *Anal. Chem.*, **23**, 757 (1951).
15. Spedding, F. H., and Daane, A. H., *J. Metals*, **6**, 504 (1954).
16. Spedding, F. H., and Daane, A. H., Chapter 5 in "Progress in Nuclear Energy," Vol. 1, edited by H. M. Finniston and J. P. Howe, New York, McGraw-Hill Book Co., 1956.
17. Spedding, F. H., Powell, J. E., Daane, A. H., Miller, M. A., and Adams, W. H., *J. Electrochem. Soc.*, **105**, 683 (1958).
18. Wakefield, G. F., Spedding, F. H., and Daane, A. H., *Trans. AIME*, **218**, 608 (1960).

A. H. DAANE

SELENIUM

Introduction

Selenium was identified as an element in 1817 by John Jacob Berzelius, a professor of chemistry in Stockholm, Sweden. Berzelius and a colleague, J. G. Gahn, were investigating the lead chamber method for the production of sulfuric acid. They observed that the sediment in the bottom of the lead chambers emitted an offensive odor which they believed to be indicative of the presence of tellurium, an element discovered thirty-five years earlier. In the hope of finding a new source of the then rare element, tellurium, Berzelius obtained larger quantities of the material, but his work proved to be of no avail for he could find no trace whatsoever of tellurium. He did notice, however, that the new substance possessed chemical properties closely resembling those of tellurium. So closely akin were these two elements that he decided to call the former selenium, from the Greek word *selene*, meaning the moon, or moon goddess; tellurium having been named from the latin word *tellus*, meaning the earth.

Selenium remained a laboratory curiosity for over fifty years. Finally, in 1873, Willoughby Smith, while testing various materials for electrical conductivity, discovered that the current resistance of the element decreased as the intensity of illumination increased. He also observed that the resistance increased slightly as the temperature increased above 170°C (338°F). This discovery led, among other things, to the development of the photoelectric cell. This was the first important step in bringing the element selenium into the public eye. Since then, a multitude of applications developed which now play a definite part in our everyday lives.

Occurrence

Selenium is one of the less common elements in the earth's crust, falling between bismuth and gold in abundance. It rarely occurs in its native state. It occasionally occurs with native sulfur and in the form of selenides of other metals in such minerals as eucairite, $CuAgSe$; clausthalite, $PbSe$; naumannite, Ag_2Se; crookesite, $(CuTlAg)_2Se$; and zorgite, $PbCuSe$. There are no known deposits of sufficient selenium concentration to be worked profitably for selenium alone under present technology.

Selenium also occurs in certain soils and will concentrate in certain species of local vegetation to levels as high as 1.0%.

The main sources of selenium today are the copper ores, from which selenium is recovered as a by-product.

Recovery

In the United States, selenium is recovered by American Smelting and Refining Company, Anaconda Mining Company, the American Metal Climax Company, Phelps Dodge Refining Company, and recently, Kennecott Copper Corporation; in Canada, the International Nickel Company of Canada, Ltd., and the Canadian Copper Refiners, Ltd., of Montreal; in Australia, selenium is produced by the Electrolytic Refining and Smelting Company, Pty. Ltd., in Sweden by the Boliden Mining Company, and in Belgium by the Societe General of Hoboken. Other producers are Taihi, Besshi, and Nippon mining companies in Japan, Cerro de Pasco Corporation in Peru and Norddeutsche Affinerie of Hamburg in the Western Zone of Germany. Selenium recovery in the U.S.S.R. and the Soviet-dominated countries is at present an unknown quantity.

Extraction and Production

Years ago, the major source of selenium was the flue dusts of metallurgical processes utilizing lead and copper sulfide ores, but that source is practically nonexistent today. Most of the world's selenium now comes from the anode muds, or slimes, from electrolytic copper refineries.

The extraction of selenium is a complex process involving many metallurgical treatments. Basically, there would appear to be three main methods of treating the electrolytic slimes—by roasting with sulfuric acid, by roasting with soda, and by smelting with soda and niter. Variations of these three methods are found to accommodate variations in the basic raw materials handled.

In the sulfuric acid roast, the raw slimes are treated with sulfuric acid prior to roasting. During roasting, most of the selenium is driven off as the dioxide which is collected in

a wet scrubber Cottrell system. The remainder is largely recovered by the conventional soda smelting process.

Prior to the soda roast, the slimes are usually decopperized by aeration in hot, dilute sulfuric acid. The slimes are then intimately mixed with soda and the mixture roasted at temperatures below the sintering point. The charge may be rabbled during heating, with sufficient air admitted to oxidize the selenium. The calcine is then leached with water to dissolve the selenate. The selenate solution is treated either with concentrated hydrochloric acid and sulfur dioxide to precipitate elemental selenium, or is evaporated to dryness, the selenate reduced with coke to sodium selenide, and the resultant calcine leached with water. The selenide solution is blown with air, precipitating elemental selenium and regenerating sodium hydroxide.

In the soda smelting process, the decopperized slimes are mixed with soda and silica and charged to the furnace. After removal of the first slags, the molten charge is rabbled with air. Some of the selenium is volatilized and is caught in a scrubber Cottrell system. Caustic and niter are now added to the charge, producing slags high in both selenium and tellurium. These slags are crushed, leached with water and treated with sulfuric acid, precipitating the tellurium as the dioxide. The solution is then gassed with sulfur dioxide, precipitating the elemental selenium. Commercial grade selenium, 99.0% Se minimum, is obtained from all three processes. It can be further refined to produce high-purity selenium and selenium compounds. Selenium is commercially available in a number of forms, some of which are:

Commercial grade—powder or lumps
High-purity, 99.99% Se and 99.999% Se—
  pellets
Ferroselenium—lumps
Nickel selenium—lumps
Selenium dioxide—powder
Sodium selenate—powder
Sodium selenite—powder
Zinc selenite—powder
Copper-selenium master alloy—tablets.

The free world production of selenium has increased steadily from about 800,000 pounds in 1945 to 2,100,000 pounds in 1964. The seven producers of primary selenium in the United States and Canada accounted for approximately 65% of the Free World total.

Increased demand for selenium, especially for rectifier manufacture, led to an acute shortage in the early 1950's. This induced producers to make material improvements in recoveries, bringing an end to the shortage in the fall of 1956. At present, and for the immediate future, the supply of selenium appears adequate to take care of any reasonable demand, based on production potential and producers' stocks.

Selenium can hardly be considered an inexpensive commodity. The price for domestic material in its commercial form has ranged from $1.50 per pound in the 1930's to a high of $15.50 per pound in 1956. The quoted price in 1967 was about $4.50 per pound. High-purity selenium was listed at $6.00 per pound.

High-Purity Selenium

Since many of the electrical and photoelectrical properties of selenium are affected by impurities, considerable emphasis has been placed in recent years on the preparation and analysis of high-purity selenium.

Several methods of purification have been used successfully. Three of the most interesting are:

(1) Selenium dioxide vapor is reacted with ammonia in the temperature range 600–800°C (1112–1472°F).

(2) Purified hydrogen is bubbled through molten selenium and the resulting hydrogen selenide is decomposed at 1000°C (1832°F).

(3) Distillation is the most satisfactory method for producing high-purity selenium on a commercial scale. The commercial product is of the order of 99.994% pure. Individual impurity levels are usually less than one ppm.

Metallic impurities in selenium are determined customarily by optical emission spectroscopy. This method is rapid and suited to routine determinations. Limits of detection are less than one ppm. Sulfur and chlorine are determined by chemical methods.

Spark source mass spectrometry has recently been applied to the analysis of high-purity selenium. Detection limits for the metals are of the order of one-tenth ppm. Disadvantages of this method at present are the length of time required, and the strong memory effect produced by selenium which is deposited within the instrument during each determination. Neutron activation analysis is of some interest in measuring impurity levels below one ppm.

Physical Properties

Selenium, atomic number 34, is the third member of Group VIA of the periodic arrangement of the elements. In metallic properties, it falls between sulfur and tellurium, the two adjacent elements in the group. Other comparisons of some of the properties of the four principal elements in the group are given in Table 1.

Selenium can exist as a solid, a liquid, or a vapor at temperatures easily obtained in any metallurgical laboratory.

The Solid State. Solid selenium exists in many different forms, but considerably less is known of its allotropic modifications than is known about those of sulfur.

Amorphous selenium occurs as a red powder, a black mass, and in the colloidal form. The red powder is obtained by treating solutions of selenous acid with hydrochloric or sulfuric acid and such reducing agents as sulfur dioxide, hydrazine or hydroxylamine hydrochloride. It will turn black on standing, yielding hexagonal selenium on heating.

When selenium is heated above its melting temperature and quench cooled, a tarlike vitreous mass results. This material becomes glassy and brittle, exhibiting a conchoidal fracture. It has no true melting point, but will start to soften at 40–50°C (104–122°F). By reflected light, it is mirror black but thin layers appear blood-red by transmitted light. The plasticity of the normally brittle mass is increased by adding various impurities (e.g.), 1% chlorine, or as little as 0.0003% tellurium. The vitreous material, like the red powder, tends to revert to the crystalline, hexagonal form. The rate depends on temperature, purity, and conditions of storage.

Vitreous selenium is a very poor conductor of heat and may be considered an electrical insulator. It does find some use as a semiconductor in xerography and photocells.

TABLE 1. PROPERTIES OF THE OXYGEN-SULFUR FAMILY

	Oxygen	Sulfur	Selenium	Tellurium
Atomic number	8	16	34	52
Atomic weight	15.9994	32.064	78.96	127.60
Isotopes	7	9	22	29
Specific gravity (solid)	1.426	Monoclinic 1.96 Rhombic 2.07	Vitreous 4.28 Hexagonal 4.79	6.24
at	$-252.5°C$ $(-422°F)$	20°C (68°F)	20°C (68°F)	20°C (68°F)
Color	Blue	Yellow	Dark red, gray, metallic	Silver
Melting point	$-218.4°C$ $(-361.1°F)$	119.0°C(mon.) (246.2°F	217°C(hex.) (422.6°F)	$449.5°C \pm 0.3$ $(841°F \pm 0.5)$
Boiling point	$-183.0°C$ $(-297.4°F)$	444.6°C (822.3°F)	$684.9°C \pm 1.0$ $(1265°F \pm 1.0)$	$990°C \pm 3.8$ $(1814°F \pm 6.8)$
Atomic volume	14	15.5	16.5	20.5
Entropy, e.u., 25°C (77°F)	49.0	7.62	10.14	11.88
Covalent radius, Å	0.73	1.02	1.16	1.35
Electronegativity (Pauling scale)	3.5	2.5	2.4	2.1
Heat of fusion, kcal/g-atom	0.053	0.34	1.25	4.28
Heat of vaporization, kcal/g-atom at boiling point	0.815	0.301	3.34	11.9

TABLE 2. PROPERTIES OF THE ALLOTROPIC FORMS OF SELENIUM

Form	Amorphous		Crystalline	
Color	Powder Red	Vitreous Black (red in thin layers)	Monoclinic Deep red	Hexagonal Gray to black
Specific gravity, 20°C	4.25	4.28	4.46	4.79
Melting point	Changes to vitreous at 40–50°C (104–112°F)	Indefinite	170–180°C (338–356°F)	217°C (423°F)
Boiling point	$684.9°C \pm 1.0$ $(1265°F \pm 1.8)$	$684.9°C \pm 1.0$ $(1265°F \pm 1.8)$	$684.9°C \pm 1.0$ $(1265°F \pm 1.8)$	$684.9°C \pm 1.0$ $(1265°F \pm 1.8)$
Solubility,				
Water	Insoluble	Insoluble	Insoluble	Insoluble
Conc. H_2SO_4	Soluble	Soluble	Soluble	Soluble
CS_2	Soluble	Soluble	Soluble	Insoluble
HNO_3	Soluble	Soluble	Soluble	Soluble
C_2H_5OH	Insoluble	Insoluble	Insoluble	Insoluble

Colloidal selenium can be prepared by electrolysis of selenous acid solutions, using a platinum anode and a selenium-coated cathode. It is also obtained by pouring a solution of selenium in carbon disulfide into a large volume of ether, and by the chemical reduction of aqueous solutions of soluble selenium compounds with such reagents as sulfur dioxide, dextrose, titanium trichloride or hydrazine hydrate or sulfate.

The colors of the element in the colloidal form vary from red to violet, depending upon the conditions of preparation.

Crystalline selenium occurs in either the hexagonal or monoclinic forms.

Hexagonal selenium, considered to be the most stable form under normal conditions, is readily prepared by heating any form of selenium below the melting point until crystallization is complete. It is a gray, metallic substance with fair heat and electrical conductivities, has fair mechanical strength and is relatively inert to atmospheric conditions.

Some of the properties of the various allotropic forms of selenium are shown in Table 2.

The Liquid State. Crystalline, hexagonal selenium melts at 217°C (423°F), exhibiting a definite transition from solid to liquid. Unlike sulfur, it becomes more fluid with increasing temperature, but does not become very fluid until heated somewhat above its melting point.

Amorphous selenium will begin to soften at temperatures as low as 40°C (104°F), but finally liquifies at 217°C (423°F).

Liquid selenium probably contains a number of molecular species.

The Vapor State. Selenium boils at 684.9°C (1265°F) at atmospheric pressure. The vapor at the boiling point is a mixture of Se_8 and Se_2. The vapor pressure is represented by $\log_{10}$ pressure $= -4989.5 \pm 4.5/T + 8.0886 \pm 0.0048$ where pressure is in millimeters of mercury and T is in degrees Kelvin. Vapor pressure curves for three members of the family, sulfur selenium and tellurium, are given in Fig. 1.

Electrical Properties

Solid, hexagonal selenium is a typical semiconductor. Its resistivity lies between that of a metal and the high resistivity of an insulator. As a semiconductor, many of its properties are in sharp contrast to those of metals. As the temperature is raised, the resistivity of selenium decreases rapidly, while that of a metal increases relatively slowly. The conductivity of selenium is quite sensitive to light, being higher when illuminated than in the dark. The Hall coefficient is larger for selenium than for metals.

Major achievements in the studies of the solid state and the study of the selenium single crystal have given information on the properties of the element as a semiconductor. Selenium is classed as a positive, or p-type, extrinsic semiconductor. Impurities, such as the halogens, will increase the p-type conductivity. The presence of impurities may also account for the fact that the electrical properties of selenium are so dependent upon the methods of purification.

The resistivity of liquid selenium between 200 and 500°C (392–932°F) also is inversely proportional to the temperature. The

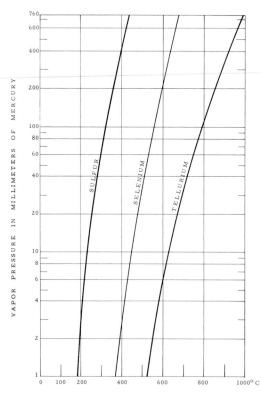

FIG. 1. Vapor pressure-temperature curves for sulfur, selenium and tellurium.

resistivity in ohm-centimeters is expressed by the following equation:

$$\log_{10} p = A + \frac{B}{T}$$

where $A = -3.81$, $B = 5850$, $T =$ degrees Kelvin, and $p =$ specific resistivity in ohm-centimeters.

The three electrical properties of selenium which are best known and give rise to its widest applications are its action as a rectifier, its photoconductivity and its photovoltaic action.

Selenium can be considered a unipolar conductor, thus permitting the element to act as a rectifier. In a commercial rectifier, a base plate, normally aluminum, is coated with the p-type, extrinsic semiconductor, selenium. A barrier layer of an n-type semiconductor, such as cadmium sulfide, is then applied to increase the resistance of the unit to the flow of current in the reverse direction. Finally a counterelectrode, Bi-Cd or Cd-Sn, is applied. The rectifying action occurs at the interface between the selenium and the barrier layer.

The photoconductive action of selenium was discovered in 1873 by Willoughby Smith, who reported an increase in the electrical conductivity of the element upon illumination. Advances in the field of the quantum theory of solids have brought understanding of the effect of radiant energy on selenium. The increase in conductivity during illumination is the result of an increase in the number of carriers; i.e., holes (deficits) and electrons caused by the action of the photons of light. This increase is normally eight to ten times the dark current flow, but may be as high as twenty-five times in some cells. When the illumination is cut off, the conductivity drops rapidly to its original value.

In commercial application, this photo-electric cell consists primarily of an emitter, a metal surface covered with a thin layer of selenium, and a collector, both enclosed in an evacuated container. It requires an external source of emf, and its output cannot be readily amplified. It has the disadvantage of variability which makes it unsuitable for precision instruments.

The photovoltaic action of selenium refers to the conversion of light energy directly into electrical energy. An example of the commercial application of this effect is the photographic exposure meter. This photo-voltaic cell, or barrier layer cell, is quite similar in construction to the dry-plate rectifier. A metal plate is coated with selenium which in turn is coated with an n-type semiconductor. The latter is often cadmium oxide. The photons of light pass through the p-n junction, entering the p-type layer of selenium. The conditions of the p-n junction become such that an electron moves in the direction from the selenium through the cadmium oxide to the collecting grid and around through the external electrical circuit back to the selenium.

The energy of the photon must exceed the photoelectric threshold value of the cell to cause voltaic action, and the wave frequency of the light must exceed a minimum value to trigger the cell.

Chemical Properties

The chemical properties of selenium are as might be expected of an element in Group VIA, between sulfur and tellurium.

The oxidation states of selenium are -2 in the selenides, $+4$ in the selenites and $+6$ in the selenates. Potential values in acid solutions for the oxidation states are reported as $+0.36$, -0.74, and -1.15 volts, respectively.

Selenium displays the properties of a nonmetal in all of its compounds, with a marked acid-forming tendency, especially in its higher valence.

Selenium forms two oxides, selenium dioxide, a white crystalline solid, and selenium trioxide, a pale yellow, amorphous, relatively unstable solid. With water, the two oxides react to form selenous acid, H_2SeO_3, and selenic acid, H_2SeO_4, respectively.

Selenium will combine directly with hydrogen at temperatures below 250°C (482°F) to form the extremely toxic gas hydrogen selenide, H_2Se. Hydrogen selenide is also prepared by the action of dilute acids on metallic selenides, as sodium selenide, iron selenide, or aluminum selenide.

Fluorine, chlorine, bromine and iodine also combine directly with selenium, giving the corresponding halides.

Hydrochloric acid does not react with selenium and dilute nitric and sulfuric acids are poor solvents for the element. Concentrated nitric acid dissolves crude selenium

631

TABLE 3. SELENIUM BINARY SYSTEMS

System	Composition, weight %	Eutectic Temperature, °C	°F	Compounds Formed
Ag-Se	26% Se (approx.)	840	1544	Ag_2Se
Cu-Se	2.2% Se	1063	1945	Cu_2Se
Pb-Se	55% Se	681	1258	PbSe
Zn-Se	—	—	—	ZnSe
Tl-Se	23% Se	284	543	Tl_2Se_3
Te-Se	Freezes to mass of mixed crystals	—	—	—
Fe-Se	No true eutectic	—	—	$FeSe$ and $FeSe_2$
Hg-Se	Lies very close to 100% Se	—	—	HgSe
S-Se	62–63% Se	105	221	—
Sb-Se	40% Se	530	986	Sb_2Se_3

even when cold, but reacts poorly with high-purity selenium.

Common alkalies will dissolve or react with selenium when fused.

Sulfur is miscible with selenium in all proportions, as is tellurium. Molten selenium is either partly or completely miscible with most metals. Usually the fused mass consists of the metal selenide or a mixture of the metal selenide and selenium, but definite compounds are formed with most of the metals. Table 3 gives the eutectic points of some of the metal-selenium binary systems.

Uses of Selenium

The principal users of selenium and its compounds are the electronics industry, the ceramics industry, and the steel industry.

Electronic Applications require a high-quality selenium in the purity range of 99.99 to 99.999%, with a halogen content compatible with the specific use.

Most of this selenium is consumed in the manufacture of dry-plate rectifiers, which range in size from plates eight inches across to miniature encapsulated-type rectifiers smaller than a match head. Some applications of selenium rectifiers have slackened in recent years with the development of germanium and silicon rectifiers.

Other uses of selenium in the electronics field include:

(1) *Xerography* is a method for the reproduction of images which makes use of the effect of light and a static electrical charge on a thin layer of vitreous selenium. It is especially useful for copying letters, drawings and prints.

(2) *Vidicon Television Camera.* This camera, or pick-up tube, makes use of the photoconducting property of amorphous selenium. The illuminated portions of the pattern projected upon the selenium layer transmit a light signal when scanned by the electron beam.

(3) *Photocell.* The photocell, or photovoltaic cell, is best known in the exposure meter and is widely used in photography. Solar batteries may be considered photovoltaic cells designed for the maximum conversion of solar radiations into electrical energy.

Glass and Ceramics Industry. The glass and ceramics industry is perhaps the oldest and largest user of selenium and its compounds. As a decolorizer, selenium is added to glass to counteract the greenish tint effect caused by the iron present therein. Selenium combined with cadmium forms cadmium selenide reds which are widely used in the glass industry to produce the familiar ruby colored glass. These same cadmium selenide reds also find wide application in the field of ceramics and enamels. These so-called glass colors have proved a boon to the bottling industry where they are widely used in attractive permanent labeling to replace paper labels or uncolored raised lettering on milk bottles, beer bottles and the like.

Steel Industry. In the mid-thirties, one of the large steel companies found that the addition of selenium to stainless steel acted not only as an excellent degasifier, but also increased the machinability of the stainless steel. It is currently used for this purpose.

Miscellaneous Uses. Selenium has been used as a vulcanizing agent in the rubber industry and in concentrations of 0.1 to 2% to promote resistance to heat, oxidation and abrasion and to increase resilience. In its acid form, it is used to etch steel. As selenium dioxide, it was used as an oxidizing agent in the preparation of the wonder drug, cortisone. Some metal selenides, WSe_2, $MoSe_2$, $NbSe_2$, $TaSe_2$, and $TeSe_2$, show much promise as solid lubricants for vacuum and elevated temperature applications.

In the elemental form, or as metal selenides and selenites, selenium has found application as a catalyst in such reactions as oxidation, hydrogenation, isomerization, and polymer treatment. Specific areas include chemical synthesis, resin preparation, oil and rosin treatment and hydrocarbon processing.

Mixtures of arsenic with selenium form low melting point glasses with interesting infrared transmitting characteristics.

Recent work has shown selenium, as sodium selenate, added to a chrome plating bath, to be the most effective addition agent known for inducing microcracks of chrome plate which in turn control corrosion of the substrate.

Some selenium is used as an alloying ingredient in bismuth telluride thermoelectric compounds. Current passed through a couple made of "n" and "p" type material, generates heat at one junction (Seebeck effect), or refrigeration at the other junction (Peltier effect).

The photographic industry looks to selenium for use not only in the manufacture of photoelectric cells, but also in its toning baths for sepia prints.

Not only does selenium increase the machinability of stainless steel, but as an addition to copper, transmits the same benefits. Another interesting application for this element has been its suggested use as a flameproofing agent for electric switchboard cables. In addition to its many and varied uses, in its oxychloride form, it is one of the most powerful solvents known and finds use as a solvent of synthetic phenic resins, at one time considered insoluble.

The idea of introducing a toxic substance into the tissues of living plants as a means of protecting them against insect attack, while perhaps somewhat revolutionary, is an accepted practice in the case of sodium selenate in the control of red spider on certain greenhouse plants.

Investigations have also shown the nutritional value of trace amounts of selenium in animals, especially in the treatment of nutritional muscular dystrophy in sheep and cattle. The use of trace amounts of selenium in diets of humans suffering from certain nutritional deficiencies appears to be beneficial.

Toxicity

While elemental selenium is relatively nontoxic, some of its compounds are extremely toxic. The maximum allowable limit in air, recommended by the American Conference of Governmental and Industrial Hygienists, is 0.1 milligram per cubic meter of air. This level is based largely on the observed effects of hydrogen selenide, H_2Se.

Contact with crystalline or amorphous selenium has not been reported as a source of skin injury. The exposure to selenium fumes can result in intense irritation of the eyes, nose and throat. Severe toxic effects can result from inhaling the vapor.

References

1. Brackin, R. B., "Occurrence, Extraction, Availability and Economics of Selenium and Tellurium," paper presented at Symposium on Selenium and Tellurium, New York, Selenium and Tellurium Development Committee, 1965.
2. Brasted, R. C., "Comprehensive Inorganic Chemistry," Vol. 8, New York, D. Van Nostrand Company, Inc., 1961.
3. Butts, A., "Copper," New York, Reinhold Publishing Corp., 1954.
4. Clark, G. L., and Hawley, G. G., "The Encyclopedia of Chemistry," 2nd Ed., New York, Reinhold Publishing Corp., 1966.
5. Cooper, W. C., "The Physical, Chemical and Toxicological Properties of Selenium and Tellurium," paper presented at the Selenium and Tellurium Symposium, New York, Selenium and Tellurium Development Committee, 1965.
6. Hampel, C. A., "Rare Metals Handbook," 2nd Ed., New York, Reinhold Publishing Corp., 1961.

7. "Handbook of Chemistry and Physics," 46th Ed., Cleveland, Chemical Rubber Co., 1965.
8. Latimer, W. M., "The Oxidation States of the Elements and Their Potentials in Aqueous Solutions," New York, Prentice-Hall, Inc., 1938.
9. Sax, N. I., "Dangerous Properties of Industrial Materials," 2nd Ed., New York, Reinhold Publishing Corp., 1965.
10. "The Bulletin of Selenium-Tellurium Development Committee," Nos. 1–5, New York, Selenium and Tellurium Development Committee, 1965.

JOHN R. STONE

SILICON

Silicon, symbol Si, atomic number 14, atomic weight 28.086, is the second most abundant element, making up 25.7% of the earth's crust. It is a nonmetal, the second element in Group IVA of the Periodic Table. In elemental form it is known only in one dark-colored crystalline form, namely, the octahedral form in which the silicon atoms have the diamond arrangement. The so-called amorphous form consists of minute crystals of this form.

History

Berzelius prepared elemental silicon in 1823 by passing silicon tetrafluoride over heated potassium. It is possible that Gay-Lussac and Thenard may have prepared very impure amorphous silicon by the same method in 1809. Berzelius purified the product by prolonged leaching. In addition, he obtained silicon from the reaction of potassium fluosilicate with potassium.

Crystalline silicon was first prepared by Deville, in 1854, by electrolysis of impure sodium aluminum chloride which contained about 10% silicon in the melt. Shiny platelets of silicon were obtained when the aluminum was dissolved.

The forerunner of the present large-scale commercial process was developed by Potter (1907), who studied the interaction of silica and carbon.

Occurrence

Silicon occurs in nature combined with oxygen in various forms of silicon dioxide and with oxygen and metals in the many types of silicates, but is never found uncombined. The various silicates plus silica make up about 60% of the earth's crust. The SiO_4 tetrahedra is the primary structural unit in all these substances. The silicates are actually a very large group of compounds composed of metal ions and negative ions (often very complex) composed of SiO_4 units. Mineral silicates may contain any or all of 42 metals and nonmetals besides rare earths. The classification of natural silicates is presented later in this article, pp. 643–645.

Derivation

Elemental silicon (96 to 98% pure) is prepared commercially by heating silicon dioxide with carbon (coke) in an electric furnace. This material can be purified by repeated leaching to yield a 99.7 + % product. A highly crystalline product is obtained by crystallization from aluminum or zinc. "Hyper-pure" silicon (99.97%) is prepared by reducing the tetrachloride with zinc. Further purification by zone refining removes phosphorus.

The Czochralski method is commonly employed to grow single crystals of silicon used in semiconductor devices. A single crystal "seed" is dipped into molten silicon held at the melting point and then slowly withdrawn. Pure quartz crucibles are generally used, but a recent technique for growing small

FIG. 1. Typical single silicon crystals grown by the Czochralski technique.

perfect crystals utilizes a silicon pedestal on which a molten puddle of silicon is maintained as the feed stock. Typical single crystals are shown in Fig. 1.

Physical Properties

Data about various physical properties of silicon are presented in Table 1.

Chemical Properties

Silicon is just below carbon in the Periodic Table. Since they both have two electrons in each of the outer s and p orbitals, silicon resembles carbon in a number of ways. For example, they both have tetrahedral arrangement in their molecules and optical isomerism

TABLE 1. PHYSICAL PROPERTIES OF SILICON

Atomic number	14
Atomic weight	28.086
Covalent radius	1.173 Å
Electronegativity	1.8
Outer electron arrangement	$3s^2 3p^2$
Oxidation number	± 4 ($+2$ in SiO)
Melting point	1420°C
Boiling point	2355°C
Density	2.33 g/cc at 20°C
Hardness	7 (Mohs Scale)
Critical pressure	1,450 atm
Critical temperature	4,920°C (calculated)
Coefficient of thermal expansion	
Mean value between 15–1000°C	4.68×10^{-6}
At 25°C	4.2×10^{-6}
At -157°C	zero
At liquid air temperatures	negative
Dielectric constant	12
Electric conductivity, ohm-cm	
-190°C	2×10^3
300°C	15
500°C	0.4
Cathodoluminescence, minimum voltage for excitation	
Amorphous silicon (whitish yellow)	1,600
Crystalline silicon (red)	2,400
Energy gap	1.12 eV
Entropy, cal/mole/°K	
Solid silicon	
298°K	4.50
500°K	7.58
1000°K	11.85
1500°K	15.48
Liquid silicon,	
2000°K	23.75
Gaseous silicon,	
2000°K	49.66
Free energy, cal/mole/°K	$\dfrac{-(F-H_{298})}{T}$
Solid silicon	
298°K	4.50
500°K	5.46
1000°K	7.70
1500°K	10.56
Hardness	240 (Brinell)
Heat of combustion, Si to SiO_2, cal	191,000
Heat of fusion, kcal/mole	11.1

TABLE 1—*continued*

Heat of vaporization, kcal/mole	71
Lattice constant, 25°C, 77°F	5.429×10^{-8}cm
Magnetic susceptibility, Si with 0.085% Fe	0.13×10^{-6}
Specific heat, c of 99.2% Si	
0°C	0.1597 cal/g/°C
0–100°C	0.181 cal/g/°C
Equation:	
$C = 0.165428\,(\theta - 17) + 0.0001584310\,(\theta - 17)^2 - 0.0000003742\,(\theta - 17)^3$	
Thermal conductivity, cal/cm/sec/°C	0.20
Resistivity, intrisic, 300°K	230,000 ohm-cm
Heat content	
Solid silicon, $H_T - H_{298}$	
500°K	1.06
1000°K	4.15
1500°K	7.37
Liquid silicon,	
2000°K	22.92
Gaseous silicon	
500°K	1.065
1000°K	3.60
1500°K	6.12
2000°K	8.70

occurs in silicon compounds. Silicon is less electronegative than carbon, resulting in its acidic properties being very weak. However, salts of the hypothetical orthosilicic acid, H_4SiO_4, are known. The low electronegativity also results in its halides being somewhat ionized and reactive.

Silicon differs from carbon in that no silicon compounds containing double or triple bonds have been discovered; also it does not combine with itself to form structures containing more than six silicon atoms joined together. The Si-Si bond is weaker than the C-C bond and the SiH- bond weaker than the C-H bond, as shown in Table 2. Consequently, the hydrides of silicon are few in number and much less stable than the hydrocarbons.

TABLE 2.   BOND ENERGIES

Bond	Energy, kcal/mole
Si-Si	42.5
C-C	58.6
Si-C	57.6
Si-O	89.3
C-O	70.0
Si-H	75.1
C-H	87.3

From the bond energy it is evident that the Si-C bond found in silicones is about as strong as the C-C bond. Since these bonds are much alike in character, the Si-C bond accounts in part for the high stability of silicones.

The most important chemical property of silicon is its tendency to combine with oxygen to form tetrahedral structures in which one silicon atom is surrounded by four oxygen atoms. This SiO_4 tetrahedron is the basic structure in silicon dioxide and in the silicates in which the tetrahedra are joined together into complex rings or chains. The Si-O bond distance in the tetrahedron is 1.62 Å and the O-O distance is 2.7 Å.

Silicon has a maximum coordination number of six in the fluosilicates which contain the $SiF_6^=$ ion.

Elementary silicon is rather inert at room temperatures, becoming active at higher temperatures, reacting directly with chlorine at 450°C to form silicon tetrachloride and at still higher temperatures reacting with many metals to form silicides. It also reacts directly with many nonmetals as it does with carbon. Above 1710°C it reacts completely with oxygen to form silicon dioxide. With HF it reacts to form fluosilicic acid, H_2SiF_6, and

H_2. Also it reacts with HCl to form silicon tetrachloride and H_2. With strong bases silicon reacts to form silicates and H_2.

Silicon Compounds

Silicon is one of the three elements capable of forming the largest number of compounds. Only hydrogen and carbon have the possibility of forming more. This is evident since in addition to other compounds, over 800 natural silicates are known and the number of possible organosilicon compounds is very large.

Fluosilicic Acid and the Fluosilicates. Fluosilicic acid, H_2SiF_6, is an active acid. It is a colorless fuming liquid which is quite soluble in water. The commercial 30% solution is sold in wax bottles since it attacks glass. Its salts are toxic and the sodium and potassium salts have been used as rat poisons and insecticides for chewing type insects such as crickets, cockroaches, etc. Sodium aluminum fluosilicate, $NaAl(SiF_6)_2$, is a good mothproofing agent for woolen articles. Barium fluosilicate, $BaSiF_6$, is effective against Japanese beetles and Mexican bean beetles.

Hydrides. Of the silanes, a saturated series having the type formula, Si_nH_{2n+2}, only the first six members are known. These compounds can be prepared by treating magnesium silicide, Mg_2Si, with 20% HCl in an atmosphere of H_2. One set of conditions produces the hydrides in the proportions 40% SiH_4, 30% Si_2H_6, 15% Si_3H_8, 10% Si_4H_{10}, and 5% $Si_5H_{12} + Si_6H_{14}$. Monosilane, SiH_4, and disilane, Si_2H_6, can be prepared in 70 to 80% yields by reaction of Mg_2Si with NH_4Br in liquid ammonia in a current of H_2. The silanes ignite spontaneously in air and become progressively less stable to heat with increase in chain length. SiH_4 is stable up to red heat while Si_6H_{14} (hexasilane) is unstable at room temperature. The silanes react violently with halogens to form silicon tetrahalides, SiX_4, and HX.

Silicon Carbide (SiC), or "Carborundum," has a diamond-like structure and is nearly as hard as the diamond. It is prepared by heating fine SiO_2 and coke with a little salt and sawdust in an electric furnace. The crystals obtained are greenish blue to black. It is one of the most widely used abrasives for grinding and cutting metals.

Silicon Dioxide or Silica. $(SiO_2)_x$, m.p. 1710°C, is one of the most important compounds of silicon occurring in nature. It has a solubility (colloidal) in water of 0.0426 g/100 cc H_2O at 90°C and a solubility of 0.0160 g/100 cc H_2O at 25°C. This slight solubility change accounts for the formation of petrified wood, geyserite, etc.

All forms of silicon dioxide are composed of SiO_4 tetrahedra in which each oxygen is shared with another tetrahedron, with the result that each crystal is a giant molecule with the average stoichiometry SiO_2. Silica exists in three crystalline forms in nature, namely, quartz, tridymite, and cristobalite. The latter two are found only in volcanic rock and have no industrial use. Keatite, another crystalline form of silica, was produced by the first atomic bomb explosion in New Mexico.

The relationship among the three crystalline forms of silica occurring in nature is given by the following diagram.

$$\alpha \text{ quartz} \underset{\rightarrow}{\overset{573°C}{\leftarrow}} \beta \text{ quartz} \underset{\rightarrow}{\overset{870°C}{\leftarrow}} \beta \text{ tridymite} \underset{\leftarrow}{\overset{1470°C}{\rightarrow}}$$

$$\updownarrow \begin{smallmatrix} 160 \text{ to} \\ 120°C \end{smallmatrix}$$

$$\alpha \text{ tridymite}$$

$$\beta \text{ cristobalite} \overset{1710°C}{\underset{\rightarrow}{}} \text{ liquid}$$

$$\updownarrow \begin{smallmatrix} 200 \text{ to} \\ 275°C \end{smallmatrix}$$

$$\alpha \text{ cristobalite}$$

The differences among the three major forms are due to the difference in the arrangement of the silica tetrahedra. The α and β form differences are slight distortions of the crystals.

Quartz is very common, occurring in granite, sand, sandstone, crystals, etc. It has a hardness of 7 and several crystalline varieties such as amethyst (purple), citrine (yellow), rock crystal (colorless), and smoky quartz are important gems. Agate, petrified wood, flint, chert, etc., are composed cryptocrystalline quartz. Crystals of natural quartz are shown in Fig. 2.

Quartz is a piezoelectric substance and is used in stabilizing amplifier tube circuits. It is also used in apparatus for measuring electrical potentials up to several thousand volts and to measure instantaneous high pressures. Natural crystals of a size and purity satisfactory for optical and resonator plate use are very uncommon and are found primarily in Brazil. Large crystals for such

FIG. 2. Quartz crystals, probably from Arkansas.

uses are now grown from alkaline solutions at high temperatures and pressures.

Fused quartz transmits ultraviolet light and due to a low coefficient of expansion (5.46×10^{-7}) is resistant to breakage under temperature changes. It is one of the best electrical insulators and is the only good one not damaged by heating to red heat.

Several forms of amorphous silica containing water, such as opal, geyserite and diatomaceous silica, are found in nature. Australian black opal is one of the most precious gems. Silica gel belongs in this same class and can be prepared by mixing dilute sodium silicate and sulfuric acid solutions. After standing about four hours the gel is cut into pieces and washed with water until the acid is removed. It is then dried in an oven at 150°C or higher for several hours. The

resulting gel is very porous and may have an apparent density as low as 0.7 g/cc. Due to its porosity and high specific surface area it is used in solvent and gas recovery. Gasoline can be removed from natural gas by the gel and water can be removed from blast furnace gas. It has·been used as a contact catalyst and is a good catalyst carrier. In some cases it acts as a promoter.

Diatomaceous silica, skeletal remains of water plants, known as diatoms, is widely used because of its high insulating value, high absorptive capacity, mildly abrasive character, and its finely divided character making it a good raw material for preparing other silicon compounds.

Silica is unreactive toward most nonmetals, acids, and metal oxides at ordinary temperatures. It is attacked by fluorine or HF to form SiF_4, and by strong bases to form silicates. An example of the latter is the reaction of SiO_2 with NaOH to form water glass, a substance used as a glue, etc. At elevated temperatures it becomes active and can be reduced by carbon and several active metals; it reacts with metallic oxides and carbonates. An example of the latter is the formation of glass from SiO_2 and various metallic oxides or carbonates.

Glass. Common glass used for windows, bottles, etc., has a composition of 75% SiO_2, 15% Na_2O, 8% CaO and 2.7% Al_2O_3. "Pyrex" glass is a borosilicate glass containing 80.75% SiO_2, 12.00% B_2O_3, 4.10% Na_2O, 0.10% K_2O, 2.20% Al_2O_3–Fe_2O_3 and 0.40% As_2O_5. This glass resists breakage with temperature change due to its low coefficient of linear expansion (0.036×10^{-4}). Lead glass used in optical instruments and ornamental ware contains 55% SiO_2, 33% PbO, 11% K_2O, and 1% Al_2O_3. Silex used in coffee pots, etc., is 98.7% SiO_2. Fluorescent glass commonly contains U_3O_8 or $U_2O_2(OH)_2$.

Silicon Monoxide. SiO is the only divalent silicon compound for which there is any good evidence. If silica is heated with elementary silicon in vacuo at 1,450°C, practically the whole of the silicon sublimes as an oxide. The spectrum of the vapor shows it to be SiO. If the vapor is cooled rapidly, a light brown solid is obtained which gives no x-ray pattern and might be amorphous SiO. If the vapor is cooled slowly or the amorphous solid is heated, the x-ray pattern indicates that the product is silica plus elementary silicon. The amorphous powder burns to silica in air, and is oxidized by water at 400°C and by carbon dioxide at 500°C.

Silicon tetrachloride (tetrachlorosilane) is a colorless liquid with a boiling point of 57.57°C and a density of 1.483 at 20°C. It is prepared commercially by heating silicon dioxide and carbon in a stream of chlorine. It is quite active chemically as the bonds are 30% ionic. It reacts readily with H_2O to form SiO_2 and HCl, making a dense smoke screen.

It reacts with alcohols to form esters of orthosilicic acid such as $Si(OC_2H_5)_4$ which is called tetraethyl orthosilicate or tetraethoxysilane. The most important reaction of $SiCl_4$ is the one with Grignard reagents, RMgCl, to form compounds such as alkyltrichlorosilanes, $RSiCl_3$, dialkyldichlorosilanes, R_2SiCl_2, trialkylchlorosilanes, R_3SiCl, and tetraalkylsilanes, R_4Si. The hydrolysis of the chlorosilanes produces the various types of silicones. Hydrolysis of trialkylchlorosilanes produces a group of compounds known as sylil ethers, R_3Si–O–SiR_3. Alkylchlorosilanes are produced industrially by the reaction between elementary silicon and alkyl chlorides. This reaction requires finely-divided copper as a catalyst. This reaction produces mostly the dialkyl dichlorosilane, R_2SiCl_2, but some of the others are also formed. This type of reaction will also work to produce arylchlorosilanes if finely-divided silver is used as a catalyst. The diaryldichlorosilanes are the main product.

Silicon tetrachloride is widely used in preparing organosilicon compounds such as silicones and makes excellent smoke screens for military purposes. This important compound was first prepared by Berzelius in 1823. Hexachlorodisilane, Si_2Cl_6, and octachlorotrisilane, Si_3Cl_8, are also known. Silicon tetrafluoride, silicon tetrabromide and silicon tetraiodide are known and are like silicon tetrachloride in properties.

Silicon disulfide, $(SiS_2)_x$, consists of infinite chains of SiS_4 tetrahedra with opposite edges in common.

This compound is prepared by heating the elements together and purifying by sublimation. It reacts with water to form hydrogen sulfide and silica. It is said to form thiosilicates when heated with alkaline sulfides.

Silicon nitride, Si_3N_4, is made directly by heating silicon in nitrogen at 1300 to 1380°C. It can also be made by heating tetraaminosilane, $Si(NH_2)_4$, which loses ammonia. This compound is very stable and probably exists as a giant molecule.

Aminosilanes are of interest as they can be used as intermediates for preparing silicones and silizane polymers. The NH_2 groups of dialkyl diaminosilanes react with water to form the corresponding silicols which condense to form silicones. Silizane polymers are formed by simply warming the alkylaminosilanes. Ammonia is lost and structures of the

type
$$-N-Si-N-S-N-Si-$$
are formed.

with the substituent pattern H, R, H, R, H, R above and R, R, R below.

Even though
$$-N-Si-$$
groups react with (H, R above; R below)

moisture, recent work indicates some useful polymers of this type may be developed.

Organosilicon chemistry has become quite extensive since Ebelmen prepared the first compound containing both silicon and carbon. He prepared tetraethoxysilane (ethyl orthosilicate) by the reaction of silicon tetrachloride with ethyl alcohol: $SiCl_4 + 4C_2H_5OH \rightarrow Si(OC_2H_5)_4 + 4HCl$. Many compounds of this type have since been prepared. This type of compound hydrolyzes slowly to liberate silica and the alcohol. In 1863 Fridel and Crafts prepared the first compounds in which silicon and carbon were bonded together. They made tertaalkylsilanes by action of zinc alkyls on silicon tetrachloride:

$$2Zn(C_2H_5)_2 + SiCl_4 \rightarrow 2ZnCl_2 + Si(C_2H_5)_4.$$

Tetraacetoxysilane (silicon tetraacetate) was prepared by Fridel and Ladenburg in 1867

639

from silicon tetrachloride and acetic anhydride:

$$SiCl_4 + 4(CH_3C)_2O \rightarrow$$
$$\underset{\displaystyle \parallel \atop \displaystyle O}{}$$
$$Si(O-C-CH_3)_4 + 4CH_3C-Cl$$
$$\underset{\displaystyle \parallel \atop \displaystyle O}{} \qquad \underset{\displaystyle \parallel \atop \displaystyle O}{}$$

This is one of a group of compounds known as acyloxysilanes. These compounds can be made more readily by reaction of sodium salts of organic acids with silicon tetrachloride. This method was discovered in 1947 by Schuyten, Weaver and Reid: $SiCl_4 + 4NaO-C-R \rightarrow$
$$\underset{\displaystyle \parallel \atop \displaystyle O}{}$$
$Si(OC-R)_4 + 4NaCl$. This method has been
$$\underset{\displaystyle \parallel \atop \displaystyle O}{}$$

widely used since then to make simple acyloxysilanes and mixed alkyl or aryl acyloxysilanes such as $R_2Si(OCR)_2$.
$$\underset{\displaystyle \parallel \atop \displaystyle O}{}$$

In 1873 Ladenburg prepared the first aromatic silicon derivative, C_6H_5–$SiCl_3$, by heating silicon tetrachloride with mercury biphenyl:

$$Hg(C_6H_5)_2 + SiCl_4 \rightarrow$$
$$C_6H_5SiCl_3 + HgC_6H_5Cl$$

In 1899 Kipping began the study of optical activity in silicon compounds. He prepared

$$\begin{array}{ccc} C_3H_7 & & CH_2-C_6H_5 \\ & \diagdown \quad \diagup & \\ & Si & \\ & \diagup \quad \diagdown & \\ C_2H_5 & & CH_2-C_6H_5SO_3H \end{array}$$

and was able to separate the isomers. In the years following he did the foundation work for silicone chemistry by discovering that silicon tetrachloride reacts with Grignard reagents to form Si–C bonds. This is the most important method of producing Si–C bonds. This is discussed later under silicones.

Silicon-carbon bonds can be produced by a Wurtz type reaction. This involves the reaction between silicon tetrachloride an alkyl chloride and sodium:

$$SiCl_4 + 4RCl + 8Na \rightarrow Si(C_4H_9)_4 + 8NaCl.$$

This type of reaction is only successful in preparing tetraalkyls which have very little use. Silicon tetrachloride will also add on to unsaturated hydrocarbons to form compounds with carbon silicon bonds:

$$\begin{array}{c} \quad\quad\quad\quad H\ \ H \\ \quad\quad\quad\quad |\ \ \ | \\ H_2C=CH_2 + SiCl_4 \rightarrow HC-C-SiCl_3 \\ \quad\quad\quad\quad |\ \ \ | \\ \quad\quad\quad\quad Cl\ H \end{array}$$

$$\begin{array}{c} \quad\quad\quad\quad H\ \ H \\ \quad\quad\quad\quad |\ \ \ | \\ HC\equiv CH + SiCl_4 \rightarrow Cl-C=C-SiCl_3 \end{array}$$

Carbon monoxide also reacts with silicon tetrachloride to form a compound with silicon carbon bonds,

$$CO + SiCl_4 \rightarrow Cl-C-SiCl_3$$
$$\underset{\displaystyle \parallel \atop \displaystyle O}{}$$

Tetraacyloxysilanes react with Grignard reagents to produce hydrolysis products such as ketones, tertiary alcohols and silicones. Many complex organic compounds can be made this way. The tetraacyloxy silanes react with water and alcohols.

Mixed alkyl or aryl acyloxysilanes also react with water and produce silicols such as $R_2Si(OH)_2$ which condense to form siloxanes (silicones). They will also react with Grignard reagents and it is possible to prepare many interesting organosilicon and organic compounds this way.

Silicon has a coordination number of six and forms chelate coordination complexes of the type $[SiA_3]$ X in which silicon is in the cation. A may be one of several B-diketones (acetyl acetone, methyl-acetyl acetone, dibenzoyl methane, etc.), X may be Cl^-, $FeCl_4^-$, $AuCl_4^-$, $ZnCl_3^-$, $PtCl_6^{-2}$, etc. These complexes are mostly insoluble in benzene, easily soluble in chloroform and are quickly hydrolyzed by water. Tris (acetylacetone) silicon (IV) tetrachloraurate is a good example of this type of compound:

$$\left[Si \left(\begin{array}{c} O - C \overset{CH_3}{\underset{\diagup}{\diagdown}} CH \\ O = C \diagup \end{array} \right)_3 \right]^+ AuCl_4^-$$

Alkaline compounds of the type R_3SiM exist but are less known than for germanium, tin or lead. $LiSi(C_2H_5)_3$ can be formed by treating $(C_2H_5)_3Si\text{-}Ge(\varphi)_3$ in ethylamine solution with lithium metal. The silicon-germanium compound is formed by treating $(C_2H_5)_3Cl$ with $NaGe\varphi_3$ in benzene solution. $LiSi\varphi_3$ is produced by action of lithium on φ_6Si_2 in ethylamine. Compounds of this type are white crystalline solids.

Organosilicon compounds containing Si–Si bonds are known but often are not very stable. The Si–Si bond is easily oxidized and is subject to hydrolysis. With water, an OH group is added to each silicon atom and hydrogen is produced. Compounds such as $(C_2H_5)_6Si_2$ and φ_6Si_2 where there is only one Si–Si bond are quite resistant to hydrolysis even in the presence of a base. The alkyl disilanes can be made by treating Si_2Cl_6 with zinc alkyls, or a Grignard reagent. Aryldisilanes can be made by heating ether free Grignard reagent residues with Si_2Cl_6. There is evidence that aryl silanes may have been produced that contain 4 silicon atoms in a ring:

$$\begin{array}{ccc} Ar_2 \diagdown & & \diagup Ar_2 \\ & Si - Si & \\ & | \quad\;\; | & \\ & Si - Si & \\ Ar_2 \diagup & & \diagdown Ar_2 \end{array}$$

Silicon can replace carbon atoms in organic compounds and a large number of such compounds are known. This includes both chain and ring compounds. Such compounds are stable as a silicon-carbon bond has almost exactly the same strength as a carbon-to-carbon bond and is just as resistant to oxidation and hydrolysis. These compounds are very similar in physical and chemical properties to the corresponding all carbon compounds. Recent discoveries indicate that silicon may be used as a molecular variant in drugs. When a carbon atom is replaced by a silicon atom in some biologically active compounds, little change in activity is observed. Meprobamate and silameprobamate, for example, show almost identical muscle-relaxing capacity. In some cases the addition of a silicon atom changes the type of biological activity. For example 3,3-dimethyl-l-butanol carbamate is a slow-acting convulsant whereas 3,3-dimethyl-3-sila-l-butanol carbamate is a fast-acting muscle relaxant.

Silicones. This term covers a class of compounds scientifically called organosiloxanes. The name silicone came about because the empirical formula R_2SiO is like that of ketones, R_2CO. However, these substances are complex organosilicon oxides and do not contain any $Si=O$ bonds. Much of the research work on silicones before 1940 was conducted by F. S. Kipping and co-workers at University College, Nottingham, England. Soon after the discovery of Grignard reagents, Kipping found that they would react with $SiCl_4$ to form alkylchlorosilanes such as $RSiCl_3$, R_2SiCl_2 and R_3SiCl_2. The alkylchlorosilanes were found to hydrolyze to form silicols such as $RSi(OH)_3$, $R_2Si(OH)_2$ and R_3SiOH. The silicols spontaneously lost water to produce polymeric organosiloxanes. These polymers were of both ring and chain types and were difficult to separate. The development of useful products began about 1940. The linear siloxanes are the useful ones and have the following type structure:

$$\begin{array}{ccccc} R & & R & & R \\ | & & | & & | \\ -Si-O-&Si-O-&Si-O-. \\ | & & | & & | \\ R & & R & & R \end{array}$$

R is commonly a CH_3-radical but may be C_6H_5- or other radicals. These structures are quite stable since they have Si–O–Si bonds such as occur in silica and the C–Si bond is quite stable. Such a structure would have excellent thermal stability, chemical resistance and water repellency. A carbon-carbon bond such as occurs in an ethyl group would lower the thermal stability.

Silicone oils are straight chain methyl siloxanes.

$$CH_3[(CH_3)_2SiO]_xSi(CH_3)_3 \quad R/S = 2$$

The viscosity and boiling point increase with x. Vicosities may range from thinner than water to ones that barely flow at 20°C. They are made by hydrolyzing a mixture of $(CH_3)_2SiCl_2$ and the right amount of $(CH_3)_3SiCl$ along with 4% concentrated sulfuric acid. Silicone oils are very stable chemically, do not react with metals, are stable at temperatures as high as 260°C, and do not form acids or sludge. They have very desirable physical properties in that they have a wide liquid range and the viscosity increases only about 7 times in going from 35°C to −35°C. When $x = 4$, the melting point is −70°C and the boiling point 194°C at 760 mm. They do not cause rubber to swell, are good electrical insulators, and have low dielectric losses.

The oils are used as antifoaming agents (diesels), in high-vacuum diffusion pumps, in sealed-in motor units, in motor vehicles used in arctic exploration and as dielectric media in transformers. They are often used in hydraulic pumps and brakes the year around. They are also used in hand lotions, in water repellent preparations for shoes and to coat baking pans.

Silicone rubber elastomer is made by hydrolyzing $(CH_3)_2SiCl_2$ in the presence of a reagent that increases the chain length without cross linking. By carefully avoiding trifunctional groups, chains of 2,000 or more $(CH_3)_2SiO$ units can be built up. Inorganic fillers such as ZnO, TiO_2 or SiO_2 and a curing catalyst are then added. The mixture is shaped by extrusion or molding and is then vulcanized. Some cross linking occurs between the chains and the material sets into an infusible elastic mass with a CH_3/Si value somewhat less than 2. Silicone rubbers are much more resistant chemically than natural rubber and can be used at 240°C for long periods of time without loss of elasticity. They do not melt in air below 300°C. Their elasticity persists down to −55°C. They have excellent electrical properties and can be bonded to metals in the curing process. After curing they will not stick to metals. They are resistant to most solvents but are affected by strong acids, strong bases and swell some in mineral oil, benzene, etc. Silicone rubber has a lower elastic limit, abrasion resistance, resistance to tearing and tensile strength than natural rubber. The latter two factors can be overcome by laminating with cloth, glass, etc.

The laminated products are used in heat resistant conveyor belts and gaskets for motors. The rubbers are also used in low-temperature gaskets for refrigerators, heat resistant tubing and rollers, wire insulation and protective coatings for metals.

Silicone resins are highly cross linked. In methyl silicones the CH_3/Si ratio is commonly from 1.2 to 1.5. If $CH_3/Si = 1$ every silicon atom would be cross linked. These resins are sticky syrups but set to colorless solids when cured by heat. They are very resistant to heat and have not been damaged by being heated at 200°C for one year. For ethyl silicone resins the C_2H_5/Si ratio can be between 0.5 to 1.5.

Methyl phenyl silicone resins have a greater resistance to abrasion and better dielectric properties. The methyl to phenyl ratio is about 1 to 1. An R/Si ratio 1.8 makes a good methyl phenyl resin.

Methyl silicone resins are commonly produced by hydrolysis of various mixtures of methyl chlorosilanes in ice water. Condensation of the resulting silicols to form resins takes place almost simultaneously with the hydrolysis. Advanced condensation to resinous materials of satisfactory thermosetting properties is generally brought about by heating. The resins are only slightly soluble in water so mixed solvents such as water and dioxane are commonly used.

Silicone resins make very tough, resistant paints that are stable to above 250°C and are used on smoke stacks and other areas subject to high temperatures. They are used on electric motor windings for this same reason and because they are excellent insulators. Motors can be operated satisfactorily at 300°C. The resins do not discolor on heating and permit greater retention of color.

Silicone resins are good water repellents and masonry and other materials are treated with dilute solutions of these resins. Such coatings prevent freezing and thawing damage and keep the surface cleaner. Ordinary resin solutions do not work on limestone. However, very satisfactory repellent coatings are produced with water solutions of sodium methyl siliconate, $Na-O-\overset{\displaystyle OH}{\underset{\displaystyle OH}{\vert}}\overset{}{\underset{}{\vert}}Si-CH_3$, or a silicone having the type formula $RSiY_3$ where R is a methyl group and Y a water-attracting group alcoholic in nature. Such coatings have been known to be effective for seven years or more.

Copolymers of silicone resins containing allyl or vinyl groups with vinyl acetate or vinyl butyl resins are satisfactory for use in lamination of wood, glass and metals. Silicone resins containing vinyl groups are used as adhesives. Others find use as wood sealers. Combination expoxide-silicone resins are being investigated. Silicone resins are being used in new type dental impression materials.

A silicone putty contains a benzene-soluble silicone polymer, powdered silica and another inorganic filler. Silicone greases are made of a silicone polymer (oil) and a filler. Ordinary silicones are nontoxic. Intermediates such as the chlorosilanes are hazardous because they react with moisture to produce hydrochloric acid.

Silicates

Natural Silicates. Natural silicates are best classified by the arrangement of the silica tetrahedra making up the negative ions of the compound. By means of x-ray studies W. L. Bragg, Pauling and others have determined the structures of many silicates since 1930. The simplest class of silicates is that of the orthosilicates which contain SiO_4^{-4} ions. Olivine, $9Mg_2SiO_4 \cdot Fe_2SiO_4$, a main constituent of basalt, belongs in this classification. Zircon, $ZrSiO_4$, a gem stone, and the various garnets, $R_3^{II}R_2^{III}(SiO_4)_3$, also belong in this class. R^{II} in garnets may be Ca, Mn or Fe and R^{III} may be Al, Cr, or Fe. Almandite or common garnet has the formula $Fe_3Al_2(SiO_4)_3$. Spessartite, $Mn_3Al_2(SiO_4)_3$, and pyrope, $Mg_3Al_2(SiO_4)_3$, are gem garnets. Chromium produces green garnets called uvarovite, $Ca_3Cr_2(SiO_4)_3$. The hardness of garnets varies from 6.5 to 7.5 on the Mohs scale and they are often used as abrasives.

The second class of silicates is the group containing $Si_2O_7^{-6}$ ions. The structure of this class is as follows:

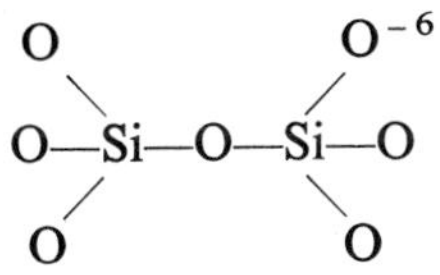

Hemimorphite, $Zn_4(OH)_2Si_2O_7 \cdot H_2O$, is an example of this class.

Another class of silicates is that with ring structures having $(SiO_3)_n^{-2n}$ ions. This class can be divided into two subclasses: those with 3 Si and 3 oxygen atoms in a ring and those with 6 Si and 6 oxygen atoms in the ring. Benitoite, $BaTiSi_3O_9$, belongs to the first subclass and contains the following silicon-oxygen ring structure:

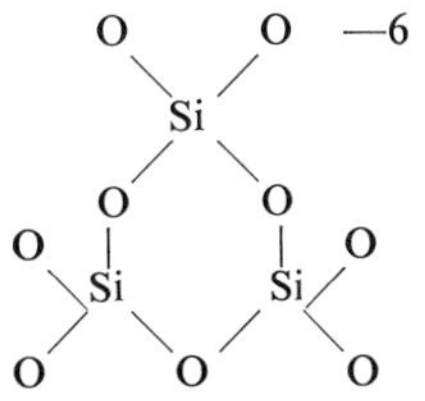

Beryl, $Be_3Al_2Si_6O_{18}$, belongs to the second subclass. The silicon and oxygen atoms are arranged as follows:

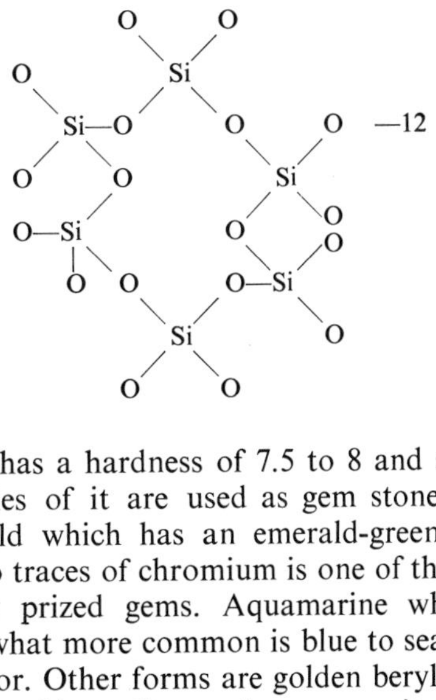

Beryl has a hardness of 7.5 to 8 and several varieties of it are used as gem stones. The emerald which has an emerald-green color due to traces of chromium is one of the most highly prized gems. Aquamarine which is somewhat more common is blue to sea green in color. Other forms are golden beryl which has a golden-yellow color, morganite which is pink or rose red and goshenite which is a very pure, colorless variety. Common beryl is usually pale green-yellowish or grayish white in color. It is the main source of the element beryllium (q.v.).

A fourth class consists of silicates with silicon-oxygen chain complexes. This class is divided into a group with simple chains and a group composed of hexagonal rings (band structure) arranged in chains. The first contains ions of the $(SiO_3)_n{}^{-2n}$ and has the following arrangement:

These chains can be very long and a very large number of minerals are possible. These minerals are commonly called pyroxenes. Enstatite, $(MgSiO_3)_n$, is an example of a mineral in this class. Serpentine asbestos belongs in this group. It is flexible and can be woven into cloth for fire-proof curtains, etc. Serpentine, $H_4Mg_3Si_2O_9$, is a green color and has a greasy luster. Serpentine rock often contains other minerals. Jadeite, $NaAl(SiO_3)_2$, a form of jade, belongs to this class. It is tough, hard (6.5 to 7) and has a splintery fracture. Its luster is subvitreous to pearly and commonly varies in color from white to emerald green. Other colors such as brown, orange, red or black occur.

The band-structured chain silicates are called amphiboles and have $(Si_4O_{11})_n{}^{-6n}$ ions. The arrangement is as follows:

glistening luster and is translucent to opaque. This is the type of jade commonly used for carvings.

The fifth class of silicates consists of silicates containing sheet structures. The sheets are made up of the same type of silicon-oxygen rings that occur in the band structure of the amphiboles but are built up in two dimensions instead of one. The various micas and clays belong in this classification. Two common micas are muscovite, $H_2KAl_3(SiO_4)_3$, or colorless mica and biotite, $(HK)_2(MgFe)_2Al_2(SiO_4)_3$, or black mica. Muscovite is used for stove and furnace doors as well as in electrical work. There are many types of clays but two common ones are kaolin, $H_8Al_4Si_4O_{18}$, and montmorillonite, $H_2Al_2Si_4O_{12}$. Kaolin is china clay and finds wide use in pottery and china of various types. The second type mentioned is a good ion exchanger and is a common constituent of good soils. The ceramic industry is dependent on clays; this includes bricks, pipes and tiles as well as the before mentioned items. Some clays swell greatly when wet and can be used to seal leaks in dams, etc. Others absorb oils and greases and can be used to clean wool, etc. (fullers earth). Some clays are useful as cracking catalysts.

Tremolite, $Ca_2Mg_5(OH)_2Si_8O_{22}$, belongs to this class of minerals. Amphibole asbestos is not flexible enough for weaving but it is just as good for insulation and filtering as serpentine asbestos. Nephrite, $Ca(Mg,Fe)_3(SiO_3)_4$, the most common form of jade, belongs to this class. The mineral is compact, very tough, hard (6 to 6.5) and the fracture is splintery. It is usually green due to ferrous iron but may be other colors from white to black. It has a

The last class of silicates includes those that have three dimensional framework structures. This includes the feldspars, zeolites and ultramarines. A common zeolite has the formula $Na_2O \cdot 2Al_2O_3 \cdot 5SiO_2 \cdot 5H_2O$. Orthoclase and microcline are feldspars having the same formula, $KAlSi_3O_8$, but different crystal structures. They are both found in granites and gneisses. The Pikes Peak region is the best known area for microline crystals.

Large green colored crystals are known as amazon stone, a gem. Another common constituent of granite is a sodium feldspar known as albite, $NaAlSi_3O_8$. Opalescent forms of orthoclase and albite are the gems known as moonstone.

Lazurite is an ultramarine and has a deep blue color. The formula is rather complex, being $(Na_2,Ca)_2Al_2[Al(NaSO_4,NaS_3,Cl)](SiO_4)_3$. It has been used in gems and as a pigment.

Two other gem silicates that contain non-metals are topaz, $Al_2SiO_4F_2$, and tourmaline, $(H,Li,K,Na)_9Al_3(BOH)_2Si_4O_{19}$. Topaz has a hardness of 8 and the crystals are frequently colored. The colors include yellow, brown, pale blue, green, violet and red. Tourmaline has a hardness of 7 to 7.5 and like topaz occurs in various colors. The color often varies within a single crystal. Common colors are black, brown, gray, yellow, green, red, pink, blue or colorless.

Synthetic Silicates. The only soluble silicates are those of the alkali metal and quaternary ammonium ions. Lithium silicates are only slightly soluble. Sodium silicate or water glass is the best known of the soluble silicates.

The composition of sodium silicates is usually expressed in terms of the ratio of Na_2O to SiO_2. $Na_2O:3SiO_2$ is called sodium trisilicate or "neutral" glass. This may be either solid or powdered. $Na_2O:2SiO_2$ is called sodium disilicate or "alkaline" glass. The crystalline soluble silicates are all synthetic and are often mixtures of crystals. For example, commercial anhydrous sodium orthosilicate is a mixture of crystals of NaOH and Na_2SiO_3. The higher the ratio of SiO_2 the more slowly and less soluble they become. Sodium disilicate even though it is very soluble in water dissolves slowly. If the ratio is 1 Na_2O to 13 SiO_2 the substance is nearly insoluble in water.

Liquid silicates (aqueous) are commonly made by treating the solid glasses with steam and water in special pressure dissolvers. A variety of solutions of sodium and potassium silicates are available commercially. They may range in ratio by weight from 1.5 SiO_2 to 3.5 SiO_2 per unit of Na_2O and from 1.5 SiO_2 to 2.5 SiO_2 per unit of K_2O. They are viscous and are often differentiated by density in degrees Baume.

The soluble silicates are widely used commercially. About 1.5 million tons (on a liquid basis) of soluble silicates are used annually. They are widely used in detergents and as detergent builders. They maintain a pH of 10.5 or higher and furnish a high concentration of colloidal silica.

The sodium silicates are very important in protecting metals, alloys, enamels and glazes from corrosion. They react with metal oxides to form metal silicate coatings which prevent further corrosion. Large quantities are used as adhesives for fibrous materials, thin metal sheets and ceramics. Also they find wide use in sealers, cements and molded products. These uses are dependent on their setting by either chemical reaction or evaporation.

The potassium silicates are used primarily as binders for phosphors in the manufacture of television screens, in special cements and in coatings for welding rods. "Silicate gardens" are made by adding water-soluble salts to dilute sodium silicate solution. Branching fungoid growths form as the salts dissolve and then form insoluble silicates.

Synthetic zeolites are a continuous gel of sodium aluminate with sodium silicate, $Na_2O:Al_2O_3:5SiO_2: \times H_2O$. These synthetic zeolites have a higher base exchange capacity than a natural zeolite such as "greensand" and make good water softeners. "Molecular sieves" are made of similar composition crystallized by heat treatment.

Reaction of metal salts with silicate solutions produces products that are used as pigments, fillers, absorbents and decolorizing agents. A calcium silicate having a formula of about $CaO:3.5 SiO_2:1.8 H_2O$, has been used as a reinforcing filler for rubber and similar compositions are used as absorbents and as decolorizing agents. A magnesium silicate, $2MgO:3SiO_2:2H_2O$, is a decolorizing agent and, with higher water content, has been prescribed for treatment of ulcers. Lead and zinc silicates are pigments and phosphors, respectively.

Portland Cement

Portland cement is one of the most important industrial materials containing silicon. No other material is more important to the building industry than concrete. The process now used to produce it was developed in 1824.

Portland cement is made by heating a mixture of finely ground limestone and clay or shale in a 5 to 1 ratio, respectively. Occasionally some blast furnace slag is used. The heating is carried out in large rotary kilns which operate continuously and may produce 200 tons of cement in a day. The kilns are a revolving inclined tube from 9 to 11 ft in internal diameter, and 200 to 400 ft long, of sheet steel, lined with firebrick. The furnace is fired at the lower end with a blast of compressed air and fuel oil, powdered coal or natural gas. The lower end of this kiln is at an intense white heat, somewhat above 1400°C. The upper end where the gases escape is at a temperature of 600 to 800°C. The clinker from the kiln is cooled and finely ground. Before the final grinding, small amounts of gypsum, $CaSO_4 \cdot 2H_2O$, and other materials are added. The calcium sulfate is added to delay the initial set of the concrete. Other additives such as resins tend to make it more waterproof and others decrease time of grinding.

Portland cement usually has a composition of from 60 to 67% CaO, 17 to 25% SiO_2, 0.1 to 5.5% MgO, 3 to 8% Al_2O_3, 0.5 to 6.0% Fe_2O_3, trace to 1.0% Mn_2O_3, 0.5 to 1.3% $Na_2O + K_2O$, and 1 to 3% SO_3. The gray color of the cement is due to the presence of iron and manganese.

The more important compounds present in portland cement are dicalcium silicate, Ca_2SiO_4, tricalcium silicate, Ca_3SiO_5, tricalcium aluminate, $Ca_3Al_2O_6$, and tetracalcium aluminoferrite, $Ca_4Al_2Fe_2O_{10}$. There may also be small amounts of free MgO and CaO. Na_2O, K_2O and MgO contents need to be kept low as they tend to give a product of inferior strength. Too much gypsum may result in crumbling of the concrete.

The initial set of portland cement (first 10 hours) involves reactions of tricalcium aluminate and tricalcium silicate. The tricalcium aluminate promptly combines with water to form crystalline hydrates such as $3CaO \cdot Al_2O_3 \cdot 6H_2O$. Tricalcium silicate is hydrolyzed to produce $Ca(OH)_2$ and gelatinous low-calcium silicates which deposit on the surface of what remains of the original cement particle. Further setting is largely due to action of dicalcium silicate with water. It reacts much like tricalcium silicate only much slower. The low-calcium gelatinous silicate materials gradually dry and stiffen to a horn-like solid, which finally becomes hard as stone and acts as an effective binder between the aggregate particles. Much of the hardening takes place in 28 days but some hardening takes place for several months afterward. Finished concrete may have an effective compressive strength of 4,400 pounds per square inch.

Application of Silicon

Elementary silicon is used in the preparation of silicones, in various alloys of iron, aluminum, copper and manganese, as a deoxidizing agent in the manufacture of steel. Ferrosilicon, which is an important alloy of iron and silicon, is produced by simultaneous reduction of ferric oxide and silica with carbon at a high temperature in an electric furnace. This alloy is used as a deoxidizing agent and an alloying agent in the manufacture of steels. It is also used as a reducing agent in the preparation of metals such as magnesium (Pidgeon Process) and chromium.

Spring steel contains 1.80 to 2.20% Si which toughens and increases the elastic

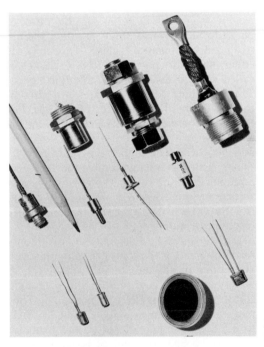

FIG. 3. Silicon semiconductor devices. The upper seven items are rectifiers. In the lower row from left to right are two diodes, a solar cell, and a transistor.

limit. Steels containing 3.5 to 4% Si have much better magnetic properties. Tantiron and duriron containing 14 to 15% Si are very resistant to corrosion and are used in acid-resistant pipes and tanks. Silicon adds strength and corrosion resistance to aluminum alloys. Aluminum alloys containing up to 17% Si are used in making intricate castings having low shrinkage and good resistance to salt water corrosion.

Pure elementary silicon when doped with traces of elements such as boron and phosphorus is one of the best semiconductors. For such purposes single crystals of silicon must be used. It is widely used in power rectifiers, transistors, diodes and solar cells. Typical silicon semiconductor devices are illustrated in Fig. 3.

Silicon rectifiers are becoming increasingly important and have almost revolutionized the conversion of a-c to d-c in the electrolytic industries.

Silica in Living Organisms

Silica occurs in living organisms and it is possible that silicon may have played an important, perhaps necessary role, in the origin of life on the earth. Lower forms of life, such as diatoms often use silica in their skeletal structure. It seems likely that some organosilicon type compounds may occur in living organisms. Bonds of the Si-O-R type appears quite likely.

Silica occurs in considerable quantity in the tissues of many higher plants and to a much lesser degree in the tissues of animals. Animals can excrete silica in solution. Some plants exclude silica and others such as rice absorb a great deal as it is beneficial for the normal growth of this plant. The silica in plants is usually opaline but a quartz has been found in leaves of lantana, strawberries and black raspberries. Silica can deposit in all parts of a plant and the percentage is often very high. For example, sorghum leaf sheath epidermis has been found to contain 11.13% silica on a dry weight basis. Members of the grass family tend to have high contents of opaline silica in their tissues. The pattern of deposition of silica in plants is biologically specific and it is possible to identify plants by microscopic examination of silica particles. In some cases silica appears to be a factor in the resistance that plants have to diseases and insects.

Human tissues often contain from 6 to 90 mg of silica per 100 grams of dry tissues. Lung tissue may vary from 10 mg in infancy to as much as 2000 mg per 100 grams in old age. Miners, stonecutters, potters and others engaged in work where siliceous dust is breathed in large amounts often develop a serious lung disease called silicosis.

References

1. Bazant, V. B., Chevalousky, V., and Rathousky, J., "Chemistry of Organosilicon Compounds," Prague, Czechoslovak Academy of Science, 1965. English translation by Kotyk, A. and Salák, J., New York, Academic Press, 1965.
2. Bazant, V. B., Chevalousky, V., and Rathousky, J., "Register of Organosilicon Compounds," Prague, Czechoslovak Academy of Science, 1965. English translation by Kotyk, A. and Salák, J., New York, Academic Press, 1965.
3. Hampel, C. A., "Rare Metals Handbook," 2nd Ed., New York, Reinhold Publishing Corp., 1961.
4. Iler, R. K., "The Colloid Chemistry of Silica and Silicates," Ithaca, New York, Cornell University Press, 1955.
5. Lanning, F. C., Ponnaiya, B. W. X., and Crumpton, C. F., "The Chemical Nature of Silicon in Plants," *Plant. Physiol.*, **33** (5): 339 (1958).
6. Lanning, F. C., "Silica and Calcium Deposition in the Tissues of Certain Plants," *Advancing Frontiers of Plant Sciences*, **13**, 55 (1965).
7. McGregor, R. R., "Silicones and Their Uses," New York, McGraw-Hill Publishing Co., 1954.
8. Meals, R. N., and Lewis, F. M., "Silicones," New York, Reinhold Publishing Corp., 1957.
9. Rochow, E. G., "Chemistry of the Silicones," 2nd Ed., New York, John Wiley and Sons, Inc., 1951.
10. Wells, A. F., "Structural Inorganic Chemistry," 3rd Ed., pp. 765–816, Oxford, England, Clarendon Press, 1962.

F. C. LANNING

SILVER

History

Silver is among the oldest metals known to man. Its discovery probably came just after that of gold and copper. As far back as 3500 B.C. the Code of Menes decreed that two and one-half parts of silver were equal to one part of gold. Silver is also mentioned in the book of Genesis. The Egyptians gave to gold, which they considered the perfect metal, the symbol of the circle and to silver, which they considered the next metal to gold in perfection, the symbol of a semicircle. This semicircle eventually became a cresent moon probably due to the similarity between the metal and the shining silvery color of the moon.

It was the Romans who gave us the word *argentum* which is even now the international name for silver. The word silver came to us from the Assyrians.

Since silver, like gold, was held precious and even sacred by the ancients, its use was very limited. The three principal uses were: (1) payment of debts or as gifts, (2) decorations and articles used for religious rites and (3) eating utensils for the noble classes. Its malleability and ductility made it ideal for decorative designs and ornaments. Since the sulfur content of the atmosphere was not as great as it is at the present time, the silver ornamentation kept its lustre. It was relatively easy for the ancients to beat silver and gold into foils that were formed into many exquisite decorative patterns.

The slag dumps in Asia Minor and on the islands in the Aegean Sea indicate that man learned to separate silver from lead as early as 3000 B.C. Gold and silver were extracted from their ores by alloying them with lead and oxidizing the product. Any precious metals present remained in the metallic state unoxidized. This was the foundation of the cupellation process used at the present time. Jeremiah and Ezekiel (about 590 B.C.) refer to "trials by fire" as a means of purification of precious metals from the base metals. There is some evidence that the ancients of 13 B.C. were making use of mercury to extract silver from cloth in which it was interwoven.

Occurrence

The chief silver mineral is the sulfide, argentite, Ag_2S, which is usually associated with other sulfides, such as those of lead and copper. Other silver minerals are cerargyrite (horn silver), $AgCl$; proustite, $3Ag_2S \cdot Ag_2S$; pyrargyrite, $3Ag_2S \cdot Sb_2S_3$; stephanite, $5Ag_2S \cdot$ Sb_2S_3; and native silver. In addition to being present in most lead ores and copper ores, silver is found in the Canadian cobalt arsenide ores and is commonly associated with gold in nature.

Most of the silver is derived as a by-product from ores mined and processed for other metals: lead, copper, cobalt, gold, etc. However, some mines have been and still are operated chiefly for their silver values. A notable example is Silver Isle on the north shore of Lake Superior, a region also noted for deposits of native copper, from which over 1,750,000 oz of native silver were extracted in the 1870's. Others are the Potosi mine in Bolivia, the Real del Monte near Pachuca, Mexico and the La Valenciana-Rayas mine near Guanajuato, Mexico, all of which were discovered over 400 years ago. The Potosi mine, probably the most productive in history, produced more than one billion oz of silver until the veins ran out many years ago; the other two are still producing silver.

Production

The total annual production of silver in the world is over 250,000,000 troy oz, and of this Mexico accounts for some 16%; the United States, 16%; and Canada, 13%, making the total for North America 45% of the world's silver production. Peru contributes another 14%. Other principal silver-producing countries are the USSR, Australia and Germany.

Despite the steady rate of production, the annual Free World consumption in the arts, industry and coinage is almost 500,000,000 oz greater than new production. Coinage requirements of some 375,000,000 oz and industrial use of almost as much account for substantially all of the annual silver consumption. Excluding United States coinage, the annual production deficit of about 175,000,000 oz has been balanced by withdrawals from world stocks, chiefly the United States Treasury. This situation portends increasing strictures on the applications of silver in industry and the arts.

Since more than half the silver produced is a by-product of the extraction of lead and copper, its availability is greatly influenced by the supply and demand situation of these two metals.

Price

Since 1939 the price of silver has been fixed by the United States Treasury; in 1963 it was raised to $1.29/troy oz. However, in July 1967 the ceiling was removed and the price promptly jumped to the world price of about $1.80/oz. The introduction in the past few years of silverless coins by the United States is the chief reason given for the removal of the price ceiling. For example, of the estimated 8.5 billion dimes and quarters in circulation nearly 8.3 billion are silverless. The decreasing use of silver in coinage is expected to make more available for industrial use.

Derivation

Since the concentration of silver in ores is measured in ounces per ton, its recovery depends in most cases on the extraction methods used for other metals being recovered. One method for obtaining the silver is that of amalgamating it with mercury from which the silver is separated by distillation of the mercury, a technique long used on the high-grade silver ores of Mexico. Another is to treat the ground ore, often first roasted with sodium chloride, with sodium cyanide solution to form a stable silver cyanide complex, $[Ag(CN)_2]^-$, from which silver is precipitated by means of metallic zinc. In the processing of lead and copper ores the silver remains with the lead and the copper. The Parkes' process for extracting silver from lead involves the use of zinc added to the molten lead to dissolve the silver. The zinc-silver alloy solidifies on top of the molten lead, is lifted off, and the zinc distilled from it to leave metallic silver. In the case of silver associated with copper, the silver remains in the anode mud in the electrolytic refining of copper and is recovered from the mud by treatment with sulfuric acid to remove the base metals, leaving the silver mixed with any gold present in the original mud. These can be separated by electrolysis.

Refining Methods

The two principal methods of purifying silver are cupellation and electrorefining. As far as the purity of the final silver is concerned, electrorefining has a slight advantage over cupellation.

Cupellation is the process in which silver and lead are melted together and the lead then oxidized and removed from the silver. This process involves much skill since it is necessary to know when the lead has been removed from the silver so that the process can be stopped to prevent volatilization of the silver. The purity of silver achieved by this method is from 99.5 to 99.7%.

Two basic methods of electrorefining make use of the Thum cell and the Moebius cell. Both methods make use of impure anodes of silver bullion, called doré, which contains gold, one or more of the platinum metals, and other impurities. The doré anodes are electrolyzed in a solution of silver and copper nitrates and crystals of commercially pure silver are loosely deposited on cathodes of silver, stainless steel or graphite from which the metal is easily removed. The two cells used differ in design and operating characteristics but both yield silver of desired high purity, 99.9 to 99.98%.

Physical Properties

Silver has a brilliant white metallic luster. It is very ductile and malleable exceeded only by gold and palladium. Pure silver has the highest electrical and thermal conductivity and possesses the lowest contact resistance of all metals. At its melting point, silver has a great capacity to absorb oxygen. In fact, it absorbs about twenty times its own volume of oxygen. However, when the temperature is lowered by 50°C the oxygen absorption drops to only 0.1 times the volume of silver. Therefore, as silver that has been melted in air is cooled; it appears to boil due to the evolution of the large amounts of dissolved oxygen. Whatever oxygen that remains in the silver is detrimental since it forms blisters on the silver piece upon annealing. Its physical properties are listed in Table 1.

Chemical Properties

In dry or moist air, silver is not affected. When contaminants such as ozone or hydrogen sulfide are present, the silver is attacked at room temperature. In fact, practically all sulfides react with silver at room temperature to form the well-known tarnish of silver

TABLE 1. PHYSICAL PROPERTIES

Symbol	Ag
Period	5
Group	1B
Atomic number	47
Atomic weight	107.870
Chemical valence	1
Density, g/cc, 20°C	10.5
1100°C	9.18
Melting point	960.8°C
Boiling point	2210°C
Crystal structure	face-centered cubic
Electrical conductance, microhm-cm	0.616
Heat of fusion kcal/g-atom	2.70
Heat of vaporization, kcal/g-atom, 2210°C	60.7
Specific heat, cal/g/°C	0.056
Electronegativity, Pauling's	1.9
Thermal conductivity, cal/cm²/cm/°C/sec, ambient	0.975
Coefficient of linear thermal expansivity, ambient	$19.7 \times 10^{-6}/°C$
Coefficient of cubical expansion, 0° to 100°C,	$58.31 \times 10^{-6}/°C$
EMF. $Ag^+ - Ag$, volts	0.7991
Atomic diameter, Å	2.884
Ionization potential, electron volts	7.574
Strongest spectral line, Å	3280.68
Terrestrial abundance, g/ton	0.10
Emissivity, 940°C	0.044
Thermal neutron absorption cross section, barns	63 ± 1

sulfide. It is for this reason that silver plate or silver is not used as extensively as in the past. Present day sulfide ladened atmospheres play havoc with any unprotected silver article.

The most useful reaction of silver with another chemical is the reaction with nitric acid to form silver nitrate:

$$Ag + 2HNO_3 \rightarrow AgNO_3 + NO_2 + H_2O$$

This reaction is self-sustaining and the reaction generates its own heat since the formation of silver nitrate is somewhat more exothermic than is the endothermic dissolution of the silver nitrate in water.

Silver dissolves very slowly in hot concentrated sulfuric acid to form silver sulfate. There is also a reaction with silver and hydrochloric acid but the formation of a protective layer of silver chloride prevents completion of the reaction.

Isotopes

There are only two naturally occurring isotopes of silver. Neither of these is radioactive. First, there is silver-107 whose natural abundance comprises 51.82% of the silver as mined. Second is silver-109 whose natural abundance comprises 48.18% of the metal. Silver-107 has an atomic mass of 106.9041 and silver-109 has an atomic mass of 108.9074.

Twenty-three other isotopes of silver have been produced artificially. Radiation emitted by the active silver isotopes are either negative beta particles or positrons. The half-lives of artificial silver isotopes range from 20 seconds for silver-114 to 249 days for silver-110.

Inorganic Compounds

Probably the most important of the inorganic silver salts is silver nitrate. It is the starting point for many processes and reactions for the manufacture of other silver salts. Among the uses of silver nitrate are photography, xerography, electroplating chemicals, battery chemicals, medicine, fungicides and catalysts.

Some of the basic reactions are:

(1) Silver nitrate and hydrochloric acid to form silver chloride used in batteries and photography.

(2) Silver nitrate and sodium cyanide to form silver cyanide used in silver plating.

(3) Silver nitrate and sodium hydroxide to form silver oxide used in batteries and as a catalyst.

Silver chloride is one of the silver salts which demonstrates many interesting properties. It can be melted and cast very much like a metal. Also, similar to a metal, it can be rolled into sheets or coils or even extruded into rods or pipe. From the silver chloride sheet, practically any shape can be punched on a punch press. The only limitation is that this salt reacts with iron, zinc or aluminum.

In recent years, not only silver chloride but also the other silver halides have been used to form some very sophisticated batteries. Also, combinations and modifications of these halides are used in modern photographic film making procedures. About 30% of the United States industrial silver is used for photography.

Organic Compounds

There is not a great variety of silver organic compounds. The most useful of these are the acetate, benzoate, citrate, fulminate, lactate, laurate, myristate, oxalate, palmitate, propionate, salicylate, stearate and tartrate. Most of these silver organic compounds are used in the electroless plating of metals and in printed circuitry. The most common of the silver organic salts is the silver fulminate which is used in primer caps for dynamite and other explosives.

Alloys

Probably the most important metal to be alloyed with silver is copper. Copper-silver alloys have been studied more thoroughly than any other alloy of silver. The eutectic of the silver-copper binary alloy is 71.9 weight % silver and 28.1 weight % copper. This eutectic has a melting point of 779.4°C. Among the many alloys containing or consisting of copper-silver are sterling silver, coin silver and the brazing alloys.

Sterling silver, which contains 92.5 weight % silver and 7.5 weight % copper, is used in flat and hollow tableware as well as in various items of jewelry. Coin silver, containing 90 weight % silver and 10 weight % copper finds use in United States silver coins. The use of coin silver however is being replaced by a copper, copper-nickel sandwich. Electrical contacts also make use of coin silver since it has a greater resistance to pitting and is harder than pure silver.

Silver brazing alloys and silver solders hold their own unique position among the silver alloys. These alloys have a silver content ranging from less than 1 to 100 weight % and have melting points from 304 to 960°C.

Several methods of brazing can be utilized. Torch, furnace, resistance and vacuum are the most commonly used methods. Unless an inert or reducing atmosphere is used in any of these methods, a flux is required to prevent the oxidation of the components of the alloy and the parts being brazed or soldered.

Silver brazing alloys have a corrosion resistance which is comparable to that of brass, copper, nickel-silver and copper-nickel. With some ferrous metals, such as iron-chromium-nickel and monel, silver brazing alloys are cathodic in many corrosive conditions thus effecting quicker corrosion of the metals.

A properly designed joint will have strength equal to or greater than the metals being joined. A temperature increase will greatly reduce the effective strength of any braze.

The use of silver brazing alloys has spread to practically every industry. Some of these are automotive (car radiators), refrigeration (heat exchangers), electricity (steam tubes), electrical (contacts), and musical (instruments). These are just a few of the ever increasing uses for silver brazing alloys.

Batteries

Silver is being used as an expensive but effective means of supplying electrical power. It is used in both "primary" (single use) and "secondary" (rechargeable) batteries. The principal "primary" battery is the silver chloride-magnesium battery. These batteries find use in sonar devices and emergency lighting. They require a saline solution for activation. Several types of batteries make up the group of "secondary" batteries. The two main types presently under intense investigation are the silver-cadmium and the silver-zinc batteries. Both of these types of batteries are of the sealed storage type using an electrolyte of 20 to 40% potassium hydroxide. The nominal open circuit potential of the silver-cadmium battery is 1.40 volts while that of silver-zinc is 1.86 volts.

There has also been much work done on the solid-state silver cell. This cell eliminates the necessity of using a liquid electrolyte. There are however, many problems in this field which need investigation.

The high cost of silver batteries prohibits their more widespread use. However, recent advances have made their use more economic than in the past.

Other Uses of Silver

Silver and silver compounds are used in many industries. Among these is the field of catalysis. Such reactions as the oxidation of ethanol and other unsaturated alcohols use metallic silver as a catalyst, while reactions such as the hydration of ethylene use silver, silver oxide, silver sulfate or silver sulfide as a catalyst. Several processes in the petroleum industry make use of silver nitrate as a catalyst.

Another use of silver is in the mirror industry. A brilliant surface is produced by either chemical or vapor deposition of silver on a surface. Until recently, almost all mirrors were manufactured in this manner. Today however, this silver mirroring has been largely replaced by aluminizing.

Biological and Toxicological Aspects

Silver as such is not extremely toxic, although most of its salts are poisonous due to the anions present. The compounds of silver can be absorbed into the circulatory system and reduced silver can be deposited in various tissues of the body. After a period of time, there results a greyish pigmentation of the skin and mucous membranes. This condition is known as argyria. From two to twenty-five years of exposure to dusts from either silver salts or of the metal usually produces this condition to some degree. The pigmentation is permanent since no known method is available to eliminate the silver.

It is believed that excessive exposure to silver vapor and/or dusts would result in heavy metal poisoning. This statement has not been proved to be true, for even though deposits of silver have been found in the blood vessel walls, kidneys, testes, pituitary, chorioid plexus and mucous membranes of the nose, maxillary antra, trachea and brinchi, death could not be attributed to silver.

The fire hazard for silver in the form of dust is only moderate even when the dust is exposed to flame or chemical oxidizers. However, the same cannot be stated for many of its salts.

Silver has a definite germicidal or oligodynamic effect and effectively kills many lower organisms without being harmful to higher animals. Silver compounds have caustic, astringent and antiseptic effects caused by free silver ions. Silver nitrate in fused form, called lunar caustic, has been used as a cauterizing agent on wounds and sores. Solutions of silver nitrate are effective as an antiseptic on mucous membranes in the mouth and throat, and are widely used as eyedrops for newborn babies. Silver protein preparations, such as "Argyrol," are non-irritating anti-infective agents for the treatment of the mucous membranes of eye, ear, nose, throat and genitourinary tract that are effective against both gram-positive and gram-negative bacteria.

Silver, the metal of royalty, has found a place in the everyday life of man. Its increased use and its constantly dwindling supply make it necessary to search for more efficient and effective methods and processes of finding, extracting, purifying and recovering this most useful metal.

References

1. Addicks, Lawrence, Editor, "Silver in Industry," New York, Reinhold Publishing Corp., 1940.
2. "ASTM Standards," Part 2, Philadelphia, American Society for Testing Materials, 1958.
3. Berkman, Sophia, Morrell, Jacque C., and Egloff, Gustav, "Catalysis," New York, Reinhold Publishing Corp., 1940.
4. Hampel, Clifford A., Editor, "Encyclopedia of Electrochemistry," New York, Reinhold Publishing Corp., 1964.
5. "Handbook of Chemistry and Physics," 46th Ed., Cleveland, Chemical Rubber Co., 1965–1966.
6. Hunter, Donald, "Diseases of Occupation," New York, Little Brown and Co., 1962.
7. Meggers, William F., "Chart of the Atoms," Chicago, W. M. Welch Scientific Co., 1959.

8. Mellor, J. W., "A Comprehensive Treatise on Inorganic and Theoretical Chemistry," Vol. 3, New York, John Wiley and Sons, Inc., 1961.
9. "Metals Handbook," Vol. 1, 8th Ed., Metals Park, Ohio, American Society for Metals, 1961.

GEORGE R. KOTRBA

SODIUM

Some of chemistry's most famous names figure prominently in the discovery of metallic sodium and its early history. In studies of the electrolysis of potassium hydroxide and of sodium hydroxide, Sir Humphry Davy isolated first potassium and then sodium in the fall of 1807 and announced their discovery before the Royal Society in London on November 19 of that year. The next year Gay-Lussac and Thenard obtained the metal by nonelectrolytic means, reducing sodium hydroxide by iron at high temperature. The conflict between electrolytic and chemical reductions, launched at that early date, raged for over a century and was not resolved until the development of the Downs cell in 1921 made sodium the cheapest available non-ferrous metal at a current price of 17 cents per pound.

Incentive for the development of a commercial method for sodium production was provided in 1824 by Oersted's discovery that sodium could be used to prepare pure aluminum by the reduction of aluminum chloride. This was developed into a workable process by Deville and Bunsen in 1854. Deville in the same year described a process for preparing sodium by reducing a mixture of sodium carbonate and lime with charcoal at a temperature above the boiling point of sodium, removing the sodium as a vapor. Although not too efficient, Deville's process remained in use for 30 years. It was displaced by an improved chemical reduction process patented in 1886 by Castner based on the reduction of sodium hydroxide by iron carbide. Castner's process was operated successfully in England for two years until Hall's discovery of the electrolytic route to aluminum abruptly eliminated the major market for sodium. Reluctant to abandon the sodium reduction process for aluminum manufacture, Castner set out to develop a still cheaper route to metallic sodium. By 1891 he had patented a process based on the electrolytic reduction of sodium hydroxide, thus completing the full circle which started in Davy's laboratory in 1807. While this source of sodium failed to challenge seriously Hall's electrolytic process for aluminum production, the Castner cell was operated commercially for thirty years. Annual production of sodium by this method had reached 30 million pounds by 1921 when the Downs cell was introduced.

Sources

Sodium is the sixth most abundant element, occurring naturally in many forms. Its major source is sodium chloride, the major inorganic constituent in sea water, but deposits of crystalline salt in underground salt domes and dry lake beds are a more convenient source. Extensive deposits occur in New York, Michigan, Kansas, Ohio, Texas, Louisiana, Great Britain, France, Germany, India, and China. Evaporation of sea water is practiced commercially in some areas, particularly in hot, arid climates where solar heat is used to vaporize the water from large shallow pans. Sodium also occurs naturally in a wide variety of other minerals. Some of the most common are borax, $Na_2B_4O_7$; cryolite, Na_3AlF_6, Chile saltpeter, $NaNO_3$, and soda ash, Na_2CO_3.

Manufacture

Faraday in 1833 and a succession of later workers had attempted to obtain sodium by the electrolysis of sodium chloride. A number of these early efforts led to issued patents, but none was a commercial success until the Downs cell was introduced in du Pont's Niagara Falls plant about 1921 and patented in 1924. The high current efficiency which is the major advantage of the Downs cell is a result of good mechanical arrangements for the removal of sodium and chlorine and of the simplicity of the electrode reactions:

$$\text{Anode: } Cl^- \rightarrow \tfrac{1}{2}Cl_2 + e^-$$

$$\text{Cathode: } Na^+ + e^- \rightarrow Na$$

In contrast, the anode reaction in a Castner cell is more complex:

$$\text{Anode: } 2OH^- \rightarrow H_2O + \tfrac{1}{2}O_2 + 2e^-$$

The water formed at the anode is not easily removed from the molten NaOH electrolyte and diffuses to the cathode, where it reacts with half of the sodium produced:

$$Na + H_2O \rightarrow NaOH + \tfrac{1}{2}H_2$$

Thus, the overall reaction in a Castner cell is:

$$2NaOH \rightarrow Na + NaOH + \tfrac{1}{2}H_2 + \tfrac{1}{2}O_2,$$

and the maximum current efficiency theoretically is 50%. Moreover, since the sodium hydroxide fed to a Castner cell is made by the electrolysis of aqueous sodium chloride, obtaining sodium by the Castner process requires the passage of three electrons for the same result which requires only one electron in a Downs cell.

The Downs cell is constructed of a steel outer jacket lined on the inside with refractory brick. The graphite anode is centrally located and projects upward from the bottom of the cell. It is surrounded at the top by a nickel collector dome maintained at a slight vacuum in order to remove chlorine vapor as it is formed and conduct it to the chlorine collection and purification system. A cast-steel cathode surrounds the anode with an electrode spacing of about $1\tfrac{1}{2}$ inches. Between the anode and the cathode, an iron gauze diaphragm is suspended which prevents recombination of the sodium and chlorine. An inverted circular trough at the top of the cell suspends this diaphragm and collects the sodium which rises on its side of the diaphragm. A riser pipe attached to this trough conducts the lighter sodium (density $=0.88$ vs 2.1 for the electrolyte) upward, cools it, and allows it to overflow into a collector vessel. The electrolyte is a mixture of sodium chloride and calcium chloride, containing usually 58–59% of the latter in order to depress the melting point to the 575–585°C range which is the operating temperature of the cell. The cell has a voltage drop of about 7 volts and operates with a current efficiency of about 85%. Small amounts of calcium are formed as well as sodium. Most of the calcium precipitates as a sodium-calcium sludge when the sodium is cooled, and is removed by filtration at 100–105°C. Some calcium also collects on the walls of the riser pipe, which must be scraped from time to time to prevent pluggage.

Production and Use

Sodium. Total United States sodium production capacity in 1966 has been estimated at 360 million pounds per year. Usage in 1966 is estimated at 316 million pounds, with an estimated 1970 demand of 384 million pounds. Growth from 1955 to 1965 was 2.7% per year, and is estimated at 5% annually through 1970. Currently 83% of production is used in the synthesis of tetraethyllead and tetramethyllead, 7% in titanium reduction, 2% in sodium peroxide synthesis, and 8% in all other uses. Its uses in titanium reduction and in electrical conductors are expected to grow sharply during the next decade.

Compounds. Sodium chloride is, of course, the most important commercial compound, since most other sodium compounds are prepared from it either directly or indirectly. The other important compounds are listed below, with estimates of 1966 consumption.

Compound	Millions of Pounds
Sodium carbonate	12,700
Sodium hydroxide	12,000
Sodium sulfate	2,800
Sodium-lead alloy	2,600
Sodium tripolyphosphate	1,900
Sodium silicate	1,200
Sodium tetraborate	870
Sodium sulfite	440
Sodium linear dodecylbenzenesulfonate	400
Sodium bicarbonate	330
Sodium chlorate	300
Sodium bichromate	280
Sodium sulfide	65
Sodium thiosulfate	55
Sodium hydrosulfide	54

Isotopes

Na^{23} is the only naturally occurring isotope. Some sodium is converted to Na^{24} in the heat exchangers of nuclear reactors, while Na^{22} finds some use as a radioactive tracer. Half-lives of the known sodium isotopes are summarized below.

Mass Number	Half-Life
20	0.23 second
21	23.0 seconds
22	2.6 years
23	Not radioactive
24	15.0 hours
25	60 seconds

Physical Properties

(Selected from Thomson, G. W., and Garelis, E., "Physical and Thermodynamic Properties of Sodium," in Sittig, M., "Sodium. Its Manufacture, Properties and Uses," New York, Reinhold Publishing Corp., 1956.)

Atomic number, 11

Atomic weight, 22.9898

Melting point, 97.83°C

Boiling point, 882.9°C

Heat of fusion, 622.2 cal/g-atom

Heat of vaporization, 20,629.8 cal/g-atom at boiling point (Complicated by the occurrence of appreciable amounts of dimeric sodium in the vapor phase. See Thomson and Garelis for a complete discussion.)

Heat of dimerization, Na_1 (g) $\rightarrow \frac{1}{2}Na_2$ (g)
$-\Delta D^\circ_o = 9100$ cal/g-atom

Heat capacity at constant pressure,
  Solid at 25°C, 0.292 cal/deg/g
  Liquid at 100°C, 0.330 cal/deg/g
  Liquid at boiling point, 0.331 cal/deg/g

Heat capacity at constant volume
  Liquid at boiling point, 0.300 cal/deg/g

Entropy
  Solid, 12.23 cal/deg/g-atom
  Ideal monatomic gas, 36.715 cal/deg/g-atom

Parachlor, 92.4 for liquid at boiling point

Acoustical velocity, 252,600 cm/sec for liquid at boiling point

Volume change on fusion, 2.5% of solid volume

Compressibility, liquid at boiling point
  Adiabatic, 1.713×10^{-5}/atm
  Isothermal, 1.888×10^{-5}/atm

Density

Temperature, °C	g/cc
0	0.9725
25	0.9674
97.83 (solid)	0.9514
97.83 (liquid)	0.9270
200	0.9037
300	0.8805
400	0.8570
500	0.8331
600	0.8089

Vapor Pressure

Temperature, °C	mm Hg
97.83	9.839×10^{-8}
200	1.481×10^{-4}
300	1.474×10^{-2}
400	3.678×10^{-1}
500	3.958
600	24.58
700	104.4
800	336.7
900	885.2
1000	1988
1100	3943

Viscosity

Temperature, °C	centipoise	centistokes
97.83	0.690	0.744
200	0.450	0.498
300	0.340	0.387
400	0.278	0.325
500	0.239	0.287
600	0.212	0.263
700	0.193	0.246
800	0.179	0.235
900	0.167	0.228

Surface tension

Temperature, °C	dynes/cm
97.83	192.2
200	182.0
300	172.0
400	162.0
500	152.0

Thermal conductivity

Temperature, °C	cal/cm²(sec)(°C/cm)
0	0.324
25	0.314
97.83 (solid)	0.285
97.83 (liquid)	0.205
200	0.193
300	0.182
400	0.170
500	0.159

Electrical resistivity

Temperature, °C	microhm-cm
0	4.477
25	4.985
97.83 (solid)	6.750
97.83 (liquid)	9.600
200	13.125
300	16.575
400	20.025

Neutron absorption cross section, 0.505 barns.

Reactions with Inorganic Compounds

Hydrogen. Although normally a reducing agent in its own right, hydrogen is reduced by sodium to form sodium hydride. The reaction is slow at ordinary temperatures, but proceeds rapidly at 200–300°C, particularly if the sodium is dispersed in an inert hydrocarbon or spread over the surface of an inert solid. Sodium hydride itself can serve as the inert solid, so that the reaction of molten sodium with hydrogen can appear autocatalytic under certain conditions.

Sodium and hydrogen will react with a variety of other substances to give complex metal hydrides. With powdered aluminum, usually in the presence of a trace of aluminum alkyl catalyst, either the hexahydride, Na_3AlH_6, or the tetrahydride, $NaAlH_4$, may be obtained depending on conditions, with higher pressures and a higher aluminum: sodium ratio favoring the tetrahydride. The analogous reaction with metallic boron has not been described, but powdered borosilicate glass will react with sodium and hydrogen at elevated temperatures to give a mixture of sodium borohydride and sodium silicate which can be readily separated. The present commercial synthesis of sodium borohydride, however, involves the reaction of sodium hydride with trimethylborate:

$$4NaH + B(OCH_3)_3 \rightarrow NaBH_4 + 3NaOCH_3$$

Oxygen. Sodium forms four distinct compounds with oxygen: the monoxide, Na_2O; the peroxide, Na_2O_2; the superoxide, NaO_2; and the ozonide, NaO_3. Sodium monoxide is of little commercial significance, except as an intermediate to sodium peroxide, since it is not as cheap as sodium hydroxide. Sodium peroxide is the most important member of the series and is widely used as a strong oxidizing agent, particularly for bleaching textiles and wood pulp. It is prepared by heating sodium at 300–400°C with air or oxygen at elevated pressure. The superoxide is believed to be the initial product formed in the reaction of sodium with oxygen, reacting rapidly with additional sodium to give the monoxide or the peroxide. The superoxide can be isolated in impure form by rapid reaction of oxygen with sodium in liquid ammonia. The pure compound is best prepared by the reaction of the peroxide with oxygen at high temperature and pressure. Sodium ozonide, like the superoxide, is mainly a laboratory curiosity. It can be prepared by the reaction of sodium with ozone.

Water. Sodium reacts vigorously with water at temperatures at least as low as −80°C to give sodium hydroxide and hydrogen. The

reaction is highly exothermic and can generate explosive pressures in a closed system. It is also dangerous in the presence of air, since explosive mixtures of air and hydrogen are formed in the presence of a source of ignition. In an inert atmosphere, with a suitable means for removing the heat of reaction (by refluxing the water, for instance), this reaction can be controlled and is no more dangerous than any other highly exothermic reaction. There are cheaper ways to make sodium hydroxide, however, and the reaction has no practical significance except for the use of sodium wire to remove the last traces of water from organic solvents.

Ammonia. In a clean system, sodium will dissolve in liquid ammonia to give a dark blue solution, and in more concentrated solutions, a bronze-colored phase as well. If metal catalysts such as iron, cobalt, or nickel are present, sodium reacts with ammonia to give sodamide:

$$Na + NH_3 \rightarrow NaNH_2 + \tfrac{1}{2}H_2$$

The reaction may also be carried out at elevated temperatures (300–400°C) in an iron vessel. At still higher temperatures (600°C) in the presence of coke, sodium cyanamide is formed, and can be reacted with additional coke at 800°C to give sodium cyanide in a process developed by Castner:

$$2NaNH_2 + C \rightarrow Na_2CN_2 + 2H_2$$

$$Na_2CN_2 + C \rightarrow 2NaCN$$

This reaction was formerly one of the more important commercial uses for sodium. Substitution of nitrous oxide for coke can lead to the synthesis of sodium azide:

$$2NaNH_2 + N_2O \rightarrow NaN_3 + NaOH + NH_3$$

This reaction can be carried out either in liquid ammonia or at 200°C without a solvent. Sodium will also react with other nitrogen derivatives besides ammonia. With urea, for example, sodium cyanate is formed at 200–300°C:

$$Na + H_2NCONH_2 \rightarrow NaOCN + NH_3 + \tfrac{1}{2}H_2$$

Metal Chlorides. Most metal chlorides are reduced by sodium to the free metal. The reduction of titanium tetrachloride is the most important of these reactions industrially and has been used in place of magnesium reduction in recent installations. The reduction of zirconium tetrachloride is also practiced commercially. Sodium has a number of advantages over magnesium in these reductions. Its greater reducing power permits the use of only a small excess (2%) vs the 15% excess of magnesium needed. This simplifies the purification of the crude titanium or zirconium. The major advantage of sodium, however, is in the physical characteristics of the crude sponge, which is relatively easy to remove from the reactor while magnesium-produced sponge must be removed with the aid of a heavy lathe. Calcium chloride, magnesium chloride, and potassium chloride are only partially reduced by sodium to an equilibrium mixture containing both free metals and both chlorides. In the case of potassium, the equilibrium can be displaced by distillation, since potassium boils more than 100° lower than sodium.

Metal Oxides. A number of metal oxides can be reduced by sodium, although the list is not nearly so extensive as in the case of the metal chlorides. Most of the common structural metals are on the list, and sodium is frequently used for deoxidizing these metals, particularly lead, copper, iron, steel, chromium, and various alloys of these metals. Sodium hydride is also frequently used in a related application, removal of an oxide coating from the metal surface. In this case the descaling bath, as it is called, consists of a 2% solution of sodium hydride in molten sodium hydroxide.

Nonmetals. Sodium reacts with a wide variety of nonmetallic compounds, but except for those cases already described above, the reactions are not commercially significant. Sodium will react with nitrogen only at very high temperatures, particularly if the nitrogen is activated by an electrical discharge. The products of the reaction are sodium azide, NaN_3, and sodium nitride, Na_3N. Perhaps the most interesting exceptions to the reactivity of nonmetals toward sodium are bromine and iodine, which are reported to be unreactive toward sodium at room temperature. It is even claimed that no reaction occurs when sodium and iodine are melted together. The problem is evidently one of kinetics, for the heat of reaction is favorable in the case of all of the halogens.

Metals. Sodium forms alloys with a large number of other metals. Of the common metals, those which do not form alloys include aluminum, boron, silicon, iron and chromium. The most important sodium alloys are those with lead and with mercury. Sodium-lead alloy is widely used in the synthesis of lead alkyls, while sodium amalgam is widely used for the production of sodium hydroxide after its formation by the electrolysis of sodium chloride in the mercury cathode chlor-alkali cell. Other alloys of sodium have minor uses. Sodium-potassium alloy, for instance, is used sometimes as a high-temperature heat exchanger fluid where its lower melting point offers an advantage over the use of sodium in certain applications. Other sodium alloys are used in metallurgy, particularly for the removal of antimony, bismuth, arsenic, copper, and tin from lead.

Reactions with Organic Compounds

Since all reactions of sodium involve the transfer of an electron from the metal to the reacting species, it is surprising to realize that the dominant characteristic of every organic molecule which reacts with sodium is a localized center of high electron density. Typical examples of such nucleophilic centers are the unshared electron pairs of halogen, oxygen, or nitrogen atoms and the pi-electron clouds of olefinic and aromatic hydrocarbons. The compensating centers of low electron density in these molecules are frequently dispersed among several carbon and hydrogen atoms and do not appear to play an important role in initiating the reaction. It is likely that the first step in all reactions is an attack by the nucleophilic center on the positively charged sodium nucleus. This attack is facilitated by the ready polarizability of the sodium electrons, which recede from the point of attack and permit formation of at least a partial ion-pair bond between the sodium cation and the nucleophilic center. Subsequent or perhaps simultaneous electron rearrangements then lead to the final products of the reaction. For heterogeneous reactions, these products must be removed from the sodium surface before further reaction can occur, and this removal frequently limits the overall

657

reaction rate. Thus, choice of a solvent is frequently all-important in organosodium chemistry. The most commonly chosen solvents are paraffins, aromatics, and ethers, particularly the more polar ethers such as tetrahydrofuran, dimethyl ether, and the dimethyl ether of diethylene glycol. The ethers are frequently the only solvents in which the products of a sodium reaction are soluble. Another common solvent choice is liquid ammonia, which dissolves sodium and thus permits a homogeneous reaction so that product removal rate is not a key consideration. For heterogeneous reactions, the state of subdivision of the sodium frequently determines the reaction rate, and the reactions are often accelerated several thousand-fold through the use of sodium dispersions or solid carriers having a high surface area.

The most important industrial reaction of sodium is the manufacture of the gasoline antiknock compounds, tetraethyllead and tetramethyllead, by the reaction of ethyl chloride or methyl chloride with sodium-lead alloy:

$$4C_2H_5Cl + 4NaPb \rightarrow (C_2H_5)_4Pb$$
$$+3Pb + 4NaCl$$

An alloy containing about 10% sodium by weight is used, and the reaction is carried out without solvent at 60–70°C under modest pressure to contain the ethyl chloride, which is used in excess and flashed off at the end of the reaction. Tetraethyllead is recovered from the reaction mass by steam distillation and the by-product lead is resmelted and converted to more alloy.

Sodium will displace hydrogen from a wide variety of organic compounds, as illustrated below with an alcohol:

$$ROH + Na \rightarrow RO^- Na^+ + \tfrac{1}{2}H_2$$

With alcohols, the reaction rate decreases as the chain length increases, and is slower with secondary and especially tertiary alcohols than with primary alcohols. Other compounds having labile hydrogens also undergo this reaction, such as nitroalkanes, nitriles, esters, aldehydes, and ketones. In these cases, it is the hydrogen in the position adjacent to the unsaturated group which is displaced, leading to a resonance-stabilized carbanion, as illustrated below with acetophenone:

$$C_6H_5COCH_3 + Na \rightarrow$$
$$\left[C_6H_5-\underset{\underset{O^-}{|}}{C}=CH_2 \leftrightarrow C_6H_5-\underset{\underset{O}{\|}}{C}-CH_2{}^- \right] Na^+$$
$$+ \tfrac{1}{2}H_2$$

In most cases, further reaction of the carbanion takes place. With esters, for instance, the carbanion can displace an alkoxide anion from a second ester molecule, as in the familiar Claisen condensation:

$$Na^+{}^-CH_2\overset{\overset{O}{\|}}{C}-OEt + CH_3\overset{\overset{O}{\|}}{C}-OEt$$
$$\rightarrow CHC_3-CH_2-\overset{\overset{O}{\|}}{C}-OEt + Na^+{}^-OEt$$
$$\underset{\downarrow}{}$$
$$\underset{\underset{CH_3\overset{\overset{O^-}{|}}{C}=CH-\overset{\overset{O}{\|}}{C}-OEt + EtOH}{}}{Na^+O^-}$$

Sodium will also displace hydrogen from acetylene, leading to either monosodium acetylide. $HC\equiv C^-Na^+$, or disodium acetylide, Na^+ $^-C\equiv C^-$ Na^+, depending upon the stoichiometry and the temperature employed. This reaction is useful in the preparation of substituted acetylene derivatives, via treatment with carbon dioxide to give propiolic acid, $HC\equiv C-COOH$, or acetylenediacarboxylic acid, $HOOC-C\equiv C-COOH$, or by reaction with an alkyl halide to give an alkylacetylene derivative, $RC\equiv CH$ or $RC\equiv CR$. Sodium will also displace hydrogen from a few aromatic compounds such as fluorene, indene, cyclopentadiene, and triphenylmethane. These are about the least acidic compounds with which sodium reacts, and elevated temperatures are required.

Displacement of a halogen by sodium is also a common reaction. One of the most familiar examples is the Wurtz reaction:

$$2RX + 2Na \rightarrow R\text{-}R + 2NaX$$

There is some dispute about whether this is an ionic or a free-radical reaction, but the most common opinion is that an intermediate organo-sodium compound, $R^- \ Na^+$, is formed and reacts with a second molecule of RX. The synthesis of phenylsodium is a more clear-cut example of halogen displacement:

$$C_6H_5Cl + 2Na \rightarrow C_6H_5^- \ Na^+ + NaCl$$

This reaction proceeds readily at room temperature or slightly above if chlorobenzene is dropped slowly into a dispersion of sodium in toluene. If the toluene solution of phenylsodium is then heated, benzylsodium can be formed by an acid-base interchange:

$$C_6H_5^- Na^+ + C_6H_5 - CH_3 \rightarrow C_6H_6$$
$$+ \ C_6H_5\text{-}CH_2^- \ Na^+$$

Another related reaction is the cleavage of diaryl ethers by sodium:

$$Ar\text{-}O\text{-}Ar + 2Na \rightarrow Ar^- Na^+ + Ar\text{-}O^- Na^+$$

This reaction is not usually as straightforward as shown in the above equation. In many cases, the isolation of coupling products (Ar-Ar) suggests that a free-radical intermediate is involved:

$$Ar\text{-}O\text{-}Ar + Na \rightarrow Ar\text{-}O^- Na^+ + Ar\cdot \rightarrow \tfrac{1}{2}Ar\text{-}Ar$$

Aliphatic ethers are not attacked by sodium except at very high temperatures. They can be cleaved indirectly, however, as in the synthesis of the Alfin catalyst from the reaction of amyl chloride and sodium in diisopropyl ether:

$$C_5H_{11}Cl + 2Na \rightarrow C_5H_{11}^- Na^+ + NaCl$$

$$C_5H_{11}^- Na^+ + (CH_3)_2CHOCH(CH_3)_2 \rightarrow$$
$$C_5H_{12} + (CH_3)_2CHO^- Na^+ + CH_3CH{=}CH_2$$

$$CH_3CH = CH_2 + C_5H_{11}^- Na^+ \rightarrow$$
$$Na^+ \ ^-CH_2CH = CH_2 + C_5H_{12}$$

Thus the amylsodium produced initially cleaves the diisopropyl ether to sodium isopropoxide plus propylene, which is trans-metallated by amylsodium to give allylsodium. The true catalyst, useful in the polymerization of butadiene and isoprene to 1,4-polymers, is a ternary salt mixture of allylsodium, sodium isopropoxide, and sodium chloride; all three components are needed for an effective catalyst.

In the presence of the polar type of ether solvents, sodium will add to polynuclear aromatic hydrocarbons or to conjugated dienes to give an intensely colored, highly paramagnetic solution which is best described as a charged free radical:

Formation of these charged free radicals is reversible; under some conditions these solutions can serve as a form of "soluble sodium." They can also be used as polymerization catalysts. This is the basis of the polymerization of butadiene to "Buna" rubber. With most electrophilic reagents, however, the initial attack at the ionic center of the sodium adduct reduces its stability and leads to a disproportionation reaction, the net result of which is regeneration of a portion of the original aromatic hydrocarbon and formation of a disubstituted product. With naphthalene, for instance, a mixture of 1,4- and 1,2-dihydronaphthalenedicarboxylic acid is formed when the sodium adduct is treated with carbon dioxide:

Still more complex disproportion-type reactions are possible. With fluorene, for instance, the sodium adduct is unstable and reacts with itself in an intramolecular acid-base interchange to give 9-fluorenylsodium:

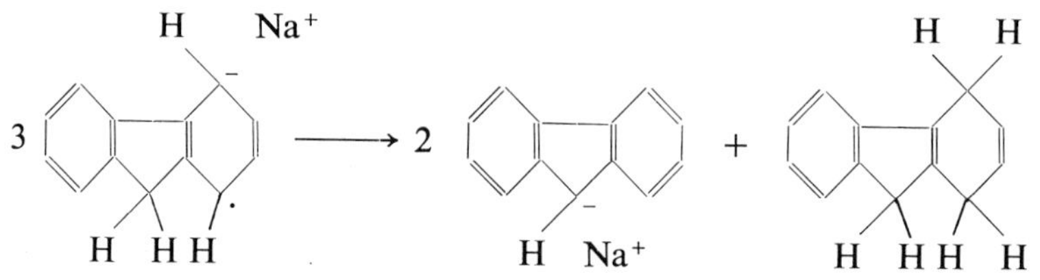

Similarly, diphenylmethane, which does not form a sodium adduct, is converted to diphenylmethylsodium by reaction with sodium in the presence of naphthalene:

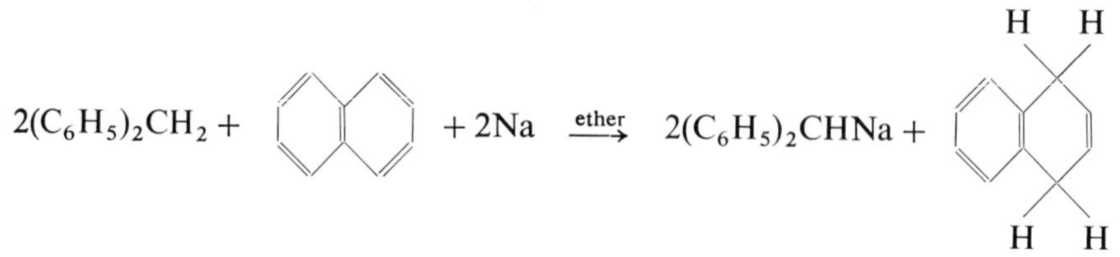

The reduction of fatty acid esters to fatty alcohols by reaction with sodium and a source of hydrogen was formerly of considerable importance, but has been largely replaced by catalytic hydrogenation in recent years. Ethanol was used as a source of hydrogen in the reaction originally described by Bouveault and Blanc, but secondary alcohols are now preferred in order to avoid wasting sodium through direct reaction with the hydrogen source. The over-all equation is shown below:

$$RCH_2COOR' + 4Na + 2R''OH \rightarrow$$
$$RCH_2CH_2ONa + R'ONa + 2R''ONa$$

The initial step is the reaction of sodium with the carbonyl group of the ester to give a sodium ketyl. If no hydrogen source is present, two sodium ketyl molecules can dimerize to give an acyloin:

$$RCH_2COOR' + Na \rightarrow RCH_2 - \overset{\overset{\displaystyle O^-Na^+}{|}}{\underset{\displaystyle \cdot}{C}} - OR' \rightarrow$$

$$Na^+ {}^-OR' + \tfrac{1}{2}RCH_2 - \overset{\overset{\displaystyle O}{\|}}{C} - \overset{\overset{\displaystyle O}{\|}}{C} - CH_2R$$

Nonchemical Applications

Uses which depend upon sodium's physical rather than its chemical properties are based upon its excellent thermal and electrical conductivity. Thus sodium is an important high-temperature heat exchange medium and is finding increasing usage as an electrical conductor. In addition to its high thermal conductivity, sodium possesses a number of other properties which make it an outstanding heat exchange fluid. These include a large liquid range (98–883°C), low viscosity, excellent thermal stability, noncorrosivity toward steel, and a neutron absorption cross section, 0.505 barns, which is acceptably low for use in nuclear power plants. After two decades of experimentation with various types of nuclear installations, sodium-cooled reactors appear to be gaining rapidly in popularity. Some estimates predict that several hundred million pounds of sodium will be in use in this application by the end of this century. A number of other more prosaic heat-transfer uses consume modest amounts of sodium. Many heavy-duty internal combustion engines have sodium-cooled valves. These are merely hollow valves partially filled with sodium, which splashes back and forth in order to conduct heat more rapidly from the head to the stem. A related use is in shale-oil retorting, where a hollow, sodium-filled plow agitator conducts heat rapidly away from the tip of the plow and maintains it at a temperature of 1000°F even though it is exposed to a temperature of 2200°F. Sodium is also used in place of water as a coolant in cores used for the die-casting of magnesium in order to avoid the hazard of accidental contact of water with molten magnesium.

As an electrical conductor, sodium is surpassed only by silver, copper, aluminum, and gold. Because of its lower density and lower cost, sodium is preferred over each of these conductors on a cost-effectiveness basis and would be used extensively except for the hazards associated with its high chemical reactivity. Recently an attempt has been made to circumvent these hazards through encapsulation of sodium in polyethylene tubing. Such conductors are now being field-tested and show promising results. They are four times as flexible as copper, and maintain flexibility even down to $-40°C$. They can also withstand short circuits better because of sodium's low melting point; with conventional conductors it is the insulation which melts first. Initial application for sodium cables is expected to be in underground residential distribution lines, where a service life of 40 years has been estimated. This use for sodium is expected to grow rapidly, particularly because of the present shortage of copper. Encapsulation of sodium in rigid steel containers has been practiced for years. These heavy-duty conductors give excellent service in high-amperage direct current bus bars. The sodium vapor lamp is another application of sodium as an electrical conductor. The yellow light from these lamps is the familiar "D" line of the sodium spectrum. It is not aesthetically pleasing, but is in a wave-length range to which the eye is extremely sensitive, so that it is particularly effective for highway lighting.

Safe-Handling Techniques

Sodium is available commercially in bricks, drums and tank cars from Du Pont, Ethyl Corporation, and U.S. Industrial Chemicals Company. Full details on safe handling techniques are available in brochures supplied by these manufacturers. These should be consulted by anyone planning to work with sodium. Key precautions in working with sodium are maintaining an inert atmosphere and avoiding contact with water and other substances with which sodium reacts readily. Nitrogen, or occasionally helium or argon,

is used as an inert blanket to exclude air from vessels and lines in sodium service. Steam heat is never used with sodium, and water is never used as a coolant. Electric heating is frequently used, and oil or "Dowtherm" is used in heat exchangers as both a heating and cooling medium. These may be heated with steam or cooled with water in secondary exchangers. Dry powder fire extinguishers should be used on sodium fires; other common fire-fighting chemicals such as carbon dioxide, carbon tetrachloride, and water react with sodium. Contact with the skin and eyes should be avoided through the use of goggles (or preferably face shields) and protective clothing. Gloves, long-sleeved shirts, and a rubber apron are usually adequate when handling small quantities of sodium in the laboratory. For larger scale operation more elaborate haberdashery is available. Contact with the skin and eyes can lead to both thermal burns and chemical burns resulting from the conversion of sodium into strong caustic by reaction with traces of moisture on the skin. Particles of sodium should be removed from the skin quickly and the affected area washed thoroughly with water. This is the only exception to the rule that contact between sodium and water should be avoided.

Sodium is usually transferred from one vessel to another on a commercial scale in the liquid form. This requires insulated lines to maintain the temperature above its melting point of 98°C. Gravity flow may be used, or a pressure differential may be maintained by applying a vacuum at one end of the line or nitrogen pressure at the other. The use of vacuum is preferred since this avoids exposing sodium to the atmosphere in the event of a leaking joint. With a vacuum system, a nitrogen blanket is still required on the vessel from which sodium is flowing, so that air will not be sucked in to fill the depleted volume. A mechanical vacuum pump should be used instead of a water or steam ejector in order to avoid the accidental introduction of water. A gas-sealed centrifugal pump with a vertical shaft may be used to transfer sodium in a more conventional manner; other common types of pumps are not as satisfactory because of leaking seals. The high electrical conductivity of sodium has permitted the development of specialized induction-type pumps with no moving parts and no seals of any kind. These are commonly used in high-temperature applications.

At temperatures below its melting point, sodium in brick form may be introduced into a reaction vessel through the use of a nitrogen-purged charging port. At ambient temperatures sodium may also be transferred conveniently in the form of a dispersion in an inert hydrocarbon or ether solvent. These dispersions, with particles as small as one micron, are easily prepared by stirring molten sodium at high speed (10–20,000 rpm in a laboratory preparation; lower speeds in larger equipment) and then allowing the mixture to cool. A small amount of a surface-active agent is usually added, typically 0.5–1.0% of oleic acid. Such dispersions are easily handled and have the added advantage of increasing the reactivity of the sodium by several orders of magnitude because of the tremendous increase in surface area. Molten sodium may also be distributed over the surface of an inert solid carrier such as alumina, charcoal, sodium carbonate, or sodium chloride to give highly reactive, free-flowing powders of large surface area. These powders can be transferred at ambient temperature in inert-gas pneumatic systems; they are highly effective in fluidized-bed reactor systems, particularly those in which the solid carrier is one of the products of the sodium reaction, as in the reduction of a metal chloride with sodium using sodium chloride as an inert carrier.

Biological and Biochemical Aspects

Sodium ion is essential to the higher animals which regulate the composition of their body fluids and it is the principal cation of their extracellular fluids. In contrast to potassium ion which is essential for all or nearly all forms of life, sodium ion is dispensable for many bacteria and most plants. However, it is found in these organisms.

The difference in the ratios of Na/K in intracellular fluids and in extracellular fluids is responsible for ion transport across membranes, membrane potentials, regulation of osmotic pressure within the cell, and nerve impulse conduction, among other functions which are classed as electrophysiological.

Since there is no reserve store of sodium ion in the animal body, losses above the amount of intake come from the functional supply of cells and tissues. This depletion results in serious symptoms and even death. Thus, the importance of NaCl in nutrition has been recognized since prehistoric times. Human populations living on grains, vegetables and fruits experience a salt hunger that causes them to go to great lengths to obtain salt. The same hunger exists among herbivorous animals. On the other hand, men and animals living on meat, milk and other foods are provided with sodium salts in their diets and need little additional salt for subsistence.

Sodium deficiency may result from extreme excretion of sodium ion by sweating and other loss of body fluids. It is evidenced by thirst, anorexia and nausea. Other results of severe sodium loss are lassitude, muscle cramps and mental disturbances. Replacement of the lost salt corrects the abnormalities.

References

General
1. Sitting, M., "Sodium. Its Manufacture, Properties and Uses," New York, Reinhold Publishing Corp., 1956.

History
2. Perkins, M., *Trans. Faraday Soc.*, **3**, 205–19 (1908).
3. Batsford, H. E., *Chem. Met. Eng.*, **26**, 888–94, 932–5 (1922).
4. Hampel, C. A., Editor, "Encyclopedia of Electrochemistry," biographies of Castner, Davy, Downs, Oersted; New York, Reinhold Publishing Corp., 1964.

Sodium in Liquid Ammonia
5. Audrieth, L. M., and Kleinberg, J., "Non-Aqueous Solvents," New York, John Wiley and Sons, 1953.

Handling Properties and Uses
6. Jackson, C. B., "Liquid Metals Handbook. Sodium-NaK Supplement," Washington, D.C., U.S. Govt. Printing Office, 1955.
7. Lyon, R. N., Editor, "Liquid Metals Handbook," Navexos P-733, Washington, D.C., U.S. Government Printing Office, 1952.
8. "Handling and Uses of the Alkali Metals," Advances in Chemistry Series No. 19, Washington, D.C., American Chemical Society, 1957.

Chemistry
9. Bergstrom, F. W., and Fernelius, W. C., *Chem. Rev.*, **12**, 43–179 (1933).

10. Morton, A. A., "Solid Organoalkali Metal Reagents," New York, Gordon and Breach, 1964.
11. Watt, G. W., *Chem. Rev.*, **46**, 289–379 (1950).
12. Wooster, C. B., *Chem. Rev.*, **11**, 1–92 (1932).

KENNETH L. LINDSAY

STRONTIUM

Strontium, symbol Sr, atomic number 38, atomic weight 87.62, is one of the alkaline earth elements located in Group IIA of the Periodic Table between calcium and barium. Its physical and chemical properties are intermediate between those of calcium and barium.

Strontium was first detected by Crawford of Edinburgh in 1790, although some sources credit its discovery to William Cruikshank, also a Scotsman, in 1787. Both men worked with strontianite, $SrCO_3$, found at Strontian, Scotland, from which the element's name is derived. The metallic element was isolated by Davy in 1808 by the electrolysis of a mixture of moist strontium hydroxide or chloride with mercuric oxide, using a mercury cathode and power from the giant Wollaston battery.

Strontium exists in nature as a mixture of four stable isotopes: Sr^{88} (82.74%), Sr^{86} (9.75%), Sr^{87} (6.96%) and Sr^{84} (0.55%). Several artificial radioactive isotopes have been prepared, of which Sr^{90} has received the most attention because of its presence in radioactive fallout.

Occurrence

Strontium comprises about 0.0002% of igneous rocks and about 0.02 to 0.03% of the earth's crust. It is distributed in small quantities in many rocks and soils and is present to a minor extent in bones where it displaces small amounts of calcium.

There are two principal ores: celestite, $SrSO_4$, and strontianite, $SrCO_3$, the former the more plentiful. Strontium minerals are found in Arkansas, Arizona, California (e.g., Strontium Hills), New York and West Virginia in the United States. The United Kingdom is the world's largest producer and Germany, Italy and Mexico are other major sources.

Derivation

Celestite, the $SrSO_4$ mineral, is the chief source of strontium compounds made in the United States. It is usually first converted to the carbonate by treatment with sodium carbonate or to the sulfide by reduction with coke at high temperatures. The carbonate and the sulfide are used to produce other strontium compounds.

Metallic strontium is derived by several methods. The electrolysis of fused KCl and $SrCl_2$ by a process in which a cooled iron rod cathode touching the surface of the fused salt bath is slowly raised as the strontium metal collects on it results in the formation of a stick of strontium. The oxide may be reduced with aluminum by heating a mixture of SrO and Al in a vacuum at high temperature so that the strontium distills out of the reaction zone. High-purity metal can also be made by heating strontium hydride in a vacuum at 1000C°, and by distilling the mercury from a strontium amalgam.

Elemental strontium is not produced commercially in more than small quantities because calcium and barium are more abundant and serve all the purposes for which metallic strontium might be applied.

Physical Properties

Strontium is a hard silver-white metal somewhat softer than calcium, and is malleable, ductile, machinable and capable of being drawn into wire. Its melting point, 770°C, is intermediate between those of calcium, 851°C, and barium, 710°C. Similarly, its density of 2.6 g/cc falls between those of calcium, 1.54, and barium, 3.5.

Physical property values are given in Table 1.

TABLE 1. PHYSICAL PROPERTIES OF STRONTIUM

Symbol	Sr
Atomic number	38
Atomic weight	87.62
Atomic volume, cc/g-atom	34.5
Atomic radius, Å	2.13
Ionic radius, Å	1.13
Electron configuration	2–8–18–8–2
Electron distribution	$1s^2$, $2s^2$, $2p^6$, $3s^2$, $3p^6$, $3d^{10}$, $4s^2$, $4p^6$, $5s^2$
Density, g/cc, 20°C	2.6

TABLE 1—*continued*

Melting point, °C	770
Boiling point, °C	1380
Latent heat of fusion, cal/g	25
Latent heat of vaporization, cal/g, 1380°C	447
Specific heat, cal/g/°C, 20°C	0.176
Vapor pressure, atm, 877°C	0.01
1081°C	0.1
1279°C	0.5
1380°C	1.0
Electrical resistivity, microhm-cm, 20°C	23
Temperature coefficient of resistivity	5.0×10^{-3}
Ionization potential (gaseous element), volts	
1st electron	5.69
2nd electron	10.98
Surface tension, dyne/cm	165
Thermal neutron absorption cross section, barns	1.21

Chemical Properties

The chemistry of strontium closely parallels that of calcium. Strontium is a reactive metal and in the air quickly forms an oxide coating which is somewhat protective at room temperature. Finely divided strontium is pyrophoric. It forms only divalent compounds. Its base-forming characteristics are less pronounced than those of barium and greater than those of calcium. An active reducing agent, strontium reacts vigorously with water to liberate hydrogen and form $Sr(OH)_2$ and with acids to form hydrogen and the strontium salt of the acid. At elevated temperatures it reduces the halides and oxides of many metals to produce the corresponding metal.

Noted for the brilliant crimson color which its volatile compounds impart to flames, the element burns brightly when heated in air, oxygen, chlorine, bromine gas and sulfur. It does not form the nitride unless heated above about 380°C in nitrogen. When it reacts with oxygen both the oxide, SrO, and the peroxide, SrO_2, may be formed.

Chemical Compounds and Their Uses

Strontium forms compounds that are the counterparts of the corresponding calcium compounds. For example, the sulfide, chloride, bromide, iodide, nitrate, etc. are soluble, while the carbonate, fluoride, sulfate, oxalate and phosphate are insoluble. With respect to solubility of compounds, one major difference occurs with $Sr(OH)_2$ which is quite soluble in hot water, 22 g/100 g H_2O at 100°C, while $Ca(OH)_2$ is not.

Two oxides exist: SrO, which resembles CaO and is made by thermal decomposition of the hydroxide, carbonate or nitrate, and the peroxide, SrO_2, formed by the addition of an alkali to an aqueous solution of a strontium salt containing hydrogen peroxide. The latter is a bleaching agent.

Strontium hydroxide, $Sr(OH)_2$, can be prepared by the action of water on SrO, and by heating SrS or $SrCO_3$ in steam at 500–600°C. It can be used in the extraction of sugar from beet sugar molasses where it combines with sugar to form a soluble saccharide which is separated and reconverted to sugar by reaction of CO_2 on the saccharide. The process has been, and may still be, used in Europe but has never found more than minor application in the United States. Strontium hydroxide also reacts with organic acids to yield lubricant soaps and greases that are structurally stable and which resist quite well oxidation and thermal breakdown over wide ranges of temperature in addition to being resistant to disintegration by water and leaching by hydrocarbons.

Strontium nitrate, $Sr(NO_3)_2$, is used in flares, pyrotechnic devices and tracer bullets because of the intense red color it imparts to compositions used for such purposes. It is made by the action of nitric acid on $SrCO_3$. Strontium chlorate, $Sr(ClO_3)_2$, is similarly used.

The preparation of fireworks, flares, etc. represents the largest application of strontium compounds in this country.

Strontium sulfide, SrS, is prepared by the carbon reduction of the sulfate in a furnace or by heating $SrCO_3$ with hydrogen sulfide. It has luminescent properties and is used in some luminous paints; it also is a depilatory.

Strontium is one of the small group of elements (others are the alkali metals, calcium and barium) which form an ionic hydride that is a stable crystalline compound. SrH_2 has a density of 3.27 g/cc (higher than that of the metal) and melts at 650°C. It is made by heating elemental strontium or strontium amalgam in a hydrogen atmosphere, or by the reduction of SrO with zinc in a hydrogen atmosphere. The hydride is a strong reducing agent and reacts readily with water and acids to liberate hydrogen.

Strontium nitride, Sr_3N_2, forms when strontium or strontium amalgam is heated in a stream of nitrogen. It is decomposed by water to form ammonia.

Strontium carbide, SrC_2, produced by the reaction of carbon on strontium carbonate in an electric furnace, is similar to calcium carbide and yields acetylene when exposed to water.

Other compounds are made by methods used to make to corresponding calcium compounds.

Applications

The possible applications of elemental strontium are similar to those of calcium and barium, and since strontium offers no advantage over calcium, its production and use are very minor. A small amount is used in the composition of special "getters" for vacuum tubes. The price of strontium metal is in the neighborhood of $6–8/lb.

Biological and Toxicological Aspects

Strontium resembles calcium in its metabolism and behavior in the body. It is similar to calcium also in its low toxicity level, as contrasted with the poisonous nature of soluble barium compounds.

However, the artificial isotopes Sr^{89} and Sr^{90} are extremely hazardous. Sr^{89}, half-life 50 days, emits beta radiation of 1.5 MeV. Sr^{90}, the more dangerous because of its half-life of 28 years, emits beta particles of 0.61 MeV. These isotopes are among the most hazardous handled in laboratory and plant operations and extreme care must be used to prevent exposure to them.

The chief problem with Sr^{89} and more especially with Sr^{90} is that they seek out and are deposited in bones where, like natural strontium (which does not contain either Sr^{89} or Sr^{90}), they replace calcium in the normal bone structure. In this location they act as a source of internal radiation that damages bone marrow and blood-forming organs and induces cancer.

Much work has been conducted on the presence of and hazard caused by fallout of Sr^{90} from nuclear explosions, mainly those occurring in the atmosphere. The Sr^{90} deposited on grass and fodder eaten by cows enters the human body through the milk from cows and deposited in the bones and teeth, particularly those of children. It appears possible to remove most of this damaging isotope from milk by treatment with a vermiculite adsorbent.

The bromide and chloride of strontium are used in medicine for certain nervous disorders, and a few other strontium compounds are used for the treatment of rheumatism and gout.

There appears to be no specific value of strontium in plant and animal life such as is associated with other trace elements.

References

"Strontium Chemicals," *Chem. Met. Eng.*, **53**, No. 1, 152–155 (Jan. 1946).

Mellor, J. W., "A Comprehensive Treatise on Inorganic and Theoretical Chemistry," Vol. 3, New York, Longmans, Green & Co., Inc. 1946.

Guntz, A., *Compt rend.*, **143**, 339 (1906).

Ephraim, F., "Inorganic Chemistry," 3rd Ed., P. C. Thorne and A. M. Ward, Editors, London, Gurney and Jackson, 1939.

"Minerals Yearbook," Washington, D.C., U.S. Bureau of Mines, published annually.

Mantell, C. L., "Rare Metals Handbook," 2nd Edition, C. A. Hampel, Editor, p. 28, New York, Reinhold Publishing Corp., 1961.

CLIFFORD A. HAMPEL

SULFUR

Sulfur, atomic number 16, atomic weight 32.064, is in Group VIA of the Periodic Table below oxygen and above selenium, tellurium and polonium. It is one of the few elements found in the earth's crust in elemental form.

Discovery and History

The ancients recognized elemental sulfur because of its color, its combustibility, and the penetrating odor of its combustion products. Very early it was used in religious ceremonies, in witchcraft, and in medicine. The early literature indicates that sulfur was employed as a bleaching agent, in pigments and cosmetics, and in the arts of war.

Sulfur figured prominently in theories developed by alchemists. The phlogiston theory proposed by early chemists regarded sulfur both as an element and a spirit. In 1772 Lavoisier proved that sulfur was an element and a new era in the chemistry of sulfur began.

Occurrence

Sulfur has been detected in certain stars, in novae, in cosmic clouds, and in the sun. It is widely distributed in nature. It is present in the earths' crust, the ocean, the meteorites that come from cosmic space, sometimes in the atmosphere, and in practically all animal and plant life. It is estimated that sulfur is the ninth most abundant element in the universe, one atom out of 20,000 to 30,000 being sulfur.

Meteorites on the average contain about 2% sulfur in the form of troilite. Average sulfur contents calculated from analyses of many samples from outcrops, mines, and drill holes are: igneous rock 0.052%, limestone 0.11%, sandstone and shale 0.27%. The much less abundant evaporite deposits average about 10% sulfur.

It is believed that the bulk of the earth's sulfur supply is iron sulfides lying deep in the mantle. In the crust it occurs as elemental sulfur, sulfides, and sulfates. The most important sulfides are iron pyrite, FeS_2; chalcopyrite, $CuFeS_2$; sphalerite, ZnS; and galena, PbS. The principal naturally occurring sulfates are anhydrite, $CaSO_4$; gypsum, $CaSO_4.2H_2O$; and kieserite, $MgSO_4.H_2O$. Significant quantities of free and combined sulfur are found in coal and petroleum. Sulfates are found in the ocean, and various sulfates and hydrogen sulfide occur in many mineral waters. Sulfur is not plentiful in the atmosphere but sulfur dioxide and other sulfur gases may be detected in the atmosphere of many urban areas and industrialized districts and near volcanoes.

The sulfur cycle in nature is a complex one. In accumulating sediments, in soil and subsoil above the water table, in surface waters, and in the sea, the sulfur cycle is dominated by the biological synthesis and destruction of sulfur-containing amino acids and by the activities of the sulfate-reducing and the sulfur-oxidizing and sulfide-oxidizing bacteria. Organic sulfur in vegetable matter averages 0.44%, in animal bodies 1.60%, and in fossil fuels probably about 2% but with wide variations. The largest deposits of elemental sulfur were formed by reduction (probably biological) of sedimentary sulfate. Many smaller deposits have been formed from volcanic gases; and small amounts of elemental sulfur are commonly found in many presently-forming sediments.

The cycle of sulfur is linked with that of iron in two places. The sulfur is ultimately derived from volcanic gases and from weathering of metallic sulfides. The most abundant sulfides are pyrite, FeS_2; pyrrhotite, iron-deficient FeS; chalcopyrite, $CuFeS_2$; pentlandite, $(Fe, Ni, Co)_9S_8$; and bornite, Cu_5FeS_4, all of which contain iron. Iron is also present in the common ore mineral sphalerite, $(Fe, Zn)S$. The weathering of these iron-containing sulfides in igneous rocks yields dissolved sulfates plus solid ferric oxide. This constitutes the first link. In the biological cycle, iron removes sulfide as FeS and FeS_2, from which sulfate may be recovered by later weathering. This is the second link.

Derivation

Industry uses sulfur in several forms and from many sources. These sources include: elemental sulfur, iron pyrites, gypsum, and by-product sulfur from the processing of sulfide ores, coal, petroleum, and natural gas. Most important to industry however, are the sources and supplies of elemental sulfur (both native and by-product) and iron pyrites.

Elemental sulfur is recovered from many types of ore deposits widely distributed throughout the world. The most important deposits are in the caprock of salt domes located in Louisiana, Texas, and Mexico and are mined by the Frasch process. In this process, hot water under pressure is pumped into the underground deposits and the liquid sulfur (m.p. about 116°C) is brought to the surface. See Fig. 1. Important also are the sulfur deposits in Sicily, Poland, Russia, South America, and Japan. Conventional mining methods are used. The ore is often concentrated by flotation. Sulfur is recovered by various processes, chiefly distillation and autoclaving.

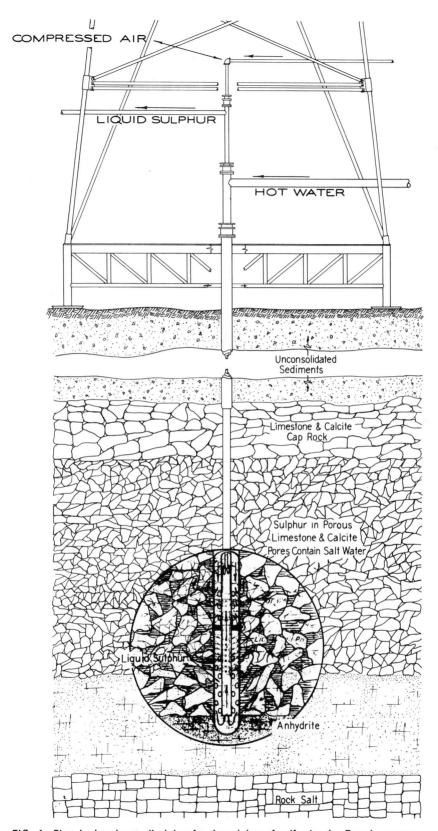

COMPRESSED AIR

LIQUID SULPHUR

HOT WATER

Unconsolidated
Sediments

Limestone & Calcite
Cap Rock

Sulphur in Porous
Limestone & Calcite
Pores Contain Salt Water

Liquid Sulphur

Anhydrite

Rock Salt

FIG. 1. Sketch showing well piping for the mining of sulfur by the Frasch process.

TABLE 1. NUCLEAR AND ATOMIC PROPERTIES

Atomic Number	Neutron Number	Mass Number	Atomic Mass	% Natural Abundance	Half-life	Mode of Decay
16	15	31	30.988865	—	2.4 sec	4.5 MeV β^+
	16	32	31.9822377	95.018	—	—
	17	33	32.9819473	0.750	—	—
	18	34	33.9787664	4.215	—	—
	19	35	34.980354	—	87 days	0.167 MeV β^-
	20	36	35.978525	0.017	—	—
	21	37	36.98212	—	5.0 min	1.6 MeV β^- (90%) 4.3 MeV β^- (10%) 2.6 MeV γ
	22	38	—	—	172 min	1.1 MeV β^- (95%) 3.0 MeV β^- (5%) 1.88 MeV γ

Atomic weight 32.064 ± 0.003
Electronic configuration $1s^2, 2s^2, 2p^6, 3s^2, 3p^4$
Spectroscopic ground state $3p_2$
Electronegativity 2.5
Thermal neutron absorption cross section, barns 0.52

In recent years elemental sulfur recovered as a by-product in the processing of natural gas and petroleum has become an important source of supply, at present amounting to about 20% of all sulfur consumed in the world. Hydrogen sulfide naturally present or produced in refining operations is separated from hydrocarbon gases by absorption in an alkaline solvent, most commonly an aqueous solution of monoethanolamine. The concentrated hydrogen sulfide stripped from the solvent is converted to elemental sulfur by the Claus process, which consists of air oxidation at high temperature followed by catalytic conversion at lower temperature.

Iron pyrites, the other main source of sulfur, presently supplies about 25% of the world's sulfur requirements. Japan, Spain, Norway, Canada, Sweden, Finland, Italy, Russia, Germany, France, Greece, and the United States have large reserves of iron pyrites. Almost all of the sulfur dioxide produced by burning pyrites is converted to sulfuric acid. The same is true of sulfur dioxide from the processing of sulfide ores, insofar as it is recovered. Elemental sulfur has been recovered by reductive smelting of sulfide ores and by the action of reducing agents such as coke or natural gas on sulfur dioxide, but the application of such processes has been limited by unfavorable economics.

Anhydrite and gypsum deposits are probably the most abundant sulfur-containing ores. Sulfuric acid and portland cement are obtained by burning a mixture of anhydrite or gypsum, clay, and coal. The cost is so great that the process is only used where it is desired to lessen dependence on imported sulfur and pyrites.

Physical Properties

The atomic and nuclear properties of sulfur are given in Table 1. Sulfur exists in a number of molecular species. The sulfur atom exists in substantial concentration in the gas phase only at low pressures above 1500°C; the oxygen-like S_2 molecule predominates from that temperature down to about 500–700°C at subatmospheric pressures; the S_3 and S_4 molecules of unknown structure are minor components of the vapor. Besides these, there are sulfur rings of 5 to 10 atoms, and unbranched sulfur chains of up to about 100,000 atoms. Structural parameters of some typical sulfur molecules are given in Table 2.

Sulfur vapor is a mixture of the small molecules S_1 through S_4 and the known rings S_5 through S_{10}, although S_9 and S_{10} are never quantitatively important. The liquid is a strongly temperature-dependent mixture of three chief components: (1) a linear polymer with a random distribution of chain lengths,

TABLE 2. POLYATOMIC SULFUR MOLECULES

Structural Type	Formula of Example	Unpaired Electrons	Bond Length, Å	Bond Angle	Torsion Angle
Diatomic triplet, like O_2	S_2	2	1.89	—	—
Unbranched chain	S_x (X > 2)	2	2.07	107°	87°
Puckered ring	S_6	0	2.057	102.2°	74.5°
Puckered ring	S_8	0	2.059	107.9°	98.9°

which predominates above 159°C; (2) cyclic S_8 molecules, which predominate at lower temperatures, and (3) an unidentified component, possibly small rings such as S_6. This unidentified component is required to account for the observed freezing point lowering and for the presence of a few per cent of polymer in solid sulfur obtained by quenching liquid sulfur from temperatures below 159°C. Most of the properties of liquid sulfur, including the 14,000-fold increase in viscosity from 157 to 187°C, have been satisfactorily accounted for by a theory which considers the equilibria within the polymer system and between chains and S_8 rings, and ignores the existence of the third component (Fig. 2). Both this

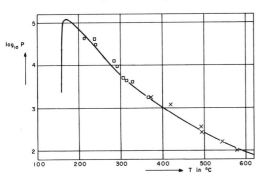

FIG. 2. The chain length, P, of sulfur polymers versus temperature. From ESR measurements. X from magnetic susceptibility measurements. The line (drawn) represents theory.

theory and the magnetic data agree that the concentration of chain sulfur molecules is negligible below 159°C.

In the solid state the orthorhombic alpha allotrope is stable below 95.5°C, while the monoclinic beta allotrope is stable between 95.5°C and its melting point. Both of these are composed of S_8 rings. There may be a cubic form stable only above 28,000

atmospheres. There are at least two, and possibly as many as twelve, metastable allotropes believed to consist of S_8 rings, though some are evidently impure and others may be duplications. One solid allotrope of the S_6 ring and one of the S_{10} ring have been prepared in fairly pure form, but both revert via the polymer to a stable octatomic form. Polymeric sulfur also has at least one solid form which is stable at high pressures, and more than one metastable form. The better known crystalline forms of sulfur are described in Table 3.

Many of the reactions among the molecular species of sulfur, even in the vapor and up to 500°C, are measurably slow, and many of them are notably influenced by traces of impurities or by heterogeneous catalysis. The physical properties of sulfur are therefore time-dependent and impurity-dependent to an unusual degree. Insofar as possible, the properties tabulated for the alpha orthorhombic and beta monoclinic solids and for the liquid and vapor, within the ranges of pressure and temperature where they are stable, are for pure sulfur at equilibrium. More limited data are given for alpha and beta sulfur outside their field of stability, and for some of the unstable solids.

The effects of high pressure on elemental sulfur are currently under investigation, but the situation is still far from clear. Four new solid phases have been reported for pressures between 16 and 18 kilobars, with hints of a metallic phase above 250 kilobars. The beta monoclinic solid exists only below 1.4 kilobar, and the nonpolymeric liquid only below 1.2–1.4 kilobar. The freezing point seems to rise much less steeply above 4 kilobars than at lower pressures, perhaps reflecting the appearance of other solid phases.

Solid sulfur allotropes which consist of ring

TABLE 3. CRYSTALLINE FORMS OF SULFUR

	Low-Pressure Forms					High-Pressure Forms		
Usual name Basic unit Crystal type	Alpha S_8 Ring Ortho- rhombic	Beta S_8 Ring Mono- clinic	Gamma S_8 Ring Mono- clinic	Epsilon S_6 Ring Rhombo- hedral	Fibrous Chain Pseudo- hexagonal	Cubic Unknown Cubic?	Foliated Chain Pseudo- tetragonal	Fibrous Chain Pseudo- hexagonal
Space group	D_{2h}^{24}–(Fddd)	C_{2h}^{5}–(P2/c)	C_{2h}^{4}–(B2/a)	C_{31}^{2}–(R_3)				Ccmm?
Atoms/unit cell	128	48	32	18	10	104		160?
Calc. density, g/cc	2.07	1.94		2.17				2.06
Obs. density, g/cc	2.07	1.96	2.04	2.14	2.01	2.18		2.06
Atomic volume, cc	15.5	16.4						
Cell dimensions, a_0	10.4646	11.04	13.96	10.818	13.7	13.66	32.4	13.8
b_0	12.8660	10.98	13.16	4.280	4.7	—	6.65	32.4
c_0	24.4860	10.92	9.29	—	4.7	—	6.65	9.75
B	—	96.7°	91.47°	—	—	—	—	—
Minimum pressure, atm	0	0	0	0	0	28,000	16,000	27,000
Type of stability	Stable	Stable	Metastable	Unstable	Unstable	Stable?	Metastable	Stable
Relationships to other forms			May also occur in plastic sulfur		Constituent of plastic sulfur	May be formed from high-pressure fibrous form	Related to omega sulfur of Das	Related to low-pressure fibrous form

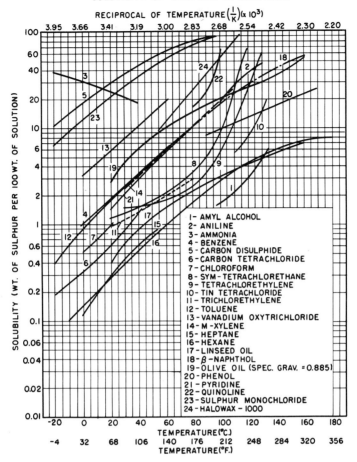

FIG. 3. Solubility of sulfur in solvents.

molecules dissolve without decomposition in many nonelectrolyte solvents. See Fig. 3. The beta monoclinic form is more soluble than alpha orthorhombic sulfur. Only carbon disulfide and a few halogen compounds will dissolve more than 2 mole % of orthorhombic sulfur at 25°C. In polar solvents, solid sulfur is either extremely insoluble (water, neutral and acidic aqueous solution, liquid H_2S) or dissolves extensively, but with chemical reaction (liquid ammonia, liquid H_2S with added triethylamine, aqueous sodium hydroxide). Solid polymeric sulfur is essentially insoluble in all solvents. Systems of nonpolymeric liquid sulfur and another nonelectrolyte solvent frequently form two liquid phases, with complete miscibility above an upper critical solution temperature (80 to 200°C). In many cases phase separation takes place again above 200–230°C, that being the

polymerization temperature of sulfur in the presence of 30 to 40% solvent. Polymeric liquid sulfur reacts more or less rapidly with all but a very few solvents. This may have some bearing on the fact that the solubility of elemental sulfur in hydrogen sulfide at about 400 atmospheres increases much more rapidly with temperature above 150–175°C than in the lower temperature range.

Tables 3 through 11 and Figs. 2 and 3 present much data on the physical properties of elemental sulfur.

Chemical Properties

Sulfur is a very reactive element and exists in compound form in the valence states of 2, 4 and 6. In sulfides the valence is 2; in sulfites, SO_2 and many organic compounds is 4; and in sulfates and SO_3 is 6.

The chemistry of those reactions in which

671

TABLE 4. PHYSICAL PROPERTIES OF SULFUR

Densities, g/cc
    Alpha orthorhombic, 25°C   2.07
    Beta monoclinic, 25°C   1.96
    Liquid at freezing point   1.808
    Liquid at boiling point   1.610
Melting point   115.21°C
Boiling point   444.60°C
Heat of fusion   410 cal/g-atom
Heat of vaporization   2200 cal/g-atom
Thermal conductivity, cal/cm/sec/°C
    α-orthorhombic, 0–95.5°C, 6.67×10^{-4}—0.81×10^{-6}t
    β-monoclinic, 95.5–119°C, 3.67×10^{-4}—0.24×10^{-6}t
Diamagnetic susceptibility, c.g.s. units,
    α-orthorhombic   0.49 at 18°C
    β-monoclinic   0.49 at 112°C
Refractive index, at 589 millimicrons, room temperature,
    α-orthorhombic   1.957, 2.0377, 2.2454
    β-monoclinic   2.038
    amorphous   1.998
Polarization, cc/g, orthorhombic   0.245 at room temp.
Standard electrode potential, S to $S^=$ 0.47 to 0.51 volts
Frictional electricity   When rubbed with practically any other substance, e.g., glass, fur, silk, wool or hard rubber, orthorhombic sulfur becomes charged with negative electricity.

Electrical Resistivity of Orthorhombic Sulfur

Temperature, °C	ohm-cm
20	1.9×10^{17}
30	3.9×10^{16}
55	3.95×10^{15}
69	1.78×10^{14}
110	4.8×10^{12}
115	9.5×10^{11}

Thermal Expansion of Orthorhombic Sulfur

	Temperature Range, °C	Expansion
Linear	0–13	4.567×10^{-5}
	13–50	7.433×10^{-5}
	50–78	8.633×10^{-5}
	78–97	20.67×10^{-5}
	97–110	103.2×10^{-5}
Cubic	0–13	13.70×10^{-5}
	13–50	22.30×10^{-5}
	50–78	25.90×10^{-5}
	78–97	62.01×10^{-5}
	97–110	309.6×10^{-5}

TABLE 5. VAPOR PRESSURE

Rhombic	(Temperature range 20–80°C)
	$\log P = 11.664 - \dfrac{5166}{T}$
Monoclinic	(Temperature range 96–116°C)
	$\log P = 11.364 - \dfrac{5082}{T}$
Liquid	(Temperature range 25–74°C)
	$\log P = 8.70 - \dfrac{4055}{T}$
	(Temperature range 120–325°C)
	$\log P = 14.70000 -$
	$0.0062238T - \dfrac{5405.1}{T}$
	(Temperature range 325–550°C)
	$\log P = 7.43287 - \dfrac{3268.2}{T}$

(Pressures given in mm of mercury, temperature in degrees Kelvin)

elemental sulfur is a reactant or a product is complicated by and merges into the chemistry of the interconversions of the various molecular forms of elemental sulfur. Substances, such as alumina and many bases, which are catalysts for these interconversions, are also effective catalysts for many other reactions involving elemental sulfur. Under more energetic conditions, as in photochemical reactions, the reacting sulfur species is monatomic sulfur.

While oxygen can use for bands only *s*-orbitals and *p*-orbitals, sulfur has available five vacant *d*-orbitals. These orbitals are used not only in compounds of high coordination and oxidation number, such as SF_6, but also in many compounds of divalent sulfur, particularly those with S-S bonds. This partial double bond character of the S-S bond is consistent with the following observations: (1) sulfur atoms in rings or chains behave

TABLE 6. SOME PROPERTIES OF LIQUID SULFUR

t	c	ρ	$\beta_{ad} \times 10^6$	$\alpha \times 10^6$	C_p	$(\beta_{is} - \beta_{ad}) \times 10^6$	$\dfrac{C_p}{C_v}$
120	1349	1.805	30.8	430	0.232	4.2	1.14
140	1325	1.793	32.2	465	0.236	5.1	1.16
160	1301	1.773	33.7	135	0.354	0.2	1.01
180	1277	1.768	35	298	0.309	1.8	1.051
200	1253	1.755	37	308	0.290	2.1	1.058
250	1192	1.727	41	366	0.266	3.7	1.09
300	1131	1.697	47	366	0.261	4.2	1.09
350	1070	1.667	53	366	0.263	5	1.09
400	1009	1.637	61	366	0.273	5	1.08

Thermal conductivity, cal/cm/sec/°C, 119–159°C	$3.06 \times 10^{-4} + 0.69 \times 10^{-6}$ (t–119)
Surface tension, dynes/cm, 119–159°C	60.93–0.105(t–119)
159–444°C	56.73–0.0563(t–159)
Diffusivity, cm²/sec, 119–148°C	204.7 exp(– 14,900/RT)
above 240°C	0.00113 exp(– 7,250/RT)
Diamagnetic susceptibility, 119–159°C	0.49×10^{-6}
Electrical conductivity, mho-cm	2.2×10^{-12} at 231°C, 79×10^{-12} at 360°C
Cryoscopic constant, °C/g-atom	686
Refractive index, at 589 millimicrons	1.929 at 110°C, 1.890 at 130°C

t—temperature, °C
c—velocity of sound, meters/sec
ρ—density, g/cc
β_{ad}—adiabatic compressibility, 1/atm
β_{is}—isothermal compressibility, 1/atm
α—cubic coefficient of thermal expansion, 1/°C
C_p—specific heat at constant pressure, cal/g/°C
C_v—specific heat at constant volume, cal/g/°C

electrophilically toward bases; (2) sulfur atoms are easily removed from or inserted into sulfur chains but no branched chains are present, and (3) S-S bonds are much stronger than O-O bonds.

Sulfur appears to form binary compounds with all of the elements except iodine and the noble gases. However, gold, platinum, tellurium, and nitrogen do not unite directly with sulfur. It is doubtful that tellurium disulfide exists except as a component of thiosalts. A large number of mixed sulfur-selenium chains and rings are formed in liquid mixtures of the two elements, but there

TABLE 7. VISCOSITY OF LIQUID SULFUR

Temperature, °C	Viscosity, poises	Temperature, °C	Viscosity, poises
119	0.1152	280	54
120	0.1125	300	29
130	0.0941	306	22
140	0.0777		
150	0.0676	Viscosity of Sulfur Vapor	
158	0.0673		micropoises
159.2	0.116	444.6 (b.p.)	197
165	190	450	198
170	446	500	207
180	843	600	192
187	932	700	153
200	800	800	164
220	488	900	178
240	244	1000	196
260	117	1040 (critical point)	200

TABLE 8. TEMPERATURES AND HEATS OF TRANSFORMATION, AND TRIPLE POINTS

Transformation	Type	At one Atmosphere		At Triple Point		
		Temp., °C	Heat, cal/g-atom	Third Phase	Temp., °C	Pressure, atm
Glass Transition, Quenched Sulfur	E	−30				
Glass Transition, "Pure Polymer"	E	75				
α-Orthorhombic → β-Monoclinic	E	95.4	95.9	Vapor	95.31	4.95×10^{-6}
				Liquid	152	1400
α-Orthorhombic → S$_8$-Liquid	M	112.8	382	Vapor	112.8	9.9×10^{-6}
α-Orthorhombic → Equil. liquid	M	110.4				
β-Monoclinic → S$_8$-Liquid	M	119.3	295	Vapor	119.3	1.37×10^{-5}
β-Monoclinic → Equil. liquid	E	(A) 115.21	410	Vapor	115.176	
Equil. Liquid → Polymer	E	159.9	88.2			
Equil. Liquid → Vapor	E	(B) 444.60	2200	(C) Vapor	1040	116
					(Density = 0.403 g/ml)	

Type: E = Equilibrium, M = Metastable
(A) Melting point and heat of fusion
(B) Boiling point and heat of vaporization
(C) Critical pressure, temperature, and density

674

TABLE 9. ENTROPY, FREE ENERGY, AND HEAT OF FORMATION

Form of Sulfur	State	Entropy	Free Energy	Heat of Formation	Heat Capacity
α-Orthorhombic, S_8	solid	7.62	0	0	5.416
β-Monoclinic, S_8	solid	7.78		0.009	5.65
S	gas	40.094	56.949	66.636	5.658
S_2	gas	27.255	9.45	15.34	3.88
S_3	gas			10.57	
S_4	gas			8.18	
S_5	gas			5.92	
S_6	gas			4.08	
S_7	gas			3.87	
S_8	gas	12.872	1.484	3.056	4.674

Standard state: 298.16°K, 1 atmosphere
Units: kcal/g-atom

seems to be no simple selenium sulfide. It is not known whether tellurium behaves similarly.

At room temperature, sulfur reacts vigorously with lithium, sodium, potassium, rubidium, cesium, calcium, strontium, and barium, and combines readily with copper, silver, and mercury. The application of heat causes a vigorous combination in mixtures of powdered sulfur and zinc, aluminum, tin, or iron; but not even boiling sulfur attacks zinc, cadmium, aluminum, and tin in massive form. Chromium, tungsten, uranium, iron, cobalt, and nickel are comparatively resistant to sulfur.

Elemental sulfur attacks iron above 300°C and aluminum above 500–600°C. High-chromium stainless steels are often used above 500°C to resist corrosion by sulfur.

Many metal sulfides are in fact polysulfides, and liberate elemental sulfur when dissolved in acids.

At high temperatures sulfur vapor reacts with boron, carbon, and silicon to form sulfides.

With a considerable evolution of heat, sulfur combines with fluorine to form SF_6 and S_2F_{10}. The existence of SF_2 and SF_4 has been reported but no evidence has been found indicating their formation from sulfur. Both chlorine and bromine, but not iodine, react readily with sulfur to form the liquids sulfur monochloride, S_2Cl_2, and sulfur monobromide, S_2Br_2. At −30°C and below, the action of chlorine on sulfur leads to sulfur tetrachloride, SCl_4. A similar bromide does not appear to exist. Solid sulfur reacts rather violently with chlorine monoxide to give thionyl chloride, $SOCl_2$. The monochloride and monobromide are slowly hydrolyzed by water, yielding elemental sulfur and a variety of sulfur-containing anions.

Sulfides may be formed with arsenic, phosphorus, antimony, and bismuth by melting them with sulfur. While the sulfides of antimony and bismuth may be classed with the heavy metal sulfides, the arsenic sulfides, As_4S_4, As_4S_6, As_4S_{10}, and the sulfides of phosphorus, P_4S_3, P_4S_5, P_4S_7, P_4S_{10}, have covalent cage structures related in various ways to the P_4 or As_4 tetrahedron. Reaction of sulfur with liquid ammonia yields two cyclic compounds, S_4N_4 and S_7NH. Other nitrogen sulfides include the cyclic S_4N_2 and the fibrous polymer $(SN)_x$.

Sulfur burns in air at 250–260°C and higher temperatures. The uncatalyzed reaction of hydrogen with sulfur is fairly slow at 260–340°C and does not go to completion. Sulfur reacts rapidly with carbon only at red heat. There exists a set of reversible gas reactions involving some or all of the compounds H_2, H_2O, H_2S, SO_2, SO_3, CO, CO_2, COS, CS_2, the lower aliphatic hydrocarbons, S_2 and other sulfur vapor species, which are of considerable technical importance. Most of the reactions in question can proceed by free-radical chain mechanisms or by heterogeneous catalysis, the predominating reaction path depending upon the experimental conditions. It is significant that activated alumina is an effective catalyst for reactions consuming

TABLE 10. THERMODYNAMIC PROPERTIES OF SOLID AND LIQUID SULFUR AT EQUILIBRIUM

		Entropy of Sulfur Above 25°C		Enthalpy of Sulfur Above 25°C		Heat Capacity of Sulfur	
	Temperature		Entropy		Enthalpy		Heat Capacity
°C		cal/g-atom/°C or Btu/lb-atom/°F	cal/g/°C or Btu/lb/°F	cal/g-atom	cal/g	cal/g-atom/°C or Btu/lb-atom/°F	cal/g/°C or Btu/lb/°F
30	↑	0.09028	0.002815	27.14	0.8464	5.4426	0.16973
40		0.26782	0.0083521	81.84	2.552	5.4981	0.17146
50		0.44147	0.013768	137.1	4.276	5.5518	0.17314
60	rhombic	0.61146	0.019069	192.9	6.016	5.6041	0.17477
70		0.77794	0.024261	249.16	7.7702	5.6548	0.17635
80		0.94108	0.029348	305.97	9.5419	5.7035	0.17787
90		1.1010	0.034335	363.23	11.328	5.7508	0.17934
95.39	↓	1.1859	0.036984	394.31	12.297	5.7756	0.18012
95.39	↑	1.4464	0.045106	490.27	15.289	5.9101	0.1843
100		1.5191	0.047375	517.24	16.130	5.776	0.1801
101	monoclinic	1.5345	0.047855	523.00	16.310	5.733	0.1788
101		1.5355	0.047887	523.38	16.322	5.9529	0.18565
110		1.7668	0.055098	577.23	18.001	6.0145	0.18757
115.207	↓	1.8987	0.059214	608.64	18.981	6.0501	0.18868
115.207	↑	2.9553	0.092163	1019.0	31.778	7.5752	0.23624
120		3.0487	0.095076	1055.4	32.913	7.6404	0.23827
130		3.2422	0.10111	1132.5	35.318	7.7720	0.24328
140		3.4343	0.10710	1211.0	37.766	7.9319	0.24736
150		3.6271	0.11311	1291.5	40.276	8.2307	0.25668
160		3.8459	0.11994	1385.2	43.198	11.76	0.3668
170		4.1060	0.12805	1496.7	46.676	10.655	0.33229
180	liquid	4.3372	0.13526	1600.4	49.910	10.142	0.31627
200		4.7620	0.14851	1796.9	56.038	9.5586	0.29818
250		5.6791	0.17711	2253.2	70.268	8.7849	0.27396
300		6.4603	0.20147	2680.8	83.603	8.3537	0.26052
350		7.1471	0.22289	3091.5	96.410	8.0919	0.25235
400		7.7649	0.24215	3491.4	108.88	7.9123	0.24675
440		8.2166	0.25624	3804.3	118.64	7.7207	0.24077
444.60	↓	8.2661	0.25778	3839.9	119.75	7.6906	0.23984

Heat Capacity Equations

S(rh)
$$C_p = 2.9863 + 0.01058T + 0.8160 \times 10^{-5}T^2$$
$$(35\text{–}95°C)$$

S(mono)
$$C_p = 3.388 + 0.006854\,T + \frac{0.080351}{(388.336\text{—}T)^2}$$
$$(101\text{–}115.18°C)$$

Sλ (liq.)
$$C_p = 5.4 + 5 \times 10^{-3}T$$
$$(118.9\text{–}444.9°C)$$

S (gas)
$$C_p = 5.43 - 0.26 \times 10^{-3}T + 0.27 \times 10^5 T^{-2}$$
$$(25\text{–}1727°C)$$

S$_2$ (gas)
$$C_p = 8.54 + 0.28 \times 10^{-3}T - 0.79 \times 10^5 T^{-2}$$
$$(25\text{–}1727°C)$$

The heat capacity is given as cal/g mole/°C. To convert these to cal/g/°C, divide by the respective molecular weights. Temperature in degrees Kelvin.

TABLE 11. COMPRESSIBILITY OF ORTHORHOMBIC SULFUR

| Pressure, | | Change in Length per unit Length | | | | | | Change in Volume per Unit Volume | |
| | | Direction "a" | | Direction "b" | | Direction "c" | | | |
kg/cm	atm	30°C	75°C	30°C	75°C	30°C	75°C	30°C	75°C
2,000	1,936	0.0099	0.0104	0.0093	0.0113	0.0042	0.0043	0.0233	0.0258
4,000	3,872	0.0180	0.0190	0.0165	0.0201	0.0079	0.0082	0.0419	0.0466
6,000	5,808	0.0246	0.0261	0.0224	0.0273	0.0113	0.0116	0.0571	0.0638
8,000	7,744	0.0304	0.0323	0.0277	0.0334	0.0143	0.0148	0.0707	0.0784
10,000	9,680	0.0357	0.0372	0.0323	0.0388	0.0171	0.0177	0.0839	0.0908
12,000	11,616	0.0412	0.0427	0.0370	0.0433	0.0198	0.0203	0.0949	0.1027

or producing elemental sulfur, especially under conditions where the sulfur is present mostly as molecules larger than S_2, since activated alumina is a particularly good catalyst for the interconversion of various sulfur species.

Elemental sulfur reacts with oxygen to yield SO_2 and SO_3, reacts with SO_2 under electric discharge to yield S_2O, reacts with water in the presence of bases to yield sulfide and thiosulfate, reacts with aqueous sulfide, sulfite, and cyanide to yield polysulfide, thiosulfate, and thiocyanate, respectively, reacts with liquid SO_3 to yield S_2O_3, and reacts with excess chlorine or fluorine to yield SCl_4 or SF_6. In each of these cases, the elemental sulfur contributes only one atom to the resulting molecule or ion, yet the equilibrium concentration of monatomic sulfur is essentially zero. Also, some of the above reactions can be reversed, yielding polymeric sulfur.

In those reactions where sulfur is attacked by a Lewis acid one can often show the existence of a chain reaction in which successive S radicals are detached from the elemental sulfur ring or chain. In the case of reactions involving Lewis bases, the evidence supports neucleophilic degradation mechanisms such as

$$S_8 + H_2SO_3 \rightarrow HO_3S - S_7 - SH$$
$$HO_3S - S_7 - SH + H_2SO_3 \rightarrow$$
$$HO_3S - S_6 - SH + H_2S_2O_3, \text{ etc.}$$
$$HO_3S - S - SH + H_2SO_3 \rightarrow 2H_2S_2O_3.$$

With excess sulfite, the conversion of sulfur to thiosulfate is complete. These long-chain intermediates are often unstable. In this particular case, if excess sulfur is used, the sulfane monosulfonic acids condense with one another yielding sulfide and a variety of sulfane disulfonic acids (polythionic acids), while the sulfide also attacks the sulfur forming various polysulfides. The resulting mixture, called Wackenroder's liquid, was a puzzle for a long time. As a result of investigations of such systems, chemists have learned to synthesize chain compounds such as H_2S_6 and S_4Cl_2, and to condense them to form unusual elemental sulfur rings, in this case S_{10}.

Sulfur, either pure or as polysulfide ion, is an important oxidizing or dehydrogenating reagent in organic chemistry. Catalysis by bases is important in many of the organic reactions of elemental sulfur just as in the inorganic reactions previously discussed. It has recently been found that sulfur atoms in either singlet or triplet states can be generated by photolysis of suitable sulfur compounds, and that the electronic state of the sulfur atom determines which compounds will result. The better understanding of the reactions of elemental sulfur has resulted largely from the interaction of studies of its inorganic and its organic reactions.

Importance and Applications of Sulfur

Sulfur is used in the manufacture of sulfuric acid, sulfur dioxide, carbon disulfide, textiles, paper pulp, dyes, cosmetics, drugs, black gunpowder, rocket fuels, insecticides, cements and chemicals. In elemental form it is used as a fertilizer, as a soil conditioner, as a fungicide, and in the vulcanization of rubber. Sulfur compounds are often used in large quantities in the manufacture of materials which contain little or no sulfur, notable examples being the use of sulfuric acid to make wet-process phosphoric acid and triple

TABLE 12. CONSUMPTION OF SULFUR BY INDUSTRIES IN THE UNITED STATES DURING 1966

Source	Per Cent of Total Sulfur	Intermediate	Industry	Per Cent of Total Sulfur
Element	8	Element	Carbon disulfide	3
Other	0		Insecticides and	
	—		fungicides	2
	8		Other chemicals	2
			Miscellaneous	1
				—
				8
Element	6	Sulfur dioxide	Sulfite pulp	5
Other	0		Miscellaneous	1
	—			—
	6			6
Element	75	Sulfuric acid	Fertilizer	48
Other	11		Chemicals	20
	—		Petroleum	3
	86		Paints and pigments	5
			Steel	3
			Rayon	3
			Other	4
				—
				86

100% = 8,950,000 long tons

TABLE 13. INDUSTRIALLY IMPORTANT COMPOUNDS OF SULFUR

Sulfuric acid, oleum, and sulfur trioxide
Iron pyrites (natural)
Calcium sulfate (natural)
Hydrogen sulfide
Sulfur dioxide
Aluminum sulfate
Ammonium sulfate
Potassium sulfate
Sodium sulfate
Carbon disulfide
Sulfur monochloride
Sodium lauryl sulfate
Numerous classes of organic compounds, including:
    Vulcanized rubbers
    Polysulfide rubbers
    Sulfa drugs
    Penicillins
    Some classes of insecticides
    Sulfur dyes
    Azo dyes having sulfonic acid groups

superphosphate fertilizer, and the use of carbon disulfide to make carbon tetrachloride and viscose rayon. Sulfur is essential to plant growth, but in many localities enough sulfur is available from rainfall, from the subsoil, or as an incidental ingredient in fertilizers such as single superphosphate, ammonium sulfate, and potassium sulfate that further addition of sulfur is not needed. Table 12 shows the consumption of sulfur, from all sources, by industries in the United States in 1966.

By far the most important sulfur compound is sulfuric acid. However, there are between 200 and 300 sulfur compounds produced industrially. A few of the more important ones are listed in Table 13.

Biology and Toxicology

Sulfur is one of the elements necessary to life. Plants manufacture their sulfur-containing essential amino acids, cystine and methionine, by reducing dissolved sulfate. Sulfur is also a minor constituent of fats, body fluids, and

TABLE 14. TOXICOLOGICAL PROPERTIES OF SOME SULFUR COMPOUNDS

Compound	Sulfur Dioxide	Hydrogen Sulfide	Carbon Disulfide
Threshold limit value	5	10	20
Beginning of irritation	6–20	70–150	300–400
Dangerous	150	170–300	1200
Possibly fatal	500	600	3000–4000
	Suffocation	Respiratory paralysis	Respiratory paralysis

skeletal minerals. It is about as abundant as phosphorus in organisms, which is on the order of 1% of dry weight.

Bacteria are important in the geochemical cycles of carbon, nitrogen, phosphorus, sulfur, and iron. Various microorganisms break down protein to hydrogen sulfide, oxidize hydrogen sulfide to sulfur or sulfuric acid, or reduce sulfate to sulfur or sulfide. The sulfur-oxidizing and the ferrous iron-oxidizing bacteria, which are closely related or possibly interchangeable, play an important part in the weathering of metallic sulfides, and have been provisionally identified in sediments containing some of the oldest known fossils.

In the human body, sulfur is present as sulfate or is bound up in organic compounds. Elemental sulfur is physiologically inert. Hydrogen sulfide in small concentrations can be metabolized, but in high concentrations it quickly causes death by respiratory paralysis. Carbon disulfide and carbonyl sulfide cause death by respiratory paralysis more slowly than H_2S. Carbon disulfide also has a narcotic effect. Hydrogen sulfide, the sulfur chlorides and oxychlorides, and especially sulfur dioxide are highly irritating to the respiratory tract. Sulfur compounds are not cumulative poisons, and recovery is usually complete. Table 14 shows some of the toxicological properties of H_2S, SO_2, and CS_2. It is important to emphasize that hydrogen sulfide is more dangerous than sulfur dioxide since it is much less irritating on first contact and since it deadens the sense of smell.

References

1. Mellor, J. W., "A Comprehensive Treatise on Inorganic and Theoretical Chemistry," Vol. 10, New York, Longmans-Green and Co., 1930.
2. Gmelin, L, "Handbuch der Anorganischen Chemie," 8th Edition, Vol. 9a, Weinheim, Verlag Chemie, 1954.
3. Pascal, P., Editor, "Nouveau Traité de Chimie Minérale," Vol. 13, Paris, Masson et Cie., 1960.
4. Brasted, R. C., "Comprehensive Inorganic Chemistry," Vol. 8, New York, D. Van Nostrand Co., 1961.
5. Yost, D. M., and Russell, H., "Systematic Inorganic Chemistry of the Fifth-and-Sixth-Group Non-Metallic Elements," New York, Prentice Hall, 1944.
6. Wells, A. F., "Structural Inorganic Chemistry," 3rd Edition, London, Oxford University Press, 1962.
7. Sidgwick, N. V., "The Chemical Elements and Their Compounds," London, Oxford University Press, 1950.
8. Meyer, B., Editor, "Elemental Sulfur, Chemistry and Physics," New York, Interscience Publishers, 1965.
9. Meyer, B., *Chem. Rev.*, **62**, 429, 1964.
10. Stone, F. G. A., and Graham, F., Editors, "Inorganic Polymers," New York, Academic Press, 1962.
11. Tobolsky, A. V., and MacKnight, W. J., "Polymeric Sulfur and Related Polymers," New York, Interscience Publishers, 1965.
12. Tuller, W. N., "The Sulfur Data Book," New York, McGraw-Hill Book Co., 1954.
13. Landolt, H. H., and Boernstein, R., "Zahlenwerte und Funktionen," 6th Edition, Vol. 2, Berlin, Springer-Verlag, 1961.
14. Kelley, K. K., U.S. Bur. Mines Bull. 601, Washington, D.C., U.S. Government Printing Office, 1962.
15. Rossini, F. D., Wagman, D. D., Evans, W. H., Levine, S., and Jaffe, I., "Selected Values of Chemical Thermodynamic Properties," National Bur. Stds. Circular 500, 1952.
16. Wagman, D. D., Evans, W. H., Halow, I., Parker, V. B., Bailey, S. M., and Schumm, R. H., "Selected Values of Chemical Thermodynamic Properties," National Bur. Stds. Technical Note 270–1, 1965.

17. Linke, W. F., "Solubilities," 4th Edition, Vol. 2, Washington, American Chemical Society, 1965.

18. Hildebrand, J. H., and Scott, R. L., "Solubility of Nonelectrolytes," 3rd Edition, New York, Dover, 1964.

19. Rice, F. O., "Free Radicals in Inorganic Chemistry," Advances in Chemistry Series, No. 36, Washington, American Chemical Society, 1962.

20. Pryor, W. A., "Mechanism of Sulfur Reactions," New York, McGraw-Hill, 1962.

21. Kharasch, N., Editor, "Organic Sulfur Compounds," Vol. 1, London, Pergamon Press, 1961.

22. Foss, O., *Advan. Inorg. Chem. Radiochem.,* **2** (1960).

23. Gee, G., Special Pub. No. 12, London, The Chemical Society, (1958).

24. Rankama, K., and Sahama, T. G., "Geochemistry," Chicago, Univ. of Chicago Press, 1950.

25. Patty, F. A., "Industrial Hygiene and Toxicology," Vol. 2, 2nd Edition, New York, Interscience Publishers, 1963.

EDWARD H. CONROY

T

TANTALUM

Tantalum is a strong, ductile, high-melting, corrosion-resistant, metallic element of high density. Its atomic number is 73 and it has an atomic weight of 180.948. Eleven isotopes are known, the mass number range being 176 through 186. The natural and only stable isotope is Ta^{181}. Among the radioactive isotopes, Ta^{179}, which has a half-life of 600 days, is the most stable. Isomeric transitions are rather common in the isotopes of tantalum; thus far a total of five have been detected.

History

While the history of the discovery of tantalum is relatively well established, that of element 41 (tantalum's sister metal) is characterized by controversy and confusion which has not been resolved completely. Factors largely responsible for this situation are the pronounced chemical similarity of the two elements and their close association in nature. (See also **Niobium.**)

After examining some mineral samples from Sweden and Finland, the Swedish chemist Anders Ekeberg reported the "discovery of a new substance of a metallic nature" in 1802. He proposed the name "tantalum" after Tantalus, a character in Greek mythology, because of the frustrating difficulties encountered in attempting to define and elucidate the chemical nature and other properties of the new element. Subsequent research confirmed the authenticity of Ekeberg's claim to discovery, and thus tantalum became the accepted name for element 73.

Brief mention of the tribulations encountered in the selection and acceptance of a name for element 41 is in order because tantalum is involved. In 1801, Charles Hatchett, an English chemist, described the results of an analysis he had made of a mineral fragment obtained from the British Museum. He claimed discovery of "a metal hitherto unknown" and, since the original source of the mineral was North America (probably Connecticut, but possibly Massachusetts), he proposed for the new element the name "columbium" in honor of Columbia, the eponymous name for America. A few years later (1810) another English chemist, William Wollaston, judged columbium and tantalum to be identical. Apparently that conclusion was accepted without question until 1844 when Heinrich Rose, a German chemist, published the results of some mineral analyses. He claimed to have found, in a Bavarian mineral, a new element for which he proposed the name "niobium," after Niobe, daughter of Tantalus. This development rekindled interest in the tantalum-columbium issue. During the next several years experimental evidence was obtained which definitely established tantalum and columbium as separate elements, and which proved columbium and niobium to be identical. Jean-Charles de Marignac, in 1866, disclosed a successful method for separating tantalum and columbium. The columbium-niobium name controversy was not, however, resolved because Europe accepted the latter and America retained the former. The International Union of Pure and Applied Chemistry, in 1950, selected niobium as the name for element 41. The justice of this decision appears somewhat questionable, because Hatchett actually and validly discovered the element, whereas Rose merely rediscovered it.

Occurrence

Tantalum does not occur in nature in the free (elemental) state, but rather in chemical combination with oxygen, and other elements. Tantalum minerals almost always contain columbium. Tantalum ranks fifty-fourth in the abundance order of the elements of the earth's crust, which is estimated to contain 0.0002% tantalum. Approximate abundance ratios of tantalum with respect to some other elements are: copper, 0.01; columbium, 0.05; tin, 1; silver, 10; and gold, 1000. The ultimate source of tantalum is granite-type rocks. Tantalum concentrations of commercial significance are found in pegmatite dykes and placer deposits which occur in, or were derived from, granites. The placer deposits frequently contain industrially important quantities of tin (as cassiterite). Tantalum, unlike its sister element columbium, is not found in significant amounts in alkalic igneous rocks. Tantalite, $(Fe,Mn)(Ta,Cb)_2O_6$, is the most important mineral source of tantalum. (If the columbium content exceeds that of tantalum, as is generally the situation, the name is changed to columbite.) Other industrial minerals containing tantalum, usually as a minor constituent, are samarskite, pyrochlore, fergusonite, and euxenite.

According to U.S. Bureau of Mines estimates the tantalum resources in the free world are less than 100,000 tons of contained Ta_2O_5; and much of this total cannot be recovered economically by current industrial processing methods. The largest known ore reserves are located in Africa and South America. No commercially important deposits have been found in the United States. During the past decade the major producers of ore concentrate were South America (Brazil), Africa (Southern Rhodesia, Republic of the Congo, Nigeria, Mozambique), Europe (Portugal), and Oceania (Australia). In 1964, the free world mine production (Ta_2O_5 basis) was approximately 300,000 pounds. Although nominal price quotations for tantalite ore during 1964 ranged from $6 to $7 per pound of contained pentoxides (60% minimum Ta_2O_5 plus Cb_2O_5, and Ta_2O_5 to Cb_2O_5 ratio of 3 to 1), actual sales were a matter of market negotiation. Tantalum metal prices, for the same year, were $30 to $49 for powder, $47 to $60 for sheet, and $52 to $65 for rod, all on a per pound basis.

The paucity of domestic ore places the United States in a very unfavorable situation with respect to tantalum. There appears to be no alternative to continued dependence on imports. During World War II the submarine attacks made it necessary to air-lift tantalum ore to the United States to assure an adequate supply for military purposes. Since the war the Government has continued to stockpile tantalum for defense and strategic uses. In 1964 such stocks totaled approximately three million pounds. Known ore reserves throughout the free world, while adequate for the immediate future, are insufficient to meet the demands indicated in longer range projections. In general, it can be expected that the supply will increase with the demand. However, should a serious supply deficiency develop it probably could be corrected through use of special incentives of the type applied to uranium a few years ago. Tantalum and uranium are equally abundant and are similar with respect to the complexity and distribution of their minerals.

Derivation

Various techniques, including hand sorting, hydraulic washing, dredging, etc., are used in mining tantalum. It should be remembered that tantalum is nearly always obtained as a by-product in the mining of another ore, usually cassiterite. This, plus the nature of the ore body and local conditions, determines the method employed in a particular mining location. The product obtained from the mine is crushed and milled, if necessary, and the tantalum portion (tantalite) is then concentrated by wet or dry processes which usually involve gravity, magnetic, and/or electrostatic separations. The high specific gravity of tantalite aids beneficiation. Tantalum ore concentrates ordinarily contain 60%, or more, combined oxides (Ta_2O_5 and Cb_2O_5). Generally the ratio of Ta_2O_5 to Cb_2O_5 falls within the range 12:1 to 1:1. Tantalum is also obtained from columbite concentrates.

Although tantalite ore concentrates usually contain a variety of impurities (tin, silica, titanium, zirconium) in addition to the iron and manganese constituents, the most trouble-some problem encountered in extracting the tantalum is its separation from columbium. (See **Niobium**.) This, of course, is a conse-quence of the very closely related chemical properties of the two elements. Of the many processes which have been investigated for the isolation of tantalum only two have achieved commercial status. The classical fractional crystallization method of Marignac takes advantage of the fact that potassium fluotantalate, K_2TaF_7, is less soluble than potassium pentafluocolumbate, K_2CbOF_5, in dilute hydrofluoric acid solution. The first operation of this method involves fusion of the pulverized ore concentrate with sodium hydroxide. Treatment of the fused product, crude sodium tantalate and columbate, with hot water followed by hydrochloric acid removes most of the impurities except colum-bium, and provides a residue of tantalic and columbic acids (hydrated oxides). The res-idue is dissolved in hydrofluoric acid. A potassium compound (hydroxide, fluoride or carbonate) is then added and precipitation of K_2TaF_7 occurs when the solution is cooled. Although this process yields a tantalum salt of high purity, it is less satisfactory for the preparation of pure columbium salt.

The other industrially important method, known as liquid-liquid extraction, is relatively simple and highly efficient, and it provides tantalum, and also columbium, of exceptional purity. During recent years it has largely replaced the Marignac method. Historically, the liquid-liquid process dates back to World War II. While several individuals and organi-zations contributed to its development, the major investigations were made in the laboratories of the U.S. Bureau of Mines and the U.S. Atomic Energy Commission. According to current industrial practice, the finely-ground ore concentrate is digested with concentrated hydrofluoric acid, which dis-solves the oxides of tantalum and columbium without affecting the bulk of the impurities. Separation and purification of tantalum and columbium is achieved by contacting the acid solution with an organic solvent, methyl isobutyl ketone. A cascade extraction system is shown in Fig. 1. Tantalum is extracted by the organic liquid when the acidity of the solution is low. After removal of the tantalum

FIG. 1. Liquid-liquid extraction cascade system for separation of tantalum and columbium; mixers and settlers (center) are constructed of polyethylene. *(Courtesy Union Carbide Corporation)*

the acidity is increased and the columbium is then extracted. Any impurities dissolved during the digestion of the ore remain in the aqueous acid phase. Because of the pronounced solubility differences, very pure tantalum and very pure columbium can be obtained quantitatively in a relatively few extraction stages. The tantalum is removed from the organic solvent by extraction with pure water. Either Ta_2O_5 (hydrated form) or K_2TaF_7 can be obtained from the aqueous solution. Neutralization with ammonium hydroxide yields the former, and the addition of potas-sium fluoride provides the latter. This brief discussion is concerned with the principles of the liquid-liquid process and thus does not necessarily conform in detail to commercial procedures.

Metal Preparation

Tantalum is an "active" metal and, therefore, difficult to convert to the metallic state. The conversion procedures used for such common metals as iron or copper are not suitable. The major commercial methods for tantalum are based on fused salt electrolysis or reduction by highly active metals. Efforts to electrodeposit tantalum metal from water solution have not been successful. Tantalum, in common with aluminum and magnesium, is one of the very few structural metals produced commercially by electrodeposition from fused salts. In the tantalum electrowinning method developed by C. W. Balke and used for industrial production of the metal, potassium fluotantalate, K_2TaF_7, is the source of the element. Electrolysis is conducted at approximately 900°C using a cast-iron pot which serves as both container and cathode, and a graphite rod anode. Tantalum oxide is added to eliminate the "anode effect." The tantalum metal crystals, produced by the electrolyzing current, are separated from unreduced salt by water washing and further purified by leaching with strong acid. Typically, the finished metal powder is more than 99.9% tantalum with the major impurities being columbium, carbon, iron and silicon. Over the past forty-five years this method has provided tantalum in sufficient quantity and of adequate purity for the evaluation and utilization of the metal in a variety of industrial applications. Several modifications of the basic Balke process have been investigated, and a few of these are being utilized for production of the metal.

As mentioned, the product obtained by the above electrolytic process is in the form of individual, and relatively small, crystals. During the past several years there has been increasing interest in the development of a procedure suitable for the electrodeposition of dense, coherent, high-purity, tantalum metal for such applications as coatings and electroformed objects. Just recently, this objective has been achieved. Changes in electrolyte composition and in anode materials are, apparently, responsible for the success of the new approach. The electrolyte comprises only fluorides (K_2TaF_7 plus alkali metal fluorides) and is maintained free of common impurities, i.e., oxygen, water vapor, and chlorides. Tantalum metal is used as the anode material; and for this reason it should be recognized that the process is not a primary electrowinning method.

Another important commercial reduction method is based on the reaction of metallic sodium with potassium fluotantalate. This approach, in principle, dates back to Berzelius (1825), and was used by von Bolton (Germany) who produced the first ductile (high-purity) tantalum metal in 1903. The reaction, which is exothermic, is conducted in a steel bomb, and the product is a high-purity metal powder of quite small particle size. Among the other methods which have been investigated is one involving the interaction of tantalum carbide and tantalum oxide. This conversion requires a relatively high temperature and is conducted in vacuum. The metal sponge obtained, after embrittlement by reaction with hydrogen, is changed to powder form by crushing and milling. Aluminum and silicon are also used as reductants, and while the products obtained are established commercial materials, they are alloys rather than pure, elemental tantalum.

Although tantalum powder can be used directly in some applications, e.g., capacitors, conversion to massive form is generally required. Conventional melting and casting techniques cannot be utilized because of contamination problems arising from the lack of suitable container materials. Pressing and sintering is the classical method for consolidation and densification of tantalum. In this, as in other satisfactory consolidation processes, some improvement in purity is achieved. Sintering involves pressing the metal powder into the form of bars or rods which are then heated in vacuum by their resistance to passage of an electric current. Practical considerations limit the temperature during sintering to a maximum of approximately 2,600°C, which is 400°C below the melting point of tantalum. The density of the metal after the pressing-sintering operation is usually about 90% of the theoretical value. Higher densities can be attained by repetition of a cyclic treatment consisting of cold working followed by reheating.

Novel consolidation methods, which are gaining in popularity, involve actual melting of the metal in water-cooled copper containers. Arc melting (inert gas atmosphere) and electron beam melting (vacuum) can provide high-density, high-purity metal ingots many inches in diameter and several feet long. Ingots made by arc melting are shown in Fig. 2.

Such standard mill forms as plate, sheet, foil, rod, wire and tubing are obtained from

FIG. 2. Arc melted tantalum ingots. Those with rough surface are as they come from the arc melting furnace; they are machined to yield the smooth ingots on the right. The ingots on the scale weigh about 70 lb each, indicating the high density of tantalum, about twice that of steel. *(Courtesy Wah Chang Corp)*

the consolidated metal ingots by rolling, swaging and drawing techniques. Other conventional forming and shaping operations, including blanking, punching, shearing, spinning, slitting, crimping, bending, drilling, tapping and threading, are applicable to tantalum. Because tantalum has excellent ductility, all working and fabrication operations are usually performed at, or near, room temperature, thus avoiding oxidation. Annealing and recrystallizing treatments are generally conducted in vacuum. Cleaning (organic solvent and/or strong acids are suitable) is necessary before the metal is exposed to elevated temperatures. Tantalum is readily welded (resistance, tungsten-inert-gas arc, or electron beam) and, if precautions are taken to prevent contamination, the welds are ductile. Nickel-, silver-, and gold-based alloys can be used to braze tantalum. Tantalum is amenable to such mechanical joining processes as riveting, bolting and crimping.

Chemical Properties

Tantalum combines chemically with a majority of the elements of the Periodic Table, including nonmetals, metalloids, and metals. The reaction products can be classified using such general categories as chemical compounds, intermetallic compounds, and solid solution alloys. Tantalum also forms addition and substitution type complexes with both organic and inorganic ions, radicals, and compounds. In the organic derivatives the attachment is usually by way of oxygen atoms rather than direct tantalum-to-carbon bonding. Tantalum is a member of Group VB of the Periodic Table and, as would be expected, its principal oxidation state, or valence, is $+5$. It is also a transition element and, therefore, the fact that lower oxidation states ($+2$, $+3$, $+4$) are known is not surprising. The chemistry of tantalum, particularly the aqueous solution chemistry, is largely that of the $+5$ oxidation state because the lower oxidation states are, in general, highly unstable. The simple Ta^{+5} ion has no more than transitory existence in aqueous solution. It reacts readily with water and the reaction product, a hydrated oxide (or acid), precipitates from solution. In order to retain the tantalum in solution it is necessary that complexing agents more potent than water be present, and that the complex derivatives formed be soluble. Fluoride ions, potassium hydroxide, and

TABLE 1.   PHYSICAL AND MECHANICAL PROPERTIES

Atomic number	73
Atomic weight	180.948
Atomic diameter, Å	2.854
Atomic volume, cc/mole	10.90
Density, g/cc	16.654
Isotopes, natural, mass number	181 (100%)
Isotopes, artificial, mass number	176, 177, 178, 179, 180, 182, 183, 184, 185, 186
Cross section, thermal neutrons, barns/atom	
absorption	21.3 ± 1.0
scattering	5 ± 1
Lattice structure	body-centered cubic
Lattice constant, Å	3.2959
Coordination number	8
Melting point, °C	2996
Boiling point, °C	5427
Specific heat, cal/g/°C at 0°C	0.0340
Heat capacity, cal/mole/°C at 25°C	6.08
Entropy, cal/mole/°C at 25°C	9.90
Latent heat of fusion, cal/mole	7500
Latent heat of vaporization, kcal/mole	180
Heat of combustion, cal/g	1380
Vapor pressure, atm	
2,000°C	3×10^{-11}
2,500°C	4×10^{-8}
3,000°C	8×10^{-6}
3,500°C	2×10^{-4}
Thermal conductivity, cal/sec/cm/cm²/°C	
20°C	0.130
1830°C	0.198
Coefficient of linear thermal expansion, cm/cm/°C	
over range 20–1500°C	8.0×10^{-6}
Volume conductivity, % IACS	
18°C	13.0
Electrical resistivity, microhm-cm	
0°C	13.6
500°C	32.0
1000°C	50.4
Temperature coefficient of electrical resistivity, per °C	
over range 0–1000°C	3.0×10^{-3}
Superconduction transition temperature, °K	4.3
Work function, electron volts	4.12
Electron emission, ma/cm²	
1,000°C	1×10^{-5}
1,730°C	19.5
Electronic emission constant, amp/cm²(°K)²	60
Positive ion emission, electron volts	10.0
Spectral emissivity	
9.0 micron wavelength 25°C	0.06
1.0 micron wavelength 25°C	0.22
0.66 micron wavelength 2500°C	0.392
0.65 micron wavelength 2527°C	0.356
Total emissivity	
1400°C	0.20
2000°C	0.25

TABLE 1—*continued*

Total radiation, watt/cm²	
1330°C	7.3
1730°C	21.2
Refractive index	2.05
Magnetic susceptibility, cgs units	
25°C	0.849×10^{-6}
1870°C	0.685×10^{-6}
Electrochemical equivalent, mg/coulomb	0.3749
Standard electrode potential for Ta/Ta^{+5}, E° in volts	1.12
Ionization potential, volts	7.3
Electron configuration	$5d^3 6s^2$
Thermoelectric power	
Tantalum-platinum couple (cold junction at 0°C)	
temperature at hot junction	emf in mv
100°C	0.33
600°C	5.95
1200°C	21.41
Tantalum-tungsten couple (in vacuum)	
800°C	10.65
1200°C	16.65
1600°C	20.90
2000°C	22.90
Modulus of elasticity, psi	27×10^{-6}
Poisson's ratio	0.35
Ductile-to-brittle transition temperature	below −195°C
Tensile strength, psi	
Recrystallized condition	30,000
Worked condition (95% reduction)	60,000
Elongation, %	
Recrystallized condition	35
Worked condition (95% reduction)	< 5
Hardness, DPN	
Recrystallized condition	90
Worked condition (95% reduction)	200
Conditions for recrystallization	1300°C for 1 hour

some organic compounds, are very effective as complexing agents.

Tantalum is described as an acidic element because Ta_2O_5, in common with the oxides of other pentavalent metals, reacts chemically in a manner characteristic of an acid. Tantalic acid is a very weak acid. It combines with bases (hydroxides) to yield compounds (salts) which are called tantalates. Tantalates are complex substances, and determination of their composition and structure is difficult. From a chemical standpoint Ta_2O_5 is the most stable form of tantalum. This means that tantalum and its compounds are prone to oxidation. Although this natural tendency to oxidize cannot be eliminated, the rate of actual oxidation is subject to partial control because it is affected by the chemical state of the tantalum and by the environmental circumstances involved. Tantalum metal, for example, undergoes little apparent change during extended periods of exposure to normal atmospheric conditions. Some of the compounds of tantalum exhibit a degree of inertness resembling that of the metal; others undergo rapid decomposition if unusual and elaborate protection is not provided.

Such common compositions as halides, nitrates, phosphates, sulfates, sulfides, etc., are known for tantalum. These compounds, like the tantalates, are generally classified chemically as salts. Special precautions are required, however, in their preparation and preservation because, with the exception of the fluoride, they are decomposed by water. The halides, and their derivatives, are probably the most important group of tantalum compounds. They have low melting points and volatilize at low temperatures. Their pronounced chemical reactivity makes them useful as intermediates in the synthesis of other compounds. They are also utilized in the preparation of tantalum metal.

Tantalum reacts with many metalloids including boron, carbon, and silicon. These compounds, along with the nitrides, oxides, and phosphides, are generally described as being refractory, which means that they have high melting points. Tantalum carbide, melting point approximately 3800°C, is one of the most refractory materials known. The refractory compounds of tantalum, in addition to their high melting points, are hard and brittle, and have relatively high mechanical strength at high temperatures. With the exception of the silicides, these compounds are not oxidation resistant at moderate to high temperatures.

Tantalum forms alloys with a majority of the other metallic elements. With some of the metals only solid solution-type alloys are obtained while with others intermetallic compound formation is an important feature. Both types of behavior may be found in the same binary system, depending on composition and metallurgical history. The principal objective being sought in alloy investigations is an improvement in the performance of tantalum at high temperatures. Pertinent properties are strength, hardness, ductility, and the ratio of strength to weight. Significant progress has been made in these areas. Although advancement has also been made in regard to another important parameter, namely oxidation resistance, it has not been sufficient to qualify any of the present alloys for extended use at high temperatures in air. The more promising compositions investigated thus far are binary and ternary systems containing relatively low percentages of such other refractory metals as tungsten, rhenium, molybdenum, columbium (niobium), vanadium, and hafnium.

A layer of tantalum oxide is normally present on the surface of tantalum metal, and this film is responsible for a number of characteristics, particularly the lack of chemical reactivity, of the metal. These characteristics, in turn, determine the performance of tantalum in many of its most important applications. Although tantalum is regarded as an active metal, the oxide surface film renders it inert to attack by many chemical agents. Thus, only those reagents which attack the film, thereby exposing the metal, have a deleterious effect on tantalum. Tantalum is either completely inert or highly resistant to attack by nearly all inorganic acids, regardless of temperature or concentration. Hydrofluoric acid, which readily dissolves the metal, and hot fuming sulfuric acid are the notable exceptions. In the absense of fluorides, tantalum is highly resistant to salt solutions. Alkalis attack tantalum, and the rate increases with concentration and temperature. Tantalum is resistant to attack by most molten metals, including molten plutonium, at temperatures up to approximately 1,000°C. Details of the outstanding corrosion resistance of tantalum are found in Ref. 5.

Tantalum combines with molecular hydrogen at temperatures above 250°C, but the hydride formed decomposes, and the hydrogen is liberated, at temperatures above 800°C in vacuum. When in galvanic circuit, tantalum becomes cathodic to nearly all metals. This situation can lead to the liberation of atomic hydrogen which is readily absorbed by the tantalum, even at room temperature. Galvanic coupling and stray currents are to be avoided because absorbed hydrogen embrittles the metal.

Applications

Applications of tantalum are based on its high melting point, good strength and ductility, low vapor pressure, inertness to chemical attack at temperatures below about 150°C, gettering properties at elevated temperatures, and the rectifying and dielectric properties of its oxide surface film.

The largest uses for tantalum are in the manufacture of capacitors, both liquid and solid types, and in the fabrication of a variety of components for corrosion resistant chemical equipment. The dielectric film (oxide) on tantalum which makes the metal useful as a capacitor component can also be utilized as a rectifier for converting alternating current to direct current. This was an early use for the metal and such rectifiers continue to be made. The self-healing property of the oxide film makes this type of rectifier particularly useful in applications where rupturing of the dielectric, as a consequence of occasional current surges, may be expected. Many components for vacuum tubes, and also for high-temperature furnaces, are made from tantalum. The first significant industrial use for tantalum was as filaments in incandescent lamp bulbs. Several million tantalum filament bulbs were manufactured before the market was captured by tungsten.

Tantalum has long been used in chemical equipment where its strength, its inertness to chemical attack, with resultant absence of contamination in products exposed to it, and its extremely high heat transfer coefficient make it valuable in many processes.

Tantalum carbide imparts shock resistance and a very low coefficient of friction to tungsten carbide cutting tools and drawing dies. Tantalum oxide is an ingredient in some high refractive index optical glasses. Certain tantalum compounds are useful as catalysts for chemical reactions.

Although the nuclear absorption cross section of tantalum is sufficiently high to preclude its use in the construction of thermal reactors, it does find application as a material for the containment and transfer of liquid metals used as coolants in some types of nuclear reactors.

The complete immunity of tantalum to body fluids and its nonirritating tolerance by body tissues have resulted in its wide use for surgical repairs. It is applied as plate and sheet in bone repair (especially in cranial sites), as wire for sutures, as foil and wire for nerve repair, and as plate, sheet and woven gauze for abdominal muscle repair.

References

1. Mellor, J. W., "A Comprehensive Treatise on Inorganic and Theoretical Chemistry," Vol. IX, pp. 883–925, London, Longmans Green and Company, 1933.
2. Weeks, M. E., "Discovery of the Elements," 6th Ed., pp. 345–352, Easton, Pa., Journal of Chemical Education, 1956.
3. Aller, L. H., "The Abundance of the Elements," New York, Interscience Publishers, Inc., 1961.
4. Miller, G. L., "Tantalum and Niobium," New York, Academic Press, Inc., 1959.
5. Hampel, C. A., "Rare Metals Handbook," 2nd Ed., pp. 469–518, New York, Reinhold Publishing Corp., 1961.
6. Sisco, F. T., and Epremian, E., Eds., "Columbium and Tantalum," New York, John Wiley and Sons, Inc., 1963.
7. Quarrell, A. G., Ed., "Niobium, Tantalum, Molybdenum and Tungsten," New York, Elsevier Publishing Co., 1961.
8. Tietz, T. E., and Wilson, J. W., "Behavior and Properties of Refractory Metals," pp. 223–273, Stanford, Cal., Stanford University Press, 1965.
9. Hansen, M., "Constitution of Binary Alloys," 2nd Ed., (R. P. Elliott, First Supplement, 1965), New York, McGraw-Hill Book Co., 1958.
10. Senderoff, S., and Mellors, G. W., "Coherent Coatings of Refractory Metals," *Science*, **153**, 1475–1481 (1966).
11. Moshier, R. W., "Analytical Chemistry of Niobium and Tantalum," New York, Pergamon Press, 1964.

R. F. WEHRMANN

TECHNETIUM

History

Perrier and Segré are credited with the discovery in 1937 of element 43 which they later named technetium, Tc.[9] The element was formed by bombarding molybdenum metal with deuterons, and it was identified by noting that the pertechnetate ion, TcO_4^-, followed the chemistry of perrhenate ion, ReO_4^-, which was added as a carrier.

On the basis of powder diffraction patterns carried out by Mooney[6] on material supplied by Parker, it was later shown that technetium fits into the Periodic Table between manganese and rhenium because of its similarity in structure type and dimensions to neighboring elements of the Periodic Table (Ru, Re and Os). Thus, the position of element 43, which had been a missing member of the manganese group for a long time, was finally filled.

Occurrence

All the isotopes of technetium are radioactive. Half-lives, type of decay, decay energies, and

TABLE 1.   A NUMBER OF THE MOST IMPORTANT ISOTOPES OF TECHNETIUM

Isotope	Half-life	Radiation Energy		Method of Production
		Type	MeV	
Tc^{95m}	60 days	$\beta+$	0.4	$Mo^{95}(p,n)Tc^{95m}$
		γ	0.201	
Tc^{96}	4.2 days	γ	0.77–0.84	$Mo^{96}(p,n)Tc^{96}$
Tc^{97m}	91 days	γ	0.096	$Mo^{97}(p,n)Tc^{97m}$
Tc^{97}	2.6×10^6 yr	γ		$Mo^{97}(d,2n)Tc^{97}$; $Tc^{97m} \rightarrow Tc^{97}$
Tc^{98}	1.5×10^6 yr	$\beta-$	0.30	$Mo^{98}(p,n)Tc^{98}$
		γ	0.66, 0.75	
Tc^{99m}	6.04 hr	γ	0.14	$Mo^{98}(n,\gamma)Mo^{99} \xrightarrow{\beta} Tc^{99m}$
Tc^{99}	2.15×10^5 yr	$\beta-$	0.29	Fission product; daughter Tc^{99m}

methods of production of a number of the more important radioactive isotopes are given in Table 1.

Four of these isotopes Tc^{95m}, Tc^{96}, Tc^{97m} and Tc^{99m} are relatively short-lived and are used as tracers in studying the chemical properties of technetium. The three isotopes Tc^{97}, Tc^{98}, and Tc^{99} are long-lived with half-lives $>10^5$ years and could be accumulated in weighable amounts to study the chemistry of technetium. These long-lived isotopes of technetium are still too short to allow the existence of primordial technetium in the earth's crust. Yet, technetium has been detected in certain stars, and theories of stellar evolution and element synthesis must explain its presence in these stars.

Sources of Technetium

Relatively large quantities of long-lived Tc^{99} (half-life $= 2.15 \times 10^5$ yr) are available from the fission of U^{235}. Technetium has a fission yield of 6.1% which corresponds to the formation of 27.0 mg of technetium per gram of U^{235} burned up in fission.

Thus, considerable quantities of technetium have been produced with the advent of nuclear power. Kilogram quantities of technetium have been isolated, and production can be expanded if demand warrants it. Technetium-99 is available at $<\$100/g$ from Oak Ridge National Laboratory. Colton[4] notes that the time is ripe for a rapid expansion of technetium chemistry with the more ready availability of technetium to universities and research institutions. Colton notes also that

the chemistry of technetium resembles that of rhenium quite closely, as would be expected, but that much more is known about rhenium than about technetium chemistry.

Preparation and Properties of the Metal

Pure technetium metal is conveniently prepared by the hydrogen reduction of ammonium pertechnetate. If $KTcO_4$ is used in place of the NH_4TcO_4 salt, it is difficult to eliminate potassium from the metal product. The reduction proceeds in two stages. First, NH_4TcO_4 is reduced to TcO_2 at 200–225°C. After the reduction to TcO_2 is complete, the temperature is raised to 600–800°C in order to reduce TcO_2 to technetium metal. Spectroscopic analysis shows that the technetium metal prepared in this fashion contains less than 1 ppm of sodium, molybdenum, magnesium, and silicon.[11] However, the metal contains about 5% oxygen, and 20% of the technetium by weight is lost by volatilization of TcO_2 when the technetium metal is melted. Weight loss of technetium metal is negligible upon subsequent melting. It is possible to reduce the oxygen content of technetium metal to a few parts per million by reducing with hydrogen at 1100°C for at least 24 hours.

After melting, massive technetium metal dissolves with greater difficulty in oxidizing acids, such as hot perchloric acid, than does finely-divided technetium.

Technetium metal crystallizes in a hexagonal close-packed structure with lattice parameters of a = 2.735 and c = 4.391 Å with two atoms in the elementary cell. The average metallic radius is 1.358 Å. The metal is slightly paramagnetic and has a high critical temperature of $7.77°K$[12] which rivals the critical temperature of niobium ($T_c = 8.6°K$).

The physical properties of technetium are tabulated in Table 2. Most of these properties were estimated by Gschneidner.[5]

Chemical Properties

Technetium exists in valence states of $+7$, $+6$, $+5$, $+4$, $+2$ and 0.[7] The evidence for the existence of the $+6$, $+5$ and $+4$ states is primarily polarographic. Tc(VI) disproportionates within 3 to 4 minutes to Tc(V) and Tc(VII), whereas Tc(V) disproportionates to Tc(VII) and Tc(IV) within one hour.[1] Tc(IV) exists as the black dioxide, TcO_2, and as the chlorocomplex, $(TcCl_6)^{-2}$. The most characteristic and stable oxidation state is its heptavalent state or Tc(VII).

Technetium is ordinarily present as the pertechnetate anion, TcO_4^-, in aqueous solution.

A noteworthy separation of pertechnetate anion, TcO_4^-, from other elements in solution is based on the strong complex formed with a quaternary or tertiary amine group in a solid or liquid. Strongly basic solid anion exchangers contain quaternary or tertiary amine groups which serve as preferential sites for the sorption of TcO_4^-. Since a large volume of concentrated HCl or HNO_3 must be used to remove TcO_4^- from the solid anion exchanger, some of the advantages associated with the preliminary separation step are lost with the use of a solid anion exchanger. Nevertheless, anion exchange is a useful step in the concentration of technetium.

Liquid-liquid extraction is superior to anion exchange on a solid in the recovery of TcO_4^- because of the simplicity of the subsequent processing. Distribution coefficients (K_d) of 8000 for permanganate, MnO_4^-, 778 for pertechnetate, and 225 for perrhenate anion between pyridine and 4.0 N NaOH have been reported. Subsequently, it was shown that

TABLE 2. PHYSICAL PROPERTIES OF TECHNETIUM

Property	Unit	Value
Atomic number		43
Atomic weight		99
Atomic volume, V	cc/g-atom	8.635
Density, d	g/cc	11.49
Melting point, T_m	°C	2170
Heat of fusion, ΔH_f	kcal/g-atom	5.42
Boiling point	°C	5030
Heat of sublimation at 298°K, ΔH_s^{298}	kcal/g-atom	152
Cohesive energy, $\Delta H_o°$	kcal/g-atom	152
Electronic specific heat constant, γ	cal/g-atom/deg²	9.7×10^{-4}
Heat capacity at constant pressure, C_p	cal/g-atom/deg	5.80
Heat capacity at constant volume, $C_v = C'_v + C_v^e$	cal/g-atom/deg	5.69
Lattice contribution to the heat capacity at constant volume, C_v^1	cal/g-atom/deg	5.40
Dilation term, $A = 9a^2V/XC_p^2$	g-atom/cal	1.066×10^{-5}
Debye temperature from specific heat data θ_o^s	°K	351
Debye temperature from Lindemann equation, θ^m	°K	335
Leibfried number, $L = RT_m/\mu V$ $R = $ gas constant		0.0165
Modified Leibfried number, $L' = KT_m/\mu V$ K depends on crystal structure and equals 2.29 for technetium		0.0193
Bragg number, $Br = \Delta H_f/\mu V$		0.0173

TABLE 2—*continued*

Property	Unit	Value
Entropy of fusion, ΔS_f	e.u./g-atom	2.29
Entropy of vaporization, ΔS_v	e.u./g-atom	25.5
Gruneisen constant calculated from C^1_v data, $\gamma_G = 3\alpha V/XC_v^1$		2.75
Gruneisen constant from C_v data, $\gamma_G = 3\alpha V/XC_v$		2.61
Size factor, $SF = [(Rt_m/\mu V)(1-\sigma)/(1+\sigma)]^{0.5}$		
via Eshelby		9.73
via Friedel		11.10
mean value		10.42 ± 0.69
Metallic radius, r	Å	1.358
First ionization potential	ev	7.28
Second ionization potential	ev	15.26
Third ionization potential	ev	31.9
Work function	v	4.4
Superconducting transition temperature	°K	7.77
Thermal neutron activation cross section, σ_{ac}	barns	22
Young's (elastic) modulus, Y	kg/cm²	3.76×10^6
Shear modulus, μ	kg/cm²	1.45×10^6
Ratio of Young's modulus to shear modulus, Y/μ		2.59
Poisson's ratio,		0.293
Ratio, $(1-\sigma)/(1+\sigma)$		0.547
Compressibility at zero pressure, X	cm²/kg	3.30×10^{-6}
Ratio of compressibility constants	b/a² in equation $\Delta V/V = aP + bP^2$ where P = pressure in kg/cm²	2.19
Bulk modulus, B	kg/cm²	3.03×10^6
Linear coefficient of thermal expansion, α	per °C	8.06×10^{-6}

the methyl-substituted derivatives of pyridine were more effective than pyridine itself in recovering TcO_4^-, especially from solutions containing an appreciable amount of nitrate ion or NH_4OH.[11] Technetium can be recovered from the organic phase by adding an inert diluent, or by removing the pyridine compound by steam distillation.

Technetium is also extracted by methyl ketones[2] such as methylethylketone, MEK, but these extractants are not as effective as the pyridine derivatives in the presence of an interferring agent such as high concentration of nitrate anions.[11]

Other methods of recovery of technetium involve the distillation of Tc_2O_7 from concentrated H_2SO_4 at $>155°C$, the precipitation of Tc_2S_7 and the reduction of TcO_4^- to insoluble TcO_2 with hydrazine in alkaline

solution. These methods offer no particular advantages over solvent extraction or anion exchange with a quaternary or tertiary amine, and they do possess a number of severe disadvantages such as high distillation temperature and the use of corrosive reagents.

Other possible recovery methods are described in reviews by Pozdynakov,[10] Anders,[1] Tribalat,[14] Boyd,[2] Murin,[7] and Colton.[4]

Analytical Methods of Determination

Technetium can be weighed as the tetraphenylarsonium compound, $(C_6H_5)_4AsTcO_4$. It can be determined spectrophotometrically from characteristic peaks with absorption maxima at 247 and 285 mμ. The spectrophotometric method is particularly suitable for the simultaneous determination of technetium and rhenium. Since technetium has a specific activity of 37,300 counts/min/μg, it can be determined by 4π-beta counting in the absence of other radioactivities. Trace quantities of technetium can also be determined polarographically. Further details on these methods can be found in Ref. 10.

Applications

The pertechnetate anion, TcO_4^-, possesses anticorrosive properties.[3] A concentration of only 5 μg of Tc/ml of solution will keep steel from rusting. This corrosion protection is available only in closed systems since the technetium must be confined because of its radioactivity.

Technetium and its alloys are superconductors with critical temperatures of the same order as niobium and its compounds, and they can be used to create magnetic fields of high strength in compact units at low temperature.

The short-lived Tc^{99m} isomer with a half-life of 6.0 hours has found extensive use in clinical medicine[13] because of its desirable physical properties such as a 140-KeV gamma ray which is readily detected, a half-life of 6.0 hours which is sufficiently short to limit the radiation dose to the body, and the absence of beta radiation. It is used to locate tumors in the spleen, liver, brain, and thyroid by scintillation scanning. The pertechnetate anion, TcO_4^-, behaves like iodine by concentrating in the thyroid. As a sulfur colloid, the Tc^{99m} is scavenged by the spleen and liver, and in this form it can be used to visualize these organs by scintillation scanning.

Toxicology

The maximum permissible concentration of Tc^{99} in water $(MPC)_w$ is 0.01 μCi/cc, and the maximum permissible concentration of Tc^{99} in air $(MPC)_a$ is 2×10^{-6} μCi/cc for a 40-hour week. With continuous exposure during a 168-hour week, these values are 3×10^{-3} μCi/cc and 7×10^{-7} μCi/cc, respectively.[8] The maximum permissible burden is 10 μCi in the kidney, 200 in the liver, 200 in the total body, 400 in the skin, 500 in the bone, and 2,000 μCi in the lung. The lung is the critical organ when technetium is present as an insoluble aerosol. The $(MPC)_a$ values for this form of technetium are 6×10^{-8} μCi/cc for a 40-hour week, and 2×10^{-8} μCi/cc for a 168-hour week.

Even though Tc^{99} has a long half-life $(2.15 \times 10^5$ years) and emits only a weak 0.29-MeV beta, it is still a considerable contamination hazard, and should be handled in a glove box. Its specific activity is 16.9 mCi/g of Tc^{99} or 6.2×10^8 disintegrations/sec/g of Tc^{99}. These levels of activity must be confined and not allowed to spread. Provision must be made for the disposal of contaminated equipment because of the long half-life of the weak beta emitter.

References

1. Anders, E., "The Radiochemistry of Technetium," Washington, D.C., National Research Council, Committee on Nuclear Science, 1960; *Ann. Rev. Nucl. Sci.,* **9**, 203 (1959).
2. Boyd, G. E., *J. Chem. Educ.,* **36**, 3 (1959); and Boyd, G. E., and Larson, Q. V., *J. Phys. Chem.,* **64**, 988 (1960).
3. Cartledge, G. H., *J. Phys. Chem.,* **64**, 1882 (1960); *Corrosion,* **15**, 469 (1959); *J. Phys. Chem.,* **61**, 979 (1957).
4. Colton, R., "The Chemistry of Rhenium and Technetium," New York, Interscience Publishers, 1965.
5. Gschneidner K. A., "Solid State Physics," F. Seitz and D. Turnbull, Eds., Vol. 16, p. 275, New York, Academic Press, 1964.
6. Mooney, R. C. L., *Acta Cryst.,* **1**, 161 (1948).
7. Murin, A. W., et al., *Usp. Khim.,* **30**, 274 (1961).
8. National Bureau of Standards Handbook 69, "Maximum Permissible Body Burdens and Maximum Permissible Concentrations of Radionuclides in Air and in Water for Occupational Exposure," p. 44, Washington, D.C. U.S. Government Printing Office, June, 1959.
9. Perrier, C., and Segré, E., *J. Chem. Phys.,* **5**, 712 (1937); *J. Chem. Phys.,* **7**, 155 (1939); *Nature,* **159**, 24 (1947).
10. Poznyakov, A. A., *Usp. Khim.,* **34**, 300 (1965).
11. Rimshaw, S. J., and Malling, G. F., *Anal. Chem.,* **33**, 751 (1961).
12. Sekula, S. T., and Kernohan, R. H., *Phys. Rev.,* **155**, 364-9 (1967).
13. Silver, S., *Nucleonics,* **23**, 106 (1965).
14. Tribalat, S., "Rhenium and Technetium," p. 9, Paris, Gauthier-Villars, 1957.

S. J. RIMSHAW

TELLURIUM

History and Occurrence

Tellurium was discovered in 1782 by Franz Müller von Reichenstein as a result of studies on a bluish-white ore of gold from Transylvania. However, it was not until 1798 that Klaproth succeeded in isolating tellurium from the ore and suggested that the new element be called "tellurium" after the Latin "tellus," meaning "earth."

The terrestrial abundance of tellurium is considerably less than that of its sister element selenium, with the average amounts of sulfur, selenium and tellurium in crustal rocks being reported by Mason[9] as 520, 0.09, and 0.002 ppm, respectively. These values correspond to a S:Se:Te ratio of 260,000:45:1. Tellurium is most commonly found in small amounts in sulfide deposits in the form of independent minerals such as altaite, $PbTe$; calaverite, $AuTe_2$; coloradoite, $HgTe$; rickardite, Cu_4Te_3; petzite, Ag_3AuTe_2; sylvanite, $(Ag,Au)Te_2$; tetradymite, Bi_2Te_2S. In contrast to tellurium, selenium in such sulfide deposits occurs only as an isomorphous admixture in the sulfide lattice. This behavior is partly attributable to the difference in the covalent radii of the sulfide, selenide and telluride ions, viz., 1.04, 1.17 and 1.37 Å, respectively (see Table 2). Tellurium has also been found as the native metal and as the dioxide, TeO_2 (tellurite or tellurium ochre).

Tellurium is the only element forming a number of minerals with gold, and is commonly encountered in association with gold ores. It is most widely distributed in low-temperature hydrothermal deposits where gold and silver tellurides often occur in agglomerations of commercial importance. On the other hand, selenium is much more rarely found in gold ore deposits. Generally it combines with silver or enters isomorphously into the lattice of sulfide minerals.

The geochemistry of tellurium is not well known and there are no extensive data on its occurrence and distribution in such diversified materials as rocks and minerals, plants, soils, waters and ocean sediments. Important data on the mineralogy of tellurium as well as selenium are provided by Sindeeva.[11]

An important source of tellurium is the sulfide ores of the Canadian Shield, where tellurium occurs as a dispersed element in discrete minerals in forms of chalcopyrite and pyrrhotite. Ores containing tellurium are also mined in the United States in Montana, Utah, Arizona and New Mexico. In South America the major source of tellurium is the lead and copper ores of Peru.

Most of the Free World's production of tellurium is centered in North America, with the current annual production on this continent being around 350,000 lb. The estimated annual total Free World production is about 500,000 lb.

Extractive Metallurgy

The principal commercial source of tellurium is the anode slime encountered in electrolytic copper refining. Besides tellurium, these slimes contain silver, gold and selenium, so that their processing is geared to the recovery of all such by-products of value. Following the removal of copper and selenium, tellurium can be extracted from the slimes by caustic leaching and neutralization of the resulting leach liquor. The precipitate so obtained is an impure tellurium dioxide. Since some of the tellurium is contained in the slimes which are charged to the Doré furnace for the recovery of silver and gold, the tellurium is removed in a soda slag which, upon leaching and neutralization of the leach liquor, again results in a crude tellurium dioxide. This material can be further refined by re-solution and re-precipitation, and metallic tellurium produced by a suitable reduction process. The most satisfactory process is one in which tellurium is electrodeposited on stainless steel cathodes from a strongly caustic solution of sodium tellurite. The resulting electrodeposit is removed from the cathodes and cast in suitable form or pulverized for sale as refined or commercial-grade tellurium.

Refined tellurium contains heavy base metal impurities such as lead, copper and iron, as well as selenium and oxygen. To upgrade this product to high purity tellurium, the base metal impurities can be removed successfully by vacuum distillation or zone melting, with the former process yielding a product having a total content of heavy metals in the range 10 to 30 ppm. The zone melting process, which is operative on a much smaller scale, can lower the metallic impurities to below spectrographic detection limits. Although neither vacuum distillation nor zone melting removes selenium, this element can be removed by treatment of molten tellurium with hydrogen, which converts selenium to hydrogen selenide. An excellent discussion of various methods for the production of high-purity tellurium has been presented by Jennings and Farge.[6]

Physical Properties

As a member of Group VIA of the Periodic Table, tellurium bears a definite resemblance to selenium and sulfur in many of its proper-

ties. The increasing metallic nature of the elements in this group with increasing atomic weight is clearly indicated in the case of tellurium, as is seen by the fact that oxygen and sulfur are insulators, selenium and

TABLE 1.

Bond	Energies (kcal/mole)
O-O	33.2
S-S	50.9
Se-Se	44.0
Te-Te	33.0

Pauling, Linus, "The Nature of the Chemical Bond," 3rd ed., Ithaca, N.Y., Cornell University Press, 1960.

TABLE 2. PERIODICITY AMONG GROUP VIA ELEMENTS

	Oxygen	Sulfur	Selenium	Tellurium
Electron Configuration	2–6	2–8–6	2–8–18–6	2–8–18–18–6
Covalent Radius, Å	0.74	1.04	1.17	1.37
Electronegativity (Pauling Scale)	3.5	2.5	2.4	2.1

Pauling, Linus, "The Nature of the Chemical Bond," 3rd ed., Ithaca, N.Y., Cornell University Press, 1960.

TABLE 3. PHYSICAL PROPERTIES OF HEXAGONAL CRYSTALLINE TELLURIUM

Atomic number	52
Atomic weight	127.60
Atomic volume, cc/g-atom	20.45
Density, 25°C, g/cc	6.24
Melting point, °C	450
Boiling point, °C	990†
Heat of fusion, (at m.p.) kcal/g-atom	4.27
Heat of vaporization, (Te$_2$ at b.p.) kcal/g-atom	13.65
Heat capacity, 25°C, cal/g-atom/°C	6.14
Entropy, 25°C, e.u.	11.88
Thermal conductivity, 20°C, cal/sq cm/cm/sec/°C	0.014
Coefficient of thermal expansion, μ in./°C (∥ to c-axis)	16.75
Electrical resistivity, microhm-cm, 25°C (∥ to c-axis)	436,000
Magnetic susceptibility, 18°C, cgs	-0.31×10^{-6}
Hardness, Mohs' scale	2.3
Lattice constants	
a-axis	4.45 Å
c-axis	5.91 Å
Thermal neutron cross section, 2,200 m/sec	
absorption, barns	4.7 ± 0.1
scattering, barns	5 ± 1

†The boiling point, 990°C, is the extrapolated value based on Brooks' equation[1] for vapor pressure between 786 and 1110°K, viz., log $P_{mm} = 7.599 - (5960.2/T)$, where T = °K. The commonly reported boiling point of tellurium, 1390°C, is incorrect.

tellurium semiconductors, and polonium a metal. The resemblance between selenium and sulfur is more marked in a number of respects than that between selenium and tellurium.

The periodicity in properties which follows the periodicity in neighbouring groups of the periodic system is shown in Tables 1 and 2 which give the atom-to-atom bond energies, covalent radii and electronegativity values.

Tellurium exists in stable form as a hexagonal crystalline material having trigonal symmetry. Eight stable isotopes of tellurium are known having mass numbers of 120, 122, 123, 124, 125, 126, 128 and 130 and abundances of 0.08, 2.46, 0.87, 4.61, 6.99, 18.71, 31.79, and 34.49%, respectively.

A number of physical properties of hexagonal crystalline tellurium are given in Table 3.

Hexagonal crystalline tellurium is characterized by a marked anisotropy in many of its physical properties including the following: electrical conductivity, linear compressibility, linear coefficient of thermal expansion, optical absorption and index of refraction with respect to polarized light, and galvanomagnetic properties. Thus, the conductivity along the two major axes differs by about a factor of 2, and the Hall coefficient shows a similar behavior. In addition, the Hall coefficient illustrates one of the remarkable anomalies of tellurium, namely, at low temperatures the Hall coefficient is positive and shows the expected reversal of sign just below room temperature. However, it has a second reversal at about 500°K. Associated with this double reversal is the fact that no one has succeeded in preparing extrinsic tellurium which is n-type so that tellurium pn-junctions are not possible.

Chemical Properties

Binary and Ternary Tellurides. Tellurium forms binary tellurides with most of the elements in the Periodic Table. The most common method of synthesis involves heating stoichiometric amounts of the two elements in an evacuated ampoule. Hydrogen telluride, although highly unstable much above 0°C, will precipitate some metal ions from solution as the tellurides. Metal chlorides can yield the

corresponding telluride when heated with tellurium in a stream of hydrogen.

Many tellurides possess semiconducting properties which have been examined extensively together with thermal, crystallographic and magnetic properties. The optical properties of these materials have been investigated to some extent, and at least one is available commercially as an infrared transmitting material, viz., CdTe.

Ternary tellurides are also formed by heating the elements in question in an evacuated ampoule and many such compounds have been studied for their semiconducting properties.

Halogen Compounds. The halides of tellurium range from a colorless gas through a pale colored liquid, and white crystals to deeply colored crystals having a melting point above 360°C. Although these compounds are considered generally to be covalent, there is evidence that $TeCl_4$ exists in an ionized form, $TeCl_3{}^+Cl^-$, in the solid state. Not all of the halides are formed in which tellurium has a valency of 2, 4 and 6. Thus, tellurium hexafluoride, TeF_6, and ditellurium decafluoride, Te_2F_{10}, are the only hexagonal fluorides formed, while tellurium diiodide, TeI_2, is the only dihalide which has not yet been prepared.

The physical properties of tellurium halides are given in Table 4.

Oxides and Oxyacids. Like sulfur and selenium, tellurium readily forms oxides which can be hydrolyzed to oxyacids. The chemistry of these oxides and oxyacids of tellurium[4] reflects the more metallic nature of the element and its amphoteric behavior.

Considerable data are available on tellurium dioxide, the most stable oxide, whereas much less is known of the other oxides, TeO, TeO_3 and Te_2O_5. Thus, tellurium monoxide has not yet been formed in the solid state, although there is considerable evidence for its existence in the vapor. The pentoxide has been reported as having been formed by heating orthotelluric acid, or α-TeO_3, at 406° for 25 hours, and is said to be stable at room temperature. Thermochemical data for TeO_2 are presented in Table 5.

Of the oxyacids, H_2TeO_3, H_6TeO_6, and H_2TeO_5, orthotelluric acid, H_6TeO_6, is of particular interest, in view of the marked difference in its structural and ionization

TABLE 4. PHYSICAL PROPERTIES OF TELLURIUM HALIDES

Compound	Form	Density, g/cc	M.P., °C	B.P., °C
$TeBr_2$	Chocolate brown crystals	—	Decomposes	—
$TeBr_4$	Yellow monoclinic crystals	4.30	363°	414–27°
$TeCl_2$	Black solid and liquid purple vapor	—	208°	328°
$TeCl_4$	Pale yellow crystals Maroon liquid and vapor	3.01	227.9°	390°/755 mm.
TeF_4	Colorless needle-like crystals	—	129°	Decomp. > 194° Calc. 374°
TeF_6	Colorless gas	3.025 at −24°	−37.8° −36°	−38.9° −35.5°
Te_2F_{10}	Colorless liquid	2.839	−33.7°	59°
Te_2I_2 or TeI	Light gray glass	5.49	—	—
TeI_4	Black crystals	5.145	280° (vac.)	—
TeI_2Br_2	Garnet red crystals	—	323–5°	420° dec.
$TeCl_2Br_2$	Yellow powder Ruby red liquid	—	292°	415°

TABLE 5. RECOMMENDED THERMOCHEMICAL VALUES FOR TeO_2[4]

Melting point, °C	732.6 ± 0.1° = 1005.8°K
Vapor pressure equation	$\log P_{mm} = -13{,}222/T + 12.3284$ (450–733°)
Heat of sublimation	59 ± 2 kcal/mole
Heat of fusion	7.0 ± 0.5 kcal/mole
Heat of vaporization	51.7 kcal/mole
Molar heat capacity at 25°C	16 ± 1 cal/mole/deg
Entropy at 25°C	14 ± 2 eu.
Heat of formation	$Te(s) + O_2(g) \rightarrow TeO_2(s)$ $\triangle H_{298} = -77.75$ kcal/mole
Free energy of formation	$Te(s) + O_2(g) \rightarrow TeO_2(s)$ $\triangle F_{298} = -64.5$ kcal/mole

properties from those of the corresponding sulfur and selenium acids and of its tendency to polymerize to form metatelluric acid, $(H_2TeO_4)_n$. Recommended values for the dissociation constants of tellurous and telluric acids are given in Table 6.

TABLE 6. DISSOCIATION CONSTANTS OF TELLUROUS AND TELLURIC ACIDS
(Values recommended by Dutton and Cooper[4])

	K_1	K_2	K_3
H_2TeO_3	3×10^{-3}	2×10^{-8}	
H_6TeO_6	2.0×10^{-8}	1×10^{-11}	$\sim 3 \times 10^{-15}$
$(H_2TeO_4)_n$	2.0×10^{-8}	1×10^{-11}	

Sulfides and Oxysulfides. The simplest sulfur compound which has been prepared is tellurium sulfide. This compound is formed by reaction between tellurium and the sulfide of zinc, cadmium or mercury. The higher sulfides, TeS_2 and TeS_3, which are analogous to the oxides, are precipitated from tellurite solution by treatment with sodium sulfide or hydrogen sulfide. They are converted to tellurium dioxide by heating in air. It is interesting to note that, during formation of the disulfide in basic solution, the ions $TeS_3^=$ and $TeS_2O^=$ are formed and their stability constants have been determined. Of the oxysulfides, the red compound $TeSO_3$ is of particular interest since it can be formed by reaction between tellurium and concentrated sulfuric acid and can be used as a qualitative test for tellurium.

Organic Tellurium Compounds. The more metallic nature of tellurium compared with sulfur and selenium is manifested in the organic chemistry of the element by the decreased stability of the carbon-tellurium bond. This fact leads to difficulties in the synthesis of various compounds and the instability of these materials compared with their sulfur and selenium analogues. An excellent survey of organic tellurium compounds is given by Pheinboldt.[10]

The organic compounds of tellurium include tellurols or telluromercaptans, RTeH; tellurides and ditellurides, R_2Te and R_2Te_2; tellurium dihalides, R_2TeX_2; telluroxides, R_2TeO; tellurones, R_2TeO_2; telluronium compounds, $[R_2Te]X$ and $[RT_2eCHCOOH]X$ with a branching R′; tellurinic acid and derivatives, RTeOOH; and telluroketones, RC_2Te. It should be noted that although alkyl tellurols can be synthesized, aromatic tellurols have not yet been isolated.

Tellurate ions react with polyhydroxy organic compounds such as ethylene glycol, glycerol, and mannitol to form polyoltellurate complexes.

Analysis

Tellurium, like selenium, is commonly detected by precipitation with sulfur dioxide in hydrochloric acid solution. Solutions of tellurium(IV) or tellurium(VI) in the presence of dilute hydrochloric acid yield black elementary tellurium upon gassing with sulfur dioxide. Red-brown tellurium sulfide is formed when hydrogen sulfide reacts with tellurium(IV). Other reducing agents for tellurium(IV) or tellurium(VI) which yield the element include stannous chloride, hypophosphorous acid, hydrazine hydrochloride and aluminum amalgam, zinc or magnesium.

Tellurium or a telluride, but not oxidized tellurium compounds react in the cold with fuming sulfuric acid or with warm concentrated sulfuric acid to give a red color, the intensity of which color depends on the amount of tellurium present. When the red solution is added to water, black elementary tellurium is precipitated. This sulfuric acid test has been applied to the spectrophotometric determination of tellurium and to the detection of tellurium in minerals.

In the determination of tellurium as well as selenium, losses may occur due to coprecipitation or volatilization. Both elements may be coprecipitated with hydrous oxides of bismuth, antimony, iron, zinc, zirconium and titanium. Such precipitates can be used as a convenient means of separation. Also, separation by volatilization can be effected since tellurides may be distilled in chlorine and heating tellurites in a stream of hydrogen chloride gas results in the formation of volatile $TeO_2 \cdot 2HCl$.

Since selenium and tellurium are often associated elements, their separation can be effected, making use of the fact that selenium is completely precipitated by sulfur dioxide from concentrated hydrochloric acid, while tellurium is not.

The rapid gravimetric estimation of tellurium can be effected by precipitation of the tellurium from tellurium(IV) or tellurium(VI) solution by the use of sulfur dioxide and hydrazine hydrochloride together. It should be noted that this method does not afford a separation of tellurium from selenium.

A convenient volumetric method for the determination of tellurium involves the oxidation of tellurous acid by ceric sulfate in hot sulfuric acid solution in the presence of chromic ion as catalyst. Selenious acid does not interfere if the sulfuric acid concentration is controlled. Excess ceric sulfate is added, the excess being titrated with ferrous ammonium sulfate.

The determination of micro amounts of tellurium(IV) can be carried out spectrophotometrically on the tellurium hydrosol or on the iodotellurite complex.[7] Johnson et al recommend a red sol formed by reduction with hypophosphite and stabilized with gum arabic. Red sols are superior in conformance to Beer's Law, reproducibility and stability against agglomeration. However, the interferences are such, e.g., substances like selenium which also produce sols with hypophosphite, that a preliminary separation of tellurium is demanded in most applications.

The applicability of the iodotellurite complex, $TeI_6^=$, to the estimation of small

TABLE 7. MINIMUM DOSES FATAL TO RATS AMONG COMPOUNDS OF TELLURIUM, SELENIUM, ARSENIC, VANADIUM, AND MOLYBDENUM

Compound		Min. Fatal Dose†		
Sodium tellurite	Na_2TeO_3	2.25–2.50	mg	Te/kg.
Sodium tellurate	Na_2TeO_4	20.0–30.0	mg	Te/kg.
Sodium selenite	Na_2SeO_3	3.25–3.50	mg	Se/kg.
Sodium selenate	Na_2SeO_4	5.25–5.75	mg	Se/kg.
Sodium arsenite	Na_2HAsO_3	4.25–4.75	mg	As/kg.
Sodium arsenate	Na_2HAsO_4	14.0–18.0	mg	As/kg.
Sodium vanadate	$NaVO_3$	4.0–5.0	mg	V/kg.
Ammonium molybdate	$(NH_4)_6Mo_7O_{24}$	Above 160.0	mg	Mo/kg.

†Minimum doses fatal to at least 75% of young rats within 48 hours after substances were injected intraperitoneally. Franke, K. W., and Moxon, A. L., *Pharmacol. Exp. Ther.*, **61**, 89 (1937).

amounts of tellurium is indicated by the fact that at 335 mμ the complex obeys Beer's Law over the concentration range 0.2 to 2 ppm.[7] Since selenite is reduced to elemental selenium by iodide, a prior separation of selenium, e.g., by repeated sulfuric acid-bisulfate fuming to dryness, is mandatory. Precautions must be taken to prevent the oxidation of iodide to free iodine.

Toxicology

Considerably less is known about the toxicity of tellurium as compared with selenium, and in general it appears that tellurium is less toxic than selenium.† The principal observation with tellurium is the pronounced garlic breath which may last for a considerable period after exposure. Other symptoms of tellurium intoxication are giddiness, nausea, transient headaches, somnolence, metallic taste and dryness in the mouth. Although no serious cases of industrial intoxication have been reported, care should be exercised in handling tellurium, particularly in cases where the formation of fumes of tellurium or tellurium dioxide is possible.

As with selenium, tellurium is excreted through the lungs, urine, feces, and sweat. The garlic odor of the breath, due to dimethyl telluride, is a sensitive and characteristic sign of tellurium absorption. In the case of humans, 0.5 μg of tellurium dioxide given by mouth was found to impart a pronounced garlic odor to the breath for 30 hours, beginning 1-1/4 hours after intake. Fifteen mg gave a garlic

†For an exception, see Table 7

smell lasting 237 days. The maximum concentration of tellurium in air at which no garlic breath is observed is given as 0.01 to 0.02 mg tellurium per cubic meter of air. However, it should be noted that susceptibility to garlic breath varies considerably between individuals. As with selenium, elemental tellurium is the least toxic form of the element. The fact that tellurium as the element must be present in much larger doses than tellurium salts to cause garlic breath has led to the recommended use of ascorbic acid (Vitamin C) in the treatment of tellurium breath. Ascorbic acid functions as a reducing agent to produce elemental tellurium. In experiments with ascorbic acid, humans received 100 μg of tellurium as sodium tellurite orally, followed by 10 mg ascorbic acid per kilogram of body weight. In two out of three cases, the garlic odor of the breath was reduced considerably or eliminated. However, it should be noted that the decrease in garlic odor is only temporary, since as soon as the ascorbic acid treatment is suspended, the garlic odor reappears. Also, it should be cautioned that ascorbic acid might enhance the toxicity of tellurium, as has been observed with tellurium dioxide in the case of animals.

Tellurites are among the most toxic tellurium compounds, and it is interesting to note that sodium tellurite is more toxic than sodium selenite (Table 7.)

Hydrogen telluride is similar to hydrogen selenide in its toxic symptoms, and great care should be exercised in handling this compound.

Relatively little is known of the toxicity of

tellurium, and more studies are needed, particularly regarding the long-term effects of low doses of tellurium and its compounds.

Cerwenka and Cooper[3] have prepared a comprehensive review of the toxicology of selenium and tellurium and their compounds up to 1960.

Applications

Ferrous Metallurgy. In recent years considerable attention has been directed to the addition of tellurium to leaded steels for improved machinability. The addition of tellurium to steel dates as far back as 1923 and the first patents covering the use of tellurium for the enhancement of machinability characteristics were issued in 1935. As a result of studies since around 1960, additions of tellurium in the order of 0.04% by weight are now being made to leaded, resulfurized, low-carbon open hearth steels and to high-strength alloy steels at the 150,000 psi tensile strength level. The tellurium produces a very marked improvement in machinability with no deleterious effects on mechanical properties. Although the exact mechanism whereby tellurium affects the machinability has not been determined, it has been established that the tellurium tends to appear as a third phase attached to the lead, iron-manganese-sulfide inclusions.

Tellurium is a powerful chilling agent in iron castings. This property has been employed to control chill depth and provide a tough abrasion resistant surface. In grey cast iron, tellurium also increases the soundness and reduces subsurface pinholes. By means of balanced additions of tellurium and graphite it is possible not only to control the chill but also to minimize the mottled transition zone between the hard surface zone and the softer grey graphitic inner core.

In malleable cast iron the addition of tellurium permits the use of a higher silicon content which results in a much shorter annealing time. In addition, tellurium promotes the formation of spheroidal graphite during annealing thereby improving the ductility.

Nonferrous Metallurgy. Tellurium copper containing 0.5% tellurium has been employed for many years in applications, e.g., welding and soldering tips, requiring an alloy having good machinability and high electrical and thermal conductivity. Its relative machinability is 90 compared with 100 for free-cutting brass and both the electrical and thermal conductivity are about 90% that of copper.

Lead alloys containing about 0.05% tellurium and 0.06% copper have a higher fatigue strength and recrystallization temperature than ordinary lead. These properties have led to the application of such alloys in cable sheathing and in chemical equipment.

Copper-, lead-, and tin-base alloys have been developed as bearing alloys for automotive use. Tellurium at a concentration of around 0.1–0.2% appears to promote a more uniform dendritic structure within the alloy.

Rubber. Tellurium and certain tellurium compounds such as tellurium diethyldithiocarbamate are used in natural and synthetic rubbers as curing agents or accelerators. Tellurium can improve the aging and mechanical properties of the rubber, notably the resistance to heat and abrasion. Thus, a combination of elemental tellurium with selenium diethyldithiocarbamate as the curing system gives superior aging properties in the case of SBR compositions in the temperature range 100 to 150°C.

Catalysts. Tellurium has been investigated for its catalytic activity particularly in processes where a catalyst of moderate activity but high selectivity is required, e.g., in the controlled oxidation of propylene to acrolein. Traces of tellurium added to platinum catalysts can serve to direct the hydrogenation of nitric oxide to hydroxylamine and preventing the reaction from yielding ammonia. Kollonitsch and Kilne have reviewed tellurium catalysts through 1962.[8]

Thermoelectrics. The most promising applications of semiconducting tellurium compounds lie in the area of thermoelectricity either for power generation as with lead telluride or for refrigeration as with bismuth telluride.[2,5] These applications are based, respectively, on the Seebeck effect which gives rise to a current upon heating the junction of two dissimilar conductors, e.g., p- and n-type PbTe, and the Peltier effect which results in a heat transfer when a current is passed through the junction of two dissimilar conductors, e.g., p- and n-type Bi_2Te_3. The properties of the tellurium-containing materials which have been developed to date appear to be adequate for a number of applications, e.g., power generation at remote locations for signaling devices and relay stations and thermoelectric cooling for electronic equipment, specialized small refrigerators, and air conditioning.

References

1. Brooks, L. S., *J. Am. Chem. Soc.*, **74**, 227, (1952),
2. Cadoff, Irving B., and Miller, Edward, "Thermoelectric Materials and Devices," New York, Reinhold Publishing Corp., 1960.
3. Cerwenka, E. A., and Cooper, W. Charles, *Arch. Environ. Health*, **3**, 189 (1961).
4. Dutton, W. A., and Cooper, W. Charles *Chem. Rev.*, **66**, 657, (1966).
5. Goldsmid, H. J., "Applications of Thermoelectricity," London, Methuen, 1960.
6. Jennings, P. H., and Farge, J. C. T., *Bull. C.I.M.*, **59**, 193 (1966).
7. Johnson, R. A., and Kwan, F. P., *Anal. Chem.* **23**, 651 (1951); Johnson, R. A., Kwan, F. P., and Westland, D., *Anal. Chem.*, **25**, 1017 (1953).
8. Kollonitsch, Valerie, and Kline, Charles H., *Hydrocarbon Processing and Petroleum Refiner*, **43**, 139 (1964).
9. Mason, Brian, "Principles of Geochemistry," 2nd Ed., New York, John Wiley & Sons, Inc., 1958.
10. Pheinboldt, H., "Methoden der Organischen Chemie," "Schewefel, Selen, und Tellur Verbindungen," Band IX, Vierte Auflage, pp. 918–1209, 1955.
11. Sindeeva, N. D., "Mineralogy and Types of Deposits of Selenium and Tellurium," New York, Interscience, 1964.

W. Charles Cooper

TERBIUM

Terbium, Tb, has an atomic number 65. Its atomic weight, 158.924, reflects a natural isotopic abundance of 100% for Tb^{159}.

History

Carl Gustav Mosander (1797-1858, curator of the mineral collection of the Swedish Academy of Sciences and Professor of Chemistry and Mineralogy at the Caroline Institute, Stockholm) showed in 1843 that the oxide called yttria contained at least three earths which he named: yttria, a colorless oxide; erbia, a yellow earth; and terbia, a rose-colored one. He separated them by fractional precipitation with NH_4OH in the order erbia, terbia, and yttria. Jean-Charles Galissard de Marignac (1817–1894, Professor of Chemistry at University of Geneva) in 1878 separated terbia from yttria but switched the names between erbia and terbia so that today the name terbia is applied to the yellow fraction.

Terbia is named for the Swedish town, Ytterby. It was first prepared in fairly pure form by G. Urbain in 1905.

Occurrence and Abundance

Xenotime, a rare earth phosphate, contains about 1% terbia and is separated magnetically from the monazite deposits of Florida and South Carolina. Euxenite, a complex oxide containing about 1.3% terbia, is found in placer deposits in Idaho.

The "cosmic" abundance of Tb is among the least of the elements but about the same as In, Tm, Hf and W, and only Lu, Ta and Re are significantly less abundant, excepting the heavy radioactive elements. When values given for abundances of the elements in the earth's crust are considered the rare earths appear to be relatively higher.

Preparation

Terbium metal has a silvery appearance and can be made by the calcium reduction of the anhydrous trifluoride. The reaction takes place in an induction heated tantalum crucible assembly in either a vacuum or an inert gas atmosphere.

Further purification is necessary if metals free from calcium, oxygen and nitrogen are required. This is accomplished in various ways such as by remelting and slagging, amalgam formation, vacuum melting, distillation, floating-zone melting and chemical treatment but it is difficult to remove the last traces of oxygen, carbon and nitrogen.

Terbium is available in 99.9 + % purity either as the oxide or metal from several suppliers. Because of its relative rarity, it is one of the more expensive of the rare earth elements.

Physical Properties

Terbium follows gadolinium in the rare earth series. The latter has a stable half-filled $4f^7$ configuration in the combined state. Terbium shows an electronic configuration beyond the xenon compliment of $4f^8$ for Tb^{3+} and $4f^7$ for Tb^{4+}. Tb^{4+} is isoelectronic with the stable half-filled f shell Gd^{3+} configuration, resulting in greater stability of the tetravalent oxidation state. The electronic configuration in the metallic state is $6s^2 5d^1 4f^8$; the gaseous atom has $6s^2 4f^9$ beyond the xenon kernal.

These configurations are consistent with the reactivity of the element and also the relative localization of the $4f$ electrons which do not easily take part in chemical bonding.

Terbium has an atomic volume of 19.25 cc/mole. The mean atomic radius is 1.782 Å and the metallic valence is three.

Metallic a-Tb metal has the hexagonal, A3, Mg-type crystal structure with $a = 3.6010 \pm 3$ Å, $c = 5.6936 \pm 2$ Å. The calculated density is 8.253. It transforms to β-Tb at 1317°C with a heat of transition, $\triangle H_t = 1.06$ kcal/mole and melts at 1356 ± 5°C with the relatively low heat of fusion of 2.2 kcal/mole. This gives an entropy of fusion of 1.62 cal/deg, one of the higher ones for the rare earths but rather lower than for most other metals.

The heat of sublimation has been estimated at 72 kcal/mole at 25°C and the boiling point is estimated to be 2480°C. Heat capacity measurements reveal a lambda point due to a magnetic transition at 228°K; an anomaly has also been reported at 2.4°K; this transition is neither confirmed nor explained. At 298.16°K the value of the entropy $S_o = 17.505$ cal/mole-deg; the value of $H_T^\circ - H_0^\circ / T = 7.545$ and of $F_T^\circ - H_0^\circ / T = 9.960$ cal/mole-deg. The Debye temperature is 158°K from C_p measurements and 173°K from velocity of sound measurements. The heat capacity may be represented as $C_p = 7.136 - 11.18 \times 10^{-3} t + 103.5 \times 10^{-6} t^2$ between 0 and 65°C; while it has been estimated to be $C_p = 6.70 + 2.3 \times 10^{-3} t$ between 65 and 1317°C where t is in °C. The ground states of Tb^{3+} and Tb^{4+} are $^7F_6$ and $^8S_{7/2}$ with 8 and 7 f electrons, respectively. The effective magnetic moments are 9.7 and 7.94, respectively. Magnetochemical studies imply that the oxides intermediate between the sesquioxide and dioxide

consist of a mixture of $3+$ and $4+$ ions. a-Tb has a magnetic susceptibility at 25°C of $193,000 \times 10^{-6}$ emu/mole. The Curie-Weiss constants are $C = 739 \times 10^{-4}$ emu-°K/g and $\theta = +237$°K from studies in the temperature region -36 to $+102$°C. For a valence of three the effective moment 9.7 is observed as would be calculated. The Curie point is -36°C and the Néel point -43°C.

The thermal neutron absorption cross section is 46 barns.

The electrical properties of terbium have been studied to some extent: the resistivity is observed to be 116×10^{-6} ohm-cm at 25°C. The work function is calculated to be 3.09 eV and the first ionization potential 6.74 eV. Superconductivity has not been observed in terbium.

The thermal expansion of the lattice parameters of a-Tb in the temperature range of 20–852°C are $a = 3.5990 + 3.37 \times 10^{-5} t - 0.72 \times 10^{-8} t^2 + 1.03 \times 10^{-11} t^3$ and $c = 5.696 + 6.9 \times 10^{-5} t + 3.8 \times 10^{-8} t^2 + 0.6 \times 10^{-11} t^3$ angstroms. The adiabatic compressibility is 2.45×10^{-6} cm^2/kg. The coefficient of expansion at 25°C is $7.0 \pm 0.3 \times 10^{-6}$/°C, while the average value in the temperature range $+25$ to $+950$°C is 11.8×10^{-6}/°C. The Grüneisen constant is 0.61. a-Tb has a Vickers hardness number of 46. The Young modulus for a-Tb is 5.75×10^{11} dynes/cm^2 from velocity of sound measurements; the shear modulus is 2.28×10^{11} dynes/cm^2. Poisson's ratio is 0.261.

Chemical Properties

The rate of oxidation of Tb has not been measured; however, it is a very reactive metal and must be handled in an inert atmosphere or vacuum. Since Tb also forms a complex higher oxide system (which, in the case of Ce and Pr, is less protecting than the sesquioxide due to the more ready transport of oxygen across the oxide layer) and it is likely to be more reactive than the other heavy rare earth metals.

Alloys of terbium with Sb, Cr, Co, Ir, La, Mg, Os, Pu, Ta, and U are among those which have been studied. Because of the relative scarcity of terbium, its compounds have not been as completely studied as most. For general chemical properties reference should be made to other rare earth elements.

In solid compounds the 3+ oxidation state is most common and compounds of the halides, oxyacids and the chalcogenides are commonly known with terbium. For more general details of the typical behavior of terbium see praseodymium. Compounds with terbium in the 4+ state are known only for TbF_4 and TbO_2. Only compounds which are of special interest for terbium will be discussed.

Along with cerium and praseodymium of the lanthanide elements, terbium combines with oxygen to form so-called higher oxides. Also in common with them, the intermediate oxides TbO_x ($1.5 \leq x \leq 2.0$) are fluorite-related and belong to the homologous series R_nO_{2n-2} ($n = 4$, 7, 11, and ∞ and also possibly 10 and 12; see the discussion of

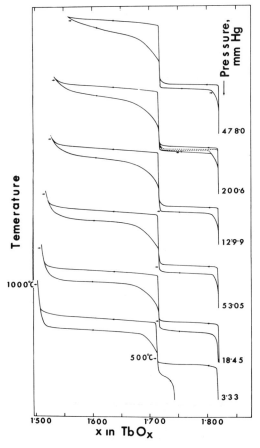

PrO_x). A wide composition phase, σ, is observed at high temperatures and moderate oxygen pressures. Fig. 1 shows a plot of composition of the oxide versus temperature at constant pressure for several isobars both in heating (reduction) and in cooling (oxidation). The stable intermediate oxides are in evidence by the vertical curves in reduction at composition of $TbO_{1.818}$ and $TbO_{1.714}$. The complicated but reproducible hysteresis phenomena exhibited in the two phase regions are characteristic also of the PrO_x system but are most marked with the terbia system. A striking feature of the curves is the absence of a stable phase of composition Tb_4O_7 which is usually listed as one of the stable oxides. Whenever this composition is prepared, it is always seen by x-ray diffraction to consist of the two phases $TbO_{1.714}$ and $TbO_{1.818}$. Tb_4O_7 is approximately the composition of the material which is formed when an ignited oxide or salt of an oxyacid is cooled slowly in air. If this oxide is leached with dilute acids, a solution of Tb^{3+} and a residue of TbO_2 results. TbO_2 can also be prepared by the oxidation of the lower oxides with atomic oxygen.

Table 1 summarizes structural, magnetic and other properties of some terbium compounds.

Solution Chemistry

The formal oxidation potential for the $Tb \rightarrow Tb^{3+} + 3e^-$ couple has been estimated at 2.39 volt. Only the trivalent ion exists in solution as $[Tb(H_2O)_n]^{3+}$ and it is only weakly hydrolyzed. Terbium ions are complexed in solution only by the strongest chelating agents.

The stability constants for the 1:1 complex at 25° for several chelating agents have been determined. For example, the common logarithm of the stability constant is for nitrilotriacetic acid, 11.59; for n-hydroxyethyl-ethylenediaminetriacetic acid, 15.32; for ethylenediaminetetraacetic acid, 17.93; for 1,2-diaminocyclohexanetetraacetic acid, 19.30; and for diethylenetriaminepentaacetic acid, 22.71.

There have been developed no important uses for pure terbium or its salts. See other rare earths for general usefulness of these substances.

FIG. 1. Typical isobaric runs showing complete heating (reduction) and cooling (oxidation) cycles. The numbers on each complete cycle show the nominal pressure, the temperatures of 500°C and 1000°C are marked on each pair with an arrow.

TABLE 1. TERBIUM COMPOUNDS

Compound	Structure	a, (Å)	b, (Å)	c, (Å)	ρ, g/cc	$x \times 10^6$ emu/mole	μ_{eff}	Curie temp., °K	Melting point, °C	Boiling point, °C	Note:
TbSb	cubic, NaCl	6.180				36232	9.57				
TbAs	cubic, NaCl	5.827				39033	9.65				
TbBe₁₃		10.251									
TbBi	cubic, NaCl	6.280				38086	9.64				
TbB₂	hexagonal	3.28		3.86	(6.579)						
TbB₄	tetragonal	7.118		4.0286	(5.385)						
TbB₆	cubic	4.1020									
TbB₁₂	cubic	7.504									
TbC₂	b.c. tetragonal, CaC₂	3.690		6.217	(7.176)	~28500	9.57				
Tb₂C₃	b.c.c., Pu₂C₃	8.2617			(8.335)						
Tb₃C	cubic, Fe₄N	5.107			(8.882)						
Tb₂Ge₃	AlB₂ defect	3.95		4.16							
TbBe₃	hexagonal	4.129		6.391					(827)	1490	
TbCl₃	monoclinic	6.163	3.848	8.357	$\beta = 107.59$				588	1550	
TbOCl	tetragonal	3.927		6.645							
TbF₃	orthorhombic	6.513	6.949	4.384	(7.236)				1172	(2277)	
TbOF	rhombohedral	6.758		7.9	$\beta = 33.02$						
TbF₄	monoclinic	12.1	10.3		$\beta = 126$				(952)	1330	TbF₃ + F₂
TbI₃	hexagonal	4.357		6.954							

TABLE 1—*continued*

Compound	Structure	a, (Å)	b, (Å)	c, (Å)		ρ, g/cc	χ × 10⁶ emu/mole	μeff	Curie temp., °K	Melting point, °C	Boiling point, °C	Note:
TbH₂	cubic	5.246										
TbH₃	hexagonal	3.700		6.658								
TbN	cubic, NaCl	4.933				(9.567)	42900	9.5	38			
Tb₂O₃	b.c.c., Mn₂O₃	10.7281					35800	9.7				
	monoclinic	13.92	3.536	8.646	$\beta = 100.2$ $\alpha = 99°21'$							
Tb₇O₁₂	rhombohedral	6.509								2387		
Tb₁₁O₂₀	triclinic	5.286	5.286	5.286	$\alpha = \beta = 89°21'$ $\gamma = 90°$							
TbO₂	cubic, CaF₂	5.220					39526	9.56				
TbP	cubic, NaCl	5.686					33755	9.82				
TbSe	cubic, NaCl	5.740										
TbSi₂	orthorhombic α-YSi₂	4.045	3.96	13.38								
TbSi₂₋ₙ	hexagonal AlB₂ defect	3.847		4.146								
Tb₂SiO₅												
Tb₂Si₂O₇												
TbS	cubic, NaCl	5.517				(7.56)	35088	9.63				
Tb₂O₂S	hexagonal	3.825		6.626								
TbTe	cubic, NaCl	6.101					38760	9.57				
Tb₂ (C₂H₄O₂) 10H₂O												−5H₂O 45°–140° −4H₂O 140°–265° −H₂O 265°–435° oxide 425°–725°

References
1. Eyring, L., Editor, "Progress in the Science and Technology of the Rare Earths," Oxford, Pergamon Press, Vol. I 1964, Vol. II 1966.
2. Gschneidner, Karl A., Jr., "Rare Earth Alloys," Princeton, New Jersey, D. Van Nostrand Company, Inc., 1961.
3. Kleber, Eugene V., and Love, Bernard, "The Technology of Scandium, Yttrium and the Rare Earth Metals," New York, The Macmillan Company, 1963.
4. Moeller, Therald, "The Chemistry of the Lanthanides," New York, Reinhold Publishing Corporation, 1963.
5. Samsonov, Grigorii Valentinovich, "High-Temperature Compounds of Rare Earth Metals with Nonmetals," Authorized Translation, New York, Consultants Bureau, 1965.
6. Topp, N. E., "The Chemistry of the Rare-Earth Elements," Amsterdam, Elsevier Publishing Company, 1965.
7. Trifonov, D. N., "The Rare Earth Elements," translated by Prasenjit Basu, translation edited by R. C. Vickery, New York, The Macmillan Company, 1963.
8. Weeks, Mary Elvira, "Discovery of the Elements," 6th Edition, Published by the Journal of Chemical Education, Easton, Pennsylvania, 1956.

LeRoy Eyring

THALLIUM

In 1861 Sir William Crookes, using spectroscopic methods in a search for tellurium in the residues of a German sulfuric acid plant, observed an unaccountable green line in the spectrum, which he concluded represented an unknown element. The bright green color of the line recalled for him the tint of new vegetation in the spring, and he gave the element the name thallium from the Latin word *thallus*—a budding twig. He was able to produce a small quantity in the metallic form for exhibit at the International Exhibition in London in 1862.

A Frenchman, Professor Lamy, also analyzing the residues of a sulfuric acid plant by spectrographic techniques, noted the same bright green line and also concluded that it was a new element.

The early assumptions that thallium belonged to the sulfur family were soon disproved as studies revealed that the element was closely associated with lead, mercury and aluminum, and it was assigned its rightful place in the atomic chart in Group IIIA under indium, between mercury and lead.

Occurrence

The abundance of thallium in the earth's crust has been estimated from 0.3 gram per ton (metric) to as high as 3 grams per ton. The most recent estimates place the abundance at 1 gram per ton. It is interesting to note that this abundance is higher than that of more commonly known metals such as mercury, antimony, bismuth, cadmium and silver. But this wide distribution does not represent its availability for recovery, for the major amount of thallium is found in potash minerals which have no commercial significance at the present time. Even deposits of the main thallium minerals having 16 to 60% thallium are so small in quantity as to be of no commercial importance. The trace amounts of thallium found in sulfide ores, although small in quantity compared with potash minerals, are the major source of commercial thallium. This is due to the concentration of the element as a by-product from the roasting of pyrite ores in the smelting of lead and zinc as well as in the production of sulfuric acid.

Production

During the smelting of lead and zinc concentrates the compounds of thallium, being volatile at the temperatures of the smelting operations, are collected in the flue dusts usually in the form of an oxide or a sulfate. The thallium compounds are associated in the flue dusts with higher concentrations of such elements as cadmium, indium, selenium and tellurium. Further concentration of the thallium compounds is accomplished during the processing to recover the above mentioned associated metals. Only under especially favorable conditions of concentration and market requirements is the thallium itself recovered as a by-product material.

The extraction of thallium is largely dependent upon the difference in solubility in water of thallium salts and other metallic compounds associated with them in the flue dust.

The purification of thallium is also accomplished by taking advantage of the difference in solubility of certain thallium compounds and the same compounds of the impurities. For example, thallium sulfate's solubility in water permits its separation from lead sulfate; thallium sulfide is insoluble in alkaline solutions but soluble in acid solutions, permitting its separation from Group I elements; and thallous chloride is only slightly soluble in cold water, permitting its separation from chlorides of cadmium, zinc, tellurium and copper.

Thallium metal may be obtained from the compounds in several ways:

1. by electrolysis of carbonates, sulfates, or perchlorates.
2. by precipitation of metallic thallium with zinc.
3. by reduction of thallous oxalate or chloride.

A number of industrial processes for the recovery of thallium have been described in the literature. Several of them depend upon the extraction of thallium from the flue dust by boiling it in acidified water. The dissolved thallium in the filtrate is then precipitated with zinc. Traces of metals such as zinc, copper, lead, cadmium, and indium are removed by dissolving the thallium in dilute sulfuric acid and precipitating the impurities with hydrogen sulfide. A saturated solution of thallous sulfate at 30°C (86°F) can be readily electrolyzed to yield thallium. An insoluble anode of platinum is suggested if a very pure metal is desired. The cathode may be of platinum, nickel, or stainless steel and is highly polished to allow easy removal of the thallium deposit. The metal is washed, compressed into blocks, melted in hydrogen, and cast into sticks.

Another process handles it as a by-product in the recovery of cadmium. The crude flue dust is leached with sulfuric acid, forming both cadmium and thallium sulfate. After the impurities are precipitated as sulfides and hydroxides, the purified solution is electrolyzed for deposition of cadmium. When the thallium content of the solution has reached a 1:10 ratio with that of the remaining cadmium, the cathodes are removed and replaced by new ones. The electrolysis is continued, depositing a cadmium-thallium alloy (5 to 20% thallium).

The cadmium-thallium cathodes are treated with boiling water and steam. The solution contains the thallium as a hydroxide with very little cadmium. The small amount of cadmium in this solution is removed by precipitation with sodium carbonate, leaving a solution of thallium carbonate. Precipitation from this solution with sodium sulfide separates the thallium from any remaining impurities.

The sulfide is dissolved with sulfuric acid, producing pure thallium sulfate. To produce thallium metal, the thallium sulfate solution is used as an electrolyte, and a thallium sponge is electrolytically deposited on aluminum cathodes, using "Duriron" anodes. The resulting thallium sponge is pressed, melted, and cast.

The only major producer in this country is the American Smelting and Refining Company.

The price of thallium has fluctuated over the last thirty years, at one time reaching a high of $22/lb. The present price, as of 1967, is $7.50/lb. for the metal.

Physical Properties

When freshly cut, metallic thallium has a metallic luster, which upon exposure to air

TABLE 1. PHYSICAL PROPERTIES OF THALLIUM

Atomic number	81
Atomic weight	204.37
Density, g/cc	
20°C (68°F)	11.85
306°C (584°F)	11.289
326°C (620°F)	11.254
330°C (626°F)	11.250
Density, lb/cu in. at 20°C (68°F)	0.428
Atomic volume, cc/g-atom	17.24
Melting point	303°C (577°F)

TABLE 1—*continued*

Boiling point	1457°C (2655°F)
Specific heat, 20°C, cal/g/°C	0.031
(303–500°C) (577–932°F)	0.036
Heat of fusion, cal/g	5.04
Latent heat of vaporization, cal/g	189.9
Coefficient of linear thermal expansion, micro-in./°C	28
Thermal conductivity, cal/sq cm/cm/°C/sec	0.093
Electrical resistivity, microhms-cm	
0°C (32°F)	18
303°C (577°F)	74
Tensile strength, psi	1300
Elongation in 5 in., %	40
Brinell hardness number (Pb–5)	2
Volume contraction on solidification, %	3.23
Cubic compressibility, 20°C (68°F), 100–500 megabars	2.83×10^{-6}
Vapor pressure, 845–900°K, mm Hg	

$$\log P_{mm} = -\frac{8.927}{T} + 7.993$$

825°C (1517°F)	1
983°C (1801°F)	10
1196°C (2185°F)	100
1274°C (2325°F)	200
1364°C (2487°F)	400
1457°C (2655°F)	760
Crystal form	
below 230°C (446°F)	$a = 3.450$
	$c = 5.514$ close-packed hexagonal
above 230°C	$a = 3.874$ body-centered cubic
Surface tension, dynes/cm, (327°C) (620°F)	401
Isotopes	

Isotope	Abundance
Thallium–203	29.5%
Thallium–205	70.5%

dulls to a bluish-gray tinge resembling lead in appearance; but, unlike lead, if thallium is allowed to remain in contact with air for a few weeks, a heavy oxide crust will build up on the surface. As may be seen by comparing the properties of thallium (Table 1) with the physical properties of lead, they are very similar.

Investigations of the systems of thallium and other elements reveal that thallium alloys readily with many other elements; the exceptions are copper, aluminum, zinc, manganese, nickel and selenium, which have limited liquid solubility. Table 2 gives the eutectic points of binary, ternary and quaternary alloys of thallium.

The resistance of various materials to attack by liquid thallium is given below:

Manganese—good resistance up to 1000°C (1832°F)

Austenitic stainless steel (18 chromium-8 nickel)—good resistance up to 649°C (1200°F)

Aluminum—good resistance up to 649°C (1200°F)

Armco iron—good resistance at m.p. 303°C (577°F)

Nickel and "Monel"—severely attacked at 649°C (1200°F)

Suggestions by Brewer for containers for liquid thallium in order of decreasing preference are iron, tungsten, tantalum, molybdenum, columbium and cobalt.

Chemical Properties

Thallium is a member of the Group IIIA family along with boron, aluminum, gallium and indium. The element forms two groups of compounds, the thallous and the thallic,

TABLE 2. EUTECTIC POINTS OF BINARY, TERNARY AND QUATERNARY ALLOYS OF THALLIUM

System	Composition	Eutectic Temperature
Ag-Tl	98.5 Tl	291°C (554°F)
Au-Tl	~73 Tl	131°C (268°F)
Cd-Tl	83 Tl	203°C (397°F)
Sn-Tl	43.5 Tl	170°C (338°F)
Sb-Tl	80 Tl	195°C (383°F)
Bi-Tl	52.5 Tl	188°C (370°F)
Bi-Tl	23.5 Tl	198°C (390°F)
Pb-Tl	No eutectic high solid solubility	
In-Tl	No eutectic high solid solubility	
Hg-Tl	40.5 Tl	0.6°C (33°F)
Hg-Tl	8.7 Tl	−59°C (−76°F)
K-Tl	96.5 Tl	173°C (343°F)
Li-Tl	99.4 Tl	211°C (412°F)
Mg-Tl	~80 Tl	203°C (397°F)
Na-Tl	93.7 Tl	238°C (460°F)
Pb-Sn-Tl	—	No ternary*
Sn-Cd-Tl	19Cd-42Sn-39Tl	129°C (265°F)
Bi-Pb-Tl	55.2Bi-33.3Pb-11.5Tl	91°C (195°F)
	42.2Bi-9.8Pb-48.0Tl	186°C (367°F)
Bi-Sn-Tl	50Bi-35.7Sn-14.3Tl	124°C (255°F)
	44Bi-31.0Sn-25Tl	167°C (333°F)
Bi-Cd-Tl	43Bi-40.8Cd-16.2Tl	124°C (255°F)
	38.2Bi-36.4Cd-25.4Tl	147°C (296°F)
Cd-Pb-Tl	—	No ternary**
Pb-Sn-Bi-Tl	46.5Bi-28.0Pb-14.0Sn-11.5Tl	93°C (199°F)
Pb-Cd-Bi-Tl	44.3Bi-11.0Cd-35.8Pb-8.9Tl	81°C (178°F)
Bi-Cd-Sn-Tl	49.1Bi-18.2Cd-23.4Sn-9.2Tl	95°C (202°F)

* A quasi-binary eutectic exists between $PbTl_2$ and Sn at 182°C (359°F) but no ternary eutectic occurs.
** In the ternary system of Pb-Cd-Tl, an invariant point exists at 210°C (410°F) which is not a eutectic.

with valences of one and three. The thallous are the most numerous and stable. Thallic salts are readily reduced to thallous salts by stannous chloride, sulfurous acid, metallic thallium, ferrous sulfate and sodium arsenite, or by boiling water.

Thallium oxidizes slowly in air at 20°C (68°F) and more rapidly as the temperature increases. Thallium metal, exposed to air at ambient temperatures for a few weeks, will form a heavy oxide crust.

Some water-soluble thallous compounds are the acetate, nitrate, nitrite, perchlorate, hydroxide, carbonate, sulfate and ferricyanide. The sulfide and chromate are insoluble, and the halides are moderately soluble in hot water.

Nitric acid will readily dissolve thallium. Dilute sulfuric acid will dissolve the metal slowly, but it is readily dissolved by concentrated sulfuric acid. Hydrochloric acid dissolves the metal very slowly.

Thallous oxide, Tl_2O, is formed by oxidizing the metal at low temperatures or heating thallous hydroxide, TlOH, at 100°C (212°F). It melts at 300°C (572°F) and will attack glass. It is easily oxidized to thallic oxide, Tl_2O_3, or reduced to thallium. Thallium tetraoxide, Tl_2O_4, must be prepared electrolytically. When thallous oxide is dissolved in water, it will form thallous hydroxide.

Thallous hydroxide is also formed when thallium contacts water containing oxygen. It reacts in water as a comparatively strong base, absorbing carbon dioxide and attacking glass and porcelain. Thallic hydroxide, $Tl(OH)_3$, is formed by adding alkali hydroxides or ammonia to a thallic solution.

The thallous halides resemble the lead salts and are formed by reaction of the acids on oxide, hydroxide, or carbonate. Thallium trichloride monohydrate, $TlCl_3 \cdot H_2O$, is formed by passing chlorine into water in which thallous chloride, $TlCl$, is suspended.

The action of fluorine on thallium is so vigorous that the metal becomes incandescent.

Thallous sulfate, Tl_2SO_4, is soluble in cold water (4.87 g in 100 g water). Alums may also be made by combining the salt with trivalent sulfates.

Selenates and tellurates are formed with selenium and tellurium.

Fabrication Technique

Thallium is a low-melting element with high malleability and low strength. It can be melted and fabricated by any one of the methods used for lead, i.e., cast, rolled, or extruded.

A smooth coherent deposit of thallium may be obtained with a perchlorate electrolyte, using peptone as an anodic depolarizer, and cresylic acid as an addition agent.

Applications

In the United States the applications of thallium as a metal or its compounds are at the present time very limited. Typical of the uses are for insecticides, rodenticides, low melting glasses for electronic encapsulation, photoelectric applications, and low melting temperature mercury switches.

In the past thallium metal and compounds have been used or experimented with in a number of applications, some of which are of limited commercial interest, and others are at the present time just of experimental interest.

For many years the only commercial application of thallium was in the form of the compound thallium sulfate. It was first used as the active ingredient of a rodenticide in Germany about 1920, and since has been employed not only as a very effective rat killer, but also in destroying the troublesome little ant. Being odorless and tasteless, thallium sulfate may be mixed with starch, sugar, glycerin and water, an appetizing treat for rats and ants, without giving the rodents or insects any warning of its presence.

The unique photosensitivity of certain thallium salts has suggested applications in special communication systems. T. W. Case discovered in 1917 that the electrical conductivity of oxidized thallium sulfide (thallofide cell) changed upon exposure to light. These cells are particularly sensitive to the long-wave, low-intensity light (infrared). Improvements in the thallofide cell have been made, and the cell has been used in war communications systems.

Mixed thallium bromide-iodide crystals were used for an unusual application during World War II. These crystals can transmit infrared radiations of very long wavelength and were employed in military equipment designed for sniper detection, and signaling where visible radiation could not be used.

Crystals of this type were first synthesized in Germany; crystals of 42 mole % thallium bromide and 58 mole % thallium iodide have been synthesized in the United States by the U.S. Naval Research Laboratory. They have properties similar to the German crystals. A mixture of the required composition is melted in a platinum or "Pyrex" crucible with a conical bottom; an angle of 60 degrees has been found satisfactory. The growth process is controlled by a temperature gradient in the furnace and the rate of movement of the crucible through the furnace. The temperature of the upper part of the furnace is 470°C (878°F). A lowering rate of 7 hr/in. gives excellent crystals 1 inch in diameter, and 32 hr/in. is used for 2 inch diameter crystals.

Increasing interest in lamps which will produce radiations in the erythemic (sun tan) range has led to investigations of materials capable of converting primary ultraviolet radiation to radiation in the erythemic range. Several types of alkaline earth silicates and phosphates activated with thallium give not only good initial erythemic emission, but also maintain a high percentage of this emission for several hundred hours.

The medicinal uses of thallium compounds are limited by the narrow margin between toxicity and therapeutic benefits. In the treatment of ringworm it has been used to produce alopecia.

The application of thallium in alloys is very limited, although alloys are formed with other elements which have unique properties.

The addition of lead to thallium raises the melting point above that of the components. These alloys have limited use in special types of fuses.

The most unique alloy of thallium is the mercury-thallium alloy which forms a eutectic at 8.5% thallium and freezes at $-60°C$ ($-76°F$), about 20°C (36°F) below the freezing point of mercury. Minus 60°C is the lowest temperature normally encountered in the arctic or stratosphere, therefore this alloy has possibility in fulfilling the need for a substitute for mercury in switches, thermometers and seals at these temperatures.

S. S. Flaschen and A. D. Pearson, of Bell Telephone Laboratories, have produced a low-melting glass using thallium as one of the components (others, arsenic and sulfur). This glass has been used to coat semiconductors, capacitors and other electronic devices to protect them from atmospheric oxidation, contamination and humidity.

Although most of the thallium now produced is used for rodenticides and insecticides, an increase in the commercial utilization of the unique properties of the metal and its compounds can be readily met with increased production.

Toxicity

When handling thallium, i.e., melting or just touching with the skin, a person must be protected against its poisonous effects. The metal readily forms soluble compounds when exposed to both air and water. Moisture on the skin may bring about this reaction, therefore the handling of thallium without protection should be prohibited. Although industrial poisoning from thallium is infrequent, many serious or fatal poisonings have resulted from accidental or therapeutic ingestion or external application of thallium. Signs of thallium poisoning are rapid loss of hair and gastrointestinal and nervous disorders.

References

1. DeMent, J., and Drake, H. C., "Rarer Metals," p. 43, New York, Chemical Publishing Co., Inc., 1946.
2. Enck, E., "Thallium and its Uses," "Foote-Prints on Chemicals, Metals, Alloys and Ores," Vol. 2, No. 1, 1929.
3. Hansen, M., "Binary Alloys," 2nd Edition, New York, McGraw-Hill Book Co., Inc., 1958.
4. Hopkins, B. S. "Chapters in the Chemistry of Less Familiar Elements," Chap. 9, Champaign, Ill., Stipes Publishing Co., 1940.
5. Howe, H. E., "Thallium," in "Rare Metals Handbook," C. A. Hampel, Editor, 2nd Ed., pp. 529–535, New York, Reinhold Publishing Corp., 1961.
6. Haughton, J. L., "Bibliography of the Literature Relating to Constitutional Diagrams of Alloys," Monograph & Rep. Series No. 2, London, Institute of Metals, 1956.
7. Kleinert, R. Z., "Thallium, a Rare Metal—an Impurity Metal," *Z. Erzbergbau*, **16**, 67–76 (1963).
8. Mellor, J. W., "A Comprehensive Treatise on Inorganic and Theoretical Chemistry," Vol. 5, p. 406, London, Longmans, Green & Co., Ltd., 1924.
9. "Metals Handbook," 8th Edition, p. 1224, Metals Park, Ohio, American Society for Metals, 1961.
10. Munch, J. C., *Chem. Trade J.*, **93**, 173, 195 (1933).
11. Petar, A., *U.S. Bur. Mines, Inform. Circ.* No. 6453 (1941).
12. Sanderson, L., *Can. Mining J.*, **65**, 624 (1944),
13. Waggaman, W. H., "Thallium," *U.S. Bur. Mines, Inform. Circ.* No. 7553 (March 1950).

HERBERT E. HOWE

THORIUM*

History

In 1815, the Swedish chemist J. J. Berzelius obtained a material which he regarded as a new earth. He assigned to this supposedly new oxide and the corresponding metal names that were intended to honor Thor, the ancient Scandinavian god of thunder. However, in 1824 he demonstrated that this supposedly new earth was essentially the phosphate of previously discovered yttrium. Four years later, the Reverend H. M. T. Esmark discovered a black mineral on the island of Lövö near Brevig, Norway; he gave a sample of this material to his father, Professor Jens Esmark, a noted mineralogist. Professor Esmark was unable to identify it as any known mineral, so he in turn sent a

*Manuscript prepared in the Ames Laboratory of the U.S. Atomic Energy Commission, Contribution No. 1990.

specimen of it to Berzelius for examination. A chemical analysis of this mineral by Berzelius demonstrated that it contained almost 60% of a new earth which he reported as being distinct from all others known. It appears that in naming this new oxide "thoria" and the mineral from which it was obtained "thorite," Berzelius fully restored the dignity of Thor from the earlier near humiliation. The discovery of thorium was announced by Berzelius by publication in 1829. He also prepared thorium in metallic form in that year by heating a mixture of potassium metal with potassium thorium fluoride in a glass tube. The metal appeared as a gray powder since the reduction reaction was not sufficiently exothermic to melt the thorium metal product.

During the next few decades, a number of investigators announced discoveries of what they believed were new elements, but these were later identified as the element thorium. Some of these workers went so far as to identify their supposedly new elements with such names as "donarium" and "wasmium." Another investigator also performed experiments in an attempt to resolve the thorium reported by Berzelius into more than one element and described means for obtaining what he thought was evidence of three different elements. However, this metal, first prepared by Berzelius, remained firmly as a single new element and he is recognized as the discoverer of thorium, element number fifty-four in the order of discoveries of the elements.

Interest in thorium and its compounds remained essentially in academic areas for over half a century following its discovery. However, by 1884, Auer von Welsbach had developed and patented the incandescent gas light mantle in which thorium oxide was the essential ingredient. The brilliant white light emitted by this mantle gave an immense breakthrough in ordinary lighting when compared to the weak yellowish flames of the kerosene lamp or of the flickering gas lamp or candle. Demands for this mantle developed rapidly and the consequent growth of the mantle industry led to search for deposits of thorium ores for increased production. The mantle industry grew to its peak in the early years of the 20th century, but as electricity

began to replace gas for general lighting purposes, mantle production decreased and by 1925 thorium was relatively unimportant to commerce.

The commercially most important mineral of thorium contains a high percentage of rare earth elements, so in the processing for thorium, the rare earths were considered as by-products. The finding of increased commercial applications for the rare earths and the dwindling of demands for thorium, however, resulted in thorium becoming the by-product by about 1932. Because of special nuclear properties of thorium atoms, thorium jumped back into prominence with the development of atomic energy in the early 1940's. A more recent development in thorium utilization has been in the production of thorium-magnesium alloys. A few per cent of thorium in such an alloy imparts to the magnesium an increased strength which remains effective above normal temperatures. The thorium addition results in only a very minor increase in density for the magnesium, so these alloys find very extensive use in the construction of vehicles and equipment for aerospace operations. Although mantle production still consumes much thorium, the use of thorium in magnesium alloys has since 1956 accounted for the major consumption of the thorium that is directed to nonenergy uses.

Occurrence

Thorium, which makes up about 0.0015% of the earth's crust, occurs in a large number of minerals in association with the rare earths and uranium; however, those minerals which contain high percentages of thorium are rather scarce. The major source of thorium has for the most part been monazite which is essentially a phosphate of the light-weight rare earths. Monazite is generally found associated with silica and a few other minerals in lesser amounts as a sand. Concentrations of thorium oxide in the monazite fractions separated from such sand mixtures can be quite varied. Deposits of monazite-containing sands occur in India, Brazil, Australia, Malagasy, Ceylon, South Africa, Canada and the United States. Domestic deposits of sands containing thorium minerals are located in Idaho, Florida, Michigan, California,

Colorado and the Carolinas. Although the sands that extend along the seacoast of Travancore in India contain less than 1% monazite, they have been considered as the world's most important proved source of thorium. The deposits are immense and the monazite sand concentrate averages about 9% thorium oxide. The monazite concentrate from the Brazilian deposits shows a thorium oxide content of about 6%. Monazite from domestic sources rarely exceeds 4% thoria. Thorite deposits of interest exist in the western states, especially in Idaho and Montana. Thorium as a by-product of uranium ore processing is important in some areas. Very limited information on thorium deposits is available from restricted areas of the world.

Ore Treatment and Purification

Since monazite sand consists essentially of rare earth phosphates, the recovery of small percentages of thorium compounds in high purity from this mineral requires somewhat extensive treatments. There are two chemical processes that are generally employed for first breaking down the chemical make-up of the mineral. One of these processes employs an acid (usually H_2SO_4) in the initial chemical treatment while the other employs caustic, NaOH. In the acid process finely ground monazite is treated with hot sulfuric acid to put the thorium and rare earths in soluble form in the presence of phosphoric and sulfuric acids. In the caustic process the monazite is treated with hot concentrated sodium hydroxide to give residues of hydrated oxides of thorium and rare earths and a solution of trisodium phosphate, which is recovered as a by-product by filtration. The oxides are then dissolved in the proper acid.

Subsequent treatment of the acid product solution from either the acid or the caustic process may include steps that depend on relative solubilities of compounds such as hydroxide, sulfate, double sulfate, oxalate, double carbonate, phosphate, iodate and nitrate. The relatively low solubility of thorium sulfate as compared to the rare earth sulfates has been the basis of a process for preparing thorium nitrate of adequate purity for use in production of mantles. For higher purity thorium, solvent extraction purification is generally employed.

One variation of the acid treatment of monazite sand employs 93% H_2SO_4 at 210°C. The resulting "monazite sulfate" is dissolved in water, separated from the insolubles and then adjusted to a pH of 1.0 with NH_4OH to precipitate the thorium with a small fraction of the rare earths. This precipitate which contains phosphate and sulfate is washed and then treated with nitric acid to give a solution. If it is desired to eliminate the phosphate and sulfate, the thorium and rare earths may be precipitated from this nitrate solution as oxalates. The oxalates are washed and calcined to oxide. The oxides are dissolved in nitric acid to give the aqueous solution for preparing feed for a solvent extraction process employing aqueous and tributyl phosphate phases. Only thorium and four-valent cerium are delivered in the organic phase. Subsequently, thorium is recovered from the organic after first reducing and removing the cerium.

A variation of the caustic treatment of monazite with subsequent solvent extraction employs a 45% NaOH solution at 138°C to open the ore. The thorium, uranium and rare earths are recovered from this treatment as water-insoluble oxides. After these compounds are washed, they are dissolved in 37% HCl at 80°C. The clear solution is subsequently treated with NaOH to adjust its pH to a value of 5.8 and thus precipitate thorium and uranium with a small amount of rare earths. The washed precipitate is then dissolved in concentrated HNO_3. Thorium and uranium are then separated from rare earths by aqueous-tributyl phosphate solvent extraction; subsequently, uranium and thorium are selectively stripped from the organic phase.

Preparation of Metal

Thorium metal can be prepared from some of its compounds by replacement with another metal or by electrolysis. The compounds that have been successfully employed were either the oxide or a halide. The oxide has a relatively high free energy of formation so it is not readily susceptible to reduction by alkali metals or by hydrogen; carbon reduction does not appear to be feasible, even at very high temperature, because of the additional problem of forming carbide as an intermediate. Although numerous means have been tested in attempts to make the metal directly from oxide, it appears that the most common process employing oxide depends on the calcium reduction. A great variety of methods have been employed for the preparation of the metal from its halides beginning with the first preparation of thorium metal by Berzelius in 1829. Alkali and alkaline earth metals as well as electrolysis have received most attention in preparation of thorium from halides. A few of these methods that have shown promise as means for large scale production of thorium metal of desirable quality are presented in some detail.

From Thorium Oxide by Calcium. The calcium reduction of thorium oxide is being employed on a relatively large scale, and although variations in the process are numerous, all have an excess of calcium in the charge. Usually a mixture of oxide and calcium in a closed steel vessel is heated at 950°C for 1 hour. After cooling, the product is leached with water to remove most of the calcium oxide and free calcium. A subsequent leaching with dilute acid, then washing and vacuum drying results in a good grade of free-flowing thorium powder. The powder may be compacted and sintered to give massive metal that is very ductile and easily fabricated into wire and sheet.

From Thorium Halides by Electrolysis. Perhaps the most successful electrolytic process for thorium has been its electrodeposition from a fused salt bath of sodium and potassium chlorides containing $KF \cdot ThF_4$. The bath was contained in a graphite crucible and the thorium deposited as a coarse powder on a centrally placed electrode of molybdenum.

Under the conditions employed, there is a fluoride buildup in the fused salt bath since fluoride is added and chloride is electrolyzed out. Some work has been done in an effort to electrolyze the chloride in a fused chloride salt bath, but further development is needed on the approach.

Ingots from Powder. Thorium metal powder by electrolysis or by calcium reduction of oxide has a high plasticity and, therefore, good compressibility with the coarser electrolytic powder showing greater compressibility than the calcium-reduced powder. The pressures employed range from 40 to 80 tons per square inch. Sintering is generally done in a vacuum at about 1200°C or higher. Massive metal has been prepared by extrusion of the powder in a copper container at much lower temperatures. Green compacts of the metal powder respond to self-induction melting and to arc melting by either consumable or nonconsumable electrodes employing low pressures and inert atmospheres. Electron beam melting of thorium compacts apparently gives some purification as well as a massive form of the metal.

By Metal Reduction of Chloride. It is reported that Berzelius obtained thorium from the tetrachloride by reaction with potassium. Others have used sodium, calcium and magnesium as well as potassium for reduction of the tetrachloride. The preparation of the tetrachloride in high purity and, due to its hygroscopic nature, the preservation of its purity in subsequent handling, however, present some problems.

In the magnesium reduction of tetrachloride, the charge mixture contains an adequate excess of magnesium metal to form an alloy of about 20 weight % magnesium. The charge is heated at about 950°C under an inert atmosphere in a titanium metal container inside a closed steel vessel for a period to permit the liquid alloy and $MgCl_2$ products to properly separate into layers. The alloy is then heated in a vacuum to about 950°C to remove the magnesium. The resulting thorium sponge is formed into massive metal by melting in an arc or electron beam furnace.

By Calcium Reduction of Fluoride. The tetrafluoride, which is not hygroscopic, is mixed with anhydrous zinc chloride and adequate calcium metal to reduce both of these compounds to give a thorium-6 weight % zinc alloy and a slag of calcium fluoride and chloride. The mixed charge in a refractory-lined closed vessel is then heated in a furnace to ignition. The preheat of the furnace and the heat of the reactions together boost the temperature of the products to above their melting points and permit separation of the liquid alloy and slag phases. The alloy is recovered as a massive piece which is subsequently heated in a vacuum to remove the zinc and leave a thorium sponge. Massive thorium metal may be obtained by melting in an induction, arc or electron-beam furnace.

In High Purity. Special-purity metal has been obtained by subsequent treatment of reduced metal. Some purification may be obtained by remelting in an electron-beam furnace. The iodide, or crystal bar, process has been found quite effective in reducing the contents of certain impurities.

Physical, Electrical and Thermodynamic Properties of Thorium Metal

Some properties of thorium metal are affected by small amounts of impurities. Values of the properties related here may be approximate since some measurements have been made on metal of normal production quality. Table 1 lists values considered as representative for certain properties of the metal.

Mechanical Properties and Fabrication

Pure thorium metal is soft and quite ductile. The metal can be cold rolled, without intermediate annealing, directly from thick sections (1 inch ±) to less than a thousandth of an inch in thickness with only minor edge cracking. The pure metal in the annealed condition has a tensile strength of about

17,000 psi, a 0.2% yield strength of about 7000 psi, a hardness of 36 VHN, an elongation in 2 inches of 36% and a reduction in area of 62%. The introduction of an impurity such as carbon or any one of a number of metals markedly increases the strength and hardness of thorium metal. Nitrogen and oxygen in concentrations of a few tenths per cent in thorium have little influence on the strength and hardness of the metal.

The metal is easily shaped by cold or hot rolling, swaging or drawing. When hot forming, however, the chemical reactivity of the metal must be considered, and adequate protection of the metal from oxidation should be provided. The metal when hot extruded is usually protected from oxidation by a jacket of another metal. In welding of thorium, usually an inert gas blanket protects the metal. Machining of thorium by turning, milling, grinding, drilling and sawing can be readily performed; however, due to the soft and ductile nature of the metal, good finishes are difficult to prepare by cutting operations.

Nuclear Properties

Soon after radioactivity was discovered, it was shown that thorium is a radioactive element. The radioactive disintegration series for thorium-232 (atomic number 90) goes

TABLE 1. PHYSICAL PROPERTIES OF THORIUM
(at 25°C unless otherwise indicated).

Atomic number	90	Heat of vaporization	140 kcal/mole
Atomic weight	232.038	Heat of fusion	< 4.6 kcal/mole
Atomic diameter	3.596 Å	Linear coefficient expansion, 25°–1000°C(mean)	12.5×10^{-6}/°C
Crystal structure			
FCC up to 1400°C	$a_o = 5.086$ Å	Atomic heat capacity	6.53 cal/°C-mole
BCC 1400°C to m.p.	$a_o = 4.11$ Å	Thermal conductivity at 200°C	0.09 cal/sec-°C-cm
Density, x-ray	11.72 g/cc	Hall coefficient	-10×10^{-5}
Electrical resistivity	14 microhm-cm	Thermal diffusion at 150°C	0.28 cm²/sec
Temp. coefficient	3.8×10^{-3} per °C	Emissivity, 1000–1700°C	0.38 at 6670 Å
Elastic constants		Work function	3.51 eV
Young's modulus	10.3×10^6 psi	Radioactive half-life	
Shear modulus	4.1×10^6 psi	α-decay	1.39×10^{10} yrs
Poisson's ratio	0.27		
Melting point	1750°C		
Boiling point	∼ 3800°C		

through ten decay steps (six alpha and four beta) before reaching the stable isotope lead-208 (atomic number 82).

Certain nuclear properties of thorium make it a source of fuel for atomic energy. By capturing a neutron, Th^{232} is converted to Th^{233} which is radioactive by beta decay to yield Pa^{233} which also decays by beta emission to give U^{233}. Uranium-233 is a fissionable isotope which can function in a manner similar to U^{235} and Pu^{239} in chain reactions to release nuclear energy. It is estimated that thorium is three times as abundant as uranium in the earth's crust; it looms, therefore, as a major source of energy.

Chemical Properties

The element thorium generally exhibits a positive valence of four in chemical reactions. Before the development of atomic energy, which brought about better understanding of the elements in relation to one another, thorium was assigned a position in Group IV of the periodic arrangement of the elements. Because of its valence, atomic weight and other properties, it was assumed that thorium was the heaviest member of the family that now includes titanium, zirconium and hafnium. However, thorium (atomic number 90) now stands as the second member of a series of elements often termed the actinides. This series of fifteen elements starts with actinium and ends with lawrencium. All elements of the series except actinium and thorium have $5f$ electrons in their ground atomic state. Uranium and plutonium, also of interest in the atomic energy program, are members of this actinide series.

In compound formation, thorium exhibits strong metal properties and stands just below magnesium in the electromotive force series. All of the nonmetallic elements, except the rare gases, form binary compounds with thorium. A number of metallic elements also form binary intermetallic compounds with thorium metal. The oxide ThO_2 which is quite stable can be obtained by thermal decomposition of compounds such as oxalate, hydroxide and nitrate, by hydrolysis of halides and by heating the metal in air or oxygen. Other oxides of thorium have been reported but these appear to be of minor

concern in the normal chemical behavior of thorium. The dioxide is generally considered as basic in salt formation, and, accordingly, many thorium salts of organic and inorganic acids are known.

The carbides of thorium, ThC and ThC_2, are formed by reacting either the metal or its dioxide with carbon. The carbides tend to hydrolyze readily and yield a gas having a very disagreeable odor. The known nitrides, ThN and Th_2N_3, are prepared by heating thorium metal in an atmosphere of pure nitrogen. The nitrides also react readily with water or moist air. The hydrides, ThH_2 and Th_4H_{15}, are formed by heating the metal in hydrogen. The dihydride is formed at about 600°C while the higher hydride is formed by heating the dihydride in hydrogen at 250°C. Formation of the hydrides from solid ingot thorium followed by thermal decomposition in a vacuum gives a means for converting solid ingot thorium to powder. The hydrides react with water, halides, hydrogen halides, acids and oxygen. They exhibit pyrophoricity. Thorium forms tetrahalides with all the halogens. These can be formed by direct union of the elements or by other reactions involving compounds of thorium.

Thorium as an alloying element in binary systems has been studied rather extensively. Nickel and cobalt metals each form five intermetallic compounds with thorium metal. Iron and aluminum are each reported to form four such compounds. Three compounds are reported for each of the metals manganese, bismuth, silicon and copper with thorium. One and two compound systems have been reported for some other binary alloy systems of thorium. A number of intermetallic compounds of thorium are quite pyrophoric. No compounds have been observed for binary systems of thorium with titanium, vanadium, chromium, zirconium, niobium, hafnium or uranium.

Applications of Thorium and its Compounds

Thorium is, as pointed out above, important in the atomic energy program. The chemical state in which the element is employed may be as metal, oxide, alloy or other compound for conversion to uranium-233. The form will depend on reactor design which may be quite varied yet consistent with principles of reactor operation and materials processing.

Nonenergy uses of thorium that have been treated in sections above include the use of thorium oxide in the incandescent gas light mantle and the use of thorium metal for imparting strength to magnesium metal. Thorium metal and thorium-rich alloys, because of a number of factors, appear to have limited use in nonenergy applications. The mechanical properties of thorium metal and thorium-rich alloys are such that these metals appear to offer no desirable features that cannot be duplicated or exceeded by other less costly and less dense metals for ordinary structural purposes. Thorium metal, because of its low work function and high emissivity for electrons, has found applications in a number of gaseous discharge lamps. It also can be used in photoelectric cells, especially where sensitivity to ultraviolet light is desired. Thorium metal may also be used as the target in x-ray tubes; it generates a strong monochromatic x-ray.

The oxide has been found useful in a variety of areas. Perhaps the most recent potentially large-scale nonenergy use found for thorium oxide is as a hardner in TD nickel. This material contains about 2% of dispersed thoria that imparts superior strength and corrosion resistance to the nickel at high temperatures. This material is finding applications in rockets, space vehicles, chemical equipment and furnace parts. For many years a small percentage of thorium oxide has been employed in tungsten filaments for incandescent lamps to facilitate fabrication and to inhibit crystallization. The thoriated tungsten filament also improves the efficiency of electronic tubes. Thoriated tungsten rods are employed as electrodes in some arc-melting operations. Thorium oxide when properly prepared is quite active as a catalyst for many chemical processes. The conversion of ammonia to nitric acid, the cracking of petroleum fractions and the preparation of sulfuric acid are areas in which thoria has found applications as a catalyst. Thoria, because of its stability at high temperatures, has for many years been employed in the preparation of special refractory crucibles for melting some metals.

Health and Safety Aspects

The effects of thorium on plants and animals have been extensively investigated. However, some consideration has been given to factors bearing on toxicity and other possible hazards connected with handling of thorium and its compounds. Although thorium has been handled in large-scale operations under controlled conditions without incident, hazards do exist, and proper health and safety measures must be regarded in operations involving thorium. Hazards of thorium or its compounds may generally be classed into three areas, namely, radiological, chemical and combustion.

The radiological hazards of thorium are connected essentially with the radioactivity of the isotopes in the decay chain from thorium-232 to lead-208. In general, the greatest danger in this regard develops when the radioactive material enters the body. The radioactive isotopes fall into several different families of the Periodic Table and, therefore, exhibit different chemical behaviors. However, because of the short half-lives of many of the members of the decay chain, the chemical behaviors are represented largely by thorium and radium. In the body the thorium-type isotopes generally will tend to concentrate in the liver, kidneys, spleen and bone marrow, and the radium-type isotopes are likely to concentrate in the skeleton. Radiation due to injection then takes place in many areas of the body.

In thorium processing certain radioactive isotopes often are separated from the thorium and collect in concentrations that are exceedingly hazardous. Even in just the storage of thorium or its compounds, the gaseous radioactive decay product, thoron (Rn^{220}), may build up to dangerous levels in the air. Radiation due to sources outside the body must also be considered. Buildup of radioactive dust on walls and on machinery can give conditions in excess of safe limits.

Ordinary chemical toxicity of thorium or its compounds by any means of introduction into the body is generally considered as low. Experiments with small animals indicate that relatively large quantities of thorium compounds (a few grams per kilogram of body weight) taken orally are necessary to produce

717

toxic reactions. The effect varies some with the compound employed, however. Intravenous injections of thorium compounds, on the other hand, are more toxic; an injection of 40 milligrams of the nitrate per kilogram of animal may produce 50% mortality in rats.

Spontaneous combustion of thorium metal or alloys must be given due consideration. Thorium metal in massive form has not been observed to offer any fire or explosion hazard; however, some alloys of thorium are pyrophoric and may, even in massive form, ignite or rapidly disintegrate on exposure to air. The greatest danger of fire and explosion from the metal and alloys is when they are in powder form. The ignition temperatures of such dusts in air are low; for example, thorium hydride dust exposed to air has ignited at 20°C. The reaction of thorium with oxygen is highly exothermic and thorium dust in air can produce a violent explosion. In thorium metal preparation, the process may involve a charge that is highly exothermic; adequate safeguards must be provided in such cases to prevent preignition of the charge.

For further information and more details on health and safety in connection with thorium, reference should be made to a report by A. F. Voigt in the book "The Metal Thorium."

References

1. Weeks, M. E., "Discovery of the Elements," 6th ed. Easton Pa., Journal of Chemical Education, 1956.
2. Wilhelm, H. A., Ed., "The Metal Thorium," Metals Park, Ohio, American Society for Metals, 1958.
3. Hampel, C. A., Ed., "Rare Metals Handbook," 2nd Ed., Chapter 28 "Thorium," New York, Reinhold Publishing Corp., 1961.
4. "Mineral Facts and Problems," 1965 Edition by Staff, Bureau of Mines, Chapter on Thorium. Available as Bulletin 630 Bureau of Mines from Superintendent of Documents, U.S. Government Printing Office, Washington, D.C. 20402.
5. Cuthbert, F. L., "Thorium Production Technology," Reading, Mass., Addison-Wesley Publishing Co., 1958.

HARLEY A. WILHELM

THULIUM

Thulium, atomic number 69, must be considered a truly minor element. Nevertheless, it possesses unique physical and nuclear properties which render it useful in a technological sense. Should the demand arise, thulia, Tm_2O_3, could be isolated readily, as one of a number of individual rare earth by-products from the current (1967) commercial production of yttria by ion exchange, at a rate exceeding 1000 pounds per annum.

History [1,2,3]

The element was "discovered" in 1879 by Cleve and named after Thule, the most northerly part of the habitable world, but actually it was not isolated in the form of "pure thulia" until 1911 (James). Due to the low natural abundance, thulium was neither available in a truly pure state (e.g., >99.99% Tm_2O_3) in pound quantities nor prepared in consolidated metallic form until adequate ion-exchange separation and metallothermic reduction techniques were developed by Spedding and co-workers some 40 years later.

Occurrence and Sources [1,4]

Thulium is the least abundant of the naturally occurring rare earths (excluding promethium), yet it ranks 65th in order of abundance among the components of the earth's crust. It is in fact more prevalent than some of the more familiar elements (cadmium, silver, indium, palladium, platinum, gold, selenium, etc.). The more important sources of thulium are the yttrium-rich minerals—xenotime, gadolinite, euxenite, samarskite, fergusonite, blomstrandine, loparite, and yttroparisite. Nevertheless, thulium also occurs as a trace element in many of the more common rocks and minerals, including apatite and cerium-rich monazite. The yttrium-rich minerals are occasionally discovered in pegmatites but are found more frequently in erosion concentrates along with monazite. Xenotime occurs in Norway, Sweden, Brazil, Switzerland, Malaysia, Korea, North Carolina, South Carolina, and Colorado. Gadolinite occurs in Sweden, Norway, Malagasy Republic (Madagascar), Texas, Arizona, and Colorado. Euxenite is found in Brazil, Finland, Norway, Australia,

Madagascar, North Carolina, and Idaho; fergusonite in Greenland, Sweden, Norway, North Carolina, South Carolina, and Texas; samarskite in Madagascar, North Carolina, and Ontario; blomstrandine in Norway; loparite and yttroparisite in Russia. Of these minerals, xenotime and gadolinite are the most easily opened by chemical action, and yield the cleanest rare earth concentrates. Because it is worked for its uranium, thorium, and yttrium values, euxenite is also an important source of thulium.

Derivation[1-5]

Processing of Ores.[1,3,4] After physical concentration, finely ground xenotime (essentially $(Y)PO_4$) is heated with excess 95% sulfuric acid to obtain a paste of yttrium and rare earth sulfates in sulfuric and phosphoric acids, and the sulfates are leached from unreacted mineral, silica, etc., with cold water. The pregnant liquor is filtered and fed directly into the ion-exchange system used to isolate yttrium and the individual rare earths.

Pulverized gadolinite (ostensibly $Be_2Fe(Y)_2Si_2O_{10}$) is attacked by hot, concentrated nitric and hydrochloric acids, and the dissolved beryllium, iron, yttrium, and various rare earths are diluted and filtered free of the silicaceous residue. Oxalic acid is added next to precipitate yttrium and the rare earths, leaving behind the beryllium and iron; and the oxalate precipitate is roasted to a mixture of yttrium and rare earth oxides at about 800°. It is expedient to redissolve the oxide mixture in hydrochloric acid and to filter the solution (to reduce the silica content) before proceeding with the isolation of yttrium and the individual rare earths. Gadolinite can also be attacked by caustic fusion. The sodium silicate formed is leached away, and the residue of mixed yttrium and rare earth hydroxides is taken into solution by adding an acid.

Euxenite, samarskite, fergusonite, blomstrandine, polycrase, loparite, and a host of less important minerals are generically either niobate-tantalate or niobate-titanate minerals of a complex and refractory nature. They are sometimes treated with hydrofluoric acid to solubilize the niobium, tantalum, and titanium values, leaving an insoluble yttrium and rare earth fluoride residue. This is decomposed subsequently with hot concentrated sulfuric acid. The refractory minerals also have been opened successfully by direct chlorination procedures and by other means.

Separation of Rare Earth Mixtures.[1,3-5] Thulium is separated from its mixtures by displacement ion-exchange techniques. An yttrium-group concentrate, containing perhaps 0.5 per cent Tm_2O_3, is dissolved in a mineral acid; and the tripositive cations are sorbed on an appropriate cation-exchange system and eluted a distance equal to one-fourth the length of the sorbed band with 0.015M ammonium ethylenediaminetetraacetate (EDTA) solution at pH 8.4–8.5, over cation-exchange resin pretreated with 1M $CuSO_4$–1M H_2SO_4 solution. The leading one-tenth of the partially developed displacement chromatogram (containing all of the lutetium, ytterbium, and thulium values, most of the erbium and perhaps half of the holmium; but very little of the dysprosium or yttrium contents of the charge) is diverted onto an appropriately dimensioned bed of acidified cupric-form cation-exchange resin. At this point the thulium will have been concentrated ten-fold. The auxiliary bed, charged with the elements Ho-Lu, is detached from the original system and connected at the head of a series of ion-exchange columns of smaller diameter. Usually a diameter one-fifth that of the original column is chosen so that the developed thulium band will be lengthened 25-fold as elution is continued. (1) Elution may be continued with EDTA over H+-form resin, provided the ammonium EDTA solution is diluted to 0.01M and the system is operated at 90–95°C. (2) The eluant may be switched to 0.018M diammonium monohydrogen β-hydroxyethylethylenediaminetriacetate solution at pH 7.5, and elution continued over H+-form resin at room temperature. In either case a series of fractions of the eluate are collected eventually and treated with oxalic acid. The resulting precipitates are filtered off, calcined individually at 800–900°, and analyzed. Appropriate combinations are then made. As a general rule, more than 90% of the recovered Tm_2O_3 exceeds a purity of 99.9%. Comparable yields of equally pure Lu_2O_3, Yb_2O_3, and Er_2O_3 are obtained by this technique.

TABLE 1. PHYSICAL PROPERTIES OF THULIUM METAL

Atomic number		69
Atomic weight, $^{12}C = 12.0000$		168.934
Atomic volume, cc/g-atom		18.151
Structure		Hcp
Lattice parameters, Å	$a_o =$	3.5375
	$c_o =$	5.5546
Density, g/cc		9.318
Metallic radius, Å		1.746
Melting point, °C		1545
Heat of fusion, kcal/g-atom		4.22
Vapor pressure, $\log P_{torr} = A/T + B$	$A =$	$-12,552$
	$B =$	9.176
Heat capacity, cal/g-atom/°C	$C_{p298} =$	6.45
	$C_{p1900} =$	8.85
Entropy of metal, eu	$S_{298} =$	17.1
Boiling point, °C		1725
Heat of sublimation, kcal/g-atom at 25°C		58.3
Coefficient of linear thermal expansion $\times 10^6$, per °C		11.6
Cohesive energy, kcal/g-atom		58
Debye temperature, °K		200
Susceptibility, emu/g-atom $\times 10^6$		26,200
Effective magnetic moment, Bohr magnetons		7.62
Curie temperature, °K		22
Neel temperature, °K		60
Compressibility, cm²/kg $\times 10^6$		2.6
Hardness, DPH		48
Ultimate compressive strength, psi $\times 10^{-3}$		78.1
Electrical resistivity, μ ohm-cm		79
Temperature coefficient of resistivity $\times 10^3$, per °C		1.95
Thermal neutron absorption cross section, barns/atom		118 ± 6
cm²/g		0.42

Preparation of the Metal [2,4,5]

Metallic thulium is prepared readily by direct reaction of thulium oxide and lanthanum metal near the melting point of thulium, 1545°. Thulium metal is sufficiently volatile at this temperature that it sublimes rapidly *in vacuo* and can be condensed in consolidated crystalline form free of lanthanum. Although thulium trifluoride can be reduced metallo-thermically by calcium in tantalum or in tungsten, marked solubility of these container materials in thulium at its melting point reduces the quality of the metal product.

Physical Properties [4,5,6]

The more significant properties of metallic thulium are listed in Table 1.

Chemical Properties [1,3-6,8]

Thulium metal is relatively stable in air at room temperature; in fact, the corrosion rate is less than one mil per year up to 200°C. This behavior is apparently related to the similar densities of the metal and the sequioxide (9.3 and 8.6) and to the fact that Tm_2O_3 does not react with moist air to form the hydroxide as is the case with cerium-group rare earth oxides. Elemental thulium is readily attacked and dissolved with the evolution of hydrogen by dilute and concentrated mineral acids, yet a 1:1 mixture of nitric acid and 48% hydrofluoric acid does not appear to affect the metal.

Thulium reacts slowly at room temperature with the halogen gases to form the trihalides; above 200°C the reaction is vigorous. At high temperatures thulium also combines with oxygen, sulfur, nitrogen, carbon, boron, hydrogen, and water, forming Tm_2O_3; TmS; TmN; TmC_2, Tm_2C_3, and Tm_3C; TmB_4, TmB_6, and TmB_{12}; TmH_2 and TmH_3; and Tm_2O_3, respectively. $TmBe_{13}$, $TmZn_{12}$,

Tm_6Zn_{23}, $TmNi_5$, $TmGa_3$, $TmSi_2$, $TmGe_3$, TmP, TmAs, TmSb, TmBi, TmSe, TmTe, and TmPo have also been prepared by direct combination of the elements.

Halides.[1,3-5] Anhydrous thulium trifluoride is readily prepared by the reactions

$$Tm_2O_3 + 6HF \xrightarrow{heat} 2TmF_3 + 3H_2O$$

$$Tm_2O_3 + 6(NH_4)HF_2 \xrightarrow{heat} 2TmF_3 + 3H_2O + 6NH_4F.$$

The latter reaction is generally preferred for the preparation of high-purity TmF_3. The anhydrous trichloride, tribromide, and triiodide are more generally prepared by careful dehydration of the corresponding hydrated trihalides at relatively low temperatures and pressures in an atmosphere of the respective hydrogen halide. TmOX is a common hydrolysis product observed.

Subhalides having the stoichiometry TmX_2 are known, but Tm^{+2} apparently does not exist in aqueous solutions.

Oxides.[1,3-6] Tm_2O_3 is obtained by burning the metal in air and by thermally decomposing a variety of thulium compounds in air, including the hydroxide, carbonate, tricarballylate, and oxalate which are not soluble in water, and the nitrate and acetate which are. The oxide is attacked readily by most common mineral acids and many water-soluble hydrated thulium salts have been prepared, for example, $TmCl_3 \cdot 6H_2O$, $TmBr_3 \cdot 6H_2O$, $Tm(NO_3)_3 \cdot 5H_2O$, $Tm_2(SO_4)_3 \cdot 8H_2O$, $Tm(BrO_3)_3 \cdot 9H_2O$, $Tm(CH_3COO)_3 \cdot 4H_2O$, and $Tm(C_2H_5OSO_3)_3 \cdot 9H_2O$.

Other Salts.[1,3,4] The water-insoluble hydroxide, fluoride, carbonate, oxalate, and tricarballylate are frequently formed in chemical separation of the rare earths as a group from other elements. The complex salts $TmCrO_3$, $TmMnO_3$, $TmBO_3$, $LaTmO_3$, $TmPO_4$, $TmCrO_4$, $TmVO_4$, $TmNbO_4$, $TmTaO_4$, Tm_2MoO_6, Tm_2WO_6, $Tm_2Ru_2O_7$, $Tm_3Al_5O_{12}$, $Tm_3Fe_5O_{12}$, and $Tm_2Ga_5O_{12}$ have also been prepared (generally by fusion of appropriate oxide mixtures). Both Tm_2S_3 and Tm_2O_2S have been prepared by passing H_2S over Tm_2O_3 at elevated temperatures.

Valency.[3] Only the tripositive ion of thulium is encountered in aqueous media. However, the stoichiometries TmI_2, TmH_2, TmS, etc., suggest that Tm^{+2} is a reality in nonaqueous systems.

Applications[1,4-6,9]

Thulium probably will never be attainable at what would be considered low cost, due to its low relative abundance and inherent difficulty associated with isolating it from its congeners. Currently (1967), >99.9% Tm_2O_3 is valued at more than $1500 per pound, and future costs will depend largely on its status as a by-product derived from the commercial production of yttrium oxide. Conceivably the cost of Tm_2O_3 and Lu_2O_3 (both comparatively rare) could drop below $100 per pound without the development of new separation techniques should adequate markets develop for dysprosium, holmium, erbium, and ytterbium.

One important application of thulium, relatively independent of its high cost, is the use of a (0.1–0.2)-gram pellet of the metal or oxide as a portable source of diagnostic x-radiation. Small pellets of natural Tm^{169} are bombarded about four months in a nuclear reactor with a high flux of thermal neutrons to convert a part of the Tm^{169} to radioactive Tm^{170}, which decays subsequently by β^- emission to Yb^{170}. Considerable internal conversion occurs, and the resultant radiation is complex, being comprised of characteristic ytterbium x-rays, soft gamma rays, and bremsstrahlung. Such sources are useful for a period of about one year (the half-life is 127 days) as medical and dental diagnostic tools, and for detecting flaws or failures in small inaccessible components of electrical and mechanical devices. Shielding requirements are not excessive, so that the source needs only to be encased in a small lead container, equipped with a shutter system to "turn the radiation on and off."

Another interesting isotope of thulium is Tm^{171} with its two-year half-life. The decay proceeds by β emission with no associated gamma ray. Tm^{171} is thus potentially useful as an energy source, and may be derived conveniently from natural Tm^{169}, *via* Tm^{170}, by continued bombardment with neutrons since Tm^{170} has an even greater cross section for thermal neutrons than does Tm^{169} (*ca.* 2000 compared to 118 barns). A very high flux of neutrons is required, however, to circumvent the decay of Tm^{170} to Yb^{170}. Tm^{171} can also be prepared from calutron separated Er^{170} by neutron capture and subsequent β decay, *via* 7.5-hour Er^{171}. Er^{170} has a cross section of 9 barns and occurs in natural erbium to the extent of 14.9%. Because erbium is about 10 times as plentiful as thulium, Er^{170} is slightly more abundant than Tm^{169}.

It is possible that thulium will also find use in magnetic ceramic materials (ferrites) similar to yttrium-iron garnet which is presently employed in microwave relay stations.

Biological and Biochemical Nature[10]

The rare earths, including thulium, have a low acute toxicity rating, but chronic effects from repeated intravenous and intraperitoneal injections include degeneration of the liver and spleen and changes in hemoglobin content, leukocyte count, etc. Liver damage due to ingestion of 0.01 to 1.0% of the diet as thulium over a 5-month period was more prominent in males than in females (mice).

References

1. Vickery, R. C., "Chemistry of the Lanthanides," New York, Academic Press, 1953.
2. Daane, A. H., Dennison, D. H., and Spedding, F. H., *J. Am. Chem. Soc.*, **75**, 2272 (1953).
3. Moeller, T., "The Chemistry of the Lanthanides," New York, Reinhold Publishing Corp., 1963.
4. Love, B., and Kleber, E. V., "Technology of Scandium, Ytterbium and the Rare Earth Metals," New York, Macmillan, 1963.
5. Spedding, F. H., and Daane, A. H., Ed., "The Rare Earths," New York, John Wiley and Sons, 1961.
6. Gschneidner, K. A., Jr., "Rare Earth Alloys," Princeton, New Jersey, Van Nostrand, 1961.
7. Hall, H. T., Barnett, J. D., and Merrill, L., *Science*, **139**, 111 (1963); Stager, R. A., and Drickamer, H. S., *Science*, **139**, 1284 (1963); Souers, P. C., and Jura, G., *Science*, **140**, 481 (1963); Hall, H. T., and Merrill, L., *Inorg. Chem.*, **2**, 618 (1963); Jayaraman, A., *Phys. Rev.*, **135**, A1056 (1964); and Stephens, D. R., *J. Phys. Chem. Solids*, **26**, 943 (1965).
8. Love, B., and Kleber, E. V., *Materials in Design Eng.*, **52**, [5], 134 (1960); and Lee, L., and Green, N. D., *Corrosion*, **20**, 145t (1964).
9. Mandle, R. M., and Mandle, H. H., "Progress in the Science and Technology of the Rare Earths," Eyring, L., Ed., Vol. 1, p. 416, New York, Pergamon Press, 1964.
10. Haley, T. J., *J. Pharmaceutical Sciences*, **54**, 663 (1965).

JACK E. POWELL

TIN

Tin (Sn), atomic number 50, atomic weight 118.69, is in Group IVA of the Periodic Table and is a member of the subgroup containing carbon, silicon, germanium and lead. The valence numbers are $+2$ and $+4$. There are ten naturally occurring isotopes.

The relative percentage of tin in the earth's crust (0.004) is far down in the list of the commonly used metals. The tonnage of tin that is mined is small in comparison to other metals since it seldom exceeds 180,000 long tons annually, but the applications and uses are widespread.

Two allotropic forms of tin can exist: white tin (β) and gray tin (α). White tin, the form which is most familiar, crystallizes in the body-centered tetragonal system. Gray tin has a diamond cubic structure and is formed when high-purity tin is exposed to temperatures well below zero. The allotropic transformation of tin is retarded when small amounts of bismuth, antimony and lead are present in the tin as impurities. The spontaneous appearance of gray tin at low temperatures is a rare occurrence requiring, in some cases, years of exposure at $-40°F$.

History and Development

The discovery of tin is uncertain as to time and place but there is evidence that it was one of the earliest metals known to mankind. The finding of ancient objects in the form of weapons and tools coupled with the chemical analysis of the objects, showed that bronze articles, containing 10 and 15% tin, were used about 3500 B.C. The Phoenicians played an important part in spreading the bronze culture through their trading activities, in the course of which they took tin from Britain and Spain to the bronze-working countries of the Eastern Mediterranean. Tin is mentioned by Pliny in A.D. 79. He described two alloys of tin and lead (now commonly called solder).

TABLE 1. TYPICAL ANALYSES OF COMMERCIAL TIN

Brand	Minimum Sn content	Maximum Impurity Limits %								
		Sb	Bi	Pb	As	Cu	Fe	S	Ni and Co	Zn and Cd
American										
U S Spec (Grade AA)	99.95	.02	.01	.02	.01	.02	.01		.01	.001
U S Spec (Grade A)	99.80	.04	.015	.05	.05	.04	.015	.01	.003	.001
Longhorn 3 Star	99.86	.033	.006	.036	.033	.021	.001	.002	.002	nil
M & T Electrolytic	99.98	.007	trace	.008	trace	trace	.004			
Vulcan Electrolytic	99.98	.010		.006	nil	.004	.006			
English										
U K Standard Tin	99.75	.05	.02	.10	.05	.05	.01	.01	.02	
Pass No 1	99.975	.02		.001	.003		.002			
Mellanear (Guar. 99.9%)	99.935	.007	.006	.025	.008	.007	.005		.003	
Mellanear (Refined)	99.813	.035	.022	.065	.018	.020	.005		.013	
Cornish (Refined)	99.775	.050	.030	.072	.020	.023	.005		.014	
Straits										
E S Coy (Penang)	99.898	.003	.004	.037	.027	.023	.005	.001	.002	
S T Co (Singapore)	99.891	.003	.008	.038	.038	.015	.005		.002	
Thailand										
Thaisarco	99.93	.003	.006	.020	.025	.010	.010	trace		
Indonesian										
Banka	99.935	.004	.001	.033	.014	.006	.007			
Dutch										
Billiton	99.935	.004	.004	.034	.010	.006	.007			
Tulip	99.863	.014	.010	.085	.010	.011	.007			
Belgian										
UMHK	99.966		trace	.012	.006	.013	.003			
Congo										
Geomines	99.93	.002		.030	.015	.013	.003		.007	

Metal Statistics: 1966 American Metal Market

The Romans were known to use solder and tinned copper vessels. Tinned iron vessels did not appear until the 14th Century in Bohemia. Tinned steel sheet (tinplate) made its appearance in England and Saxony about the middle of the 17th Century. Tinplate manufacture in the United States did not appear until the early 19th Century, but production increased steadily and has outstripped all other countries for many years.

The development of fast machinery and mechanical means of transportation surged forward with the introduction of the tin-base babbitt bearing in 1839.

Tin-producing areas, confined first to England and Spain, gradually opened up in southeastern Asia in the 9th Century. Tin production in Bolivia, Congo and Nigeria is more recent but production has increased substantially since 1910.

Prior to 1945, a few large smelters in Malaya, England, Holland and Belgium handled the refining and smelting of the tin ore. The present trend is to operate smelters close to the mining areas; there are now over twenty-five tin smelters located throughout the world. Typical analyses of various brands of tin are given in Table 1.

Prevalence and Sources

The important tin-producing countries are Malaysia, Thailand, Indonesia, Bolivia, Republic of the Congo, Nigeria and China which account for 90% of world production. Small tonnages are produced in Australia, England, Burma, Japan, Canada, Portugal and Spain. No workable deposits are found in the United States.

The only tin-bearing mineral of commercial importance is the oxide, SnO_2, commonly called cassiterite. There are no high-grade tin deposits. The bulk of the world's tin ore is obtained from low-grade alluvial deposits averaging about 0.4 lb of tin metal content per cubic yard (3,000 lbs). Lode deposits containing up to 4% tin are found mainly in Bolivia and Cornwall where the cassiterite is associated with granitic rock and complex sulfides.

Mining

Methods for mining of the tin ore depend on whether the cassiterite is in the form of an alluvial sand or is embedded in granitic rock underground.

The cassiterite is recovered from alluvial deposits by dredging, gravel-pump mining on level ground, hydraulicing where a head of water permits, and open-pit mining.

Dredging is mining with a floating dredge on an artificial pond in a placer (see Fig. 1). This method of mining allows profitable exploitation of low-grade deposits unworkable by panning. The tin-bearing material is obtained by either chain buckets or suction cutters digging below the surface of the artificial pond, sometimes at a depth of 140 feet. Preliminary roughing and cleaning with water is accomplished on the dredge using screens, hydrocyclones, jigs, shaking tables, etc. to remove the sand and dirt. Final concentration is done on shore. Dredges operate on tin ore averaging 0.4 lbs of tin metal per cubic yard (3,000 lbs). Final concentrates contain between 70 and 77% tin. Offshore dredging is now in operation in Thailand and Indonesia.

Gravel-pump mining is widely used in southeastern Asia. Powerful jets of water are directed on the face of the mine and wash down the tin-bearing soil. A gravel pump in the sump elevates the ore to a wooden trough or palong. The palong has a gentle slope and as the ore flows down the slope, the heavy tin oxide particles are trapped behind wooden slats or riffles. The cassiterite is $2\frac{1}{2}$ times heavier than the sand. Further concentration using magnetic and electrostatic separators and shaking tables is needed to remove associated minerals.

Underground lode deposits in Bolivia are located at very high altitudes, 12,000 to 15,000 feet above sea level. Lode deposits in Cornwall are 1300 feet below sea level. The ore is broken up by blasting and drilling. Further crushing and grinding above ground is necessary to produce the finely divided ore capable of being separated by gravity concentration methods, by flotation and heavy-media separations. Tin concentrates from lode deposits are of low grade (from 40 to 60% tin) and must be upgraded before smelting. Roasting the ore removes sulfur and arsenic; the sulfides of iron, copper, bismuth and zinc are converted to oxides; the lead sulfide is oxidized to sulfate. The

FIG. 1. Tin mining dredge in Malaysia.

roasted concentrates are leached with hydro-chloric acid which removes the oxides. Specific treatments with soda are sometimes needed to remove tungsten. The refined concentrates are then ready for smelting.

Refining

Tin oxide is easily reduced to metal by heating at high temperatures with carbon. Concentrates from placer or alluvial deposits require little fluxing material but vein deposits may contain oxides of other metals. Limestone and sand are used with coal to remove the impurities. Several complicating factors are involved in tin smelting practice. Tin at smelting temperatures is more fluid than mercury; it finds minute openings for escape and soaks into porous refractories. Tin oxide reacts with the furnace linings, thus the slags contain appreciable quantities of tin and require retreatment.

The primary smelting is usually done in a reverberatory furnace with a sloping hearth 30 to 40 feet long and 12 to 15 feet wide. A charge of 8 to 15 tons containing the tin concentrates, 15 to 20% anthracite, and smaller amounts of limestone, sand and by-products from previous melts are added through openings in the roof, and stirred at intervals. The furnaces are operated at 1200–1300°C and the smelting time is 12 hours. The tin is tapped into a settler or forehearth and the slag overflows into cast iron pots. The molten tin from the bottom of the settler is cast into slabs of about 75 lbs. Electric arc furnaces are used at some smelters.

Resmelting of the slags is carried out in the same type of furnace. A higher tem-perature, up to 1480°C, is needed because the tin in the slags is combined as silicate and requires a higher reducing temperature. Slags containing 1% tin are discarded.

The slab tin is remelted in a small rever-beratory furnace to just above its melting point. The pure tin melts and flows away from the higher melting metal impurities in this liquation process. Iron, copper, arsenic and antimony are largely removed, but lead and bismuth remain in the tin.

The purified tin is heated in a huge crucible while being stirred with green wood poles or agitated with steam. The wood poles decompose with the heat and the evolved gases stir up the liquid and cause the impurities to form lighter compounds which rise to the surface. This process is known as poling or boiling. The refined tin, 99.8% or better, is cast into ingots.

Several thousand tons of high-purity tin metal (99.97%) are recovered annually from the detinning of tinplate scrap with a hot caustic solution and is recovered electrolytically from the sodium stannate solution. A small quantity of zone refined tin is available commercially for research purposes; impurities are in parts per million.

Specifications and Standards

Pure tin is usually sold to the large consumer in ingots 28 to 100 lbs in weight. One pound bars and tin shot can be purchased from chemical supply houses and metal dealers.

Seven grades of tin are listed in the ASTM Classification for Pig Tin, B-339. ASTM Grade A tin (99.8% tin, minimum) covers about 90% of the fire-refined tin produced. Two extra high-purity grades, are available commercially—AAA (99.98%+) and AA (99.95%+) are electrolytically refined. These grades are offered for analytical standards, making reagents and for research purposes. Lower Grades B to E (99.8 to 99.0% tin, minimum) are also available for alloying with other metals and for less exacting general purposes. Impurities in the Grade B or higher purity tin are limited by ASTM to minor amounts of lead, antimony, copper, arsenic, antimony, iron, bismuth and sulfur.

Physical Properties

The physical and mechanical constants of tin are shown in Table 2.

Tin is a nontoxic, soft pliable metal easily adaptable to cold-working by rolling, extrusion and spinning. Tin has a white, silvery color and when highly polished has high light reflectivity. It retains its brightness well both outdoors and indoors. The melting point is low compared with those of the common structural metals. On the other hand, the boiling point is high and loss by volatilization from a liquid melt or during alloying with other metals is insignificant. It alloys readily with most common metals imparting hardness and strength to the alloys. A tin coating adheres well to many metal surfaces and improves the corrosion protection, appearance and workability of the basis metals. Tin does not take into solution many other metals and where it does the amounts dissolved are quite small. The improvement in hardness of the tin is not uniform for different elements —zinc and cadmium give greater hardening effects than indium or antimony. Small amounts of tin oxide dispersed in tin have a hardening effect.

The physical properties of tin are not affected to any appreciable extent by small amounts of impurities in the tin. The mechanical properties, however, are sensitive to impurities in the tin and different values for the same property may be obtained according to the test method used.

Chemical Properties

Tin can be considered a truly chemical metal. While it is mechanically a weak metal for constructional uses, its nontoxicity and relative freedom from corrosion by weak acids, alkalies and other electrolytes, makes it useful in handling foods and in other exacting applications. Tin, spread thinly on steel or copper acts as a chemical barrier to reactions which would occur on the uncoated basis metal. The high overpotential of tin (0.75 volt) and the peculiar reversal of potential of the tin-iron couple in vacuum-packed containers makes the tin anodic to steel. It is the tin, not the iron, which is slowly attacked. The small amount of tin dissolved by the contents of the can is not only nontoxic but also tasteless. A corresponding amount of iron would affect the flavor and appearance of foods. Again, copper wire is tinned to provide a chemically resistant surface to insulating rubber and to prevent the sulfur in the rubber from attacking the copper. Tinned copper is resistant to water and milk products.

Oxygen or dry air combine with tin to form an invisible and protective oxide film which thickens as the temperature is raised.

TABLE 2.   PROPERTIES OF PURE TIN

	Sn
Symbol	Sn
Atomic number	50
Atomic weight	118.69
Isotopes (in order of abundance)	120, 118, 116, 119, 117, 124, 122, 112, 114, 115
Crystal system, white tin (β)	body-centered tetragonal
gray tin (α)	diamond cubic
Melting point, °C	231.9
Boiling point, °C	2270
Density, g/cc, white tin (β)	7.29
gray tin (α)	5.77
liquid at m.p.	6.97
Brinell hardness, 10 kg/5 mm/180 sec at	
20°C	3.9
220°C	0.7
Tensile strength as cast, psi at	
15°C	2100
200°C	650
-40°C	2900
Electrical resistivity, microhm-cm at	
0°C	11.0
100°C	15.5
Thermal conductivity, cal/cm/cm²/sec/°C at	
100°C	0.145
500°C	0.078
Magnetic susceptibility, cgs units	0.027×10^{-6}
Modulus of elasticity, million psi	6 to 6.5
Specific heat, cal/g at	
25°C	0.053
250°C	0.058
Latent heat of fusion, cal/g	14.2
Latent heat of vaporization, cal/g	520 ± 20
Shrinkage of solidification, %	2.8
Viscosity, centipoise at	
240°C	1.91
400°C	1.38
600°C	1.05
Surface tension, dyne/cm at	
300°C	5.26
400°C	5.18
500°C	5.10
Coefficient of linear expansion, per degree at	
0°C	19.9×10^{-6}
100°C	23.8×10^{-6}
Thermal neutron absorption cross section, barns	0.625

Tin does not react directly with nitrogen, hydrogen, carbon dioxide or gaseous ammonia. Sulfur dioxide, when moist, attacks tin. Chlorine, bromine and iodine readily react with tin; with fluorine the action is slow at room temperature.

Tin reacts with both strong acids and strong bases, but it is relatively resistant to solutions that are nearly neutral. Distilled water has no effect on tin.

The halogen acids attack tin, particularly when hot and concentrated. Hot sulfuric acid dissolves tin, especially in the presence of oxidizers. Nitric acid attacks tin slowly but the hot concentrated acid converts the tin to an insoluble hydrated stannic oxide. Sulfurous, chlorosulfonic and pyrosulfuric acids react rapidly with tin. Phosphoric acid dissolves tin less readily than the other mineral acids. Organic acids, such as lactic, citric, tartaric and oxalic, attack tin slowly in presence of air or other oxidizing substances.

Dilute solutions of ammonium hydroxide and sodium carbonate have little effect on tin, but strong alkaline solutions of sodium hydroxide and potassium hydroxide dissolve tin to form the stannate.

Neutral aqueous salt solutions react slowly with tin when oxygen is present, but oxidizing salt solutions, such as potassium persulfate, ferric sulfate and stannic chloride, dissolve tin. Nonaqueous solutions of lubricating oils, organic solvents and gasoline have little effect on tin.

Principal Chemical Compounds

Stannous and stannic tin salts have a number of uses in electroplating, ceramics, as starting chemicals in making organotin compounds, in pharmaceuticals.

Stannic oxide, SnO_2, is a white powder insoluble in acids and alkalies. It is prepared by atomizing tin with high-pressure steam or by calcination of the hydrated oxide. As an opacifier in vitreous enamels, it produces a glaze which has a pleasing whiteness, good chemical shock resistance and wearing properties. Other uses are for resistor and dielectric bodies and as a component of putty for polishing marble and decorative stones.

Stannous oxide, SnO, is a black powder soluble in acids and strong alkalies. It is used in making stannous salts for plating and for chemical reagents.

Stannous chloride, $SnCl_2$, is available in the anhydrous and hydrated forms. It is a major ingredient in acid tin plating baths and is an intermediate for tin chemicals. Equally important materials in the electrotinning industry are stannous sulfate, stannous fluoborate, and sodium and potassium stannate.

Heavy metal stannates of lead, barium, calcium, and copper are important in the manufacture of capacitor bodies.

Stannous fluoride and stannous pyrophosphate are extensively used as toothpaste additives. Stannous octoate is a prominent urethane foam catalyst. Stannic chloride, $SnCl_4$, is used in the preparation of organotin

compounds and as a stabilizer of perfume in soaps and in weighting silk.

Organotin compounds are those compounds in which a tin atom is linked directly to one or more carbon atoms. Industrial interest started with the discovery that dibutyl tin compounds, notably the dilaurate and maleate, were effective in preventing the discoloration by heat and light of polyvinyl chloride resins during processing. Incorporating about 2% of the stabilizer was found to be satisfactory. Modified tin stabilizers to suit all conditions of resin manufacture are produced in the United States, England, Germany and Japan and hundreds of tons are used annually. The starting material for the manufacture of tin stabilizers is dibutyltin dichloride.

The chemistry of organotin compounds has advanced considerably in recent years. When the tin atom is combined directly with three carbon atoms, the resulting compounds possess biocidal properties which are at a maximum in trialkyl and triaryl compounds when the total number of carbon atoms in the molecule is about twelve. The practical use of these compounds is mainly in the direction of fungicides, insecticides and antimicrobial agents in the fields of agriculture, antifouling paints, wood preservation, textiles and paper. Tributyltin oxide (TBTO) and tributyltin acetate are commercially available and in use as biostats. A large number of compounds are under study for an evaluation of their biocidal activity and industrial use.

Uses Related to Properties

Tin is generally used in conjunction with something else and for that reason the user is not always conscious of its use. The weight of the tin coating on a container is only a fraction of the filled can of fruit that it protects; the monetary value of the tin in an automobile bearing is extremely small in relation to the cost of the car; the amount of tin in a soldered joint in a computer is quite out of proportion to the importance of the purpose it serves.

The mechanical weakness of tin is put to good purpose when tin is used as foil for wrapping or as a collapsible tube. Tin does not work-harden.

The ease of tinning the various stronger metals is related to a number of physical properties. In the first place, the melting point of tin is low (232°C) and molten tin can be handled in simple steel pots. The molten tin is highly fluid which permits it to drain rapidly from an article before solidifying so that thin, even coatings can be produced. The surface-chemical activity of tin towards steel, brass, copper and many other metals allows the tin to wet and adhere to the surface in a smooth layer.

Electrodeposited coatings of tin are plated in a semibright or matte condition. However, momentarily fusing the matte tin coating in hot oil or by induction heating provides a good reflecting surface with improved corrosion resistance.

The wetting power of liquid tin is not only important in surface coating with tin but it makes the joining of metals by soldering possible. Solders melting below that of tin are easily applied with the minimum of external heat. Solders with a pasty range during solidification are useful in making wipe joints. It is the tin in the solder that wets the surface and makes the joint stronger than the solder itself.

Most low-melting fusible alloys contain a high percentage of tin with lead, bismuth, cadmium and indium. The low melting point and good casting properties bring tin into the field of die-casting alloys and type metals.

Tin has a low coefficient of friction which is the first consideration in its use as a bearing material for which purpose it is hardened with a few per cent of antimony and copper. Tin-base bearings are known for the properties of excellent conformability to the shaft and for the ease with which grit is embedded in the bearing material so that it does not wear the shaft. Tin-base bearings hold the lubricating oil on the surface and improve lubrication. The bearing melts under severe galling and prevents the failure of more expensive parts of the machine.

Antimony strengthens the bearing alloy matrix by dissolving in tin up to about 8%. Above this, hard cubic particles of tin-antimony compound are formed which tend to float. Copper additions are necessary to secure a uniform distribution of these hard cubic particles which provide a relatively hard "pavement" in a soft but reasonably rigid bearing alloy matrix—the classic bearing structure. Tin-aluminum bearings also provide soft lubricating particles of tin dispersed in the harder aluminum matrix and enhance bearing properties.

Tin is a strong pearlite stabilizer in both flake and nodular cast iron. A residual content of 0.10% tin is usually sufficient to produce a matrix that is completely pearlitic. Soft spots due to ferrite are eliminated without the risk of the formation of massive cementite which gives rise to machining difficulties. Cast iron automotive engine blocks with tin additions have been successfully used for a number of years.

General Applications

The United States is by far the largest consumer of tin. Annual consumption amounts to approximately 58,000 long tons of virgin tin and 24,000 long tons of secondary tin recovered from metal scrap and tinplate scrap. Uses for pure tin may be divided into four main categories: viz. as metal, coatings, alloys and chemical compounds.

Cast tin metal is used as pipe and in lining valves and fittings for conveying distilled water, beer and carbonated beverages. Thousands of tons of tin are cast as anodes for electrotin plating installations. Tin rolled to sheet is used to line tanks for the storage of distilled water and pharmaceutical chemical solutions. Further reduction of the sheet to foil thickness provides uses as cap liners for whiskey bottles, electrical condenser plates, fuses, gun charges, and wrappings for food, candy and tobacco. Collapsible tubes, extruded from cast slugs are used for pharmaceutical products such as creams and ointments, artist's colors, toiletries and some paste-type foods. Tin powder is used for coating paper, for tinning pastes, metal spraying, paints, as a laboratory reagent and for metal powder compacts. Baths of molten tin metal are the heart of the "Float Glass" process for the production of smooth glass plate that does not need grinding.

Pure tin can be applied as a coating to all common metals by hot dipping, electrodeposition, immersion plating, and by cladding. Tin-coated steel (tinplate), the largest use of tin, consumes about 30,000 long tons of tin each year in making over 46 billion containers for food products and beverages,

FIG. 2. Tin-nickel plated articles.

containers for nonfood products of every kind such as paints, shave cream, hair spray, bug sprays, other aerosol products, gas meters, kitchen aids, dairy and brewery equipment, automotive parts, electronic parts and many other uses. The ten-gallon tinned steel milk can sees long service in dairy and milk handling. The above figures are for the United States alone. The worldwide use of tinplate consumes 72,000 long tons of tin to make 100 billion containers.

Tin-coated copper is used in the electronics and electrical industries as sheet and wire for components, connectors, pigtails, etc. Tinned copper pots and pans are standard implements in restaurants for the preparation of food.

Tin coatings protect aluminum pistons and bearings, steel couplings for oil-drilling pipe strings, pins and paper clips, water cooler tubing, cast iron food choppers and slicers, chain links, eyelets, printed circuit boards, etc.

Electrodeposited tin alloy coatings (tin-copper, tin-lead, tin-zinc, tin-cadmium and tin-nickel) can be applied readily to steel, copper and brass. They provide decorative coatings and solderable coatings that are denser and harder, and more corrosion resistant than pure tin coatings. Many industrial uses for tin-alloy coatings have been developed in electronics, watch making, surgical and scientific instrument making (see Fig. 2).

Tin, when alloyed with a nonferrous metal or a combination of nonferrous metals, alters the properties of the alloy greatly and many industrial uses result. With lead, it forms a group of alloys known as soft solders. Moving the percentage of tin up or down alters the melting characteristics and uses of the alloys. The lowest melting tin-lead solder contains 63% tin (eutectic) and has no melting range. A 50:50 mixture of tin and lead makes the strongest joints. The tin-base solders have no serious competitors in the field of low-temperature soldering.

Copper-tin alloys, with or without modifying elements, are classed under the general name of tin bronzes. The phosphor bronzes, containing up to 10% tin with small additions of phosphorus are extra-strength alloys used for ship propellors, gears, bushings, electrical contacts, springs, pressure-tight castings. The gun metals, modified with 1–6% zinc, are used for valves and fittings, and corrosion-resistant castings. Both types can be further modified with lead to give better machinability.

The tin-antimony-copper alloys of varying percentage of the three constituents find applications and uses as babbitt bearings, modern pewter, and die-casting alloys. These alloys contain 65 to 91% tin, balance copper and antimony (Fig. 3 and Fig. 4.)

The lead-base alloys containing tin and antimony are used as bearing alloys (lead babbitts). Type metals may contain from 10

FIG. 3. Pewterware.

FIG. 4. Tin-base babbitted bearings.

to 25% antimony, 3 to 13% tin, balance lead. Good casting characteristics are more important than resistance to wear in this case.

Among the newer alloys of tin are the high-strength titanium-tin-aluminum and zirconium-tin-aluminum alloys. Niobium-tin alloys are finding use as superconducting magnet wire. The most common dental amalgams for filling teeth contain 12% tin.

Toxicological Factors

The small percentage of tin present in canned foods of good quality is quite harmless. The agreed limit of tin content in foods is 300 mg per kilogram in the United States and 286 ppm in the United Kingdom. Tests have shown that many times these concentrations can be consumed without adverse effects on the human system.

Soldered seams in containers or vessels exposed directly to food products should be made with pure tin, tin-silver, or 95 tin-5 antimony solders. The ordinary food can has a doubly-folded body seam and the solder is on the outside of the seam. Pure tin coatings are a safe surface treatment for children's toys.

The trialkyl and triaryl tin compounds have toxic properties and their use as biocides must be under strict supervision and they must be adequately labeled to indicate hazards in handling.

References

1. Mantell, C. L., "Tin: Its Mining, Production and Technology," 2nd Ed., New York, Reinhold Publishing Corp., 1949.
2. Hedges, E. S., "Tin and Its Alloys," London, Edward Arnold, Ltd., 1960.
3. Faulkner, C. J., "The Properties of Tin," Columbus, Ohio, Tin Research Institute, Publication No. 218, 1954.

ROBERT M. MACINTOSH

TITANIUM

Discovery

The element titanium was discovered in 1790 by William Gregor, an English clergyman, who was also an amateur chemist and minerologist. Gregor's analysis of the black sand found along the beach in the County of Cornwall showed 45.25 per cent of a white metallic oxide up to that time unrecognized. A few years later Kloprath noticed the close agreement between Gregor's findings and his own investigation of the oxide recovered from "red schorl" (rutile) found in Hungary. Acknowledging Gregor's priority, Klaproth applied to the new element the name titanium from the Titans, the mythical first sons of the earth.

Occurrence

Titanium is widely distributed in nature. It is ninth in abundance of the elements making up the crust of the earth and accounts for 0.63% of the total. Of the metals suitable for structural use, it is exceeded in amount only by aluminum, iron and magnesium. Titanium is a persistent constituent of most igneous, metamorphic and sedimentary rocks, and is present in many of the minerals. Of 801 igneous rocks analyzed in the laboratories of the U.S. Geological Survey, 784 contained this element. It is present in soils, clays, sand, water, the dust of the atmosphere, and in coal and oil. The proportion of titanium in soils of the different parts of the world ranges from about 0.5 to 1.5%. Noteworthy amounts of the element have been observed in volcanic material, in meteorites and in interstellar space. By means of the spectrograph it has been detected in the atmosphere of the sun and in many stars. Titanium is also present in plants and animals including man. Eggs and milk contain a small proportion of this element.

The more common titanium minerals are ilmenite and arizonite (iron titanate), rutile, brookite, anatase and leucoxene (titanium dioxide), perovskite (calcium titanate), geikielite (magnesium titanate), pyrophanite (manganese titanate), and titanite or sphene (titanium calcium silicate). Of these ilmenite and rutile, and to a minor extent leucoxene, are mined as ores of titanium.

Deposits of ilmenite and rutile of commercial importance occur in Florida, New Jersey, New York, North Carolina and Virginia in the United States, in Argentina, Australia, Brazil, Canada, Egypt, India, Malaya, Norway, Republic of South Africa, Senegal, Sierra Leona, The Congo, and the Union of Soviet Socialist Republics. The largest deposits of rutile are in Australia.

Derivation

The production of elemental titanium is fraught with many difficulties since the hot metal combines actively with oxygen, nitrogen and moisture of the air as well as with carbon and most construction materials. It decomposes the present refractory materials absorbing the oxygen. These contaminants render the metal so hard and brittle as to be useless. Once picked up there is no practical method of removing these impurities. This difficulty is overcome by carrying out the reduction of $TiCl_4$ with magnesium (the Kroll process) or with sodium in a mild steel vessel under an atmosphere of argon or helium at around 800°C. At this temperature alloying of the titanium with the iron is at a low level, but even so, the layer of metal in contact with the surface of the reactor contains too much iron for use and must be discarded.

In operation of the Kroll process commercially, clean dry magnesium ingots are charged into a cylindrical, flat-bottomed, mild steel pot. After securing the cover in place the closed reactor is evacuated and then filled with argon or helium. The magnesium-charged reactor is then lowered into a vertical, cylindrical furnace heated by electricity or burning fuel and equipped for temperature regulation. As soon as the magnesium begins to melt, highly purified titanium tetrachloride is introduced at a controlled rate while the inert gas pressure is maintained to prevent inward leakage of air. Since the reduction reaction is highly exothermic, external heat is no longer needed to maintain the temperature between the required 750 and 1000°C.

Although the actual reaction mechanism is probably more complex, the net reduction is represented by the equation: $TiCl_4 + 2Mg \rightarrow Ti + 2MgCl_2 + heat$. This equation shows that approximately 4 lb of titanium tetrachloride reacts with 1 lb of magnesium to produce 1 lb of titanium and 4 lb of magnesium chloride. In practice excess magnesium is employed to prevent side reactions with the result that the magnesium efficiency does not exceed 90%. The magnesium chloride produced is tapped from the pot in the molten form from time to time during the reaction period and it is drained as completely as possible after the reaction is completed. Care is taken to prevent air entering the reactor.

After removal from the furnace, the vessel is cooled and then opened in a dry room to prevent moisture pickup by the hygroscopic magnesium chloride. During subsequent heating in the purification step any moisture absorbed contributes its oxygen to the titanium. The pot with its reaction product of titanium along with some magnesium chloride and magnesium is chucked in a lathe, and the mixed products are turned out in chips up to 0.5 in. size. The turnings are collected in a steel basket in which they are later distilled to remove $MgCl_2$ and excess Mg.

The basket of chips is placed in a clean condenser which is sealed without delay. After evacuation to a pressure of 1/20,000 of an atmosphere, the retort is placed in an electrically heated vacuum furnace so designed that the pressure in the furnace outside the condenser is approximately the same as that inside the condenser. This prevents retort collapse at the distillation temperature, around 930°C. In operation the lower part of the retort extends into the furnace and is supported by a flange. The upper portion of the retort is water jacketed and thus serves as a condenser for the magnesium chloride and magnesium distilled from the hot chips. After the impurities have been distilled from the titanium sponge, the vacuum in the retort is released with inert gas simultaneously with the release of the vacuum in the furnace with air. The retort is removed from the furnace and cooled. At this stage the vessel is opened and the titanium sponge is chipped from the basket, passed through a crusher and screened to obtain pieces of the required size. The sponge form titanium must be melted into an ingot before it can be rolled, forged or extruded. This is accomplished by first pressing it into bars which serve as consumable electrodes in the arc melting of the titanium in a water-cooled copper crucible the size and shape of the desired ingot. An inert atmosphere is maintained.

A very similar procedure employs sodium as the reducing agent. Although the use of sodium permits a lower temperature for the reduction of the titanium tetrachloride, the heat of the reaction is greater. The entire quantity of sodium chloride produced must be distilled or leached from the titanium, while in the magnesium process 90% of the magnesium chloride may be tapped from the furnace.

Many modifications of the process have been proposed. For example, by carrying out the reaction in a centrifuge, separation of the titanium from the other materials is effected. Vapors of titanium tetrachloride and magnesium or sodium are introduced simultaneously into a columnar, steel reaction chamber at 800 to 950°C. The titanium tetrachloride is reduced with magnesium or sodium in a molten salt bath so that continuous billet compacted metal is extracted. Titanium tetrachloride dissolved in liquid ammonia is reduced with sodium amalgam at room temperature to form titanium amalgam. Reduction of the tetrachloride with hydrogen is effected at high temperature.

Electrolytic methods of producing titanium metal from a bath of fused salts have been developed. One such method will soon be employed commercially.[5] Titanium tetrachloride or lower chlorides are electrolyzed in a fused bath of alkali or alkaline earth metal chlorides to produce the metal. Sodium

733

and potassium fluotitanates are electrolyzed in a similar manner. Titanium dioxide is electrolyzed in a fused bath of calcium fluoride, magnesium fluoride, alkali metal phosphates, alkali metal borates or alkali metal fluorides to produce pure titanium. Anodes of titanium carbide, nitride or monoxide are electrolyzed in a fused salt electrolyte to produce titanium. The electrolytic preparation of titanium is presented in detail in Ref. 6.

Titanium metal of very high purity is prepared by the thermal decomposition of titanium tetraiodide; however, the method does not seem to be amenable to large scale operation.

Physical and Mechanical Properties

Titanium is a silvery colored metal with a density of 4.5, a melting point of 1668°C and a hardness of 80 to 100, Vickers. It is 45% lighter than steel but just as strong, and although 60% heavier than aluminum it is more than twice as strong. Although titanium has a higher melting point than steel, above 800°F the strength of the metal drops rapidly, and above 1300°F it absorbs oxygen and nitrogen from the air which cause embrittlement.

It has an atomic number of 22 and an atomic mass of 47.90. Proportions of principal isotopes are 46, 10.82; 47, 10.56; 48, 100; 49, 7.50; and 50, 7.27. Titanium is reported to become very radioactive after bombardment with deuterons, and the emitted radiations are mainly positrons and hard gamma rays. A radioactive isotope of half-life 41.9 minutes is produced by alpha particle bombardment. Titanium occurs in two modifications; alpha which crystallizes in the hexagonal system is stable up to 882°C, and beta having a body-centered cubic lattice is stable above this transition temperature. Its heat capacity varies uniformly from 6.507 calories per mole at 200°C to 8.901 calories per mole at 817°C, and then increases to a very high value as the temperature approaches 882°C. Above this temperature the heat capacity seems to remain practically constant at 7.525 calories per mole, which value corresponds to that of the beta modification. Table 1 lists physical and mechanical properties.

Titanium can be machined and worked with the same equipment and in the same way as stainless steel. However, fusion welding requires an inert atmosphere of argon or helium to prevent contamination by oxygen, nitrogen and hydrogen with consequent brittleness at the weld.

Details about the mechanical properties, physical metallurgy, processing and fabrication of titanium are given in Ref. 4.

Chemical Properties

Titanium falls in Group IVB of the transition elements in the periodic classification of the elements. Consequently it shows variable valence and yields colored ions. However, the titanic ions carrying a positive charge of 4 are colorless. Salts of quadrivalent titanium are readily hydrolyzed in solution. Analogous salts of the other members of the group show increasing stability as their atomic weight increases, and metallic properties become more pronounced in the same direction. Similarly the amphoteric nature of the dioxides which is well pronounced with titanium, becomes slight with zirconium, and thorium oxide exhibits basic properties only. The metallic role of titanium is exhibited in such compounds as the chloride, nitrate, phosphate and sulfate, while the nonmetallic characteristic appears in a long series of titanates, as exemplified by calcium, iron and sodium titanates.

Titanium metal is very resistant to corrosion and is unaffected by atmospheric conditions and by sea water. Nitric acid has no appreciable effect, but it is attacked rapidly by concentrated sulfuric and hydrochloric acids, and slowly by dilute sulfuric acid. It is not affected by strong alkalis, sulfur or sulfur compounds, chlorinated solvents, chlorides and wet chlorine. The metal ignites in air at 1200°C and burns with incandescence. Heat of combustion to the dioxide is 4700 calories per gram. In contact with liquid oxygen titanium can be ignited by impact. Titanium dust is very explosive. It is one of the few elements that will burn in an atmosphere of nitrogen, that is, it reacts to form the nitride with the liberation of heat and light. Combination begins at a temperature of around 800°C. At 700°C it decomposes steam to form the oxide with the liberation of hydrogen.

TABLE 1. PROPERTIES OF HIGH-PURITY TITANIUM METAL

Atomic number	22
Atomic weight	47.90
Atomic volume, cc per gram-atom	10.6
Atomic radius in Angstrom units	1.54
Density at 20°C, g/cc	4.507
Melting point, °C	1668
Boiling point, °C	3260
Linear coefficient of expansion, 20 to 300°C, microinches per inch per °C	8.2
Latent heat of fusion, kcal/mole	5
Latent heat of vaporization, kcal/mole	112.5
Latent heat of transformation, kcal/mole	1.05
Electrical conductivity, per cent of copper	3.6
Electrical resistivity, microhm-cm	42
Superconductivity, °K	below 1.73
Specific heat, cal/g/°C at 20°C	0.13
Thermal conductivity, cal/cm/sec/°C	0.041
Surface tension at melting point, dynes per centimeter	1427
Crystal structure	
Below 882°C	Close-packed hexagonal Alpha form
Above 882°C	Body-centered cubic Beta form
Lattice constants	
Alpha	a = 2.9504
	c = 4.6833
Beta	a = 3.3065
Work function, eV	4.17
Thermal neutron absorption cross section, barns	5.8
Modulus of elasticity, psi	15.5×10^6
Tensile strength, ultimate 25°C, psi	34,000
yield, 25°C, psi	20,000
Elongation, 25°C, %	54
Hardness, Vickers	80–100

It combines directly with the halogens to form the corresponding tetrahalides.

Compounds

Oxides. Titanium forms four well defined oxides: the monoxide, TiO, which shows weakly basic properties; dititanium trioxide Ti_2O_3, which is decidedly basic; the dioxide, TiO_2, which is amphoteric; and the trioxide or pertitanic acid, TiO_3, which exhibits acid properties only.

Industrially, the dioxide is by far the most important compound of titanium. Titanium dioxide for pigment use is produced by hydrolytic precipitation from titanyl sulfate solution on heating, and by the vapor phase oxidation of anhydrous titanium tetrachloride

with oxygen or air at high temperatures. The hydrolytically precipitated oxide is in the hydrous form but the closely held water is driven off by calcination at an elevated temperature. Titanium dioxide exists in three crystal modifications: anatase, brookite and rutile. Hydrolysis of sulfate solutions normally yields anatase, but by proper nucleation titanium dioxide of the rutile crystal form is produced. The vapor phase oxidation of the tetrachloride yields rutile directly.

As a result of its extreme whiteness and brightness and its high index of refraction, titanium dioxide is widely used as a white pigment in paints, lacquers and enamels, paper, floor coverings, rubber, coated fabrics and textiles, printing ink, plastics, roofing granules, welding rods, synthetic fabrics, ceramics and cosmetics. A synthetic rutile may be cut and polished into gem stones that outsparkle diamonds.

The lower oxides are usually prepared by the reduction of the dioxide. Reduction by hydrogen, aluminum and carbon usually fail to give well-defined lower oxides, but by reduction with an excess of the metal itself, dititanium trioxide is formed at 700°C and the monoxide at 1500°C. Peroxides or pertitanic acid are prepared by adding hydrogen peroxide to freshly prepared titanic acid, or by treating a solution of titanic sulfate or chloride with hydrogen peroxide and then adding ammonium hydroxide to precipitate the yellow, horny mass corresponding to the formula, $TiO_3 \cdot H_2O$.

Many compounds of titanium in solution have a tendency to assume the colloidal form and this property is applied in the commercial production of titanium dioxide pigments. These compounds are unusual in that they exist in the colloidal state in solutions containing large proportions of electrolytes. For example, dispersed systems containing 60 g of colloidal titanium dioxide in a liter of a solution containing 400 g of sulfuric acid may be prepared readily.

Inorganic Compounds. Titanic sulfate is produced in large quantities as an intermediate step in the manufacture of titanium dioxide pigments by the action of concentrated sulfuric acid on finely ground ilmenite ore. Such solutions contain the titanyl sulfate, $TiOSO_4$, and the experimental evidence indicates that the titanyl salt is the only sulfate of tetravalent titanium stable enough to persist under ordinary conditions. The disulfate, $Ti(SO_4)_2$, can be formed by the action of hot sulfuric acid on the dioxide and it may be crystallized from fuming sulfuric acid, but it decomposes on contact even with moisture of the air. A number of double salts such as titanic potassium sulfate, titanic sodium sulfate and titanic calcium sulfate are known.

Titanous sulfate, $Ti_2(SO_4)_3$, may be prepared readily by the electrolytic reduction of the tetravalent salt in water solution. If the introduction of impurities is not objectionable, the reduction may be effected by metallic zinc or iron, sodium thiosulfate, sulfur dioxide and other reducing agents. This has a blue color, as do the other titanous salts, and is not hydrolyzed in solution but is easily oxidized to the tetravalent state. It is a strong reducing agent. Titanium monosulfate, $TiSO_4$, may be obtained in crystalline form by evaporating the solution produced by dissolving the monoxide in dilute sulfuric acid.

Anhydrous titanium tetrachloride is produced by the action of chlorine on titanium dioxide and coke in a fluidized bed. It is a colorless liquid with a boiling point of 136°C and a density of 1.74 at 10°C; it is soluble in organic solvents as well as in water. The anhydrous tetrachloride is reduced to titanium metal by magnesium or sodium at elevated temperatures in an inert atmosphere of argon or helium, and it is oxidized with air or oxygen to titanium dioxide and chlorine at high temperatures. Both of these reactions are employed commercially. It fumes strongly in moist air and dissolves in water to form solutions which are hydrolyzed readily to yield hydrous titanium dioxide and hydrochloric acid. Similar solutions may be obtained by dissolving orthotitanic acid in hydrochloric acid, by adding an alkaline earth chloride to titanic sulfate solution, or by dissolving sodium titanate in hydrochloric acid. The anhydrous liquid is employed in producing smoke screens and it serves as a catalyst in many organic reactions.

Titanous chloride may be prepared by reducing titanic chloride with aluminum, magnesium, zinc, tin or hydrogen, or by electrolytic reduction of the solution. Anhydrous titanous chloride obtained by reducing the tetrachloride with hydrogen at 600°C is a crystalline, violet-colored solid. A brown variety has also been reported. Titanous chloride is oxidized slowly on exposure to the atmosphere at ordinary temperature. It is soluble in water to form stable solutions which act as strong reducing agents. Titanium dichloride may be prepared by the reduction of the tetrachloride with sodium amalgam, by the extreme reduction of a stream of the tetrachloride in a current of hydrogen at 700°C, and by dissolving the metal in hydrochloric acid. Solutions of the dichloride are unstable and readily convert to the trichloride.

Titanium tetrafluoride may be obtained

by the action of fluorine or of anhydrous hydrofluoric acid on metallic titanium at elevated temperatures. It is a white solid having a boiling point of 280°C, and is soluble in water. The product obtained by dissolving titanium dioxide in aqueous hydrofluoric acid is probably fluotitanic acid. Potassium fluotitanate can be prepared by the action of potassium hydrogen fluoride on a solution of titanium dioxide in an excess of concentrated hydrofluoric acid. The trifluoride is obtained as an insoluble violet-colored powder by heating potassium fluotitanate in a current of hydrogen, or by reducing potassium fluotitanate in solution with zinc and hydrochloric acid or with sodium amalgam.

The tetrabromide and tetraiodide are produced by the action of bromine or iodine vapor, respectively, on heated titanium metal. These compounds may also be produced by the action of the corresponding halide vapor on a mixture of titanium dioxide and carbon at elevated temperatures. Solutions of both compounds are hydrolyzed readily. Titanous bromide and iodide are formed by the electrolytic reduction of the corresponding titanic salt.

Titanic phosphate precipitated from aqueous solutions on addition of a soluble phosphate to salts of tetravalent titanium is more or less basic and consequently of variable composition, so that in general more uniform products may be obtained by heating the dioxide with an alkali metal phosphate or phosphoric acid. Complex titanic salts that hydrolyze only with difficulty, for use in dyeing, mordanting, lake formation and tanning, may be prepared by treating titanic phosphate with an organic acid as oxalic, lactic and tartaric. The blue-colored titanous phosphate may be prepared by the reaction between a soluble phosphate and a solution of titanous chloride or sulfate.

Titanium forms a number of sulfides under nonaqueous conditions in addition to the characteristic disulfide, TiS_2, dititanium trisulfide, Ti_2S_3, and the monosulfide, TiS.

The tetranitrate is formed by dissolving hydrous titanic oxide or titanates, sodium titanate or barium titanate, in nitric acid. These solutions hydrolyze readily on heating or on dilution to yield hydrous titanium dioxide and nitric acid.

Titanium carbide formed by heating titanium dioxide with carbon at a high temperature is a hard crystalline solid used in making cutting tools and grinding stones.

Titanium forms an extensive series of titanates with the alkali, alkaline earth and heavy base metals. Iron and calcium titanates are found extensively in nature, and the minerals ilmenite and arizonite, corresponding to ferrous and ferric titanates, respectively, are important raw materials of titanium. Titanates are usually formed by heating the corresponding oxide, hydroxide or carbonate with titanium dioxide at an elevated temperature to effect a direct reaction. With some of the stronger bases, the reaction takes place in aqueous media. For example, sodium and barium titanates may be prepared by heating a water suspension of hydrous titanium dioxide in a concentrated solution of the corresponding hydroxide at atmospheric pressure. Barium titanate possesses piezoelectric properties and has some uses as an application of this characteristic.

Organic Compounds. Many organic compounds of titanium such as esters, alcoholates, phenylates and complexes have been prepared. Examples are titanium phthalate, titanium oxalate, titanium gluconate, titanium tetraethylate, titanium stearate, triphenylcatechol titanate and butyl titanate. Titanium is a constituent of a number of permanent metallized azo dyes. Organometallic compounds may be prepared from titanium tetrachloride and a primary, secondary or tertiary amine. Methyl ether combines with anhydrous titanium tetrachloride to give a complex having the formula, $TiCl_4 \cdot CH_3 \cdot O \cdot CH_3$. A double titanium-benzoic chloride corresponds to the formula, $TiCl_4 \cdot C_6H_5COCl$. Compounds have been made in which there is a titanium-to-carbon bond. An example is, $C_6H_5Ti(OC_3H_7)_3$.

Uses

Unfortunately, all of the known processes for winning titanium from its ores in commercial quantities are difficult, slow and expensive. At the present price of $5.90/lb average for mill products, almost 90% of the output goes into military hardware, mostly (70%) for airplane parts (compressor wheels, rotor blades, jet engines and frames). Smaller amounts go into artillery recoil mechanisms, guided missile parts, air-borne equipment and space vehicles. The 2,000 mile/hour A-11 jet plane is constructed largely of titanium. The largest industrial uses are in the construction of airplanes and of chemical plant equipment.

Although currently only 8% of the titanium metal consumed goes into chemical plant equipment, its use is of vital and increasing importance to the chemical industry. More and more chlorine plants are installing titanium towers, pumps, heat exchangers, etc., because of the metal's excellent resistance to wet chlorine, an exposure that previously required ceramic and other nonmetallic equipment. Other applications of titanium equipment take advantage of its corrosion resistance to chloride solutions, including sea water; to nitric acid; to chlorine dioxide and other bleaching agents; and to sulfur dioxide.

As the price of producing the metal is reduced, it has great potential uses where the properties of light weight, high strength and resistance to corrosion are important factors. By 1970 it is expected that some 20,000 tons/year of titanium metal will be marketed as mill products, compared with about 15,000 tons in 1966.

Alloys

A major part of titanium used as a construction material is in the form of alloys, most of which have superior strength to that of pure titanium without being unduly affected with respect to corrosion resistance. The alloy of Ti-6A1-4V, for example, which is used in chemical equipment, has a room temperature tensile strength at the yield point of about 120,000 psi, while commercial (99.2%) titanium's value is about 63,000 psi. The alloying agents are seldom present in more than 10–15% concentrations.

Alloying elements in titanium fall into two groups: those that strengthen and stabilize the alpha or room temperature-modification and those that strengthen the high-temperature, beta, modification. Agents of the first group are oxygen, nitrogen, carbon and aluminum, and those falling into the second group are iron, manganese, chromium, molybdenum and vanadium. Alloying agents are employed to raise the tensile strength and

hardness of the titanium, but at the same time they reduce the ductility. Consequently the highest strength alloys are relatively brittle. Successful alloys have been developed with aluminum, chromium, iron, manganese, molybdenum and tin. These alloys are produced commercially by adding the alloying metal to the titanium during melting of the sponge. Additional information and data about alloy composition and properties are presented in Ref. 4.

Physiological Effects

The nontoxic nature of titanium dioxide, the most important industrial compound of titanium, has been demonstrated many times with test animals and with man. Some organic compounds of titanium show a degree of toxicity but this is attributed to the effect of the acid radical. Growth and fermentation are accelerated by ascorbic acid complexes of titanium. Titanium compounds have been reported to act as catalysts in the oxidation reactions of vegetable cells and there is evidence that the element is essential in the formation of soil from rocks. An ointment of titanium dioxide hastens the healing of diseased skin areas. Titanium dioxide powder exerts an insecticidal effect against tribolium ferrugineau. Titanium tetrachloride is a severe skin irritant, but this effect appears to be caused by hydrochloric acid liberated by hydrolysis. Inhalation of titanium tetrachloride vapor is also harmful.

References

1. Barksdale, Jelks, "Titanium, Its Occurrence, Chemistry and Technology," New York, The Ronald Press Co., 1966.
2. Barksdale, Jelks, Section on Titanium in "Economic Geography of Industrial Minerals," New York, Reinhold Publishing Corp., 1956.
3. Miller, J. A., "Titanium, A Materials Survey," Washington, D.C. U.S. Bureau of Mines, Information Circular 7791, 1957.
4. Ogden, H. R., chapter on "Titanium," in "Rare Metals Handbook," C. A. Hampel, Editor, 2nd Ed., pp. 559-579, New York, Reinhold Publishing Corp., 1961.
5. Carmichael, R. L., Chem. Eng., 73, No. 24, 109–114 (Nov. 21, 1966).

6. Sibert, M. E., "Titanium, Electrolytic Preparation," in "Encyclopedia of Electrochemistry," C. A. Hampel, Editor, pp. 1130–1135, New York, Reinhold Publishing Corp., 1964.

JELKS BARKSDALE

TRANSURANIUM ELEMENTS

The transuranium elements are the man-made chemical elements with atomic numbers greater than that of the heaviest natural element, uranium, which has the atomic number 92. The eleven, or perhaps twelve, known (in the mid-1960's) transuranium elements are listed in Table 1 with their names and chemical symbols. They are, for all practical purposes, synthetic in origin and must be produced by transmutation, starting in the first instance with uranium.

The key to the discovery of these "synthetic elements" was their position in the Periodic Table. Prior to the discovery of the transuranium elements, the relationship of the heaviest naturally occurring elements, actinium, thorium, protactinium and uranium, to the Periodic Table was not clearly understood.

TABLE 1. THE ATOMIC NUMBERS, NAMES, AND SYMBOLS OF THE TRANSURANIUM ELEMENTS

Atomic Number	Name	Symbol
93	Neptunium	Np
94	Plutonium	Pu
95	Americium	Am
96	Curium	Cm
97	Berkelium	Bk
98	Californium	Cf
99	Einsteinium	Es
100	Fermium	Fm
101	Mendelevium	Md
102	Nobelium	No
103	Lawrencium	Lr
104	—	—

Today, it is known that the first eleven transuranium elements fit in as a separate row at the bottom—as shown in Fig. 1—set apart from the Periodic Table along with the previously known naturally occurring elements—thorium, protactinium and uranium.

These fourteen elements constitute what is known as the "actinide" series, and are

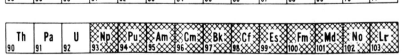

FIG. 1. Periodic table of the elements.

analogous to the previously known rare earth series—the lanthanide series. (See **Lanthanide Elements.**) An inner-electron shell, the $5f$ shell, is being filled in this actinide series just as the inner $4f$ electron shell is being filled in the members of the "lanthanide" series. There is an element-by-element analogy of the chemical properties between the two series and this has made it possible to predict the chemical properties of these elements.

Recognition of the fact that these elements represented a whole new family of actinide elements (that is, "like actinium") analogous to the rare earth series of elements, the lanthanides, permitted the discoverers to predict the chemical properties of the unknown transuranium elements, and thereby enabled them to discover and separate a number of them from all the other elements in the Periodic Table, which is the classical test for the discovery of a new chemical element.

Chemically the transuranium elements are very similar, although the observed differences are those expected and anticipated from their unique position in the periodic system as part of a second rare earth series. All have trivalent ions, which form inorganic complex ions and organic chelates. Also in common are acid-insoluble trifluorides and oxalates, soluble sulfates, nitrates, chlorides and perchlorates. Neptunium, plutonium, and americium have higher oxidation states in aqueous solution (similar to uranium), but the relative stability of these higher states compared to that of the common trivalent ion becomes progressively less as one proceeds to the higher atomic numbers. This is a direct consequence, indeed an identifying feature, of the actinide role as a second rare earth-type transition series.

The electronic configurations of the gaseous atoms of the transuranium elements (beyond the electronic structure of radon) as determined by spectroscopic means and atomic beam experiments are as follows (with predicted values given in parentheses)

neptunium, $5f^46d7s^2$; plutonium, $5f^67s^2$; americium, $5f^77s^2$; curium, $5f^76d7s^2$; berkelium, ($5f^86d7s^2$ or $5f^97s^2$); californium, ($5f^{10}7s^2$); einsteinium, ($5f^{11}7s^2$);

fermium, ($5f^{12}7s^2$); mendelevium, ($5f^{13}7s^2$); nobelium, ($5f^{14}7s^2$); lawrencium, ($5f^{14}6d7s^2$); element 104, ($5f^{14}6d^27s^2$).

One of the most important methods for study and elucidation of chemical behavior of the actinide elements has been ion-exchange chromatography. Adsorption on and elution from ion exchange columns has made possible the identification and separation of the transuranium elements. The behavior of each transuranium element in this respect is very similar to its analogous rare earth element. This has made it possible to detect as little as one or two atoms when this small a number has been made in some of the transmutation experiments.

Prediction of the chemical properties of the yet undiscovered transuranium elements is quite straightforward. Lawrencium, the element with the atomic number 103, completes the actinide series. Accordingly, the elements with atomic numbers greater than 103 are known as transactinide elements. One of these, element 104, may have been discovered in experiments performed in the Soviet Union in 1966. It is expected that these transactinide elements will fit into the Periodic Table as shown in Fig. 1. Thus we can predict the chemical properties of the "transactinide" elements 104 to 118, inclusive, and we suggest that they will have an element-by-element chemical analogy with the elements immediately above them in the Periodic Table. In other words, element 104 should chemically be like hafnium, element 105 like tantalum, element 106 like tungsten, and so on across the Periodic Table to element 118, which should be a noble gas like radon.

All the transuranium elements are unstable and, therefore, are radioactive. The half-lives of the various isotopes decrease in general with increasing atomic number—this means that as heavier and heavier elements are created they exist for shorter and shorter periods, and as a result their production, separation and identification become progressively more difficult. However, it is possible that regions of stability will be found as will be described in a later section.

The transuranium elements have been

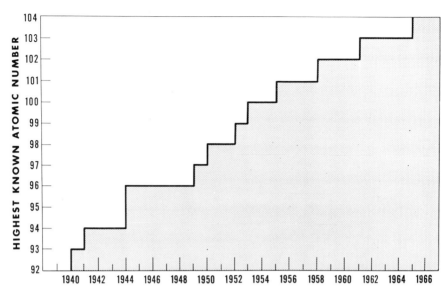

FIG. 2. Increase in number of known transuranium elements with time.

produced in nuclear reactors, as products of the explosion of nuclear devices, and by the use of particle accelerators. In both a nuclear reactor or a nuclear explosion, the atomic nucleus of the starting element is subjected to bombardment with neutrons. Because neutrons are electrically neutral, they have little difficulty in entering the nucleus, where they are absorbed and bound to other neutrons and to protons by strong short-range, nuclear forces. This, in itself, does not create a new element, because the capture of a neutron does not affect the number of protons in the nucleus. Rather, a new isotope of the starting element is created. Subsequent nuclear beta decay, which transforms neutrons into protons, leads to the new element. The third method of synthesizing an element is based on the bombardment of the starting element by the nuclei of light elements. Protons, deuterons, or the nuclei of helium, carbon, nitrogen, oxygen, or other elements, can be used as projectiles.

Beta radioactivity results from one form of nuclear instability common to all regions of the periodic system, but among the heavy elements nuclei may decay by alpha-particle emission and spontaneous fission as well. Since these forms of instability are independent of each other, a particular nuclear species may be observed to decay by any one or all

three modes, depending upon the relative rates. Further, the specific characteristics of the decay of transuranium isotopes generally changes in a uniform manner from element to element, so that the decay properties of isotopes of undiscovered elements, or of undiscovered isotopes of known elements, can often be predicted with some success.

It is interesting to observe how the discovery of the individual transuranium elements has been spread over time. The pace of discovery to the mid-1960's is shown in Fig. 2 where the atomic number of each new element is related to the time of its discovery. In terms of mass number (the sum of protons and neutrons in the nucleus) it has been possible to synthesize isotopes as high as mass number 257 in easily detectable quantity, and perhaps as high as mass number 260 in quantities of a few atoms. The advancement of mass number with time is shown in Fig. 3.

Many radioactive isotopes have been synthesized for each of the transuranium elements, giving a total of about 100 transuranium isotopes. The increase with time of the total number of transuranium isotopes is shown in Fig. 4.

The transuranium elements up to and including element 99, einsteinium, have been isolated in weighable quantities—those beyond element 99 have been investigated only

741

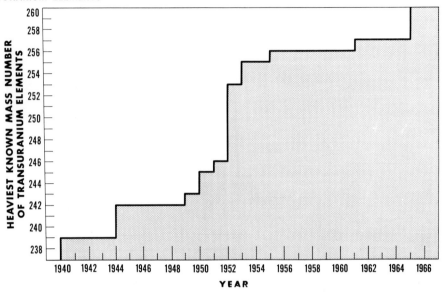

FIG. 3. Increase in heaviest known mass number of transuranium isotopes with time.

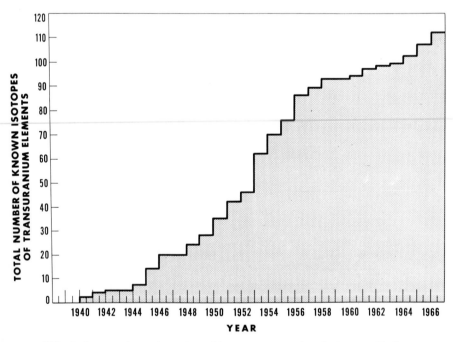

FIG. 4. Increase in total number of known transuranium isotopes with time.

with tracer quantities, that is, quantities not visible to the eye and too small to be weighed. Element 98, californium, was available in the mid-1960's in only rather small quantities— microgram quantities, and element 99, einsteinium, was available only in submicrogram or nanogram (billionths of a gram) quantities, as described in a later section. The U.S. Atomic Energy Commission has a program for the production of these elements which makes larger quantities, grams of californium and milligrams of einsteinium, available.

The transuranium elements are discussed individually in the following sections.

Neptunium

Neptunium (Np, atomic number 93) was named after the planet Neptune. It was the first of the synthetic transuranium elements to be discovered; the isotope Np^{239} was produced by McMillan and Abelson in 1940 at the University of California, Berkeley, as the result of the bombardment of uranium with cyclotron-produced neutrons. The isotope Np^{237} (half-life of 2.14×10^6 years) is obtained in kilogram quantities as a by-product from nuclear reactors. Trace quantities of the element are actually found in nature due to transmutation reactions in uranium ores produced by neutrons which are present from natural sources.

The known isotopes of neptunium, with their radioactive decay characteristics, and some methods of production, are listed in Table 2.

The first isolation of a weighable amount of neptunium in the form of the long-lived isotope, neptunium-237, took place October, 1944, when L. B. Magnusson and T. J. LaChapelle were able to isolate the material at the wartime Metallurgical Laboratory of the University of Chicago. The neptunium was produced in a nuclear reactor as a by-product of the beta decay of uranium-237 formed by a nuclear reaction on uranium-238.

Neptunium metal has a silvery appearance, is chemically reactive, melts at 640°C and exists in at least three structural modifications: α-neptunium, orthorhombic, density = 20.45 g/cc (25°C); β-neptunium (above 280°C), tetragonal, density (313°C) = 19.36 g/cc; γ-neptunium (above 577°C), cubic, density (600°C) = 18.0 g/cc.

Neptunium gives rise to four ionic oxidation states in solution: Np^{+3} (pale purple),

TABLE 2. ISOTOPES OF NEPTUNIUM

Isotope	Half-Life	Mode of Disintegration†	Formation
Np^{231}	~ 50 m	$\alpha(6.28)$	U^{238} (d,9n)
			U^{235} (d,6n)
Np^{232}	~ 13 m	E.C.	U^{233} (d,3n)
Np^{233}	35 m	E.C. (>99%)	U^{235} (d,4n)
		$\alpha(10^{-3}\%)$ (5.53)	U^{233} (d,2n)
Np^{234}	4.4 d	E.C. (>99%)	U^{235} (d,3n)
		$\beta^+(4.6 \times 10^{-2}\%)$	U^{236} (d,4n)
		(0.8)	U^{235} (α,p4n)
			Pa^{231} (α,n)
			U^{234} (d,2n)
			U^{233} (d,n)
			U^{233}(α,p2n)
			U^{233}(α,3n)Pu^{234} $\xrightarrow{E.C.}$
			U^{235}(p,2n)
Np^{235}	410 d	E.C. (>99%)	U^{235}(d,2n)
		$\alpha(1.6 \times 10^{-3}\%)$	U^{235}(α,p3n)
		(5.095, 5.015, 4.925, 4.864)	U^{235}(α,4n)Pu^{235} $\xrightarrow{E.C.}$
			U^{233}(α,pn)
			U^{233}(α,2n)Pu^{235} $\xrightarrow{E.C.}$
Np^{236}	> 5000 y		U^{238}(d,4n)
Np^{236m}	22 h	$\beta^-(49\%)$ (0.52, 0.48)	Np^{237}(n,2n)
			U^{238}(d,4n)
		E.C. (51%)	U^{235}(d,n)
			U^{235}(α,p2n)
			Np^{237}(α,αn)
			U^{233}(α,p)
Np^{237m} 2	5.4×10^{-9} s	I.T. (0.27)	$U^{237}\beta^-$ decay

TABLE 2—*continued*

Isotope	Half-Life	Mode of Disintegration†	Formation
Np^{237m} 1	6.3×10^{-8} s	I.T. (0.060)	Am$^{241}\alpha$ decay
			U$^{237}\beta^-$ decay
Np^{237}	2.14×10^6 y	α(4.781, 4.764 plus others ranging from 4.87 to 4.52) β stable	U$^{237}\beta^-$ decay
Np^{238}	2.10 d	β^-(1.25, 0.28, 0.25)	U^{238}(d,2n)
			Np^{237}(n,γ)
			U^{238}(α,p3n)
			U^{235}(α,p)
Np^{239}	2.35 d	β^-(0.713, 0.654, 0.437, 0.393, 0.332)	U$^{239}\beta^-$ decay
			U^{238}(d,n)
			U^{238},(αp2n)
Np^{240m} 2	7.3 m	β^-(2.16, 1.60, 1.30 0.65)	U$^{240}\beta^-$ decay
			Np^{239}(n,γ)
Np^{240m} 1	63 m	β^-(0.89)	U^{238}(α,pn)
			Np^{239}(n,γ)
Np^{241m}	3.4 h	(β^-)	U^{238}(d,p)
Np^{241}	16 m	β^-(1.4)	U^{238}(α,p)

† Energy of radiation in million electron volts, E.C. = electron capture, I.T. = isomeric transition.

analogous to the rare earth ion Pm^{+3}, Np^{+4} (yellow-green), NpO$_2{}^+$ (green-blue), and NpO$_2{}^{++}$ (pale pink). These latter oxygenated species are in contrast to the rare earths which exhibit only simple ions of the (II), (III), and (IV) oxidation states in aqueous solution. The element forms tri- and tetra-halides such as NpF$_3$, NpF$_4$, NpCl$_4$, NpBr$_3$, NpI$_3$, and oxides of various compositions such as are found in the uranium-oxygen systems, including Np$_3$O$_8$ and NpO$_2$.

The standard oxidation potentials (where the hydrogen-hydrogen ion couple is taken as zero volts) for neptunium are as follows:

Plutonium

Plutonium (Pu, atomic number 94) was named after the planet Pluto. It was the second transuranium element to be discovered; the isotope Pu^{238} was produced in 1940 by Seaborg, McMillan, Kennedy and Wahl at the University of California, Berkeley, by deuteron bombardment of uranium in the 60-inch cyclotron. By far the most important is the isotope Pu^{239} (half-life of 2.44×10^4 years), produced in extensive quantities in nuclear reactors from natural uranium:

$$U^{238} \ (n,\gamma) \ U^{239} \xrightarrow{\beta^-} Np^{239} \xrightarrow{\beta^-} Pu^{239}.$$

Acid aqueous solution (1M *perchloric acid*):

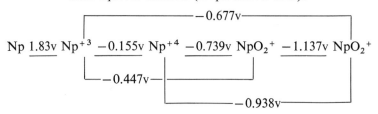

Alkaline aqueous solution (1M *sodium hydroxide*):

Np 2.25v Np(OH)$_3$ 1.76v Np(OH)$_4$ −0.39v NpO$_2$OH −0.48v NpO$_2$(OH)$_2$

(−0.43v)est.

TABLE 3. ISOTOPES OF PLUTONIUM

Isotope	Half-Life	Mode of Disintegration†	Formation
Pu^{232}	36 m	E.C. ($\geq 98\%$) $\alpha(\leq 2\%)$ (6.58)	$U^{235}(\alpha,7n)$ $U^{233}(\alpha,5n)$
Pu^{233}	20 m	E.C. ($>99\%$) $\alpha(0.1\%)$ (6.30)	$U^{233}(\alpha,4n)$
Pu^{234}	9.0 h	E.C. (94%) $\alpha(6\%)$ (6.196, 6.145, 6.025)	$U^{235}(\alpha,5n)$ $U^{233}(\alpha,3n)$ $Cm^{238}\alpha$ decay
Pu^{235}	26 m	E.C ($>99\%$) $\alpha(3 \times 10^{-3}\%)$ (5.85)	$U^{235}(\alpha,4n)$ $U^{233}(\alpha,2n)$
Pu^{236}	2.85 y	α(5.763, 5.716, 5.610, 5.448) β stable	$U^{235}(d,n)$ $Cm^{240}\alpha$ decay $U^{235}(\alpha,3n)$ $U^{238}(\alpha,6n)$ $Np^{237}(d,3n)$ $Np^{237}(\alpha,p4n)$ $Np^{237}(\alpha,5n) \xrightarrow{\text{E.C.}}$ $U^{233}(\alpha,n)$ $Np^{236}\beta^-$ decay
Pu^{237m}	0.18 s	I.T. (0.145)	$Cm^{241}\alpha$ recoils
Pu^{237}	45.6 d	E.C. ($>99\%$) $\alpha(3.3 \times 10^{-3}\%)$ (5.65, 5.36)	$U^{238}(\alpha,5n)$ $U^{235}(\alpha,2n)$ $Np^{237}(d,2n)$
Pu^{238}	86.4 y	α(5.491, 5.452, 5.352) β stable	$U^{238}(d,2n)$ $Cm^{242}\alpha$ decay $Np^{237}(n,\gamma)Np^{238} \xrightarrow{\beta^-}$ $U^{238}(\alpha,4n)$ $U^{238}(\alpha,p3n)N^{238}\,p\xrightarrow{\beta^-}$ $U^{235}(\alpha,n)$ $U^{235}(\alpha,p)$
$Pu^{239m}2$	1.93×10^{-7} s	I.T. (0.392)	$Cm^{243}\alpha$ decay $Np^{239}\beta^-$ decay
$Pu^{239m}1$	1.1×10^{-9} s	I.T. (0.286)	$Cm^{243}\alpha$ decay $Np^{239}\beta^-$ decay
Pu^{239}	2.44×10^4 y	α(5.147, 5.134 plus others ranging from 5.10 to 4.92) β stable	$Np^{239}\beta^-$ decay
Pu^{240}	6580 y	α(5.159, 5.115 plus others ranging from 5.01 to 4.85) β stable	$Pu^{239}(n,\gamma)$ $U^{238}(\alpha,pn)Np^{240} \xrightarrow{\beta^-}$
Pu^{241}	13.2 y	$\beta^-(>99\%)$ (0.0205) $\alpha(2.3 \times 10^{-3}\%)$ (4.890, 4.845)	$Pu^{240}(n,\gamma)$ $U^{238}(\alpha,n)$ $Cm^{245}\alpha$ decay
Pu^{242}	3.79×10^5 y	α(4.898, 4.854) β stable	$Pu^{241}(n,\gamma)$ Am^{242m} E.C. decay
Pu^{243}	4.98 h	β^-(0.58, 0.49)	$Pu^{242}(n,\gamma)$
Pu^{244}	7.6×10^7 y	α(4.55 est.) β stable	$Pu^{243}(n,\gamma)$ U^{238} multiple neutron capture
Pu^{245}	10.6 h	β^-	$Pu^{244}(n,\gamma)$
Pu^{246}	10.85 d	β^-(0.33, 0.15)	$Pu^{245}(n,\gamma)$

† Energy of radiation in million electron volts, E.C. = electron capture, I.T. = isomeric transition.

The known isotopes of plutonium with their radioactive decay characteristics, and some methods of production, are listed in Table 3.

In August, 1942, B. B. Cunningham and L. B. Werner, working at the wartime Metallurgical Laboratory at the University of Chicago, succeeded in isolating about a microgram of plutonium-239 which had been prepared by cyclotron irradiations. Thus, plutonium was the first man-made element to be obtained in visible quantity. The first weighing of this man-made element, using a larger sample (2.77 micrograms), was made by these investigators on September 10, 1942.

Plutonium has assumed the position of dominant importance among the transuranium elements because of its successful use as an explosive ingredient in nuclear weapons

ance, is chemically reactive, and melts at 641°C. It exhibits at least six crystalline modifications: α-plutonium (below 122°C), monoclinic, density $= 19.737$ g/cc (25°C); β-plutonium (below 203°C) BC monoclinic, density $= 17.77$ g/cc (150°C); γ-plutonium (below 317°C), orthorhombic, density $= 17.19$ g/cc (210°C); δ-plutonium (below 453°C) FC cubic, density $= 15.92$ g/cc (320°C); δ'-plutonium (below 477°C) tetragonal, density $= 15.99$ g/cc (465°C); and ε-plutonium (above 477°C) BC cubic, density $= 16.48$ g/cc (500°C).

Plutonium exhibits four ionic valence states in aqueous solutions: Pu^{+3} (blue-lavender), Pu^{+4} (yellow-brown), PuO_2^+ (presumably pink), and PuO_2^{++} (pink-orange). The ion PuO_2^+ is unstable in aqueous solutions, disproportionating into Pu^{+4} and

Acid aqueous solution (1M perchloric acid):

$$Pu \xrightarrow{2.03v} Pu^{+3} \xrightarrow{0.9818v} Pu^{+4} \xrightarrow{-1.1721v} PuO_2^+ \xrightarrow{-0.9133v} PuO_2^{+2}$$

with $-1.0228v$ bridging Pu^{+3} to PuO_2^+, $-1.09v$ bridging Pu^{+4} to PuO_2^+, and $-1.0433v$ bridging Pu^{+4} to PuO_2^{+2}.

Alkaline aqueous solution (1M sodium hydroxide):

$$\xrightarrow{(2.42v)\text{est.}} Pu(OH)_3xH_2O \xrightarrow{0.95} Pu(OH)_4 \cdot yH_2O \xrightarrow{-0.76v} PuO_2(OH) \text{ aq} \xrightarrow{-0.26v} PuO_2(OH)2aq$$

with $\sim -0.5v$ bridging $Pu(OH)_4 \cdot yH_2O$ to $PuO_2(OH)2aq$.

and the place which it holds as a key material in the development of industrial utilization of nuclear energy, one pound being equivalent to about 10,000,000 kilowatt hours of heat energy. Its importance depends on the nuclear property of being readily fissionable with neutrons and its availability in quantity.

Plutonium also exists in trace quantities in naturally occurring uranium ores. It is formed in much the same manner as neptunium, by irradiation of natural uranium with the neutrons which are present.

Plutonium metal can be prepared, in common with neptunium and uranium, by reduction of the tetrafluoride with alkaline earth metals. The metal has a silvery appear-

PuO_2^+; the Pu^{+4} thus formed, however, oxidizes the PuO_2^+ to PuO_2^{++}, itself being reduced to Pu^{+3}, giving finally Pu^{+3} and PuO_2^{++}.

The standard oxidation potentials (where the hydrogen-hydrogen ion couple is taken as zero volts) for plutonium are as above.

Plutonium forms binary compounds with oxygen: PuO, PuO_2, and intermediate oxides of variable composition; with the halides: PuF_3, PuF_4, $PuCl_3$, $PuBr_3$, PuI_3; with carbon, nitrogen and silicon: PuC, PuN, $PuSi_2$; in addition, oxyhalides are well known: $PuOCl$, $PuOBr$, $PuOI$.

Because of the high rate of emission of alpha particles, and the physiological fact that the element is specifically absorbed by bone marrow, plutonium, to an even larger extent than other transuranium elements, is a radiological poison and must be handled with special equipment and precautions.

Americium

Americium (Am, atomic number 95) was named after the Americas. It was the fourth transuranium element to be discovered; the isotope Am^{241} was identified by Seaborg, James, Morgan and Ghiorso late in 1944 at the wartime Metallurgical Laboratory (now the Argonne National Laboratory) of the University of Chicago as the result of successive neutron capture reactions by plutonium isotopes in a nuclear reactor:

$$Pu^{239} (n,\gamma) \; Pu^{240} (n,\gamma) \; Pu^{241} \xrightarrow{\beta^-} Am^{241}.$$

The known isotopes of americium, with their radioactive decay characteristics and some methods of production, are listed in Table 4.

Americium was first isolated by B. B. Cunningham, as the isotope americium-241 in the form of a pure compound, the hydroxide, in the fall of 1945 at the wartime Metallurgical Laboratory. It can be produced in kilogram quantities. Since the isotope Am^{241} can be

TABLE 4. ISOTOPES OF AMERICIUM

Isotope	Half-Life	Mode of Disintegration†	Formation
Am^{237}	1.3 h	E.C. (99%) $\alpha(5 \times 10^{-3}\%)$ (6.01)	$Pu^{239}(d,4n)$
Am^{238}	1.9 h	E.C.	$Pu^{239}(d,3n)$ $Pu^{239}(p,2n)$ $Np^{237}(\alpha,3n)$
Am^{239}	12.1 h	E.C. (>99%) $\alpha(5.0 \times 10^{-3}\%)$ (5.78)	$Pu^{239}(d, 2n)$ $Np^{237}(\alpha,2n)$ $Pu^{239}(p,n)$ $Pu^{239}(\alpha,p3n)$
Am^{240}	51 h	E.C.	$Pu^{239}(d,n)$ $Np^{237}(\alpha,n)$ $Pu^{239}(\alpha,p2n)$
Am^{241}	433 y	$\alpha(5.476, 5.433$ plus others ranging from 5.54 to 5.24) β stable	$Pu^{241}\beta^-$ decay
Am^{242}	16.01 h	$\beta^-(84\%)$ (0.667, 0.625) E.C. (16%)	$Am^{241}(n,\gamma)$
$Am^{242m}1$	152 y	I.T. (0.049) $\beta^-(<2\%$ of I.T.) $\alpha(0.48\%)$	$Am^{241}(n,\gamma)$
$Am^{242m}2$	0.014 s	S.F.	$Am^{243}(n,2n)$ $U^{238}(O^{16},5p7n)$ $U^{238}(Ne^{22},7p11n)$
Am^{243}	7700 y	$\alpha(5.267, 5.224$ plus others ranging from 5.340 to 5.169) β stable	$Am^{242m}(n,\gamma)$ $Pu^{243}\beta^-$ decay
Am^{244m}	26 m	$\beta^-(>99\%)$ (1.50) E.C. $(4 \times 10^{-2}\%)$	$Am^{243}(n,\gamma)$
Am^{244}	10.1 h	$\beta^-(0.387)$	$Am^{243}(n,\gamma)$
Am^{245}	2.07 h	$\beta^-(0.91)$	$Pu^{245}\beta^-$ decay
Am^{246}	25 m	$\beta^-(2.10, 1.60, 1.31)$	$Pu^{246}\beta^-$ decay
Am^{247}	24 m	β^-	$Pu^{244}(\alpha,p)$

† Energy of radiation in million electron volts, E.C. = electron capture, I.T. = isomeric transition, S.F. = spontaneous fission.

prepared in relatively pure form by extraction as a decay product over a period of years from intensely neutron-irradiated plutonium containing Pu^{241}, this isotope has been used for much of the chemical investigation of this element. Better suited is the isotope Am^{243} due to its longer half-life (7700 years as compared to 433 years for Am^{241}).

Am^{+2} has been prepared in tracer experiments at very low concentrations; this would be very similar to the analogous lanthanide, europium, which can be reduced to the divalent state.

The standard oxidation potentials (where the hydrogen-hydrogen ion couple is taken as zero volts) for americium are as follows:

Acid aqueous solution (1M *perchloric acid*):

$$Am(<2.7v)est.\ Am^{+2}>1.5v\ Am^{+3}\ (-2.7v)\ est.\ Am^{+4}\ -0.14v\ AmO_2^+\ -1.60v\ AmO_2^{+2}$$

(brackets: $-1.69v$; $2.32v$; $-1.74v$)

Alkaline aqueous solution (1M *sodium hydroxide*):

$$Am\ \xrightarrow{2.71v}\ Am(OH)_3\ \xrightarrow{-0.4\ to\ -0.5v}\ Am(OH)_4\ \xrightarrow{(-0.7v)est.}\ AmO_2OH\ \xrightarrow{(1.1v)est.}\ AmO_2(OH)_2$$

(bracket: $(-0.9v)est.$)

Nearly isotopically pure Am^{243} can be prepared by neutron irradiation of Pu^{242} and the Am^{243} can be chemically separated. Fairly pure Pu^{242} can be prepared by very intense neutron irradiation of Pu^{239} as the result of successive neutron capture reactions. This Pu^{242} can be irradiated with neutrons to produce Am^{243} by the reactions

$$Pu^{242}\ (n,\gamma)\ Pu^{243}\ \xrightarrow{\beta^-}\ Am^{243}.$$

Americium can be obtained as a silvery white reactive metal by reduction of americium trifluoride with barium vapor at 1000°C to 1200°C. It appears to be more malleable than uranium or neptunium and tarnishes slowly in dry air at room temperature. The density is 13.67 g/cc (20°C) and the melting point is 995°C.

The element exists in three oxidation states in aqueous solution: Am^{+3} (light salmon), AmO_2^+ (color unknown), and AmO_2^{+2} (light tan). The trivalent state is highly stable and difficult to oxidize, and forms precipitates of low solubility with hydroxide, fluoride, oxalate, iodate, etc. AmO_2^+, like plutonium, is unstable with respect to disproportionation into Am^{+3} and AmO_2^{+2}. The ion Am^{+4} has been observed in the form of a stable complex in solution. There is some evidence that

Americium dioxide, AmO_2, is the important oxide; Am_2O_3 and, as with lighter actinide elements, oxides of variable composition between $AmO_{1.5}$ and AmO_2 are known. The halides AmF_3, AmF_4, $AmCl_3$, $AmBr_3$, and AmI_3 have also been prepared, and their molecular structures have been determined by x-ray diffraction methods.

Curium

Curium (Cm, atomic number 96) is named after Pierre and Marie Curie. Although curium comes after americium in the periodic system, it was actually known before americium and was the third transuranium element to be discovered. It was identified by Seaborg, James, and Ghiorso in the summer of 1944 at the wartime Metallurgical Laboratory in Chicago as a result of helium-ion bombardment of Pu^{239} in the Berkeley, California, 60-inch cyclotron. It is of special interest because it is in this element that the first half of the transition series of actinide elements is completed.

The known isotopes of curium, with their radioactive decay characteristics and some methods of production, are listed in Table 5.

Curium was first isolated in the form of a pure compound, the hydroxide, of curium-242

TABLE 5. ISOTOPES OF CURIUM

Isotope	Half-Life	Mode of Disintegration†	Formation
Cm^{238}	2.5 h	E.C. ($\sim 99\%$ est.) $\alpha(\sim 1\%$ est.) (6.50)	$Pu^{239}(\alpha,5n)$
Cm^{239}	2.9 h	E.C.	$Pu^{239}(\alpha,4n)$
Cm^{240}	26.8 d	$\alpha(6.25, 6.21)$	$Pu^{239}(\alpha,3n)$
Cm^{241}	35 d	E.C. (99%) $\alpha(1\%)$ (5.94, 5.93, 5.88)	$Pu^{239}(\alpha,2n)$
Cm^{242}	163 d	$\alpha(6.110, 6.066$ plus others ranging from 5.97 to 5.20) β stable	$Pu^{239}(\alpha,n)$ $Am^{242}\beta^-$ decay
Cm^{243}	32 y	$\alpha(>99\%)$ (5.780, 5.736 plus others ranging from 6.061 to 5.58) E.C. (0.3%)	$Cm^{242}(n,\gamma)$
Cm^{244}	17.6 y	$\alpha(5.801, 5.759, 5.661, 5.515)$ β stable	$Cm^{243}(n,\gamma)$ $Am^{243}(n,\gamma)Am^{244m} \xrightarrow{\beta^-}$ Pu^{239} multiple neutron capture
Cm^{244m}	0.034 s	I.T. (1.032)	Am^{244} β^- decay
Cm^{245}	9320 y	$\alpha(5.36, 5.31)$ β stable	$Cm^{244}(n,\gamma)$ Pu^{239} multiple neutron capture U^{238} multiple neutron capture
Cm^{246}	5480 y	$\alpha(5.37)$ β stable	$Cm^{245}(n,\gamma)$ Pu^{239} multiple neutron capture U^{238} multiple neutron capture
Cm^{247}	1.6×10^7 y	α β stable	Pu^{239} multiple neutron capture U^{238} multiple neutron capture
Cm^{248}	4.7×10^5 y	$\alpha(89\%)$ (5.054) S.F. (11%) β stable	Pu^{239} multiple neutron capture U^{238} multiple neutron capture Cf^{252} α decay
Cm^{249}	64 m	$\beta^-(0.9)$	$Cm^{248}(n,\gamma)$ Pu^{239} multiple neutron capture U^{238} multiple neutron capture
Cm^{250}	1.7×10^4 y	S.F. β stable(?)	Pu^{239} multiple neutron capture U^{238} multiple neutron capture

† Energy of radiation in million electron volts, E.C. = electron capture, I.T. = isomeric transition, S.F. = spontaneous fission.

(produced by the neutron irradiation of americium-241) by L. B. Werner and I. Perlman at the University of California during the fall of 1947.

The isotope Cm^{242} (half-life 163 days) produced from Am^{241} by the reactions

$$Am^{241} \ (n,\gamma) \ Am^{242} \xrightarrow{\beta^-} Cm^{242}$$

was used for much of the early work with macroscopic quantities, although this is difficult due to the extremely high specific alpha activity. An excellent isotope for the investigation of curium in weighable amounts is Cm^{244} because it has a half-life of 17.6 years and can be prepared in fairly pure form by a sequence of neutron irradiations and chemical separations. Fairly pure Pu^{242} can be prepared by very intense neutron irradiation of Pu^{239} as the result of successive neutron capture reactions. This can be transmuted to Am^{243} which can be chemically separated and finally transmuted to Cm^{244} through neutron bombardment by the reactions

$$Am^{243} \ (n,\gamma) \ Am^{244} \xrightarrow{\beta^-} Cm^{244}.$$

Further neutron bombardment of Cm^{244}, as shown later in Fig. 6, produces higher-mass isotopes of longer half-life which are even better for use in the investigation of curium.

Curium metal which melts at 1340°C resembles the other actinide metals quite closely; it has a density of 13.51 g/cc (20°C). In common with other metals, it can be prepared by heating curium trifluoride with barium vapor at 1275°C.

Curium exists in aqueous solution predominantly as Cm^{+3}, although Cm^{+4} exists as complex fluoride ion. Slightly soluble compounds include $Cm(OH)_3$, CmF_3, $Cm_2(C_2O_4)_3$. Solid CmO_2 and CmF_4 have been prepared as well as solid Cm_2O_3, CmF_3, $CmCl_3$, $CmBr_3$ and CmI_3, and their molecular structures have been determined by x-ray diffraction methods. It has been demonstrated that curium (III) cannot be reduced in aqueous solutions.

Berkelium

Berkelium (Bk, atomic number 97) was named after Berkeley, California. The eighth member of the actinide transition series, it was discovered in December, 1949, by Thompson, Ghiorso and Seaborg and was the fifth transuranium element synthesized. It was produced in the form of the isotope Bk^{243} by cyclotron bombardment of Am^{241} with helium ions at the University of California, Berkeley.

The known isotopes of berkelium, with their radioactive decay characteristics and some methods of production, are listed in Table 6.

In 1958, B. B. Cunningham and S. G. Thompson, at Berkeley, succeeded in isolating, for the first time, macroscopic amounts of berkelium using the isotope Bk^{249} produced by the long-time irradiation with neutrons of Pu^{239} and its transmutation products. Chemical studies have demonstrated that berkelium exists in aqueous solutions in two oxidation states, berkelium (III) and berkelium (IV). The chemistry and solubility of compounds appears to follow closely the other transuranium elements in these oxidation states. The standard oxidation potential (where the hydrogen-hydrogen ion couple is taken as zero volts) for the berkelium (III)—berkelium (IV) couple is estimated to be:

$$Bk^{+3} \xrightarrow{(-1.6v)est.} Bk^{+4}.$$

The existence of Bk^{249} with a half-life of 314 days makes it feasible to work with berkelium in weighable amounts so that its properties can be investigated with macroscopic quantities. This isotope can be prepared by the intense neutron bombardment of lighter transuranium isotopes such as Cm^{244} as the result of the capture of successive neutrons by the reactions

$$Cm^{244} \ (n,\gamma) \ Cm^{245} \ (n,\gamma)$$
$$Cm^{246} \ (n,\gamma) \ Cm^{247} \ (n,\gamma) \ Cm^{248} \ (n,\gamma)$$
$$Cm^{249} \xrightarrow{\beta^-} Bk^{249}.$$

Another method of production is the irradiation of isotopes such as U^{238} with neutrons produced in nuclear explosions as illustrated later in Fig. 5.

Slightly soluble compounds include $Bk(OH)_3$, $Bk(OH)_4$ and BkF_3 and the following compounds are among those that have had their molecular structures determined by x-ray diffraction methods: Bk_2O_3, BkO_2, BkF_3, $BkCl_3$, $BkOCl$.

TABLE 6. ISOTOPES OF BERKELIUM

Isotope	Half-Life	Mode of Disintegration†	Formation
Bk^{243}	4.5 h	E.C. ($> 99\%$) α(6.76, 6.72, 6.57, 6.54, 6.21)	$Am^{241}(\alpha,2n)$ $Am^{243}(\alpha,4n)$ $Cm^{242}(d,n)$ $Cm^{244}(d,3n)$
Bk^{244}	4.4 h	E.C. ($> 99\%$) α($6 \times 10^{-3}\%$) (6.67)	$Am^{241}(\alpha,n)$ $Am^{243}(\alpha,3n)$
Bk^{245}	4.98 d	E.C. ($> 99\%$) α(0.1%) (6.36, 6.32, 6.15, 6.12, 5.89)	$Am^{243}(\alpha,2n)$ $Cm^{242}(\alpha,p)$ $Cm^{244}(d,n)$
Bk^{246}	1.8 d	E.C.	$Am^{243}(\alpha,n)$ $Cm^{244}(\alpha,pn)$
Bk^{247}	1.4×10^3 y	α(5.67, 5.51, 5.30)	Cf^{247} E.C. decay $Cm^{244}(\alpha,p)$ $Cm^{245}(\alpha,pn)$ $Cm^{246}(\alpha,p2n)$
Bk^{248}	> 9 y	$T_{1/2}(\beta^-) > 10^4$y	Cm^{246} (d,pn)
$Bk^{248}{}_m$	16 h	β^-(70%) (0.65) E.C. (30%)	$Bk^{247}(n,\gamma)$ $Cm^{245}(\alpha,p)$ $Cm^{246}(\alpha,pn)$
Bk^{249}	314 d	β^-($> 99\%$) (0.125) α($10^{-3}\%$) (5.43, 5.41, 5.38 and others ranging from 5.04 to 5.34)	Pu^{239} multiple neutron capture U^{238} multiple neutron capture
Bk^{250m}	3.9×10^{-8} s	I.T.	$Es^{254}\alpha$ decay
Bk^{250}	193 m	β^-(1.760, 0.725)	$Bk^{249}(n,\gamma)$ $Es^{254}\alpha$ decay
Bk^{251}	57.0 m	β^-(0.5, 1.0)	$Es^{255}\alpha$ decay

† Energy of radiation in million electron volts, E.C. = electron capture, I.T. = isomeric transition.

TABLE 7. ISOTOPES OF CALIFORNIUM

Isotope	Half-Life	Mode of Disintegration†	Formation
Cf^{242}	3.4 m	α(7.4)	$U^{235}(C^{12},5n)$ $Cm^{244}(He^3,5n)$
Cf^{243}	~ 10 m	E.C. (90%) α(10%) (7.05)	$U^{235}(C^{12},4n)$ $Cm^{244}(He^3,4n)$
Cf^{244}	20 m	α($> 99\%$) (7.21, 7.17) E.C. (?)	$Cm^{242}(\alpha,2n)$ $Cm^{244}(\alpha,4n)$ $U^{238}(C^{12},6n)$
Cf^{245}	44 m	E.C. (70%) α(30%) (7.14)	$Cm^{242}(\alpha,n)$ $Cm^{244}(\alpha,3n)$ $U^{238}(C^{12},5n)$
Cf^{246}	35.7 h	α(6.753, 6.711) β stable	$Cm^{244}(\alpha,2n)$ $Cm^{243}(\alpha,n)$ $U^{238}(C^{12},4n)$
Cf^{247}	2.5 h	E.C.	$Cm^{244}(\alpha,n)$ $U^{238}(N^{14},p4n)$

751

TABLE 7—*continued*

Isotope	Half-Life	Mode of Disintegration†	Formation
Cf^{248}	350 d	$\alpha(6.26, 6.22)$ β stable	$U^{238}(N^{14},p3n)$ $Cm^{245}(\alpha,n)$ $Cm^{246}(\alpha,2n)$ $Cm^{247}(\alpha,3n)$ $Cm^{248}(\alpha,4n)$
Cf^{249}	360 y	$\alpha(5.806$ plus others ranging from 6.194 to 5.687) β stable	$Bk^{249}\beta^-$ decay
Cf^{250}	13 y	$\alpha(6.024, 5.980)$ S.F. (0.1%) β stable	Pu^{239} multiple neutron capture $Bk^{250}\beta^-$ decay $Cm^{247}(\alpha,n)$ $Cm^{248}(\alpha,2n)$ $Es^{254}\alpha$ decay
Cf^{251}	800 y	$\alpha(5.844, 5.667)$ β stable	Pu^{239} multiple neutron capture U^{238} multiple neutron capture
Cf^{252}	2.65 y	$\alpha(96.9\%)$ (6.112, 6.069, 5.970) S.F. (3.1%) β stable	Pu^{239} multiple neutron capture U^{238} multiple neutron capture
Cf^{253}	17.6 d	$\beta^-(0.27)$ $\alpha(0.31\%)$ (5.98)	Pu^{239} multiple neutron capture U^{238} multiple neutron capture
Cf^{254}	60.5 d	S.F. ($>99\%$) $\alpha(\approx 0.2\%)$ (5.84) β stable	Es^{254}E.C. decay Pu^{239} multiple neutron capture U^{238} multiple neutron capture

† Energy of radiation in million electron volts, E.C. = electron capture, S.F. = spontaneous fission.

Californium

Californium (Cf, atomic number 98) was named after the state and University of California. The sixth transuranium element to be discovered, it was produced in the form of the isotope Cf^{245} by Thompson, Street, Ghiorso and Seaborg in January, 1950 by helium-ion bombardment of microgram quantities of Cm^{242} in the 60-inch cyclotron at the University of California, Berkeley.

The known isotopes of californium, with their radioactive decay characteristics and some methods of production, are listed in Table 7.

In 1958, B. B. Cunningham and S. G. Thompson, at Berkeley, succeeded in isolating, for the first time, macroscopic amounts of californium as a mixture of the isotopes californium-249, -250, -251, and -252. It was synthesized by the long-term irradiation with neutrons of Pu^{239} and its transmutation products.

Californium (III) is the only ion stable in aqueous solutions, all attempts to reduce or oxidize californium (III) having failed. The existence of the isotopes Cf^{249}, Cf^{250}, Cf^{251} and Cf^{252} makes it feasible to work with californium in weighable amounts so that its properties can be investigated with macroscopic quantities. The isotope Cf^{249} results from the beta decay of Bk^{249} while the heavier isotopes are produced by intense neutron irradiation by the reactions

$$Bk^{249} (n,\gamma) Bk^{250} \xrightarrow{\beta^-} Cf^{250}$$

and $Cf^{249} (n,\gamma) Cf^{250}$ followed by $Cf^{250} (n,\gamma)$ $Cf^{251} (n,\gamma) Cf^{252}$.

Methods of production are illustrated later in Figs. 5 and 6.

Slightly soluble compounds include $Cf(OH)_3$ and CfF_3; Cf_2O_3 and $CfCl_3$ are among the compounds that have had their molecular structures determined by x-ray diffraction methods.

Einsteinium

Einsteinium (Es, atomic number 99) was named after Albert Einstein. The seventh transuranium element to be discovered, it was identified by Ghiorso *et al*, in December, 1952, in the debris from a thermonuclear explosion in work involving the University of California Radiation Laboratory, the Argonne National Laboratory, and the Los Alamos Scientific Laboratory. The isotope produced by successive neutron capture in U^{238} was the 20.5-day Es^{253}, originating from beta decay of U^{253} and daughters.

The known isotopes of einsteinium, with their radioactive decay characteristics and some methods of production, are listed in Table 8.

TABLE 8. ISOTOPES OF EINSTEINIUM

Isotope	Half-Life	Mode of Disintegration†	Formation
Es^{245}	1.3 m	$\alpha(17\%)$ (7.70) E.C. (83%)	$Np^{237}(C^{12},4n)$ $Pu^{240}(B,xn)$ $U^{238}(N^{14},7n)$ $U^{235}(N^{14},4n)$
Es^{246}	7.3 m	E.C. ($\sim$90%) $\alpha(\sim 10\%)$ (7.35)	$U^{238}(N^{14},6n)$
Es^{247}	5.0 m	$\alpha(\sim 7\%)$ (7.33) E.C. ($\sim$93%)	$U^{238}(N^{14},5n)$
Es^{248}	25 m	E.C. ($>$99%) $\alpha(0.3\%)$ (6.87)	$Cf^{249}(d,3n)$
Es^{249}	2 h	E.C. ($>$99%) $\alpha(0.1\%)$ (6.76)	$Bk^{249}(\alpha,4n)$ $Cf^{249}(\alpha,p3n)$ $Cf^{249}(d,2n)$
Es^{250}	8 h	E.C.	$Bk^{249}(\alpha,3n)$ $Cf^{249}(\alpha,p2n)$ $Cf^{249}(\alpha,3n)Fm^{250}\xrightarrow{\text{E.C.}}$ $Cf^{249}(\alpha,H^3)$ $Cf^{249}(d,n)$
Es^{251}	1.5 d	E.C. (99.5%) $\alpha(0.5\%)$ (6.48)	$Bk^{249}(\alpha,2n)$
Es^{252}	$\sim$ 140 d	α(6.64, 6.58)	$Bk^{249}(\alpha,n)$
Es^{253}	20.5 d	α(6.633, 6.592 plus others ranging from 6.62 to 6.16) β stable	Cf^{253} β^- decay Pu^{239} multiple neutron capture U^{238} multiple neutron capture
Es^{254m}	39.3 h	β^-(99.9%) (1.04, 0.381) E.C. ($\sim$0.1%)	$Es^{253}(n,\gamma)$ Pu^{239} multiple neutron capture
Es^{254}	276 d	α(6.43)	$Es^{253}(n,\gamma)$ Pu^{239} multiple neutron capture
Es^{255}	38.3 d	β^-(91.5%) $\alpha(8.5\%)$ (6.31)	Pu^{239} multiple neutron capture U^{238} multiple neutron capture $Es^{253}(n,\gamma)Es^{254}(n,\gamma)$
Es^{256}	$<$1 h	β^-	$Es^{255}(n,\gamma)$

† Energy of radiation in million electron volts, E.C. = electron capture.

It was not until 1961 that sufficient einsteinium had been produced through intense neutron bombardments of plutonium-239 to permit separation of a macroscopic and weighable amount. B. B. Cunningham, J. C. Wallmann, L. Phillips, and R. C. Gatti, working on the submicrogram scale, were able to separate a small sample of pure einsteinium compound utilizing the isotope Es^{253}. This was a remarkable feat, since the total amount of material involved was only a few hundredths of a microgram of einsteinium.

Its chemical properties have been studied with tracer amounts and indicate that the (III) oxidation state may be the only one which exists in aqueous solution.

Existence of Es^{254} with a half-life of 276 days makes it possible to work more conveniently with this element in weighable amounts. The isotope Es^{253} and heavier isotopes can be produced by intense neutron irradiation of lower elements such as plutonium, by a process of successive neutron capture interspersed with beta decays until

TABLE 9. ISOTOPES OF FERMIUM

Isotope	Half-Life	Mode of Disintegration†	Formation
Fm^{244}	3.0 ms	S.F.	
Fm^{245}	4.5 s	$\alpha(8.6)$	
Fm^{246}	1.5 s	$\alpha(\sim 92\%)$ (8.2)	$U^{235}(O^{16},5n)$
		S.F.$(\sim 8\%)$	$Pu^{239}(C^{12},5n)$
Fm^{247}	35 s	$\alpha(7.9)$	$Pu^{239}(C^{12},4n)$
Fm^{247}	9.2 s	$\alpha(8.2)$	$Pu^{239}(C^{12},4n)$
Fm^{248}	0.6 m	$\alpha(7.8)$	$Pu^{240}(C^{12},4n)$
		S.F.$(\sim 0.1\%)$	$Np^{237}(N^{15},4n)$
			$U^{238}(O^{16},6n)$
Fm^{249}	2.5 m	$\alpha(7.5)$	$Pu^{242}(C^{12},5n)$
			$U^{238}(O^{16},5n)$
Fm^{250}	~ 0.5 h	$\alpha(7.43)$	$Cf^{249, 250, 251, 252}(\alpha,xn)$
		S.F.$(\sim 5 \times 10^{-3}\%)$	$Cm^{244}(C^{12},\alpha 2n)$
			$U^{238}(O^{16},4n)$
Fm^{251}	7 h	E.C. (99%)	$Cf^{249}(\alpha,2n)$
		$\alpha(\sim 1\%)$ (6.89)	
Fm^{252}	23 h	$\alpha(7.05)$	$Cf^{249, 250, 251, 252}(\alpha,xn)$
		β stable	$Cf^{250}(Be^9,\alpha 3n)$
Fm^{253}	3.0 d	E.C. (89%)	$Cf^{252}(\alpha,3n)$
		$\alpha(11\%)$ (6.94)	
Fm^{254}	3.24 h	$\alpha(7.20, 7.16, 7.06)$	Pu^{239} multiple
		S.F. (0.06%)	neutron capture
		β stable	Es^{254m} β^- decay
Fm^{255}	20.1 h	$\alpha(7.02$ and others ranging from 6.4 to 7.1)	Pu^{239} multiple neutron capture
		S.F. $(2.5 \times 10^{-5}\%)$	U^{238} multiple
		β stable	neutron capture
Fm^{256}	160 m	S.F. (97%)	$Es^{255}(n,\gamma)Es^{256}$ $\xrightarrow{\beta^-}$
		$\alpha(3\%)$ (6.86)	
		β stable	
			$Es^{253}(\alpha,n)Md^{256}$ $\xrightarrow{E.C.}$
			$Es^{253}(\alpha,p)$
Fm^{257}	80 d	$\alpha(6.53)$	U^{238} multiple
		β stable	neutron capture
			Pu^{239} multiple neutron capture

† Energy of radiation in million electron volts, E.C. = electron capture, S.F. = spontaneous fission.

these mass numbers and atomic numbers are reached, as illustrated later in Fig. 6. Another method of production is illustrated later in Fig. 5.

Fermium

Fermium (Fm, atomic number 100) was named after Enrico Fermi. It was the eighth transuranium element to be discovered, and was identified by Ghiorso, *et al*, early in 1953 in the debris from a thermonuclear explosion in work involving the University of California Radiation Laboratory, the Argonne National Laboratory, and the Los Alamos Scientific Laboratory. The isotope produced by successive neutron capture in U^{238} was the 20.1-hour Fm^{255}, originating from the beta decay of U^{255} and daughters.

The known isotopes of fermium, with their radioactive decay characteristics and some methods of production, are listed in Table 9.

Its chemical properties have been studied solely with tracer amounts, and in normal aqueous media only the (III) oxidation state appears to exist. The isotope Fm^{254} and heavier isotopes can be produced by intense irradiation of lower elements, such as plutonium, by a process of successive neutron capture interspersed with beta decays until these mass numbers and atomic numbers are reached, as illustrated later in Fig. 6. The isotope Fm^{257}, with a half-life of 80 days, makes it possible to work with weighable amounts of fermium. This isotope can be produced by the method later illustrated in Fig. 5 as well as the method illustrated in Fig. 6.

Mendelevium

Mendelevium (Md, atomic number 101) was named after Dmitri Mendeleev. It was the ninth transuranium element to be discovered and was first identified by Ghiorso, Harvey, Choppin, Thompson and Seaborg in early 1955 as a result of the bombardment of the isotope Es^{253} with helium ions in the 60-inch cyclotron at the University of California, Berkeley. The isotope produced was Md^{256} which decays by electron capture to Fm^{256}, which in turn decays predominantly by spontaneous fission with a half-life of about 3 hours. The first identification was notable in that only of the order of one to three atoms per experiment were produced, making the discovery experiments very difficult. The extreme sensitivity for its detection depended on the fact that its chemical properties could be accurately predicted as those of eka-thulium and there was a high sensitivity for detection because of the spontaneous fission decay.

The known isotopes of mendelevium, with their radioactive decay characteristics and some methods of production, are listed in Table 10.

The chemical properties have been investigated solely by the tracer technique and seem to indicate that the predominant oxidation state in aqueous solution is the (III) state; the (II) state has been observed corresponding to a value of about $+0.2$ volts for the couple $Md^{++} \rightarrow Md^{+++}$. The isotope Md^{258} (half-life about 2 months) may make it possible eventually to work with this element in macroscopic quantity.

TABLE 10. ISOTOPES OF MENDELEVIUM

Isotope	Half-Life	Mode of Disintegration†	Formation
Md^{252}	8 m	E.C.	$U^{238}(F^{19},5n)$
Md^{255}	0.6 h	E.C. (90%) $\alpha(10\%)$ (7.34)	$Es^{253}(\alpha,2n)$
Md^{256}	1.5 h	E.C. (97%) $\alpha(3\%)$	$Es^{253}(\alpha,n)$
Md^{257}	3 h	E.C. ($\sim 92\%$) $\alpha(\sim 8\%)$ (7.08)	$Cf^{252}(B^{11},2p4n)$ $Cf^{252}(C^{12},3p4n)$ $Cf^{252}(C^{13},3p5n)$
Md^{258}	60 d	α	$Es^{255}(\alpha,n)$

† Energy of radiation in million electron volts, E.C. = electron capture.

TABLE 11. ISOTOPES OF NOBELIUM

Isotope	Half-Life	Mode of Disintegration†	Formation
No^{251}	~ 0.85	$\alpha(8.6)$	$Cm^{244}(C^{12},5n)$
No^{252}	2.3 s	$\alpha(8.4)$	$Pu^{239}(O^{18},5n)$
			$Cm^{244}(C^{12},4n)$
No^{253}	1.7 m	$\alpha(8.0)$	$Pu^{242}(O^{16},5n)$
			$Pu^{239}(O^{18},4n)$
			$Cm^{246}(C^{12},5n)$
No^{254}	~ 1 m	$\alpha(8.1)$	$Cm^{246}(C^{12},4n)$
			$Am^{243}(N^{15},4n)$
			$U^{238}(Ne^{22},6n)$
			$Pu^{242}(O^{16},4n)$
No^{255}	~ 3 m	$\alpha(8.1)$	$Cm^{246}(C^{13},4n)$
			$U^{238}(Ne^{22},5n)$
			$Pu^{242}(O^{18},5n)$
No^{256}	~ 3 s	$\alpha(8.4)$	$Cm^{248}(C^{12},4n)$
			$Pu^{242}(O^{18},4n)$
			$U^{238}(Ne^{22},4n)$
No^{257}	~ 20 s	$\alpha(8.3)$	$Cf^{252}(B^{10},p4n)$
			$Cm^{248}(C^{13},4n)$

† Energy of radiation in million electron volts.

Nobelium

Nobelium (No, atomic number 102) the tenth transuranium element to be discovered, was identified by Ghiorso, Sikkeland, Walton and Seaborg in 1958 as a result of the bombardment of curium with C^{12} ions in the heavy ion linear accelerator (HILAC) at Berkeley, California. The isotope produced was No^{254} which is now known to decay with a half-life of about a minute. This element, like mendelevium, was produced in extremely small amounts, one atom at a time. An earlier claim to discovery of nobelium, based on work performed in 1957 at the Nobel Institute for Physics in Stockholm, has never been confirmed. Soviet scientists at the Dubna Laboratory near Moscow and Ghiorso and coworkers at Berkeley have produced a number of additional isotopes of nobelium. Its known isotopes, with their radioactive decay characteristics and methods of production, are listed in Table 11.

Nobelium has had its chemical properties investigated using the tracer technique (using the isotope No^{255}); it exhibits the II and III oxidation states in aqueous solution with a value of about -1.2 volts for the couple $No^{++} \rightarrow No^{+++}$.

Lawrencium

Lawrencium (Lr, atomic number 103) was named after Ernest O. Lawrence. It was the eleventh transuranium element to be discovered, and was identified in 1961 by Ghiorso, Sikkeland, Larsh and Latimer as a result of the bombardment of californium with boron ions in the HILAC at Berkeley, California. The activity produced was assigned to Lr^{257} which decays with a half-life of 8 seconds; it is now thought to be due to Lr^{258} or Lr^{259}. It was also produced on an atom-by-atom basis, as in the case of mendelevium and nobelium.

The known isotopes of lawrencium, with their radioactive decay characteristics and some methods of production, are listed in Table 12.

Lawrencium has been shown experimentally to exhibit a stable III oxidation state in aqueous solution as expected. The element lawrencium is the last member of the 14-member actinide series.

Transactinide Elements

The transuranium elements with atomic numbers greater than 103, beyond the actinide

TABLE 12. ISOTOPES OF LAWRENCIUM

Isotope	Half-Life	Mode of Disintegration†	Formation
Lr^{256}	45 s	α	$Am^{243}(O^{18},5n)$
		E.C.	
Lr^{257}	35 s	α	$Am^{243}(O^{18},4n)$
$Lr^{258, 259}$	8 s	$\alpha(8.6)$	$Cf^{250, 251, 252}(B^{11},xn)$
			$Cf^{250, 251, 252}(B^{10},xn)$

† Energy of radiation in million electron volts, E.C. = electron capture.

series, are known as the transactinide elements. There was evidence in the mid-1960's that one such element, element 104, may have been discovered. It seems certain that a substantial number of additional transactinide elements will be synthesized and identified. Chemical identification may not be possible in all cases, making it necessary to base the identification on an analysis of the methods of production and the nuclear properties of the isotopes produced.

These heavier elements will be produced either by the bombardment of heavy isotopic targets with heavy ion projectiles or the irradiation of uranium or of other heavy isotopes with the instantaneous high flux of neutrons produced in nuclear explosions, or by both methods. (A United States program for the production of substantial quantities of heavy isotopes that might be used as starting target materials for these purposes, and for other purposes, is described in a later section of this article.) The yields of the new heavy elements produced by these nuclear reactions and their half-lives for radioactive decay (by alpha-particle emission and spontaneous fission) are apparently decreasing as we go up the atomic number scale. If this should prove to be true it will be very difficult and will require many years to synthesize and identify such elements, based on an extrapolation of the great difficulties in producing and identifying elements 101, 102, 103, and 104.

The small yields and short half-lives are exemplified by the work on element 104. Soviet groups of scientists working at the Dubna Laboratory near Moscow in the mid-1960's bombarded Pu^{242} with Ne^{22} ions and detected an isotope which decays by spontaneous fission. They suggested that this isotope, which has a half-life of 0.3 second, might be 104^{260}. Element 104, as the first transactinide element, is expected to have chemical properties similar to those of hafnium, and hence is expected to form a relatively volatile compound with chlorine (a tetrachloride). These investigators feel that their chemical experiments have shown that the chloride compound of the 0.3 second activity is more volatile than the relatively nonvolatile actinide chlorides (which are trichlorides). However, their chemical evidence was not sufficient to be convincing in the mid-1960's.

There are, of course, many combinations of target nuclei and heavy ion projectiles for the production of still heavier elements; for example, californium (No. 98) and nitrogen ions (No. 7) or americium (No. 95) and neon ions (No.10) might lead to element 105, etc.

There are some reasons for optimism that the production of heavier elements will not be as difficult as a simple extrapolation might suggest. One particularly hopeful sign is the theoretical suggestion that the difficulties are in part due to the fact that a pocket of instability has been encountered in the region of elements 102 and 103, leading to abnormally short half-lives. This theory suggests that this region of instability will begin to "heal" around element 105, leading to heavier isotopes with longer half-lives.

The cause for optimism goes even beyond these prospects. There is reason to believe that there may be regions of extra stability in the very heavy unexplored transuranium region. These would correspond to the so-called closed nucleon (the collective name for protons and neutrons) shells that exist much lower down in the Periodic Table and which give rise to relatively stable nuclei such as those of tin and lead. A particularly exciting possibility is that isotopes with about 126 protons and 184 neutrons, corresponding to predicted stable nucleon shells—that is, isotopes like the one with the atomic number 126 and the mass number 310—will be sufficiently stable to make discovery and identification possible. There may be another similar region of stability around the element with the atomic number 114. The production of such elements will require accelerators capable of making bombardments with ions as heavy as krypton or xenon or even heavier ions.

A very fascinating and quite different method for producing new transuranium isotopes, and perhaps even new transuranium elements, uses the neutrons from nuclear explosions to transmute target materials to heavier and heavier isotopes by means of neutron capture reactions. This brief—of the order of a millionth of a second—but very intense source of neutrons makes it possible to capture successively a very large number of neutrons all in one element, such as uranium. This type of reaction to synthesize

heavy elements occurs in some of the stars.

A possible sequence of nuclear reactions is illustrated in Fig. 5. The starting material, uranium-238, might, in less than a millionth of a second, capture successively as many as thirty-seven neutrons, for example, and produce uranium-275, as shown in the right-hand part of the mass number scale. Then the uranium-275 might undergo fourteen successive beta-particle (electron) emissions, converting its excess neutrons to protons, and as a result might end up as an isotope of the undiscovered element 106. The net result would be the addition of fourteen protons and twenty-three neutrons to the uranium-238. Of course, any of the transuranium elements, when they become available in quantity, or other heavy isotopes, might be used as the target material instead of uranium.

The transuranium elements einsteinium and fermium were discovered as a result of their production by this method of thermonuclear explosions as indicated in the foregoing sections devoted to these elements. The present rather extensive United States program in this field utilizes, and undoubtedly

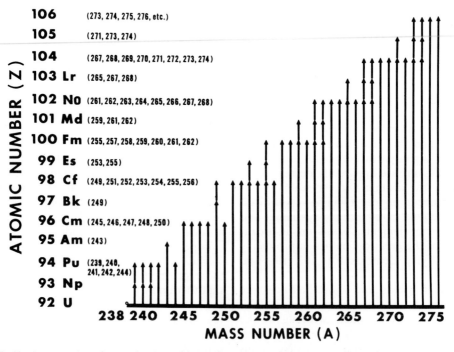

FIG. 5. Nuclear reactions for production of heavy isotopes by intense irradiation of uranium by neutrons furnished by a nuclear explosive. Neutron capture reactions all occur in uranium, to increase the mass number, followed by series of beta particle (electron) decays, to increase the atomic number.

TABLE 13. PREDICTED ELECTRONIC STRUCTURES OF SOME TRANSACTINIDE ELEMENTS

Element	Electronic Structure†	Element	Electronic Structure†
104	$5f^{14}6d^27s^2$	112	$5f^{14}6d^{10}7s^2$
105	$5f^{14}6d^37s^2$	114	$5f^{14}6d^{10}7s^27p^2$
106	$5f^{14}6d^47s^2$	118	$5f^{14}6d^{10}7s^27p^6$
107	$5f^{14}6d^57s^2$	120	$5f^{14}6d^{10}7s^27p^68s^2$
108	$5f^{14}6d^67s^2$	126	$5f^{14}5g^66d^{10}7s^27p^68s^2$

† In addition to the electronic structure of radon (element number 86).

will continue to utilize, underground nuclear explosions.

Table 13 shows predicted electronic structures for some transactinide elements on the basis of their position in Fig. 1. The predictions for elements 120 and 126 are on the basis of suggested points of addition of the inner, 5g type, electrons.

Quantity Production of Isotopes

The U.S. Atomic Energy Commission program for the production of heavy isotopes in quantity was mentioned earlier in this article. The program starts by irradiating plutonium with neutrons and continues on to irradiate the products of the plutonium irradiation, and then the products of that irradiation, and so on. In this way it is possible to proceed up the scale of mass numbers (and eventually atomic numbers) by adding one neutron after another. A required "high neutron flux" reactor, known as the High Flux Isotope Reactor (HFIR), has been built and is operating at the Oak Ridge National Laboratory, which also includes the special facilities required for the chemical isolation of the transuranium products of this reactor.

The AEC program for the larger scale production of heavy transuranium elements uses the HFIR in conjunction with existing facilities. The first step is to irradiate large amounts of plutonium—tens of kilograms— with neutrons in the huge plutonium production reactors at the Savannah River Plant. Several years of this type of neutron irradiation produces intermediate isotopes, such as plutonium-242, americium-243 and curium-244, which are separated and purified. These can then be placed in the HFIR reactor for further neutron irradiation in order to produce the heavier transuranium elements. A special reactor at the Savannah River Plant has also been configured to a very high flux mode of operation (the highest neutron flux ever obtained anywhere) as a further contribution to this effort. Under this program it is planned to produce more than gram amounts of californium and corresponding quantities of other heavy transuranium elements. Fig. 6 shows the nuclear reactions by which plutonium is built up through the successive addition of thermal or slow neutrons. As the isotope plutonium-239 is irradiated, the neutrons are captured one after the other and the mass number builds up, going from left to right. Then, as the number of neutrons becomes large enough there is the emission of a beta particle converting a neutron in the nucleus to a proton, thus transforming the isotope into the element one higher on the atomic number scale. That element, in turn, can capture more neutrons and a product again decays by the emission of electrons until we reach the isotopes high up on the atomic number and mass number scales.

The largest mass number reached by this method of production by the mid-1960's was fermium-257, that is, the element with the atomic number 100 and the isotope with mass number 257. This means that six protons and twelve neutrons had been successfully added to plutonium-239. The heights that can be reached ultimately by this method are apparently quite limited. The reason for this is that the chain of buildup includes nuclei which decay so quickly (chiefly by undergoing spontaneous fission) that it is very difficult to accumulate them in the quantity required to make the successive capture of neutrons

759

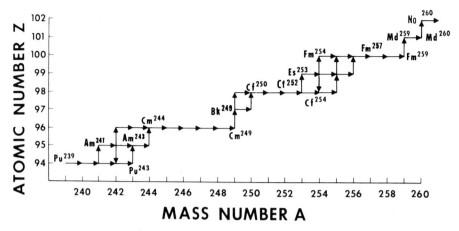

FIG. 6. Nuclear reactions for the production of heavy elements by intense slow neutron irradiation. Neutron capture reactions are interspersed with beta decays. Each neutron capture adds one unit to the mass number (horizontal arrows), and each beta decay increases the atomic number by one unit leaving the mass number unchanged (vertical arrows).

possible—in other words, their quick disappearance effectively blocks the buildup of still heavier nuclei. The isotopes beyond fermium-257 in Fig. 6 represent the predicted course of future additional buildup after these difficulties have been overcome.

Some Practical Applications

Although the research on the transuranium elements has had as its prime objective the increase of knowledge, particularly in the fields of atomic and nuclear structure, a number of practical applications of great importance have resulted.

The enormous practical importance of plutonium in the form of the fissionable isotope plutonium-239 is, of course, well known. This material can be used not only as the explosive ingredient for nuclear weapons, but also as a nuclear fuel to generate electricity to serve the world's needs for centuries to come. The future importance of plutonium-239 as a nuclear fuel arises, of course, from the fact that it can be readily produced from the abundant, but nonfissionable isotope of uranium, uranium-238, thereby unlocking the enormous stores of nuclear energy contained in uranium.

The transuranium isotopes—plutonium-239 and plutonium-241 (produced by the successive absorption of two neutrons by plutonium-239)—which are both fissionable by thermal neutrons, can be used in power-producing reactors. No large-scale reactors fueled exclusively with plutonium are expected to be in operation before about 1970 (due in large part to the difficulty of handling plutonium because of its alpha-radioactivity); rather, natural uranium or enriched uranium (i.e., uranium containing a larger proportion of uranium-235 than the 0.7% present in natural uranium) will continue to be used for some years. Most large power reactors using either natural or slightly enriched uranium produce considerable quantities of plutonium, some of which is utilized in the nuclear reaction as it proceeds. The remainder is available upon chemical separation of the fuel material. As more reactors come into operation, more plutonium will be produced; and as the problems of handling plutonium are solved, it will become feasible to use this increasing supply of plutonium for fueling reactors—first, perhaps, by providing a slight plutonium enrichment to natural uranium.

The really important role of plutonium-239 in peaceful applications lies in the fact that it is a fissionable nuclide that can be produced from uranium-238, an isotope that is not readily fissionable. In any analysis of the world's energy resources, it is evident that gas, oil, and coal are not inexhaustible, but supplies of these are eventually limited. Studies to date indicate that the energy locked in uranium is greater by many powers of ten than that of fossil fuels. This total nuclear energy resource is calculated, however, on the basis of utilization of not only the 0.7% of uranium-235 present, but also on the basis of the inherent energy of the 99.3% of uranium-238 that can be converted into plutonium-239.

The complete utilization of nonfissionable uranium-238 (through conversion to fissionable plutonium-239) can be accomplished through the development of breeder reactors. In essence, these reactors produce more fissionable material than they use in the nuclear reaction. This is possible because a fissioning atom of plutonium-239 emits in excess of two neutrons. In a simplified view, one neutron is required to continue the chain reaction. The remaining neutrons (more than one) theoretically can be captured in uranium-238 to produce more new fissionable material, plutonium-239, than is consumed in the process.

There are also major potential uses of another plutonium isotope, plutonium-238. This isotope, which has an 86-year half-life, and was the first isotope of plutonium to be discovered, may prove to be one of the most valuable assets of mankind. It can be used as a compact source of electricity through the conversion of its heat from radioactive decay by thermoelectric or thermionic devices. Such plutonium-238-fueled power units, one of which is illustrated in Fig. 7, are very compact and light in weight and hence are admirably suited for long-lived power sources in space and terrestrial applications. They can be handled safely and directly by technicians, since very little external radiation is emitted from power units fueled with plutonium-238.

The first space orbiting of such a nuclear battery took place on June 29, 1961. It was still powering equipment that was still sending signals back to earth in 1966. Among the many potential uses of such nuclear batteries in the space program is the plan to have astronauts deliver such a power source to the moon and leave it there to power radio transmission equipment for a year or more after their return to earth. There are also many potential uses of plutonium-238 on earth. One is to power pacemakers for heart patients. Even more exciting is the possibility of using plutonium-238 to power an entirely artificial heart which can be surgically implanted in the patient.

The projected requirements for plutonium-238 in space nuclear batteries over the next decade or two run into tons of material. If the artificial heart application should materialize, the requirements will be substantially greater than this. Fortunately, plutonium-238 is derived from neptunium-237 which is produced as a by-product in the operation of nuclear reactors, including electricity-

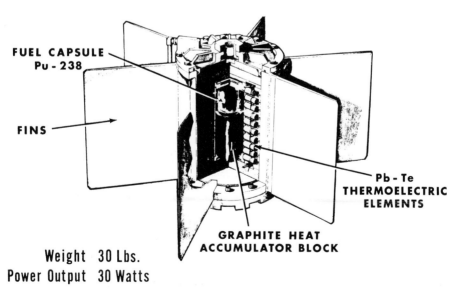

FUEL CAPSULE
Pu - 238

FINS

Pb - Te
THERMOELECTRIC
ELEMENTS

GRAPHITE HEAT
ACCUMULATOR BLOCK

Weight   30 Lbs.
Power Output   30 Watts

FIG. 7. SNAP-19 generator. SNAP stands for Systems for Nuclear Auxiliary Power.

producing nuclear power reactors, according to the reactions shown in Fig. 8; neutron irradiation of the chemically separated neptunium-237 isotope results in its conversion to plutonium-238.

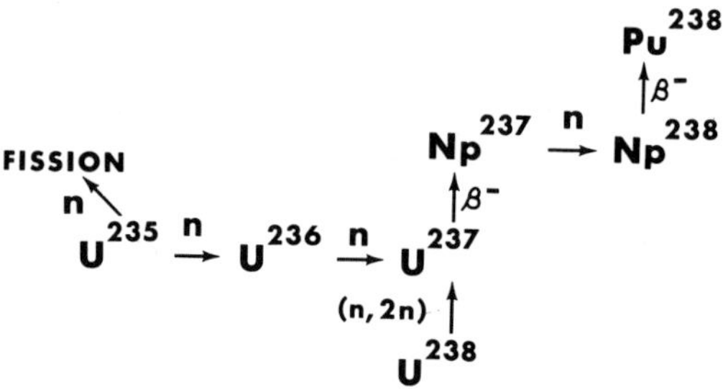

FIG. 8. Production of plutonium-238 from uranium-235 and uranium-238.

The isotope americium-241, which has a half-life of 433 years, has a number of important industrial uses due to its 60 KeV gamma ray. It has a wide range of uses in fluid density gauges, in thickness gauges, in aircraft fuel gauges, in distance sensing devices and a number of other uses.

The possible practical applications of other transuranium isotopes are also very interesting. For example, the isotope curium-244, with a 17.6-year half-life, is produced by neutron irradiation of plutonium in a nuclear reactor as indicated earlier in Fig. 6. This isotope, like plutonium-238, can also be used as a fuel for nuclear batteries. While curium-244 would require greater shielding than plutonium-238 in its applications, it has the advantage that it can be more readily produced in very large quantities, should the assessment of its properties turn out favorably.

Isotope heat sources of these types develop very high temperatures in the process of the conversion of their heat energy into electricity. The energy emission rates are: about one hundred and twenty thermal watts per gram of curium-242, about three thermal watts per gram of curium-244, and about one-half thermal watt per gram of plutonium-238; these emission rates are continuous, diminishing only at the same rate as that of the isotope's radioactive decay.

Another isotope of interest is californium-252, which is produced through successive neutron capture in high-flux nuclear reactors, according to the reactions indicated earlier (Fig. 6). This isotope, due to its high rate of neutron emission, has potential widespread applications as a point neutron source for radiography or as a portable and reliable source for conducting neutron activation analyses in locations on earth and out in space where conventional neutron generators are not possible. It may also have special useful widespread applications for therapy in a number of medical uses.

Impressive as are the uses already found or being considered for the heavier transuranium elements, it is certain that even more noteworthy applications will be found. Although the addition to basic knowledge alone would justify the program of fundamental research on the transuranium elements, there seems little doubt that the practical applications will also in themselves justify a continuing investigation of the transuranium elements.

References

1. Seaborg, Glenn T., "Man-Made Transuranium Elements," Englewood Cliffs, N.J., Prentice-Hall, Inc., 120 pp., 1963.
2. Katz, Joseph J., and Seaborg, Glenn T., "The Chemistry of the Actinide Elements," New York, John Wiley & Sons, Inc., 508 pp., 1957.
3. Seaborg, Glenn T., "The Transuranium Elements," New Haven, Yale University Press, 328 pp., 1958.
4. Seaborg, Glenn T., and Valens, Evans G., "The Elements of the Universe," New York, E. P. Dutton and Co., Inc., 253 pp., 1958.
5. Nouveau Traitè de Chimie Minérale, Series Ed. by Paul Pascal, Vol. XV, Troisième Fascicule "Transuranium," under direction of M. Haissinsky, Masson et Cie, Editeurs Paris, 1962.
6. Coffinberry, A. S., and Miner, W. N., (Eds.), "The Metal Plutonium," Chicago, University of Chicago Press, 446 pp., 1961.
7. Seaborg, G. T., and Katz, J. J., "The Actinide Elements," National Nuclear Energy Series, Div. IV, 14A, New York, McGraw-Hill Book Co., 1949.
8. Seaborg, G. T., Katz, J. J., and Manning, W. M., (Eds.), "The Transuranium Elements: Research Papers," National Nuclear Energy Series, Div. IV, 14B, New York, McGraw-Hill Book Co., 1949.

9. Hyde, Earl K., Perlman, Isadore, and Seaborg, Glenn T., "Nuclear Properties of the Heavy Elements," Vol. I, "Systematics of Nuclear Structure and Radioactivity;" Vol. II, "Detailed Radioactivity Properties," ibid; Earl K. Hyde, Vol. III, "Fission Phenomena," Englewood Cliffs, N. J., Prentice-Hall, Inc., 1964.

10. Wilkinson, W. D., (Ed.), "Extractive and Physical Metallurgy of Plutonium and Its Alloys," New York, Interscience Publishers, 1960.

GLENN T. SEABORG

TUNGSTEN

History

The mineral now called wolframite, an iron-manganese tungstate, was first described about 1574 by Lazarus Ecker. The word wolfram, first applied to this ore, apparently referred to its "wolflike" nature whereby it "devoured" tin and caused low recoveries in the tin smelting operation. (Wolframite inhibits the reduction of tin oxides during smelting.) Another mineral, a calcium tungstate now called scheelite, was originally called tungsten after the Swedish words *tung* (heavy) and *sten* (stone). In 1781 the Swedish chemist C. W. Scheele showed that this ore is composed of lime and a new acid similar to, but distinct from, molybdic acid. At one time wolframite and scheelite were both considered to be ores of tin.

The two Spanish brothers, J. J. and F. de Elhuyar, in about 1783 isolated what was probably the first sample of "metallic" tungsten. They also showed that tungsten is associated with manganese and iron in the mineral wolframite.

Immediate interest in the study of the properties of the new element led to experimentation by the de Elhuyar brothers in 1786 on the use of tungsten to harden steel. A British patent (No. 11848) by R. Oxland for the manufacture of sodium tungstate and tungstic acid marked the first attempt to industrialize tungsten. In 1900 tungsten high-speed tool steel was brought to the attention of the general public by an exhibit of Bethlehem Steel Company at the Paris Exposition of 1900.

By 1909, W. D. Coolidge at General Electric Company had developed a powder metallurgical process to produce ductile tungsten filaments for electric lamps. A new age in the use of tungsten was introduced by the development of cemented tungsten carbides in 1917 to 1923 for use as tool materials.

Although tungsten did not find industrial application until early in the present century, it has since become one of the most important of the industrial less common metals.

Tungsten Minerals

Quantity. Tungsten comprises approximately 0.01% of the earth's crust and ranks as the 26th most plentiful element. World resources of tungsten deposits are estimated to be about 175 million short ton units† of WO_3 with Chinese deposits accounting for three-fourths of this amount. Tungsten is more common in the earth's crust than the other refractory metals (molybdenum, niobium, and tantalum), only slightly less common than nickel and copper, one-half as plentiful as zinc and four times as plentiful as lead.

Mineral Forms. Uncombined tungsten is never found in nature. Except for tungstenite, WS_2, tungsten always occurs as tungsten trioxide combined with oxides of iron, manganese or calcium, and to a limited extent with the oxides of lead and copper. The most important minerals are scheelite and the wolframites.

Scheelite is nearly pure calcium tungstate, $CaWO_4$, with an opaque, waxy appearance. In color the mineral varies from black through pale yellow to white.

The term wolframite applies to a series of ferrous and manganous tungstates ranging from pure $FeWO_4$ to pure $MnWO_4$. Minerals containing less than 20% manganous tungstate are called ferberite, while minerals containing less than 20% iron tungstate are termed hubnerite. The remaining minerals in the series are simply called wolframite.

Two additional tungsten minerals which are of minor commercial importance are tungstite, H_2WO_4, and cuprotungstite, $CuWO_4$.

Raw tungsten ores are generally of low

† A short ton unit is 20 pounds of WO_3.

grade, the tungsten trioxide content rarely being greater than 2% and averaging approximately 0.5%.

World Production of Tungsten Concentrates. During the relatively brief industrial history of tungsten, the world production of its ore concentrates has fluctuated widely in response to changing demand and changing economic conditions. Fig. 1 shows that mineral con-

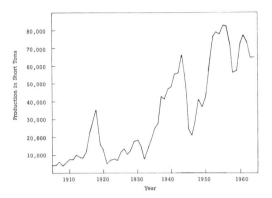

FIG. 1. Estimated world production of tungsten concentrates containing 60% WO3 (short tons).

centrate production has been especially influenced by the increased demand in war time. From 1905 to 1964, estimated world production has fluctuated from 4,025 short tons of 60% WO_3 (1905) to 82,500 short tons (1956).

Geography. It is interesting to note from data presented by Li and Wang[1] that nearly three-fourths of the estimated world resources of tungsten ore occur in China. The remainder of important reserves occur in the United States, the Koreas, Burma, Bolivia, Brazil, Russia, Australia, Malaysia, Portugal, Spain, Thailand, Peru, Argentina and Canada. Other countries with lesser but significant deposits include Mexico, South Africa, Japan, The Congo and Rhodesia.

Extraction Metallurgy

Most tungsten is beneficiated in mills located at or very near the mine site. The objective of most of these mills is to produce for shipment a concentrate containing at least 60% WO_3. Some concentrates are used directly in electric steel furnaces or for reduction to ferrotungsten, but most con-

centrates must undergo chemical purification to produce tungsten end-products.

Decomposition and Purification. Ore concentrates are converted to alkali metal or ammonium tungstate solutions which are further purified before evaporation to crystallize ammonium paratungstate for reduction to metal powder. Scheelite concentrates are digested with HCl to form soluble calcium chloride and insoluble tungstic acid, H_2WO_4, which is then washed and dissolved in NaOH to form Na_2WO_4 or digested at elevated temperature and pressure to produce Na_2WO_4 and $CaCO_3$. Wolframite concentrates may be boiled or pressure digested with 50% caustic, or they may be fused or sintered with sodium or potassium hydroxide or carbonate followed by leaching. After filtration of the soluble tungstates, it is usually necessary to remove such impurities as molybdenum, phosphorus and arsenic.

The ammonium paratungstate (APT) crystals may be reduced directly or they may first be converted to oxide either by simply calcining or by converting to H_2WO_4 and dehydrating.

Reduction to Tungsten Metal

For the production of tungsten powder, the only two large-scale commercial processes are carbon reduction and hydrogen reduction. The purest tungsten powder is produced by hydrogen reduction. Carbon reduction is sometimes performed using carbon or carbonaceous gases to produce a less expensive powder suitable for certain applications. However, only hydrogen-reduced tungsten powder is satisfactory for the production of tungsten wire, rod, sheet and forgings.

Hydrogen Reduction. Starting material for the hydrogen reduction may be tungstic oxide, WO_3; tungstic acid, H_2WO_4; or ammonium paratungstate, $5(NH_4)_2O\cdot12WO_3\cdot11H_2O$. Reduction is usually performed in an electrically heated or gas-fired tube furnace at temperatures up to about 1100°C (2012°F). A typical tube furnace contains several horizontal tubes of $1\frac{1}{2}$ inches to 3 inches inside diameter by 12 to 18 feet long. The tungstic oxide or APT is loaded into boats 12 to 18 inches long made from molybdenum or a nickel-chromium alloy. As a new boat is loaded into the tube furnace at regular intervals another is

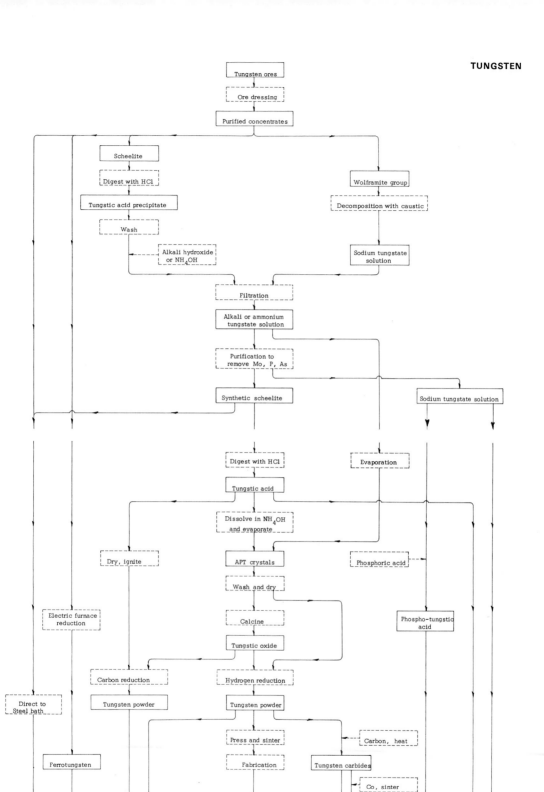

FIG. 2. Composite flow sheet of typical industrial processes to convert tungsten ores to commercial products.

TABLE 1. PHYSICAL PROPERTIES OF TUNGSTEN

Property		Value
Symbol		W
Atomic number		74
Atomic weight		183.85
Electronic configuration		$1s^2$, $2s^2$, $2p^6$, $3s^2$, $3p^6$, $3d^{10}$, $4s^2$, $4p^6$, $4d^{10}$, $4f^{14}$, $5s^2$, $5p^6$, $5d^4$, $6s^2$
Lattice type		Body-centered cubic
Lattice constant, Å		3.1585
Melting point		3410°C (6170°F)
Boiling point		5930°C (10,710°F)
Density, g/cc, at 20°C	(68°F)	19.3
Vapor pressure, torr		
1527°C	(2781°F)	1.93×10^{-15}
2127°C	(3861°F)	7.9×10^{-9}
2727°C	(4941°F)	6.5×10^{-5}
3227°C	(5841°F)	4.68×10^{-3}
Specific heat, cal/g/°C		
−200°C	(−328°F)	0.016
−100°C	(−148°F)	0.026
20°C	(68°F)	0.0321
100°C	(212°F)	0.0325
600°C	(1112°F)	0.035
1000°C	(1832°F)	0.036
Thermal conductivity, cal/cm/sec/°C		
20°C	(68°F)	0.31
927°C	(1700°F)	0.275
1327°C	(2421°F)	0.260
1727°C	(3141°F)	0.245
Coefficient of linear thermal expansion, 1/°C		
27°C	(81°F)	4.6×10^{-6}
1027°C	(1880°F)	5.2×10^{-6}
2100°C	(3812°F)	7.3×10^{-6}
Entropy at 25°C, cal/mole/°C		8
Enthalpy (basis, 0°K) at 25°C, cal/mole		1102
Heat of fusion, cal/g		44
Heat of vaporization, cal/g		1150
Electrical resistivity, microhm-cm		
20°C	(68°F)	5.5
227°C	(440°F)	10.5
727°C	(1340°F)	24.3
1727°C	(3141°F)	55.7
2727°C	(4941°F)	90.4
3227°C	(5841°F)	108.5
Temperature coefficient of resistivity		
0–170°C (32–338°F) (1/°C)		5.1×10^{-3}
Electron emission, milliamperes/cm²		
1000°C	(1832°F)	3.2×10^{-10}
2000°C	(3632°F)	3×10^{-2}
3000°C	(5432°F)	84
Thermionic data		
Apparent electron work function, eV		4.55
Apparent positive ion emission, eV		11.93
Radiation emission coefficient		0.43
1st ionization potential		7.60
Magnetic susceptibility, cgs units		$+ 59 \times 10^{-6}$

TABLE 1—*continued*

Property	Value
Thermal neutron absorption cross section (2200 m/sec), barns	19.2 ± 1.0
Compressibility, per megabar	
at 20°C (68°F)	2.8×10^{-7}
Modulus of elasticity at 20°C (68°F)	
(single crystal), psi	50×10^6—57×10^6
Poisson's ratio	0.17
Minimum interatomic distance, Å	2.734
Spectral emissivity at 4670 Å	
227°C (441°F)	0.498
727°C (1341°F)	0.486
1727°C (3141°F)	0.469
2727°C (4941°F)	0.455
3227°F (5841°F)	0.449
Total radiation intensity, watt/cm²	
400°K	0.00495
800°K	0.173
1400°K	3.82
2000°K	23.65
2600°K	80.6
3200°K	203
Radiation for 5500 Å	
(In % of the radiation of a black body)	48% at 20°C
Reflectivity for 5500 Å	50% at 20°C
Velocity of sound, ft/sec	about 13,000
Natural isotopes	
% Abundance	
180	0.14
182	26.41
183	14.40
184	30.64
186	28.41
Wave length of the characteristic x-ray radiation, Å	
K-series	About 0.21
L-series	About 1.48

removed from the water-cooled discharge end of the tube.

Carbon Reduction. Carbon-reduced tungsten powder is produced for certain non-ferrous alloys and for manufacture of cast tungsten carbide and certain grades of cemented carbides. In one method stoichiometric amounts of low-ash-content lamp black are mixed with the oxide and packed in graphite crucibles for reduction in gas-fired kilns or induction furnaces. Tungsten purities are in the 99.0 to 99.7% range.

Newer Developmental Reduction Methods. Hydrogen reduction of tungsten hexafluoride and hexachloride is under study for several applications including a joining method (vapor deposition bonding), vapor plating, production of semispherical high-purity tungsten powder, and production of ultrafine (250 to 450 Å) tungsten powders. Electrolytic reduction of tungsten has been studied as a possible method for direct treatment of ore concentrates. "Electrowinning" of tungsten is performed in fused salt electolytes at temperatures in the 750 to 1100°C (1382 to 2012°F) range.

Production of Ferrotungsten. Commercial ferrotungsten is generally produced in an electric furnace by carbon reduction of wolframite, ferberite, hubnerite or scheelite separately or in combination. Iron scrap is added in such quantity as to form a ferro-tungsten alloy containing about 70 to 80% tungsten. The ferrotungsten is not tapped from the furnace because of its high melting temperature but is removed as a huge solid button after cooling the furnace. The button is crushed and graded into convenient sizes for addition to steel baths.

Physical Properties

The most notable among the physical properties of tungsten presented in Table 1 are its high melting point, 3410°C (6170°F) (the highest of all metallic elements); high boiling point, 5930°C (10,710°F) and high modulus of elasticity (about 53×10^6 psi). Tungsten's compressibility and vapor pressure are the lowest of all metallic elements. Tungsten has a high density, 19.3 g/cc, a high thermal neutron absorption cross section and excellent electrical conductivity.

Chemical Properties and Compounds

The more notable reactions of tungsten are summarized in Table 2. Behaving very similarly to the other transition elements in Group VIB, tungsten exhibits valences of 0, $+2$, $+3$, $+4$, $+5$, and $+6$. Compounds of the lower oxidation states are relatively unstable and tend to exhibit alkaline properties. The most stable and most common valence state of tungsten compounds is $+6$ and such compounds are acidic.

Metallic tungsten is highly resistant to attack by many liquid metals and is relatively resistant to nonoxidizing mineral acids. Tungsten begins to oxidize in air at about 400°C (752°F) and oxidizes rapidly in oxygen or in air at red heat forming the trioxide, but it may be protected by a hydrogen atmosphere. Fine tungsten powder is pyrophoric.

Tungsten Oxides. There are three well-defined oxides of tungsten:[1] WO_2 (brown), W_2O_5 (blue) and WO_3 (yellow). In addition about nine other oxides have been reported

TABLE 2. REACTIONS OF TUNGSTEN WITH VARIOUS CHEMICAL REAGENTS

Reagent	Reaction
Water	No reaction at room temperature.
Carbon	Carburization above approximately 1200°C (2192°F).
Sulfur	Slow attack when molten or boiling.
HCl (conc.)	Very slow attack at 100°C (212°F).
HF	Only slight attack at 100°C (212°F).
HNO_3 (dilute or conc.)	Nearly stable when cold; forms at most a slight film of oxide which passivates the surface. Hot, dilute HNO_3 corrodes tungsten and forms oxide. Hot, concentrated HNO_3 rapidly oxidizes tungsten powder, slowly dissolves metal.
H_2O_2, 30%	Rapid attack at room temperature.
H_2SO_4 (dilute)	Slight attack at 100°C (212°F).
H_2SO_4 (conc.)	Slight attack at 20°C (68°F); slow reaction when hot.
Aqua regia	Only superficial oxidation to WO_3 at room temperature.
$HF + HNO_3$	Oxidation to WO_3, rapid solution.
NaOH or KOH (aqueous)	None at 20°C (68°F).
NaOH or KOH (molten)	Slow attack, slowly oxidizes in air, rapid solution with oxidizing agents such as KNO_2, KNO_3 $KClO_3$ and PbO_2.
NH_4OH (aqueous)	Practically no reaction at room temperature; attacks compact tungsten and powder in the presence of H_2O_2.
$K_3Fe(CN)_6$ (basic solution)	Tungsten dissolves.
$NaClO_3$ (saturated solution)	Tungsten dissolves.
$NaNO_2$	Tungsten dissolves in sodium nitrite at 300°C (572°F).
Na_2CO_3, K_2CO_3 or mixtures (fused)	Tungsten dissolves slowly. Reaction is hastened by addition of KNO_3.
Boron	Forms borides at elevated temperatures.
Silicon	Forms silicides at elevated temperatures.
H_3PO_4 (viscous, aqueous)	Dissolves tungsten powder at 230°C (446°F).
Chromic acid	No reaction with ductile tungsten even when mixed with H_2SO_4.
NH_4OH solution of a cupric salt	Dissolves tungsten slowly in air.

TABLE 2—*continued*

Reagent	Reaction
Sea water	Corrodes tungsten.
Fusions of KNO_2, KNO_3, $KClO_3$, PbO_2	Dissolves very rapidly.
$CuCl_2$ solution	Corrodes tungsten.
$FeCl_3$ solution	Corrodes tungsten.
Gaseous Reagents	
Air or oxygen	Oxidation begins at 400°C (752°F); rapid at red heat, forms WO_3 which spalls easily.
Ammonia or NH_3–H_2 mixtures	Tungstic nitrides and amides are formed at elevated temperatures with consolidated tungsten and at low temperatures with powder.
Hydrogen	Forms no hydrides.
Water vapor	Oxidation at red heat.
Carbon monoxide	Carburization as low as 800°C (1472°F).
Hydrocarbon gases and gasoline vapor	Carburization as low as 900°C (1652°F).
Nitrogen	No reaction up to 1500°C (2732°F).
Carbon dioxide	Oxidation above 1200°C (2192°F).
Carbon disulfide	Reaction at red heat forms WS_2.
Hydrogen sulfide	Superficial attack at red heat; metal is only coated.
Sulfur dioxide	Slight oxidation at elevated temperatures.
Fluorine	Forms a volatile hexafluoride, WF_6 at 20°C (68°F).
Chlorine	Pure, dry chlorine forms the hexachloride, WCl_6, above 250°C (482°F); if air or moisture is present, oxychlorides or tungstic oxides are formed.
Bromine vapor	Forms pentabromide, WBr_5, at red heat.
Iodine vapor	Forms tetraiodide, WI_4 at red heat; forms diiodide, WI_2, at about 727°C (1340°F).

including W_3O, W_4O_3, WO, W_2O_3, W_5O_9, W_4O_8, W_3O_8, W_4O_{11}, and W_5O_{14}. Most of these are unstable and the existence of W_3O is questionable. The oxidation states of tungsten vary in color from gray through brown and then violet to blue and finally yellow as the oxidation level is increased. Tungstic trioxide, WO_3, is the anhydride of the weak acid, H_2WO_4. When metallic tungsten; tungstic acid, H_2WO_4; the lower oxides or the tungsten carbides are heated in air, WO_3 is formed.

Tungsten Carbides. By heating tungsten and carbon together at about 1500–1600°C (2732–2912°F) it is possible to prepare the tungsten carbides, WC and W_2C. Both carbides have high densities (15.7 and 16.06 g/cc, respectively), high hardnesses (DPH approximately 2000) and high melting points —W_2C melts at approximately 2700°C (4892°F) and WC decomposes at about 2600°C (4712°F). Insoluble in water, the carbides are readily attacked by a mixture of nitric and hydrofluoric acids.

The *tungsten borides* are also dense, hard, crystalline, refractory materials. Silvery, octahedral crystals of the diboride, WB_2, may be formed from tungsten and boron in an electric furnace. This compound is insoluble in water but is attacked by concentrated acids and decomposed by chlorine at 100°C (212°F) or by a fused mixture of Na_2CO_3 and $NaNO_3$. This series is completed by W_2B and WB.

Tungsten Silicides. Another group of hard, refractory tungsten compounds are the silicides, including W_2Si_3, WSi_2, and WSi_3. These insoluble compounds are readily attacked by fused alkalies or a mixture of nitric and hydrofluoric acids.

Tungsten Nitrides. Although tungsten does not ordinarily react directly with nitrogen, it is possible to form WN_2 and W_2N by reaction

769

of tungsten powder with ammonia, and W_2N_3 by reacting dry ammonia with tungsten hexachloride.

Tungsten hexacarbonyl, $W(CO)_6$, may be prepared by reaction of carbon monoxide with tungsten at 275–300°C (527–572°F) and 200 atmospheres or by reduction of WCl_6 with aluminum in anhydrous ether under 100 atm of carbon monoxide at 70°C (158°F). The hexacarbonyl is a nontoxic, volatile, white, crystalline solid which decomposes at about 150°C (302°F).

Tungsten Halides and Oxyhalides. Tungsten halides exist in the +2, +3, +4, +5, and +6 valence states and are characterized by their low boiling points and instability toward both air and moisture.

Tungsten hexachloride, WCl_6, is prepared by heating tungsten to a red heat in the presence of pure, dry chlorine. In the presence of moisture or oxygen, the oxytetrachloride, $WOCl_4$, is formed. Other chlorides and oxychlorides which may be prepared include WCl_2 and WO_2Cl_2.

Other halides and oxyhalides which have been prepared include WBr_6, WBr_5, WBr_2, WO_2Br_2, $WOBr_4$, WI_4, WI_2, WF_6, WOF_4 and WOF_2. Tungsten oxyiodides have not been prepared, however, nor has tungsten hexaiodide. Although neither tungsten trifluoride nor the dioxydifluoride are known as such, they do exist in such complex salts as $KF \cdot WF_3 \cdot H_2O$ and $NH_4F \cdot WO_2F_2 \cdot H_2O$.

The *tungsten sulfides* include the disulfide, WS_2, which occurs in nature as tungstenite, and the trisulfide, WS_3. In addition, there is a series of thiotungstates which correspond to the normal tungstate salts but with one, two, three or all four of the oxygen atoms replaced by sulfur.

The *tungsten phosphides* include W_4P_2, WP, WP_2, and W_3P_4.

Tungstic Acid and Monotungstates. Tungstic acid, H_2WO_4, one of the hydrates of tungstic oxide, WO_3, may be precipitated from a tungstate solution by a hot mineral acid.

The normal tungstates or monotungstates have the general formula $R_2O \cdot WO_3 \cdot xH_2O$. Normal tungstates of the alkali metals can be produced by fusion of WO_3 with the alkali hydroxide or carbonate. Other tungstates may be prepared by fusing together an alkali tungstate and the chloride of the metal.

Paratungstates. In crystalline form the paratungstates are represented by the general formulas $5M_2O \cdot 12WO_3 \cdot xH_2O$ and $3M_2O \cdot 7WO_3 \cdot xH_2O$. Generally, they are crystallized from slightly acid solutions. The most commercially important salt in the series, ammonium paratungstate, $5(NH_4)_2O \cdot 12WO_3 \cdot 11H_2O$, is obtained by reacting tungstic acid and ammonia or by concentrating an ammoniacal solution of ammonium monotungstate. Heating in air removes ammonia from the dry salt at about 60°C (140°F), and waters of hydration are driven off at about 100°C (212°F). Heating the salt in hydrogen reduces it to metallic tungsten.

Physical Metallurgy

Consolidation. Tungsten is usually consolidated by powder metallurgy techniques including mechanical or hydrostatic pressing followed by sintering. In the preparation of rod blanks for drawing into tungsten wire, tungsten powder is mechanically pressed in steel dies at 20,000 to 70,000 psi, presintered at about 1200°C in hydrogen to strengthen the fragile compact, and finally, sintered in hydrogen, the heat being supplied by direct resistance of current through the compact. Larger parts, such as forging billets, are compacted isostatically in vacuum-sealed elastic molds at fluid pressures of 20,000 to 40,000 psi and sintered by indirect heating in hydrogen at 1600 to 2500°C depending on powder characteristics.

Tungsten is sometimes consolidated by vacuum arc casting, and electron beam melting has been demonstrated, but these seldom used methods are expensive and lead to large as-cast grains which cause a problem during forming. Tungsten alloys of 2% and 15% molybdenum for rocket propulsion applications have both been centrifically cast extensively in a vacuum arc-skull melting and casting apparatus.

Hot pressing has been applied to tungsten. A newer technique is gas pressure bonding, a high-temperature isostatic hot pressing of powder in an evacuated molybdenum sheet metal "can."

Complex shapes of tungsten have been prepared by the ceramic process of slip casting followed by sintering. Tungsten coatings are often applied to substrates in the aerospace industry by plasma arc spraying of tungsten powder or wire. Tungsten coatings may also be applied by vapor plating in which WF_6 is reduced by hydrogen above 300°C (572°F). Another vapor plating technique involves the pyrolysis of tungsten hexacarbonyl.

Forming and Fabrication. Tungsten can be hot worked below its recrystallization temperature by all of the conventional forming operations. Heating is usually performed in hydrogen.

Machining of tungsten, while difficult, may be improved by heating the work piece to about 300°C (572°F). Tungsten can be cut relatively well with an abrasive grinding wheel and can be machined fairly well by grinding.

Welding of tungsten is exceedingly difficult and, at best, leads to brittle welds. Brazing is possible with adequate precautions.

Mechanical and Metallurgical Properties. The high strength and hardness of tungsten are notable both at room temperature and at elevated temperatures. At very high temperatures the strength-to-density ratio of tungsten, in spite of its high density, is one of the highest (if not the highest) of all metallic elements. The tensile properties vary over a wide range depending upon purity and fabrication history.[5] Tungsten exhibits a classical, sharp brittle-to-ductile transition behavior wit increasing temperature. The recrystallization temperature for tungsten, which may vary from 800 to 1550°C (1472 to 2822°F), depends upon several factors and is markedly reduced by metallurgical cold work.

Production of Tungsten Carbides

Tungsten carbide, WC, powder is usually produced by heating a mixture of tungsten powder and finely divided lamp black in hydrogen at about 1500°C (2732°F). The carbide is ball milled with 5 to 30% of binder (usually cobalt), pressed at 10 to 30 tons/sq inch, preheated in hydrogen at about 900°C (1972°F), machined to final shape and packed in carbon black for the final sinter at 1300 to 1450°C (2372 to 2642°F).

Cast carbides are produced by melting at 3000–3200°C (5432–5792°F) a mixture of carbon-reduced tungsten powder and the requisite amount of carbonaceous material.

Commercial Applications for Tungsten Products

The largest consumption of tungsten (about 40%) is in tungsten carbide tools and dies. Based on recent data, steel manufacturers use about one-fourth of the national tungsten production as an alloying addition. About one-fifth of the tungsten concentrate production is consumed in tungsten metal products including wire, rod, sheet and other forms of pure, "doped" and alloyed tungsten. Nonferrous alloys account for one-eighth of our tungsten consumption and include a wide range of cutting and wear resistant alloys (such as the "Stellite" alloys), high-density alloys and high-temperature alloys. Finally, the consumption of tungsten in chemical forms requires only about 1.5% of total tungsten concentrate production.

Applications of Unalloyed Tungsten. The major advantage of tungsten is its extremely high melting point; yet the usefulness of tungsten at high temperatures is severely limited by its catastrophic oxidation behavior at elevated temperatures in air or other oxidizing atmospheres. Protective coatings, many of which involve silicides, are being developed.

The most common types of commercial application of unalloyed tungsten are electric lamp filaments, electrical contacts, and electrodes for various arc-welding processes. Tungsten is used for targets in x-ray machines, for emitters in electronic tubes and for heating elements in high-temperature furnaces. Recently the use of tungsten wire heating elements for vacuum metallizing equipment has become a major source of tungsten consumption.

Wrought tungsten products are finding use in aerospace applications for which high strength is required at extreme temperatures. Forged, spun or formed and welded tungsten is used in rocket nozzles, and porous tungsten is used in experimental ion rocket propulsion engines.

Applications of Tungsten Alloys and Composites. "Heavy metal" alloys, containing upwards of 90% tungsten with nickel and usually copper or iron additions, are machineable, moderately ductile alloys produced by powder metallurgy techniques for use as counter-weights and in other applications requiring high-density materials.

Tungsten-silver and tungsten-copper composites are prepared by powder metallurgy methods and are used as electrical contacts and switches.

Tungsten-molybdenum alloys are centrifugally vacuum arc cast into aerospace components.

Tungsten as an Alloying Addition. Next to carbides the most extensive application of tungsten is in various types of steels and cast irons. Among the benefits imparted to steels by tungsten are increased hardness, improved high-temperature performance and improved corrosion resistance. Li and Wang[1] list over 300 domestic, commercial ferrous tungsten alloys with wide ranging percentages of tungsten additions. Tungsten exists in steel mainly as carbide.

Tungsten is also an important component in several common nonferrous alloys including the "Stellite" alloys of cobalt, chromium and tungsten, which are noted for their hardness and abrasion resistance, and the nickel-base alloys which have good resistance to corrosion and erosion as well as high strength at elevated temperatures. Tungsten is also one of the most important alloying additions to tantalum and columbium and significantly improves their high-temperature strength.

Applications of tungsten carbide account for the largest consumption of tungsten. Because they are extremely hard at both ordinary and elevated temperatures, tungsten carbide and mixed carbides make excellent cutting materials and have replaced some of the usage of tungsten alloys and high-speed steel in the tool-and-die industry. A major and rapidly growing application of cemented tungsten carbide in the United States is in studs used to increase the traction of tires; this use is about 20% of the total consumption of tungsten carbide. Cemented carbides are also used in wear-resistant parts and in dies for drawing wire or tubing. Militarily they have been used in armor-piercing bullets. Hard-facing applications of cast carbides for wear resistance include deep-well drilling tools. Fused carbides are also cast into such abrasion resisting parts as sandblasting nozzles and cutting tools.

Applications of Various Tungsten Compounds. Calcium and magnesium tungstates are phosphorescent materials used in fluorescent lighting. Other commercially significant tungsten compounds include tungsten hexacarbonyl and tungsten hexafluoride, both used for vapor plating. Tungsten disulfide, WS_2, has been considered as a replacement for MoS_2 as a high-temperature lubricant. Certain tungsten compounds are important as catalysts for several important chemical processes including hydration reactions in the oil industry. Tungsten disulfide is used as a catalyst for the hydration of coal.

Tungsten compounds are used in paints and pigments. Tungsten trioxide is used for pigmentation in oil and water colors. Tungsten bronzes (reduction products of alkali and alkaline earth tungstates) are used in paints. Lead tungstates are sometimes substituted for white lead in paints, and phosphotungstic acid is used as a mordant in pigments.

References

1. Li, K. C., and Wang, C. Y., "Tungsten," 3rd Ed., New York, Reinhold Publishing Corp., 1955.
2. Hampel, Clifford A., "Rare Metals Handbook," 2nd Ed., New York, Reinhold Publishing Corp., 1961.
3. Smithells, Colin J., "Tungsten," 1st American Ed., New York, Chemical Publishing Co., 1953.
4. Agte, C., and Vacek, J., "Tungsten and Molybdenum," Washington, NASA, Office of Scientific and Technical Information, 1963, Translation of "Wolfram a Molybden," Prague, State Publishing House of Technical Literature, 1954.
5. Schmidt, F. F., and Ogden, H. R., "The Engineering Properties of Tungsten and Tungsten Alloys," Columbus, Defense Metals Information Center, Battelle Memorial Institute, 1963.
6. Kieffer, R. A., and Benesovsky, F., "Hartmetalle," Vienna, Springer-Verlag, 1965.
7. Mellor, J. W., "A Comprehensive Treatise on Inorganic and Theoretical Chemistry," New York, Longmans, Green and Co., Vol. XI, p. 673, 1931.
8. Thieler, E., "Ullmanns Encyklopaide der Technischen Chemie," 3rd Ed., Munich, Urban & Schwarzenberg, 1967.

BERNARD E. DAVIS

U

URANIUM

In 1789, the German chemist M. S. Klaproth discovered a new element in pitchblende ores which he named uranium in honor of the planet Uranus, which had been discovered just eight years previously. The French scientist Henri Becquerel discovered the radioactive property of uranium in 1896.

Uranium has the atomic number 92 and is the heaviest naturally occurring element. Its three natural isotopes are U^{238}, U^{235} and U^{234} which comprise 99.28, 0.71 and 0.0054 weight % of the element, respectively. Uranium is now known to be the third member of the rare earth-like transition series (the actinide series), in which the inner $5f$ electron shell is being filled. The gaseous atom has the electronic structure of radon (atomic number 86) plus three $5f$, one $6d$ and two $7s$ electrons.

History

Enrico Fermi and his coworkers observed in 1934 that the bombardment of uranium by neutrons produced beta radioactivity, although the full significance of this observation was not understood at the time. Late in 1938, Otto Hahn and Fritz Strassmann showed that when uranium was bombarded by thermal neutrons it fissioned into radioactive isotopes of lighter elements, such as krypton and barium, and that part of the binding energy holding the component protons and neutrons together in the heavy uranium nucleus was released.

In 1939, at a conference in the United States, Fermi suggested that when uranium nuclei are split under neutron bombardment, other neutrons might also be released in sufficient numbers to cause a continuous, self-sustaining fission reaction.

The existence of these fission neutrons was confirmed in 1939 in studies by F. Joliot, Leo Szilard, H. L. Anderson and their coworkers. Later investigations disclosed that during each occurrence of the fissioning process an average of 2-1/2 such neutrons are released. Further study proved that it is the comparatively rare U^{235} isotope that is split in the fissioning process, and still further investigation showed that neutron irradiation transmutes U^{238} into the synthetic element plutonium, which is fissionable by thermal neutrons, as is U^{235}.

The first self-sustaining nuclear chain reaction was achieved by Fermi and a team of scientists in a pile of 400 tons of graphite, six tons of uranium metal and 58 tons of uranium oxide underneath the stands of Stagg Field at the University of Chicago, on December 2, 1942. Methods of controlling the rate of fission on a large scale then were developed and the first wartime and peaceful application of nuclear energy followed.

The first test of a nuclear explosive device occurred at Alamogordo, New Mexico, on July 16, 1945, and the first nuclear weapon was used in warfare August 6, 1945, on Hiroshima. Nuclear power for propulsion was used for the first time in 1955 in the submarine U.S.S. Nautilus.

Production and distribution of radioisotopes began under the Manhattan Engineer District, wartime predecessor of the Atomic Energy Commission, as one of the earliest peaceful applications of nuclear energy. Other programs followed. On December 20, 1951, heat from an experimental reactor produced electrical power to light four bulbs at the AEC's National Reactor Testing

773

Station in Idaho—the first practical demonstration of electrical generation from nuclear power. The world's first full-scale nuclear powered electrical generating station began operation at Shippingport, Pennsylvania, on December 2, 1957. By the mid-1960's approximately 50% of the AEC's annual operating budget was devoted to a wide variety of peaceful applications of the atom.

Occurrence

Uranium is found to some extent in the majority of rocks and sediments making up the earth's crust. The concentration appears to vary from about 0.2 to 10 ppm in most igneous rocks, running somewhat higher in rocks enriched in sodium, potassium and silicon. At an average abundance of 4 ppm there would be about 10^{13} to 10^{14} tons of uranium in the upper 20 kilometers of the earth's crust.

Uranium is considerably less abundant in concentrated deposits. The black unoxidized deposits containing pitchblende (uraninite), an oxide intermediate between UO_2 and U_3O_8 in composition, are by far the most important and common of the different types of uranium deposits known today. The bulk of these ores occurs in sandstones and conglomerates; however, significant reserves have also been found in vein deposits. Coffinite, a hydrous uranium silicate, is also usually associated with these deposits. The yellow oxidized uranium deposits are of less importance. The most common of these are the deposits of carnotite, a potassium uranium vanadate, which are abundant in the Colorado Plateau region of the United States. Many other types of uranium ores have been found, but they are relatively less important. Table 1 presents a selected list of some of the uranium minerals.

Since the advent of the discovery of the release of nuclear energy from uranium, many countries have carried on extensive exploration of this valuable substance. Until the early 1950's the largest known sources of uranium were in the pitchblende deposits of the Congo (Leopoldville) and the Great Bear Lake area in Canada and the carnotite-type deposits of the Colorado Plateau. These sources, however, were overshadowed by the development in the mid-1950's of much larger reserves of pitchblende and coffinite ores in the United States, Canada and South Africa. Other important deposits are now also known to exist in France and the USSR. Less extensive reserves have been found in Australia and in various countries of Asia, Africa, South America and Europe.

Major reasonably assured resources of uranium, economically recoverable at prices less than $10 per pound U_3O_8, were estimated in the mid-1960's to be approximately 210,000 tons in Canada; 200,000 tons in the United States; 180,000 tons in the Republic of South Africa; 40,000 tons in France; and approximately 60,000 tons among other non-Communist nations. Important deposits were also believed to exist in the Communist countries. The Blind River area of Ontario has over 90% of Canada's resource, the remainder being mostly in Northern Saskatchewan. The United States resources at this price in the mid-1960's consisted of 175,000 tons U_3O_8 in conventional sandstone impregnation deposits and veins and 20,000 tons recoverable as a by-product of processing phosphate rock for triple superphosphate. The conventional reserves were distributed as follows: New Mexico, 88,000 tons; Wyoming, 62,000 tons; Colorado, 11,700 tons; Utah, 5,500 tons; and all other states combined, 7,800 tons. The United States was the largest producer of uranium in the Western World during the period 1955-1965; Canada and the Republic of South Africa were also important producers of uranium during this period.

A large amount of uranium ore must be processed to extract a small amount of uranium since the average ore contains only from about 2 to 5 pounds of U_3O_8 per ton. First the ore is crushed and finely ground and then leached with either acid or alkali. The uranium is finally recovered from the pregnant leach liquors by various precipitation, solvent extraction, or ion exchange procedures. The uranium, a concentrate resulting from this treatment in the ore processing mill, generally contains at least 75% U_3O_8. The further purification steps generally involve the dissolution of the concentrate in nitric acid to yield a solution of uranyl nitrate. The uranyl nitrate can then be separated from impurities by solvent extraction employing, for example,

TABLE 1. SELECTED URANIUM MINERALS

Name	Chemical Composition	% Uranium	Color	Typical Occurrence
Uraninite	UO_2	45–85	Black, gray	The Congo, Africa
Pitchblende (variety of uraninite)	$UO_{2.2}–UO_{2.67}$	45–85	Black	Western USA
Euxenite	$(Y,Ca,Ce,U,Th)(Nb,Ta,Ti)_2O_6$	0.6–9	Black	Bear Valley, Idaho
Brannerite	$(U,Ca,Fe,Y,Th)_3(Ti,Si)_5O_{16}$	27–43	Black to brown	Blind River, Canada
Francevillite	$(Ba,Pb)O(2UO_3)V_2O_5 \cdot 5H_2O$	17–55	Yellow, gold, orange	Mounana, Gabon
Ningyoite	$U_{1-x}Ca_{1-x}R.E._{-2x}(PO_4)_2 \cdot 1–2H_2O$ [x = 0.1–0.2]	23	Brownish green, brown	Ningyo Pass, Japan
Davidite	$(Fe,Ce,U)(Ti,Fe,V,Cr)_3(O,OH)_7$	4	Black	Radium Hill, South Australia
Carnotite	$K_2(UO_2)_2(VO_4)_2 \cdot nH_2O$ [n = 1–3]	52–55	Yellow	Colorado Plateau
Autunite	$Ca(UO_2)_2(PO_4)_2 \cdot nH_2O$ [n = 10–12]	45–48	Yellow	Autun, France
Tyuyamunite (metatyuyamunite)	$Ca(UO_2)_2(VO_4)_2 \cdot nH_2O$ [n = 3–8.5]	50–56	Yellow	Ferghana, Turkestan
Uranophane	$Ca(UO_2)_2(SiO_3)_2(OH)_2 \cdot 5H_2O$	55	Yellow, green	The Congo, Africa
Torbernite (metatorbernite)	$Cu(UO_2)_2(PO_4)_2 \cdot nH_2O$ [n = 4–12]	47–50	Green	Erzgebirge, Saxony and Bohemia
Coffinite	$U(SiO_4)_{1-x}(OH)_{4x}$	60	Black	Colorado Plateau
Thucholite (asphaltite)	Uranium oxide and hydrocarbons	Variable	Black	Colorado Plateau

tributyl phosphate as the active extractant.

Deposits of phosphate rock and carbonaceous shales, containing low concentrations (50–150 ppm) but overall very large quantities of uranium, may become important sources of uranium as high-grade resources dwindle. Limited quantities of uranium can be obtained economically as a by-product of processing phosphate rock to make chemical fertilizers. Uranium can be recovered from shale only at several times the costs prevailing in the mid-1960's.

The uranium content of sea water is about 3 parts per 1,000,000,000. Living matter contains uranium in varying amounts—from 10^{-4} to 10^{-9} % by weight. The biological significance of uranium is still not clear. Sulfate-reducing microbes may have contributed to the formation of certain uranium ore deposits. In ancient times, these bacteria generated hydrogen sulfide while feeding on plant matter buried in river channels. This gas is a very effective reductant and precipitant, and may have been responsible for the deposition of uranium as well as other metals such as copper, iron, and vanadium in sedimentary rocks.

Isotopes

Natural uranium consists of three isotopes: U^{238}, U^{235}, and U^{234} as shown in Table 2. The chemical atomic weight is thus largely determined by the U^{238} and is 238.03 on the scale where $C^{12} = 12.0000$.

Recent studies have shown that the weight % of U^{235} in natural uranium may vary by as much as 0.1% depending on the source of the sample. In 1963 an official announcement of the U.S. Atomic Energy Commission declared that no single value carried to four places can be established as truly representing the U^{235} content of natural uranium. The official value for purposes of that agency was set at 0.711 weight % U^{235}.

The nominal value given in Table 2 for the U^{234} content of natural uranium is the equilibrium value calculated from the ratio of the U^{238} and U^{234} half-lives. The U^{234} content of natural uranium shows some variations from this equilibrium value depending on the geological origin and past history of the sample. However, the specific activity of natural uranium is not significantly changed by these slight variations in U^{234}.

All of these isotopes have unstable nuclei, and U^{238} and U^{235} are the parents of rather complicated decay chains which give rise to natural alpha and beta radioactivities. The isotope U^{238} is the parent of the natural uranium $(4n + 2)$ radioactive series; the isotope U^{234} is also a member of this series, and thus these two are linked by radioactive decay. The isotope U^{235} is of other origin and is the parent of the actinium $(4n + 3)$ radioactive series. Both series eventually decay into stable lead isotopes, but the U^{238} chain passes through Ra^{226}, the normal radium of commerce which was and still is very valuable for certain therapeutic uses. Since the half-life relationships of all of the members of the chains are known, and further since the half-lives of the U^{238} and U^{235} parents $(4.51 \times 10^9$ and 7.13×10^8 years, respectively), are known to be comparable

TABLE 2. COMPOSITION OF NATURAL URANIUM (NOMINAL VALUE)

Isotope	Abundance (atom %)	Abundance (weight %)
234	0.0055	0.0054
235	0.7204	0.7110
238	99.2741	99.2830

Atom ratio U^{238}/U^{234}	=	18,180
Atom ratio U^{238}/U^{235}	=	137.80
Specific activity	=	1501 dis/min/mg total uranium
Contribution of U^{235}	=	33.7 dis/min/mg total uranium
Contribution of U^{238}	=	733.6 dis/min/mg total uranium
Contribution of U^{234}	=	733.6 dis/min/mg total uranium

TABLE 3. ISOTOPES OF URANIUM

Isotope	Half-life	Mode of Disintegration†	Source
U^{227}	1.3 m	$\alpha(6.8)$	$Th^{232}(\alpha,9n)$
U^{228}	9.3 m	$\alpha(80\%)$ (6.67)	$Th^{232}(\alpha,8n)$
		E.C. (20%)	
U^{229}	58 m	E.C. (80%)	$Th^{232}(\alpha,7n)$
		$\alpha(20\%)$ (6.42)	
U^{230}	20.8 d	$\alpha(5.884, 5.813, 5.658)$	$Pa^{231}(d,3n)$
U^{231}	4.2 d	E.C. (>99%)	$Pa^{231}(d,2n)$
		$\alpha(6 \times 10^{-3}\%)$ (5.45)	
U^{232}	73.6 y	$\alpha(5.318, 5.261, 5.134)$	$Th^{232}(\alpha,4n)$
U^{233}	1.62×10^5 y	$\alpha(4.816, 4.773, 4.717, 4.655, 4.582, 4.489)$	Pa^{233} decay
$U^{234}(U_{II})$	2.48×10^5 y	$\alpha(4.77, 4.72)$	Natural
$U^{235}(AcU)$	7.13×10^8 y	$\alpha(4.58, 4.47, 4.40, 4.20)$	Natural
U^{236}	2.39×10^7 y	$\alpha(4.50)$	$U^{235}(n,\gamma)$
U^{237}	6.75 d	$\beta^-(0.249, 0.084)$	$U^{238}(n,2n)$
$U^{238}U_I$	4.51×10^9 y	$\alpha(4.18)$	Natural
U^{239}	23.5 m	$\beta^-(1.22)$	$U^{238}(n,\gamma)$
U^{240}	14.1 h	$\beta^-(0.36)$	$U^{239}(n,\gamma)$

†Energy of radiation in million electron volts; E.C. = electron capture

TABLE 4. CRYSTAL STRUCTURES OF THE VARIOUS URANIUM PHASES

Phase	Region of Stability	Symmetry Class	Lattice Parameters, Å			Space Group	Density, g/cc
			a_o	b_o	c_o		
α†	R.T.–667°C	Orthorhombic	2.8541	5.8692	4.9563	Cmcm	18.97
β‡	667–772°C	Tetragonal	10.759		5.656	P4/mnm	18.11
γ§	772–1132°C	Body-centered cubic	3.525				18.06

† The parameters given here are for 25°C.
‡ Parameters are for temperature of 720°C.
§ Parameters are for temperature of 805°C.

to the age of the earth, the ratios of various uranium and lead isotopes have been used to date the age of formation of the oldest minerals and, in turn, the age of the earth itself.

In addition to the three natural radioactive isotopes, there are a number of other artificial radioactive isotopes of uranium. The known isotopes and their radioactive decay information are listed in Table 3.

Uranium Metal

Metallic uranium initially prepared is a lustrous, silvery metal which melts at 1132°C and boils at about 3818°C. It can be prepared by reduction of the halides by alkali and alkaline earth metals or by reduction of

various oxides, UO_3, U_3O_8, UO_2, by carbon, aluminum, or calcium at high temperature. Electrolysis of uranium compounds in molten salt baths of alkali halides also gives good results.

The metal crystallizes in the orthorhombic form stable at room temperature but undergoes two transitions at 667°C and 772°C, respectively, on heating as shown in Table 4. The calculated density of alpha-uranium (the room temperature form) from x-ray data is 18.97. Some additional physical and thermal properties of uranium metal are given in Table 5.

It is a malleable, ductile metal, slightly paramagnetic, and highly reactive chemically; initially lustrous metallic pieces eventually

TABLE 5. PHYSICAL AND THERMAL PROPERTIES OF URANIUM METAL

Property	Value
Melting point	$1132.3 \pm 0.8°C$
Vapor pressure,	$\log P \text{ mm} =$
1630–1970°K	$-\dfrac{2330}{T} + 8.583$
Boiling point	3818°C
Density, 25°C	18.97 g/cc
Transformation points	
$\alpha \rightarrow \beta$	667°C
$\beta \rightarrow \gamma$	772°C
Heat of fusion	4.7 kcal/mole
Heat of vaporization	106.7 kcal/mole
Heat of sublimation, 0°K	116.6 kcal/mole
Enthalpy, 25°C	1521.4 cal/mole
Heat capacity, 25°C	6.612 cal/°C/mole
Entropy, 25°C	11.99 ± 0.02 cal/°C/mole
Thermal conductivity, 70°C	0.071 cal/cm/sec/°C
Electrical conductivity	$2–4 \times 10^4$ (ohm-cm)$^{-1}$

TABLE 6. CHEMICAL REACTIONS OF URANIUM METAL

Reactant	Reaction Temperature†, °C	Products
H_2	250	α^- and $\beta-UH_3$
C	1800–2400	UC; U_2C_3; UC_2
N_2	700	UN; UN_2
P	1000‡	U_3P_4
O_2	150–350	UO_2; U_3O_8
S	500	US_2
F_2	250	UF_6
Cl_2	500	UCl_4; UCl_5; UCl_6
Br_2	650	UBr_4
I_2	350	UI_3; UI_4
H_2O	100	UO_2
HF (g)	350‡	UF_4
HCl (g)	300‡	UCl_3
NH_3	700	$UN_{1.75}$
H_2S	500‡	US; U_2S_3; US_2
NO	400	U_3O_8
N_2O_4	25	$UO_2(NO_3)_2 \cdot 2NO_2$
CH_4	635–900‡	UC
CO	750	$UO_2 + UC$
CO_2	750	$UO_2 + UC$

† Reaction temperature with massive metal.
‡ Reaction temperature with powdered uranium (formed by decomposition of UH_3).

become coated with a dull black oxide coating. Pyrophoric metal can be prepared, and even massive metal will combine directly with oxygen, the halogens, and gaseous hydrogen, nitrogen, carbon monoxide, and carbon dioxide. It is not attacked by alkalies but reacts directly with water and dissolves readily in acids to give compounds of uranium (III) and uranium (IV). The chemical reactions of uranium metal are given in Table 6.

It has not been possible to assign an unambiguous radius to uranium in the metallic state. The abnormalities of the uranium structure are reflected in various properties such as abnormally high electrical resistivity ($32–76 \times 10^{-6}$ ohm-cm) of the metal at room temperature.

Chemical Properties

Uranium Ions. Uranium ions representing four different oxidation states have been prepared in aqueous solutions: U^{+3} (red), U^{+4} (green), UO_2^+ (unstable), and UO_2^{++} (yellow). The oxidation-reduction potential of uranium ions in acid solution on the scale $1/2H_2 \longrightarrow H^+$ equals zero is indicated below:

$$U \xrightarrow{+1.80 \text{ v}} U^{+3} \xrightarrow{+0.631 \text{ v}}$$

$$U^{+4} \xrightarrow{-0.58 \text{ v}} UO_2^+ \xrightarrow{-0.063 \text{ v}} UO_2^{+2}.$$
$$\underset{-0.32 \text{ v}}{\underline{\hspace{3cm}}}$$

Uranium also exhibits a formal oxidation number of uranium (II) in a few solid, semi-metallic compounds such as UO and US. No simple ions of oxidation state uranium (II) are known in solution.

The U^{+3} ion is highly unstable, since it will liberate hydrogen from water, and UO_2^+, representing uranium (V), disproportionates with the production of U^{+4} and UO_2^{++}. Although definitely unstable, millimolar solutions of uranium (V) do appear to form complexes with the inorganic ions, chloride, sulfate, carbonate, etc., and with numerous organic chelating agents.

Since the uranium (IV) and uranium (VI)

TABLE 7. COMPLEX CONSTANTS FOR URANIUM (IV) COMPLEX FORMATION WITH CHLORIDE, SULFATE, AND THIOCYANATE ($\mu = 2.0$)

Reaction	Constants		
	10°C	25°C	40°C
$U^{+4} + Cl^- \rightarrow UCl^{+3}$	3.3	1.21	0.91
$U^{+4} + 2Cl^- \rightarrow UCl_2^{+2}$	—	1.14	0.80
$U^{+4} + SCN^- \rightarrow USCN^{+3}$	60	31	20
$U^{+4} + 2SCN^- \rightarrow U(SCN)_2^{+2}$	2.0×10^2	1.3×10^2	95
$U^{+4} + HSO_4^- \rightarrow USO_4^{+2} + H^+$	4.3×10^2	3.3×10^2	2.4×10^2
$U^{+4} + 2HSO_4^- \rightarrow U(SO_4)_2 + 2H^+$	9.3×10^3	7.4×10^3	5.7×10^3

compounds represent the most important oxidation states, the chemistry of uranium may be related to the two corresponding oxides, UO_2 and UO_3. The former dissolves in acid solutions to form U^{+4} solutions and also gives rise to solid salts of the type UCl_4 and $U(SO_4)_2 \cdot 9H_2O$. The UO_2^{++} ion in acid solution leads to uranyl derivatives of the type $UO_2(NO_3)_2 \cdot 6H_2O$ and UO_2Cl_2. Closely related are the basic derivatives of the trioxide, the uranates, and the polyuranates. Alkali metal diuranates, $M_2U_2O_7$, are well known, and the simple uranates such as Na_2UO_4 have also been prepared.

No trivalent uranium compounds can be precipitated from aqueous uranium (III) solutions because of the very rapid oxidation to uranium (IV). The common water-soluble salts of uranium (IV) are the chloride, bromide, sulfate, and perchlorate; all of these solutions are hydrolyzed. Chloride and bromide ions form weak complexes in dilute

solutions; sulfate ion complexes U^{+4} more strongly. Some of the complex constants are shown in Table 7.

The main adsorption bands of uranium (IV) solutions are at 650 mμ, 550 mμ, 495 mμ, and 430 mμ. A number of different types of experiments indicate that in one molar acid the uranium (IV) ion is essentially U^{+4} (in the absence of complexing agents). Uranium (IV) oxalate, phosphate, fluoride, molybdate, arsenate, ferricyanide, and hydroxide are insoluble in nearly neutral solutions.

The interesting oxygenated cations MO_2^{++} and MO_2^+ are almost unique to the actinide elements. The uranyl ion, UO_2^{++}, behaves in many respects as a simple doubly charged ion and in many respects resembles Ca^{++}. There also appears to be evidence that more complicated polymeric species of this ion, such as $U_2O_5^{++}$, $U_3O_8^{++}$, etc., are formed in concentrated uranyl solutions as a result of hydrolytic phenomena.

TABLE 8. DISTRIBUTION OF URANYL NITRATE BETWEEN WATER AND VARIOUS ORGANIC SOLVENTS AT 25°C.

Organic Solvent	Distribution Coefficient (Organic/Aqueous†) in Terms of Molalities for	
	0.2 molal Uranyl Nitrate	1.0 molal Uranyl Nitrate
Diethyl ether‡	0.003	0.14
Dibutyl cellosolve	<0.001	0.026
Dibutyl carbitol	0.01	0.32
Pentaether	0.12	1.0
Methyl isobutyl ketone	<0.004	0.16
Cyclohexanone	0.17	0.9
Isoamyl alcohol	0.004	0.15
Tributyl phosphate	5.5	1.8

† Aqueous phase at equilibrium.
‡ At 18°C.

An interesting property of uranyl nitrate solutions known since the mid-19th Century is the extractability with diethyl ether; uranyl nitrate hydrates are markedly soluble in ether. The distribution of uranyl nitrate between water and diethyl ether and other organic solvents is shown in Table 8.

The addition of hydroxide, phosphate, ferricyanide, oxalate, etc., to solutions containing uranyl ions results in the precipitation of insoluble salts. The uranyl ion has, however, a strong tendency to form soluble complex ions with an excess of carbonate or oxalate ions. In general, uranyl salts of weak acids have a marked tendency to form complex ions. Some of the stability constants of uranyl complexes are shown in Table 9. Character-

gives some of the physical properties of the stoichiometric uranium oxides.

Uranium trioxide exists in a number of crystal modifications. It is usually prepared by thermal decomposition of uranyl nitrate at about 300°C. The oxide U_3O_8 is formed when any uranium oxide is ignited in air at about 700°C. Uranium dioxide is usually obtained by hydrogen reduction of UO_3 at elevated temperatures (700°C). All these oxides dissolve readily in nitric acid to give uranyl solutions. Uranium trioxide decomposes to U_3O_8 upon ignition at 500 to 700°C; UO_2 is refractory, melting above 2000°C.

Uranium peroxide, the formula of which is usually given as $UO_4 \cdot 2H_2O$, is formed by precipitation from solutions of uranyl nitrate

TABLE 9. STABILITY CONSTANTS OF URANYL COMPLEXES ($\mu = 2.00$, $t = 25°C$)

Reaction	Temperature		
	10°C	25°C	40°C
$UO_2^{++} + Cl^- \rightarrow UO_2Cl^+$	0.58	0.88	1.14
$UO_2^{++} + NO_3^- \rightarrow UO_2NO_3^+$	0.30	0.24	0.17
$UO_2^{++} + SO_4^= \rightarrow UO_2SO_4$	63	76	96
$UO_2^{++} + 2SO_4^= \rightarrow UO_2(SO_4)_2^=$	5.8×10^2	7.1×10^2	8.2×10^2
$UO_2^{++} + HSO_4^- \rightarrow UO_2SO_4 + H^+$	6.1	6.4	6.5
$UO_2^{++} + HF \rightarrow UO_2F^+ + H^+$	55†	26‡	21§

† 51 for $\mu = 0.05$ ‡ 37 for $\mu = 0.25$ § 24 for $\mu = 0.50$, 27 for $\mu = 1.00$.

istic is the precipitation of double salts such as sodium uranyl acetate, $NaUO_2(C_2H_3O_2)_3$, and sodium magnesium uranyl acetate, $NaMg(UO_2)_3(C_2H_3O_2)_9 \cdot 9H_2O$. The latter type has considerable analytical significance. Uranyl solutions are fluorescent and undergo a great variety of photochemical reactions in the presence of organic compounds.

Uranium Oxides. In addition to UO_2 and UO_3 the oxides UO, U_2O_5, and U_3O_8 are also known. There is also some evidence for the existence of U_4O_7 and U_6O_{17}, and several crystal modifications of U_3O_8 are known. In fact, the phase relationships for the uranium-oxygen system are so complex because of solid solution formation that it is possible to obtain almost any oxide ranging in composition between UO and UO_3. The same is also true to a somewhat lesser extent with the transuranium elements. Table 10

by hydrogen peroxide. Alkali hydroxide, hydrogen peroxide, and sodium peroxide form soluble peroxyuranates, $Na_2UO_6 \cdot 4H_2O$ and $Na_4UO_8 \cdot 8H_2O$, when added to solutions of uranyl salts.

Uranium Carbides, Nitrides and Hydrides. Three uranium carbides have been prepared: a monocarbide, UC; the dicarbide, UC_2; and the sesquicarbide, U_2C_3. The first two are formed by either direct reaction of carbon with molten uranium or by the action of carbon monoxide on the metal at high temperatures. The sesquicarbide, stable below 1800°C, can be formed by heating mixtures of UC and UC_2; the sesquicarbide will form only if the reaction mixture is subjected to mechanical stress.

Uranium metal also reacts directly with nitrogen to give nitrides such as UN, U_2N_3, and UN_2. Both nitrides and carbides are

TABLE 10. PHYSICAL PROPERTIES OF THE STOICHIOMETRIC URANIUM OXIDES

Formula	Color	M.P., °C	Thermochemical Data			Crystallographic Data				Density, g/cc
			$\Delta H°$ kcal/mole	$\Delta F°$ kcal/mole	$\Delta S°$ cal/mole/°C	Symmetry Class	Lattice Parameters, Å			
							a_o	b_o	c_o	
UO_2	Brown to black	2800 ± 200	-259.2	-246.6	18.63	F.C. cubic	5.468		4.149	10.97
$\alpha\text{-}U_3O_8$	Greenish black	1450 (dec.)	-853.5	-804	66	Orthorhombic	6.721	3.988	4.149	8.39
$\beta\text{-}U_3O_8$						Orthorhombic	7.04	11.40	8.27	8.38
UO_3	Yellow to orange	450 (dec.)	-291.6	-273.1	23.6	Hexagonal	3.971		4.168	8.34
$UO_4 \cdot 2H_2O$	Yellow	150 (dec.)	-436			Orthorhombic	8.74	6.50	4.21	4.66

semimetallic compounds; they can be converted to U_3O_8 by ignition in air and they also react with water.

The carbides and nitrides of uranium are relatively inert, semimetallic compounds. Uranium mononitride is stable in the absence of air to temperatures above 2000°C; the monocarbide is likewise refractory. Both carbides and nitrides are converted to U_3O_8 by ignition in air. They are soluble with difficulty in acids.

At temperatures of 250 to 300°C uranium metal will react with hydrogen to form a hydride, UH_3. At higher temperatures the hydride loses hydrogen reversibly. The compound is conveniently used as a starting material for the preparation of reactive uranium powder and is itself reactive enough to be used directly to prepare halides, carbides and nitrides; it is thus a very important compound from which a great many uranium compounds can be conveniently prepared. An interesting observation on UH_3 is that it exhibits ferromagnetism at low temperatures. Uranium hydride exists in two crystal modifications: the α form is obtained when the hydride is prepared at low temperatures; the β form is obtained when the temperature of formation is greater than 250°C. β-UH_3 is ferromagnetic below the Curie temperature (173°K). The hydride undergoes decomposition with increasing temperature; the dissociation pressure of UH_3 is one atmosphere at 436°C.

Uranium Halides. The halides of uranium also constitute a numerous and important group of compounds. Table 11 lists some of the known uranium halides.

Uranium tetrafluoride serves as a starting material for the preparation of the other fluorides. It is best prepared by hydrofluorination of uranium dioxide. Uranium trifluoride can be prepared by reduction of UF_4 with hydrogen at 1000°C. The intermediate fluorides U_2F_9, U_4F_{17} and UF_5 are prepared by reaction of solid UF_4 and gaseous UF_6 under appropriate conditions of temperature and pressure.

The most important compound of this class and probably the most interesting is the hexafluoride, UF_6. This substance very fortunately has a high vapor pressure at room temperature (120 mm) and is thus well suited

for use in the gaseous-diffusion process for the separation of the isotopes U^{238} and U^{235}. It can be prepared from uranium dioxide as follows:

$$UO_2 + 4HF \xrightarrow{500°C} UF_4 + 2H_2O$$

$$UF_4 + F_2 \xrightarrow{350°C} UF_6.$$

Under ordinary conditions uranium hexafluoride is a dense, white solid with a vapor pressure of about 120 mm at room temperature. It can be readily sublimed or distilled and is the most volatile uranium compound known. Despite its high molecular weight, gaseous UF_6 is almost a perfect gas, and many of the properties of the vapor can be predicted from kinetic theory. Uranium hexafluoride is a strong fluorinating agent and is therefore reactive; it is sensitive to traces of moisture and must be handled by special techniques.

Uranium tetrachloride can be prepared by direct combination of chlorine with uranium metal or hydride; it can also be obtained by chlorination of uranium oxides with carbon tetrachloride, phosgene, sulfur monochloride, or other powerful chlorinating agents. The trichloride is obtained by reduction of UCl_4 with hydrogen, and the higher chlorides by reaction of UCl_4 with chlorine. Uranium pentachloride disproportionates on heating to UCl_4 and UCl_6. Uranium hexachloride is a rather volatile, somewhat unstable substance. All the uranium chlorides dissolve in or react readily with water to give solutions in which the initial oxidation state of the ion corresponds to that in the solid. All the solid chlorides are sensitive to moisture and air.

The bromides and iodides of uranium are obtained either by reaction of the elements or by treatment of UH_3 with the appropriate halogen acid. The thermal stability of the halides decreases as the atomic number of the halogen increases. The uranium bromides and iodides, UBr_3, UBr_4, UI_3, and UI_4, are known. A series of oxyhalides of the type UO_2F_2, $UOCl_2$, UO_2Cl_2, UO_2BR_2, etc., is known. They are water-soluble substances which become increasingly less stable in going from fluoride to iodide.

Uses

Before the advent of nuclear energy, uranium had very limited uses. It has been suggested

TABLE 11. HALIDES OF URANIUM†

Fluorides	Melting point, °C	Chlorides	Melting point, °C	Bromides	Melting point, °C	Iodides	Melting point, °C
UF_3	(>1140‡)	UCl_3	835	UBr_3	730	UI_3	(680)
UF_4	960	UCl_4	590	UBr_4	519	UI_4	506
U_2F_9	—‡	UCl_5	(327)				
U_4F_{17}	—‡	UCl_6	179				
UF_5	(<400‡)						
UF_6	64§						

† Parentheses indicate estimated values.
‡ Indicates undergoes disproportionation; in the case of UF_3, into UF_4 and U; in the case of the remaining fluorides, into UF_4 and UF_6.
§ Indicates under pressure; UF_6 sublimes below its melting point.

for filaments of lamps. A small tube of uranium dioxide, UO_2, connected in series with the tungsten filaments of large incandescent lamps used for photography and motion pictures, tends to eliminate the sudden surge of current through the bulbs when the light is turned on, thereby extending their life. Compounds of uranium have been used in photography for toning, and in the leather and wood industries uranium compounds have been used for stains and dyes. Uranium salts are mordants of silk or wool. In making special steels, a little ferrouranium has been utilized, but its value is questionable in this connection. Such alloys have not proved commercially attractive. In the production of ceramics, sodium and ammonium diuranates have been used to produce colored glazes. Only 0.006% is needed to give good yellow colors. By increasing the percentage of uranium in the glaze, the color may be changed progressively to orange, brown, green, or black.

Uranium carbide has been suggested as a good catalyst for the production of synthetic ammonia. Uranium salts in small quantities are claimed to stimulate plant growth, but large quantities are clearly poisonous to plants. Uranium metal also has some application as counterweights in aircraft wings.

By far the most important use of uranium lies in its application for nuclear (or atomic) energy. This use, in fact, has so increased the value of uranium as to eliminate its use for many of the purposes mentioned above.

Three isotopes of uranium are of prime importance to the development of nuclear fuels and explosives: U^{238} and U^{235}, in natural uranium, and U^{233} whose short half-life (1.62×10^5 years) precludes the possibility of its natural occurrence as it is not being formed in any of the natural decay series.

U^{235} is the key to the utilization of uranium. Although its natural abundance is only 0.71% it undergoes fission so readily with slow neutrons that a self-sustaining fission chain reaction can be brought about in a nuclear reactor. Such a nuclear reactor can be constructed from natural uranium and a suitable moderator (graphite, heavy water, etc.) alone.

While the abundant isotope, U^{238}, will not in itself undergo fission with slow neutrons in a nuclear reactor, it does capture neutrons to eventually produce Pu^{239}:

$$U^{238} (n,\gamma)\ U^{239} \xrightarrow{\beta^-} Np^{239} \xrightarrow{\beta^-} Pu^{239}.$$

Pu^{239}, like U^{235}, is also very fissionable and is used both as a concentrated form of nuclear fuel and as a nuclear explosive. It is therefore possible to convert most of the natural uranium into fissionable nuclear fuels, instead of realizing the energy from the rare isotope U^{235} alone, and thereby multiply some 100-fold the amount of energy which can be realized from uranium. This nuclear conversion of U^{238} into Pu^{239} can be performed in "breeder" reactors where it is possible to produce more new fissionable material than the fissionable material consumed in sustaining the chain reaction.

Instead of being used to fuel natural uranium nuclear reactors, the rare isotope U^{235} can be concentrated by physical methods (usually gaseous diffusion) and used directly in a more concentrated form as a nuclear fuel or explosive. Uranium slightly enriched in U^{235} (a few %) is often used to fuel nuclear power reactors for the generation of electricity.

The third isotope of importance, U^{233}, can only be produced in quantity by irradiation of natural thorium (Th^{232}) with neutrons from a nuclear chain reaction:

$$Th^{232} (n,\gamma)\ Th^{233} \xrightarrow{\beta^-} Pa^{233} \xrightarrow{\beta^-} U^{233}.$$

Since thorium itself is not readily fissionable, U^{233} must be produced initially at the expense of some other fissionable material. However, in "breeder" reactors, thorium can be converted essentially completely into the useable nuclear fuel U^{233} and thus such reactors can operate on thorium and increase the world's total nuclear power resources.

Table 12 gives the neutron cross section and other fission parameters for U^{233} and U^{235}.

The chemical forms of uranium fuel most commonly used in nuclear reactors include uranium metal and alloys and uranium dioxide. Other forms such as uranium carbide or uranium nitride may also find wide use.

In the United States, reactor development has emphasized the light water-cooled and light water-moderated power reactors which

TABLE 12. FISSION PARAMETERS OF FISSIONABLE ISOTOPES OF URANIUM FOR NEUTRONS (2200 METERS PER SECOND)

	Uranium-233
σ_{abs} †(barns)	573 ± 4
σ_{fiss} ‡(barns)	524 ± 4
α §	0.0935 ± 0.0038
η ‖	2.291 ± 0.009
v ¶	2.50 ± 0.012
	Uranium-235
σ_{abs} (barns)	679 ± 3
σ_{fiss} (barns)	580 ± 2
α	0.172 ± 0.01
η	2.07 ± 0.02
v	2.43 ± 0.02

† σ_{abs} is the absorption cross section.
‡ σ_{fiss} is the fission cross section.
§ α is the ratio of radiative capture to fission.
‖ η is the average number of neutrons emitted per neutron absorbed.
¶ v is the average number of neutrons emitted per fission event.

use uranium enriched in the fissionable isotope U^{235} as nuclear fuel. Power reactors in the Soviet Union are also of the light water-type utilizing enriched uranium as fuel. In European countries, such as England and France, emphasis has been placed on gas-cooled graphite-moderated reactors utilizing natural uranium as fuel. Later power reactors in England utilize enriched uranium. Other countries have the opportunity to choose between the enriched or natural uranium fuel types. In Canada emphasis has been given to heavy water-moderated reactors fueled with natural uranium. Estimated worldwide capacity of nuclear power reactors is 25,000,000 KW by 1970 and 200,000,000 to 250,000,000 KW by 1980.

Despite the projected growth of such first generation nuclear power reactors, which are economically competitive in the generation of electricity, it will still be necessary to develop breeder and other advanced type reactors. Such reactors will utilize the nuclear fuel even more efficiently and more economically in order to fulfill the potential of uranium and thorium in supplementing conventional sources of electrical power as conventional fuels begin to be depleted and increase in cost.

Among the many other applications of nuclear power utilizing uranium as the nuclear fuel, an important area is for marine propulsion, as in submarines, other warships, and merchant ships. Because it represents a concentrated form of energy, nuclear power finds special application in power stations located in remote terrestrial regions. Nuclear power reactors also can heat propellants for the propulsion of long-range, heavy payload space vehicles which might be used for manned missions to the moon and the nearer planets. Another special application in space of lightweight compact power reactors is to furnish electric power for such space missions and for communication and other satellites.

The isotope U^{235} can of course be used as the explosive ingredient for nuclear (atomic) weapons. The isotope U^{235} is also used in nuclear explosives which will have important peaceful applications to large-scale excavations and mining and research uses.

Highly useful radioactive isotopes for use in industry, agriculture, and medicine are also produced in nuclear reactors fueled with uranium. The diagnostic and therapeutic applications of such isotopes in medicine are particularly noteworthy.

Many other physical and chemical properties of uranium and its compounds are now known, and it is interesting to note that this element which remained rather obscure and unknown for 150 years has been the object of more scientific investigation in recent times than almost any of the other more "common" elements.

References

1. Katz, J. J., "Uranium and Uranium Compounds," in "Encyclopedia of Chemical Technology," Raymond E. Kirk and Donald F. Othmer (Eds.), Vol. 14, pp. 432–458, New York, Interscience Publishers, 1955.
2. Hoekstra, H. R., and Katz, J. J., "Actinide Elements," National Nuclear Energy Series, Div. IV, Vol. 14A, Chapt. 6, New York, McGraw-Hill Book Co., 1954.
3. Katz, J. J., and Rabinowitch, E., "The Chemistry of Uranium," National Nuclear Energy Series, Div. VIII, Vol. 5, New York, McGraw-Hill Book Co., 1951.
4. Seaborg, G. T., and Katz, J. J., "The Chemistry of the Actinide Elements," New York, John Wiley & Sons, 1957.

5. Seaborg, G. T., and Katz, J. J., (Eds.) "The Actinide Elements," National Nuclear Energy Series, Div. IV, Vol. 14A, New York, McGraw-Hill Book Co., 1949.

6. Hyde, Earl K., Perlman, Isadore, and Seaborg, Glenn T., "Nuclear Properties of the Heavy Elements," Vol. I, "Systematics of Nuclear Structure and Radioactivity;" Vol. II, "Detailed Radioactivity Properties," ibid; Earl K. Hyde, Vol. III, "Fission Phenomena," Englewood Cliffs, N. J., Prentice-Hall, Inc., 1964.

7. Sidgwick, N. V., "The Chemical Elements and Their Compounds," Vol. I, pp. 1069–1091, Oxford, Oxford University Press, 1950.

8. Mellor, J. W., "A Comprehensive Treatise on Inorganic and Theoretical Chemistry," Vol. XII, pp. 1–138, New York, Longmans-Green and Co., 1932.

9. Cotton, F. Albert, and Wilkinson, G., "Advanced Inorganic Chemistry, A Comprehensive Text," Second Ed., New York, Interscience Publishers, Div. of John Wiley & Sons, 1966.

GLENN T. SEABORG

V

VANADIUM

Vanadium, symbol V, has an atomic number of 23 and an atomic weight of 50.942. It is a ductile metal located in Group VB of the Periodic Table above niobium and tantalum and between titanium and chromium. For many years it was incorrectly placed in Group VA with phosphorus which it resembles closely in the chemical properties of its compounds, especially the ability to form ortho-, meta-, pyro-, and polyacids and salts analogous to the phosphates.

Vanadium was discovered in the year 1801 by Manuel del Rio, Professor of Mineralogy at the School of Mines, Mexico City, in lead ore from Zamapan in the State of Hidalgo, and named "erythronium" by him, because of the property of its salts of becoming red when heated with acids. In 1830, Sefstrom found what he thought was an unrecognized metal in the iron ores of Taberg, Sweden, and named it "vanadium" in honor of the Scandinavian goddess Vanadis, because of its beautiful multicolored compounds. Wohler in 1830 demonstrated that erythronium and vanadium were the same element.

In 1831 Berzelius published a description of the compounds, but the chemistry of the metal was not thoroughly worked out until Roscoe made extensive studies of vanadium and its compounds in the 1860's.

Roscoe's silvery-white powder, first produced in 1867 by hydrogen reduction of the chloride, VCl_2, was probably the first nearly pure vanadium metal. Efforts of other workers, notably Moissan, Helouis, Goldschmidt, Weiss and Aichel, Prandtl and Bleyer, and Ruff and Martin, to produce the pure metal by electrothermic carbon reduction or aluminothermic reduction of vanadium pentoxide or trioxide, during the interim until 1920, were not successful, in that the metal product always contained either substantial residual quantities of the reducer or lower oxides of vanadium.

In 1923, Hunter and Jones reduced vanadium trichloride with sodium in a steel bomb, obtaining a fine gray powder analyzing 99.5–100% vanadium, but no coherent grains were formed that could be utilized in physical research.

In 1927 Marden and Rich announced the production of 99.3 to 99.8% vanadium metal in the form of ductile globules or shot, 3/8 inch and smaller in diameter, by means of the reaction:

$$V_2O_5 + 5Ca + 5CaCl_2 \rightarrow 2V + 5CaO \cdot 5CaCl_2$$

conducted in a heated steel bomb at 900 to 950°C for one hour, thus providing for the first time metal of high purity in a ductile form which could be worked and shaped in sufficient quantities to determine its physical properties, and moreover, finally proving that the metal is not like arsenic or bismuth but resembles tantalum.

Though Van Arkel produced metal of slightly higher purity by thermal decomposition of the iodide, the method was not practical, and for the next two decades the process of Marden and Rich was the source of the few hundred grams of metal produced annually.

Occurrence

Vanadium is one of the more abundant trace elements, ranking twenty-second among the elements in the earth's crust. It is widely spread in minute quantities, but in only a few places does it occur in sufficient quantities for economical mining and processing.

Most rocks and meteorites carry from a trace to a few hundredths of a per cent expressed as V_2O_5. Coal ash may contain a similar amount. Petroleum crudes have varying vanadium contents but not sufficient to justify treatment for vanadium extraction. However, in burning the residual oils, the vanadium is concentrated in the ash from which it may be recovered economically.

Magnetite iron ores may carry up to 1.0% or more V_2O_5. Where economically justified, steelmaking operations may be conducted to concentrate the vanadium and produce converter, open hearth, or basic oxygen furnace slags which are amenable to vanadium extractive processes.

Ilmenite and other titanium minerals commonly carry 0.1 to 0.3% V_2O_5 which is currently being removed as impurity residues in processing the mineral concentrates for production of titanium dioxide pigments and titanium metal.

Certain phosphate-rock deposits of Idaho and Montana contain from 0.1 to 0.5% V_2O_5. In electric furnace smelting of the phosphate rock to produce elemental phosphorus, the vanadium is concentrated in the ferrophosphorus by-product. The ferrophosphorus is then further processed for recovery of the vanadium. The vanadium is also recovered as an impurity residue in the sulfuric acid process for manufacture of phosphoric acid and phosphate fertilizers.

Mineralogy

More than sixty-five minerals containing vanadium have been identified, but only five primary minerals are known:

1. Patronite, $V_2S_5 + nS$—found only at Mina Ragra, Peru, where it formed the largest known vanadium deposit. It is a greenish-black amorphous mineral, usually carrying some iron, nickel, molybdenum, phosphorus, and carbon.

2. Bravoite, $(Fe,Ni)S_2$—wherein cobalt or vanadium substitutes for nickel and iron. As found in small quantities in Mina Ragra, it occurs in brassy cubes of metallic luster carrying 25% sulfur.

3. Sulvanite, $3Cu_2S \cdot V_2S_5$—a bronze-yellow crystalline sulfide found only in small quantities in Burra-Burra, South Australia

and in Utah. It contains 51% copper, 14% vanadium, and 35% sulfur.

4. Davidite—a titanium-iron mineral from Mt. Painter, South Australia carrying some vanadium.

5. Roscoelite, $2K_2O \cdot Al_2O_3(Mg,Fe)O \cdot 3V_2O_5 \cdot 10SiO_2 \cdot 4H_2O$—a vanadium-bearing mica found as a vein mineral in a number of rich gold-bearing veins, but in important quantity as a secondary mineral in the sandstones of Colorado and Utah. It carries 20% V_2O_5, 7.5% K_2O, 14% Al_2O_3, 2% MgO, 1.5% FeO, and 47.5% SiO_2.

All other known vanadium minerals are secondary products formed by alteration of primary minerals in the oxidizing zone of the upper lithosphere. The most important are:

Vanadinite—$Pb_5(VO_4)_3Cl$—a red, brown, crystalline mineral occurring in Mexico, Arizona, New Mexico, and Argentina.

Cuprodescloizite—$4(Cu,Zn,Pb)O \cdot (V,As)_2O_5 \cdot H_2O$—greenish-brown crystalline mineral. Found in Mexico, Arizona, Nevada, Argentina, Spain, Turkestan, and Rhodesia.

Carnotite—$K_2O \cdot 2UO_3 \cdot V_2O_5 \cdot 3H_2O$—yellow, earthy aggregate. Found in Colorado, Arizona, New Mexico, Utah.

Uvanite—$2UO_3 \cdot 3V_2O_5 \cdot 15H_2O$—brownish-yellow, fine granular aggregate. Found in Utah.

Tyuyamunite—$CaO \cdot 2UO_3 \cdot V_2O_5 \cdot 4H_2O$—yellow, very fine crystals. Found in Colorado, Utah, and Russia.

Roscoelite—Same as in primary mineral.

Hewettite and metahewettite—$CaO \cdot 3V_2O_5 \cdot 9H_2O$—deep red, fibrous aggregate. Found in Colorado.

Vanadium Sources

For many years the patronite deposit at Mina Ragra, Peru, was the major source of vanadium, with smaller quantities being derived from carnotite, roscoelite and vanadinite. With the gradual depletion of the Peru deposit, increasing proportions of vanadium are derived from carnotite and roscoelite. After the advent of atomic energy, processing of carnotite ore increased sharply to meet uranium requirements and for many years the vanadium obtained as a co-product exceeded United States requirements. Recent cutbacks in uranium output combined with increased vanadium consumption have made it necessary to seek other sources of vanadium. Increasing quantities are being recovered from ferrophosphorus obtained from the Idaho and Montana phosphate deposits, from vanadium-bearing boiler residues, and spent vanadium catalysts. Large reserves of vanadium have been reported in Arkansas and a plant for processing the ore has been constructed. Increasing attention is being given to recovering vanadium from titaniferous magnetites. Construction of iron and steel works is underway in the Transvaal which includes recovery of large quantities of vanadium in a slag product.

Ore Processing

At the present time vanadium is generally extracted by leaching the raw ore with hot dilute sulfuric acid. The ore may also be roasted with common salt to convert the vanadium to water-soluble sodium vanadates. The vanadium is then extracted from the roasted ore by leaching with water or soda ash solution, usually followed by leaching with dilute sulfuric acid for extraction of some additional vanadium. Vanadium is precipitated from water leach or alkaline leach solutions by addition of sulfuric acid to a pH between 2 and 3. The vanadium precipitates as red cake, a sodium polyvanadate which fuses readily at 700°C to yield the commercial-grade fused vanadium pentoxide. The red cake also finds use in the chemical industry and may be redissolved in soda ash and precipitated by ammonium salts to form ammonium metavanadate. Ammonium metavanadate is decomposed by heating to 320–430°C, yielding a high-purity V_2O_5.

Purification of acid leach liquors is generally necessary before precipitation of the vanadium. The vanadium is extracted from the acid leach liquors by solvent extraction using an aliphatic amine or as an alternative an alkyl phosphoric acid in kerosene. The vanadium is stripped from the organic with aqueous solutions of sulfuric acid, soda ash, or ammonia and ammonium chloride. Precipitation of vanadium as red cake from sulfuric acid or soda ash solutions is accomplished by pH control. The ammonia-ammonium chloride solution results in the direct formation of ammonium metavanadate.

Derivation

Most of the vanadium metal currently available is made by calcium reduction of V_2O_5 in a pressure vessel. This is an adaptation of the process developed by McKechnie and Seybolt. The important improvement in their method over the procedures of Marden and Rich, Van Arkel, and Gregory, is the inclusion of iodine. This combines with calcium at a relatively low temperature, 425°C, giving off enough heat to initiate the $V_2O_5 + Ca$ reaction. The presence of calcium iodide causes the formation of a slag which will permit the metal to collect as a solid regulus. McKechnie and Seybolt produced metal of better than 99% purity; carbon was the greatest impurity, about 0.2%, with oxygen 0.02 to 0.08%, nitrogen 0.01 to 0.05% and hydrogen 0.002 to 0.01%.

Block and Ferrante have shown that high-purity ductile vanadium can be made by the reduction of vanadium trichloride with magnesium or magnesium-sodium mixtures.

The range in chemical composition of the metal produced currently is:

V	C	Fe
99.5 +	0.02–0.10	0.01–0.08
Si	Ni	Cr
about 0.05	about 0.01	about 0.01
O_2	N_2	H_2
0.04–0.15	0.02–0.06	0.002–0.006

An electrorefining process developed by Baker and Ramsdell of the Bureau of Mines may provide a better and cheaper method for commercial production of vanadium metal. The process consists of electrolytically refining a relatively impure vanadium metal in a fused chloride electrolyte such as $NaCl$-$LiCl$-VCl_2. In this manner calcium-reduced vanadium metal may be upgraded from 99.8 to 99.95% V, or low-cost aluminum-reduced metal containing about 90% V can be refined to ductile 99.6% V metal. The process is particularly effective in removing the interstitial elements, oxygen, nitrogen, and hydrogen, and consequently produces vanadium metal with low hardness and good ductility.

TABLE 1. PHYSICAL PROPERTIES OF VANADIUM METAL

Atomic number	23
Atomic weight	50.942
Isotope, natural	50 (0.25%), 51 (99.75%)
Crystal structure, to 1550° ± 10°C	Body-centered cubic
Lattice constant, A	3.026
Density, g/cc	6.11
Melting point, °C	1890°C
Boiling point, °C	3000°C
Vapor pressure, 1393–1609°C	$R \ln p = 121.95 \times 10^3 T^{-1} - 5.123 \times 10^{-4} T + 36.29$
	R = gas constant, cal/mole/deg
	p = pressure in atmosphere
	$\ln$ = logarithm to base e
	T = absolute temperature, °K
Volatility at melting point	Very low
Specific heat 20–100°C, cal/g	0.120
Latent heat of fusion, kcal/mole	4
Latent heat of vaporization, kcal/mole	106
Enthalpy, 25°C, kcal/mole	1.26
Entropy, 25°C, cal/mole/°C	7.05
Thermal conductivity, cal/°C/cm/sec	
100°C	0.074
500°C	0.088
700°C	0.084
Electrical resistance 20°C, microhm-cm	24.8
30.6°C	25.2
58.9°C	27.4
Temperature coefficient of resistance, microhm-cm/°C	
0–100°C	0.0034
0–200°C	0.0033
Thermal emf versus platinum cold junction, 0°C, mv	
100°C	0.63
200°C	1.56
400°C	3.97
700°C	9.26
900°C	13.97
1000°C	16.71
Magnetic susceptibility, cgs units	1.4×10^{-6}
Superconductive transition temperature, °K	5.13
Coefficient of linear thermal expansion, per °C	$9.7 \pm 0.3 \times 10^{-6}$, x-ray, 20–720°C
	8.95×10^{-6}, dilatometer 200–1000°C
Thermal expansion, μ-in./in./°C	
20°C	8.84
23–500°C	9.6
23–900°C	10.4
23–1100°C	10.9
Recrystallization temperature, °C	700–800 (for 70% cold-rolled sheet)
Modulus of elasticity, psi	18 to 19×10^6
Shear modulus, psi	6.73×10^6
Poisson ratio	0.36
Thermal neutron absorption cross-section, barns/atom	5.00 ± 0.01

Physical Properties

Pure vanadium has a body-centered crystal structure throughout the temperature range normally encountered during fabrication and treatment. It will recrystallize at about 700 to 800°C if cold worked. Its intermediate density of 6.1 g/cc provides an interesting strength-to-weight ratio for structural applications, particularly when the metal is strengthened by cold work or alloying. Its electrical resistivity is considerably higher than that of copper or aluminum. Its thermal conductivity is relatively low. The physical properties of vanadium are listed in Table 1.

Mechanical Properties

Pure vanadium has relatively low strength and hardness with very good ductility. With higher-than-normal interstitial elements, oxygen, nitrogen, and hydrogen, its strength is substantially higher and its ductility much lower.

The tensile properties of vanadium varying in composition and treatment are given in Table 2. Vanadium work hardens to a minor degree and has a very high capacity to withstand cold reduction without intermediate annealing. Metal cold rolled 75% has a tensile strength of about 110,000 psi and an elongation in 2 in. of about 5%. After annealing this metal at 800–900°C, the tensile strength drops to about 70,000 psi and the elongation increases to about 25%. Tensile test results indicate that pure vanadium increases in strength mildly (from 91,000 to 99,000 psi) as its temperature is raised from ambient to 400°C. As its temperature is raised above this, its strength drops to 40,000 psi at 600°C and 7100 psi at 1000°C, a somewhat slower rate than shown by many other metals.

TABLE 2. TENSILE PROPERTIES OF HOT OR COLD WORKED AND ANNEALED VANADIUM METAL

| Composition (%) | | | | Condition | Yield strength (drop of beam) (psi) | Tensile strength (psi) | Elongation (% in 1 in.) | Reduction of area (%) | Hardness (Rockwell) |
C	O	H	N						
0.024	<0.010	0.001	0.005	a	13200[c]	28700	38.3	95.0	A21
0.08	0.015	0.006	0.02	b	23000[c]	37600	33.7	36.7	A38
0.05	0.08	0.008	0.04	d	42000	55000	32	72	B71
0.07	0.08	0.004	0.04	d	63000	69600	32	66	B78
0.09	0.06	0.006	0.04	d	56000	63600	36	68	B75
0.06	0.08	0.004	0.05	d	52000	60300	34	69	B79
0.06	0.10	0.005	0.05	d	64000	66400	38	82	B81
0.10	0.09	0.007	0.07	d	64000	74600	26	68	B77
0.047	0.07	0.0043	0.052	e	55400[c]	68000	34	68	—
0.045	0.048	0.0028	0.047	e	43000[c]	83400	24	50	—
0.13	0.045	0.0043	0.0072	f	47800[i]	56000	44.5	78.5	—
0.17	0.031	0.0021	0.026	g	55100[i]	61700	37.0	79.0	—
0.075	0.032	0.0025	0.0009	h	48600[i]	58400	33.0	80.5	—

(a) ¾-in.-diameter arc welded iodide vanadium ingot cold swaged to ⁷⁄₁₆ in.-diameter 1100°C (2012°F), 48 hr, furnace cool.
(b) Arc welded calcium reduced vanadium ingot rolled at 400°C (752°F) to 45% reduction + 900°C (1652°F), 5 hr, furnace cool.
(c) 0.2% offset.
(d) Calcium reduced vanadium hot rolled from 2-in.-square ingot + 800°C (1472°F), ½ hr, furnace cool.
(e) Arc welded calcium reduced vanadium ingot (2-in.-square, hot-worked + 800°C (1472°F) furnace cool.
(f) Hot extruded 1100–1150°C (2012–2100°F), cold swaged 63%, anneal for 1 hr at 900–950°C (1650–1740°F).
(g) Same as (f) except 50% cold swaging.
(h) Same as (f) except 47% cold swaging.
(i) Upper yield point.

The brittle-ductile transition temperature of unalloyed vanadium is influenced significantly by the level of interstitial elements, carbon, oxygen, nitrogen, and hydrogen. This is well illustrated by the results of an investigation by Loomis and Carlson which show that the lower the content of H or O or N or C, the lower the transition temperature.

Chemical Properties

Vanadium, like most of the other elements in Groups VA and VB, combines in different valencies, 2, 3, 4 and 5, and forms basic as well as acid radicals, which includes the power of functioning as the central atom in polyacids. The interrelation among vanadium acids is shown in Fig. 1.

When the metal is heated in air it is oxidized, showing various colors: brownish black, (V_2O_3); blue-black, V_2O_4; and red

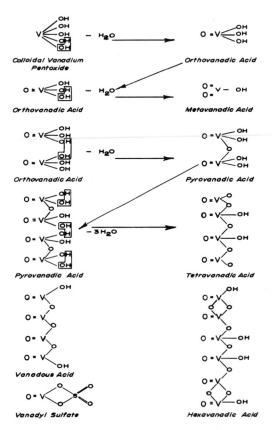

Colloidal Vanadium Pentoxide

Orthovanadic Acid

Orthovanadic Acid

Metavanadic Acid

Orthovanadic Acid

Pyrovanadic Acid

Pyrovanadic Acid

Tetravanadic Acid

Vanadous Acid

Vanadyl Sulfate

Hexavanadic Acid

FIG. 1. Typical structural formulas illustrating the interrelation of vanadium acids. From Alexander, Jerome, "Vanadium and Some of Its Industrial Applications," *J. Soc. Chem, Ind.,* **46**, 36-37 (1929).

to orange, V_2O_5. When heated in chlorine at 180°C it combines directly to form vanadium tetrachloride, VCl_4. At high temperature it combines directly with nitrogen to form vanadium nitride, VN, and with carbon to form vanadium carbide, VC. The metal is not soluble in hydrochloric acid nor in dilute sulfuric acid, but dissolves in nitric acid, hydrofluoric acid, and concentrated sulfuric acid. Solutions of alkalis have little action, but fused alkalis react readily to form water-soluble vanadates, liberating hydrogen.

Compounds

Vanadium pentoxide or vanadic anhydride, V_2O_5, is the most important oxide from which nearly all vanadium compounds are derived. In its commercial form it normally ranges from 88 to 98% V_2O_5.

By fusing vanadium pentoxide with two, four, and six molecular proportions of caustic soda, a series of water-soluble sodium vanadates can be made: sodium metavanadate, $NaVO_3$, sodium pyrovanadate, $Na_4V_2O_7$, and sodium orthovanadate, Na_3VO_4.

When vanadium pentoxide is treated with sulfuric acid while gassing with sulfur dioxide, the following reaction occurs to produce vanadyl sulfate, which can be crystallized from solution in beautiful blue crystals:

$$V_2O_5 + H_2SO_4 + H_2O + SO_2 \rightarrow V_2O_2 \cdot (SO_4)_2 + 2H_2O$$

Application of this reaction, more often using ferrous ammonium sulfate as the reducer, is made in the analytical determination of vanadium. The excess of reducer is then destroyed with ammonium persulfate, and the vanadyl sulfate titrated with potassium permanganate, as orthovanadic acid, thus:

$$5V_2O_2(SO_4)_2 + 2KMnO_4 + 22H_2O \rightarrow 10H_3VO_4 + K_2SO_4 + 2MnSO_4 + 7H_2SO_4$$

Vanadium pentoxide can be chlorinated at 500°C when mixed with carbon to give vanadium oxytrichloride:

$$V_2O_5 + 3C + 3Cl_2 \rightarrow 2VOCl_3 + 3CO$$

When conducted at 750°C the process yields principally vanadium tetrachloride, which when refluxed is converted to vanadium trichloride, as described by Block and Ferrante.

Vanadium acetate, citrate, linoleate, oleate, oxalate, palmitate, phenolate, resinate, and stearate are examples of vanadyl organic compounds that can be formed. Metal vanadates such as those of Bi, Cd, Ca, Cr, Co, Cu, Fe, Pb, Mg, Mn, Mo, Ni, K, Ag, Na, Sn, and Zn have been produced for special purposes—mostly as catalysts or interprocess materials in purification of ore concentrates.

Corrosion Resistance

According to Kinzel, vanadium is highly resistant to reducing acids in moderate concentrations but is not resistant to oxidizing acids. Unalloyed vanadium is resistant to pitting and corrosion by salt spray and sea water. Schlain, Kenahan, and Acherman reported that vanadium is resistant to corrosion in simulated ocean water at 35°C, 60% sulfuric acid and 20% hydrochloric acid at 35°C. Vanadium resists corrosion in 3% nitric acid solution, corrodes slowly in 12% acid, and corrodes very rapidly in 17% acid. Vanadium has shown considerable promise as a container material in nuclear reactors for its ability to resist corrosion by liquid sodium and various bismuth alloys.

Ferrovanadium

Ferrovanadium, the alloy used for many years to add vanadium to steel and iron—the major use of vanadium—contains either 50–55% or 70–80% vanadium. It is produced by aluminum or silicon reduction of the oxide in the presence of iron in an electric arc furnace. In aluminum reduction the reaction is exothermic and little additional heat from the arc is required. Silicon reduction requires a two-stage reduction to achieve an efficient operation.

A new product, essentially vanadium carbide containing about 85% vanadium, 12% carbon, and 2% iron, has replaced ferrovanadium in many applications in the steel industry. It is produced by solid state carbon reduction of vanadium oxide in a vacuum furnace.

Somewhat similar in purpose, vanadium-aluminum alloys containing 40 and 85% vanadium are available for the preparation of titanium alloys containing these two ele-ments. The vanadium-aluminum alloys are prepared by the reduction of vanadium pentoxide with aluminum metal, an excess of the latter being used to provide the desired final ratio of vanadium to aluminum in the alloy.

Fabrication

The metal button resulting from direct reduction, either cut into strips or crushed and agglomerated into convenient shapes, is usually remelted into ingot form for more convenient shaping operations. The metal lends itself to common fabricating methods such as forging, rolling, extruding, swaging, drawing, bending, stamping, pressing, machining, and welding. Hot working and welding require precautions to prevent em-brittlement by reaction with air.

Consumable vacuum arc and electron beam melting are the most common methods used for melting vanadium. Ingots up to 6 in. diameter are common and larger ones can be made.

An inert atmosphere such as argon is necessary for heating prior to hot working to prevent contamination by oxygen and nitrogen. Sheathing of the ingot is sometimes used. The optimum hot-working temperature range is 1100–1150°C. Reductions similar to those for stainless steels have been found satisfactory. The lower limit for hot working is usually imposed by the rather rapid hard-ening of the metal as it cools.

Vanadium can be successfully rolled, swaged, extruded, and drawn at temperatures below the recrystallization point. There is a distinct advantage in performing these opera-tions at low temperatures to avoid the surface contamination resulting from hot working. If the metal is sufficiently pure with respect to oxygen, nitrogen, and hydrogen, cold working can be started on small ingots. Vanadium is unique in that it can be cold worked to more than 90% reduction in area without intermediate annealing. Its machining characteristics are like those of austenitic stainless steel.

Applications

Recently over 80% of the vanadium pro-duced is made into ferrovanadium or vanadium carbide and added to steel as an alloying agent. About 11% is used in vanadium-aluminum alloys whose use by the titanium industry has become substantial. Several titanium alloys containing vanadium are being used in modern aircraft construction. Vanadium pentoxide accounts for 3.6% of the vanadium consumed and ammonium meta-vanadate for another 2.9%. These compounds are used by the chemical industry as catalysts. For example, nearly all of the sulfuric acid is made by use of a vanadium catalyst. Vanadium oxytrichloride is being used as a catalyst in the production of ethylene propylene rubber.

There have been no commercial applications of ductile vanadium developed, perhaps because its utility has not been fully explored. It has been of interest as a structural material for fast nuclear reactors since it has a relatively low neutron capture cross section and good strength and corrosion resistance at elevated temperatures. Vanadium foil has been tried as a bonding material in the cladding of titanium to steel. Vanadium alloyed with other metals, such as titanium, to increase its strength at elevated temperatures has been considered as a structural material for space craft, particularly in sheet form. There has been considerable study of the usefulness of vanadium in various wrought forms in a wide area of our technology.

Biological, Biochemical and Toxicological Aspects

Vanadium compounds have variable toxicity which appears to be limited to their irritant action on conjunctiva and the respiratory tract, although prolonged exposure may lead to pulmonary involvement. The chief offender seems to be vanadium pentoxide, but some investigators report that patronite ore dust, which contains chiefly V_2S_5, is quite toxic to animals and causes acute pulmonary edema in them. The more recent studies describe no evidence of effects by vanadium compounds on the gastrointestinal tract, kidneys, blood or central nervous system. However, vanadium compounds should be regarded as toxic materials and proper precautions should be taken in handling them.

Dr. Robert D. Solomon has found that small doses of vanadium, in the form of salts, can reverse hardening of the arteries in experimental animals. A clinical study by Dr. Charles E. Lewis of the University of Cincinnati showed that workers engaged in the mining and milling of vanadium had a significantly lower serum cholesterol level than unexposed workers in the same geographical area.

Vanadium appears to have no biological role in animals. There is some evidence that in small quantities it stimulates plant growth and that it resembles molybdenum in promoting growth and activation of azotobacter. It has also been found that a vanadium-containing respiratory pigment is in the blood of a group of marine worms, *ascidia*.

Vanadium is isomorphous with phosphorus and V_2O_5 can replace P_2O_5 in the apatite molecule; thus, it has been found in human teeth. Studies on small animals have shown that V_2O_5 added to a caries-producing diet induced a marked reduction of new enamel caries and a cessation of progress of dentin caries. It is possible that the presence of V_2O_5 increases the hardness of hydroxyl apatite in teeth.

References

1. Baker, D. H., Jr., and Ramsdell, J. D., "Electrolytic Vanadium and Its Properties," *J. Electrochem. Soc.,* **107**, 985–989 (1960).
2. Block, F. E., and Ferrante, M. J., "Vanadium by Metallic Reduction of Vanadium Trichloride," *J. Electrochem. Soc.,* **108**, 464–468 (1961).
3. Dunn, H. E., and Edlund, D. L., "Vanadium" in "Rare Metals Handbook," C. A. Hampel, Editor, 2nd Ed., pp. 629–652, New York, Reinhold Publishing Corp., 1961.
4. Gregory, E. D., *J. Electrochem. Soc.,* **98**, 395 (1951).
5. Kinzel, A. B., *Metals Progr.,* **58**, 315 (1950).
6. Lacey, C. E., and Beck, C. J., "Properties of Vanadium Consolidated by Extrusion," *Trans. A.S.M.,* **48**, 579–94 (1956).
7. Loomis, B. A., and Carlson, O. N., "Brittle-Ductile Transition in Vanadium," *A.E.C., ISC 1037* (March 1958).
8. McKechnie, R. K., and Seybolt, A. U., *J. Electrochem. Soc.,* **97**, 311 (1950).
9. Marden, J. W., and Rich, M. N., *Ind. Eng. Chem.,* **19**, 786–788 (1927).

10. "The Reactor Handbook," Vol. 3, Section 1, A.E.C. Publication *AECD 3647*, pp. 437–449 (1955).
11. Schlain, D., Kenahan, C. B., and Acherman, W. L., *Corrosion,* **16**, 70–72 (1960).
12. Smith, K. F., and Van Thyne, R. J., "Selected Properties of Vanadium Alloys for Reactor Application," A.E.C. Publication *ANL 5661* (1957).
13. Underwood, E. J., "Trace Elements in Human and Animal Nutrition," New York, Academic Press, Inc., 1956.
14. Van Arkel, A. E., "Reine Metalle," p. 202, Berlin, J. Springer, 1939.

Technical Staff
Foote Mineral Co.

XENON †

The element xenon has an atomic number 54 and an atomic weight of 131.30 on the C^{12}-scale. It is a member of Group 0 of elements in the Periodic Table, otherwise known as the noble or rare gases. At room temperature xenon is a colorless, odorless, and nontoxic gas. Although numerous compounds of xenon are now known, the element is nevertheless chemically rather inert, reacting under certain conditions directly only with fluorine, the most electronegative element, or some of its derivatives. (See **Noble Gases**.)

Xenon is found in nature as a constituent of the atmosphere where it occurs to the extent of $8.6 \times 10^{-6}\%$ by volume of dry air. It is the rarest of the stable elements with an estimated abundance of $2.9 \times 10^{-9}\%$ of the earth's crust (including the oceans and the atmosphere). Most of the xenon in nature is of primordial origin, but it has been estimated that about 0.5% of the total results from spontaneous or neutron induced fission of uranium and thorium.

The element was discovered in 1898 by Sir William Ramsay and M. W. Travers. In the course of purification of krypton by fractional distillation, a gas of abnormally high density was isolated which was identified as a new element by its characteristic spectrum. Xenon is a Greek word meaning "the stranger."

Production

Xenon is produced as a by-product in the liquefaction and fractional distillation of air. Because of its relatively high boiling point, it collects in the liquid oxygen fraction along

with krypton, acetylene, and other hydrocarbons present in air. (See **Oxygen**.) The latter present a serious hazard because of the possibility of chance ignition and explosion if they are allowed to become too concentrated. The fraction enriched in xenon is flash vaporized and the hydrocarbons burned over a catalyst. The xenon is absorbed on refrigerated silica gel and finally separated from krypton by selective adsorption and desorption from charcoal. Xenon is commercially obtainable in "Pyrex" glass bulbs at one atmosphere pressure or in pressurized steel cylinders. The current price is about $20 per liter at STP. The isotopes of xenon have been separated by thermal diffusion. Xe^{131} has been obtained in 99% enrichment by this method.

Nuclear Properties

Xenon occurs in nature as a mixture of nine stable isotopes with mass numbers ranging from 124 to 136. In addition to the stable isotopes, about twenty radioactive nuclides and isomers have been characterized. Table 1 lists the known nuclides of xenon together with a number of their properties. Many of the radioactive nuclides of xenon are products of fission of U^{235}, U^{233}, and Pu^{239} by thermal neutrons or of fast fission of U^{238} and Th^{232}. Of the radioactive species, Xe^{135} must be singled out because of its extremely high thermal neutron cross section. As a fission product, its presence in nuclear reactors requires considerable excess fuel to overcome the detrimental poisoning effects of the isotope.

Atomic Structure

The ground state of xenon is an ^1S_o singlet state with the following electron configuration:

† Based on work performed under the auspices of the U.S. Atomic Energy Commission.

TABLE 1. STABLE AND RADIOACTIVE NUCLIDES OF XENON

Mass Number	Abundance, %	Atomic Mass, C^{12}-Scale	Half-Life	Mode of Decay	Total Decay Energy, MeV	Gamma Energies, MeV	Thermal Neutron Cross Section, barns
120			43m	β^+		0.096	
121			34m	β^+ E.C.	2.8	0.080 0.132 0.440	
122			19h	E.C. β^+		0.148 0.090 0.187 0.238	
123			1.85h	E.C. β^+(1.5)	2.8	0.149 0.178 0.328	
124	0.096	123.9061					110
125m			60s	IT	0.186	0.075 0.110	
125			18h	E.C.		0.056 0.096 0.106 0.187 0.243 0.460	
126	0.090	125.9043					
127m			75s	IT	0.300	0.175 0.125	
127			36.4d	E.C.	0.7	0.057 0.145 0.170 0.203	
128	1.92	127.9035					<5
129m			8d	IT	0.236	0.196 0.040	
129	26.44	128.9048					25
130	4.08	129.9035					<5

TABLE 1—*continued*

Mass Number	Abundance, %	Atomic Mass, C¹²-Scale	Half-Life	Mode of Decay	Total Decay Energy, MeV	Gamma Energies, MeV	Thermal Neutron Cross Section, barns
131m			12d	IT	0.164	0.164	
131	21.18	130.9051					85
132	26.89	131.9042					<5
133m			2.3d	IT	0.233	0.233	
133			5.27d	β^-	0.43	0.081, 0.160, 0.30, 0.38	190
134	10.44	133.9054					
135m			16m	IT	0.53	0.53	<5
135			9.2h	β^-(.91, .55)	1.16	0.249, 0.36, 0.607	2.7×10^6
136	8.87	135.9072					0.15
137			3.9m	β^-	3.5	0.42, 0.51, 1.78, 2.01	
138			14m	β^-(2.4, 3.7)			
139			41s	β^-	β^-(~4.6)	0.22, 0.30, 0.17, 0.40	
140			16s	β^-			
141			2s	β^-			
142			~1.5s	β^-			
143			1s	β^-			
144			~1s	β^-			

Legend: s = seconds, m = minutes, h = hours, y = years
IT = isomeric transition
E.C. = electron capture
β^+ = positron emission
β^- = beta emission

$1s^2$, $2s^2$, $2p^6$, $3s^2$, $3p^6$, $3d^{10}$, $4s^2$, $4p^6$, $4d^{10}$, $5s^2$, $5p^6$. In common with the other noble gases, xenon possesses a so-called "closed" shell of electrons. The filled electron shells in xenon result in a higher first ionization potential relative to those of neighboring elements. The first, second, and third ionization potentials of xenon are 12.127, 21.2, and 32.1 electron volts, respectively. The optical spectra of xenon played an important part in the initial identification of xenon as a new element and currently are significant for analysis and certain specialized uses of the gas in light sources. The lowest excited level lies 8.315 eV above the ground state.

Physical Properties

With the exception of helium, the physical properties of the noble gases vary smoothly with their atomic weights. As a consequence of their nonpolar, spherical structures, noble gas atoms have been used as model substances for physical theories. Many of the published properties of xenon (and the other noble gases) were obtained solely to test such theories.

The closed shell configuration plays a crucial role in determining the properties of xenon. The attractive forces between atoms are of the Van der Waals type. Their magnitude depends on the number of extranuclear electrons and is thus stronger for xenon than for the lighter noble gases. Nevertheless, they are so weak that liquid and solid phases exist only at temperatures where the thermal energy, kT, is low enough so that condensed phases are not shaken apart by thermal agitation.

A measure of the interatomic forces in noble gases is given by the Leonard-Jones

TABLE 2. PHYSICAL PROPERTIES OF XENON

Solid State

Triple point	Temperature	°K	161.36
	Pressure	mm Hg	611 ± 1.5
	Density (solid)	g/cc	3.540
	Density (liquid)	g/cc	3.076
Heat of fusion		cal/mole	548.5
Entropy of fusion		cal/mole/deg	3.40

Liquid State

Normal boiling point	°C	− 108.12 ± .01
Heat of vaporization at b.p.	cal/mole	3020 ± 3
Density at boiling point	g/cc	2.987
Calorimetric entropy at b.p.	cal/mole/deg	37.66 ± .10
Statistical entropy at b.p.	cal/mole/deg	37.58
Critical temperature	°C	+16.59
Critical pressure	atm	57.64
Critical density	g/cc	1.100

Gaseous State

Density at STP	g/l	5.8971
Specific heat at 25°C at 1 atm., Cp	cal/mole	4.968
Thermal conductivity at 0°C, 1 atm	cal/cm/sec	1.23×10^{-5}
Refractive index at 0°C, 5893 Å		1.000702
Dielectric constant 25°C, 1 atm		1.001238
Viscosity at 1 atm, 20°C	micropoise	227.40
Solubility in water at 1 atm		
partial pressure	cc(STP)/l	
0°C		203.2
20°C		108.1
30°C		85.4

potential. The form of this equation is similar for all the gases, but the constants vary. For xenon it is given by

$$E = 1244 \left[\left(\frac{4.07 \times 10^{-8}}{r} \right)^{12} - \left(\frac{4.07 \times 10^{-8}}{r} \right)^{6} \right] \quad (1)$$

where E is the potential energy of the xenon atoms with respect to each other, and r is the distance between their centers.

The constants have been evaluated from the temperature dependence of the second virial coefficient.

In principle, it should be possible to calculate all the physical properties of xenon from this equation. From a practical standpoint, however, such calculations are inaccurate because of the simplifying assumptions required to make such calculations feasible and the inexactitude with which the constants are known. A number of the measured physical properties of xenon have been collected in Table 2.

Solid xenon is a white, crystalline substance with a face-centered cubic lattice. The variation in melting point with pressure is given by the equation

$$T = T_o + 0.03987p - 0.00000342p^2 \quad (2)$$

where T_o is 161.328°K, the temperature of the melting point at one atmosphere pressure, and p is the pressure in atmospheres. This equation is valid for pressures up to 100 atmospheres.

Smoothed values of the molar heat capacities, C_s, of the solid and liquid are given in Table 3.

The liquid range of xenon between the triple point and the critical point spans about 128 degrees. The vapor pressure of the liquid over its entire range can be represented by the following equation:

$$\log_{10} p_{mm} = 23.20334 - \frac{1040.76}{T} \\ - 8.25369 \log_{10} T + 0.0085216\, T. \quad (3)$$

Values obtained from Eq. (3) agree very well with those calculated from calorimetric data. For vapor pressures of the solid serious discrepancies exist. Smoothed values of the vapor pressures of the solid which have been adjusted to conform to calorimetric data are

given in Table 4. Data on the densities of solid and liquid xenon are given in Table 5. Solid densities obtained by different investigations

TABLE 3. HEAT CAPACITY OF XENON

T, °K	Cs, cal/mole/deg
Solid	
10	2.00
15	3.28
20	4.15
25	4.75
30	5.12
40	5.68
60	6.16
80	6.48
100	6.80
120	7.20
140	7.70
158	8.50
Liquid	
163–166	10.65

TABLE 4. VAPOR PRESSURE OF SOLID XENON

T, °K	P, mm
70	1.39×10^{-4}
80	4.24×10^{-3}
90	5.99×10^{-2}
100	4.95×10^{-1}
110	2.76
120	11.5
130	38.2
140	101
150	258
160	562

TABLE 5. DENSITY OF XENON

Solid		Liquid	
T, °K	Density, g/cc	T, °K	Density, g/cc
58	3.686	210	2.726
77.4	3.649	220	2.642
88	3.588	230	2.548
88.9	3.630	240	2.445
100	3.695	250	2.331
161.3	3.540	260	2.204
		270	2.041
		280	1.830
		285	1.677

are in poor agreement. For liquid xenon, the data are more reliable.

The behavior of xenon gas differs appreciably from that of an ideal gas. These deviations, however, have been accurately determined and formulated in terms of a number of equations of state. At low pressures the Van der Waals equation can be used as follows:

$$\left(p + \frac{4.194}{V^2}\right)(V - 0.05105) = RT \quad (4)$$

where V is the volume in liters and p the pressure in atmospheres. Another equation of state which is valid up to 10 atmospheres pressure and for temperatures ranging from the critical point to 300°C is the Beattie-Bridgman equation

$$P = \frac{RT}{V^2}\left[1 - \frac{C}{VT^3}\right][V + B] - \frac{A_0}{V^2}\left(1 - \frac{a}{V}\right) (5)$$

In this equation, the constants have the following values: $R = 0.08206$ liter-atm/mole, $C = 30.02 \times 10^4$ lit-deg^3, $B = 0.07503$ liter, $A_0 = 4.6715$ atm-liter^2, and $a = 0.03311$ liter.

A useful parameter measuring deviations from ideality is the second virial coefficient, B. Knowledge of its temperature dependence permits calculations of the intermolecular potential function. It is used with a simple equation of state of the form

$$pV = RT + Bp. \quad (6)$$

The second virial coefficient increases from -133.0 cc/mole at 25.0°C to -81.5 cc/mole at 100°C to -23.6 cc/mole at 400°C and finally becomes zero at around 500°C, the so-called Boyle temperature. At higher temperatures, the second virial coefficient becomes positive passing through a maximum near 5000°C.

The transport properties of xenon are of considerable theoretical and practical interest. Included here are such properties as the thermal conductivity, viscosity and diffusion coefficients. The viscosity of xenon gas at atmospheric pressure as a function of temperature is given in Table 6 and the thermal conductivity of gaseous xenon as a function of temperature is given in Table 7. The self-diffusion coefficient of xenon gas at one

TABLE 6. VISCOSITY OF XENON GAS AT ATMOSPHERIC PRESSURE

T, °K	Viscosity, micropoise
273	210.1
289.8	223.5
293.2	226.0
400	300.9
450	335.1
500	365.2
550	395.4

TABLE 7. THERMAL CONDUCTIVITY OF XENON GAS AT 1 ATMOSPHERE PRESSURE

t, °C	$K \times 10^5$
−78.5	0.915
0	1.23
100	1.68
218.0	2.08
305.9	2.37

atmosphere is 0.0480 cm^2/sec at 273°K, 0.0684 cm^2/sec at 329.9°K, and 0.0900 cm^2/sec at 378.0°K. The self-diffusion coefficients of xenon in combination with those of other gases permit the derivation of the diffusion coefficients of the gas mixtures and calculations of mixing times for two gases.

Certain of the transport constants are related by equations derivable from the kinetic theory of gases and hence some properties not easily accessible to experimental measurements may be determined by measuring another property.

Chemical Properties

Until recently the noble gas elements were believed to be completely inert with respect to other elements. This belief was reinforced by the remarkable success of the "closed" electron shell configuration or "octet" concept in correlating a vast body of chemical knowledge, combined with many unsuccessful or unsubstantiated experiments to produce compounds of the noble gases.

It has been known for many years that some of the heavier noble gases, notably xenon,

801

could be trapped in the form of "clathrates." These are compounds in which the noble gases are held in a crystalline cage formed by a so-called host substance. Although clathrates are chemical compounds in the sense that they conform to a definite stoichiometry, the forces holding them together are of the Van der Waals type which are considerably weaker than normal chemical bonds. Clathrates are known in which the host is either water, an organic molecule, or a mixture of water and an organic molecule. The ideal formula of the hydrate is $Xe \cdot 5.75 H_2O$. Some of the properties of xenon hydrate are: decomposition temp at 1 atmosphere pressure $-3.4°C$; dissociation pressure at $0°C$, 1.5 atm; heat of formation, 16.7 cal/mole; and crystal lattice constant, 11.97 Å.

The ease with which the hydrate forms is related to the high solubility of xenon in water. The solubility of xenon in water as a function of temperature is expressed by the following relationship

$$\log S = -60.836 + \frac{3605}{T} + 20.5 \log_{10} T \quad (7)$$

where S is the absorption coefficient in cc xenon (STP) per 1000 g of H_2O at a partial gas pressure of 1 atmosphere.

Relatively stable clathrates of xenon with hydroquinone, p-cresol, and phenol are known. These are generally prepared by cooling aqueous solutions or a liquid melt of the host substance under a high xenon pressure until the clathrate crystals form. Mixed crystals of the type $A \cdot 2Xe \cdot 17H_2O$ where A is an organic molecule, such as carbon tetrachloride, acetone, or chloroform, have been prepared as well.

Certain transient species involving xenon, such as $ArXe^+$, $KrXe^+$, have been identified in optical and mass spectra. Furthermore, radioactive transformations where Xe is a decay product can give rise to compounds containing Xe. Some examples are

$$CH_3I^{131} \xrightarrow{\beta^-} (CH_3Xe^{131})^+$$

$$KI^{129}Cl_4 \xrightarrow{\beta^-} (Xe^{129}Cl_4)^+$$

$$KI^{129}O_3 \xrightarrow{\beta^-} (Xe^{129}O_3)^+$$

The species thus produced are all unstable with lifetimes of 10^{-5} second or less. Nevertheless, important information on the nature of the Xe-O and Xe-Cl bond have been obtained from them.

In 1962, the first stable compound of xenon was prepared by Bartlett. This followed his earlier discovery that a compound dioxygenyl hexafluoroplatinate, $O_2^+ PtF_6^-$, could be prepared by direct reaction of oxygen and platinum hexafluoride at room temperature. On the basis that the first ionization potentials of oxygen and xenon are identical, a similar reaction involving xenon and platinum hexafluoride was carried out. Shortly thereafter a research group at the Argonne National Laboratory succeeded in preparing xenon tetrafluoride by direct combination of the elements. (See figure, p. 470.) Since then, xenon compounds of all even valencies from 2 to 8 have been characterized. The three simple fluorides are prepared in successive steps as follows:

$$Xe + F_2 \longrightarrow XeF_2$$
$$XeF_2 + F_2 \longrightarrow XeF_4$$
$$XeF_4 + F_2 \longrightarrow XeF_6$$

The proportions of the various fluorides present in a xenon-fluorine mixture are governed by an appropriate set of equilibrium constants for these reactions. Although the most useful method to initiate these reactions is to heat the gas mixtures, any method which provides fluorine atoms in the presence of xenon will suffice. Electric discharge, ultraviolet radiation and electron beam irradiations have been used. It is noteworthy that xenon difluoride can be prepared photochemically by exposing a mixture of the component gases to sunlight. The best known oxyfluoride of xenon, $XeOF_4$, is prepared by partial hydrolysis of XeF_6 according to the following reaction:

$$XeF_6 + H_2O \longrightarrow XeOF_4 + 2HF.$$

If the hydrolysis is carried to completion xenon trioxide, XeO_3, is formed. In solution xenon trioxide is stable and nonhazardous. If the solutions are evaporated to dryness, solid xenon trioxide forms. This is a colorless, nonvolatile solid with dangerous explosive properties!

The hydrolyses of the binary fluorides can be summarized by the set of reactions:

$$XeF_2 + H_2O \rightarrow Xe + \frac{1}{2}O_2 + 2HF$$

$$XeF_4 + 2H_2O \rightarrow \frac{1}{3}XeO_3 + \frac{2}{3}Xe + \frac{1}{2}O_2 + 4HF$$

$$XeF_6 + 3H_2O \rightarrow XeO_3 + 6HF$$

If the xenon hexafluoride is hydrolyzed with strong base, the XeO_3 disproportionates and perxenate is formed according to

$$2XeF_6 + 16NaOH \longrightarrow Na_4XeO_6 + Xe + O_2 + 12NaF + 8H_2O.$$

Since this disproportionation reaction proceeds relatively slowly, the xenon can be recovered nearly quantitatively as perxenate by passing ozone through the solution. The alkali perxenates are relatively insoluble salts and stable at room temperature. They are powerful oxidizing agents and show promise of important applications in analytical chemistry.

Numerous complex compounds of xenon have been prepared. In particular, the hexavalent xenon compounds, XeF_6 and $XeOF_4$, are capable of forming a series of complex salts in a manner suggesting strong analogies to the chemistry of the neighboring halogen fluorides.

The known compounds of xenon are listed in Table 8 where they are classified according to type and valence. Several compounds of xenon are known for which the valence is not yet conclusively established. These are the metal hexafluoride adducts of the type $Xe(MF_6)_n$, where M = Pt, Ru, Rh and Pu and n may vary from 1 to 2 for Pt and from 1 to 3 for Ru. The first compound of

TABLE 8. COMPOUNDS OF XENON

Valence	2	4	6	8
Simple Fluorides	XeF_2 $\qquad$ XeF_4 $XeF_2 \cdot XeF_4$		XeF_6	
Oxyfluorides		$XeOF_2$	$XeOF_4$ XeO_2F_2	
Oxides			XeO_3	XeO_4
Oxysalts			$CsHXeO_4$ $Na_2H_8Xe_2O_{11}$ $CsF \cdot XeO_3$	$Na_4XeO_6 \cdot nH_2O$ $(n = 0,2,6,8)$ $K_4XeO_6 \cdot 9H_2O$ $Ba_2XeO_6 \cdot \frac{3}{2}H_2O$
			$K_4XeO_6 \cdot 2XeO_3$	
Complexes	$XeF_2 \cdot 2SbF_5$ $XeF_2 \cdot 2TaF_5$ $XeF_2 \cdot 2PtF_5$		$XeF_6 \cdot BF_3$ $XeF_6 \cdot AsF_5$ $2XeF_6 \cdot SbF_5$ $XeF_6 \cdot SbF_5$ $XeF_6 \cdot 2SbF_5$ $XeF_6 \cdot PtF_5$ $XeF_6 \cdot 2VF_5$ $4XeF_6 \cdot SnF_4$ $MXeF_7$ (M = Cs,Rb) M_2XeF_8 (M = Cs,Rb,K,Na) $(NO)_2XeF_8$ $CsF \cdot XeOF_4$ $3RbF \cdot 2XeOF_4$ $3KF \cdot XeOF_4$ $XeOF_4 \cdot 2SbF_5$ $(NO)XeOF_5$ $XeOF_4 \cdot 2VF_5$	

xenon prepared, which Bartlett described as $Xe^+PtF_6^-$, belongs to this category and its composition is still in doubt.

Practical Applications

Although xenon has been found to have a number of useful applications, the low abundance and high price preclude its widespread utilization. Because of its high atomic number, xenon has a large cross section for ionization by x-rays, gamma photons and neutral mesons. For this reason it has found application as a filling for proportional counters and in liquid xenon bubble chambers.

Xenon has been used as a filling gas for light bulbs and is especially useful for high-intensity lamps. Xenon flash lamps have long lifetimes and have been used in photography.

Besides the below mentioned uses as an anesthetic, radioactive xenon has been utilized as a biological tracer and has been particularly useful in elucidating lipid metabolic processes.

In the form of compounds, xenon has thus far found limited application. The fluorides may eventually play a role as specialized fluorinating agents, particularly if processes can be devised where the xenon gas is recovered and reutilized. The perxenates have already found application as oxidizing agents in analytical chemistry.

By far the most widespread impact that xenon will have had in years to come will probably be the role it played in stimulating a critical re-examination of the nature of chemical bond formation and the banishment of the concept of the inviolability of the electron octet.

Biological Properties

Xenon has been found to possess considerable narcotic potency and has been used as an anesthetic in human surgery. There is evidence indicating that this property is related to its high solubility in lipid-rich nervous tissue. Xenon has the ability to affect metabolic processes and is effective in reducing oxygen-dependent radiosensitivity. Xenon itself is nontoxic, but compounds of xenon are highly toxic because of their strong oxidizing properties.

References

1. Cook, Gerhard A., Editor, "Argon, Helium, and the Rare Gases," New York, Interscience Publishers, 1961.
2. Hyman, H. H., Editor, "Noble Gas Compounds," Chicago, University of Chicago Press, 1963.
3. Malm, J. G., Selig, H., Jortner, J., and Rice, S. A., "The Chemistry of Xenon," *Chem. Rev.*, **65**, 199 (1965).

HENRY SELIG

Y

YTTERBIUM*

Ytterbium is one of the more fascinating elements of the Periodic Table, primarily because of its ability to vary its valence in different environments. In the divalent state ytterbium has completed $4f$ level ($4f^{14}$), but in the trivalent state the $4f$ level is incomplete and has thirteen electrons. The dual valence states of ytterbium give rise to interesting and variable chemical and alloying behaviors. In aqueous solutions the oxidation-reduction potential of the Yb^{+2}/Yb^{+3} couple is 1.15 v, and thus Yb^{+2} is easily oxidized to the trivalent state. In general, the trivalent state is more stable than the corresponding divalent state in chemical compounds, but metallic ytterbium is divalent.

In the elemental state, the application of modest pressure ($\sim16,000$ atm) changes the electrical conductivity from metallic to semiconducting. Higher pressures increase the semiconducting properties until at a pressure of about 40,000 atm, ytterbium suddenly becomes a metallic conductor once more.

Presently, ytterbium is not too important technologically, but current scientific investigations indicate that many new and perhaps exciting applications will be developed.

History[1,2,3]

Ytterbium was discovered by J. C. G. de Marignac in 1878, as a component of Mosander's so-called pure erbium oxide. The ytterbium fraction isolated by de Marignac was later found by other workers to contain scandium and lutetium.

Ytterbium is named after the city of Ytterby and the nearby Ytterby feldspar mine in the

*Work was performed in the Ames Laboratory of the U.S. Atomic Energy Commission. Contribution No. 1988.

archipelago of Stockholm. It was at this quarry that a mineral which contains the rare earths was first found.

Metallic ytterbium was first prepared by Klemm and Bommer in 1937 by reducing ytterbium trichloride with potassium. However, their metal was mixed together with potassium chloride. It was not until 1953 that Daane, Dennison and Spedding prepared gram quantities of ytterbium metal which was free from slag impurities and could be used in studies to characterize its physical and chemical properties.

Occurrence and Sources[1,4]

Ytterbium is one of the less abundant elements of the rare earth group, eleventh of 17. (See **Lanthanide Elements**.) It ranks 53rd in the abundances of the 83 naturally occurring elements of the earth's lithosphere. Ytterbium is slightly less abundant than boron, molybdenum and thallium, but slightly more abundant than antimony and tantalum. The more important minerals containing ytterbium are euxenite, gadolinite, monazite and xenotime. Euxenite is a complex titanium niobo-tantalate containing rare earths, thorium, and uranium. The principal deposit of this mineral is found in Idaho.

Gadolinite, which is a rare earth, iron, beryllium silicate, is found primarily in Scandinavia. This mineral has an unusually high rare earth content, about 40% oxide.

Monazite is a phosphate containing thorium, light rare earths and small amounts of heavy rare earths. Although the heavy rare earths are obtained as by-products from monazite, this mineral is still one of the more important sources of these elements. The most important deposits are located in Florida and Idaho-Montana in the United

805

States, and also in Australia, Brazil, India and South Africa. Deposits of lesser importance are found in Egypt, Malagasy Republic and Malawi in Africa, Ceylon, Indonesia, Malaysia, and Republic of Korea in Asia, and Uruguay and Argentina in South America.

Xenotime is a rare earth, thorium phosphate. It is found along with monazite, but in general the proportion of xenotime varies from one-half to five % of the amount of monazite.

Derivation[1,2,3,4,5]

Processing of Ores.[1,3,4] Euxenite is decomposed by fusion with potassium bisulfate. The resultant melt is digested in water precipitating niobium, tantalum and titanium as hydrated oxides. The soluble rare earths are then precipitated as oxalates. A second method, in which the ore is treated with hydrofluoric acid, may be used. The rare earth fluorides are insoluble and are separated from the soluble constituents by filtration. The rare earth fluorides may be dissolved by treating with concentrated sulfuric acid and volatilizing the hydrofluoric acid. The separation of ytterbium from the rare earths is discussed in the next section.

Gadolinite is treated with either hydrochloric or nitric acid to dissolve the rare earths. The rare earth solution is separated from the insoluble materials by filtering. The rare earths are recovered by precipitation as the oxalate.

Monazite or xenotime is heated in sulfuric acid to convert the phosphate to a thorium-rare earth sulfate mixture. The thorium, yttrium and heavy rare earths are separated from the light rare earths by fractional precipitation and filtration. The thorium, yttrium and heavy rare earths are recovered as the precipitate. An alternative method involves digestion of the monazite or xenotime by using sodium hydroxide at elevated temperatures to give the insoluble rare earth hydroxide in a trisodium phosphate solution. Following filtration, the hydroxide is carefully neutralized to dissolve the light rare earths, leaving the thorium and the heavy rare earths as insolubles. The thorium is separated in either case by any of three techniques: selective precipitation, selective extraction by nonaqueous solvents, or selective anion exchange.

Separation from Rare Earth Mixtures.[1,3,4,5] If one is just interested in separating ytterbium from a mixture of the heavy rare earths, this is most easily accomplished by the sodium amalgam reduction technique. A buffered acidic solution containing the trivalent heavy rare earths is mixed with the molten sodium-mercury alloy and trivalent ytterbium is reduced and dissolved in the molten sodium-mercury alloy. The separated mercury alloy is treated with hydrochloric acid to extract the ytterbium back into an aqueous solution. The ytterbium is recovered by precipitation as the oxalate.

Ytterbium may also be reduced electrolytically and simultaneously extracted into mercury. The separation is continued as noted above.

Ordinarily, however, since the heavy rare earths are separated from each other by ion exchange or perhaps solvent extraction techniques, the ytterbium is isolated from the other rare earths as a natural step in these processes.

Preparation of the Metal.[2,4,5] After chemical separation from the other rare earths, ytterbium is usually in the form of Yb_2O_3. The oxide is easily converted to the metal by heating a mixture of lanthanum metal and ytterbium oxide in a high vacuum. Because of the large differences in the vapor pressures ($>10^9$ at 1000°C) ytterbium metal sublimes and is collected on a condenser plate; simultaneously the lanthanum is oxidized to the sesquioxide. The ytterbium may be further purified by resublimation.

Aluminum, zirconium, cerium and mischmetal (a lanthanum-cerium-light rare earth alloy) have been substituted for lanthanum as reducing agents. But to date lanthanum appears to be the most popular reducing agent.

Allotropy[4,5,6,7]

For about twelve years ytterbium has been known to have two polymorphic forms (a room-temperature face-centered cubic modification, α, $a = 5.483$Å, and a high-temperature body-centered cubic form, β, $a = 4.44$Å). But it was not until the last three years that the body-centered cubic phase was found to be stable at high pressures and room temperature (see Fig. 1). Furthermore, these high pressure studies revealed that α, which

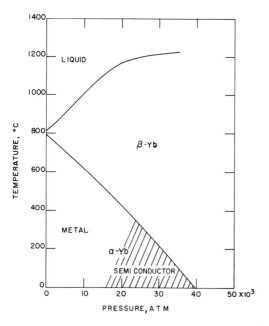

FIG. 1. Pressure-temperature diagram of ytterbium. Also shown is the region in which α-Yb behaves as a semiconductor.

has metallic type of conductivity at standard temperature and pressure, becomes a semiconductor when the pressure is increased above 16,000 atm. The electrical resistance increases by a factor of about ten as the pressure is raised to 39,000 atm and then drops drastically at 40,000 atm to a value which is about 0.8 of its standard temperature-pressure resistivity. The energy gap, E_g,

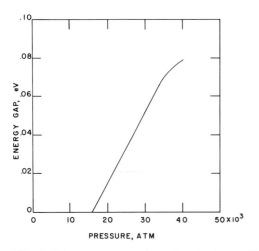

FIG. 2. The energy gap of semiconducting α-Yb as a function of pressure.

which was determined from resistivity data, increases with increasing pressure (Fig. 2). But when the pressure reaches 39,500 atm at room temperature, a structural transformation takes place and ytterbium again becomes a metallic type conductor. The semiconducting region of α-Yb is indicated by the shading in Fig. 1.

Electronic Structure[1,3,4,5,6,7]

The ground state configuration of ytterbium, as determined by spectral studies, is $4f^{14}6s^2$.

Metallic ytterbium has fourteen $4f$ electrons and two valence electrons. Because of the existence of semiconducting type of electrical conductivity at high pressure (see Fig. 1), it is thought that the $6s$ band of ytterbium is almost entirely filled with a slight overlap of the $5d$ band at atmospheric pressure. But as the pressure is increased, the s and d bands shift with respect to one another giving rise to an energy gap at pressures greater than 16,000 atm.

Ytterbium in many solutions and in many of its ionic, covalent and metallic type compounds exists as the trivalent ion, which has thirteen $4f$ electrons. The divalent ion, which has fourteen $4f$ electrons, is not very stable in most solutions and is easily oxidized to the trivalent state by air. The divalent state and states in which the valence of ytterbium lies between two and three are also found in many of ytterbium's ionic, covalent and metallic type compounds.

Physical Properties[4,5,6]

The physical properties of metallic ytterbium are given in Table 1. Most of the values refer to measurements at 298° K(25°C). The magnetic data clearly indicate that ytterbium has no unpaired $4f$ electrons,* and thus is a divalent metal. Many of ytterbium's physical properties, such as atomic volume, density, metallic radius, melting point, heat of sublimation, thermal expansion, hardness, elastic properties and compressibility, are more similar

---

*If ytterbium had one unpaired $4f$ electron, a magnetic susceptibility of 7,000 x 10^{-6} to 9,000 x 10^{-6} emu/mole would be expected. If ytterbium had no unpaired $4f$ electrons, a susceptibility between 10 x 10^{-6} and 100 x 10^{-6} emu/mole would be expected. The experimental value is 71 x 10^{-6} emu/mole.

TABLE 1. PHYSICAL PROPERTIES OF YTTERBIUM[4,5,6]

Property	Value
Atomic number	70
Atomic weight, $C^{12} = 12.00$	173.04
Atomic volume, cc/mole	24.82
Lattice parameter, Å α (fcc)	5.483
β (bcc)	4.44[a]
Density, gm/cc	6.972
Metallic radius, CN = 12[b] (Å)	1.939
α-β Transformation temperature, °C	792
Heat of transformation, kcal/g-atom	0.418
Melting point, °C	816
Heat of fusion, kcal/g-atom	1.830
Vapor pressure, A	−7696
log $P_{torr} = A/T + B$ B	8.295
Boiling point, °C	1193
Heat of sublimation at 25°C, kcal/g-atom	38.2
Heat capacity, C_p, cal/g-atom-deg	6.14
Electronic specific heat constant, cal/g-atom-deg$^2 \times 10^4$	6.93
Debye temperature, °K	118
Magnetic susceptibility, emu/mole $\times 10^6$	71
Electric resistivity, μ ohm-cm	29.4
Hall coefficient, volt-cm/amp-Oe $\times 10^{12}$	3.77
Ionization potentials, eV	
I	6.25
II	12.17
Thermal expansion, per °C $\times 10^6$	25.0
Grüneisen constant	1.02
Compressibility, cm^2/kg $\times 10^6$	7.39
Young's modulus, kg/cm$^2 \times 10^{-6}$	0.182
Shear modulus, kg/cm$^2 \times 10^{-6}$	0.071
Poisson's ratio	0.284
Hardness, Vickers, kg/mm^2	21
Yield strength, kg/mm^2	6.7
Ultimate strength, kg/mm^2	7.3
Elongation, %	6
Thermal neutron absorption cross section, barns	37

[a] Measured at 798°C.
[b] CN means coordination number.

to those of the alkaline earth metals than to those of the trivalent rare earth metals. This also supports the conclusion derived from magnetic susceptibility data concerning the divalent nature of this metal.

Ytterbium has 17 different isotopes, mass 154, 155, 162, and 164 through 177. Of these, seven are naturally occurring. These naturally occurring isotopes and their percentage abundances (given in parentheses) are as follows; 168 (0.14), 170 (3.03), 171 (14.31), 172 (21.82), 173 (16.13), 174 (31.84) and 176 (12.73).

Chemical Properties[1,3,4,5,8]

Ytterium is quite stable in moist or dry air up to temperatures of 200°C. At higher temperatures the rate of oxidation is significant and increases with increasing temperatures. The rate of oxidation at 400°C is 170 mg/dm^2/day. Little, however, is known about the mode of oxidation of ytterbium and the role played by YbO and Yb_2O_3 in the oxidation process.

Ytterbium is readily attacked and dissolved by dilute and concentrated mineral acids.

The rate of attack is about the same as observed for the majority of the normal trivalent rare earth metals. Sodium and ammonium hydroxide solutions and sodium nitrate solution slowly corrode ytterbium at room temperature at about the same rate at which the other rare earth metals corrode.[8]

Ytterbium easily dissolves in liquid ammonia to give a dark blue color. This behavior is very typical of the alkali and alkaline earth elements, and europium.

Ytterbium reacts slowly at room temperature with the halogen gases to form the corresponding ytterbium trihalide. Above 200°C, ytterbium is thought to react very rapidly with these gases. At high temperatures in contact with sulfur, carbon, nitrogen, boron and hydrogen, ytterbium reacts to form ytterbium metalloid compounds. The stoichiometry of the compound depends upon the temperature and the relative amounts of the materials present.

Principal Compounds[1,3,4,5,6]

Halides.[1,3,4,5] The ytterbium trihalides, $YbCl_3$, $YbBr_3$ and YbI_3, are quite hygroscopic, and generally are found as hydrated salts. These halides are soluble in water. Ytterbium trifluoride is nonhygroscopic and insoluble in water. The dihalides may be prepared by reduction of the corresponding ytterbium trihalide with hydrogen or ytterbium metal, or by thermal decomposition at elevated temperatures. Ytterbium dichloride is soluble in water but liberates hydrogen as the divalent ytterbium ion is oxidized to the trivalent state.

Oxides.[1,3,4,5,6] Ytterbium and oxygen form two compounds of the Yb_2O_3 and YbO stoichiometries. Yb_2O_3 has a melting point of 2346°C, and it crystallizes in the C-type cubic Mn_2O_3 type lattice. The sesquioxide may be dissolved in mineral acids. Little is known about the monoxide, other than its crystal structure, which is of the NaCl type.

Other Salts.[1,3,4] Ytterbic hydroxide, sulfate and carbonate are formed in the chemical separation of the rare earths from the other elements in their ores. Ytterbic hydroxide is very insoluble and is easily precipitated by the addition of sodium, potassium or ammonium hydroxide to a solution containing ytterbium. The sulfate is moderately soluble in water, and its solubility decreases when the temperature of the solution is raised. The carbonate is readily formed by precipitation from most salt solutions. Ytterbous sulfate may be prepared from crystalline ytterbic sulfate by methods similar to those described above to prepare the dihalides.

Metalloid Compounds.[1,3,4,5,6] Ytterbium reacts with hydrogen to form a dihydride which is orthorhombic and isostructural with the alkaline earth dihydrides. A cubic dihydride, which is isostructural with the normal trivalent rare earth dihydrides, can be prepared at high pressures.

Ytterbium forms three carbides, Yb_3C, Yb_2C_3 and YbC_2. The former has a NaCl type structure with missing C atoms, and it reacts with water to give methane gas. The latter two carbides are considered saline carbides because they contain C_2 groups or ions. Both Yb_2C_3 and YbC_2 react with water to form hydrocarbons and hydrogen.

Of the other metalloids (boron, silicon, nitrogen, phosphorus, sulfur, selenium and tellurium) all form at least one compound with ytterbium. Most of the compounds have high melting points and are reasonably stable at room temperature.

Intermetallic.[4,5,6] Ytterbium does not form intermetallic compounds with the elements which lie to the left of iron and its cogeners, ruthenium and osmium. Very little is known about the crystal chemistry of ytterbium, other than the structures of a few of the possible intermetallic compounds which may be expected to be formed with the elements which lie to the right of iron and its cogeners.

Applications[1,4,5,6,9]

Individual Element. Ytterbium free from other rare earths presently has very limited commercial usage. Ytterbium is being used as a laser source which has a wave length of 1.02μ, and as a dopant in garnets. Radioisotope Yb^{169} is being used in portable industrial units to inspect thin steel and aluminum sections and in medical radiographic units for diagnostic purposes. Probably one of the most important uses is the sale of high-purity ytterbium and ytterbium compounds to scientists for applied and fundamental research purposes.

Mixed Forms. By far the largest usage of

809

ytterbium is in the form of mixed rare earth salts and metals. The mixed oxides, containing ytterbium, are used in cored carbon rods for industrial lighting and in titanate insulated capacitors, as catalysts and glass additives. The mixed rare earth metals are used to control the grain size and improve the strength and other mechanical properties of stainless steels, and nonferrous alloys.

Biological and Chemical Nature[10]

Most of the biological, biochemical, pharmacological and toxicological studies on ytterbium have been carried out on small animals such as mice, rats and guinea pigs.

Oral administration of ytterbium or ytterbium compounds, unless the anion is toxic, has very little or no effect. This is primarily due to the fact that very little ytterbium is absorbed by the body. Subcutaneous injection gives a greater absorption. The excretion of ytterbium, however, is slow. About 25% of the ytterbium absorbed is deposited in the liver and 60% in the skeleton, and the elimination half-lives are about 15 days and 2.5 years, respectively. Ytterbium was found to produce granulomas from intradermal injections. Intraperitoneal administration of ytterbium in concentrations of 0.01, 0.1 and 1% in the diet for 90 days produced liver damage, which was more prominent in males than females. Inhalation of the sesquioxide and/or trifluoride induces granulomas in the lung.

The rare earths, including ytterbium, have a low acute toxicity rating.

References

1. Vickery R. C., "Chemistry of the Lanthanides," New York, Academic Press, 1953.
2. Daane, A. H., Dennison, D. H., and Spedding, F. H., *J. Am. Chem. Soc.*, **75**, 2272 (1953).
3. Moeller, T., "Chemistry of the Lanthanides," New York, Reinhold Publishing Corp., 1963.
4. Love, B., and Kleber, E. V., "Technology of Scandium, Ytterbium and the Rare Earth Metals," New York, Macmillan, 1963.
5. Spedding, F. H., and Daane, A. H., Ed., "The Rare Earths," New York, John Wiley and Sons, 1961.
6. Gschneidner, K. A., Jr., "Rare Earth Alloys," Princeton, New Jersey, Van Nostrand, 1961.
7. Hall, H. T., Barnett, J. D., and Merrill, L., *Science*, **139**, 111 (1963); Stager, R. A., and Drickamer, H. G., *Science*, **139**, 1284 (1963); Souers, P. C., and Jura, G., *Science*, **140**, 481 (1963); Hall, H. T., and Merrill, L., *Inorg. Chem.*, **2**, 618 (1963); Jayaraman, A., *Phys. Rev.*, **135**, A1056 (1964); and Stephens, D. R., *J. Phys. Chem. Solids*, **26**, 943 (1965).
8. Love, B., and Kleber, E. V., *Materials in Design Eng.*, **52**, [5], 134 (1960); and Lee, L., and Green, N. D., *Corrosion*, **20**, 145t (1964).
9. Mandle, R. M., and Mandle, H. H., "Progress in the Science and Technology of the Rare Earths," Eyring, L., Ed., Vol. 1, p. 416, New York, Pergamon Press, 1964.
10. Haley, T. J., *J. Pharmaceutical Sciences*, **54**, 663 (1965).

KARL A. GSCHNEIDNER, JR.

YTTRIUM

Yttrium, symbol Y, atomic number 39, atomic weight 88.905, was discovered in 1794 by the Scandinavian chemist Gadolin. He named it after the small town of Ytterby in Sweden, which also bears the honor of having given names to the elements terbium, erbium, and ytterbium. Yttrium always occurs with the rare earth elements and is very similar to them in both chemical and metallurgical respects. The first element of the second transition group, it is in Group IIIB of the Periodic Table, and resembles the rare earth elements more than it resembles scandium. A few early experimental preparations of yttrium metal were made in the 1800's but they were of a quality that did not permit characterization of the metal. Recently, newly developed separation processes for the rare earths have made yttrium much more available, and it has been prepared and studied in many laboratories. Interest in the use of yttrium metal in nuclear reactor programs prompted support of a research program by the U.S. Atomic Energy Commission, and a detailed description of the development of large scale processes for the separation of yttrium from its ores, the preparation and purification of the metal, and the analytical methods associated with such work has been described in a report of the Ames Laboratory of the U.S. Atomic Energy Commission.[1] Also, the proceedings of a 1959 symposium on "The Rare Earths and Related Metals," sponsored by the American Society for Metals and the U.S. Atomic Energy Commission,[29] and a paper by McGurity and Simmons[18] include many additional details on the preparation, properties, fabrication and uses of yttrium. Mandle and Mandle[17] have made detailed analyses of the uses of yttrium as well as the rare earths and have presented their data in a very convenient form. Kremers[16] has compared the uses of yttrium and the rare earths in 1946 and in 1966 and reports the greatest increase to be in the area of phosphors. The use of metallic yttrium in alloys is receiving much attention, but practical use has not increased significantly in the last 20 years, although some very interesting uses have been reported. Gschneidner[11] has prepared an extensive and critical review of rare earth metal alloy systems. Interest in yttrium has been heightened by its low neutron cross section, its melting point, 1509°C, its density, 4.47 g/cc, and its behavior with other metals.

Occurrence

In the geochemical processes in which the earth's crust was formed, yttrium and the rare earth elements remained together. Today we find them together as phosphates in xenotime and monazite, as silicates in gadolinite, as columbates in samarskite, as well as in other important minerals such as fergusonite, apatite, blomstrandite, and euxenite. Norway has been a rich source of supply of many of these minerals, and more recently, mining operations have been carried out in this hemisphere in the Fair Valley, Idaho; Blind River, Ontario; Aiken, South Carolina; and Brazilian areas. Yttrium is present in the earth's crust to the extent of 40 ppm compared to concentrations of 46 ppm for cerium, 24 ppm for neodynium, 18 ppm for lanthanum, and less than 10 ppm for the other rare earths and scandium. For comparison, the concentration of copper is 45 ppm. This is somewhat misleading, as the copper deposits are much more concentrated.

Ore Treatment and Separation

Development of pilot plant scale processing of ores for their yttrium and rare earth content has been carried out by Spedding and Powell,[1,22,23,29a] and a typical treatment by their process follows. Starting with electromagnetically concentrated xenotime (36% Y_2O_3, 24% RE_2O_3 as phosphates), the ore is broken down with a high-temperature sulfuric acid treatment. The leachate from this digestion is then loaded onto cation exchange resin beds, which are then eluted with an ammonia buffered ethylenediamine-tatraacetic acid (EDTA) solution containing cupric ion which prevents precipitation of the insoluble EDTA on the resin bed. Yttrium and the rare earths are obtained in separate fractions of the eluent and are precipitated as their oxalates and ignited to their oxides. Other complexing agents have been studied for this process, but EDTA appears to be most suited for this separation. This process is operated using 30-in. diameter columns containing 10-ft beds, and with 12 such columns a throughput of about 500 pounds of 99.9% pure Y_2O_3/cycle is achieved; a cycle consists of two months. Several companies have constructed separation plants based on the above process. Silvernail and Woyski[27] have reported the use of successive complexing agents to achieve separation of yttrium from the rare earths on ion exchange columns in large scale operations. Morton and James[21] have examined the effect of temperature on the separation of yttrium from its associated rare earth elements, and have been able to drastically shift the position of yttrium in the eluting order by adjusting the temperature of the ion exchange column. As a consequence of their study, they have been able to prescribe conditions to enhance the isolation of yttrium on a large scale.

Preparation

Metallic yttrium was first prepared by Wöhler[32] in 1828; he reduced the anhydrous chloride, and since that time metallothermic reductions of yttrium halides have been employed by several workers. The largest scale application of this type of reaction has been that described by Spedding, Carlson, and Daane,[29b] who have reduced yttrium trifluoride with calcium in several variations as described below. The halides are the only yttrium compounds that have been successfully reduced to the metal on any scale of

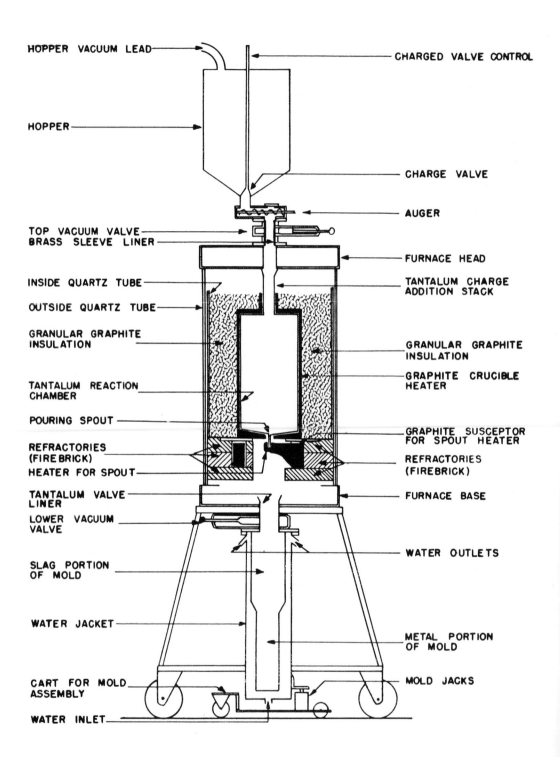

FIG. 1. Furnace for 40-kilogram scale preparation of yttrium.

operations. Their preparation is described below.

Preparation of Halides

Yttrium Fluoride. The preparation of yttrium fluoride may be carried out by the same procedures described in this book for scandium fluoride: (1) ammonium hydrogen fluoride may be mixed with yttrium oxide and heated to 400°C in a stream of dry air or helium; (2) yttrium oxide may be heated to 750°C in a stream of anhydrous hydrogen fluoride. The latter method is preferable for large scale operations.

Yttrium Chloride. The very hygroscopic nature of yttrium chloride, as well as the bromide and iodide, makes it necessary to handle these salts under dry conditions. Yttrium chloride may be prepared by mixing 9 moles of ammonium chloride and 1 mole of yttrium oxide together, and adding 4 moles of hydroxylamine hydrochloride. This mixture is heated to 400°C in a stream of dry air or helium to effect the conversion to the trichloride.

Brugger and Greinacher[4] have reported a process for the preparation of anhydrous rare earth chlorides (including YCl_3) by chlorination of oxides. Although the process was designed for treatment of ores, it is capable of handling large quantities of oxides also.

Yttrium Metal Preparation

Calcium Reduction of Yttrium Fluoride. Yttrium fluoride prepared by the methods described above has a relatively large surface area and a tendency to adsorb atmospheric gases. A vacuum sintering or melting operation is helpful in eliminating some of the adsorbed gases before the actual reduction. The fluoride is then mixed with 10% more than the stoichiometric amount of redistilled calcium required to reduce the salt by the reaction:

$$2YF_3 + 3Ca \rightarrow 2Y + 3CaF_2.$$

To prepare the metal on a scale of from 32 to 40 kg per charge, the induction furnace shown in Fig. 1 has been devised. In this unit the stainless steel charge hopper is discharged into the reaction chamber by means of an auger feed. The temperature of the reaction chamber is maintained at 1500–1550°C, and the charge is fed in intermittently as each previous addition melts down. The tantalum reaction chamber is 9 in. in diameter and 16 in. high, with 35-mil (0.035 in.) walls, and as indicated in Fig. 1, is contained in a graphite crucible surrounded by a 2-in. layer of granular graphite insulation.

A bottom pour spout on the crucible extends out of the heated zone and stays at a sufficiently low temperature for the first metal running into it to freeze and seal the chamber. To tap the heat, the induction coil is lowered to melt out the plug, and the metal flows into the water-cooled copper mold, followed by the slag. The charge hopper is reloaded and flushed with argon, and a new mold is set in place; this allows another heat to be run through immediately on a schedule of 80 minutes per heat.

The mold contents of a run, i.e., yttrium ingots, contain 1% calcium, 0.5 to 2% tantalum, 1000 to 2000 ppm, oxygen, 200 ppm carbon, and 50 ppm nitrogen. Vacuum melting the ingots in an arc melting furnace or an induction furnace eliminates the calcium leaving the other impurities essentially unchanged.

Magnesium Alloy Process. The most successful application of a lower temperature metallothermic reaction to the preparation of yttrium has been that of Spedding and Carlson.[1,29b] This process utilizes a lower melting magnesium alloy of yttrium and operates with a lower melting slag by the addition of calcium chloride to the reaction mixture. In a typical run the process is operated as follows: A mixture of 83 pounds of redistilled calcium and 35 pounds of redistilled magnesium are placed in a 20-in. diameter titanium vessel 48 in. high: this in turn is placed in a 24-in. diameter mild steel retort 54-in. long having ½-in. walls. After evacuating, the retort is lowered into a furnace at 750°C, as shown in Fig. 2, and when the calcium-magnesium mixture is molten, 1 atm of helium is admitted to the system. A sealed hopper system is attached to the retort, and a mixture of 180 pounds of YF_3 and 160 pounds of $CaCl_2$ is added and the temperature is increased to 960°C to finish the reaction. The retort is then cooled in an inclined position; this allows the slag

FIG. 2. Retort entering furnace; 110 pound scale, magnesium alloy process.

and metal to freeze in a configuration that may be easily broken out of the container. The resulting 150 pounds of 27 weight % magnesium alloy, is quite brittle, and is crushed to $\frac{1}{2}$-in. diameter chunks with as little exposure to atmospheric moisture as possible. These chunks are loaded into a titanium container and heated in a vacuum in an induction furnace or a resistance furnace for 6 hours at 900°C, followed by 24 hours at 950°C.

During the operation (called "demaging") the magnesium and residual calcium are slowly sublimed from the alloy, leaving behind a porous, soft, slightly sintered mass of metal called "sponge," which has a calcium and magnesium content of about 100 ppm each. To arc melt this material into ingots the granular sponge particles are pressed into 12 $\times 1\frac{1}{2} \times 1\frac{1}{2}$ in. sticks which are welded end-to-end to make an electrode. This is consumably arc melted into a 4-in. diameter ingot in an

arc of 22 to 24 volts and 1000 to 1200 amperes in a vacuum. The resulting 4-in. diameter ingots are welded together to make a 60-in. long electrode which may be arc melted in a vacuum at a rate of 4.5 pounds per minute, requiring 20 to 24 volts at 2800 to 3200 amperes. A typical 6-in. ingot of such a run will have the following analysis: Ca less than 10 ppm, Mg 30 ppm, oxygen 500 to 1650 ppm, titanium 0.5 to 1%. Such an ingot is shown at the left in Fig. 3, with 4-in. ingots in the center and pressed sponge electrodes on the right.

Dennison[6] has attempted the preparation of yttrium metal by the hot wire decomposition of yttrium iodide, but under a variety of conditions has never been able to obtain yttrium metal.

Electrolysis of Fused Salts. Morrice, Shedd and Henrie[20] have devised cells for the preparation of yttrium by the electrolysis of a bath of 50-50 mole % LiF-YF$_3$ to which

FIG. 3. Six-in. diameter arc melted ingot at left, four-in. diameter ingots in center, and pressed "sponge" electrodes on right.

Y_2O_3 is added as the primary reactant. The bath is heated to nearly 1700°C by the electrolytic current. The yttrium metal is produced as a liquid on molybdenum cathodes and drops to a frozen electrolyte "skull" in the bottom of the graphite crucible. The high temperature required for the preparation of yttrium by this method severely strains the materials of construction of the cell. Metallothermic methods of preparing yttrium still seem to be much the preferable approach.

Purification of metal

As the fabricability of yttrium appears to improve with lower oxygen content, much effort has been expended to achieve lower oxygen content in the metal. Some of the approaches have involved high-vacuum high-temperature distillation of the metal, purification of the reactants by distilling them into the reaction chamber, and extraction of oxygen from the metal into a YF_3-$CaCl_2$ or YCl_3 fused salt bath. From this work samples of metal with oxygen contents of only 120 ppm (by distillation of the metal) and 150 ppm (by fused salt extraction) have been obtained, and these specimens show greatly improved fabricability.

However, the most fruitful approach for improving the quality of the metal appears to be to achieve purer reactants and conditions in the preparation and handling of the metal.

Physical Properties

In many of its physical properties yttrium is quite similar to the heavy rare earth metals, and if properties are plotted against atomic number for the heavy rare earths, yttrium would have an apparent atomic number of from 64.5 to 67.5 (i.e., between gadolinium and erbium).

Table 1 gives the physical and mechanical properties of yttrium, and Tables 2, 3 and 4 give data on some of the properties of yttrium that have been studied over a temperature range at the General Electric ANP Department and the Battelle Memorial Institute Laboratories as reported by Simmons.[29d] Much of the data on physical properties has been obtained with quite pure specimens, particularly where only small specimens are involved, and is not likely to require much modification in the future. Mechanical properties and other properties requiring bulk specimens have generally been determined with production grade yttrium, and these figures, given in Table 1, will undoubtedly have to be modified when purer metal is available in quantity to permit examination

815

TABLE 1. PHYSICAL PROPERTIES OF YTTRIUM

Atomic number	39
Atomic weight	88.905 (100% isotope 89)
Melting point, °C	1509
Boiling point, °C	3200
Density, g/cc	4.472
Crystal structure	
Room temperature to 1490°C	Hexagonal close packed
	a = 3.6457 Å, c = 5.7305 Å
1490–1509°C	Body-centered cubic, a = 3.90 Å
Atomic volume, cc/mole	19.86
Metallic radius, Å	1.802
Heat capacity, 25°C, cal/mole/°C	6.50
Heat of fusion, kcal/mole	4.1
Heat of vaporization, 25°C, kcal/mole	93
Thermal conductivity, cal/sec/cm/°C	0.0240
Linear coefficient of expansion, per °C	10.8×10^{-6}
Compressibility, cm²/kg	2.09×10^{-6}
Young's modulus, psi	9.62×10^{6}
Shear modulus, psi	3.8×10^{6}
Poisson's ratio	0.265
Hardness	Brinell 32
Ultimate tensile strength, psi	22,000 (24,000 after 10% reduction in area)
Yield strength, psi	9,800 (21,000 after 10% reduction in area)
Elongation, %	25 (7% after 10% reduction in area)
Thermal neutron absorption cross section, barns/atom	1.31 ± 0.08
Electrical resistivity, microhm-cm	
25°C	65
100°C	83.5
400°C	133.5
700°C	169.5
1000°C	190.6

TABLE 2. ENTHALPY AND INSTANTANEOUS SPECIFIC HEAT VALUES FOR YTTRIUM METAL AS A FUNCTION OF TEMPERATURE

°C	Enthalpy, H_0^t, cal/g	°C	Specific heat	
			cal/g/°c	cal/mole/°C
0	0	50	.074	6.57
177.0	13.4	100	.076	6.75
		200	.077	6.84
		300	.078	6.93
243.4	18.4	—	—	—
343.1	24.8	500	.084	7.46
—	—	600	.088	7.82
—	—	800	.105	9.33
—	—	1000	.124	11.02
403.9	31.6			
536.3	41.8			
722.0	58.8			
996.2	89.4			

Enthalpy data H^t (total heat content between the temperature and the ice point) were obtained by ice calorimetric measurements for GE-ANPD at the Battelle Memorial Institute. Instantaneous specific heats were measured graphically as slopes of H_0^t vs. T°C plots. The error in specific heats reportedly did not exceed $\pm$ 1 per cent.

TABLE 3. LINEAR THERMAL EXPANSION COEFFICIENT OF YTTRIUM METAL AS A FUNCTION OF TEMPERATURE

°C	Coefficient, alpha $\times 10^{-6}$
25–300	7.6
25–600	9.3
25–900	9.9
25–1000	10.1

Most probable values for polycrystalline metal of random grain orientation.
From paper, "The Preparation and Properties of High Purity Yttrium Metal," by H. J. Nolting and C. R. Simmons of GE-ANPD and J. J. Klingenberg of Dept. of Chemistry, Xavier University, *J. Inorganic & Nuclear Chem.*, **14**, 208 (1960).
Data obtained by dilatometric measurements.

TABLE 4. THERMAL CONDUCTIVITY OF YTTRIUM AS A FUNCTION OF TEMPERATURE

°C	Thermal conductivity	
	BTU/hr/ft²/°F/ft	cal/sec/cm/°C
−18	5.6	0.0231
0	5.7	.0236
38	6.0	.0248
93	6.3	.0260
204	7.1	.0293
315	8.1	.0334
427	9.5	.0392
538	11.3	.0466

Measurements made on longitudinal rod specimen. Results are average of GE-ANPD measurements and those made for GE-ANPD at the Battelle Memorial Institute. These and specific heat data are from "Chemistry and Metallurgy of Yttrium," APEX 475 (deleted) by C. R. Simmons, C. B. Magee, J. A. McGurty, E. S. Funston, and V. P. Calkins, GE-ANPD, issued from the Technical Information Service Extension (TISE), Oak Ridge National Laboratory, Oak Ridge, Tenn.

of these properties. Hardness increases with increasing oxygen content, and there is some indication of a variation with heat treatment and degree of working. There is also a distinct decrease in hardness with increasing temperature. Tensile data given by Simmons[29d] show an increasing strength and decreasing ductility with increasing oxygen content, and a decreasing strength and increasing ductility with increasing temperature.

Chemical Properties

The chemistry of yttrium is very like that of the rare earths except that only a trivalent state is known for this element whereas about half the rare earths exhibit other valences in addition to their normal valence of three. In aqueous solutions yttrium forms an insoluble hydroxide, oxalate, and fluoride, all of which may be used for gravimetric analytical procedures. The chloride, bromide, iodide, nitrate, and sulfate are all soluble. Because of the absence of "d" and "f" electrons, the Y^{+3} ion is colorless in solutions, and direct spectrophotometric determination of this species is not possible. The Y^{+3} ion is so nearly the same size as the heavy rare earth ions that it behaves as one of them in solutions; in many chemical separations and reactions yttrium falls between gadolinium and erbium in order of reaction. Because of its occurrence with, and similarity to, the heavy rare earths, and because of its greater abundance, this group of elements is often called the "yttrium earths." This similarity of yttrium to the heavy rare earths extends to the metallic state.

Yttrium and hydrogen form compositions of about 1:1 atom ratio that are quite stable at temperatures in the neighborhood of 1000°C. In air and oxygen yttrium is only slightly tarnished at room temperature and never loses its metallic sheen, but at higher temperatures, i.e., over 400°C, the reaction increases and the metal can ignite, especially if in sponge or small particle form. A nitride, YN, is formed in nitrogen at over 1000°C. In water vapor at 750°C, an oxide coating 10^5 Å thick is formed which protects the metal from further attack.

Yttrium is not rapidly attacked by a 1:1 mixture of concentrated nitric acid and 48% hydrofluoric acid; it is, however, rapidly attacked by other acids.

The halogens attack yttrium at temperatures above about 200°C to form trihalides. Sulfur, carbon, silicon, phosphorus and selenium all react with yttrium at elevated temperatures to form binary compounds. Three carbides, Y_3C, Y_2C_3 and YC_2, are known and each hydrolyzes to form hydrocarbons.

Principal Compounds

The most important compound of yttrium is yttrium oxide, Y_2O_3, which accounts for most of the consumption of yttrium and its compounds. The chief application of Y_2O_3 is in the YVO_4:Eu and Y_2O_3:Eu phosphors that give the red color in color television tubes, an application which has grown from a few thousand pounds in 1963 to several hundred thousand pounds in 1968. The europium emits the red color while the yttrium gathers energy from the electron gun and transfers it to the europium phosphor.

The more important YVO_4:Eu phosphor is made by several techniques, all of which end up with a mixture of oxides in the right proportions to form YVO_4:Eu_2O_3 in which the atom ratio of Y to Eu is 19 to 1. One method starts with a solution of YCl_3, $EuCl_3$ and NH_4VO_3 that is treated with alkali to precipitate hydrous oxides which are washed and dried. All types are calcined at 1200°C to yield the desired compounds.

Another outlet for Y_2O_3 is in yttrium-iron garnets which are extremely effective microwave filters, an outlet which requires some 10,000 lb/year of Y_2O_3. The garnets are mixed yttrium and iron oxides that have a composition of roughly $Y_3Fe_5O_{12}$, and must be of the correct geometric form to be effective. Their use permits the pickup of lower powered radiation and the use of smaller radar collectors due to their noise elimination action.

Alloys

Alloying Behavior. Yttrium is a large atom among metal atoms; there are only a few metals with which it can form substantial solid solutions. As might be expected, yttrium forms nearly complete solid solutions with the rare earth metals and thorium. Yttrium and magnesium show significant solid solubility in one another. Other metals appear to have a very restricted solubility relationship with yttrium, but Collins et al.[29e], Daane[5] and Gschneidner[11] describe the very striking effects obtained when yttrium is added to iron, chromium, vanadium, columbium and some of their alloys.

Yttrium additions improve workability, cause grain refinement, promote resistance to high-temperature recrystallization, and most of all, enhance the high-temperature oxidation resistance of the metals and alloys. In iron alloys the improvement seems to be associated with the spheridizing of graphite by yttrium.

Among the metals and alloys studied recently whose properties have been improved by very small amounts of yttrium are chromium,[25] Nb-W-Hf alloys,[30] tantalum[15] and molybdenum.[10]

Alloy Systems. Some of the more important features found in alloy systems of yttrium with other metals are given in the following paragraphs. A more detailed review of yttrium alloy systems has been given by Lundin.[29f]

Group IA (Alkali metals). Lithium, sodium, and potassium, used as reductants for the preparation of yttrium, do not form stable intermetallic compounds and have little affinity for yttrium.

Group IIA (Alkaline earth metals). The yttrium-magnesium system has been investigated by Gibson and Carlson[9] who found three peritectic compounds to exist. The maximum solubility of yttrium in magnesium is 9 weight % at 567°C, while 15 weight % magnesium is soluble in beta yttrium (body centered cubic) at 935°C; this latter phase may be quenched to room temperature. The possibility of heat treating the terminal solutions is suggested in this work. Calcium does not alloy readily with yttrium and appears to form immiscible liquids like those found in the lanthanum-calcium system.

Group IIIB (Rare earth metals). Valletta[31] has found yttrium and gadolinium to form a nearly perfect solid solution at all compositions. With lanthanum, cerium, praseodymium, and neodymium, however, yttrium forms terminal solid solutions that are quite extensive, with an intervening solid solution that appears to have the unusual samarium structure.

Group IVB (Ti, Zr, Hf.) The yttrium-titanium system has a simple eutectic with less than 1 weight % yttrium soluble in titanium and about 0.5 % titanium soluble in yttrium.[2] The yttrium-zirconium system is similar.

Group VB (V, Cb, Ta). Vanadium and columbium form a eutectic near the yttrium side of these systems. Tantalum is soluble in liquid yttrium to the extent of about 2% at 1550°C. There is no solid solubility of these metals in one another.

Group VIB (Cr, Mo, W). Yttrium and chromium form a simple eutectic system. Molybdenum and tungsten are only slightly soluble in liquid yttrium; tungsten less so than tantalum.

Group VIIB (Mn, Tc, Re). Yttrium and manganese form a Laves phase YMn_2 and other compounds.

Group VIIIB (Fe, Co, Ni, Ru, Rh, Pd, Os, Ir, Pt). Yttrium and iron form several intermetallic compounds and show little solid solubility in each other. The yttrium-nickel system has been found to contain 9 intermetallic compounds.[3] The yttrium-cobalt system is similar.

Group IB (Cu, Ag, Au). Yttrium and copper form several intermetallic compounds and have little solubility in each other. In this system a eutectic is the limiting factor in choosing the soaking temperature for copper clad yttrium for hot fabrication.

Group IIB (Zn, Cd, Hg).—

Group IIIA (B, Al, Ga, In, Tl). Yttrium forms several borides that are quite refractory; yttrium dissolves in boron to stabilize a new phase of boron.[24] Yttrium is soluble in solid aluminum to the extent of about 0.2 weight % and forms at least one compound.

Group IVA (C, Si, Ge, Sn, Pb). Yttrium forms three carbides, Y_3C, Y_2C_3, and YC_2, all of which hydrolyze to form hydrocarbons.[28] Silicides of yttrium are refractory.

Group VA (N, P, As, Sb, Bi), Yttrium forms a nitride, YN, that is unstable to water vapor.

Group VIA (O, S, Se, Te). Y_2O_3 is the only reported stable oxide of yttrium. YS and YSe have been observed.

Group VIIA (F, Cl, Br, I). The halides of yttrium have the following melting points: YF_3, 1152°C; YCl_3, 709°C; YBr_3, 913°C; YK_3, 964°C.[6]

Actinides. Yttrium and thorium form a complete solid solution in the beta body-centered cubic) forms of these metals, with extensive solid solubility in the room temperature close packed forms.[6] Yttrium is immiscible with uranium in the liquid and solid states,[13] and Scheinhartz[26] has suggested the use of uranium metal dispersions in yttrium as nuclear reactor fuel elements to alleviate the problem of radiation damage. The use of yttrium to contain liquid uranium alloys is especially interesting.

Compositions of yttrium and hydrogen have also occasioned much interest in nuclear reactor circles in that the hydrogen is held tightly by the yttrium at high temperatures and provides a very effective neutron reflector and shield. Anderson[29g] has described work done at several laboratories (GE-KAPL, GE-ANP, Denver Research Institute) in which pressure-temperature-composition measurements were made on yttrium-hydrogen samples showing that at approximately a 1 : 1 atom ratio, a hydrogen pressure of less than 1 atm is generated at 1300°C. Significantly higher hydrogen contents (between 1 and 2 atoms of hydrogen/yttrium) were achieved having hydrogen pressures of 1 atm at temperatures between 900–1200°C. Samples of these materials are found to be compatible with stainless steel jackets which permits exposure of the clad specimens to the atmosphere at high temperatures. These compositions represent some of the most stable hydrogen containing materials available for this type of reactor application; further study and consideration of this material is in order.

Fabrication

Yttrium can be melted under vacuum by the consumable electrode arc melting process previously described. The ingots obtained can be extruded or forged at temperatures of 250 to 480°C after being heated to a higher temperature in an inert atmosphere.

The metal can be cold rolled, hot rolled in air at 760–870°C, swaged hot, drawn into rod and tubing, and machined. It can be welded by the use of inert atmosphere methods. Chips formed during machining operations are a distinct fire hazard and should be stored with care or reprocessed as soon as possible. Both Bohlender and Guidoboni give detailed information about the fabrication of yttrium.

Toxicity

Although extensive data on the toxicity of yttrium are not available, no apparent toxic effects have been reported despite considerable exposure of workers to this element.

The Future of Yttrium

Yttrium promises to have an interesting future. It is the most abundant of the heavy rare earths, and methods of producing it in large quantity have been devised. In the field of nuclear reactor technology, the low cross section of yttrium for neutron capture and the high temperature stability of yttrium-hydrogen compositions have already occasioned much interest and study. The relatively high melting point of yttrium and its inertness toward liquid uranium metal and many liquid uranium alloys have been demonstrated; should further tests confirm the results of preliminary experiments, yttrium will most certainly be considered seriously as a prime material for some nuclear reactors involving bolder approaches to economic nuclear power.

Although yttrium is too large an atom to form solid solution alloys with many of our more useful metals, it has shown promise in the case of magnesium. Perhaps the most striking application of yttrium may be as an additive to some of the more refractory metals and alloys, where its ability to form stable adherent oxide coatings on high temperature alloys has been demonstrated. Further developments in this area are likely.

A "Rare Earth Information Center" has been established at the Ames Laboratory, Iowa State University, Ames, Iowa, 50010, and requests for detailed information on yttrium as well as the rare earths may be directed there.

References

1. Ames Laboratory Staff, *U.S. Atomic Energy Commission Report, IS*-1 (1959).
2. Bare, D., and Carlson, O. N., paper accepted for publication in *Trans. Am. Soc. Metals,* 1960.
3. Beaudry, B. J., Master of Science Thesis, Iowa State University, Ames, Iowa, 1959.
4. Brugger, W., and Greinacher, E., *Proceedings of the 6th Rare Earth Research Conference,* 1967, 702. Gatlinburg, Tenn.
5. Daane, A. H., "Yttrium," chapter in "Rare Metals Handbook," C. A. Hampel, Editor, 2nd edition, pp. 653–666, New York, Reinhold Publishing Corp., 1961.
6. Dennison, D. H., *U.S. Atomic Energy Commission Report, ISC*-617 (1955); also unpublished data, Ames Laboratory, Ames, Iowa, 1960.
7. Eash, D. T., and Carlson, O. N., *Trans. Am. Soc. Metals,* **52**, 1097 (1960).
8. Fisher, R. W., and Fullhart, C. B., *Second United Nations Conference on Peaceful Use of Atomic Energy, Geneva,* 7, 216 (1958).
9. Gibson, E. D., and Carlson, O. N., *Trans. Am. Soc. Metals,* **52**, 1084 (1960).
10. Golstev, V. P., *Dokl. Akad. Nauk Belorussk. SSR,* **10**, 196, (1966).
11. Gschneidner, K. A., "A Critical Review of Rare Earth Alloy Systems," U.S. Atomic Energy Commission, 1961; and "Rare Earth Alloys," Princeton, N.J., D. Van Nostrand Co., 1961.
12. Guidoboni, S. E., Huntress, A. M., and Lowenstein, P., *U.S. Atomic Energy Commission Report, NMI-1223* (1959).
13. Haefling, J. F., and Daane, A. H., *Trans. AIME,* **215**, 336 (1959).
14. Jaffee, R. I., "High Temperature Technology," chapter on "Refractory Metals," New York, McGraw-Hill Book Company, Inc., 1960.
15. Kirkbride, L. D., Ferguson, W. E., Basmajian, J. A., Perkins, R. H., Stoller, D. R., and Dunning, D. N., *J. Less-Common Metals,* **9**, 393 (1965).
16. Kremers, H. E., *Proceedings of the 6th Rare Earth Research Conference,* 1967, 1. Gatlinburg, Tenn.
17. Mandle, R. M., and Mandle, H. H., "Uses and Applications," Chapter in "The Science and Technology of The Rare Earths," Edited by L. Eyring, Vol. 1 (1964) and Vol. 2 (1966), New York, Pergamon Press.
18. McGurty, J. A., and Simmons, C. R., paper presented at National Western Mining and Engineering Conference, Denver, 1960.
19. Moiseev, U. V., Zatulovskii, S. S., and Chornovol, A. V., *Dopov. Akad. Nauk Ukr. RSR Ser. A.* **29**, 373 (1967).
20. Morrice, E., Shedd, E. S., and Henrie, T. A., *Proceedings of the 6th Rare Earth Research Conference,* 1967, 715. Gatlinburg, Tenn.
21. Morton, J. R., and James, D. B., *Proceedings of the 6th Rare Earth Research Conference,* 1967, 667. Gatlingburg, Tenn.
22. Powell, J. E., and Spedding, F. H., *U.S. Atomic Energy Commission Report, ISC-617* (1955).
23. Powell, J. E., and Spedding, F. H., *Chem. Eng. Progr. Symposium Ser.,* **55**, 101 (1959).
24. Seybolt, A. U., *Trans. Am. Soc. Metals,* **52**, 971, (1960).
25. Seybolt, A. U., *Corrosion Sci.,* **6**, 263 (1966).
26. Sheinhartz, I., Sylvania-Corning Nuclear Corporation, Quarterly Progress Reports, 1959.
27. Silvernail, W. L., and Woyski, M. M., *Proceedings of the 6th Rare Earth Research Conference,* 1967, 687. Gatlinburg, Tenn.

28. Spedding, F. H., Gschneidner, K. A., and Daane, A. H., *J. Am. Chem. Soc.,* **80**, 4499 (1958).

29. Spedding, F. H., and Daane, A. H., Editors, "The Rare Earths and Related Metals," Novelty, Ohio, American Society for Metals, 1960.

CHAPTERS IN REFERENCE 29

29a. Powell, J. E., "The Separation of Rare Earth by Ion Exchange."

29b. Carlson, O. N., and Schmidt, F. A., "Metallothermic Preparation of Yttrium Metal."

29c. Huffine, C. L., and Williams, J. M., "Refining and Purification of Rare Earth Metals."

29d. Simmons, C. R., "The Mechanical Properties of Yttrium, Scandium, and The Rare Earths."

29e. Collins, J. F., Calkins, V. P., and McGurty, J. A., "Application of Rare Earths to Ferrous and Non-ferrous Alloys."

29f. Lundin, C. E., "Rare Earth Metal Phase Diagrams."

29g. Anderson, W. K., "Nuclear Applications of Yttrium, Scandium, and The Lanthanons."

29h. Bohlender, K. M., "Mechanical Fabrication of Rare Earth Metals."

30. Torgerson, R. T., and Baginski, W. A., *Trans. Met. Soc. AIME,* **236**, 158 (1966).

31. Valletta, R. M., Doctoral Thesis, Iowa State University, Ames, Iowa, 1959.

32. Wöhler, F., *Pogg. Ann. chim. phys.,* (2), 39, **77** (1828).

A. H. DAANE

Z

ZINC

Zinc, atomic number 30, atomic weight 65.37, is located in Group IIB of the Periodic Table above cadmium and mercury.

Discovery and History

Zinc as a metal of relatively high purity (i.e., more than 98% zinc) is not commonly used, and as such is not familiar to the average person in any fabricated article, whereas vessels and pipe of copper and lead were known even in ancient times. Zinc ornaments 2500 or more years old have been discovered, but would now be considered as alloys since a composition of only 80 to 90% zinc, with the remainder lead including iron and antimony as impurities, could not under modern concepts be called a commercially saleable metal.

The first smelting and extraction of the impure metal was carried out in China and India, thought to be around 1000 A.D. The first slab zinc or spelter was imported from the East in the early Seventeenth Century, historically late when compared with iron, copper or lead. The metal did not even have a universally accepted name at this time, but was known as tutanego, Indian tin, calamine or spiauter. The term "Zink" was first used by Löhneyes in 1697. The commercial designation for zinc from a distillation process is still spelter.

Knowledge of smelting zinc was brought from China about 1740, and a zinc smelter was erected in Bristol, England. A patent was granted in 1758 for smelting zinc from a roasted blende or zinc sulfide, fundamentally the present distillation process.

Not until 1836 did the beginning of the horizontal retort process evolve, mainly in Belgium. The ore was calamine (zinc oxide) mixed with coal. No great improvements in the distillation of zinc were made until 1880. Until this time, with the enormous consumption of coal per ton of ore, the European smelters established the principle that for the extraction of zinc it is better to carry the ore to the coal rather than coal to the ore. In the United States with introduction of the mechanical gas producer in 1878, the gas-fired horizontal retort distilling furnace became successful. Continuous distilling was not practically realized until 1925 in the United States.

The electrolytic process did not come into being until 1916 in Anaconda, Montana, and Trail, British Columbia. The development of better analytical methods in determining trace amounts of impurities, and understanding their effects on current efficiencies during plating of zinc from sulfate solutions, probably gave the technological breakthrough for economically successful electrolytic operations.

With distillation and electrolysis as the two fundamental processes, any recent new developments have been in the application of physical and chemical principles to new equipment such as fluidized bed roasting and the lead-zinc blast furnace.

Prevalence

Zinc is found as a mineral in the earth's crust, usually associated with other base metals such as copper and lead. The world tonnage mined is about 20% less than copper but 50% more than lead. Virtually all zinc produced is recovered from mine production of a sulfide ore.

Zinc deposits are widely distributed throughout the world. The mineral when found in massive deposits, where by far the largest tonnage occurs, usually has a high iron impurity

content. This ore, known as marmatitic zinc, may be as high as 10% iron, with total zinc only 40–45% in the concentrate. The large sources are British Columbia in Canada; Utah, Colorado and Idaho in the United States; Cerro de Pasco Mine in Peru; Broken Hill and Mount Isa in Australia; and Upper Silesia in Poland.

The other common sulfide mineral is sphalerite, found in vein type deposits. Although individual mine tonnage is comparatively low, there are a great number of producing mines. This is economically possible since a high-purity zinc sulfide concentrate is produced assaying 60–62% zinc. The large production from numerous mines originates in Northern Ontario and Quebec, the Tri-State District centered around Joplin, Missouri, the Central Peruvian Andes and Japan.

New deposits have recently been found which should insure sufficient zinc reserves for the foreseeable future.

Sources

The major proportion of the slab zinc is produced in smelters and refineries located near the ultimate industrial consumers with the exception of electrolytic plants where cheap hydroelectric power close to mine production dictates the preference of shipping slab great distances. Another factor taken into account where low-grade concentrates are produced is the savings made by extracting the zinc at the source to save smelter penalties and transportation costs. The principal slab producing countries are also heavily industrialized and import concentrate to satisfy demands.

For example, most European countries, the United States and Japan produce more zinc than the zinc content of the output of their mines, that is, they import zinc concentrates. In contrast, Canada, Mexico, Peru, Australia and several African nations produce less zinc than their mines yield. However, most of the latter group of countries produce sufficient zinc to satisfy their internal demands and some export zinc metal as well as zinc concentrates to the United States and Europe.

Derivation

Zinc is extracted from its ores by two distinct methods, both starting with zinc oxide formed by initially roasting the ores: (1) the pyrometallurgical or distillation process wherein the zinc oxide is reduced with carbon in horizontal or vertical retorts from which the resultant zinc is distilled and condensed; and (2) the hydrometallurgical or electrolytic process wherein the zinc oxide is leached from the roasted or calcined material with sulfuric acid to form zinc sulfate solution which is electrolyzed in cells to deposit zinc on cathodes.

In recent years in the United States approximately 60% of the slab zinc produced has been derived by the distillation process and 40% by the electrolytic process.

Both methods use a roasted froth flotation concentrate as the primary feed. Since the primary material is a sulfide, whose major constituent is zinc but which also contains sulfides of iron, lead, copper and cadmium in this order of diminishing proportions, and is insoluble in weak acid, a sulfur elimination or roasting step is necessary. In distillation, roasting is also important to improve the reduction efficiency and avoid the undesirable accumulation of matte in the retort residues.

The primary reaction in roasting is: $2ZnS + 3O_2 \rightarrow 2ZnO + 2SO_2$. However, some zinc sulfate is also produced by the reaction: $2ZnO + 2SO_2 + O_2 \rightarrow 2ZnSO_4$.

Several types of roasters have been used of which the most widely accepted up to 1950 was the vertical multiple-hearth roaster. The hearth roasters have yielded to the modern fluid-bed systems which have high unit capacity, an autogenous roast reaction, efficient waste heat recovery, and which produce rich sulfur dioxide gas for sulfuric acid production.

Where dead roasted, finely divided calcine is required as in the electrolytical process, the fluidized-bed roaster is ideal. The concentrate may be charged as a wet slurry, or as-received containing up to 8% moisture and with extra water injection into the bed, to control temperature and maintain gas strength. The roast reaction is carried out at temperatures close to 1000°C producing a calcine with relatively low ferrites as compared to the wedge roaster.

Another type of roaster uses pelletized feed to the fluidized bed, producing an excellent feed for the distillation process.

All fluidized systems employ the same principle. Air sufficient to burn the sulfur in the concentrates with an excess to cool the bed, is forced through a grate with small openings (to prevent material falling into the ducts) at a velocity designed to keep the charge in suspension. Retention time for complete sulfur elimination is determined by the height of overflow for the larger particles and volume of the reaction chamber for the smaller particles. The formation of sulfates can be controlled by regulating the time a particle remains in a zone of reaction at a temperature of approximately 450°C.

The Electrolytic Zinc Process. The electrolytic production of zinc from roasted concentrates consists of three steps. First, the ZnO is leached with sulfuric acid from spent electrolyte; second, the $ZnSO_4$ solution is carefully purified to eliminate copper, iron, tin, cadium, arsenic, antimony, germanium, cobalt, etc.; and third, the purified solution is electrolyzed, whereby zinc is deposited on aluminum cathode sheets, oxygen is liberated at lead alloy anodes, and sulfuric acid is generated in the cell. The leaching stage can be exemplified by the reaction: $ZnO + H_2SO_4 \rightarrow ZnSO_4 + H_2O$, and the electrolysis operation by the reaction: $2ZnSO_4 + 2H_2O \rightarrow 2Zn + 2H_2SO_4 + O_2$.

A choice as to the use of this process depends not so much on the availability of concentrates, but on primary electric power and its cost as compared to the cost of natural gas or coal. The fact that the electrolytic process tends to produce a higher quality zinc, added to the increased insistence on purity from die casters, has shaped a trend toward preference for electrolytic zinc. Certain high-marmatitic or high-iron concentrates cannot be treated by a distillation process, whereas in the leaching step of the electrolytic process iron is essential to purify the solutions from arsenic and antimony.

Zinc oxide is soluble in dilute sulfuric acid and the zinc sulfate produced is soluble in water. Zinc ferrite, however, is practically insoluble in dilute acid under ordinary leaching conditions. The amount of ferrite formed during roasting is a function of the amount of iron in the concentrates and the control of the roasting process. Ferrites directly influence zinc recovery.

Spent electrolyte from the cellroom supplies the acid to dissolve the zinc. An acid balance is maintained by the amount of sulfate produced in roasting being equal to the sulfate lost in washing and the lead content in the calcine. The lead is eliminated by forming an insoluble sulfate and follows the leach residue to disposal after filtering.

Leaching may be carried out continuously in air agitated Pachuca tanks or batch-wise in cylindrical flat bottom tanks with rake or propeller agitators. Calcine is added to spent electrolyte and when a pH of 2.6 is approached ferric hydroxide begins to form. At this point the "iron purification" begins. As an excess of zinc oxide is added, the zinc sulfate solution becomes buffered at a pH of 4.0 to 5.0. When sampled, visible flocs can be seen. The theory now generally accepted is that impurities, such as arsenic, antimony and germanium, are occluded into the ferric hydroxide flocs and like lead, enter the leach residue.

After filtration the $ZnSO_4$ solution is further purified. The main impurities in the neutral leach solution are copper and cadmium, with small amounts of cobalt. Metallic zinc dust is added to precipitate both the copper and cadmium. Nitroso-beta-naphthol is used in the removal of cobalt, in an additional purification step. All solutions are clarified of precipitated elements through Shriver presses. The purification residue or cake may contain as much as 10% cadmium and 6% copper. Cadmium from zinc plant residues is the major source of this metal. The solution now contains less than 1 ppm of either copper or cadmium and is added to the circulating electrolyte in the cellroom.

The care taken in leaching and purification, and in the removal of impurities, dictates the purity of the zinc deposited by electrolysis in the tankhouse. A current efficiency of over 90% can be expected with lead content as low as 10 ppm in the cathode deposit, if the electrolyte is sufficiently free of impurities.

The zinc is deposited on the aluminum cathodes by the application of direct current through insoluble lead anodes. Simultaneously, the electrolyte is decomposed to form oxygen at the anode and sulfuric acid at the cathode. The operation is affected by several factors, one of the most important being polarization caused by overvoltage. The potential required to deposit zinc on a zinc surface in sulfuric acid is 2.35 volts and the potential to deposit hydrogen under the same conditions is 2.4 volts. This difference of 0.05 volts is the narrow margin which spells success or failure of the commercial production of electrolytic zinc. Any controllable factor that will cause a lowering of the hydrogen overvoltage on zinc should be avoided. The electrode surface should be smooth, circulation must be adequate to provide plenty of zinc ions at each cathode surface and temperature in electrolyte should ideally be kept below 35°C. Deposition time normally is 24 hours with current densities in the range of 65–70 amperes per sq ft.

If these factors are controlled and the electrolyte is pure, a good deposit will result. The sheets of zinc deposit are hand stripped from the cathodes and are sent to electric furnaces for melting. Molten zinc from the furnace is pumped to a casting machine where 55-pound slabs are formed. A much larger casting in the form of a 2400-pound block is also supplied by many producers and is rapidly gaining favor with consumers.

The Distillation Process. In this process zinc oxide in the roasted calcine is mixed with carbon or carbonaceous material, charged into retorts, and reduced at elevated temperatures by the reaction: $ZnO + C \rightarrow Zn(g) + CO(g)$. The zinc vapor is condensed and collected in vessels connected with the reduction retorts.

After dead roasting the zinc concentrate, in most cases the calcine is sintered to produce a massive charge for retorting. The common practice is to mix the calcine with carbonaceous fuel (coal or coke) in a paddle mixer and feed it to a sinter machine. Sintering is usually done in a two-stage process. Double-over sintering has definite advantages as the sinter is denser and more uniform in quality and the elimination of lead, cadmium and sulfur is improved.

The original distillation process was carried out in horizontal retorts made of fire-clay, where each batch hardly produced a hundred pounds of zinc. Banks of as many as 800 retorts are mounted four high along two sides of a Hegeler furnace and heated indirectly with natural gas to maintain the distillation temperature above 950°C. Usually a 48-hour cycle is used. Zinc from the fire-clay condensers attached to each retort is cast by hand in

the same size molds as in the electrolytic process. The iron-rich slag produced may contain 26–28% iron with 5–10% of the new zinc charged. The charging of the retorts is a hot, arduous job and is done by hand. Charging machines have not been too successful.

To reduce labor and increase recoveries and production, a continuous process has been developed. The vertical retort process also takes roasted concentrates and coal, but in the form of a briquet to insure a free movement of the charge through the retort and provide good heat transfer and sufficient porosity for the escape of the gases. The briquets are passed through an autogenous coker at 700°C. Carbon in excess of that required for reduction of zinc is included in order to prevent disintegration of the briquets on discharge of retort. The external walls of the charge column are heated by gas to a temperature of 1300°C.

The electrothermic process for the production of zinc in continuously operated electric furnaces is conducted successfully in several zinc smelters. In one type of furnace the sinter-coke charge is the electrical resistance, while in others open electric arcs are used as the energy source. The thermal efficiency of the electrothermic process is high.

Efficient condensation of zinc is the core of the continuous processes. By developing a "splash condenser" with a motor-driven graphite impeller partially immersed in molten zinc, the zinc vapor condenses on the drops of zinc thrown up, before they fall back into the bath. 95% of the zinc vapor is condensed with the remainder being collected as blue powder in a scrubber with a Venturi ejector. The powder is recovered in settling tanks. Carbon monoxide produced is returned to gas mains. The zinc produced in most cases is further refined in distillation columns to separate cadmium and lead.

Recently, the Imperial Smelting process has been developed, using a blast furnace to produce both lead and zinc simultaneously from a bulk concentrate. Here, a lead splash condenser is used, and although the zinc vapors are more dilute than in the conventional processes, the copious spray shock chills the zinc and allows very little reoxidation. Lead is collected in the classic blast furnace way. The method allows recovery of zinc and lead from concentrates that heretofore could not be treated because of too high a concentration cost.

Physical Properties

Zinc is a bluish white metal, somewhat less dense than iron (7.133 vs 7.86 g/cc). As cast it has a brittle, hexagonal crystal structure, but loses its brittleness at about 120°C so that it can be rolled and drawn. Above 200°C it again becomes brittle. After being rolled or drawn in the range of 100–150°C it is no longer brittle when cold.

Zinc crystals are highly anisotropic and some of its properties are different for single crystals than they are for polycrystalline zinc. Further, small amounts of impurities change

mechanical properties and increase the rate of solution in acids.

Physical properties of zinc are listed in Table 1.

Chemical Properties

The outstanding property of zinc is its strong electropositive character, surpassed only by aluminum and magnesium. This property is used in galvanizing, where zinc in contact with iron or steel undergoes sacrificial corrosion.

Zinc exhibits divalency in all of its compounds.

Pure zinc is highly resistant to attack by dry air at normal ambient temperatures but the rate of attack increases rapidly above 225°C. In the presence of moist air, attack will occur at room temperature, and is accelerated by

TABLE 1. PHYSICAL PROPERTIES OF ZINC

Atomic number	30
Atomic weight	65.37
Isotopes, % natural abundance	
64	48.86
66	27.62
67	4.12
68	18.71
70	0.69
Electron configuration	2–8–18–2
Crystal structure	Hexagonal close-packed
a = 2.664Å, c = 4.9469Å, c/a = 1.856	
Density, g/cc	
solid, 25°C	7.133
solid, 419.5°C	6.83
liquid, 419.5°C	6.62
liquid, 800°C	6.25
Melting point, °C	419.5°C
Boiling point, °C	907
Heat of fusion, cal/g, 419.5°C	24.4
Heat of vaporization, cal/g, 907°C	419.5
Heat capacity, cal/mole	
solid, $C_p = 5.35 + 2.40 \times 10^{-3}T$ (298–693°K)	
liquid, $C_p = 7.50$	
gas (monatomic), $C_p = 4.969$	
Vapor pressure, mm Hg	
487°C	1
593°C	10
736°C	100
788°C	200
844°C	400
Linear coefficient of thermal expansion, per °C	
polycrystalline, 20–250°C	39.7×10^{-6}
a axis, 20–100°C	14.3×10^{-6}
c axis, 20–100°C	60.8×10^{-6}

TABLE 1—*continued*

Volume coefficient of thermal expansion, per °C, 20–400°C	8.9×10^{-5}
Thermal conductivity, cal/sec/cm/°C	
solid, 18°C	0.27
liquid, 419.5°C	0.415
Modulus of elasticity, psi	10 to 20 $\times 10^6$
Surface tension, dynes/cm	
510°C	785
550°C	778
600°C	768
640°C	761
$\gamma = 758 - 0.09\,(t - 419.5°C)$	
Viscosity, centipoise	
450°C	3.17
600°C	2.24
700°C	1.88
Electrical resistivity, microhm-cm	
419.5°C	35.3
600°C	35.0
800°C	35.7
polycrystalline, t = 0–100°C, $R = 5.46\,(t + 0.0042t)$ microhm-cm	
Magnetic susceptibility (diamagnetic), 20°C, polycrystalline, cgs units	0.139×10^{-6}
Thermal neutron absorption cross section, barns	1.1

carbon dioxide and sulfur dioxide with a hydrated basic carbonate being the end product of normal atmospheric corrosion. Dry halogen gases will not attack zinc at ordinary temperatures but in the presence of moisture zinc foil will actually ignite. Steam begins to react on the metal at 350°C and reacts rapidly at red heat.

Zinc is attacked by mineral acids evincing the strongest reaction with sulfuric, then hydrochloric and nitric in descending order. Impurities in the metal expedite the attack. The reaction with nitric acid does not result in the evolution of hydrogen, as is the case with the other mineral acids, but rather the reduction in part of the pentavalent nitrogen to lower valences. This reaction shows the vigorous reducing power of zinc, which can be intensified by increasing the surface area exposed per unit weight.

Zinc also has an amphoteric property. The metal will dissolve in hot caustic solutions evolving hydrogen and forming zincates.

Principal Compounds

Zinc oxide, ZnO. This compound is the most important zinc chemical with respect to both tonnage and total value. It can also be the starting point for all zinc chemicals.

For some time now, the rubber industry has been the greatest user of zinc oxide, followed by the paint and ceramic industries. The commercial consumption of oxide in 1965 was 160,000 tons.

Zinc oxide crystallizes in the hexagonal system. Commercial zinc oxide is white, but other colors such as yellow, green and brown do exist. The darker colors usually indicate the presence of iron or manganese. Indices of refraction of pure artificially produced oxide are given as 2.004 and 2.020 with somewhat higher figures for the mineral oxide. These high refractivity values and the normally fine particle size explain the high covering power and suitability for use in paints. Density varies slightly from 5.4 to 5.7. Zinc oxide is a refractory material melting at 1975°C ± 25°.

The greatest tonnage of oxide is produced commercially from mineral concentrates or zinciferous materials by a method known as the "American process." The primary material is oxidized to produce a sintered calcine which is subsequently reduced to a metallic vapor and oxidized. The needle-like product is used in exterior house paints. The nodular oxide is generally preferred for rubber compounding. The ceramic industry uses the oxide in frits and glazes to improve the brilliance of the glass. Oxide is also used in the production of viscose rayon in a bath with sulfuric acid reacting to form zinc sulfate giving a high-strength, satisfactory fatigue resistance textile.

The other method of commercial production is known as the "French process" which uses high-purity metal of Special High Grade quality. The oxide is made by vaporizing and burning zinc from a retort to obtain a product of higher purity than that made in the "American process." For this reason "French process" oxide is preferred for pharmaceutical preparations such as salves, lotions, and cosmetics.

Zinc sulfide ZnS crystallizes in two forms: hexagonal (wurtzite), indices of refraction 2.356 and 2.378 and sp. gr. 4.087; and cubic (sphalerite), refractive index 2.368 and sp. gr. 4.102. The hexagonal form is stable above 1020°C and wurtzite is the preferred form for pigments with the higher index of refractory.

Zinc sulfide is mixed with barium sulfate for use in interior low-gloss house paints.

Phosphors contain zinc sulfide to give luminescence upon irradiation by light and are used in cathode-ray tubes for television and fluorescent lamps.

Zinc sulfate, ZnSO₄, sp. gr. 3.74, forms a colorless rhombohedral crystal with indices of refraction of 1.658, 1.669 and 1.670.

The major uses are in textiles, in concentrators as a flotation reagent, and in soil conditioning in zinc deficient areas.

Zinc chloride, ZnCl₂, sp. gr. 2.91, has a melting point of about 300°C. It is an important industrial compound. In aqueous solution it is used as a wood preservative and for fireproofing timber; as a deodorant in

disinfecting fluids; as a mordant in printing; in mercerizing cotton and in the manufacture of dry batteries.

Applications

Elemental zinc of high-purity seldom forms part of a manufactured article. More often it is alloyed with copper and aluminum to produce castings, or is used in galvanizing to protect steel structures, or is present as a chemical additive in rubber and paints.

Each use requires certain industrial standards as to purity, governed by the American Society of Testing Materials for the United States, and similar societies in other countries. Table 2 gives the ASTM designation B6–62T (1962) for maximum impurities in slab zinc made by a process of distillation or electrolysis, but not by remelting of secondary zinc.

As seen previously, zinc for die casting will be in the future the major outlet of slab and this use requires metal of Special High Grade purity. A die casting made with zinc of ordinary purity is subject to damaging intercrystalline corrosion and swelling. High-purity zinc is alloyed with 3.5 to 4.3% aluminum and small amounts of copper and magnesium. Dimensionally accurate equipment parts are produced in a die casting machine in fractions of a minute giving this method of production distinct advantages by eliminating several finishing operations.

Zinc for galvanizing is well-known, having been in use for over one hundred years. It is estimated that more than 8.5 million tons of steel were galvanized in the United States in 1965. Galvanized steel originally protected building structures and everyone is familiar with the galvanized water bucket. More recently, the use of galvanized parts in cars and appliances has noticeably increased.

Steel when galvanized is protected from corrosive attack by the thin zinc skin. When

TABLE 2. GRADES OF ZINC

	Lead, Max.	Iron, Max.	Cadmium, Max.	Zinc, Min. by Diff.
Special High Grade	0.003%	0.003%	0.003%	99.990%
High Grade	0.07	0.02	0.03	99.90
Intermediate	0.20	0.03	0.40	99.5
Brass Special	0.6	0.03	0.50	99.0
Prime Western	1.6	0.05	0.50	98.0

the protective coating is broken by scratches or cracks the protection continues by means of galvanic action whereby the zinc slowly sacrifices itself. This action takes place because zinc is less noble than iron in the electromotive series. The steel will continue to be protected as long as sufficient zinc remains. The coating is applied by hot-dip method or by electrodeposition. The latter gives a relatively thin coating that is usually used as a base for paint.

The same electrochemical reaction applies to the cathodic protection on steel boats and buried steel structures. The difference is that in cathodic protection the solid piece of zinc is connected to the steel by a conductor. The zinc anode directs the flow of current to the steel, preventing corrosion as it slowly dissolves.

Brass, the designation for a series of copper-base alloys containing between 3 and 45% zinc, is generally stronger and more ductile than copper. It has superior corrosion resistance and is widely used in water valves, hardware, instruments and communication equipment.

Rolled zinc forms part of the container of the common dry cell used to supply electrical current for small portable radios and flashlights. It has a dual function of also being one component of the electrical cell. Sheet zinc can be quickly and easily etched and large quantities are used in the printing industry for photoengraving.

Although plastics have made inroads in various applications of zinc, the essential uses that depend on its unique properties such as galvanizing and die casting will continue to expand as the standard of living increases throughout the world.

Consumption

The importance of zinc can be indicated by the total world consumption of about 4.5 million tons annually. In the United States the consumption approaches 1.5 million tons per year, and in the United Kingdom about 400,000 tons. In the United States the largest use is in die castings, 45% of the total, followed by 35% for galvanizing, 10% in brass products, and 10% in miscellaneous applications. The usage in the United Kingdom is comprised of 34% in brass products, 26% for galvanizing, 20% in die castings, and the balance in miscellaneous uses.

In both countries the use of zinc for galvanizing is almost constant. The striking increase in the United States in the use of die castings, mainly in automotive and appliance components, illustrates the ready acceptance of zinc in industry. This use now substantially exceeds galvanizing, formerly the principal application of zinc.

Biological, Biochemical, and Toxicological Significance

Zinc has been found to be an essential element in the growth of humans and animals. Laboratory tests demonstrate that zinc-deficient animals require 50% more ration to gain the equivalent weight of an animal supplied with sufficient zinc. Recently it has also been proved that a zinc-rich diet promotes fast healing of wounds.

In agriculture, zinc compounds are used as a nutritive supplement to promote growth, in addition to their use as fungicides.

Zinc is not regarded as inherently toxic. However, zinc oxide when freshly formed and inhaled will cause a mild disorder known as "zinc chills" or "oxide shakes." The attacks are normally of brief duration and no cumulative or chronic aftereffects have been noted. With continuous exposure, the human body can develop a high degree of resistance. When not freshly formed, zinc oxide dust is practically harmless. Soluble salts of zinc have a harsh metallic taste and if taken internally can cause nausea and purging. Small repetitive doses may affect the digestion and cause constipation. Inhalation of zinc chloride fumes can injure the lungs and respiratory tract, the damage very likely being due to hydrolysis and consequent release of hydrochloric acid.

The prevention of metal fume fever which may occur during melting and distilling of zinc is more important than its treatment. Good ventilation to insure a concentration of less than 15 milligrams of zinc oxide per cubic meter over an eight-hour exposure is the best preventive measure.

References

Mathewson, C. H., Editor, "Zinc, The Metal, Its Alloys and Compounds," New York, Reinhold Publishing Corp., 1959.

Lund, R. E., "Zinc, Electrothermic Production," in "Encyclopedia of Electrochemistry," Hampel, C. A., Editor, pp. 1184–1188, New York, Reinhold Publishing Corp., 1964.

Hampel, C. A., "Zinc and Cadmium Electrowinning," *ibid.*, pp. 1180–1184.

"Year Book of the American Bureau of Metal Statistics—1965," New York, 1966.

R. S. Lehto

ZIRCONIUM

Zirconium, symbol Zr, atomic number 40, atomic weight 91.22, is one of the more reactive elements in the Periodic Table where it occupies a position as a transition metal in Group IVA, Period 6. The metal is about three times as sensitive to nitrogen and oxygen as is titanium. The sponge and powder are highly pyrophoric and cannot be pulverized in the presence of air or water without explosive results. It has a valance of four and strong tendencies to unite simultaneously with a variety of atoms or radicals. This characteristic is notable in the formation of compounds of complex nature and of polymers.

The uses for the compounds are numerous and of wide scope, but the most important single application of zirconium is in the form of hafnium-free metal in atomic reactors of the boiling water type. A low thermal neutron absorption cross section of 0.18 barns, amenability to fabrication techniques, adequate strength, dimensional stability, good heat transfer properties, excellent corrosion resistance, and good bonding characteristics are the important properties which make zirconium especially useful in thermal reactors.

Discovery and History

Zirconium was discovered as zirconium oxide in 1789 by N. H. Klaproth who worked with the mineral zircon, $ZrSiO_4$, zirconium silicate, in the form of semiprecious gemstones from Ceylon. Such zircon gems derive their name from the Arabic *zargun* (gold color) and Klaproth named the element zirconium. J. J. Berzelius first produced the metal in 1824 in impure form by the reduction of K_2ZrF_6 with potassium.

The first ductile metal of good purity was made by the reduction of resublimed zirconium tetrachloride with high-purity sodium, first by Lely and Hamburger in 1914 in Germany and later in the early 1920's by Cooper and by Hunter and Jones in the United States. In 1925 van Arkel and de Boer applied their iodide decomposition process, actually a refining process, to make very pure zirconium.

The U.S. Bureau of Mines in 1944 began work under the direction of W. J. Kroll at Albany, Oregon to adapt his magnesium reduction process to the production of zirconium from $ZrCl_4$. The production plant that was thus developed evolved into several commercial production plants whose construction was largely stimulated by the demands for high-purity zirconium for nuclear reactors. This need arose chiefly because of the decision by Admiral H. G. Rickover to use zirconium as a cladding and structural material in the atomic reactor of the submarine *Nautilus*.

For this purpose hafnium-free metal had to be produced to attain the desired low neutron absorption cross section of 0.18 barns of zirconium. Natural zirconium containing about 2% Hf has a cross section of over 2 barns because of the 105 barns cross section of hafnium. To accomplish the separation of zirconium from hafnium special techniques had to be developed to overcome the close chemical similarity of Zr and Hf. The one presently used was first placed in operation in 1950 at Oak Ridge National Laboratory.

Occurrence

The mineral zircon, zirconium orthosilicate (theoretically 67.2% ZrO_2 and 32.8% SiO_2), is the only commercial source of zirconium utilized at present. It is found in alluvial deposits laid down in stream beds, ocean beaches and old lake beds throughout the world. Zircon is rarely ever mined for its own value, but is an important by-product or co-product of other operations.

In Australia, ocean beaches are mined for rutile and at the same time provide the most important source of zircon. A second important source of zircon results from the mining of ilmenite from old beach deposits in Florida. Both sources yield a very pure, discrete mineral due to the eons of washing and tumbling in nature. Other similar sources are found in India and Brazil.

Altered zircons such as those occurring as by-product of tin mining operations in Nigeria are not important sources of zircon but do contain higher ratios of hafnium.

There are at least thirty-five known minerals of zirconium, most of which will have no commercial significance until the need for hafnium, sister of zirconium, becomes much greater than that associated with the normal zircon. One of the altered zircons, cyrtolite, contains nine times as much hafnium as zirconium.

Baddeleyite, another important zirconium mineral, is essentially pure zirconium oxide in crystalline form having a hafnium content of approximately 1%; it is found in Brazil in the form of alluvial pebbles.

Mining and Beneficiation

Zircon and baddeleyite are produced by dredging or strip mining alluvial placer deposits. Conventional bucket, suction or dragline dredges and stripping equipment are used. Once the minerals are removed from the earth, the preliminary segregation is accomplished using screens and simple gravity methods such as jigs, tables, riffles or spirals.

In Australia, a typical concentrate would contain 60% zircon, 20% rutile, and 15% ilmenite, the remaining constituents being monazite, garnet, cassiterite, tourmaline, spinel, and ferromagnesium minerals. A typical Florida concentrate contains 11% zircon, 7% rutile, 40% ilmenite, 4% leucoxene, 0.5% monazite and the remainder kyanite and various silicates.

Final cleaning of dried concentrates is accomplished in high tension electrostatic separators which effectively remove the titanium group minerals from the less conductive zircon, monazite and quartz. Magnetic separators are also used.

Extraction and Separation

All major producers of zirconium metal use the Kroll reduction process or modifications of it. Other production methods which are of historical interest only are described completely in literature recommended in the reference list. The important steps are described briefly in the following and may be followed by reference to Fig. 1, a schematic flowsheet.

Cracking the Ore. One of the great obstacles in the path of early researchers was the inertness of zircon to attack by most chemicals. Breaking down of the ore is accomplished by direct chlorination or by smelting with carbon in an arc furnace.

Arc furnace smelting is a straightforward reaction at about 3500°C when a mixture of coke and zircon is fed into an arc furnace. During the reaction silica is driven off as SiO and zirconium carbide, sometimes referred to as zirconium carbonitride or cyanonitride, is formed. On completion of a batch the charged material is removed from the furnace and the unreacted mix separated from the product by screening. The product is crushed and sized to provide a uniform feed to the chlorinator.

Chlorination of the Carbonitride. The carbonitride is charged to a simple steel shell chlorinator. The initial charge is heated to promote chlorination which then continues without external heating. Chlorine gas admitted to the bottom of the chlorinator passes through and reacts with the charge to produce a crude zirconium-hafnium tetrachloride. This is collected in a condenser and discharged periodically into containers.

Separation of Hafnium from Zirconium. The function of this step in the production of zirconium metal is the removal of hafnium which is always associated with zirconium in the natural state and which has followed it through all the previous operations. Hafnium accounts for about 2% of the total metal present in zircon. Following this separation step, the processing of hafnium to metal follows the same procedure as for the zirconium. While the separation step is requisite for the production of hafnium, zirconium not destined for nuclear applications need not be freed from hafnium. However, since the major portion of all zirconium is used in reactors, most of it must undergo the separation step.

The crude tetrachloride is solubilized in water with ammonium thiocyanate and fed to liquid-liquid extraction columns. Methyl isobutyl ketone passed countercurrent to the aqueous mixture extracts the hafnium preferentially. Zirconium leaving the system as

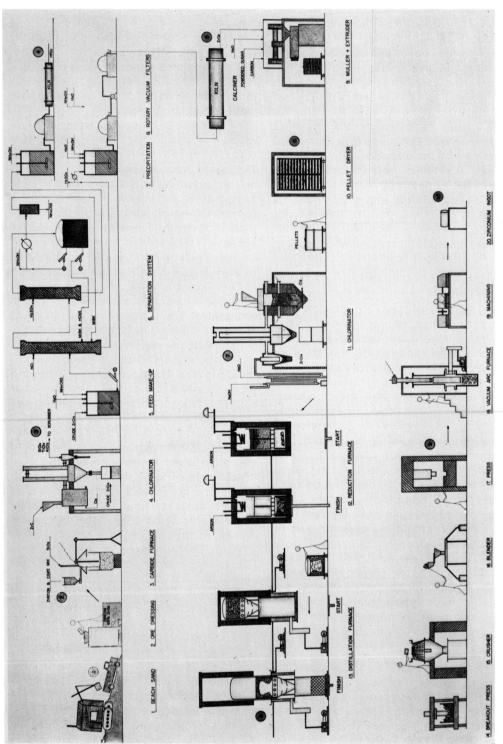

FIG. 1. Flowsheet for the production of hafnium-free zirconium. *(Courtesy Wah Chang Albany Corporation.)*

1. BEACH SAND   2. ORE DRESSING   3. CARBIDE FURNACE   4. CHLORINATOR   5. FEED MAKE-UP   6. SEPARATION SYSTEM   7. PRECIPITATION   8. ROTARY VACUUM FILTERS   9. MULLER + EXTRUDER   10. PELLET DRYER   11. CHLORINATOR   12. REDUCTION FURNACE   13. DISTILLATION FURNACE   14. BREAKOUT PRESS   15. CRUSHER   16. BLENDER   17. PRESS   18. VACUUM ARC FURNACE   19. MACHINING   20. ZIRCONIUM INGOT

zirconyl chloride, $ZrOCl_2$, in the water solution is precipitated as a basic zirconium sulfate with H_2SO_4. Because other metallic ions will not precipitate under the conditions employed an excellent purification results. The sulfate is converted to hydroxide with NH_4OH, dried and calcined to pure zirconium oxide.

Chlorination of the Pure Oxide. The oxide is mixed with lampblack, powdered sugar and water in the proper proportions and pelletized. The pellets are dried and charged to a shaft-type chlorinator lined with silica brick.

The chloride resulting from the reaction: $ZrO_2 + 2C + 2Cl_2 \rightarrow ZrCl_4 + 2CO$, is collected in a nickel-lined condenser from which it falls into a can and is ready for charging to the reduction furnaces.

Zirconium Metal Production

The can of tetrachloride is placed on a baffle over a crucible containing magnesium ingots and located in the bottom of the furnace retort. After charging, the furnace is sealed, evacuated and backfilled twice with helium. When the temperature has increased sufficiently and the magnesium becomes molten, the $ZrCl_4$ vapor and magnesium react to form zirconium sponge and magnesium chloride by the reaction: $2Mg + ZrCl_4 \rightarrow Zr + 2MgCl_2$.

Distillation Procedure. Removal of the magnesium chloride salt from the sponge zirconium is accomplished in a long vertical tube which is heated in the top portion and water-cooled in the lower section. The reduction crucible is mounted on several baffles that rest on a salt collecting can and the assembly is loaded into the distillation retort. The furnace is sealed and evacuated. The entire salt removal is then accomplished by heating the upper portion of the retort under reduced pressures. As heat is applied, the magnesium chloride and excess magnesium are distilled to the cold wall of the retort. When the distillation is completed and the furnace is cooled, the sponge is conditioned to the atmosphere to prevent rapid oxidation. The sponge zirconium is then removed from the crucible and segregated into fractions related to position in the crucible and sorted into storage cans. Each fraction of sponge in every batch is chopped and crushed to pass through $\frac{3}{8}$ in. screen, sampled, and analyzed.

Ingot Production. Ingot production from sponge is accomplished using consumable electrode arc melting of sponge pressed into compacts and joined by electron beam or plasma arc welding. The consumable electrode is melted by the arc and forms an ingot in a water-cooled copper crucible. Ingots produced in this manner can be joined together and remelted to obtain ingots several tons in weight. Sounder ingots and better distribution of alloying elements (added in the original sponge compact) are obtained by the double melting.

Purification of Zirconium. Small amounts of impurities, such as oxygen and nitrogen, seriously affect the properties of zirconium and several processes have been studied for the elimination or decrease of O, N and other elements in zirconium. Among them are: (1) the iodide decomposition process; (2) electron beam melting; (3) zone refining; and (4) electrorefining of metal in a molten salt bath containing K_2ZrF_6.

Physical and Mechanical Properties

The physical properties of zirconium are listed in Table 1. Notable among them are the relatively low density of 6.506 g/cc (greater than that of titanium, 4.507, but considerably less than that of steel, about 7.8); a melting point of 1850°C, over 300°C higher than that of iron; a very long liquid range to a boiling point of almost 4400°C; and a very low thermal neutron absorption cross section of 0.18 barns.

Some mechanical properties of zirconium are given in Table 2. As with other metals, the values of various mechanical properties are affected by small amounts of impurities, especially elements like oxygen and nitrogen which increase drastically both tensile strength and hardness. For example, in one study it was found that 0.2% oxygen raised the tensile strength from 30,000 psi to 50,000 psi, and 0.1% nitrogen increased it from 25,000 psi to 90,000 psi. Hayes gives many additional detailed data on the mechanical properties of zirconium. The values given in Table 2 are then to be regarded as typical of quite pure metal.

TABLE 1. PHYSICAL PROPERTIES OF ZIRCONIUM

Atomic number	40
Atomic weight	91.22
Atomic volume, cc/mole	14.02
Naturally occurring isotopes	90, 91, 92, 94, 96
Density, 20°C, g/cc	6.506
Melting point, °C	1850
Boiling point, °C	4377
Heat of fusion, kcal/mole	5.5
Heat of vaporization, kcal/mole	124
Heat capacity, C_p, cal/g-atom/°C	6.06
Electronic specific heat constant, cal/g-atom/deg$^2 \times 10^4$	6.95
Debye temperature, °K	250
Coefficient of lineal thermal expansion, 20°C, cm/cm/°C	5.85×10^{-6}
Thermal conductivity, 20°C, cal/cm/°C/sec	0.0505
Electrical resistivity, 0°C, microhm-cm	40.0
Superconducting transition temperature, °K	0.56
Hall coefficient, volt-cm/amp-Oer $\times 10^{12}$	0.18
Ionization potentials, eV	
I	6.835
II	13.13
III	24.00
IV	33.8
Electron work function, ϕ, eV	3.84
Oxidation potential, $Zr \rightarrow Zr^{+4} + 4e^-$, volts	1.53
Chemical valence	4
Electrochemical equivalent, Zr^{+4}, g/amp-hr	0.85076
Ionic radius, Å, Zr^{+4}	0.79
Valence electron potential, Zr^{+4}	73.0
Electronic configuration	$1s^2\ 2s^2\ 2p^6\ 3s^2\ 3p^6$
	$3d^{10}\ 4s^2\ 4p^6\ 4d^2\ 5s^2$
Valence electrons	$4d^2\ 5s^2$
Transition temperature, $\alpha \rightarrow \beta$, °C	867
Crystal structure, alpha phase	close-packed hexagonal
	a = 3.2321 Å,
	c = 5.1474 Å,
	c/a = 1.59
beta phase	body-centered cubic
	a = 3.609 Å
Magnetic susceptibility, at 20°K	1.2×10^{-6} cgs units
at 1000°K	1.55×10^{-6} cgs units
Emissivity, E, red (0.652)	0.48 under 1500°K
red (0.652)	0.42 above 1500°K
green (0.541)	0.50 under 1500°K
green (0.541)	0.46 above 1500°K
Thermal neutron absorption, cross section, barns/atom	0.18

TABLE 2. MECHANICAL PROPERTIES OF ZIRCONIUM

Compressibility, at 30°C	$10.97 \times 10^{-7} - 7.44 \times 10^{-22} p^6$
at 75°C	$11.06 \times 10^{-7} - 7.80 \times 10^{-12} p^6$
Young's modulus, hard-drawn	14.5×10^6 psi
tempered at 650°F	14.0×10^6 psi
annealed	11.35×10^6 psi
Shear modulus	5.42×10^6 psi
Poisson's ratio	0.33

Chemical Properties

Although quite resistant to reaction with a wide variety of reagents at ordinary temperatures, zirconium is a very reactive metal as the temperature is raised. The presence of hafnium in the naturally found ratios appears to have no effect on the chemical reactions of zirconium. The element is essentially quadrivalent in its compounds although some lower valency compounds do exist; their stability is much less than those of titanium and they are exemplified by $ZrCl_2$ and $ZrCl_3$.

Zirconium reacts readily with oxygen. Reaction with the massive metal is measurable at 200°C, but very slow, and the rate increases at higher temperatures. Zirconium powder ignites spontaneously at much lower temperatures and a hazard exists in the preparation and handling of powder, machine turnings, sponge, etc.

The reaction of nitrogen and zirconium is slow at 400°C but increases rapidly at 800°C and above. Amounts up to 20 atomic% N form solid solutions and above this amount ZrN is formed. Nitrogen in zirconium drastically reduces the metal's resistance to attack by water, and since the inertness of zirconium to corrosion by high-temperature water is one reason for its use in nuclear reactors, great care must be taken to prevent nitrogen uptake during preparation and fabrication of the metal. The presence of tin in zirconium

counteracts the above effect of nitrogen and this is the reason for the use of tin in the "Zircaloy" alloys.

Hydrogen is rapidly absorbed by zirconium at temperatures of 300–1000°C and brittle ZrH_2 can be formed. Heating in a vacuum above 1000°C completely removes the hydrogen.

All of the halogens react with zirconium in the range of 200–400°C to form tetrahalides which are solids subliming at 300°C and above. With the exception of ZrF_4 the halides are readily hydrolyzed in water to form oxyhalide compounds, such as zirconium oxychloride, $ZrOCl_2$. Sulfur, carbon, boron, silicon, phosphorus and aluminum react directly with zirconium at elevated temperatures to form binary compounds. The metal reacts rapidly with CO above 800°C and with CO_2 above 1000°C to form ZrO_2 along with zirconium carbide, ZrC. The action of SO_2 on Zr is rapid above 500°C, as is the action of propane above 900°C. Molten zirconium reacts with metal oxides and other refractory materials so it cannot be melted in ceramic containers.

Zirconium is stable to steam and to high-pressure water at temperatures up to about 600°C, but for long exposures the temperature is limited to about 400°C.

Data on the corrosion of zirconium by a variety of reagents are given in Table 3. Additional details are given by Hayes, by

TABLE 3. CORROSION DATA ON ZIRCONIUM

Reagent	Conc.	Temp., °F	Zirconium Resistance
INORGANIC ACIDS			
Aqua regia	—	65	Poor
	—	140	Poor
Chromic	Dilute	Boiling	Excellent
	Conc.	Boiling	Excellent
Hydrochloric	Dilute	All	Excellent
	Conc.	Room	Excellent
	Conc.	Boiling	Poor
Nitric	Dilute	65	Excellent
	Dilute	212	Excellent
	Conc.	212	Excellent
Phosphoric	Dilute	Room	Excellent
	Dilute	212	Good
	Conc.	Room	Fair
	Conc.	212	Fair
	Conc.	410	Poor

TABLE 3—*continued*

Reagent	Conc.	Temp., °F	Zirconium Resistance
Sulfuric	Dilute	65	Excellent
	Dilute	95	Excellent
	Dilute	212	Excellent
	Conc.	65	Good
	Conc.	212	Poor
	Conc.	570	Poor
ORGANIC ACIDS			
Acetic	Conc.	Boiling	Excellent
Formic	Dilute	Boiling	Excellent
	Conc.	Boiling	Excellent
Lactic	Dilute	Boiling	Excellent
	Conc.	Boiling	Excellent
Oxalic	Dilute	Boiling	Excellent
	Conc.	Boiling	Excellent
CHLORIDE SOLUTIONS			
$AlCl_3$	Satd	Boiling	Excellent
$CuCl_2$	10%	Boiling	Poor
$FeCl_3$	10%	Boiling	Poor
$HgCl_2$	Satd	Boiling	Excellent
NaCl	Satd	Boiling	Excellent
$SnCl_4$	24%	Boiling	Excellent
ALKALINE SOLUTIONS AND FUSED ALKALIS			
Molten KOH	—	—	Good
Molten NaOH	—	—	Excellent
KOH	5–10%	Room	Excellent
	5–10%	Boiling	Excellent
	40%	Room	Excellent
	40%	Boiling	Excellent
NaOH	5–10%	Room	Excellent
	5–10%	Boiling	Excellent
	40%	Room	Excellent
	40%	Boiling	Excellent

Rating System: Excellent 0.5
     mpy   Good ....0.5 to 5.0
              Fair ....5.0 to 10.0
              Poor 10.0

Hampel and by Schlechten. In addition to being quite resistant to HCl, zirconium is outstanding in its inertness to alkalis.

Zirconium Compounds

The important compounds of zirconium and their applications, except for metal production, are discussed in the following. For a complete treatise, compilation and list of compounds as well as theoretical dissertation, readers are urged to consult, "The Chemical Behavior of Zirconium" by W. B. Blumenthal.

Zircon, Zirconium Orthosilicate, ZrO_2SiO_2. Zircon is a transparent brown or yellowish semiprecious stone, often used in jewelry. The gem quality crystals are generally found buried in granite or other rock formations.

However, most gem stones are now produced synthetically by adding clean sand and zirconia to a "growing pedestal" in an oxygen flame.

Zircon is the most important zirconium chemical and it represents 60 to 75% of all zirconium consumed. Primarily it is used in foundries where its high melting point of 2430°C and refractory nature make it a valuable material for cores and molds. Secondarily it is used as an abrasive and polishing agent and as a ceramic constituent in insulators, refractory bricks, glazes, bodies, etc.

Zirconium Oxide, ZrO_2, m.p. 2765°C, is a white, dense highly refractory material that resists attack by most acids. It is useful in the production of piezoelectric crystals because of its dielectric properties. Rings made of zirconia can be used as high-frequency induction coils because of high resistivity at low temperatures and low resistivity at high temperatures. Zirconium oxide stabilized usually by the addition of 5% CaO is used for refractories, refractory furnace parts, crucibles, tubes, and laboratory gear. Solid electrolytes for batteries operating at 1000°C or more are made of sintered mixtures of 15 mole% CaO in ZrO_2, one of the most intriguing recent applications for zirconia.

Hydrous zirconium oxide is used to cure dermatitis resulting from the urushiol irritant of poison ivy and as a powerful adsorbent of organic and inorganic substances, making it useful as an ingredient in personal deodorants.

Zirconium oxide is used to produce highly reflective colored glazes for the enamel and ceramics industry.

Zirconium Carbide, ZrC, m.p. 3400°C; *Zirconium Diboride, ZrB_2,* m.p. 3060°C; and *Zirconium Nitride, ZrN,* m.p. 2980°C, are high-melting refractory compounds that have been studied a great deal in recent years. ZrB_2 and ZrC are very hard materials that have use as cladding materials and cutting tool components. ZrB_2 is also an excellent electrical and thermal conductor that is quite resistant to oxidation and chemical attack by such materials as molten aluminum and cryolite. It can be used to coat metals such as tantalum for oxidation protection, and to act as a cathode in high-temperature electrochemical systems.

Zirconium Hydride, ZrH_2, contains as many hydrogen atoms per cc as does water, and can be used at temperatures as high as 800°C. It is used as a moderator in nuclear reactors and as a source of pure hydrogen. Since ZrH_2 is brittle it can be crushed and dehydrogenated to form zirconium powder.

Ammonium Zirconyl Carbonate, $(NH_4)_3$-$ZrOH(CO_3)_3 \cdot 2H_2O$, is used in the preparation of water repellants and waterproof coatings for paper, as a stabilizer in latex base paints, as an ingredient in floor wax to cause it to resist the attack of detergents, and as a lubricant in the fabrication of glass fibers.

Potassium Zirconium Fluoride, K_2ZrF_6. This salt is used chiefly as a grain refiner in the magnesium and aluminum industry. It is also used in the preparation of welding flux, optical glass and as a catalyst.

Zirconium Acetate, $H_2ZrO_2(C_2H_3O_2)_2$, is useful in the preparation of water repellants, pharmaceuticals and other chemicals.

Zirconium Molybdate, $ZrO_2 \cdot xMoO_3 \cdot yH_2O$; Zirconium Phosphate, $(H_2PO_4)_2ZrO \cdot nH_2O$; and *Zirconium Tungstate, $5ZrO_2 \cdot xWO_3 \cdot yH_2O$,* are used as cation exchangers. They are highly selective toward alkali metals and alkaline earths. They are reportedly satisfactory for operation at temperatures up to 300°C and can withstand high-level radiation.

Zirconyl Nitrate, $ZrO(NO_3)_2 \cdot 2H_2O$, is useful in the preparation of catalysts, photographic plates, paper, and film.

Zirconium Sulfate, $Zr(SO_4)_2 \cdot 4H_2O$; Zirconium Basic Sulfate, $Zr_5O_8(SO_4)_2 \cdot xH_2O$; and *Sodium Zirconium Sulfate, $Na_2ZrO(SO_4)_2 \cdot 2H_2O$,* are used in the tanning industry and as catalysts and pigment stabilizers. The sulfate is reacted with the carbonate to form a basic zirconyl mono fatty acid which is insoluble in the normal cleaning solutions and uniquely suitable for water repellance. The sulfate is also useful in the preparation of drier catalyst in the paint industry.

Zirconium Tetrachloride, $ZrCl_4$, and *Sodium Zirconate, Na_4ZrO_4.* Zirconium tetrachloride, an intermediate in the production of zirconium metal, and sodium zirconate resulting from caustic fusion of zircon sand are the starting materials for essentially all chemical compounds of zirconium.

Zirconyl Chloride, $ZrOCl_2$, is produced by dissolving the tetrachloride or zirconate in hydrochloric acid solution followed by evaporation to form the crystals generally of high purity and satisfactory for further reactions to form other chemicals. It is also used in the preparation of catalysts, water repellant, antiperspirant, dye precipitant, and lakes and toners.

Fabrication of Zirconium

Zirconium can be forged, swaged, hot rolled, cold rolled, extruded, drawn into rod, tubing and wire, formed by bending, machined and annealed with proper precautions taken with respect to temperature and atmosphere to prevent deleterious pickup of oxygen and nitrogen. The metal can be welded using inert atmosphere techniques.

Applications of Zirconium

Zirconium is recognized as the best all-round material of construction in the thermal nuclear reactor. Because of the low neutron absorption cross section of 0.18 barns, it has a very low parasitic capture of neutrons; it also has adequate strength at high temperatures, is amenable to fabrication techniques, is dimensionally stable, has good heat transfer properties, and is resistant to attack by corrosive reagents.

Much of the zirconium used in atomic reactors is in the form of Zircaloy alloys which have superior corrosion resistance to water especially as influenced by nitrogen in the metal. Zircaloy II contains 1.46% tin, 0.124% iron and 0.104% chromium, while Zircaloy III contains 0.25% tin, 0.25% iron and 0.05% each of chromium and nickel. The major application of zirconium metal is as Zircaloy to clad uranium fuel elements. A typical 800 megawatt (electrical) nuclear power plant will use about 32 tons of Zircaloy tubing.

While scores of zirconium alloys have been studied, there is no other major zirconium alloy in use today.

Zirconium is used as an alloying constituent to improve mechanical and/or corrosion resistance properties of several metals and alloys, among them magnesium, aluminum, copper, nickel, tungsten, titanium, silicon and gold.

The chemical industry uses zirconium equipment in an increasing number of installations, e.g., in processes where alternate alkaline and acidic conditions are encountered, and in exposures to hydrochloric acid and to sulfuric acid.

Minor but important applications of zirconium metal are: photoflash bulbs, explosive primers, fireworks, flares, tracer ammunition, metal to glass seals, as a flux foil in welding tungsten to tungsten, tungsten to molybdenum, and molybdenum to molybdenum, and in various vacuum tubes.

In 1967 an estimated 2.5 million pounds of zirconium metal were consumed, compared with 1.6 million pounds in 1965. Even so, this amounts to only a few per cent of the total use of zirconium, since zircon and zirconia account for the balance.

Health and Safety

Zirconium metal has a very low order of toxicity so that no restrictions are necessary for control of health hazards unless it is combined or alloyed with other materials of higher toxicity. The major hazard to be considered in the use of the metal results from its high affinity to combine with oxygen at relatively low temperatures in spontaneous and exothermic reactions. Bars, ingots, and other massive forms can be heated to high temperatures with only a small surface oxidation resulting. Turnings and chips will often burn when being produced on machine tools and should be cooled with a small jet of air or coolant. Powder and fine dusts will explode when dispersed in air and should be handled with extreme care.

Care should be exercised in pickling or etching zirconium-uranium alloys or other alloys where residue is left on the surface of the metal. Such residues have exploded violently upon continued pickling or attendant to a scratching or tapping of the surface.

Any process involving new alloys or methods of pickling should always be tested on a small scale with appropriate physical protection to determine whether an explosive coating might form. Pickling in nitric or fuming nitric acid should be most suspect.

Finely divided residues resulting from the reduction operation are likely to generate hydrogen from contact with water vapor with resulting hazard of explosion.

References

1. Kroll, W. J., "How Commercial Titanium and Zirconium Were Born," *J. Franklin Institute*, **260**, 169 (1955).
2. Hayes, E. T., "Zirconium, Its Production and Properties," *U.S. Bureau of Mines, Bulletin 561*, (1956).
3. McClain, J. H., and Shelton, S. M., "Zirconium and Hafnium Separation," "Reactor Handbook," Vol. 1, p. 64, New York, Interscience Publishers, Inc., 1960.
4. Gilbert, H. L., Aschoff, W. A., and Brennan, W. E., "Arc Melting of Zirconium Metal," *J. Electrochem. Soc.,* **99**, 191 (1952).
5. Pemsler, J. P., Perryman, E. C. W., Smeltzer, W. W., "Zirconium and Its Alloys," New York, The Electrochemical Society, Inc., 1966.
6. Blumenthal, W. B., "The Chemical Behavior of Zirconium," Princeton, New Jersey, D. Van Nostrand Co., Inc., 1958.
7. Miller, E. C., "The Metal Zirconium and Its Place in Nuclear Power Plants," *Metal Progress*, **63**: **5**, 67 (1953).
8. Golden, L. B., "The Corrosion Resistance of Zirconium and Its Alloys," p. 305, Cleveland, Ohio, American Society for Metals, 1953.
9. Gordon, N. E., and Jacobs, R. M., "Spectrographic Determination of Impurities in Zirconium and Hafnium," *Anal. Chem.,* **25**, 1605 (1953).
10. Hampel, C. A., "Corrosion Resistance of Titanium, Zirconium and Tantalum Used for Chemical Equipment," *Corrosion*, **17**, No. 10, 9–17 (Oct. 1961).
11. Clark, D. P., and Meredith, R. E., "A High-Temperature Solid State Battery," *Electrochem. Technol.,* **5**, 446 (1967).
12. Schlechten, A. W., "Zirconium," chapter in "Rare Metals Handbook," C. A. Hampel, Editor, 2nd Edition, pp. 667–686, New York, Reinhold Publishing Corp., 1961.

J. H. McCLAIN

INDEX

841